The
GARDENER'S
YEARBOOK
—— 1994 ——

The
GARDENER'S
YEARBOOK
1994

EDITORS

Charles Quest-Ritson

&

Christopher Blair

PAN MACMILLAN

First published 1994 by Pan Macmillan Ltd
Cavaye Place London SW10 9PG
and Basingstoke

Associated companies throughout the world

ISBN 0-333-606 44-2

135798642

A CIP catalogue record for this book is available from
the British Library.

Data management and typesetting by Hodgson Associates, Tunbridge Wells, Kent
Printed and bound in Great Britain by Mackays of Chatham PLC, Kent

Contents

	Page
Introduction	vii
Calendar	1
Shows	56
A Digest of 1993 Gardening News	64
New Plants	69
Latest Scientific Research	76
Current Restoration Projects	79
Weather Records 1992–1993	82
Societies	98
Local Gardening Clubs	119
Nurseries & Garden Centres	120
Nursery Specialities	220
Importing & Exporting Plants	229
Seedsmen	232
Seed Exchange Schemes	238
Overgrown & Undergrown	241
Gardens	242
Garden Features	360
English Heritage Garden Grades	365
Garden Supplies	371
Organic Gardening	393
Buying in Bulk	395
Composts	398
Professional Services	400
Organisations	436
Colleges and Horticultural Education	441
Grant-making Trusts	457
Horticultural Libraries	460
Specialist Bookshops	464
Books, Periodicals & Videos	467
Personal Bibliography	482

Holidays	484
The French Scene	487
Britain in Bloom	489
Nature Reserves	490
Health & Safety	491
Charities	495
Nomenclature Changes	498
Index	504

Introduction

Gardeners are always in need of help and advice. The purpose of this book is to provide a compendium of useful information on every aspect of gardening for anyone who is interested in the subject. Names and addresses, facts and figures: there are thousands here. If the book does not contain the answer to a particular question, then it should at least point you to where the answer can be found. We hope it will supply a need for a single source of reliable and up to date knowledge for all those who want or need to find out more.

There is a balance to be struck between comprehensiveness and selection. Individual sections of the book lean more to one or other of these aims, but we hope that there are few serious omissions. Given the scope, we have had to rely to a great extent on information which has been submitted to us by third parties. Not everyone who was approached has replied – or replied in time – and this explains some gaps. Inclusion or exclusion should not be construed as a recommendation or condemnation.

Several sections of the book are arranged by county or region. We have tried to give the actual county in every case, regardless of postal addresses or postcodes. Please use the index or look under adjacent counties in cases of difficulty. You will also find a number of common abbreviations used freely throughout the text, including AGS – the Alpine Garden Society; EC – the European Community; MAFF – Ministry of Agriculture, Fisheries and Food; NAFAS – the National Association of Flower Arrangement Societies; NCCPG – the National Council for the Conservation of Plants and Gardens; NGS – National Gardens Scheme; RHS – Royal Horticultural Society; RNRS – the Royal National Rose Society; SGS – Scotland's Gardens Scheme; SRGC – Scottish Rock Garden Club.

The editors are very grateful to the many people who have helped in the compilation of this work. First and foremost we want to thank all the garden owners, nurseries, horticulturists, colleges, societies, tour operators, products suppliers and every one else who has responded to our requests for information. We are greatly indebted to them for their assistance and forbearance, and regret that it is not always possible to give each the personal attention which they are due. Particular thanks go to the staff of the Alpine Garden Society, the Edinburgh Climate Station, English Heritage, the Henry Doubleday Research Association, MAFF, the National Trust, the Northern Horticultural Society, and the Royal Horticultural Society.

We must also acknowledge the considerable input of others who have worked with us on this project: Julian Ashby, our publisher; Steve Benaim; Ian Crofton; Mark Griffiths; our sterling editor, Lin Hawthorne; John Hodgson and his team; our agent, Barbara Levy; Sarah Stevenson for typing; and designer Robert Updegraff. Unquantifiable thanks are due to Camilla Blair, and to Brigid and Madeline Quest-Ritson for the months of hard labour which have dominated our family life for the last year.

Calendar

The calendar, with a week to a page, lists events up and down the country which may be of interest to gardeners. Typically they include lectures and talks, shows, gardening workshops and demonstrations, garden walks, and plant sales. Many entries give a contact number or an address. Further information may also be found in other sections of the book: turn to the index first. A number of organisations, most notably the Royal Horticultural Society, have very extensive programmes. To save space, and avoid repetition, their details appear in shortened form. Full titles and booking details, where applicable, are given below. Although we have tried to be as accurate as possible, much of the information has been obtained well in advance. Arrangements can change at short notice, so do check with the organisers or in the press nearer the time, especially if you intend to travel any distance. The RHS journal, *The Garden*, publishes monthly up to date information on events at its gardens and those at Harlow Carr, Ness Gardens and the Hillier Arboretum.

Garden Events

Write to Garden Events, Honeysuckle Cottage, Maulden MK45 2DL for details and advance booking for their garden shows. There are discounts for pre-booked groups.

Harlow Carr

Harlow Carr Botanical Gardens, Crag Lane, Harrogate, North Yorkshire HG3 1QB. The home of the Northern Horticultural Society. Walks and demonstrations are free, and there is no need to book. Contact the Education Officer for details of the courses (0423 565418).

Hillier Arboretum

Sir Harold Hillier Gardens and Arboretum, Jermyns Lane, Ampfield, Romsey, Hampshire SO51 0QA. The gardens are now managed by Hampshire County Council. Meet in the car park for walks: no

need to book. You should book in advance for the workshops (0794 368787).

National Trust

A leaflet containing booking details and other information about events at National Trust gardens can be obtained by sending a sae (29p) to The Events Co-ordinator, The National Trust, 36 Queen Anne's Gate, London SW1H 9AS. Tickets for the winter lecture series are obtainable from the Royal Festival Hall (071 928 8800).

Ness Gardens

Ness Botanic Gardens, Ness, Neston, Cheshire L64 4AY. The gardens belong to the University of Liverpool. Book in advance for events where numbers are limited. There is a £1 admission charge for all lectures (051 336 7769).

RHS Hyde Hall

The RHS Garden, Hyde Hall, Rettendon, Chelmsford, Essex CM3 8ET. Walks are held at the garden, but other events take place at nearby Writtle College, Writtle, Chelmsford. Apply to the Administrator for tickets for both venues; for further information call 0245 400256.

RHS Pershore

West Midlands RHS Centre at Pershore, Pershore College of Horticulture, Avonbank, Pershore, Hereford & Worcester WR10 3JP. Write to the Administrative Secretary for tickets for the many events here: details from 0386 554609.

RHS Lectures

For tickets to both regional and London lectures, apply in writing to The Secretary (RHS Lectures), P O Box 313, Vincent Square, London SW1P 2PE. Tickets are normally free for RHS members.

RHS Rosemoor

The RHS Garden, Rosemoor, Great Torrington, Devon EX38 8PH. For tickets to the regular demonstrations and walks you should write to the Director. Some demonstrations are also staged at Cannington College, Bridgwater. The booking procedure is the same. More details are available on 0805 24067.

RHS Wisley

Walks, demonstrations and other events are held throughout the year at the RHS Garden, Wisley, Woking, Surrey GU23 6QB. Events, which are open to members and non-members, must be booked in advance. Write to the Director at Wisley. For more information ring 0483 224234.

Ryton Organic Gardens

Ryton on Dunsmore, Coventry, West Midlands CV8 3LG. Home of the Henry Doubleday Research Association and the National Centre for Organic Gardening (0203 303517).

Westminster Flower Shows

The RHS Westminster Flower Shows take place in the RHS Halls, Vincent Square and Greycoat Street, London. The nearest underground stations are St James's Park and Victoria. Recorded information is available on 071 828 1744. RHS members are admitted free.

The attitude of societies towards admitting non-members to their lectures and events varies. More detail appears in the Societies section. In general, though, clubs and societies exist for their members, so if you are interested in their events you probably ought to become a member. National societies who have local groups should be able to put you in touch with one near you. Most societies also hold open shows and plant sales (the AGS and NCCPG among them): the public is more than welcome at these events.

EVENTS	DIARY	
		MON 27
		TUE 28
		WED 29
		THU 30
		FRI 31
	G J Graham, d. 1878; plant collector in Mexico (*Salvia grahamii*) Henry Broughton, Lord Fairhaven, b. 1900; created garden at South Walsham Hall, Norfolk	SAT 1
		SUN 2

DIARY		EVENTS
MON 3		
TUE 4		
WED 5	George Forrest, d. 1932; plant collector (*Pieris forrestii*)	
THU 6		Lecture; Woking AGS, Mayford Village Hall, Saunders Lane, Mayford: 7.30 pm. Ganesh expedition, Bill Baker (0483 224269).
FRI 7		
SAT 8	Sir Herbert Maxwell, b. 1845; plantsman	North of England Orchid Show, Altrincham (061 439 5417).
SUN 9		

EVENTS	DIARY	
Lecture; East Lancashire AGS, Ramsbottom Civic Hall, Market Place: 7.45 pm. Czech gardens and gardeners, Ron and Joan Beeston (0706 356385).	Nicolas Culpeper, d. 1654; herbalist	MON 10
Demonstration; RHS Pershore. Around the garden in January. • Lecture; Cleveland AGS, Methodist Church Hall, Nunthorpe: 7.15 pm. Vanoise voyage, Dr P. Freeman (0642 315721).	William Curtis, b. 1746; founder of *The Botanical Magazine*	TUE 11
Demonstration; RHS Wisley. Propagation of garden plants. • Demonstration; RHS Hyde Hall, at Writtle College. Practical and low maintenance gardening.	Hon. & Rev. William Herbert, b. 1778; *Herbertia*	WED 12
Demonstration; RHS Pershore. Garden design 1 – using space in small gardens.	Hon. Vicary Gibbs, d. 1932; creator of garden at Aldenham, Hertfordshire	THU 13
		FRI 14
Workshop; RHS Pershore. Painting flowers for pleasure 1. • Walk; Hillier Arboretum: 11 am and 2 pm. Winter witch hazels.		SAT 15
Demonstration: RHS Wisley. Propagation of glasshouse plants. • Walk; RHS Wisley. Winter colour in the garden. • Walk; Hillier Arboretum: 11 am and 2 pm. Winter witch hazels. • Lecture; Ness Gardens. New Zealand plants in their natural habitats, Professor P. Bannister.	Sir Jeremiah Colman, d. 1942; orchid breeder and mustard manufacturer	SUN 16

DIARY		EVENTS
MON **17**	William Cavendish, 6th Duke of Devonshire, d. 1858; improved garden at Chatsworth, Derbyshire	
TUE **18**		Demonstration; RHS Pershore. Tricks and techniques for early crops.
WED **19**		Lecture; 7.30 pm, Belfast Castle. Small Gardens, Reg Maxwell. Admission free (0232 681246). ● Course; Organic garden design day, Ryton Organic Gardens.
THU **20**	Ferdinand Bauer, b. 1760; botanical artist	RBG, Edinburgh Public Lecture; 3 pm, Lecture Theatre, 20a Inverleith Row. Arid America: Cacti and other Xerophytes of the Southern United States and Mexico, Barry Miller. RBG, Edinburgh (031 552 7171). ● Lecture; RHS Hyde Hall, at Writtle College. Gardening history. ● Lecture; RHS Pershore. The ornamental kitchen garden 1 – history. ● Lecture; North Lancashire AGS, Unitarian Church, Scotforth, Lancaster: 7.30 pm. Rare and unusual northern flora, Malcolm Hutcheson (05395 34416).
FRI **21**		
SAT **22**	George Bunyard, d. 1919; pomologist and rosarian	Demonstration; RHS Pershore. Propagation 1 – getting started. ● Walk; Hillier Arboretum: 11 am and 2 pm. Winter witch hazels. ● Lecture; Dorset NCCPG, Allendale Centre, Wimborne: 2.30 pm. Abbotsbury gardens, past, present and future, Steven Griffiths.
SUN **23**		Walk; RHS Wisley. The changing face of Wisley. ● Walk; Hillier Arboretum: 11 am and 2 pm. Winter witch hazels.

EVENTS	DIARY	
Walk; RHS Wisley. The changing face of Wisley.	Henry Merryweather, b. 1839; nurseryman ('Bramley's Seedling')	MON 24
25 – 26 January; RHS Flower Show, RHS Westminster, London: 11 am – 7 pm. Royal Horticultural Society (071 828 1744). Ornamental Flower Show and Botanical Paintings. ● Workshop; RHS Pershore. Painting flowers for pleasure 2.	Lionel de Rothschild, b. 1882; creator of Exbury Gardens, Hampshire	TUE 25
26 – 27 January; Garden Leisure & Groundsmanship Exhibition, Royal Dublin Society, Ballsbridge. John Palmer (Exhibitions) (010 353 1 269 4022). ● Walk; RHS Rosemoor. Winter colour at Rosemoor. ● Demonstration; RHS Hyde Hall, at Writtle College, Writtle, Essex. Growing vegetables for small gardens (0245 400256). ● Workshop; Sir Harold Hillier Gardens and Arboretum, Hampshire. Plant propagation 1 – grafting (0794 368787). ● RHS Flower Show ends: 10 am – 5 pm.	Hugh, 5th Earl Annesley, b. 1831; creator of garden at Castlewellan, Co. Down	WED 26
Lecture; RHS Pershore. Garden history lecture. ● Garden Leisure & Groundsmanship Exhibition ends.	Lord Grenfell, d. 1925; president of the RHS	THU 27
Course; Harlow Carr. Garden Design: Garden style.	Mark Fenwick, d. 1945; creator of garden at Abbotswood, Gloucestershire	FRI 28
Workshop; Sir Harold Hillier Gardens and Arboretum, Hampshire. Plant propagation 1 – grafting (0794 368787). ● Lecture; Dorset NCCPG, St George's Church Hall, Fordington: 2.30 pm. Plants in medicine, Matthew Biggs.	Lord Digby, d. 1964; creator of garden at Minterne, Dorset	SAT 29
Lecture; Ness Gardens, Cheshire. The dwarf Ericaceae, J. K. Hulme (051 336 7769).	George Ehret, b. 1708; botanical artist	SUN 30

DIARY		EVENTS
MON **31**	Hugh Falconer, d. 1865; botanist in India (*Rhododendron falconeri*)	
TUE **1**		Demonstration; RHS Pershore. Around the garden in February.
WED **2**	William Aiton, b. 1766; RBG, Kew superintendent (1793 – 1841) and founder member of RHS	Lecture; East Yorkshire AGS, Beverley Girls' High School, Norwood: 7.30 pm. Finding a place for it, David Mowle. • Lecture; Derby Rock Garden Club (AGS), St Helen's House, King Street: 7.30 pm. Flowers of Andorra, V. Aspland.
THU **3**	Col. Frederick Bailey, b. 1882; soldier and botanist (*Meconopsis baileyi* syn. *M. betonicifolia*)	Demonstration; RHS Pershore. Unusual bulbs. • Lecture; East Dorset AGS, Lytchett Matravers Village Hall: 7.30 pm. Flowers of south west Turkey, James Compton (0202 692962). • Lecture; Woking AGS, Mayford Village Hall, Saunders Lane, Mayford: 7.30 pm. Bulbs and things, Kath Dryden (0483 224269).
FRI **4**		Lectures; Harlow Carr. History of flower painting, Penny Muter; Butterflies in Yorkshire, Michael Barnham.
SAT **5**	John Lindley, b. 1799; botanist and bibliophile	Demonstration; RHS Pershore. Propagation 2 – composts.
SUN **6**	Sir Lancelot 'Capability' Brown, d. 1783; landscaper	Walk; RHS Wisley. Winter interest under glass. • Walk; Sir Harold Hillier Gardens and Arboretum, Ampfield, Hampshire: 2 pm. Late winter tour. Meet in the car park. • RHS Regional Lecture; Ness Gardens, Cheshire: 2 pm. Gardening at the edge – the development of a maritime garden, S. Goodenough (051 336 7769).

EVENTS

DIARY

Events	Diary	
National Trust Lecture; 6 pm, Purcell Room, South Bank Centre. Shakespeare Gardens, Sir Roy Strong (071 928 8800). • Lecture; North London AGS, Oakwood Methodist Church Hall: 7.30 pm. *Galanthus*, Richard Nutt (081 445 1675).	Canon Henry Ellacombe, d. 1916; plantsman and writer (*In a Gloucestershire Garden*)	MON 7
Course; Harlow Carr. Flower arranging, Pat Reader. • Lecture; RHS Pershore. The design of Japanese gardens. • Lecture; Suffolk NCCPG, Otley College, Otley, Ipswich: 7.30 pm. Garden conservation in Poland, J. Michalak.	John Sibthorp, d. 1796; botanist	TUE 8
Lecture; 7.30 pm, Malone House, Belfast. Wildflowers of Ireland, Ray Nelson. Belfast Parks Department (0232 681246). • Demonstration; RHS Wisley. Growing plants under glass. • Lecture; Nottingham Rock Garden Club, Nethergate School, Swansdowne Drive, Clifton: 7.30 pm. Flowers of Turkey, Nick Turland. • Demonstration; RHS Hyde Hall, at Writtle College. Wall building for the garden.	William Bartram, b. 1739; American botanist	WED 9
Lecture; RHS Pershore. Garden design 2 – front gardens. • RHS Regional Lecture; Douglas, Isle of Man. Creating a cottage garden, Sue Phillips.	Rev. William Colenso, d. 1899; botanist in New Zealand	THU 10
Lecture; North East England AGS. Bulbs throughout the year, Jack Brownlees (091 286 9527). • Lecture; East Kent AGS, Furley Hall, Maidstone Road, Ashford: 7.45 pm. The rock garden at Wisley, Alan Robinson.	Robert Gathorne-Hardy, d. 1973; garden writer	FRI 11
Organic Wedding Fair, Ryton Organic Gardens. • AGS Show; Burleigh Community College, Thorpe Hill, Lougborough (0386 554790). • Course; Harlow Carr. An introduction to propagation, Nigel Hutchison. • Lecture; West Yorkshire AGS, St Chad's Parish Centre, Headingley, Leeds: 2.30 pm. Plants on limestone, Steve Furness (0423 886302). • 12 – 13 February; Open Weekend, Plant Centre, RHS Wisley. Orchids made easy, Ray Bilton. • Workshop; RHS Pershore. Winter fruit tree pruning. • 12 February – 1 May; Exhibition, Inverleith House, RBG Edinburgh: 10 am – 3.30 pm. A Sense of Place, Adrian Berg. Oils and watercolours including images of RBG Kew, Surrey and Stourhead, Wiltshire. The exhibition is free, and from April opens until 5 pm. • Lecture; Dorset NCCPG, Allendale Centre, Wimborne: 2.30 pm. Alternatives to peat, Margaret Scott.	Charles Darwin, b. 1809; naturalist	SAT 12
Demonstration; RHS Wisley. Growing plants under glass. • Walk; RHS Rosemoor. Bark, stems and evergreens. • Workshop; RHS Rosemoor. Winter propagation. • Lecture; Ness Gardens: 2 pm. Soil, air and water – the problems facing garden plants, Professor R. H. Marrs.	Sir Joseph Banks, b. 1743; botanist	SUN 13

DIARY	EVENTS
MON **14**	National Trust Lecture; 6 pm, Purcell Room, South Bank Centre. Architectural Plants for the Garden, Roderic Llewellyn (071 928 8800). • Lecture; West Sussex AGS, County Hall, Chichester: 7.30 pm. Flowers along the Silk Road, P. Cunnington (0903 241993). • Lecture; East Lancashire AGS, Ramsbottom Civic Hall: 7.45 pm. The evolution of two alpine gardens, Alan Furness (0706 356385).
TUE E. H. Wilson, b. 1876; collector (*Magnolia wilsonii*) **15**	Workshop; RHS Pershore. Propagation 3 – apple tree grafting.
WED **16**	Flower Arrangers' Day; RHS Wisley. Flowers around the world, Daphne Love. • Lecture; South Wales AGS, Pencoed College, Bridgend: 7 pm. *Cyclamen* and *Paeonia* species, R. Isherwood (0558 822960). • 16 February; Course, RBG Edinburgh, Lothian. Beginning botany, Dr Ian Darwin Edwards. 8 weeks (031 552 7171 Ext. 480). • Lecture; North Staffs AGS, Civic Hall, Alsager: 7.45 pm. Saxifrages, John Byam-Grounds (0270 874833).
THU Samuel Arnott, d. 1930; writer (*Galanthus* 'S Arnott') **17**	RBG, Edinburgh Public Lecture; Lecture Theatre: 3 pm. Irian Jaya, David Mitchell (031 552 7171). • Lecture; RHS Hyde Hall, at Writtle College. Garden design – part 1. • Workshop; RHS Pershore. The ornamental kitchen garden 2 – cropping plan. • Lecture; Berkshire AGS, Speen Parish Hall, Newbury: 7.30 pm. The genus *Iris*, Peter Maynard (0635 31759). • Lecture; North Lancashire AGS, Unitarian Church, Scotforth: 7.30 pm. Beyond the Pillars of Hercules, Charles Aitchison (05395 34416). • Lecture; Exeter AGS, St Thomas High School: 6.30 pm. Czech gardens and gardeners, Joan Beeston (0395 273636).
FRI Clarence Elliott, d. 1969; nurseryman and plantsman **18**	Course; Harlow Carr. Creative gardening: Selecting trees and shrubs, Rita Lait. • Lecture; North Cumbria Rock Garden Group (AGS), Newton Rigg College, Penrith: 7.30 pm. High summer in the rock garden, James Aitken. • Lecture; Bristol AGS, Westbury on Trym Methodist Hall: 7 pm. North African bulbs, Mike Salmon (0594 529663). • Lecture; Birmingham AGS, 36 Harborne Road: 7.30 pm. Erodiums, Dr Lionel Bacon (05646 2765). • Lecture; North Wales AGS, The Guildhall, Conwy: 7.30 pm. Inaccessible alpines – some mountain wanderings, Sylvia Morrow.
SAT William Nesfield, b. 1793; garden designer **19**	Demonstration; Rose pruning and growing, Hosford's Geraniums & Garden Centre, Co. Cork, Republic of Ireland (010 353 23 39159). • 19 – 20 February; Principles of garden design (seminar), John Brookes. RBG Kew (081 332 5626). • Lecture; Ulster AGS, Main Lecture Theatre, Ashby Building, Stranmillis Road, Belfast: 2.30 pm. Little gems for the rock garden, Harold McBride.
SUN **20**	Lecture; Ness Gardens: 2 pm. The Galapagos islands, D. Wakeham.

EVENTS | DIARY

EVENTS	DIARY	
National Trust Lecture; 6 pm, Purcell Room, South Bank Centre. Plant Introductions and Garden Design, Richard Bisgrove. The effect of the exotic discoveries of the plant hunters on the English garden. Tickets from the Festival Hall Box Office (071 928 ● 8800).	John Lewis, d. 1963; retailer and creator of Longstock Water Gardens, Hampshire	MON 21
22 – 23 February; RHS Flower Show, RHS Westminster, London: 11 am – 7 pm. Royal Horticultural Society (071 828 1744). Ornamental Plant Competition and Botanical Paintings. ● Royal Horticultural Society Annual General Meeting, RHS Old Hall, Westminster: 2 pm. ● Demonstration; RHS Pershore. Early flowering trees and shrubs.		TUE 22
Course; Alternative gardening course, Ryton Organic Gardens, Ryton on Dunsmore, West Midlands (0203 303517). ● Lecture; Leicester AGS, Church of the Martyrs Hall, Westcote Drive: 7.30 pm. The genus *Cyclamen*, Vic Aspland. ● Lecture; Ipswich AGS, Oddfellows Hall, High Street: 7.30 pm. Plants of the Great Snow mountains in China, S. G. Haw. ● RHS Flower Show ends: 10 am – 5 pm. ● Demonstration; RHS Wisley. Propagation of rock garden and alpine plants. ● Demonstration; RHS Rosemoor at Cannington College, Bridgwater, Somerset. Pruning ornamental trees and shrubs. ● Demonstration; RHS Hyde Hall, at Writtle College, Writtle, Essex . Grafting fruit trees (0245 400256).		WED 23
Workshop; RHS Pershore. Propagation 4 – plants from roots. ● RHS Regional Lecture; Chelmsford. My favourite plants, Anne Swithinbank.	Lord Redesdale, b. 1837; bamboo expert	THU 24
Course; Harlow Carr. Garden Design: Garden development from Brown to Jekyll. ● Lecture; RBG Kew, Surrey. Jodrell science behind the scenes (081 332 5626). ● Lecture; Norfolk NCCPG, Centre of East Anglian Studies, University of East Anglia, Norfolk: 7.30 pm. NCCPG and conservation in a broader context, Ian Beyer.	George Don, d. 1856; plant collector	FRI 25
Course; Harlow Carr. An introduction to propagation, Nigel Hutchison. ● Demonstration; RHS Pershore. Tools for the garden. ● Demonstration; J Bradshaw & Son, Busheyfields Nursery, Kent. A clematis pruning demonstration for the British Clematis Society. ● Demonstration; Rose pruning this weekend at John Sanday, Avon (0454 612195) ● Lecture; Hertfordshire AGS, Holy Trinity Church, Frogmore, Park Street, St Albans: 3 pm. Around the Mediterranean in 50 minutes, A. Kemp (0442 252596). ● Lecture; Dorset NCCPG, County Records Office, Dorchester: 2.30 pm. Rare, interesting and unusual plants, Jim Gardiner.		SAT 26
Demonstration; RHS Wisley. Propagation of rock garden and alpine plants. ● Lecture; Ness Gardens, Cheshire: 2pm. Growing on seedlings successfully, Dr H. A. McAllister (051 336 7769).	Mrs C W Earle, d. 1925; popular gardening writer	SUN 27

DIARY		EVENTS
MON **28**		National Trust Lecture; 6 pm, Purcell Room, South Bank Centre. Lanhydrock Garden through the Years 1909 – 1993, Peter Borlase. The speaker was the Trust's Senior Head Gardener in Cornwall. Tickets from the Festival Hall Box Office (071 928 880).
TUE **1**	Lady Clara Vyvyan, d. 1976; Cornish gardener and writer	Course; Harlow Carr. Successful soil management, Barry Brown. ● Demonstration; RHS Pershore. Around the garden in March. ● RHS Regional Lecture; Derby. Blooming containers, Tim Miles.
WED **2**	Rev. William Wilks, d. 1923; breeder of Shirley poppies	Demonstration; RHS Wisley. Rose pruning. ● Demonstration; RHS Rosemoor. Roses – planting and pruning. ● Workshop; RHS Rosemoor. Seed sowing. ● Lecture; RHS Pershore. AGM and RHS regional lecture. Clematis, Raymond Evison. ● Lecture; East Yorkshire AGS, Beverley Girls' High School, Norwood: 7.30 pm. Spring flowers from a national collection, Michael Myers. ● Lecture; Derby Rock Garden Club (AGS), St Helen's House, King Street: 7.30 pm. Flowers of the Rocky Mountains, Mrs & Mrs G. Phillips.
THU **3**	Batty Langley, d. 1751; landscaper	Workshop; RHS Pershore. Painting flowers for pleasure 3. ● AGM; East Dorset AGS, Lytchett Matravers Village Hall: 7.30 pm (0202 692962). ● Lecture; Woking AGS, Mayford Village Hall, Saunders Lane, Mayford: 7.30 pm. Propagation demonstration, John Gubbins, Auriol Hill and Chris Norton (0483 224269).
FRI **4**		Lecture; Kent Medway AGS, Bluebell Hill Village Hall, Robin Hood Lane, Chatham: 8 pm. Dwarf bulbs for the rock garden, D. Mowle. ● Lecture; Chipping Campden School Hall, Gloucestershire: 7.30 pm. Annual Ernest Wilson Memorial Garden Lecture. Roy Lancaster (0386 840764). ● Lectures; Harlow Carr. The twentieth century garden, Penny Muter; Some great Yorkshire gardens, Peggy Nicholls.
SAT **5**		5 – 6 March; Pruning demonstration, The Gardens of the Rose, Chiswell Green, St Albans: 11 am – 4 pm. Continuous demonstrations of how roses should be pruned at the headquarters of the Royal National Rose Society (0727 850461). ● Demonstration; Rose pruning demonstrations this weekend at John Sanday, Avon (0454 612195). ● AGS Early Spring Show; Mark Hall School, First Avenue, Harlow, Essex (0386 554790). ● AGM & Lecture; Lothians NCCPG, Conference Room, RBG Edinburgh: 10.30 am. National collection of *Chionodoxa*.
SUN **6**	General Sir Henry Collett, b. 1836; botanist and introducer of *Rosa gigantea; Colletia*	Craft Fair; Ryton Organic Gardens, Ryton on Dunsmore, West Midlands (0203 303517). ● Demonstration; RHS Wisley. Rose pruning. ● Walk; Sir Harold Hillier Gardens and Arboretum, Ampfield, Hampshire: 2 pm. Early spring tour. Meet in the car park. ● Lecture; Ness Gardens, Cheshire: 2pm. History and development of the gardens at Erdigg (051 336 7769). ● RNRS rose pruning demonstrations end.

EVENTS

DIARY

National Trust Lecture; 6 pm, Purcell Room, South Bank Centre. A Plantsman in the Gardens of the National Trust, Roy Lancaster (071 928 8800). • 7 – 11 March; School Organic Gardening week, Ryton Organic Gardens. • Lecture; Bedfordshire AGS, Village Hall, Wilstead: 8 pm. French Alps in summer, A. Colmer.	**MON** **7**
Course; Harlow Carr. An introduction to shrub pruning, Chris Margrave and Paul Griffiths. • Lecture; RHS Pershore. All about chrysanthemums. • Show; Cleveland AGS, Methodist Church Hall, Nunthorpe: 7.15 pm. Mini show and plant sale (0642 315721). • Lecture; Suffolk NCCPG, Otley College: 7.30 pm. Rose rescue, Peter Beales. • RHS Regional Lecture; Brecon. Kew Gardens, Brian Halliwell.	Sir William Chambers, d. 1796; garden architect (at Kew) and writer **TUE** **8**
Demonstration; RHS Wisley. Planting fruit trees. • Lecture; Oxford AGS, Halifax House, South Parks Road: 7.30 pm. With the AGS to the Andes, Capt. Peter Erskine (0865 351586). • Lecture; Nottingham Rock Garden Club, Nethergate School, Swansdowne Drive, Clifton: 7.30 pm. Mile high alpines, David King. • RHS Regional Lecture; Kidderminster. Plants and gardens of Scotland, John Basford.	Sir Thomas Hanbury, d. 1907; creator of garden at La Mortola, and benefactor of Wisley to the RHS **WED** **9**
Workshop; RHS Pershore. Garden design 3 – now get out of the rut. • RHS Regional Lecture; Bristol. Creating a garden for Chelsea, Faith Whiten.	**THU** **10**
Lecture; North East England AGS. Mountain flowers of Sichuan, David Millward (091 286 9527). • Lecture; East Kent AGS, Furley Hall, Maidstone Road, Ashford: 7.45 pm. The world of *Iris*, Brian Mathew.	Frederick Balfour, b. 1873; creator of arboretum at Dawyck, Borders **FRI** **11**
12 – 13 March; RHS Orchid Show, Westminster: 10 am – 5 pm. Specialist show devoted to orchids. • AGS Loughborough Show; Burleigh Community College, Thorpe Hill, Loughborough (0386 554790). • Course; Harlow Carr. Constructing rock gardens, Nigel Hutchison. • 12 – 13 March; Open Weekend, Plant Centre, RHS Wisley. Growing from seed. • 12 – 13 March; Garden design weekend, RHS Pershore. • Demonstration; Rose pruning demonstrations at John Sanday, Avon this weekend (0454 612195). • Lecture; Southport AGS, Hall of the Lord Street, West Church. Brian Russ. • Lecture; Dorset NCCPG, Allendale Centre, Wimborne: 2.30 pm. Salvias, Beryl Davies. • Lecture; North East NCCPG, Hancock Museum, Newcastle upon Tyne: 2.30 pm. Hepaticas, Michael Myers. • Lecture; Kent NCCPG, Horticultural Research Institute, East Malling: 2 pm. Restoration of the gardens at Belsay Hall, Stephen Anderton.	John Aubrey, b. 1626; naturalist and antiquarian; André le Nôtre, b. 1613; French royal gardener **SAT** **12**
Demonstration; RHS Wisley. Planting fruit trees. • Lecture; Ness Gardens: 2 pm. Native British orchids, T. Wells. • RHS Orchid Show ends: 10 am – 4 pm.	**SUN** **13**

DIARY	EVENTS
MON **14**	National Trust Lecture; 6 pm, Purcell Room, South Bank Centre. Gardens and Landscapes, Patrick Taylor. ● Lecture; Bluebell Nursery, Derbyshire (0283 222091). ● AGM & Lecture; West Sussex AGS, Chichester: 7.30 pm. Alpines and insects, M. Edwards (0903 241993). ● Lecture; East Lancashire AGS, Ramsbottom Civic Hall: 7.45 pm. Unusual plants for a northern garden, Thelma Kay (0706 356385). ● Lecture; Surrey NCCPG, Wisley, Surrey: 7.45 pm. Magnolias and other choice plants, Graham Rankin. Visitors £1.

| **TUE**
15 | Rev. George Engleheart, d. 1936; daffodil breeder | 15 – 16 March; RHS Flower Show, Westminster: 11 am – 7 pm. Early Camellia, Early Rhododendron, Early Daffodil and Ornamental Plant competitions. ● RHS Lecture; Westminster: 2.15 pm. Geraniums and erodiums, Trevor Bath. ● Lecture; RHS Pershore. Introducing new garden plants. |

DIARY		EVENTS
MON **14**		National Trust Lecture; 6 pm, Purcell Room, South Bank Centre. Gardens and Landscapes, Patrick Taylor. ● Lecture; Bluebell Nursery, Derbyshire (0283 222091). ● AGM & Lecture; West Sussex AGS, Chichester: 7.30 pm. Alpines and insects, M. Edwards (0903 241993). ● Lecture; East Lancashire AGS, Ramsbottom Civic Hall: 7.45 pm. Unusual plants for a northern garden, Thelma Kay (0706 356385). ● Lecture; Surrey NCCPG, Wisley, Surrey: 7.45 pm. Magnolias and other choice plants, Graham Rankin. Visitors £1.
TUE **15**	Rev. George Engleheart, d. 1936; daffodil breeder	15 – 16 March; RHS Flower Show, Westminster: 11 am – 7 pm. Early Camellia, Early Rhododendron, Early Daffodil and Ornamental Plant competitions. ● RHS Lecture; Westminster: 2.15 pm. Geraniums and erodiums, Trevor Bath. ● Lecture; RHS Pershore. Introducing new garden plants.
WED **16**		NAFAS Demonstrations; Digby Hall, Sherborne. Dorset & Guernsey area day (0258 837239). ● 16 – 17 March; NAFAS Devon & Cornwall Area Show & Exhibition, Hotel Metropole, Padstow (0579 370286). ● Lecture and AGM; South Wales AGS, Pencoed College: 7 pm. New Zealand Alpines, C. Mullins (0558 822960). ● AGM & Lecture; North Staffs AGS, Civic Hall, Alsager: 7.45 pm. Ways of growing alpines, Christine Trinder (0270 874833). ● RHS Flower Show ends: 10 am – 5 pm.
THU **17**	Ferdinand Bauer, d. 1826; botanical artist	RBG, Edinburgh Public Lecture; Lecture Theatre: 3 pm. Madagascar, Rosemary Clement (031 552 7171). ● Lecture; Berkshire AGS, Speen Parish Hall, Newbury: 7.30 pm. Eileen Larbey Lecture: Bulbs for the rock garden, Brian Mathew (0635 31759). ● Lecture; North Lancashire AGS, Unitarian Church, Scotforth: 7.30 pm. Saxifrages, Winton Harding (05395 34416). ● Lecture; Exeter AGS, St Thomas High School: 6.30 pm. Lilies, Alf Evans (0395 273636). ● RHS Regional Lecture; Beverley. The decorative vegetable garden, Joy Larkcom.
FRI **18**		Lecture; North Cumbria Rock Garden Group (AGS), Newton Rigg College, Penrith: 7.30 pm. Winton Harding. ● Lecture; Bristol AGS, Westbury on Trym Methodist Hall: 7 pm. Mountain plants in lowland gardens, Peter Cunnington (0594 529663). ● Lecture; North Wales AGS, New Arts Lecture Theatre, Bangor: 7.30 pm. Len Beer Memorial Lecture, Tony Schilling.
SAT **19**		AGS Kent Show; Rainham School, Rainham 10.30 am – 4.30 pm. AGS Medway Group (0474 703822). ● 19 – 27 March; Spring Gardens Week, Leeds Castle, Kent (0622 765400). ● AGS and SRGC Morecambe Show; Lancaster and Morecambe College of Further Education, (0386 554790). ● AGM & Lecture; Somerset & Avon NCCPG, Edington Hall: 2.30 pm. Himalayan plants in cultivation, Chris Chadwell. ● 19 – 20 March; Open Weekend, Plant Centre, RHS Wisley. Clematis, Raymond Evison.
SUN **20**	Sir Isacc Newton, d. 1727; scientist and apple grower	Walk; Isle of Wight Historic Gardens Trust, St Lawrence: 2.30 pm. ● Walk; RHS Rosemoor. Early spring at Rosemoor. ● Lecture; Ness Gardens: 2 pm. A week in the Pyrenees, P. L. Cunnington.

EVENTS	DIARY	
National Trust Lecture; 6 pm, Purcell Room, South Bank Centre. This lecture will be delivered by garden designer and writer Arabella Lennox Boyd, on a subject to be announced. Tickets from Royal Festival Hall Box Office (071 928 8800).	Wilfrid Fox, b. 1875; creator of Winkworth Arboretum, Surrey	MON 21
Course; Harlow Carr. Practical propagation workshop, Roger Brook. ● Demonstrations; RHS Wisley. Plant pests; Plant diseases and plant disorders. ● Workshop; RHS Pershore. Fix that mower. ● RHS Regional Lecture; Southampton. Plants with personality, Christopher Brickell.	Sir James Horlick, b. 1886; creator of Achamore Gardens, Strathclyde	TUE 22
Meet the Gardener; Ryton Organic Gardens, Ryton on Dunsmore, West Midlands. Late winter in the garden (0203 303517). ● Demonstration; RHS Wisley. Getting started with vegetables: managing the vegetable garden. ● Flower Arrangers' Day; RHS Wisley. The beauty of spring – Ikebana Way, Teneke Robertson. ● Demonstration; RHS Rosemoor at Cannington College, Bridgwater, Somerset. Grafting. ● AGM & Lecture; Leicester AGS, Church of the Martyrs Hall, Westcote Drive: 7.30 pm. Lost in a ½ acre, Dr John Richards.	John Bartram, b. 1699 ('the greatest natural botanist in the world', Linnaeus)	WED 23
Demonstrations; RHS Wisley. Plant pests; plant diseases and plant disorders. ● Lecture; RHS Hyde Hall, at Writtle College, Writtle, Essex. Garden design – part 2 (0245 400256). ● Workshop; RHS Pershore. Propagation 5 – dividing. ● Walk; Harlow Carr: 2 pm. Early spring walk with the curator. ● Lecture; Dorset NCCPG, County Records Office, Dorchester: 7.30 pm. Old roses at Mottisfont Abbey, Sarah Coles. ● Lecture; Strathclyde NCCPG, Greenbank Gardens, Strathclyde: 7.30 pm. Graham Pattison.	Daniel Hanbury, d. 1875; plant collector and pharmacologist	THU 24
AGM & Lecture; Norfolk NCCPG, Centre of East Anglian Studies, University of East Anglia, Norfolk: 7.30 pm. The Cottage Garden, Ethne Clarke. ● Course; Harlow Carr. Garden Design: Before the design – site and use studies. ● RHS Regional Lecture; Newport, Isle of Wight. Shrubaceous plantings, Dennis Woodland.	John Standish, b. 1814; nurseryman	FRI 25
Plant Sale; The Pavilion, North Parade, Bath: 11 am – 4 pm. Specialist nurseries from the South West. Contact Ms Derry Watkins (0225 891686). ● AGS East Lancashire Show; Hopwood Hall, Rochdale Road, Middleton, Manchester (0706 356385). ● Annual Show; North London AGS, Oakwood Methodist Church Hall (opposite Oakwood underground station): 2 – 4 pm. Includes plant sale (081 445 1675). ● Conference; Birmingham AGS, Solihull. Farrer and the rock garden (05646 2765). National Auricula & Primula Society Show, Kirkstall Lane, Leeds.	Robert Bolton, d. 1949; sweet pea breeder	SAT 26
Demonstration; RHS Wisley. Getting started with vegetables; managing the vegetable garden. ● Walk; RHS Wisley. Early flowering trees and shrubs. ● Lecture; Ness Gardens, Cheshire: 2pm. Two weeks in Japan, Dr J. Edmondson (051 336 7769).	Charles Raffill, d. 1951; plantsman	SUN 27

DIARY	EVENTS
MON **28**	National Trust Lecture; 6 pm, Purcell Room, South Bank Centre. What is a Garden For?, Nigel Nicolson. Tickets from the Royal Festival Hall Box Office (071 928 8800). • NAFAS Demonstration; Dolman Theatre, Newport, Gwent. Joyce Grimley, Newport Floral Society. • Walk; RHS Wisley. Early flowering trees and shrubs.
TUE **29**	Demonstration; RHS Pershore. Easter flower arranging – church and home.
WED **30**	Demonstration; RHS Hyde Hall, at Writtle College, Writtle, Essex . Growing herbs for cooking (0245 400256). • NAFAS Demonstration; Deans Close School Theatre, Cheltenham. George Smith, Stephen Lacey, Cheltenham Flower Club. • Flower arranging competitions and exhibitions; Jermyns House, Sir Harold Hillier Gardens and Arboretum, Hampshire. Wessex and Jersey area of NAFAS (0264 781474). • Meeting; Ipswich AGS, Oddfellows Hall, High Street: 7.30 pm. Includes alpine show and competition.
THU **31** Sir Isaac Balfour, b. 1853; botanist at RBG Edinburgh	
FRI **1**	1 April – 4 April: Crafts for Springtime & Early Garden Show, Kent County Showground, Detling: 9.30 – 5.00 pm. Rural Crafts Association (0428 682292). • 1 – 10 April; Easter Bulb display, Harlow Carr. • Lecture; Kent Medway AGS, Bluebell Hill Village Hall, Robin Hood Lane, Chatham: 8 pm. Propagation and the nursery, Tim Ingram.
SAT **2** J J Dillenius, d. 1747; German botanist	AGS South West Show; St Thomas High School, Hatherleigh Road, Exeter: 12 – 4.30 pm. Exeter group of the Alpine Garden Society (0404 881213). • AGS Cleveland Show; James Finegan Hall, Eston (0386 554790). • Primula Show, Village Hall, Horton Road, Datchet, Berkshire: 2.30 – 4.30 pm. National Primula & Auricula Society (Southern). • Demonstration; RHS Rosemoor at Cannington College, Bridgwater, Somerset. Growing vegetables for the small garden. • Crafts for Springtime & Early Garden Show continues.
SUN **3**	Crafts for Springtime & Early Garden Show continues. • Question time: Iden Croft Herbs, Kent: 2 – 4 pm (0580 891432). • 3 – 4 April; Craft Fair by Meadow Crafts at Ryton Organic Gardens, Ryton on Dunsmore, West Midlands (0203 303517). • Walk; Sir Harold Hillier Gardens and Arboretum, Ampfield, Hampshire: 2 pm. Easter garden tour. Meet in the car park.

EVENTS	DIARY	
Show; Cotswold & Malvern AGS, Pershore College of Horticulture. (0886 21576). • Garden Open; High Beeches, West Sussex: 10 am – 5 pm. Attractions include daffodil display, tasting of local wines, bookstall and watercolours by Helen Hilliard. • Lecture; Bedfordshire AGS, Village Hall, Wilstead: 8 pm. Looking back on '93, N. Crick. • Crafts for Springtime & Early Garden Show ends. • Craft Fair, Ryton Organic Gardens ends.	William Gumbleton, d. 1911; Irish botanist	MON 4
Demonstration; RHS Pershore. Around the garden in April.		TUE 5
Wildlife Gardening Day; Ryton Organic Gardens (0203 303517). • 6 – 8 April; Workshop, Harlow Carr: 10 am – 4.30 pm. Introduction to botanical illustration. • Lecture; Derby Rock Garden Club (AGS), St Helen's House, King Street: 7.30 pm. Campanulaceae, P. Lewis.	Henry Broughton, Lord Fairhaven, d. 1973; art collector and garden maker	WED 6
RBG, Edinburgh Public Lecture; 3 pm, Lecture Theatre, 20a Inverleith Row, Edinburgh. The challenge of Scottish plant conservation, Mike Scott (031 552 7171). • Lecture; RHS Pershore. Friends and foes in the garden. • Lecture; East Dorset AGS, Lytchett Matravers Village Hall: 7.30 pm. Propagation, Christine Walkden (0202 692962). • AGM; Woking AGS, Mayford Village Hall: 7.30 pm. Includes plant show (0483 224269).		THU 7
8 – 10 April; NCCPG Primula Conference, Harrogate. Primula Sale and some lectures are open to the public. Details from Booking Officer, Yorkshire NCCPG, Windy Ridge, Bolton Percy, York YO5 7BA. • 8 – 10 April; Crafts for Springtime & Early Garden Show, Lincolnshire County Showground, Grange de Lings: 9.30 – 5.00 pm (0428 682292). • Lecture; North East England AGS. Making do with what you've got, Alan Furness (091 286 9527). • Lecture; East Kent AGS, Furley Hall, Ashford: 7.45 pm. The propagation of alpines, Graham Gough and Tim Ingram.	Frank Kingdon Ward, d. 1958; plant collector	FRI 8
9 – 10 April; Gateshead Spring Flower Show, Gateshead Central Nursery, Whickham Highway: 10 am – 5 pm. Leisure Services, Gateshead Metropolitan Borough Council (091 490 1616 Ext. 272). • 9 - 10 April; Cornwall Gardens Society Spring Show, Rosewarne, Camborne. • AGS Nottingham Show; Arnold and Carlton College, Mapperley (0386 554790). • AGS Ulster Show; Greenmount College, Muckamore, Co. Antrim (0386 554790). • Show; East Dorset AGS, Ferndown Community Centre (0202 692962). • Lecture; North East NCCPG, Hancock Museum, Newcastle upon Tyne: 2.30 pm. Polemoniums, Dianne Allison; Variegated plants, Arthur Byrne. • Crafts for Springtime & Early Garden Show continues.	Francis Bacon, Viscount St Albans, d. 1626; Lord Chancellor and writer	SAT 9
Gateshead Spring Flower Show ends: 10 am – 5 pm. • Walk; RHS Wisley. Rock garden, alpine meadow and alpine house. • Crafts for Springtime & Early Garden Show ends.	William Purdom, b. 1880; plant collector	SUN 10

DIARY		EVENTS
MON **11**		Walk; RHS Wisley. Rock garden, alpine meadow and alpine house. ● Lecture; North London AGS, Oakwood Methodist Church Hall: 7.30 pm. Lewisias, Denzil Devos (081 445 1675). ● Lecture; East Lancashire AGS, Ramsbottom Civic Hall, Market Place: 7.45 pm. India, monsoon and beyond, Henry and Margaret Taylor (0706 356385). ● AGM; East Cheshire AGS, British Legion Hall, Grove Lane, Wilmslow: 8 pm. ● Lecture; Epping Forest AGS, St John's School, Tower Road, Epping: 8 pm. Cultivation of European orchids, Sandra Bell. ● RHS Regional Lecture; St Andrews. Gardening with the Edwardians, Kay Sanecki. ● Lecture; Surrey NCCPG, Wisley: 7.45 pm. Ericaceae, Barry Starling.
TUE **12**	William Kent, d. 1748; landscaper	12 – 13 April; RHS Flower Show, Westminster: 11 am – 7 pm. Main Camellia, Daffodil and Ornamental Plant competitions. Includes the AGS London Show. ● RHS Lecture; Westminster: 2.15 pm. *Lycaste* and *Anguloa*, Henry Oakeley. ● RHS Lecture; Westminster: 6 pm. Gardening up the wall, Christopher Grey-Wilson. ● Lecture; RHS Pershore. Plant trials at Wisley. ● AGM and Brains Trust; Cleveland AGS, Methodist Church Hall, Nunthorpe: 7.15 pm. (0642 315721). ● Lecture; Dorset NCCPG, Allendale Centre, Wimborne: 7.30 pm. Plant hunting in Mexico, James Compton. ● Lecture; Suffolk NCCPG, Haughley Park, Stowmarket: 7.30 pm. 500 years of English gardening, Brian Halliwell.
WED **13**	Robert Fortune, d. 1880; plant hunter (*Fortunella*)	RBG, Edinburgh Public Lecture; Lecture Theatre: 7.30 pm. The RBGE Expedition to Taiwan, Sid Clarke. ● Walk; RHS Hyde Hall, at Writtle College. Spring walk. ● Lecture; Nottingham RGC, Nethergate School: 7.30 pm. Ferns, A. R. Busby. ● RHS Flower Show ends: 10 am – 5 pm.
THU **14**	Walter Bentley, d. 1953; creator of garden at Quarry Wood, Berkshire	Workshop: Iden Croft Herbs, Kent. Propagation and potting on (0580 891432). ● Demonstration; RHS Pershore. Garden design 4 – climbers. ● AGM and Lecture; Wiltshire Gardens Trust. The garden in its setting and environment, John Brookes. Members and guests only.
FRI **15**	Rev. Adam Buddle, d. 1715; (*Buddleja*)	15 – 17 April; Crafts for Springtime & Early Garden Show, South of England Showground, Ardingly: 9.30 am – 5 pm (0428 682292). ● 15 – 17 April; Spring Gardening Show, Capel Manor, Enfield. Garden Events. ● AGM & Lecture; Bristol AGS, Westbury on Trym Methodist Hall: 7 pm. Woodland plants, Charlotte Evans. ● Meeting; North Wales AGS, Brambell Building, Bangor: 7.30 pm. ● AGM; Birmingham AGS, Birmingham Medical Institute: 7.30 pm. (05646 2765). ● Walk; Bath Botanical Gardens, Avon: 10 am. Hillier Gardening Club (0794 368966).
SAT **16**	Henry, 2nd Lord Aberconway, b. 1879; president of the RHS (1931 – 1955)	AGS & SPRC Northumberland Show; Wentworth Leisure Centre, Hexham. ● Belfast Spring Flower Show. ● Workshop; RHS Pershore. The ornamental kitchen garden 3. ● Crafts for Springtime & Early Garden Show continues. ● Spring Gardening Show, Capel Manor continues.
SUN **17**	Col. Frederick Bailey, d. 1967; soldier and botanist	Crafts for Springtime & Early Garden Show ends. ● Spring Gardening Show, Capel Manor ends.

EVENTS	DIARY	
Plant Sale; Bingham Hall, Cirencester: 10.30 am – 3 pm. Specialist nurseries from the Southwest. Contact Ms Derry Watkins (0225 891686).	Erasmus Darwin, d. 1802; scientist and poet (*Botanic Garden*)	MON **18**
Demonstration; RHS Wisley. Biological pest control. ● Workshop; RHS Pershore. Propagation 6 – alpines. ● RHS Regional Lecture; Exeter. The RHS gardens, Mike Pollock. ● Walk; Hinton Ampner House, Hampshire: 2.15 pm.	Charles Darwin, d. 1882; naturalist	TUE **19**
Meet the Gardener; Ryton Organic Gardens. Spring time. ● Demonstration; RHS Wisley. Propagation of hardy plants. ● Flower Arrangers' Day; RHS Wisley. Artistic inspirations, Carol Firmstone. ● Workshop; Hillier Arboretum. Traditional hanging baskets. ● RHS Regional Lecture; Redruth. Can the Americans garden? Timothy Walker. ● Lecture; Museum of Garden History, London: 7 pm. Unusual vegetables, Joy Larkcom.	Peter Barr, b. 1826; botanist and daffodil breeder	WED **20**
21 – 24 April; Harrogate Spring Show, Valley Gardens, Harrogate: 10 am – 7 pm. Includes North of England AGS Show. ● Lecture; RHS Hyde Hall, at Writtle College. Historic gardens of national importance. ● Lecture; Exeter AGS, St Thomas High School: 6.30 pm. Saxifrages, Byam-Grounds (0395 273636). ● Lecture; RHS Pershore. Finding plants from *The Plant Finder*.		THU **21**
Lecture; North Cumbria Rock Garden Group (AGS), Newton Rigg College, Penrith: 7.30 pm. Dolomites, Ian and Carole Bainbridge. ● RHS Regional Lecture; Nottingham. Michael Jefferson-Brown. ● Harrogate Spring Show continues: 10 am – 7 pm.	James Anderson, d. 1842; botanist and plant collector (*Carex andersonii*)	FRI **22**
AGS Dublin Show; Cabinteely Community School, Cabinteely, Co. Dublin (0386 554790). ● 23 – 24 April; Festival of Spring Gardening, Borde Hill, Sussex. Garden Events. ● Bird Watch; Ness Gardens: 5.30 am. Limited numbers. ● Plant Sale; Somerset & Avon NCCPG, Clapton Court Gardens, Somerset: 10.30 am – 4 pm. ● Workshop; RHS Pershore. Photography – plants in focus. ● Harrogate Spring Show continues: 9.30 am – 5 pm. ● Annual Show; Kent Medway AGS, Bluebell Hill Village Hall, Chatham.	Harold Comber, d. 1969; plant collector and lily breeder	SAT **23**
Specialist Plant Sale; Calke Abbey, Derbyshire (0602 830278). ● Garden Tour; Ness Gardens: 10.30 am. Part of National Plants and Gardens Week. ● Plant Sale; The Old Rectory, Oby, Great Yarmouth: 2 – 5 pm. Norfolk NCCPG. ● Plant Sale; Museum of Garden History, London: 11 am – 5 pm. ● Walk; Greenbank Gardens, Strathclyde: 2.30 pm. With head gardener, Jim May. ● Plant Sale; Kent NCCPG, Coldham, Little Chart Forstal: 2 – 5 pm. ● Walk; RHS Wisley. Wisley's birds. ● Walk; Westonbirt Arboretum, Gloucestershire: 2.30 pm. Shrubs for your garden. ● Harrogate Spring Show ends: 10 – 4 pm. ● Festival of Gardening, Borde Hill ends.	Sir Jeremiah Colman, b. 1859; mustard maker and orchid breeder	SUN **24**

DIARY		EVENTS
MON 25		
TUE 26	Sam McGredy II, d. 1926; rose breeder	Demonstration; RHS Pershore. Down the garden path.
WED 27	Lawrence Johnston, d. 1958; creator of Hidcote Manor, Gloucestershire	Course; Harlow Carr. Introduction to botanical illustration, Valerie Oxley. • Demonstration; RHS Wisley. Secrets of tender and difficult crops revealed. • NAFAS Demonstration; Armstrong Hall, Thornbury. Mrs Ann Stott, Severn Vale Flower Club. • AGM & Lecture; Ipswich AGS, Oddfellows Hall, High Street: 7.30 pm. Plants of the Peloponnese, Jill White. • Walk; RHS Rosemoor. Spring at Rosemoor. • Walk; RHS Hyde Hall. National *Malus* collection. • Lecture; Leicester AGS, Church of the Martyrs Hall: 7.30 pm. Alpines through the seasons, A. G. Cook. • RHS Regional Lecture; Hagley. Modern garden roses, John Mattock.
THU 28	Charles Sturt, b. 1795; botanist of Australia	Walk; Harlow Carr. With the curator. • Lecture; Dorset NCCPG, Digby Hall, Sherborne: 7.30 pm. Pale and interesting, Trevor Bath. • Course; West Dean College, Chichester. Container gardening (0243 811343).
FRI 29	Rev. Samuel Goodenough, b. 1743; founder and first treasurer of the Linnaean Society	Course; Harlow Carr. Garden design graphics. • Course; West Dean College, Chichester, West Sussex. Spring into summer (0243 811343).
SAT 30	Sir Gerald Loder, Lord Wakehurst, d. 1936; creator of Wakehurst Place, West Sussex	30 April – 2 May; Bath Spring Flower Show, Victoria Park (0225 314213). • 30 April – 2 May; Milton Keynes Garden Show, Milton Keynes. Garden Events. • 30 April – 2 May; Open weekend, Hydon Nurseries, Surrey (0483 860252). • Auricula Show; Church House, Holy Trinity Church, Brompton Road, London SW7: 2.30 – 4.30 pm. • Auricula Show; Knowle, West Midlands (0225 448433). • Garden Open; High Beeches, West Sussex: 1 – 5 pm. NCCPG opening.
SUN 1		Orchid Society of Great Britain Spring Show, Syon Park, London (0483 421423). • 1 – 2 May; Windsor Garden Show, Royal Windsor Race Club (0795 428242). • 1 – 2 May; Fair, Bodiam Castle, East Sussex. National Trust. • Question Time: Iden Croft Herbs, Kent: 2 – 4 pm (0580 891432). • Demonstration; RHS Wisley. Secrets of tender and difficult crops revealed. • Plant Sale; Essex NCCPG, Marks Hall, Coggleshall: 11 am – 5 pm. • Plant Sale; Kingston Maurward, Dorset: 12.30 pm. Dorset NCCPG. • Lecture; Greenbank Gardens, Strathclyde: 2.30 pm. Himalayan plants in cultivation, Cameron Carmichael. • Garden Open; Goldney Hall, Avon: 2 – 6 pm. • Garden Open; Hill House Garden, Hertfordshire. For the Herts and Middlesex Wildlife Trust. • Bath Spring Flower Show continues. • Milton Keynes Garden Show continues.

EVENTS	DIARY	
Lecture; Bedfordshire AGS, Village Hall, Wilstead: 8 pm. Nepal in the monsoon, Dr C. Bucke. • Plant Sale; Ness Gardens: 10 am. Friends of Ness Gardens. • Windsor Garden Show ends. • Bath Spring Flower Show ends. • Milton Keynes Garden Show ends.	Sir John Heathcoat Amory, b. 1894; creator of garden at Knightshayes, Devon	MON 2
3 – 4 May; RHS Flower Show, Westminster: 11 am – 7 pm. Main Rhododendron, Late Daffodil, Tulip, and Ornamental Plant competitions. • RHS Lecture; Westminster: 2.15 pm. The Queen Elizabeth, The Queen Mother's Bursary Lecture, Dr Mark Watson. • Lecture; Westminster: 6 pm. RHS and National Trust for Scotland. Osgood Mackenzie's masterpiece – the garden of Inverewe, Professor Douglas Henderson.	George Sherriff, b. 1898; plant hunter (*Paeonia lutea* var. *ludlowii*)	TUE 3
Course; Ness Gardens. Photography in the garden for beginners. Limited numbers. • Walk; RHS Hyde Hall. Viburnum collection and woodland walk. • Lecture; Westminster: 2.15 pm. RHS and RNRS lecture. Roses and rose people, John Mattock. • Lecture; East Yorkshire AGS, Beverley Girls' High School, Norwood: 7.30 pm. Plants from my travels, Colin Stephenson. • RHS Flower Show ends: 10 am – 5 pm.		WED 4
Workshop; RHS Pershore. Propagation 7 – softwood cuttings. • Lecture; East Dorset AGS, Lytchett Matravers Village Hall: 7.30 pm. The Cape floral kingdom, Dennis Woodland (0202 692962). • Lecture; Woking AGS, Mayford Village Hall: 7.30 pm. A dip in the Great Basin, Jim Archibald (0483 224269). • Plant Sale; Strathclyde NCCPG, Greenbank Gardens, Strathclyde: 11 am.	Hugh Dickson, d. 1904; rosarian	THU 5
6 – 8 May; Malvern Spring Gardening Show, Three Counties Show-ground: 10 – 6 pm (0684 892751). • 6 – 8 May; Spring Flower Show, Blenheim Palace, Oxfordshire. Garden Events. • Lectures; Harlow Carr. Medieval herb gardens, Penny Muter; The preservation of flowers and herbs, Mavis Hammond. • AGM; Kent Medway AGS, Bluebell Hill Village Hall, Chatham: 8 pm.		FRI 6
7 – 8 May; British Iris Society Show, RHS Wisley. • 7 – 8 May; Spring-fields Country Fair and Flower Parade, Spalding. • AGS East Anglia Show; Uplands Middle School, Sudbury, (0386 554790). • AGS East Cheshire Show; Ryles Park County High School, Macclesfield. • Tulip Show; Wrenthorpe, West Yorkshire (0924 375843). • Plant sale; Harlow Carr. Bring and buy. • Plant Sale; Somerset & Avon NCCPG, Armstrong Hall, Thornbury: 10.30 am – 2.30 pm. • Bird Watch; Ness Gardens: 9 am. With Colin Wells. Limited numbers. • 7 – 8 May; Bonsai Weekend, Leonardslee Gardens, West Sussex. • Malvern Spring Gardening Show continues: 9.30 am – 6 pm. • Spring Flower Show, Blenheim Palace continues.	E A Bowles, d. 1954; plantsman and writer	SAT 7
Walk; RHS Wisley. Trees, shrubs and herbaceous perennials. • Plant Sale; Felsham House, Felsham, Suffolk: 11 am – 5 pm. Suffolk NCCPG. Teas. • Malvern Spring Gardening Show ends: 9.30 am – 5 pm. • Spring Flower Show, Blenheim Palace ends. • British Iris Society Show, Wisley, ends. • Springfields Country Fair ends.	Thomas Baines, d. 1875; artist, explorer and botanist (*Aloe bainesii*)	SUN 8

DIARY		EVENTS
MON 9	Charles Turner, d. 1885; nurseryman	Walk; RHS Wisley. Trees, shrubs and herbaceous perennials. • Lecture; East Lancashire AGS, Ramsbottom Civic Hall: 7.45 pm. With the AGS to the Andes, Capt. Peter Erskine (0706 356385).
TUE 10	Rev. H H d'Ombrain, b. 1818; rose grower	Lecture; RHS Pershore. Successful Rhododendrons.
WED 11		11 – 13 May; Royal Ulster Show, Balmoral, Belfast (0232 665225). • 11 – 14 May; NAFAS Conference and competitions, Guernsey. Open to all members. • Lecture; Nottingham Rock Garden Club, Nethergate School, Clifton: 7.30 pm. Dwarf shrubs for the rock garden, Bob Straughan. • Dawn Chorus; Westonbirt Arboretum, Gloucestershire: 4.30 am. Followed by champagne breakfast.
THU 12	Reginald Cory, d. 1934; plant collector, philanthropist and garden maker (Dyffryn Botanic Garden, South Glamorgan)	Workshop: Iden Croft Herbs, Kent. Growing and using culinary herbs (0580 891432). • Demonstration; RHS Pershore. Plant association in the garden. • Walk; Harlow Carr: 2 pm. With the head gardener. • National Auricula & Primula Society Show; Houghton le Spring, Tyne & Wear. • Royal Ulster Show continues.
FRI 13		13 – 15 May; Chelsea preview and open weekend, Blackmore & Langdon, Pensford, Avon (0275 332300). • 13 – 15 May; Highclere Castle Flower Show, Newbury: 10 am (0980 611485). • Lecture; North East England AGS. In search of the pink Celmisia, Capt. Peter Erskine (091 286 9527). • AGM; East Kent AGS, Furley Hall, Ashford: 7.45 pm. • Royal Ulster Show ends.
SAT 14	Mary Delany, b. 1700; paper flower artist	AGS Midland Show; Alderbrook School, Solihull (0386 554790). • 14 – 15 May; Herts Garden Show, Knebworth House, Stevenage (0795 428242). • 14 – 15 May; English Wine Festival. Leeds Castle, Kent (0622 765400). • Tulip Show; Normanton, West Yorkshire (0924 375843). • Workshop; RHS Pershore. Hanging baskets. • Lecture; North East NCCPG, Hancock Museum, Newcastle upon Tyne: 2.30 pm. Edinburgh Botanic Garden, Chris Page. • Highclere Castle Flower Show continues.
SUN 15		South Suffolk Show, Ampton, Bury St Edmunds (0638 750879). • Walk; RHS Wisley. May-time medley. • Demonstration; RHS Rosemoor. Hanging baskets and containers. • Walk; RHS Rosemoor. Stream and bog garden. • 15 – 16 April; RHS Regional Lecture Weekend, Windermere. Martin Gardner, Michael Warren, Allen Paterson, and Trevor Bath. • Open Day; Riseholme Hall, Lincolnshire: 10.30 am – 4 pm. • Garden Open; Carclew Gardens, Cornwall. For the Army Benevolent Fund. • Garden Open; Goldney Hall, Avon: 2 – 6 pm. • Herts Garden Show ends. • Highclere Castle Flower Show ends.

EVENTS	DIARY	
Walk; RHS Wisley. May-time medley: plants, facts and artifacts.	Henry Elwes, b. 1846; dendrologist and collector (*Galanthus elwesii*)	MON 16
Walk; Hinton Ampner House, Hampshire: 2.15 pm.	George Glenny, d. 1874; popular gardening writer	TUE 17
Meet the Gardener; Ryton Organic Gardens. Spring into summer. ● AGM and Lecture; Harlow Carr. Northern Horticultural Society. ● Walk; Ness Gardens: 7pm. A conservationist's guide to Thurstaston Common, Professor Marrs. Limited numbers. ● Flower Arrangers' Day; RHS Wisley. Images, Kathleen Hyde. ● Demonstration; RHS Hyde Hall, at Writtle College, Writtle, Essex . Hanging baskets (0245 400256).		WED 18
19 – 21 May; Devon County Show, Westpoint, Clyst St Mary. Devon County Agricultural Association (0392 444777). ● Plant Sale; Berkshire AGS, Speen Parish Hall, Newbury: 7.30 pm. (0635 31759). ● Show; Exeter AGS, St Thomas High School: 6.30 pm. Includes plant sale (0395 273636). ● Demonstration; Harlow Carr: 2 pm. Planting sinks and troughs.		THU 19
20 – 22 May; Journées des Plantes de Courson, Domaine de Courson, 91680 Courson Monteloup. Prestigious French show with high quality exhibitors and a relaxed atmosphere (010 33 1 64 58 90 12). ● 20 – 21 May; Shropshire & West Mid Show, Agricultural Showground, Shrewsbury. Shropshire & West Midlands Agricultural Society (0734 362824). ● Course; Harlow Carr. Aromatic plants and herbs, Rita Lait. ● Devon County Show continues.	Richard Cox, d. 1845; brewer ('Cox's Orange Pippin')	FRI 20
AGS Southport Show; Lord Street South Church Hall, Southport (0386 554790). ● Bird Watch; Ness Gardens: 9 am. Led by Colin Wells, RSPB warden. Limited numbers. ● 21 – 22 May; Argyll & Bute Rhododendron event, Crarae Gardens, Strathclyde. ● Shropshire & West Mid Show ends. ● Devon County Show ends.	William Cavendish, 6th Duke of Devonshire, b. 1790; garden maker at Chatsworth, Derbyshire	SAT 21
Garden walk: Iden Croft Herbs, Kent. The herb garden in May (0580 891432). ● Plant Sale; Birmingham Botanical Gardens and Glasshouses, West Midlands. Friends' plant market.	Thomas Bridges, b. 1807; introducer of *Victoria amazonica*	SUN 22

DIARY		EVENTS
MON 23		
TUE 24		24 – 27 May; Chelsea Flower Show, Royal Hospital, Chelsea: 8 am – 8 pm. • Workshop; RHS Pershore. Hanging baskets.
WED 25	John, 3rd Earl Bute, b. 1713; prime minister and botanist	Workshop; Hillier Arboretum. Basic botany. • Course; Harlow Carr. Flower arranging course, Pat Reader. • NAFAS Instruction Day; Larruputz Centre, Ross on Wye. Mrs Ann Stott (0633 440223). • Lecture; Leicester AGS, Church of the Martyrs Hall: 7.30 pm. An introduction to botanical knowledge, Dolly Norledge. • Lecture; Ipswich AGS, Oddfellows Hall: 7.30 pm. Alpines of the Himalayas, Chris Chadwell. • Visit to Triscombe Nursery; Somerset & Avon NCCPG. Tickets required. • Chelsea Flower Show continues: 8 am – 8 pm.
THU 26	W J Bean, b. 1863; *Trees & Shrubs Hardy in the British Isles*	Workshop; RHS Pershore. Planting up patio containers. • Chelsea Flower Show continues: 8 am – 8 pm.
FRI 27	Countess Amherst, d. 1838; plant collector and patron (*Amherstia*)	Course; Harlow Carr. Garden Design: Designing the hard landscape. • Chelsea Flower Show ends: 8 am – 5 pm.
SAT 28		28 – 29 May; Herts County Show, The Showground (M1, Junction 9) (0582 792626). • 28 – 30 May; Gardeners Weekend Show, Wimpole Hall, Hertfordshire. Garden Events. • 28 – 29 May; Loseley Flower Festival, Guildford (0372 457375). • 28 – 30 May; Festival of Flowers, Marble Hill House, Twickenham: 10 am – 6 pm (081 460 7902). • 28 – 30 May; Fair, Felbrigg Hall, Norfolk. National Trust. • Workshop; RHS Pershore. Planting up patio containers. • Concert; Westonbirt Arboretum, Gloucestershire: 7 pm. Sweet Harmony.
SUN 29	Leopold de Rothschild, d. 1917; creator of Ascott, Buckinghamshire	29 – 30 May; Kent Garden Show, County Showground, Detling (0795 428242). • Plants and Gardens Festival; Dyffryn Gardens, Cardiff: 11 am – 4 pm (0225 891686). • Fair; Florence Court, Co. Fermanagh. National Trust. • Family Day; Nostell Priory, West Yorkshire. National Trust. • Garden Open; Carclew Gardens, Cornwall. For Mount Edgecumbe Hospice. • Garden Open; High Beeches, West Sussex: 10 am – 5 pm. Azalea opening. • Garden Open; Lakeside, Hereford & Worcester: 2 – 6 pm. For the Red Cross. • Festival of Flowers, Marble Hill continues. • Gardeners Weekend Show, Wimpole Hall continues.

EVENTS	DIARY	
Surrey County Show, Stoke Park, Guildford (0483 414651). • Northumberland County Show, Tynedale Park, Corbridge (0434 344443). • Family Day; Blickling Hall, Norfolk. National Trust. • Festival of Flowers, Marble Hill ends. • Kent Garden Show ends. • Gardeners Weekend Show, Wimpole Hall ends.		MON 30
Course; Harlow Carr. Getting the best from the kitchen garden, Barry Brown. • Workshop; RHS Pershore. Pruning and training climbers.		TUE 31
Royal Bath & West of England Show, The Showground, Shepton Mallet (0749 823211). • 1 – 2 June; Suffolk Show, Bucklesham Road, Ipswich. Suffolk Agricultural Association (0473 726847).		WED 1
The London Rare Plants Fair, Battersea Town Hall, Lavender Hill: 11 am – 7 pm (0225 891686). • Demonstration; RHS Pershore. Around the garden in June. • Demonstration; Harlow Carr: 2 pm. Plants in containers. • Family Day; Charlecote Park, Warwickshire: 11 am – 6 pm. National Trust. • Royal Bath & West Show continues. • Suffolk Show ends.	Vita Sackville-West, d. 1962; creator of Sissinghurst Castle, Kent	THU 2
3 – 5 June; Great Garden & Countryside Festival, Holker Hall, Cark in Cartmel: 10 am – 5.30 pm (05395 58328). • Lecture; Kent Medway AGS, Bluebell Hill Village Hall, Chatham: 8 pm. Heathers through the year, Tessa Forbes. • Royal Bath & West Show continues.	C H Curtis, b. 1869; editor (Gardeners Chronicle)	FRI 3
AGS Summer Show (South); Merrist Wood Agricultural College, Worplesdon (0386 554790). • 4 – 5 June; British Iris Society Show, RHS Wisley. • National Plant Sale; Brockett's Farm, Fetcham, Leatherhead, Surrey. The Cottage Garden Society. • 4 – 5 June; Craft Fair, The Gardens of the Rose, St Albans (0727 850461). • Opera; Wimpole Hall, Cambridgeshire. National Trust. • Great Garden & Countryside Festival, Holker Hall continues: 10 am – 7.30 pm. • Course; Harlow Carr. Photography in the spring garden, Peter Cordall. • Royal Bath & West Show ends.	Nathaniel Ward, d. 1868; inventor of Wardian case	SAT 4
Plant Sale; Waddesdon Manor, Buckinghamshire: 11 am – 4 pm. Oxon, Berks & Bucks NCCPG. • Plant Sale; Felley Priory, Nottinghamshire: 11 am – 4 pm. For the NCCPG. • Walk; Hillier Arboretum: 2 pm. • Teddy Bears Picnic; Sudbury Hall, Derbyshire. National Trust. • Garden Open; Hill House Garden, Hertfordshire. For the Red Cross. • Craft Fair, The Gardens of the Rose, continues. • Great Garden & Countryside Festival ends: 10 am – 5.30 pm. • British Iris Society Show, Wisley ends.		SUN 5

DIARY		EVENTS
MON **6**		6 June – 8 July; Kew School of Garden Design, John Brookes. Details from Adult Education Section, RBG Kew (081 332 5626). ● Lecture; Bedfordshire AGS, Village Hall, Wilstead: 8 pm. Daphnes, Brian Mathew.
TUE **7**		
WED **8**	Mrs C W Earle, b. 1836; popular gardening writer	8 – 9 June; Early Summer Flower Show, St Helier: 2 – 9 pm (0534 37227). ● Meet the Gardener; Ryton Organic Gardens. Summer in the Garden. ● Course; Harlow Carr. Plants of the Bible lands, Kate Garton. ● Demonstration; RHS Wisley. Summer treatment of grapes. ● Demonstration; RHS Rosemoor. Organic pest and disease control. ● Walk; RHS Rosemoor. Early summer at Rosemoor. ● Demonstration; RHS Hyde Hall, at Writtle College. Know your trees – by leaf.
THU **9**	E F Warburg, d. 1966; botanist (*Quercus warburgii*)	9 – 11 June; Royal Cornwall Show, Wadebridge (0208 812183). ● 9 – 11 June; South of England Show, Ardingly (0444 892700). ● Demonstration; RHS Wisley. Summer treatment of grapes ● Demonstration; RHS Pershore. Garden design 5 – constructing a rock garden. ● Walk; Harlow Carr: 2 pm. ● Jersey Early Summer Flower Show ends: 9.15 – 8 pm.
FRI **10**	Sir Cecil Hanbury MP, d. 1937; owner and improver of La Mortola gardens	10 – 12 June; Summer Gardening Show, Capel Manor, Enfield. Garden Events. ● 10 – 12 June; Flower Festival, The Mansion House, Luton Hoo, Bedfordshire. Bedfordshire Women's Institutes. ● Course; Harlow Carr. Introduction to garden design, Rita Lait. ● Garden Visit; Hestercombe, Somerset: 2 pm. Hillier Gardening Club (0794 368966). ● Open Air Concert; Felbrigg Hall, Norfolk. National Trust. ● Jazz Concert; Fountains Abbey, North Yorkshire. National Trust. ● Royal Cornwall Show continues. ● South of England Show continues.
SAT **11**		11 – 12 June; Craft Fair, Newby Hall, North Yorkshire. ● Plant Sale; Somerset & Avon NCCPG, Saltford Hall: 10.30 am – 2.30 pm. ● Open Air Concert; Fountains Abbey, North Yorkshire. National Trust. ● Open Air Dance; Chartwell, Kent. National Trust. ● Jazz Concert; Felbrigg Hall, Norfolk. National Trust. ● Jazz Concert; The Vyne, Hampshire. National Trust. ● Open Day; Caythorpe Court, Lincolnshire: 1.30 – 5 pm. ● Summer Gardening Show, Capel Manor continues. ● Royal Cornwall Show ends. ● South of England Show ends.
SUN **12**		Walk; RHS Wisley. Seasonal walk and model small gardens reviewed. ● Plant Sale; Belsay Hall, Northumberland. North East NCCPG. ● Open Air Concert; Felbrigg Hall, Norfolk. National Trust. ● Garden Open; Crittenden House Kent: 2 – 6 pm. For the RSPCA. ● Summer Gardening Show, Capel Manor ends. ● Craft Fair, Newby Hall ends.

EVENTS	DIARY	

Walk; RHS Wisley. Seasonal walk and model small gardens reviewed. | | **MON** 13

14 – 16 June; Three Counties Show, Three Counties Showground, Malvern (0684 892751). ● Demonstration; RHS Pershore. Garden design 6 – constructing a water garden. | Cecil Andrews, d. 1951; botanist | **TUE** 14

15 – 19 June; BBC Gardeners' World Live, National Exhibition Centre, Birmingham (081 943 5000). Includes an RHS Flower Show. ● Flower Arrangers' Day; RHS Wisley. Fred Wilkinson. ● Course; Harlow Carr. Flower arranging course, Pat Reader. ● Demonstration; RHS Rosemoor. Fruit and vegetables. ● Demonstration; RHS Hyde Hall, at Writtle College. Pests and diseases on fruit and vegetables. ● Three Counties Show continues. | | **WED** 15

Workshop; Iden Croft Herbs, Kent. Simple home herbal (0580 891432). ● Workshop; RHS Pershore. The reluctant gardener. ● Festival of Flowers; Mount Usher, Co. Wicklow: 7.30 pm. Preview (010 353 404 40116). ● Lecture; Exeter AGS, St Thomas High School: 6.30 pm. Dartmoor – seven years hard labour, Barry Stirling (0395 273636). ● BBC Gardeners' World Live continues. ● Three Counties Show ends. | William Paul, b. 1822; rose nurseryman and breeder | **THU** 16

17 – 19 June; Essex County Show, Great Leighs, Chelmsford (0733 234451). ● 17 – 19 June; Festival of Flowers, Mount Usher, Co. Wicklow: 10.30 am – 5.30 pm. ● Open Air Theatre; Killerton, Devon. National Trust. ● BBC Gardeners' World Live continues. | | **FRI** 17

18 – 19 June; Festival of Gardening, Hatfield House. (0707 262823). ● AGS Summer Show (North); Pudsey Civic Hall (0423 886302). ● Visit to Hestercombe Garden, Somerset: 2.30 pm. Somerset & Avon NCCPG. Followed by lecture: Gardens of the Italian Lakes, Roy Cheek (tickets required). ● 18 – 19 June; Flower Festival, Stanton Harcourt, Oxfordshire (0734 403587). ● Pelargonium Show; The British & European Geranium Society's National Show is being held today in the Sheffield area (0742 426200). ● Open Air Theatre; Cliveden, Buckinghamshire. National Trust. ● Opera; Sudbury Hall, Derbyshire. Details from the National Trust. ● Festival of Flowers, Mount Usher continues: 10.30 am – 5.30 pm. ● Essex County Show continues. ● BBC Gardeners' World Live continues. | William Cobbett, d. 1835; journalist, writer and horticultural economist | **SAT** 18

Elsworth Herbs, Cambridgeshire: 10 am – 5 pm. *Artemisia* day (0954 267414). ● Plant Sale; Bowerhouse, Dunbar: 2 pm. The garden opens under SGS. Includes Lothian NCCPG plant sale. ● 19 – 20 June; Fair, Charlecote Park, Warwickshire. National Trust. ● Fair; Clumber Park, Nottinghamshire. National Trust. ● Garden Open; Greystone, Oxfordshire. For the British Heart Foundation. ● Festival of Flowers, Mount Usher ends. ● Flower Festival, Stanton Harcourt ends. ● Festival of Gardening, Hatfield ends. ● Essex County Show ends. ● BBC Gardeners' World Live ends. | Sir Joseph Banks, d. 1820; botanist | **SUN** 19

DIARY		EVENTS
MON **20**	S C Atchley, d. 1936; diplomat and author (*Wild Flowers of Attica*)	Country Fair and Horse Show, Newby Hall, North Yorkshire.
TUE **21**	Sir Thomas Hanbury, b. 1832; creator of gardens at La Mortola	21 – 22 June; RHS Flower Show, Westminster: 11 am – 7 pm. Ornamental Plant competition; Delphinium Society Show. ● RHS Lecture; Westminster: 2.15 pm. Masters Memorial Lecture, Professor Harold B. Tukey Jr. ● 21 – 22 June; Cheshire Show, Knutsford (0270 73245). ● Workshop; RHS Pershore. Pictures from preserved plant material. ● Walk; Hinton Ampner House, Hampshire: 2.15 pm.
WED **22**		22 – 23 June; Lincolnshire Show, Lincolnshire Showground, Grange de Lings (0522 522900). ● Demonstration; RHS Rosemoor at Cannington College. Plant design for beds and borders. ● Walk; RHS Hyde Hall. Roses. ● Garden Visit; Petersfield Physic Garden, Hampshire. Hillier Gardening Club (0794 368966). ● 22 June – 10 July; Open Air Theatre, Polesden Lacey, Surrey. National Trust. ● RHS Flower Show ends: 10 am – 5 pm. ● Cheshire Show ends.
THU **23**	Eleanor Sinclair Rohde, d. 1950; writer	23 – 26 June; Royal Highland Show, Ingliston (031 333 2444). ● Demonstration; RHS Pershore. Movement in the garden – fountains, waterfalls and lighting. ● Course; West Dean College, Chichester, West Sussex. West Dean's garden history (0243 811343). ● Walk; Harlow Carr: 2 pm. With the trials officer. ● Lincolnshire Show ends.
FRI **24**		Course; Harlow Carr. Garden Design: Designing with plants 1. ● Course; West Dean College, Chichester, West Sussex. Summer gardening (0243 811343). ● 24 – 26 June; Open Air Concerts, Petworth Park, West Sussex. National Trust. ● Royal Highland Show continues.
SAT **25**	David Douglas, b. 1799; plant collector (Douglas Fir); T W Girdlestone, d. 1899; rose and dahlia breeder	25 – 26 June; Early Summer National Organic Gardening Weekend. HDRA (0203 303517). ● 25 – 26 June; Open Air Concert, Blickling Hall, Norfolk. National Trust. ● Open Air Concert; Belton House, Lincolnshire. National Trust. ● 25 – 26 June; Newbury Garden & Leisure Show, Newbury Showground (0635 247111). ● 25 - 26 June; Middlesex County Show ● Open Day; J Bradshaw & Son, Busheyfields Nursery, Kent. *Clematis* and *Lonicera* (0227 375415). ● Open Day; Killerton, Devon. National Trust. ● 25 – 26 June; Sandringham Country Weekend, Norfolk (0553 772675). ● 25 – 26 June; Country Craft Fair, Leonardslee Gardens, West Sussex. ● Royal Highland Show continues.
SUN **26**	Rev. Gilbert White, d. 1793; naturalist	Garden walk: Iden Croft Herbs, Kent (0580 891432). ● Plant Sale; Bingham Hall, Cirencester, Gloucestershire: 10.30 am – 3 pm (0225 891686). ● Walk; RHS Wisley. Plant diseases and disorders. ● NAFAS Kent area show; Hever Castle, Kent. ● Garden Party; Ness Gardens. Friends of Ness Gardens. ● Family Day; Petworth Park, West Sussex. National Trust. ● National Organic Gardening Weekend ends. ● Royal Highland Show ends. ● Newbury Garden & Leisure Show ends. ● Sandringham Country Weekend ends. ● Country Craft Fair, Leonardslee ends.

EVENTS	DIARY	
Walk; RHS Wisley. Plant diseases and disorders.		**MON** 27
	Robert Stephenson Clarke, b. 1862; creator of Borde Hill, Sussex	**TUE** 28
29 – 30 June; Royal Norfolk Show, Dereham Road, New Costessey (0603 748931). ● 29 – 30 June; Summer Floral Show, Sark, Channel Islands (0481 832345). ● Demonstration; RHS Wisley. Pruning of shrubs. ● Demonstrations; RHS Rosemoor. Summer pruning; Propagation of alpines. ● Dinner and Garden Tour; Ness Gardens. Limited numbers (051 336 7769).	Henry Doubleday, d. 1875; Quaker scientist	**WED** 29
30 June – 4 July; German Rose Congress, Baden-Baden. Details from the Verein Deutscher Rosenfreunde (010 49 7221 31302). ● Malton Show, Show Ground, Malton (0653 693382). ● Demonstration; RHS Pershore. Propagation 8 – growing trained plants. ● Walk; Harlow Carr: 2 pm. With the head gardener. ● Royal Norfolk Show continues. ● Summer Floral Show, Sark continues.	Sir Joseph Hooker, b. 1817; botanist	**THU** 30
Course; Harlow Carr. Introduction to dry stone walling, John Butler.		**FRI** 1
AGS Cheltenham Show; Pittville School, Cheltenham (0386 554790). ● 2 – 3 July; Southampton Ballon & Flower Festival, Southampton Common (A33) (0703 832525). ● 2 – 3 July; Delphinium Society Show, RHS Wisley. ● Exhibition; Harlow Carr. National Collection display.	Augustine Henry, b. 1857; collector	**SAT** 2
Demonstration; RHS Wisley. Pruning of shrubs. ● Open Air Concert; Polesden Lacey, Surrey. National Trust. ● Southampton Ballon & Flower Festival ends. ● Delphinium Society Show, Wisley ends.		**SUN** 3

DIARY		EVENTS
MON 4		Lecture; Bedfordshire AGS, Village Hall, Wilstead: 8 pm. Western Pyrenees, A. Powell. ● Teddy Bears Picnic; Beningborough Hall, Yorkshire. National Trust. ● 4 - 7 June; Royal Show, NAC, Stoneleigh Park (0203 696969).
TUE 5		5 - 6 July; National Sweet Pea Society National Show, City Hall, Salisbury. ● Preview day, Hampton Court Palace Flower Show. ● Demonstration; RHS Pershore. Around the garden in July.
WED 6	Sir Harry Veitch, d. 1924; nurseryman and orchidist	6 - 10 July; Hampton Court Palace Flower Show, Hampton Court. The British Rose Festival, organised by the Royal National Rose Society, is held as part of the show (0727 850461). ● Course; Ryton Organic Gardens. Sustainable Agriculture Overseas. ● Demonstration; RHS Wisley. Propagation of fruit trees by budding. ● Walks; RHS Rosemoor. The aromatic garden; Culinary herbs. ● Demonstration; RHS Hyde Hall, at Writtle College. Flower arranging economically. ● Garden Visit; Court Lodge Garden and Studio. Hillier Gardening Club (0794 368966). ● National Sweet Pea Society National Show, Salisbury ends.
THU 7	William Curtis, d. 1799; founder of *The Botanical Magazine*	Demonstration; RHS Pershore. Vegetable production - cropping secrets from the experts. ● Walk; Harlow Carr: 2 pm. With the curator. ● 7 - 9 July; Opera, Polesden Lacey, Surrey. National Trust. ● Hampton Court Palace Flower Show continues.
FRI 8	Rev. James Backhouse, b. 1794; nurseryman and botanist	8 - 10 July; Open Air Concert, Wimpole Hall, Cambridgeshire. National Trust. ● 8 - 10 July; Opera, Felbrigg Hall, Norfolk. National Trust. ● 8 - 9 July; Open Air Concert, Fountains Abbey and Studley Royal, North Yorkshire. National Trust. ● 8 - 9 July; Jazz Festival, Dyrham Park, Avon. National Trust. ● 8 - 9 July; Jazz Concert, Wimpole Hall, Cambridgeshire. National Trust. ● Open Air Concert; Erdigg Hall, Clwyd. National Trust. ● Hampton Court Palace Flower Show continues.
SAT 9	Rev. Keble Martin, b. 1877; botanist; author of *The Concise British Flora*	National Organic Food and Wine Fair, Ryton Organic Gardens. ● 9 - 10 July; Dagenham Town Show, Central Park (081 592 4500). ● Hampton Court Palace Flower Show continues. The Royal National Rose Society's National Amateur Show is held at the show today and tomorrow. ● 9 - 10 July; South Beds County Show, Toddington Manor, Toddington (0525 875170). ● Jazz Concert; Clumber Park, Nottinghamshire. National Trust.
SUN 10	Sir F Stern, d. 1967; creator of Highdown, West Sussex	National Sweet Pea Society Provincial Show, Market Bosworth, Leicestershire. ● Plant Sale; Bradley House, Maiden Bradley, Wiltshire: 2 - 5 pm. Wiltshire Gardens Trust. Open to the public. ● Plant Sale; West Wing, Horsford Hall, Horsford: 2 - 5 pm. Norfolk NCCPG. ● Demonstration; RHS Wisley. Propagation of fruit trees by budding. ● Jazz Concert; Polesden Lacey, Surrey. National Trust. ● Family Day; Cragside, Northumberland. National Trust. ● Garden Open; Malleny House Garden, Lothian: 2 - 5 pm. For the NCCPG. ● Dagenham Town Show ends. ● South Beds County Show ends. ● Hampton Court Palace Flower Show ends.

EVENTS	DIARY	
11 – 16 July; Jersey Floral Festival, Jersey (0534 78000). Events take place throughout the island, and include garden openings, talks, demonstrations, visits to the Eric Young Orchid centre and a broadcast of BBC Radio's *Gardener's Question Time*.	E C Buxton, d. 1925; plantsman (*Geranium* 'Buxton's Blue')	MON 11
12 – 14 July; Great Yorkshire Show, Hookstone Oval, Harrogate (0423 561536). ● Course; Harlow Carr. Drawing plants and flowers, Victoria Street. ● Workshop; RHS Pershore. Tree and soft fruit summer pruning. ● Visit to Barrington Court: 10.30 am . Somerset & Avon NCCPG. ● Visit to Savill Gardens; Dorset NCCPG. ● Jersey Floral Festival continues.	David Douglas d. 1834; plant collector	TUE 12
Demonstration; RHS Wisley. Sinks and troughs. ● Demonstrations; RHS Rosemoor. Drying flowers; Arranging dried flowers. ● Demonstration; RHS Hall, at Writtle College. Pests and diseases on ornamentals. ● Lecture; Museum of Garden History, London. Victorian gardens, Brent Elliott. ● 13 – 16 July; Fête Champêtre, Claremont Landscape Garden, Surrey. National Trust. ● Open Air Concert; Cliveden, Buckinghamshire. National Trust. ● Great Yorkshire Show continues. ● Jersey Floral Festival continues.	John Clare, b. 1793; nature poet	WED 13
14 – 16 July; Kent County Show, Detling (0622 630975). ● 14 – 17 July; Art in action, Waterperry Gardens, Oxfordshire (0844 339226). ● Workshop: Iden Croft Herbs, Kent. Growing Basil; making your own pesto (0580 891432). ● Demonstration; RHS Pershore. A guide to ornamental grasses. ● Walk; Harlow Carr: 2 pm. ● 14 – 17 July; Opera, Scotney Castle, Kent. National Trust. ● Jersey Floral Festival continues. ● Great Yorkshire Show ends.		THU 14
Open Air Concert; Ickworth, Suffolk. National Trust. ● Open Air Concert; Kingston Lacy, Dorset. National Trust. ● Kent County Show continues. ● Jersey Floral Festival continues.	William Robinson, b. 1838; writer (*The English Flower Garden*)	FRI 15
16 – 17 July; Durham County Agricultural Show, Lambton Park, Chester le Street (091 388 5459). ● 16 – 17 July; Clematis Weekend, The Tropical Bird Gardens, Rode, Somerset: 11.00 – 5.00 pm (0373 830326). ● 16 – 17 July; Open Air Theatre; Chirk Castle, Clwyd. National Trust. ● Course; Ness Gardens. Know your garden insects, Dr I. Wallace. Limited numbers (051 336 7769). ● 16 – 17 July; Parham Plant Fair, Parham, West Sussex: 11 am – 5 pm. ● Visit to Monteviot House Garden, Jedburgh: 11 am. Lothian NCCPG (031 243 9449). ● Jazz Concert; Killerton, Devon. National Trust. ● Kent County Show ends. ● Jersey Floral Festival ends.		SAT 16
Alton Agricultural Show, Froyle Park, Froyle (0420 563492). ● Walk; RHS Wisley. Annuals and herbaceous plants. ● Walk; RHS Rosemoor. Borders at Rosemoor. ● Workshop; RHS Rosemoor. Getting the most from your borders. ● Open Air Concert; Killerton, Devon. National Trust. ● Jazz Concert; Claremont Landscape Garden, Surrey. National Trust. ● Durham County Agricultural Show ends. ● Parham Plant Fair ends: 11 am – 5 pm. ● Clematis Weekend, Rode, ends: 11.00 am – 5.00 pm.	Rev A T Boscawen, d. 1939; creator of garden at Ludgvan, Cornwall	SUN 17

DIARY		EVENTS
MON **18**	James Bateman, b. 1811; botanist and writer (*Orchidaceae of Mexico and Guatemala*)	18 – 22 July; Royal Welsh Show, Llanelwedd, Builth Wells (0982 553683). ● NAFAS Demonstration; Wareham Middle School, Wareham: 7.30 pm. Mrs Dorothy Bye. ● Walk; RHS Wisley. Annuals and herbaceous plants.
TUE **19**	Thomas Blaikie, d. 1838; landscaper and writer (*Diary of a Scotch Gardener at the French Court*)	19 – 20 July; RHS Flower Show, Westminster: 11 am – 7 pm. Summer Fruit & Vegetable, and Ornamental Plant competitions. ● Lecture; Westminster: 6 pm. RHS and Worshipful Company of Gardeners, Michael Upward. ● 19 – 23 July; Open Air Theatre, Fountains Abbey and Studley Royal, North Yorkshire. National Trust. ● Course; Harlow Carr. Growing plants for showing, Barry Brown. ● Workshop; RHS Pershore. Propagation 9 – unusual plants. ● Walk; Hinton Ampner House, Hampshire: 2.15 pm. ● Royal Welsh Show continues.
WED **20**		Driffield Show, Showground, Kelleythorpe (0377 47494); Horticultural Secretary (0377 288256). ● Meet the Gardener; Ryton Organic Gardens. Flowers and Fruit. ● Demonstration; RHS Wisley. Pruning of fruit trees and bushes. ● Flower Arrangers' Day; RHS Wisley. Purely for pleasure, Mary Deacon. ● Demonstration; RHS Rosemoor at Cannington College. A guide to wall shrubs and climbers. ● Walk; RHS Hyde Hall. Herbaceous perennials. ● NAFAS Demonstration; Memorial Hall, Colehill, Dorset: 7.30 pm. Mrs Dorothy Bye. ● 20 – 23 July; Fête Champêtre, Stourhead, Wiltshire. National Trust. ● Royal Welsh Show continues. ● RHS Flower Show ends: 10 am – 5 pm.
THU **21**		Demonstration; RHS Pershore. Hardy ferns. ● Walk; Harlow Carr: 2 pm. With the trials officer. ● Royal Welsh Show continues.
FRI **22**	Charles Babington, d. 1895; Cambridge botanist (*Allium babingtonii*)	Evening Picnic; Hillier Arboretum. Hillier Gardening Club (0794 368966). ● Course; Harlow Carr. Garden Design: Designing with plants 2. ● 22 – 23 July; Open Air Concert, The Vyne, Hampshire. National Trust. ● Royal Welsh Show ends.
SAT **23**		23 – 24 July; Gateshead Summer Flower Show, Gateshead Central Nursery, Whickham Highway: 10 am – 7 pm (091 490 1616 Ext 272). The show includes the Royal National Rose Society's National Northern Rose Show. ● Course; Ness Gardens. Know your common grasses, Dr McAllister. Limited numbers. ● Demonstration; RHS Pershore. The *Penstemon* collection. ● Open Air Concert; Calke Abbey, Derbyshire. National Trust.
SUN **24**	Montagu Allwood, d. 1958; breeder of carnations and pinks	Garden walk: Iden Croft Herbs, Kent. The herb garden in July (0580 891432). ● Demonstration; RHS Wisley. Pruning of fruit trees and bushes. ● Fair; Nostell Priory, West Yorkshire. National Trust. ● Garden Open; Hexham Herbs, Northumberland: 2 – 6 pm. Open for Northumberland Red Cross. Details of this scheme 091 273 7961. ● Gateshead Summer Flower Show ends: 10 am – 5.30 pm.

EVENTS	DIARY	
25 – 29 July; Summer School, Harlow Carr: 10 am – 4.30 pm. Botanical illustration.	William Forsyth, d. 1804; founder of the RHS (*Forsythia*)	MON 25
26 – 27 July; Garden Competition. Royal Jersey Agricultural & Horticultural Society (0534 37227). • 26 – 28 July; New Forest & Hampshire County Show, New Park, Brockenhurst (0590 22400).	Joseph Arnold, d. 1818; botanist (*Rafflesia arnoldii*)	TUE 26
27 – 30 July; NAFAS Flower Arranging Competitions and Exhibition 1994, Brighton Centre, East Sussex: 10 am – 9.30 pm. Donation to Cystic Fibrosis Research Trust. • Cardigan Show (0239 615438). • Sandringham Flower Show, Norfolk (0553 772675). • Walks; RHS Rosemoor. Climbers and wall plants; Cottage garden plants. • Workshop; Hillier Arboretum, Hampshire. Plant propagation 2 – cuttings. • New Forest & Hampshire County Show continues. • Jersey Garden Competition ends.		WED 27
28 – 30 July; Opera, Scotney Castle, Kent. National Trust. • Walk; Harlow Carr: 2 pm. With the head gardener. • NAFAS Flower Arranging Competitions and Exhibition continues. • New Forest & Hampshire County Show ends.	Abraham Cowley, d. 1667; botanist and poet	THU 28
29 – 31 July; St Helens Show, The Showground (0744 24061). • 29 – 30 July; Jazz Concert, Mottistone Manor, Isle of Wight. National Trust. • NAFAS Flower Arranging Competitions and Exhibition continues.	E B Anderson, d. 1971; plantsman and writer	FRI 29
30 – 31 July; National Miniature Rose Show, The Gardens of the Rose, St Albans, Hertfordshire: 11 am – 5 pm (0727 850461). • Abergavenny & Borders Show (0873 853152). The 1994 show is the 150th. • 30 – 31 July; Dartford Festival (0233 343056). • 30 – 31 July; South of England Flower Show, Hudsons Field, Salisbury: 10 am (0980 611485). • 30 – 31 July; Fair, Wimpole Hall, Cambridgeshire. National Trust. • Open Air Theatre; Mottisfont Abbey, Hampshire. National Trust. • NAFAS Flower Arranging Competitions and Exhibition ends. • St Helens Show continues.		SAT 30
Craft Fair, Ryton Organic Gardens. • National Miniature Rose Show ends: 10 am – 6 pm. • Dartford Festival ends. • St Helens Show ends. • South of England Flower Show ends.	Robert Gathorne-Hardy, b. 1902; writer	SUN 31

DIARY		EVENTS
MON 1	Lord Digby, b. 1894; creator of garden at Minterne, Dorset	Turriff Show, The Haughs (0466 780267). ● Lecture; Bedfordshire AGS, Village Hall, Wilstead: 8 pm. Primulas, R. Barter and A. Papworth.
TUE 2	Joseph Thomson, d. 1895; botanist of Africa	Demonstration; RHS Pershore. Around the garden in August.
WED 3	Sir Joseph Paxton, b. 1801; garden designer	3 – 4 August; Bakewell Show, Showground, Coombs Road (0629 812736). ● 3 – 4 August; Taunton Flower Show, Vivary Park (0823 271597). ● Garden Open; Ness Gardens, Cheshire. For the NGS (051 336 7769). ● Bingley Show, Myrtle Park, Bingley (0274 564400). ● North Devon Show, Plyms Farm, Landkey, Barnstaple (0769 60205). With show by the North Devon Fuchsia Society (0271 76665).
THU 4	John Tradescant, Snr, b. 1608; royal gardener	Black Isle Show, Mannsfield, Muir of Ord, Grampian. Black Isle Farmers' Society (0463 233957). ● Workshop; RHS Pershore. Children's workshop. ● Bakewell Show ends. ● Taunton Flower Show ends.
FRI 5		5 – 6 August; Perth Show, South Inch (0738 23780). ● 5 – 7 August; Flower Festival at Hawkstone Hall, Shropshire. Mercia and North Wales area of NAFAS (0492 583626). ● 5 – 6 August; Opera, Anglesey Abbey, Cambridgeshire. National Trust. ● Lecture; Mount Usher, Co. Wicklow: 7.30 pm. White knights of summer, John Anderson (010 353 404 40116).
SAT 6	Thomas Laxton, d. 1893; nurseryman	6 -7 August; Late Summer National Organic Gardening Weekend. HDRA (0203 303517). ● Brecon County Show (0568 708760); Horticultural Secretary (0874 625654). ● Dumfries & Lockerbie Show (0461 203551). ● 6 – 7 August; Howden Horticultural & Agricultural Show (0757 630247; Horticultural Secretary (0430 430578). ● Oswestry Show, Park Hall, Whittington Road (0691 654875). ● 6 – 7 August; Open Air Concert, Stowe, Buckinghamshire. National Trust. ● Open Air Concert; Bateman's, East Sussex. National Trust. ● Jazz Concert; Clumber Park, Nottinghamshire. Details from the National Trust. ● Open Air Concert; Osterley Park, London. Details from the National Trust. ● Flower Festival, Hawkstone Hall continues.
SUN 7	Johann Gräfer, d. 1802; botanist and garden designer	Walk; RHS Wisley. Secrets of success with dahlias, chrysanthemums and other summer flowers. ● Walk; Hillier Arboretum: 2 pm. Summer surprises. ● Walk; Westonbirt Arboretum, Gloucestershire: 2.30 pm. Native Trees. ● Flower Festival, Hawkstone Hall ends. ● Howden Show ends.

EVENTS	DIARY	
Walk; RHS Wisley. Secrets of success with dahlias, chrysanthemums and other summer flowers.	Lady Amelia Hume, d. 1809; gardener	**MON** 8
9 – 10 August; Anglesey County Show, Mona Showground, Gwalchmai. Anglesey Agricultural Society (0407 720072). • 9 – 10 August; Open Air Theatre, Plas Newydd, Gwynedd. Details from the National Trust. • Open day; Harlow Carr. Trials trade day.		**TUE** 9
Demonstration; RHS Rosemoor. Propagating and growing tender perennials. • Walk; RHS Rosemoor. Structural plants – form and foliage. • Anglesey County Show ends.	Frank Ludlow, b. 1885; plant collector	**WED** 10
11 – 12 August; United Counties Show, Carmarthen (0267 232141). • 11 – 12 August; St Martin's Summer Show, Guernsey (0481 723555). • Workshop: Iden Croft Herbs, Kent. Simple home herbal (0580 891432). • 11 – 14 August; Flower Festival, St Mary's Church, Wareham, Dorset. Dorset & Guernsey area of NAFAS. • Walk; Harlow Carr: 2 pm. With the trials officer. • 11 – 12 August; Open Air Theatre, Erdigg Hall, Clwyd. Details from the National Trust.		**THU** 11
12 – 13 August; Shrewsbury Flower Show, Quarry Park (0743 364051). • 12 – 14 August; Wisley Flower Festival, RHS Wisley. Includes the National Vegetable Society's National Championships. • 12 – 14 August; Summer Gardening Show, Broadlands, Romsey. Garden Events. • 12 – 14 August; Flower Festival, Sherborne Abbey, Dorset. Dorset & Guernsey area of NAFAS (0258 837239). • Flower Festival, Wareham continues. • St Martin's Summer Show ends.	Rev. Samuel Goodenough, d. 1827; founder member of the Linnean Society	**FRI** 12
13 – 14 August; Gladiolus Society Southern Show, Squire's Garden Centre, Shepperton (0335 345443). • 13 – 14 August; Springfields Flower Show, Spalding Lincolnshire. • Flower Festival, Sherborne Abbey continues. • Flower Festival, Wareham continues. • Summer Gardening Show, Broadlands continues. • Wisley Flower Festival continues. • Shrewsbury Flower Show ends.		**SAT** 13
Walk; RHS Wisley. Heathers all year round. • Open Air Concert; Powis Castle, Powys. Details from the National Trust. • Flower Festival, Sherborne Abbey ends. • Flower Festival, Wareham ends. • Summer Gardening Show, Broadlands ends. • Wisley Flower Festival ends. • Gladiolus Society Southern Show ends.		**SUN** 14

DIARY		EVENTS
MON **15**		Walk; RHS Wisley. Heathers all year round. ● Lecture; Mount Usher, Co. Wicklow: 5.30 pm. Mount Usher garden through the seasons, John Anderson (010 353 404 40116).
TUE **16**		16 – 17 August; RHS Flower Show, Westminster: 11 am – 7 pm. Gladiolus and Ornamental Plant competitions. ● RHS Lecture; Westminster: 2.15 pm. Beetles – friends or foes? Andrew Halstead. ● Demonstration; RHS Pershore. Topiary and tree training. ● Walk; Hinton Ampner House, Hampshire: 2.15 pm.
WED **17**	Lord Lambourne, b. 1847; RHS president (*Malus* 'Lord Lambourne')	17 – 18 August; Summer Flower Show, Howard Davis Park, St Helier: 2 – 9 pm. Royal Jersey Agricultural & Horticultural Society (0534 37227). ● 17 – 21 August; Durham Castle Flower Festival, Durham. The Northumberland & Durham area of NAFAS. ● RHS Flower Show ends: 10 am – 5 pm.
THU **18**		Jersey Summer Flower Show ends: 9.15 am – 8 pm. ● Denbighshire & Flintshire Show, The Green, Denbigh, Clwyd (0352 712131). ● 18 – 20 August; Southport Flower Show, Victoria Park (0704 533133 Ext 2308). ● 18 – 19 August; L'Erée Summer Show, Guernsey (0481 723555). ● Durham Castle Flower Festival continues. ● Demonstration; RHS Pershore. Pot pourri and other fragrant delights. ● Walk; Harlow Carr: 2 pm. With the education officer.
FRI **19**	Ellen Willmott, b. 1858; plantswoman and patron; Jane Loudon, b. 1807; writer	Southport Flower Show continues. ● 19 – 20 August; County Flower & Vegetable Show, Congregational Church Hall, Kirkwall, Orkney. Orkney Horticultural & Industrial Association. ● L'Erée Summer Show ends. ● Durham Castle Flower Festival continues. ● 19 - 21 August; Europlant Show, Flanders Expo, Ghent (010 32 51 221959).
SAT **20**	Huttleston, Lord Fairhaven, d. 1966; creator of garden at Angelesey Abbey, Cambridgeshire	20 – 21 August; Bolton Show, Leverhulme Park, Bolton. Bolton Metropolitan Borough, Department of Leisure Services (0204 22311). ● 20 – 21 August; Gladiolus Society National Show, Weston super Mare. Gladiolus Society and Weston super Mare Horticultural Society (0335 345443). ● Durham Castle Flower Festival continues. ● Southport Flower Show ends. ● Orkney County Flower & Vegetable Show ends.
SUN **21**	James McBean, d. 1910; orchid nurseryman	Garden walk: Iden Croft Herbs, Kent. The herb garden in August (0580 891432). ● Walk; RHS Wisley. Something nasty in the garden. ● Open Air Concert; Blickling Hall, Norfolk. National Trust. ● Family Day; Wallington, Northumberland. National Trust. ● Durham Castle Flower Festival ends. ● Bolton Show ends. ● Gladiolus Society National Show ends.

EVENTS	DIARY	
Walk; RHS Wisley. Something nasty in the garden.		**MON** **22**
	F C Puddle, d. 1952; head gardener at Bodnant Gardens, Clwyd	**TUE** **23**
Seed Saving and Varieties Day; Ryton Organic Gardens. ● Flower Arrangers' Day; RHS Wisley. Through the decades, Brian Halliday. ● Demonstration; RHS Rosemoor at Cannington College. Summer colour – late summer plants and their propagation. ● 24 – 25 August; Open Air Theatre, Felbrigg Hall, Norfolk. National Trust.	A W Haworth, d. 1833; cactus botanist (*Haworthia*)	**WED** **24**
25 – 26 August; Guernsey Battle of Flowers, Saumarez Park, Guernsey. Details from Guernsey Tourist Office (0481 723555). ● Walk; Harlow Carr: 2 pm. With the head gardener.		**THU** **25**
26 – 27 August; Area competitions and exhibition, Ferndown School, Wimborne, Dorset. Dorset & Guernsey area of NAFAS (0258 837239). ● Guernsey Battle of Flowers ends.		**FRI** **26**
27 – 29 August; Festival of Gardening, Audley End, Essex. Garden Events. ● 27 – 28 August; Gladiolus Society Northern Show, Vincents Nurseries, Townley Park, Burnley. Gladiolus Society (0335 345443). ● Poynton Show, Poynton Park. Show Office, Social Centre, Park Lane, Poynton, Cheshire SK12 1RB. ● Jazz Concert; Emmetts Garden, Kent. National Trust. ● NAFAS Dorset & Guernsey area competitions end.	Rev. Reynolds Hole, d. 1904; rose grower	**SAT** **27**
28 – 29 August; City of Swansea Flower Show, Singleton Park (0792 302431). ● Garden Open; Hexham Herbs, Northumberland 2 – 6 pm. For the Northumbrian Red Cross. For details of other gardens in this scheme contact 091 273 7961. ● Gladiolus Society Northern Show ends. ● 28 – 29 August; Harrow Show, Headstone Manor, North Harrow. Entries Secretary (081 428 4504). ● 28 – 29 August; Eye Show. Tim Seeley (0379 870224). ● 28 – 29 August; Havering Show. Entertainment & Events Office, London Borough of Havering (0708 772879). ● Festival of Gardening, Audley End continues.		**SUN** **28**

DIARY		EVENTS
MON **29**		Keswick Agricultural Show, Crossings Field, High Hill, Keswick. Keswick Agricultural Society (07687 79737). • Aylsham Show, Blickling Park, Blickling Hall, Aylsham. Aylsham Agricultural Show Association (0263 732432). • Leominster Agricultural Show, Dishley Court Show Site. Date and venue subject to confirmation (0568 614984). • Festival of Gardening, Audley End ends. • Eye Show ends. • Havering Show ends. • Harrow Show ends.
TUE **30**	Marianne North, d. 1890; botanical artist	
WED **31**	Huttleston, Lord Fairhaven, b. 1896; creator of garden at Anglesey Abbey, Cambridgeshire	31 August – 2 September; Bristol Flower Show, Durdham Downs, Bristol: 10 am. Contact Mike Crook (0980 611485). • Demonstration day; Scottish Association of Flower Arrangement Societies, St Andrews. Open to the public (031 445 2467). • Demonstration; RHS Wisley. Digging, manuring and composting.
THU **1**		1 – 2 September; Autumn Floral Show, Sark, Channel Islands. Details from the Sark Tourist Board (0481 832345). • Demonstration; RHS Pershore. Around the garden in September. • Lecture; East Dorset AGS, Lytchett Matravers Village Hall: 7.30 pm. Spring flowers of the hills and mountains of Spain, Mr & Mrs G. S. Phillips (0202 692962). • Bristol Flower Show continues.
FRI **2**	Marion Cran, d. 1942; garden writer	2 – 4 September; Autumn Flower Show, Blenheim Palace, Oxfordshire. Garden Events • Course; West Dean College, Chichester, West Sussex. Walling in flint and stone (0243 811343). • Autumn Floral Show, Sark ends. • Bristol Flower Show ends.
SAT **3**	Sir Frederick Moore, b. 1857; Irish botanist	Dorchester Agricultural Show, Came Park, Dorchester (0305 264249). • Moreton-in-Marsh Show, Batsford Road, Moreton-in-Marsh. Moreton-in-Marsh and District Agricultural and Horse Show Society (0608 651908). • Garden Tour; Ness Gardens, Cheshire. Limited numbers: £4.50 (051 336 7769). • Autumn Flower Show, Blenheim Palace continues.
SUN **4**		Demonstration; RHS Wisley. Digging, manuring and composting. • Walk; RHS Rosemoor. Late summer colour at Rosemoor. • Walk; Sir Harold Hillier Gardens and Arboretum, Ampfield, Hampshire: 2 pm. Late summer tour. Meet in the car park. • Autumn Flower Show, Blenheim Palace ends.

EVENTS

DIARY

Lecture; North London AGS, Oakwood Methodist Church Hall (opposite Oakwood underground station): 7.30 pm. Propagating alpines, Fiona Dennis (081 445 1675). ● Lecture; Bedfordshire AGS, Village Hall, Wilstead: 8 pm. Snow melt plants, J. Lea.	**MON** **5**
6 - 7 September; City of London Flower Show, Gresham Street. ● Lecture; RHS Pershore. Garden design 7 – planting out a herb garden.	**TUE** **6**
National Dahlia Society Show, RHS New Hall, Westminster (0628 473500). ● Summer Pruning, Top Fruit Day; Ryton Organic Gardens. ● Demonstration; RHS Rosemoor. Flower arranging: inspirations from the garden. ● Walk; RHS Rosemoor. The flower arranger's garden. ● Workshop; Hillier Arboretum. What's in a plant name? ● AGM; East Yorkshire AGS, Beverley Girls' High School, Norwood: 7.30 pm. ● Lecture; Derby Rock Garden Club (AGS), St Helen's House, King Street: 7.30 pm. Gardening with tufa, P. Cunnington.	**WED** **7**
Workshop; RHS Pershore. Bulbs for containers.	**THU** **8**

9 – 11 September; Exhibition of Floral Arrangements, Jermyns House, Hillier Arboretum. Wessex and Jersey area of NAFAS (0264 781474). ● 9 – 11 September; Tewkesbury Abbey Flower Festival, Gloucestershire. Three Counties & South Wales area of NAFAS (0633 440223). ● Jazz Concert; Kingston Lacy, Dorset. National Trust.	Captain William Bligh, b. 1754, introducer of bread fruits to the West Indies; George Ehret, d. 1770; botanical artist	**FRI** **9**
Kington Agricultural Show, Recreation Ground (0497 831265). ● Penistone Show, Penistone Show Ground. Contact Huthwaite Bank, Old Mill Lane, Thurgoland, Sheffield S30 7AG. ● Romsey Show, Broadlands Park (0794 517521). ● London Rare Plants Fair; Battersea Town Hall, London: 11 am – 7 pm (0225 891686). ● Greenbank Bulb Fair, Greenbank Gardens, Strathclyde: 11 am. ● Plant sale; Surrey NCCPG Group sale. ● Tewkesbury Abbey Flower Festival continues. ● Exhibition, Jermyns Place continues: 10.30 am – 6 pm.	George Bentham, d. 1884; taxonomist	**SAT** **10**
Town & Country Show, Dereham Road, New Costessey, Norwich (0603 748931). ● Course; Ness Gardens. Saving seed from your own plants, Dr McAllister. Limited numbers. ● Walk; RHS Wisley. Model fruit garden, fruit field and tasting. ● Visit to National Collection of *Hedychium*. Somerset & Avon NCCPG, Hinton St George. ● Plant Sale; Beningborough Hall, West Yorkshire. National Trust. ● Tewkesbury Abbey Flower Festival ends. ● Exhibition, Jermyns Place ends: 10.30 am – 6 pm.	Daniel Hanbury, b. 1825; plant collector and pharmacologist	**SUN** **11**

DIARY		EVENTS
MON **12**		Walk; RHS Wisley. Model fruit garden, fruit field and tasting.
TUE **13**	Hon. Sir David Bowes-Lyon, d. 1961; president of the RHS	13 – 14 September; RHS Great Autumn Flower Show, Westminster: 10 am – 7 pm. ● RHS Lecture; Westminster: 2.15 pm. Water and bog gardening, Bill Heritage. ● RHS Lecture; Westminster: 6 pm. Gardens of the London livery companies, Brigid Boardman. ● Workshop; RHS Pershore. Propagation 10 – evergreens and conifers. ● Lecture; Dorset NCCPG, Allendale Centre, Wimborne: 7.30 pm. Campanulas, Peter Lewis.
WED **14**	Alicia Amherst, d. 1941; garden historian	Flower Arrangers' Day; RHS Wisley. Autumnal trends – fresh and dried, Judith Blacklock. ● Demonstration; RHS Hyde Hall, at Writtle College. Seed collecting and preparation. ● Lecture; Westminster: 2.15 pm. RHS and Bonsai Kai. The simple art of bonsai, Colin Ellis. ● Lecture; Nottingham Rock Garden Club, Nethergate School, Clifton: 7.30 pm. ● RHS Great Autumn Flower Show ends: 10 am – 5 pm.
THU **15**	André le Nôtre, d. 1700; Louis XIV's gardener	Workshop: Iden Croft Herbs, Kent. Herbal ideas for Christmas and birthday presents (0580 891432). ● RHS Regional Lecture; Older roses for gardens of today, Hazel le Rougetel.
FRI **16**	Robert Fortune, b. 1812; plant hunter	16 – 18 September; Harrogate Great Autumn Flower Show, Exhibition Halls, Harrogate: 10 – 8 pm (0423 561049). Includes the Royal National Rose Society's Great Autumn Rose Show. ● 16 – 19 September; Flower Festival, Leeds Castle, Kent (0622 765400). ● 16 – 17 September; Chrysanthemum, Dahlia & Industrial Show, Congregational Church Hall, Kirkwall, Orkney. Orkney Horticultural & Industrial Association. ● Lecture; Bristol AGS, Westbury on Trym Methodist Hall: 7 pm. Saxifrages in the wild and in cultivation, Winton Harding (0594 529663).
SAT **17**	Peter Barr, d. 1909; botanist and daffodil breeder	17 – 18 September; Newbury and Royal County of Berkshire Show, Newbury Showground, Priors Court (0635 247111). ● 17 – 18 September; Craft Fair, Newby Hall, North Yorkshire. ● Stokesley Show. Stokesley Agricultural Society (0642 713209). ● 17 – 18 September; Fair, Nostell Priory, West Yorkshire. National Trust. ● Workshop; RHS Pershore. The ornamental kitchen garden 4. ● Orkney Chrysanthemum, Dahlia & Industrial Show ends. ● Harrogate Great Autumn Show continues: 9.30 am – 5 pm ● Lecture; Ness Gardens: 2 pm. Conservation of birds in the Dee estuary, C. Wells.
SUN **18**	George Paul, d. 1921; rose nurseryman	Specialist Nursery Sale; Hole Park, Rolvenden, Cranbrook: 11 am – 5 pm. Kent NCCPG. ● Newbury & Royal County of Berkshire Show ends. ● Harrogate Great Autumn Flower Show ends.

EVENTS	DIARY	
Nidderdale Show, Bewerley Park, Pateley Bridge. Nidderdale Agricultural Society (0423 770888).	George Sherriff, d. 1967; plant hunter	**MON** **19**
Demonstration; RHS Pershore. Winter display 1. • RHS Regional Lecture; Ross on Wye. Gardens of the Great Park at Windsor, John Bond. • Walk; Hinton Ampner House, Hampshire: 2.15 pm.		**TUE** **20**
Frome Cheese Show, Showfield, Frome. Frome & District Agricultural Society (0373 463600). • Meet the Gardener; Ryton Organic Gardens. • Demonstration; RHS Wisley. Harvesting and storing vegetables for winter. • Demonstration; RHS Rosemoor at Cannington College. Flowers and fabrics – a guide to colour co-ordination.		**WED** **21**
Workshop; RHS Pershore. Winter display 2 – patio containers. • Demonstration; Harlow Carr: 2 pm. Autumn work in the garden. • Lecture; Dorset NCCPG, County Records Office, Dorchester: 7.30 pm. Pansies, violas and sweet violets, Elizabeth Farrer.	John Bartram, d. 1777; botanist	**THU** **22**
23 – 24 September; IDS Symposium, Botanical Institute, University of Bonn. The Conservation Status of Temperate Trees. Restricted to members of the International Dendrology Society. • Course; West Dean College, Chichester, West Sussex. Autumn gardening (0243 811343).		**FRI** **23**
AGS Wirral Show; West Cheshire Arts Centre, Blacon Avenue, Blacon, Chester (0386 554790). • 24 – 25 September; Autumn Flower Show, Borde Hill, Sussex. Garden Events. • Conference; Bristol AGS, Bristol Students Union Building. One day conference: date subject to confirmation (0594 529663). • Outing; Visit to Hillier Nurseries Propagation Unit. Hillier Gardening Club (0794 368966). • Plant Sale; Somerset & Avon NCCPG, Bristol Botanic Gardens: 2 – 5 pm.		**SAT** **24**
Demonstration; RHS Wisley. Harvesting and storing vegetables for winter. • Autumn Flower Show, Borde Hill ends.		**SUN** **25**

DIARY	EVENTS
MON **26**	RHS Regional Lecture; Preston. Lessons from the Victorian walled garden, Peter Thoday.
TUE **27**	Workshop; RHS Pershore. Winter display 3 – hanging baskets. • RHS Regional Lecture; Edinburgh. The Andes from the Caribbean to Patagonia, Brinsley Burbidge.
WED **28** Sir Henry Wickham, d. 1928; plant collector	Demonstration; RHS Wisley. Lawn maintenance. • Demonstrations; RHS Rosemoor. Seed collecting and storage; Autumn lawn maintenance. • NAFAS Area Day; Porthcawl. Three Counties & South Wales area of NAFAS (0633 440223). • Garden Tour; Ness Gardens, Cheshire: 10.30 am. Includes lunch. Limited numbers: £8.50 (051 336 7769). • Walk; RHS Hyde Hall, at Writtle College, Writtle, Essex. Autumn fruit (0245 400256).
THU **29**	NAFAS Demonstrations; New Windmill Hall, Upminster, Essex. Donald Lovatt Frazer and Ann Stott (081 460 7902). • Workshop; RHS Pershore. Pruning of soft fruit. • Course; West Dean College, Chichester, West Sussex. What is garden design? (0243 811343). • RHS Regional Lecture; Birmingham. A history of English gardens, Daphne Vince-Prue.
FRI **30** James Aitchison, d. 1898; botanist in India (*Rosa ecae*)	
SAT **1**	North of England Orchid Society Show; East Didsbury Methodist Church Hall, Manchester. • Meeting; Somerset & Avon NCCPG, Cannington College, Somerset: 10 am. Includes members' plant sale and talks on alpines and clematis.
SUN **2**	South of England Autumn Show, Ardingly, Haywards Heath. South of England Agricultural Society (0444 892700). • Craft Fair; Ryton Organic Gardens. • Demonstration; RHS Wisley. Lawn maintenance. • RHS Regional Lecture; Ardingly. Bog and waterside gardens.

EVENTS	DIARY	
3 – 7 October; Schools Recycling and Composting Week, Ryton Organic Gardens. Further details from the HDRA (0203 303517). ● Lecture; North London AGS, Oakwood Methodist Church Hall (opposite Oakwood underground station): 7.30 pm. *Cyclamen*, M. Jope (081 445 1675). ● AGM; Bedfordshire AGS, Village Hall, Wilstead: 8 pm. Includes plant sale.		MON 3
4 – 5 October; RHS Flower Show, Westminster: 11 am – 7 pm. Autumn Fruit & Vegetable and Ornamental Plant competitions. ● RHS Lecture; Westminster: 2.15 pm. Vegetables from a small garden, Richard Bailey. ● Demonstration; RHS Pershore. Around the garden in October. ● RHS Regional Lecture; Durham. *Lilium* for the garden, John Main. ● Lecture; Hillier Garden Centre, Bath, Avon: 7.30 pm. Westonbirt Arboretum. Hillier Gardening Club (0794 368966). ● Trailer Tour; Charlecote Park, Warwickshire. Details from the National Trust.	Franz Bauer, b. 1758; botanical artist	TUE 4
5 – 6 October; Autumn Flower Show. Royal Jersey Agricultural & Horticultural Society (0534 37227). ● RHS Flower Show ends: 10 am – 5 pm. ● Demonstration; RHS Wisley. Glasshouse management. ● Demonstration; RHS Rosemoor. Rocks, cascades and walls. ● Walk; RHS Rosemoor. Autumn colour at Rosemoor. ● RHS Regional Lecture; Cambridge. Bhutan – Land of the thunder dragon, Tony Schilling.	Sir Moritz Schomburgk, b. 1811; botanist	WED 5
Demonstration; RHS Pershore. Making the most of your unheated greenhouse in winter.		THU 6
Lecture; East Yorkshire AGS, Beverley Girls' High School, Norwood: 7.30 pm. Sex among the flowers, Dr Steve Furness.		FRI 7
8 – 16 October; Sulgrave Manor, Oxfordshire. Living History 1560, themed events at George Washington's ancestral house. ● Lecture; Dorset NCCPG, Allendale Centre, Wimborne: 7.30 pm. Uncommon perennials, Angela Whinfield. ● Lecture; North East NCCPG, Hancock Museum, Barras Bridge, Newcastle upon Tyne: 2.30 pm. Autumn and winter colour, Mrs Sue Robinson. ● AGM; Ness Gardens, Cheshire: 10 am. Friends of Ness Gardens (051 336 7769).		SAT 8
National Vegetable Society Show & Northern Championships, California Gardens, Howden, North Humberside. The host garden centre, California Gardens, can be contacted on 0430 430824. ● Demonstration; RHS Wisley. Glasshouse management. ● Walk; Westonbirt Arboretum, Gloucestershire: 2.30 pm. Maples and autumn colour.	William Aiton, d. 1849; superintendent of RBG, Kew	SUN 9

DIARY		EVENTS
MON **10**		Lecture; East Lancashire AGS, Ramsbottom Civic Hall, Market Place: 7.45 pm. Campanulas and some relatives, Peter Lewis (0706 356385).
TUE **11**	Alexander Dickson, d. 1880; founder of rose nursery	Lecture; RHS Pershore. ● Trailer Tour; Charlecote Park, Warwickshire. Details from the National Trust.
WED **12**	Thomas Rochford, d. 1901; nursery founder	Demonstration; RHS Wisley. Paths and patios. ● Demonstration; RHS Hyde Hall, at Writtle College. Hedges – selection and maintenance.
THU **13**	Mary Kingsley, b. 1862; botanist and traveller	Demonstration; RHS Pershore. Apple juicing and cider making. ● RHS Regional Lecture; Cheltenham. Year-round bulb garden, Christine Skelmersdale.
FRI **14**		14 - 16 October; Journées des Plantes de Courson, Courson-Monteloup (010 33 1 64 58 90 12).
SAT **15**	George Russell, d. 1951; lupin breeder	AGS Sussex Show; Millais School, Depot Road, Horsham, West Sussex (0386 554790). ● 15 – 16 October; Pruning demonstration, The Gardens of the Rose, St Albans, Hertfordshire: 11 am – 4 pm. Continuous demonstrations of pruning and training climbers and rambling roses. £2 charge (0727 850461). ● 15 – 16 October; Autumn garden design weekend, RHS Pershore. ● Plant Sale; Dorset NCCPG, Abbotsbury Nursery.
SUN **16**	Reginald Farrer, d. 1920; collector (*Viburnum farreri*)	Rose pruning demonstration ends: The Gardens of the Rose close for the winter today. ● Demonstration; RHS Wisley. Paths and patios. ● Walk; RHS Wisley. Autumn colour. ● Lecture; Ness Gardens: 2pm. Up the Amazon without a paddle, Professor R. H. Marrs. ● Garden Open; High Beeches, West Sussex: 10 am – 5 pm. Autumn colour opening, with bazaar for Red Cross Activenture appeal.

EVENTS	DIARY	
17 October – 18 November; Kew School of Garden Design, John Brookes. Details from the Adult Education Section, RBG Kew (081 332 5626). ● Walk; RHS Wisley. Autumn colour. ● RHS Regional Lecture; York. Fruit cultivation for amateur gardeners in the north of England, Jim Arbury. ● AGM and Plant Sale; Surrey NCCPG, Wisley Lecture Hall: 7.45 pm.	Thomas Rivers, d. 1877; fruit hybridiser	MON 17
Walk; Westonbirt Arboretum, Gloucestershire. Hillier Gardening Club (0794 368966). ● Trailer Tour; Charlecote Park, Warwickshire. Details from the National Trust.	Nicolas Culpeper, b. 1616; herbalist	TUE 18
Meet the Gardener; Ryton Organic Gardens. Putting the Garden to Bed (0203 303517). ● Flower Arrangers' Day; RHS Wisley. Delights of autumn, Christina Wallis. ● Demonstration; RHS Rosemoor at Cannington College. The cool glasshouse. ● Demonstration; RHS Garden, Hyde Hall. Pruning the roses – ramblers, shrubs and climbers (0245 400256). ● Workshop; Hillier Arboretum. Plant propagation 3 – seeds. (0794 368787). ● Lecture; South Wales AGS, Pencoed College, Bridgend: 7 pm (0558 822960). ● RHS Regional Lecture; Restoration and reconstruction of historic gardens, Elizabeth Banks.	Sir Thomas Browne, b. 1605, d. 1682; writer (*The Garden of Cyrus*); E A Bunyard, d. 1939; writer (*Old Garden Roses*)	WED 19
Demonstration; RHS Pershore. Using your heated greenhouse in winter. ● Lecture; Exeter AGS, St Thomas High School: 6.30 pm. Some woodland plants, Kath Dryden (0395 273636). ● RHS Regional Lecture; Melton Mowbray. Alpines, the easy ones and others, Paul Ingwersen.	Friedrich Welwitsch, d. 1872; botanist (*Welwitschia*)	THU 20
RHS Regional Lecture; Woodbridge. Bulbs of central Asia, Brian Mathew. ● National Apple Day. Events around the country, including at Ryton Organic Gardens, West Midlands; Brogdale, Kent; Sulgrave Manor, Oxfordshire. The event is co-ordinated by Common Ground.		FRI 21
22 – 23 October; Sulgrave Manor, Oxfordshire: 10 am– 5 pm. Apple Day celebrations. ● RHS Regional Lecture; Cannington. Peat and woodland gardens, Bill Tait.	James Cocker, d. 1880; nurseryman	SAT 22
Lecture; Ness Gardens, Cheshire: 2 pm. Recognition and control of garden pests, P. L. Cunnington (051 336 7769).	Rev. H H d'Ombrain, d. 1905; rose grower	SUN 23

DIARY		EVENTS
MON **24**		
TUE **25**	James Sowerby, d. 1822; botanical artist	Demonstration; RHS Pershore. Celebration of apple day. • Trailer Tour; Charlecote Park, Warwickshire. Details from the National Trust.
WED **26**		RHS Regional Lecture; Mold. Small gardens and backyards, David Stevens.
THU **27**	Rev. Clarence Bicknell, b. 1842; botanist of the Riviera	Demonstration; RHS Pershore. Designer plants – house plants. • Lecture; Dorset NCCPG, County Records Office, Dorchester: 7.30 pm. 18th and 19th century plants, Peter Jones.
FRI **28**	James Aitchison, b. 1836; botanist	
SAT **29**		
SUN **30**	John Kennedy, b. 1759; nurseryman (*Kennedia*)	

EVENTS	DIARY	
	John Evelyn, b. 1620; naturalist and diarist	MON 31
1 – 2 November; RHS Flower Show, Westminster: 11 am – 7 pm. Ornamental Plant competition and Botanical Paintings. • RHS Lecture; Westminster: 2.15 pm. The garden in winter, Rosemary Verey. • Demonstration; RHS Pershore. Around the garden in November.	Fred Streeter, d. 1975; broadcaster	TUE 1
Lecture; East Yorkshire AGS, Beverley Girls' High School, Norwood: 7.30 pm. Alliums, Dr Dilys Davies. • RHS Regional Lecture; Fishguard. Conservation – national plant collections, Graham Pattison. • RHS Flower Show ends: 10 am – 5 pm.	James Kelway, b. 1815; nurseryman; John Waterer, d. 1868; nurseryman	WED 2
Workshop; RHS Pershore. Propagation 11 – trees and shrubs from hardwood cuttings. • RHS Regional Lecture; Bath. My kind of plants, Roy Lancaster.	Clarence Elliott, b. 1881; nurseryman and plantsman; Robert Stephenson Clarke, d. 1948; creator of Borde Hill, West Sussex	THU 3
4 – 5 November; Christmas Exhibition and Competition, Mercia and North Wales area of NAFAS (0492 583626).	William Dykes, b. 1877; iris breeder	FRI 4
5 – 6 November; National Chrysanthemum Society Show, RHS Westminster, London. The National Chrysanthemum Society (0788 569039). • Christmas Exhibition and Competition, Mercia and North Wales NAFAS ends.	Richard Bradley, d. 1732; Cambridge botanist and writer	SAT 5
AGS Annual General Meeting; Details in September *Bulletin* (0386 554790). • Walk; RHS Wisley. Chrysanthemums and other plants under glass. • Walk; Hillier Arboretum: 2 pm. Farewell to autumn. • Lecture; Ness Gardens: 2pm. Trees for the smaller garden, J. K. Hulme. • National Chrysanthemum Society Show ends.	Frank Kingdon Ward, b. 1885; plant collector	SUN 6

DIARY		EVENTS
MON **7**	William Dallimore; d. 1959; dendrologist	Lecture; North London AGS, Oakwood Methodist Church Hall (opposite Oakwood underground station): 7.30 pm. The Pyrenees, Antony P. C. Powell (081 445 1675).
TUE **8**		Lecture; RHS Pershore. Hedgerow conservation. ● Lecture; Suffolk NCCPG: 7 pm. Venue to be confirmed. Penelope Hobhouse. ● RHS Regional Lecture; Consett. Creating gardens in France, Alan Mason.
WED **9**	Thomas Bridges, d. 1865; introducer of *Victoria amazonica*	Course; Ryton Organic Gardens. Flower Arranging Course (0203 303517). ● Course; Ness Gardens. Pruning. Limited numbers: £5.50 (051 336 7769). ● Demonstration; RHS Wisley. Trees: planting for 'life'. ● Demonstration; RHS Hyde Hall, at Writtle College. The ABC of fencing.
THU **10**	Robert Harkness, d. 1920; rose nurseryman	Lecture; RHS Pershore. Introducing the latest seeds. ● NAFAS Demonstration; Borough Theatre, Abergavenny: 7 pm. The tingle factor, Mrs S. Edwards, Abergavenny Flower Arrangement Society (0873 830072).
FRI **11**	E J Lowe, b. 1825; pteridologist	RHS Regional Lecture; Norwich. The Wisley glasshouse department, Ray Waite.
SAT **12**		Lecture; West Yorkshire AGS, St Chad's Parish Centre, Headingley, Leeds: 2.30 pm. Nurseryman's view of alpines, Jim Sutherland (0423 886302). ● Lecture; Dorset NCCPG, Allendale Centre, Wimborne: 2.30 pm. East Dorset AGM. Orchid hunting in Sumatra, Christine Hart-Davies. ● Lecture; North East NCCPG, Hancock Museum, Barras Bridge, Newcastle upon Tyne: 2.30 pm. Bulbous plants, Prof. R. B. Cain. ● Lecture; Kent NCCPG, Benenden Village Hall: 2.30 pm. ● Garden Visit; Hillier Arboretum. Torchlight tours and late night shopping. Hillier Gardening Club (0794 368966).
SUN **13**		Demonstration; RHS Wisley. Trees: planting for 'life'. ● Lecture; Ness Gardens: 2 pm. Some Cornish gardens, P. Matthews.

EVENTS

DIARY

Lecture; East Lancashire AGS, Ramsbottom Civic Hall, Market Place: 7.45 pm. If in doubt try a trough, Robin Brown (0706 356385). • RHS Regional Lecture; Garden plants to attract butterflies, Roy Cheek. • Lecture; Surrey NCCPG, Wisley Lecture Hall: 7.45 pm. Plant arranging in the garden with foliage and flowers, Jane Sterndale-Bennett.

Rev. A. Foster-Melliar, d. 1904; rose grower

MON

14

Lecture; RHS Pershore. Plant names explained. • NAFAS Demonstration; Country Club Theatre, Sandford Park, Wareham, Dorset: 2 pm. O little town of Bethlehem, Barry Grey. • RHS Regional Lecture; Altrincham. Magic of Magnolias, Jim Gardiner.

TUE

15

Demonstration; RHS Wisley. Pruning of fruit trees and bushes. • Flower Arrangers' Day; RHS Wisley. The Christmas Spirit, Sheila Macqueen. • Demonstration; RHS Rosemoor. Choosing and caring for your garden equipment. • Walk; RHS Rosemoor. Winter structure in your garden. • Lecture; South Wales AGS, Pencoed College, Bridgend: 7 pm. (0558 822960).

WED

16

Lecture; RHS Hyde Hall, at Writtle College. Science for gardeners. • Demonstration; RHS Pershore. A herbal Christmas – gift ideas and decorations. • Lecture; Exeter AGS, St Thomas High School: 6.30 pm. Alliums, Richard Dadd (0395 273636). • RHS Regional Lecture; Flowers of Greece and Crete, Christopher Grey-Wilson.

Rev. William Colenso, b. 1811; botanist (*Myosotis colensoi*)

THU

17

18 – 27 November; World Federation of Rose Societies Convention, Christchurch, New Zealand. Details from the RNRS (0727 850461). • Lecture; Bristol AGS, Westbury on Trym Methodist Hall: 7 pm. Pleasures of collected seed, Phillip Harris (0594 529663). • Demonstration; RHS Wisley. Pruning of fruit trees and bushes.

FRI

18

Thomas Meehan, d. 1901; collector (*Meehania*)

SAT

19

Demonstration; RHS Wisley. Pruning of fruit trees and bushes. • Lecture; Ness Gardens, Cheshire: 2 pm. The meres of Cheshire, Professor B. Moss (051 336 7769).

SUN

20

DIARY		EVENTS
MON **21**		RHS Regional Lecture; Peterborough. Cultivation and use of tender perennials, Christopher Bailes.
TUE **22**		22 – 23 November; RHS Flower Show, Westminster: 11 am – 7 pm. Late Apple & Pear and Ornamental Plant competitions, Botanical Paintings. ● RHS Lecture; Westminster: 2.15 pm. Canada's Royal Botanical Gardens, Professor Allen Paterson. ● 22 – 24 November; Orchid Society of Great Britain Autumn Show, RHS Halls, Westminster. ● Lecture; RHS Pershore. Introduction to fruit tree pruning.
WED **23**	Charles Babington, b. 1808; botanist (*Allium babingtonii*)	Demonstration; RHS Wisley. Pruning outdoor grapes. ● Demonstration; RHS Rosemoor at Cannington College. Hardy foliage plants – winter colour in the garden. ● Demonstration; RHS Hyde Hall, at Writtle College, Writtle, Essex. Growing alpines (0245 400256). ● Workshop; Sir Harold Hillier Gardens and Arboretum, Hampshire. Plant propagation 4 – division and layering (0794 368787). ● RHS Flower Show ends: 10 am – 5 pm. ● Orchid Society of Great Britain Autumn Show continues.
THU **24**		Demonstration; RHS Wisley. Pruning outdoor grapes. ● Demonstration; RHS Pershore. Garden design 8 – planting a fruit garden. ● AGM & Lecture; Dorset NCCPG, County Records Office, Dorchester: 7.30 pm. Camellias, Jennifer Trehane. ● Orchid Society of Great Britain Autumn Show ends.
FRI **25**	John Downie, d. 1892; nurseryman (*Malus* 'John Downie')	25 November – 5 December; Exhibition, Harlow Carr. National tree week exhibition. ● Demonstration; RHS Wisley. Pruning outdoor grapes.
SAT **26**	Henry Elwes, d. 1922; dendrologist and collector	Wine Tasting and Christmas Feast, Ryton Organic Gardens, Ryton on Dunsmore, West Midlands (0203 303517).
SUN **27**	James Bateman, d. 1897; orchidist and writer	Lecture; Ness Gardens, Cheshire: 2 pm. The greenhouse effect, Dr K. Hardwick (051 336 7769).

EVENTS	DIARY	
		MON **28**
Workshop; RHS Pershore. Winter fruit tree pruning.	Gertrude Jekyll, b. 1843; garden designer and writer	**TUE** **29**
30 November – 2 December; Flower Arrangers' Christmas workshop, RHS Wisley.	Sir Isaac Balfour, d. 1922; Edinburgh botanist	**WED** **30**
Demonstration; RHS Pershore. Around the garden in December. • Walk; Harlow Carr: 2 pm. With the curator.	William Dykes, d. 1925; iris breeder	**THU** **1**
	Sir Alfred Parsons, b. 1847; botanical artist (*Genus Rosa*)	**FRI** **2**
Flower Arranging Children's workshops, RHS Wisley.		**SAT** **3**
Walk; RHS Wisley. Conifers including slow growing types. • Walk; RHS Rosemoor. Winter at Rosemoor. • Walk; Hillier Arboretum: 2 pm. Advent walk. Meet in the car park. • Lecture; Ness Gardens: 2 pm. Plant breeding and selection for the amateur, Dr H. McAllister.	Hugh Armytage-Moore, d. 1954; creator of Rowallane, Co. Down	**SUN** **4**

DIARY		EVENTS
MON 5	Constance Spry, b. 1886; flower arranger and writer	Lecture; North London AGS, Oakwood Methodist Church Hall (opposite Oakwood underground station): Pleiones, Ian Butterfield 7.30 pm. (081 445 1675).
TUE 6		Lecture; RHS Pershore. Winter treasures in the garden. • NAFAS Demonstration; Church House Conference Centre, Westminster, London: 2 pm. Christmas contrasts, Michael Bowyer (081 460 7902).
WED 7	Captain William Bligh, d. 1817; Master of *The Bounty* (*Blighia*)	Planning a Vegetable Garden Day; Ryton Organic Gardens, Ryton on Dunsmore, West Midlands (0203 303517). • Demonstration; RHS Hyde Hall, at Writtle College, Writtle, Essex . Identification of trees by winter twigs (0245 400256).
THU 8	Gertrude Jekyll, d. 1932; garden designer and writer	Workshop; RHS Pershore. Flower arranging for Christmas.
FRI 9	Lord Penzance, d. 1899; rose hybridiser (Rose 'Lord Penzance')	9 – 10 December; RHS Christmas Show, Westminster: 11 am – 7 pm. Displays of wintering flowering shrubs, cyclamen and other horticultural gifts.
SAT 10	George Maw, b. 1832; collector and *Crocus* expert	RHS Christmas Show ends: 10 am – 5 pm.
SUN 11	Franz Bauer, d. 1840; botanical artist	

EVENTS	DIARY	
AGM & Lecture; East Lancashire AGS, Ramsbottom Civic Hall, Market Place: 7.45 pm. (0706 356385).	Erasmus Darwin, b. 1731; scientist and poet (*Botanic Garden*)	MON **12**
		TUE **13**
	John Loudon, d. 1843; writer and landscaper	WED **14**
Lecture; RHS Hyde Hall, at Writtle College. Plant origins and naming. ● AGM; Exeter AGS, St Thomas High School: 6.30 pm. Includes seed exchange (0395 273636).	Hugh, 5th Earl Annesley, d. 1908; creator of Castlewellan, Co. Down	THU **15**
		FRI **16**
Workshop; RHS Pershore. Flower arranging for Christmas.	Charles Hurst, d. 1947; Cambridge geneticist; hybridiser with roses and orchids	SAT **17**
	Philip Miller, d. 1771; author: *Gardeners' Dictionary*, curator at the Chelsea Physic Garden.	SUN **18**

DIARY	EVENTS
MON **19**	
TUE **20** James Gordon, d. 1780; nurseryman (*Gordonia*); Sir Reginald Blomfield, b. 1856; garden designer and writer	
WED **21** Charles Lawson, d. 1873; nurseryman (*Chamaecyparis lawsoniana*)	
THU **22**	
FRI **23** Sir Thomas Neame, b. 1885; founder of East Malling Research Station	
SAT **24** Frances, Viscountess Wolseley, d. 1936; gardener	
SUN **25** Christmas Day	

EVENTS	DIARY	
	John Fothergill, d. 1780; amateur botanist	MON 26
	Sir Thomas Gage, d. 1820; plant collector (*Gagea*); Sir Reginald Blomfield, d. 1942; garden designer and writer (*The Formal Garden in England*)	TUE 27
	Joseph Arnold, b. 1782; botanist (*Rafflesia arnoldii*)	WED 28
	G P Baker, d. 1951; textile manufacturer and alpine botanist	THU 29
		FRI 30
	Isabella Preston, d. 1965; Canadian hybridiser of *Syringa*	SAT 31
		SUN 1

Shows

NOTES FROM THE RHS SHOWS 1993

Only a minority of high-profile nurseries exhibits at Westminster shows. It is, however, a way of getting yourself noticed and the RHS both encourages new exhibitors and rewards them. The Tropical Rain Forest won a gold medal at the show on 22 & 23 March 1993 for its exhibition of Bromeliads, dominated and unified by drapes of Spanish moss, *Tillandsia usneioides*. The nursery was still winning gold medals in November.

One of the most consistently challenging exhibitors this year was Mallet Court Nursery of Somerset. At the Wisley Flower Festival (30 June & 1 July) it won a Silver-Gilt medal in the Flora range for a display which included *Carpinus laxiflora*, *Distylium myricoides* and a gold-variegated form of beech, *Fagus sylvatica* 'Luteovariegata'. On 10 & 11 August at Westminster, it showed *Carpinus polyneura*, *Diospyros glaucifolia* and *Cornus alba* 'Hessei' among other seldom-seen trees and shrubs and at the Great Autumn Show on 14 & 15 September it scored again with such rare tree forms as the spotty-leaved *Catalpa bignonioides* 'Pulverulenta' and *Ilex rugosa* in fruit.

Another reliable exhibitor throughout the year was Burncoose & South Down Nurseries of Cornwall. A fine exhibit of the many forms of *Phormium tenax* and its hybrids was one of the highlights of the Wisley Flower Festival: many were in flower, which meant that they were seen at their best. Starborough Nurseries are another faithful supporter. At the Great Autumn Show on 14 & 15 September they showed *Fothergilla* 'Blue Mist', a newish cultivar with good glaucous foliage. Their exhibit on Westminster on 5 & 6 October included

Cunninghamia lanceolata and *Fortunearia sinensis*, which was turning a clear yellow, while their exhibit in the New Hall on 2 & 3 November was outstanding. Entirely taken up with forms of *Liquidambar*, it included such rare species as *L. acalycina* and the variegated form of *L. styraciflua* known as 'Golden Treasure'. A welcome novice exhibitor at the Wisley Flower Festival was Green Farm Plants, owned by the charismatic John Coke. Coke's exhibit was composed of stunning white flowers set off by one or two - no more - stems of scarlet and crimson. The white form of willowherb *Epilobium angustifolium* 'Album' and *Antirrhinum majus* 'Taff's White', a variegated form, dominated the display. At the New Hall on 10 & 11 August Green Farm Plants was awarded a Gold Medal for its display of salvias, mainly from the CDR collections in Mexico. It concentrated upon the *S. greigii* × *microphylla* hybrids raised by James Compton under the name *Salvia* × *jamensis*. Among them were 'La Luna', white with small crimson hairs on the hood of the calyx, and the pink 'La Siesta'. At the show on 5 & 6 October Hopleys Plants also exhibited a wide range of James Compton's hybrids: clearly these salvias will be widely available within a year or so.

Some of the best exhibits at RHS shows come from the specialist societies and such institutes as Kew and Wisley. On 16 & 17 March the Director of the Royal Botanic Gardens at Kew exhibited three forms of *Iris viscaria*. This member of the rare Juno section of the genus *Iris* comes from Central Asia and is seldom seen in cultivation in the UK. On 10 & 11 August, Vincent Square welcomed back the British Gladiolus Society, exhibiting for the first time since its Golden Jubilee Year in 1975. Fortunately 1993 was the best year for growing gladiolus for a long time, due in large part to the weather: the Society considered the competition to be the best exhibition of gladiolus for many years.

At the Great Autumn Show the NCCPG mounted a fine exhibition of *Hedychium* varieties to emphasise that the genus is hardier than supposed. But perhaps the best corporate exhibit at a show in 1993 was put on by The Fruit and Vegetable Committee of the RHS on 5 & 6 October. It included all but four of the cultivars of apple and pear to which the Award of Garden Merit (New Series) had been made during the year, among them such old favourites as 'Bramley's Seedling' and 'Golden Delicious', the little known 'Dumelow's Seedling', a modern culinary variety highly prized for mincemeat, and 'Belle de Boskoop' and 'Falstaff'. Less common vegetables formed another part of the exhibit and included seven different forms of squash from orange 'Turk's Turban' to a small, near-black variety like a large passionfruit, 'Rolet'. The Fruit and Vegetable Committee was founded on 5 July 1858 and is the oldest standing committee of the RHS. Its members' aim has always been to 'examine and report upon all Fruits or Esculents brought under their notice; collecting information concerning the qualities of Fruits grown in different parts of the United Kingdom, and advising the Council generally as to the best modes of increasing the Society's power of promoting the improvement of Fruits and Esculents cultivated in Great Britain and Ireland'. In furtherance of the RHS's theme of Education Year, the Brogdale Trust showed rare varieties of apple at the same show. These included 'Curl Tail', which is only really distinguished for the strangely fleshy curving stalk, and which Brogdale cheerfully admitted was 'a somewhat small cooking apple of no particular merit', and the original 'Isaac Newton' cooker whose fall inspired the scientist to define the laws of gravity. One of the best apples shown by Brogdale, still little known, is 'Christmas Pearmain'.

Exhibits which display a large number of varieties for visitors' enlightenment are one of the features of RHS shows. The central feature of an exhibit mounted by Bodnant Gardens on 16 & 17 March was *Clivia* seedlings, dominated by a pale peach coloured form of *C. miniata* named 'Bodnant Yellow'. The individual flowers, well-spaced on the inflorescence, are creamy apricot, deepening to orange at the base of the petals, which gives almost a two-tone effect. At the same show there was an exhibition of *Primula allionii* and its hybrids on the stand of Sussex nurserymen W E Th. Ingwersen.

Unnamed seedlings of the 'Crowsley Seedling' were shown alongside more simple forms, including *Primula allionii* f. 'alba'. The best have flowers which open out to cover the entire leaf rosette.

An exhibit of a different kind dominated the Late Spring Show on 20 & 21 April. It was a huge display of orchid photographs mounted by J R Oddy to coincide with the International Orchid Conference in Glasgow and designed to illustrate the sheer variety of the world's orchids, whether species or hybrids. There were 59 sheets, each composed of 42 colour pictures, and annotated to show the flower's origin, height, hardiness and place in the natural order of the Orchidaceae. The labour and knowledge that this exhibit demonstrated were admirable.

At the Wisley Flower Festival the star of the show was the exhibit of *Umbelliferae* mounted by the Kent Group of the Hardy Plant Society under the direction of Tim Ingram. Many of the plants were rare: *Zosima absinthifolia*, *Seseli praecox* and *Laserpitium gallicum* among them, but they also included the darkest form of *Astrantia major*, which is called 'Ruby Wedding'. Other good educational exhibits during the year were the display of cannas from Bockings Exotics of Launceston on 10 & 11 August; Edrom Nurseries' amazing range of forms of autumn-flowering gentians, most of them forms or hybrids of *Gentiana sino-ornata* and *G. multiflora* (including the striped form *G.* × *macaulayi* 'White Wings', *ternifolia*, 'Strathmore' and 'Angel's Wings') at the Great Autumn Show; and Stephen Treseder's small exhibit of African succulents from four plant families - the Asclepiadaceae, the Aizoaceae, the Liliaceae and the Crassulaceae on 5 & 6 October. But the best table at that show was an exhibition of acers from Hergest Croft on behalf of the NCCPG: Hergest Croft has the National Collection. It deserved better than the Silver Medal (Flora Range) awarded by the RHS.

The weather affects every exhibitor. The Camellia competition on 16 & 17 March was well supported and the quality of the blooms exceptionally high in 1993. Both camellias and rhododendrons benefited from the absence of recent heavy rain or frost. At the Wembley Show in Easter Week the number of camellias in the competition was the largest for many years. The *reticulata* hybrids showed particularly well, after the warm weather, and the exhibits were of high standard. At the Late

Spring Show on 20 & 21 April both the daffodil and the rhododendron competition had a larger number of exhibits than seen for a long time.

The RHS has experimented with new shows in new venues recently. Hampton Court is adjudged a great success: likewise the Birmingham NEC show. But the Wembley Show in Easter Week was unpopular with both the public ('too difficult to get to, and too crowded', they said) and with the exhibitors ('not enough visitors'). Launched as the Greatest Gardening Spectacular ever staged, the idea was a good one: to combine the elements of a traditional flower show and garden sundries exhibit with practical demonstrations, seminars, lectures, competitions and the possibility of purchasing plants at this important time of the year for sales. It was a mixture between a Perfect Homes Exhibition and an ordinary fortnightly show. There was no segregation of exhibitors, which meant that Societies and Charities rubbed shoulders with Seed Merchants and Colleges, Bedroom Furniture suppliers and Hatters. It will be revived this year, not at Wembley, but at Olympia, where it should thrive.

THE CHELSEA FLOWER SHOW 1993

This was a very upbeat Chelsea. The garden designs were more innovative than ever, and the plant exhibits of higher standard. There was a new sense of optimism among the exhibitors, in response to the end of the recession. The weather had been kind. And the RHS was basking in its own success. This Chelsea was definitely better than ever.

It was the gardens which stole the show. Top prize-winner was the wild flower and seaside garden co-ordinated by Countryside Wildflowers, Hasmead (Landscape) Ltd, John Chambers Wild Flower Seeds and Julie Toll. It was set on the edge of simulated sand dunes, with sea-holly *Eryngium maritimum* and horned poppy *Glaucium flavum* among the marram grass. A clever idea, and nicely done, though some considered it too wild to be called a garden. The visitors' favourite was the series of small gardens assembled by the Miniature Garden Co of Ilminster in Somerset. They fell for the sheer variety of its lilliputian container gardens, a splendid plug for the Nursery of Miniatures which stocked it.

Many of the gardens were designed as marketing exercises to enhance their sponsors' profiles. Ursula Buchan commented that 'for those of us who have never even heard of Azzarro 9, the fact that 'the feeder fountain spilled onto a diffuser reminiscent of the shape of a perfume bottle' is altogether too subtle'. There is an unreality about such designs which puts them beyond relevance to most visitors. An increasing number of gardens are sponsored not by newspapers but by charities. Lucy Huntington designed a garden of low-allergen plants for the National Asthma Campaign garden. No wind-pollinated plants were allowed but, when so many allergens blow in from miles away, it makes little difference to asthma sufferers to be surrounded by insect-pollinated plants. But the beds of pretty herbs, foxgloves, columbines, geums, irises and lupins were effective for their very simplicity.

Small exhibitors proliferated in the great marquee. They concentrated on new herbaceous plants: charming new *Linaria* hybrids from Rougham Nurseries and *Diascia* 'Joyce's Choice' from Potterton & Martin. Not all were so exciting: Hopleys showed *Salvia patens* 'White Trophy': proof that albino forms are seldom as good as the coloured types. This anaemia was common to the design of the exhibits too: soft, subtle, colour-conscious compositions were everywhere. The cumulative effect was a shade repetitive. It was a relief to see the amazing bright colours of the Interflora stand: reds, oranges and yellows around a bronzy frame. And the most impressive exhibit was the slice of the Savill Gardens which the Crown Estates brought from Windsor Great Park to cover the Monument site.

Chelsea is for launching new roses. Best of the bunch was Kordes' 'Mary Pope', a crimson floribunda with an imbricated flower like a camellia, introduced by Mattocks as a rose for cutting. It is said to last well in water and keep its shape to the end. Other novelties from David Austin (the rugosa hybrid 'Mrs Doreen Pike') and Dicksons ('Mr JCB' - a floribunda) were worthy new variations on old themes. A welcome feature of recent Chelsea has been the proliferation of awards to exhibits of courtyard gardens, window-boxes and hanging baskets. It underlines both the broad appeal of the RHS and the wide range of its members' interests. And the expanded floristry and floral arrangement section reflects growing acceptance of the importance of floral art. Its appeal is international. The prize winners for the exhibits by Floral Arrangement Clubs included teams from Northern Ireland, Italy, Grenada and Zimbabwe.

1993 saw more and better exhibits at Chelsea than ever within the educational and scientific section. Apart from education, the emphasis was on conservation and environmental responsibility. It was good to see the Friends of Oxford Botanic Garden seeking, rather shyly, a greater public awareness of their remarkable collection of aroids. Another sign of the times was a stand for The National Institute of Medical Herbalists. And bang up to date was the exhibit manned by the Ministry of Agriculture to publicise the problems which open frontiers pose to the control of pests and diseases.

Gold Medals at the Chelsea Flower Show 1993

Gardens. B & Q (Living garden); Bridgemere Garden World (WI Woodland garden); Country Living Magazine (Gertrude Jekyll); Countryside Wildflowers (Seaside garden); Daily Telegraph (Romantic woodland garden); Douglas Knight (Rock & water garden).

Exhibits of Plants. African Violet Centre (saintpaulias); Alpine Garden Society (woodland plants); Jacques Amand (bulbs); David Austin Roses (roses); Avon Bulbs (bulbs); Steven Bailey (carnations etc.); Barbados Horticultural Society (Barbadian flowers); Belgium (ONDAH) (house plants); Walter Blom & Son (tulips); Blooms of Bressingham (herbaceous plants); Rupert Bowlby (alliums); S & N Brackley (sweet peas); British Bedding & Pot Plant Association (bedding plants); Burncoose & South Down Nurseries (trees & shrubs); Butterfields Nursery (pleiones); Cheshire Herbs (herbs); The Crown Estate (plants from Savill Gardens); Dibleys (streptocarpus); Garden Centre Association (bedding plants in hanging baskets); Glebe Cottage Plants (herbaceous plants); Goldbrook Plants (hostas); R Harkness & Co (roses); Hazeldene Nursery (violas); Herons Bonsai (bonsai); Hillier Nurseries Ltd (trees & shrubs); The Hop Shop (dried flowers); Ichiyo School of Ikebana (floral arrangements); Kirstenbosch Botanical Gardens (native plants of South Africa); Marston Exotics (carnivorous plants); Mattocks Roses (roses); McBeans Orchids (orchids); Ken Muir (strawberries); Notcutts Nurseries (trees & shrubs); Oakleigh Nurseries (fuchsias & pelargoniums); Oldbury Nurseries (fuchsias); G Reuthe (rhododendrons); Southfield Nurseries (cacti); Stapeley Water Gardens (aquatic plants); Tropical Rain Forest (bromeliads); Woodfield Brothers (lupins); ZimTrade (proteas).

Courtyard Gardens. Fittleworth & District Horticultural Society; Woking Borough Council.

Window Boxes & Hanging Baskets. Leeds & Hollingbourne Garden Society.

Floral Arrangements. Aldershot Flower Arrangement Club; Ravensbourne Floral Society.

Floristry. Berry & Saunders; Bettina Floral Artist.

HORTICULTURAL SHOWS IN 1994

Some of the major horticultural shows and floral events are listed in this section. Dates of many other shows can be found in the Calendar section. Local papers, the gardening press, especially *Garden News*, and gardening society publications are other good places to look for further show information. If you are thinking of organising your own show - or simply want to understand what makes for a winning entry - then two booklets from the Royal Horticultural Society are essential reading. *The Horticultural Show Handbook* (revised in 1990) gives clear advice on how to organise a show, suggests what rules should be adopted, and provides details of the standards by which entries should be judged. The *Horticultural Judges Register* locates accredited judges. Not all societies use the rules laid down in the RHS handbook: the Royal National Rose Society, the National Chrysanthemum Society and the National Dahlia Society have their own rules; and the National Vegetable Society is preparing its own amended system. Show stationery is supplied by many societies to their affiliates, including the National Vegetable Society and the National Association of Allotment and Leisure Gardeners (who will also duplicate schedules). Stationery can also be ordered from RHS Enterprises Ltd at Wisley (0483 211320).

Ayr Flower Show

Kyle & Carrick District Council, 30 Miller Road, Ayr KA7 2AY
☎ 0292 282842

CONTACT Mr P. M. Gibbs, Leisure Services
DATES To be confirmed: 4 August to 6 August
LOCATION Rozelle Park, Ayr

The dates for this summer flower show were not confirmed when we went to press. Contact the organisers for more details.

BBC Gardeners' World Live

BBC Haymarket Exhibitions, 60 Waldegrave Road, Teddington TW11 8LG
☎ 081 943 5000

DATES   15 June to 19 June
LOCATION   National Exhibition Centre, Birmingham
OPEN   10 am - 6 pm, daily
TICKETS   To be announced: look out for advance discounts
GROUPS   1 free ticket for every 20 purchased in advance
PARKING AND TRAVEL   Parking on site

Now in its second year, the first show was judged a great success with its mixture of displays and demonstrations. The NEC location though lacking atmosphere is spacious, and the show is considerably bigger this year. Attractions include a large out of London RHS show, spread over two marquees, and a flower arrangement display. The RHS advisory desk will be present.

Chelsea Flower Show

Shows Department, Royal Horticultural Society, 80 Vincent Square, London SW1P 2PE
☎ 071 828 1744/ 834 4333

CONTACT   See the January edition of *The Garden*
DATES   24 May to 27 May
LOCATION   Royal Hospital, Chelsea, London
OPEN   24 - 26 May: 8 am to 8 pm; 27 May: 8 am to 5 pm
TICKETS   24, 25 May (members only): £15 (£8 from 3.30 pm); 26 May: Members £11; Public £22 (£12 after 3.30 pm, £7 after 5.30 pm); 27 May: Members £9; Public £18
GROUPS   No discounts for groups
PARKING AND TRAVEL   Battersea Park, with free shuttle bus. Public transport recommended (Sloane Square underground or shuttle from Victoria station)

The world famous annual flower show remains the most prestigious event in the horticultural calendar. Nurseries, societies and charities create display stands and gardens in the huge marquee, and outside in the grounds of The Royal Hospital. An exceptional range of garden furniture, machinery and other products is displayed outside, and items can be bought or ordered. Press attention usually centres on the display gardens: months of work goes into these beautifully staged displays which only last a week. There is a large flower arranging marquee and a pavilion devoted to garden designers. Numbers are restricted, and even so the show is often very crowded. RHS members have two days set aside exclusively for them, and can buy tickets at preferential rates. Early morning and late evening are the best times to visit, especially if it is hot.

Gateshead Summer Flower Show

Gateshead Metropolitan Borough Council, Prince Consort Road, Gateshead NE8 4HJ
☎ 091 490 1616 Ext. 272

CONTACT   Leisure Services
DATES   23 July to 24 July
LOCATION   Gateshead Central Nursery, Whickham Highway
OPEN   23 July: 10 am - 7 pm; 24 July: 10 am - 5.30 pm
TICKETS   23 July: £3; 24 July: £2
PARKING AND TRAVEL   Free parking

Expanding show which is organised by Gateshead Metropolitan Borough and a local gardening society, Rosecarpe (the North of England Rose, Sweet Pea and Carnation Society). There is also a spring show on 9 - 10 April.

The Great Garden and Countryside Festival

Holker Hall, Cark in Cartmel, Grange over Sands, Cumbria LA11 7PL
☎ 05395 58328

CONTACT   Show director
DATES   3 June to 5 June
LOCATION   Holker Hall, Cumbria: west of Grange over Sands on B5277 and B5278
OPEN   3 June: 10 am to 5.30 pm; 4 June: 10 am to 7.30 pm; 5 June: 10 am to 5.30 pm
TICKETS   Adults £6, OAPs £5, Children £3, under 12s free

The show covers horticulture, the countryside and the environment. Now in its third year. Displays include nurseries and national horticultural societies, as well as a flower arranging marquee and craft stands. This year there will be lectures, demonstrations and a gardeners' Question Time chaired by television gardener Alan Mason. One of the festival's themes will be cottage gardens.

Hampton Court Palace Flower Show

Shows Department, Royal Horticultural Society, 80 Vincent Square, London SW1P 2PE
☎ 071 828 1744/ 834 4333

CONTACT   Shows department
DATES   6 July to 10 July; Preview day, 5 July
LOCATION   Hampton Court Palace, East Molesey, Surrey
OPEN   5 July: 11 am - 7.30 pm; 6 - 9 July: 10 am - 7.30 pm; 10 July: 10 - 5.30 pm
TICKETS   5, £18 (members only); 6 - 10, Members £11; Public £14 (after 3.00 pm, Members £7; Public £8)
GROUPS   Affiliated societies £11.50; Others £12 (10 or more, booked in advance)

PARKING AND TRAVEL   £6; after 3.00 pm, £3
FACILITIES FOR THE DISABLED   Free parking; one es-
cort admitted free

Spread between eight main marquees, with additional
stands and tents over a wide area, this is now the biggest
gardening show of its kind in the world. Unlike Chelsea
the exhibitors can sell direct from their stands on all
days. The show is also recommended for those who
now find Chelsea too crowded. The Royal National
Rose Society's British Rose Festival is held at the show.

Harrogate Great Autumn Flower Show

The North of England Horticultural Society,
4a South Park Road, Harrogate HG1 5QU
☎ 0423 561049

CONTACT   Show organiser
DATES   16 September to 17 September
LOCATION   Exhibition Halls, Harrogate
GROUPS   Discounts apply for advance bookings:
phone for details

As well as displays from nurseries and other trade
stands, this show is particularly recommended for the
society competitions (including dahlias and chrysanthemums), and for the National Kelsae Onion Festival
(Saturday only). There is a flower arrangement section
too.

Harrogate Spring Flower Show

North of England Horticultural Society, 4a South
Park Road, Harrogate HG1 5QU
☎ 0423 561049

CONTACT   Show secretary
DATES   21 April to 24 April
LOCATION   Valley Gardens, Harrogate
OPEN   21 - 23 April: 9.30 am to 6 pm; 24 April: 9.30
am - 4.30 pm
TICKETS   Day tickets: 21, £8.50; 22, £7; 23, £7.50; 24,
£7. RHS members, £1 less. Reduced afternoon rates
GROUPS   Discounts for groups of 20 and over. Apply
by 7 April

The show is jointly run by the North of England
Horticultural Society and the Royal Horticultural Society. As well as trade stands from nurseries, there will
be shows and competitions run by the Alpine Garden
Society, the Daffodil Society, and the National Association of Flower Arrangement Societies. The RHS advisory team will be present to answer horticultural
questions.

International Spring Gardening Fair

News International Exhibitions Ltd, P O Box 495,
Virginia Street E1 9XY
☎ 071 782 6000

DATES   31 March to 4 April
LOCATION   Olympia, London
OPEN   31 March - 3 April: 9 am - 5 pm; 4 April: 9.30
am - 5.30 pm
TICKETS   £9; £7 RHS members and last year's visitors;
£5 afternoon only; £20 family ticket
PARKING AND TRAVEL   On site and nearby parking
available

The show moves to Olympia after a mixed start at
Wembley last year. Timed to coincide with the Easter
weekend and the start of the gardening year it should
fill a gap in the show calendar. The new venue is larger
and has natural light, thus overcoming the major failings
of the previous year. The innovative lecture programme
continues. Other features to look out for include Trehane's Camellia Garden and, in a competition sponsored by *Amateur Gardening*, a window box display
right round the gallery. Ticket outlets will include all
London Underground stations in the four weeks before
the event. Keep an eye out for advance discounts for
clubs and society members.

Malvern Spring Gardening Show

Three Counties Agricultural Society, The
Showground, Malvern WR13 6NW
☎ 0684 892751

CONTACT   Show secretary
DATES   6 May to 8 May
LOCATION   Three Counties Showground, Malvern
OPEN   6 May: 9 am to 6 pm; 7 May: 9 am to 6 pm; 8
May: 9 am to 5 pm
TICKETS   £5; £3.50 (£2.50 if booked in advance) for
RHS and Three Counties Agricultural Society
members
GROUPS   Discounts for groups of 20 and over. Apply
by 30 April
PARKING AND TRAVEL   Free car parking

The Malvern Spring Gardening Show is organised by
the Three Counties Agricultural Society and the Royal
Horticultural Society together. The dramatic setting
and rural location give this show its own unique character. The exhibitors include a wide range of nurseries,
both national and local, and numerous products and
sundries stands. The RHS advisory team is present.
There is also a floral art section.

Shrewsbury Flower Show

Quarry Lodge, Shrewsbury SY1 1RN
☎ 0743 364051

CONTACT   Show secretary
DATES   12 August to 13 August
LOCATION   The Quarry, Shrewsbury
OPEN   12 August: 11 am - 10 pm; 13 August: 10 am -
10 pm

TICKETS   Details from the show office
GROUPS   1 free ticket for groups of 20 or more

A large, traditional flower show. The show closes with a firework display on both nights.

Southport Flower Show

42 Hoghton Street, Southport PR9 0PQ

CONTACT   Show administrator
DATES   18 August to 20 August
LOCATION   Victoria Park, Southport
OPEN   18 August: 9 am - 7.30 pm; 19 August: 9 am - 8.30 pm; 20 August: 9 am - 5.30 pm
TICKETS   In advance: Adults £6, OAPs £5, Children (12-16) £2.50; On the gate: £7, £6 and £3
GROUPS   15% discount for groups of 20 and over, booked in advance

Prestigious annual flower show which draws over 100,000 visitors. Worth travelling to to see nurseries who do not attend the numerous southern shows.

Wisley Flower Festival

RHS Garden, Wisley, Woking GU23 6QB
☎ 0483 224234

DATES   12 August to 14 August
LOCATION   RHS Garden, Wisley
OPEN   12, 13 August: 10 am - 6 pm; 14 August: 9 am - 5 pm
TICKETS   Normal garden admission rates (£4.50); RHS members free
GROUPS   £3.75 for advance bookings of over 20: 12, 13 August only
PARKING AND TRAVEL   Free parking

The setting in the garden at Wisley is a major attraction of this smallish show. The nurseries attending will be selling plants. This year the Flower Show hosts the National Vegetable Society's National championships: not to be missed. The RHS Garden is open only to RHS members and NVS members on Sunday 14 August.

FLORAL EVENTS 1994

Chelsea Flower Show

DATES   24 May to 27 May

The Flower Show includes a marquee which is wholly devoted to flower arranging. See the Horticultural Shows section for more details.

Durham Castle Flower Festival

DATES   17 August to 21 August
LOCATION   Durham Castle, Durham

Flower Festival, Sherborne Abbey

DATES   12 August to 14 August
LOCATION   Sherborne Abbey, Sherborne, Dorset

Hampton Court Palace Flower Show

DATES   6 July to 10 July

There is a flower arrangement section at this show: see Horticultural Shows for more information.

Harrogate Great Autumn Flower Show

DATES   16 September to 17 September

The Flower Show includes a flower arranging section: see Horticultural Shows for more details.

Harrogate Spring Flower Show

DATES   21 April to 24 April

The show includes a NAFAS competition: see Horticultural Shows section for further details.

Loseley Flower Festival

DATES   28 May to 29 May
LOCATION   Loseley Park, Guildford

Two day flower festival organised by the Surrey area of NAFAS. Details from 0372 457375.

Malvern Spring Gardening Show

DATES   6 May to 8 May

This flower show includes a flower arranging section: see Horticultural Shows for more details.

Marble Hill: A Palladian Rendezvous

DATES   28 May to 30 May
LOCATION   Marble Hill House, Richmond Road, Twickenham, Surrey
OPEN   10 am - 6 pm daily
TICKETS   £3, OAPs £2, Children £1
PARKING AND TRAVEL   Free parking

A festival of flowers organised by the London and Overseas branch of NAFAS. There is also a craft marquee and refreshments. Tickets and more details from 081 460 7902.

NAFAS Berks, Bucks & Oxon Flower Festival

DATES   18 June to 19 June
LOCATION   Stanton Harcourt, Oxfordshire
TICKETS   £5
PARKING AND TRAVEL   Free parking

Entrance includes admission to the house and grounds. Local societies will stage displays in various buildings, and there will be plant and craft stalls. The NCCPG *Buddleja* collection can also be visited.

NAFAS Devon & Cornwall Area Show and Exhibition

DATES 16 March to 17 March
LOCATION Hotel Metropole (THF), Padstow, Cornwall

NAFAS Devon & Cornwall area show: further details from 0579 370286.

NAFAS Dorset & Guernsey Area Competitions and Exhibition

DATES 26 August to 27 August
LOCATION Ferndown School, Ferndown, Wimborne, Dorset

Area competitions and exhibition by the Dorset & Guernsey area of NAFAS (0258 837239).

NAFAS Dorset & Guernsey Conference and Competitions

DATES 11 May to 14 May
LOCATION Guernsey

Open to all NAFAS members. Day school and demonstration by Johan Huisman.

NAFAS Flower Arranging Competitions and Exhibition

DATES 27 July to 30 July
LOCATION The Brighton Centre, East Sussex
OPEN 27 July: 10 am - 9.30 pm; 28 July: 10 am - 3.30 pm; 29 July: 12 - 9.30 pm; 30 July: 10 am - 3.30 pm. Last admissions 1½ hours before closing
TICKETS £6 daily; £10 season ticket

Flower arranging competitions and an exhibition. This is the main open event for the National Association of Flower Arrangement Societies this year. It includes a sales table and a tombola. The event will benefit the Cystic Fibrosis Research Trust.

NAFAS Kent Area Show

DATES 26 June
LOCATION Hever Castle, Kent

NAFAS Mercia & North Wales Flower Festival

DATES 5 August to 7 August
LOCATION Hawkstone Hall, Shropshire

Further details about this NAFAS flower festival on 0492 583626.

NAFAS Three Counties & South Wales Area Day

DATES 28 September
LOCATION Porthcawl

Area day and competitions for the Three Counties & South Wales area of NAFAS (0633 440223).

NAFAS Wessex & Jersey Area Competitions

DATES 30 March
LOCATION Barton Peveril College, Eastleigh, Hampshire
OPEN 10 am - 5 pm

Area competitions and exhibitions from the Wessex and Jersey area of NAFAS: open to the public. Barton Peveril College is off Chestnut Avenue.

NAFAS Wessex & Jersey Area Exhibition

DATES 9 September to 11 September
LOCATION Jermyns House, Sir Harold Hillier Gardens and Arboretum, Ampfield, Hampshire
OPEN 10.30 am - 6 pm daily

Exhibition of floral arrangements at this famous arboretum.

SAFAS Open Demonstration Day

DATES 31 August
LOCATION St Andrews, Fife

Open demonstrations by members of the Scottish Association of Flower Arrangement Societies. More details on 031 445 2467.

3

A Digest of 1993 Gardening News

At its Annual General Meeting in February, the President of the Royal Horticultural Society, Robin Herbert, confirmed that members' tickets would shortly become non-transferable. In the past, a member's ticket could freely be lent to someone else: possession of the ticket permitted the holder, not just the member, to see the Westminster shows free of charge, and the holder plus one guest to enter the Royal Horticultural Society's gardens. In future these rights will accrue to the member, not the holder of the ticket. The right of the member to bring a guest to the gardens is not affected by the change.

In March 1993, the President-designate of the Royal Horticultural Society, Sir Simon Hornby, told the new bimonthly magazine *Gardens Illustrated* 'I hate rose gardens'. In the same month, a survey published by Gallup in the *Daily Telegraph* in March 1993, revealed that roses are by far the most popular flower among UK gardeners, twice as popular as their nearest rival. 33% of all British gardeners regard the rose as their favourite plant, followed by 13% who opted for daffodils. The Royal National Rose Society is the largest specialist flower society in the UK: in the 1960s it had more members than the Royal Horticultural Society.

The garden at Hyde Hall in Essex opened for the first time to the public under the care of the Royal Horticultural Society on 28 March. The Society bestowed an honorary fellowship on the garden's creators, Dick and Helen Robinson. Robin Herbert, President of the Royal Horticultural Society, said at the presentation 'We are not just here to extend the Society's gratitude to Helen and Dick Robinson, but to celebrate their life-long work at Hyde Hall'. These remarks will help to underline the quality of the Robinsons' achievement: Hyde Hall is a very fine garden.

At the beginning of April, Reuter reported from Tokyo that a Japanese scientist claimed to have raised a white eight-petalled magnolia from seed found in a 2,000-year old catacomb. Hiroshi Utsunomiya said the seed came from a food storage chamber buried underground in a tomb about 500 miles south west of Tokyo.

One of the best exhibitions of the year was called 'Treasures of the Royal Horticultural Society' and was mounted at the Kew Gardens Gallery from 7 April to 31 May. It was an exhibition of works from the Society's collection of 18,000 paintings and drawings, the oldest on display being flower studies by Pieter van Kouwenhoorn which date from the 1630s. Van Kouwenhoorn's charming works are the basis of this year's Royal Horticultural Society desk diary. The other major horticultural exhibition was mounted all summer at the Museum of Garden History to celebrate the 150th anniversary of the birth of Gertrude Jekyll. Every aspect of her life and works was illustrated, including original plans of some of her gardens and first editions of all her books. The exhibition was accompanied by lectures about Miss Jekyll and her times, given every week by a different expert.

The Royal Horticultural Society gave official support and professional assistance to the Cincinnati Flower Show, which ran from the 21 to 25 April in the grounds of Ault Park in downtown Cincinnati, Ohio. As the Show has been going for no more than four years, with only 50,000-60,000 visitors expected, it was not clear to many observers just how the Royal Horticultural Society expected to benefit from the association. The Royal Horticultural Society also exhibited for the first time at the International Garden Festival in Europe (IGA Stuttgart '93).

High rainfall in April and May, following on the good rains of autumn 1992 and early winter, replenished the aquifers and avoided the need for hosepipe bans and other drought- provision in most of the country. Terry Marsh of the Institute of Hydrology at Wallingford in Oxfordshire said at the beginning of June 'In general, the early summer aquifer levels are the highest for five years... a remarkable recovery from a year ago when they were the lowest on record'.

In an article in the *Sunday Telegraph* on 2 May, the convicted train robber and prison escaper Ronnie Biggs, now living in Rio de Janeiro, confessed that he had become a keen gardener. He said that he spends 'about 90%' of his waking hours pottering in his garden among the coleus, shrimp plants, busy lizzies and dieffenbachias. But times are difficult and the money is running out. 'I would like to have a potting shed here but, sadly, funds are lacking', he confided.

In May 1993 the American Rhododendron Society announced the award of their highest honour - the Gold Medal - to Dr H Davidian, formerly of Edinburgh University and the Royal Botanic Garden in Edinburgh. Dr. Davidian has already received innumerable awards in Scotland and England for his work on rhododendrons, culminating in the publication of his multi-volume work *The Rhododendron Species,* of which volumes I - III are already available and volume IV will be published this year.

Leading members of the Royal National Rose Society were prevented from attending the Chelsea Flower Show because they were attending a planning appeal. A developer called Thaker Properties applied to build a clay pigeon firing range on a site close to the Society's Gardens of the Rose and, although the application was refused by the District Council, Thaker Properties appealed against the decision. That appeal hearing took place during Chelsea week. The Rose Society gave evidence that the Gardens, enjoyed by 60,000 visitors last year, would effectively be destroyed if permission were given for the development. The noise levels from one of the largest shooting ranges in Europe would be intolerable for visitors to the Gardens. The outcome of the appeal was not yet known at the time of going to press.

On 19 May, the Royal Horticultural Society announced that Gordon Rae had been appointed Director General to succeed Chris Brickell on 30 July. Rae started his career in tropical agriculture, after degrees from Wye College, Cambridge and the University of the West Indies. He worked for three years as a district agricultural officer in Kenya and joined ICI in 1965. For the past four before joining the Royal Horticultural Society, he was general manager of ICI's Garden & Professional Products division.

In June the London *Evening Standard* reported that Adam Nicolson, the grandson of Sir Harold Nicolson and Vita Sackville-West, was harried from a village in Leicestershire because he had allowed his quarter-acre garden to grow wild. Apparently fellow-villagers believed that he was responsible for losing them the prestigious 'Best Kept Village' award. 'They said the garden was an eyesore and let the community down' explained Nicolson 'I think it was really beautiful. It looked like a hay meadow'. Nicolson has now moved to Hammersmith and calls for the Best Kept Village competition to be scrapped.

The Garden History Society, which will celebrate its thirtieth anniversary next year, has launched an appeal to raise funds for special projects. Despite its impressive reputation as a learned society and its high profile in conservation activities, the Garden History Society operates on a tight budget. It has recently been offered grants towards the cost of some of the projects that it would like to undertake, but only if the Garden History Society can come up with matching funding. An offer of grant-aid from the Department of National Heritage, to cover half the cost of a two year publication project, had to be turned down for lack of funds.

At the end of July, Lt Cdr Tony Lowe announced that he was departing as General Secretary of the National Council for the Conservation of Plants & Gardens (NCCPG). 'It is not appropriate' he added 'to go into the details why. Suffice to say that strains have occurred within the management structure which are best solved by my departure'. Lowe spent nine years with the NCCPG: perhaps his greatest achievement was the expansion of the National Collections scheme whose numbers grew from 200 to over 600 during his tenure.

In late summer it was announced that Clay Jones, the 69-year old chairman of BBC Radio 4's *Gardener's Question Time* was to retire after seven years on the programme, following a mild heart attack. His successor as chairman was Stefan Buczacki, who has been a regular panellist for many years. Brushing aside comments that he was unhappy with plans to put the programme to independent tender, Jones said 'I wish to retire now, quietly, with the dignity the programme engenders in the minds and hearts of its faithful audience'.

In August 1993, Christopher Lloyd, the writer whose garden at Great Dixter in East Sussex is deservedly acclaimed, announced that he had dug up his roses (originally planted when the garden was designed by Sir Edward Lutyens in 1910) and replaced them with a tropical garden of exotic bedding, including banana plants, cannas and castor oil plants.

In September, a report in *Watsonia*, the journal of the Botanical Society of the British Isles, confirmed that the wild service tree *Sorbus torminalis*, was in retreat across the British Isles. Patrick Roper, who co-ordinated the 20 years of research, said that development pressures 'have clobbered it'. The tree, once prized by archers as an ideal wood for crossbows, has fallen prey to changes in forestry and agricultural practices. Indeed it is now almost exclusively found in ancient woodland sites.

For the Royal Horticultural Society, 1993 was Education Year. The educational theme started with a garden design competition for schools, launched in association with the *Daily Mirror*, and was present at most of the Society's events during the year. At the late autumn show, for example, the Fruit and Vegetable Committee fulfilled its educational mission by putting on an exhibit of all but four of the cultivars of apple and pear to which the Award of Garden Merit (New Series) had been made.

In December 1993 the Council of the Royal Horticultural Society announced the award of the Victoria Medal of Honour (VMH) to fill three vacancies which occurred during the year. The VMH is awarded to British horticulturists resident in the United Kingdom whom the Council considers deserving of special honour at the hands of the Society. The award marks the number of years of the reign of Queen Victoria and may therefore only be held by sixty three horticulturists at any one time. The three vacancies will be filled by Mr Robin Compton, Mr Alan Hardy and Mrs Mary Newnes. At the same time, the Council of the Royal Horticultural Society announced the award of the Veitch Memorial Medal to five persons who have 'helped in the advancement and improvement of the science and practice of horticulture': Dr Brent Elliott, Mrs Brenda Hyatt, Sir Peter Smithers, Mrs Joyce Stewart and Mr Hideo Suzuki.

Legacies

Two significant legacies were received by British gardening societies in 1993. First, nearly £37,000 was received by the Alpine Garden Society from the estate of the late Muriel Hodgman. In view of her interest in photography, at which she excelled, the Society has allocated £20,000 towards the provision of extra colour photographs for the *Encyclopaedia of Alpines* which will be published this year.

The other important legacy was made to the Royal National Rose Society by a Miss Sheila Haldane, a member of the Society of long standing who was a regular volunteer helper in the Gardens of the Rose. The legacy is expected to be about £200,000 and will have a substantial effect upon the fortunes of the Rose Society, which have suffered during the recession.

The Royal Botanic Gardens at Kew were the principal beneficiary under the terms of the will of John Scott-Marshall of Hill Pasture, Broxted, Essex who bequeathed them the residue of his estate. The bequest is estimated to be worth about £80,000. Marshall was once the editor of the *Gardeners Chronicle*, at that time the most distinguished and oldest of gardening magazines. About half the bequest will be used to endow and fund a travel scholarship for young horticulturists at Kew. Lead ornaments from the garden at Hill Pasture will be used in the gardens at Kew and Wakehurst.

1993 Obituaries

Arthur Hellyer

Arthur Hellyer died on 28th January 1993, aged 90. Hellyer was the most respected garden-writer of his generation, a true professional whose style was clear, informed and accessible.

Hellyer became a horticulturist quite by chance. Considering the robust health which he enjoyed for most of his long life, it comes as a surprise to learn that tuberculosis forced him to leave Dulwich College at the age of 14. The doctors prescribed work on a farm in the mild climate of Guernsey: the outdoor life suited him and in due course Hellyer moved back to a nursery in England, fully cured and committed to a career in horticulture.

Hellyer's entry into journalism began with a brief assignment as associate editor of *Commercial Horticulture* but his writings really took off in 1929 when he succeeded A J Macself as assistant editor of *Amateur Gardening*. Hellyer took over as editor in 1946 and by the time he retired (and collected his MBE) in 1967, the circulation had risen to 300,000 a week. Not that Hellyer retired from any other activity: his energy and curiosity were insatiable. One of the last articles he wrote for the *Financial Times* in November 1992 was on Nemasys, the parasitic nematodes which feed on the grubs of vine weevils.

Throughout his life, Hellyer produced a stream of reliable gardening books: *The Amateur Gardening Pocket Guide* first appeared in 1941 and is now in its 23rd edition, while *The Popular Encyclopaedia of Flowering Plants* first published in 1957, received its latest reprint last year. After his retirement from *Amateur Gardening*, Hellyer wrote an article every Saturday for the *Financial Times*, and was a frequent contributor to such magazines as *Homes & Gardens*, *Country Life* and *The Garden*.

Hellyer spoke well - his voice was robust to the end - and he was, above all, a great listener, always keen to learn more, alert and curious about everything. His interests extended to art, design and history as well as practical gardening and technical innovations. He preferred to write from experience. His Sussex garden had 7 acres but he also inherited

a one-acre garden in Jersey and the contrast between them offered endless possibilities for good articles.

Hellyer's vigour was legendary. He came to see us in Wiltshire when he was 85, driving over from his house in East Sussex. He grumbled that one of his sons, who should have shared the driving, had cried off because he did not feel up to it. Arthur Hellyer talked and questioned us energetically for an hour and a half and then went off into Somerset and Avon to visit a garden and a nursery before driving back to Sussex that evening.

He was much involved in furthering the work of the Gardeners' Royal Benevolent Society and it was at their home at Red Oaks, Henfield, that he spent the last few weeks of his own life.

Cornish Torbock

Cornish Torbock died on 17th June 1993, aged 88. Torbock was one of the great characters of the North of England garden world, a tall bachelor with a slightly giggly manner, much given to self-mockery. But his mannerisms disguised an encyclopaedic knowledge of plants and considerable artistic flair. He showed these qualities not only in the garden at Crossrigg Hall, where he and his brother planted extensively for over 50 years, but also in his enthusiasm for floral art. He was reputed to have said of the late Constance Spry, 'Oh, I taught old Connie all she knew!'

Frances Perry

Frances Perry died on 11th October 1993. Born Frances Everett, she attached herself as a young girl to her parents' neighbour at Enfield, the great plantsman Augustus Bowles. Bowles encouraged the young Frances to train professionally and continued to take an interest in her career: 'I look upon you as one of my boys', he said.

Frances Everett graduated from Swanley Horticultural College and went to work for the famous herbaceous nursery of Amos Perry, whose son Gerald she married in 1930. Although she took time off to have her two sons, Frances published her classic work *Water Gardening* in 1938 and then made the move into administration with her appointment as horticultural adviser to Middlesex County Council in 1943. Ten years later she became Principal of Norwood Hall College of Horticulture and began another career as a broadcaster and television personality.

After her retirement Frances Perry became a gardening correspondent for the *Observer*, and wrote for that newspaper for over 20 years. In 1968 she was the first woman to be invited to sit on the Council of the RHS, but the honour had to wait until after she collected the MBE in 1962 and the Veitch Memorial Medal in 1964. She went on to acquire horticulture's highest award, the Victoria Medal of Honour, in 1971.

Gerald Perry died in 1964 and in 1977 Frances married Roy Hay, himself a distinguished horticulturist whom she had known almost all her life. That second marriage brought as much pleasure to their many friends as it did to both Roy and Frances.

Sir George Taylor FRS

Sir George Taylor FRS died on 13 November 1993, aged 89. Taylor was born in Edinburgh on 15 February 1904 and educated at George Heriot's School. A short stocky Scot, he was 'tough, shrewd, forthright and relentlessly industrious'. He began his career as a taxonomic botanist, after studying at Edinburgh University under Sir William Wright Smith. His early years involved much travel and botanical exploration: Taylor considered that its highlight was his 1936 expedition to Tibet in the company of the famous Scottish collectors Frank Ludlow and George Sherriff.

In 1945 Taylor was appointed deputy keeper of botany at the British Museum; in 1950 he advanced to become keeper. In 1956 he took up his appointment as director of the Royal Botanic Gardens at Kew where he remained until he retired in 1971. Under his guidance the palm house at Kew was restored, the heath garden and the Queen's Garden were planned and planted, and a new library and herbarium wing were built. But perhaps his greatest achievement was the acquisition of Wakehurst Place as an annexe to Kew, where tender plants could flourish just as they did at Benmore for the Royal Botanic Garden in Edinburgh.

Taylor liked to bridge the gulf between botany and horticulture. He was personally a very keen gardener and always deeply involved in the affairs of the Royal Horticultural Society. He first became a member of its Council in 1951 and was appointed a Vice-President in 1974. Meanwhile he was knighted in 1962 for services to science and elected a Fellow of the Royal Society in 1968.

Although a keen gardener and an able botanist, Taylor was above all a brilliant administrator. In retirement he became chairman of the Committee of Management of the Chelsea Physic Garden and held a visiting professorship at Reading University. Another interest was the welfare of the Stanley Smith Horticultural Trust: as its director for 19 years, Taylor was responsible for supporting innumerable horticultural projects. He was also botanical secretary of the Linnean Society, general secretary of the British Association for the Advancement of Science, and botanical adviser to the Commonwealth War Graves Commission.

4

New Plants

New varieties and cultivars of plants don't just arrive in seed catalogues and nurseries. They may be the result of years of top secret work at a horticultural research laboratory or they may have turned up in someone's back garden. Either way, a keen eye and a good deal of patience are at least as important as scientific and horticultural knowledge in the business of breeding new cultivars of garden plants. Genetic engineering may change the picture one day, but raising new plants is as yet an area where in theory the amateur can participate with the professionals.

There are two stages of development. First you have to breed or select a new form which is good enough to be introduced. Then you have the problems of propagating it in sufficient quantities, and marketing and selling your new variety. Trial and error may be enough for the first stage, but you can turn to the specialist societies for advice also. Most will have knowledgeable members who can point you in the right direction and warn you against such problems as genetic incompatibility between certain species or sections within a genus. Some are more active still and make breeding material available to their members.

The Hardy Plant Society has published a useful booklet, *Raising New Plants*, which contains general information about the mechanics of plant breeding and details of how the society can help you take your hobby a stage further. The classic guide is W. J. C. Lawrence's *Practical Plant Breeding*. Many books which are devoted to individual genera include useful material on the genetic history of breeding and on how to raise new varieties.

Propagating and marketing a new plant are probably best left to the professionals, unless the plant is only likely to appeal to a small group of enthusiasts. You can test the water by sending your plant for trial at the RHS, the Royal National Rose Society, or one of the other societies which organise trials for spe-

cific genera. RHS members can also enter a plant for an award by taking it to one of the society's shows. The experts on the judging committees will assess its potential and may recommend the plant for an award or advise further trials.

A more high profile approach is to ask a commercial nursery do the work for you. Keep an eye out for the nurseries which regularly bring novelties into commerce, and contact one which handles plants of the right type. The major seed companies, for example, are always looking out for new strains which they can promote in their annual catalogues. Some have formal schemes to encourage amateur hybridisers. Thompson & Morgan produces an easy to understand leaflet which explains its procedures and gives tips on how to get started, including some plants which are easy for the beginner to experiment with.

Blooms of Bressingham are among the nurseries which are always interested in potential new additions to their list, and have a department whose sole function is to handle such plants. We give the way they deal with new plants here as an illustration. In the first instance Blooms require a photograph and a letter which describes in what way the plant is different from existing varieties. Their experienced staff will quickly recognise an improvement in type. Do not send any plant material until they ask for it. If they think the plant may be of commercial quality, they will propagate and evaluate it for up to two years. During this period Blooms keep meticulous records of its growth and performance, and also inform you of its progress; they are always careful to acknowledge the original raiser. If it still looks good after trialling, they will consider taking out Plant Breeder's Rights for the plant, after discussing this with you. A major new introduction could be marketed in Europe, the USA and worldwide, through their agency network: the rights apply overseas too. Financial arrangements would be negotiated, which could be royalty based or an outright purchase.

Self-satisfaction and local glory aside, there is a chance of making money from your intervention in nature's handiwork. Yet on your own the expense of registering your interest in the plant may prove prohibitive. The legislation in the Plant Varieties and Seeds Act 1964 and the Plant Breeders Rights (Fees) Regulations 1990 lays down stringent procedures including trials and evaluations (see below). At every stage of the process a hefty fee is payable. The result has been that PBR is usually only resorted to - even by the trade - for plants that have the chance of outstanding commercial success and which are expensive to develop. The main categories are roses, chrysanthemums and pelargoniums. Look in *The Plant Finder*, where such plants are marked.

From *The Plant Finder* you will also see that in some genera varieties proliferate for no good reason. Gardeners and nurseryman all suffer from indiscriminate introductions, which detract from the better plants and confuse the public. The following points, which echo the stages of the PBR system, offer some ground rules for hybridisers:

1. Make sure that a 'new' plant really is new. It could be growing somewhere else under a different name. In the past it was common for the same plant to circulate under several different names at once, and the confusion has not yet been eradicated. Don't add to this problem. Check against specimens in botanic gardens or the NCCPG National Collections: a trained eye may be needed.

2. Confirm that the plant is distinct in its ornamental features (as opposed to botanical characteristics). Find a variety that is closest to yours and note every way in which the two plants differ. If there is nothing else like it, you may be onto a winner.

3. Increase your stocks. This is not just a preliminary to distributing it. The form may not be stable or may be difficult to replicate. Bulk up the plants and grow them on to see how they behave. The recent introduction *Lavatera* 'Barnsley' seemed to have no drawbacks until it showed a tendency to revert back to the ordinary form of *Lavatera thuringiaca*.

4. If the plant is raised from seed, then you must make sure that it will come true from seed. You will require several generations of further crosses to develop a pure seed strain.

That said, there is no need to be put off. Hybridising is fun and frequently addictive. All your attempts, even the disastrous ones, will produce unique results. Even if you never seem to be getting anywhere there is nothing to stop you from trying again. And again.

AWARDS TO NEW PLANTS FROM TRIALS, SHOWS & EXHIBITS

Introduction

Many horticultural institutes, private and public, carry out tests and assessments on new and established varieties of plant. These include *Fleuroselect*, which is mainly concerned with annuals grown from seed for summer bedding; the *Royal Horticultural Society*, which runs both temporary and permanent trials of a very wide selection of annuals, perennials, shrubs, bulbs, fruit and vegetables; the *Northern Horticultural Society*, which tests the same range as the RHS, but limits its assessments to fewer varieties; and the *Royal National Rose Society*, which conducts three-year tests on over 200 new rose varieties every year. We report from all these institutions below. *Gardening Which?* also undertakes useful trials of many types of plant, from annuals to trees, and publishes the results month-by-month in *Gardening Which?* There is an emphasis upon established varieties, rather than novelties. The results of all these trials are a good test of what is on the market and what may be expected when the introducers have been able to bulk up their stocks to a commercial volume. One source of information about new varieties of plants and seeds is the *Plant Varieties and Seeds Gazette*, published by MAFF, which operates the whole system of Plant Breeders Rights in the UK. The Gazette is published monthly and lists applications for Plant Breeders Rights, withdrawals of applications, and decisions affecting them.

Plant Breeders Rights

The registered owner of Plant Breeders Rights is entitled, while that registration lasts, to have the exclusive right to sell propagating material or seed of the variety in question or to authorise others to do so. He enjoys, in effect, a plant patent. It is a cardinal rule of the system that the new variety should not have been offered for sale already: new means new. Samples are submitted to MAFF, who must be satisfied that the variety is clearly distinguishable in its characteristics from all other varieties and that it is both stable and uniform or homogeneous.

Most applications relate to agricultural crops, particularly grasses, fodders and brassicas. Among vegetables, the most significant subject for applications for Plant Breeders Rights is the potato. The grant lasts for twenty-five years and the varieties which are still registered (and producing royalties for the owners) include 'Cara', 'Maris Bard', 'Pentland Javelin' and 'Wilja'. Among the horticulturally important genera, chrysanthemums (as MAFF continues to call them, in preference to the more modern *Dendranthema*), pelargoniums and roses are the main plants, but especially roses. You can be certain that almost all the great roses of the last twenty years have been properly registered, including such important roses as 'Silver Jubilee' and 'Royal William'. Unfortunately, however, they are almost invariably registered under code names which continue to be used for legal purposes: the actual cultivar name under which the variety will be marketed will be different, and usually differs from one country to another. For example, the November 1993 edition of the Plant Varieties and Seeds Gazette listed 58 new varieties of rose to which it was proposed to grant Plant Breeders Rights. Most of the famous breeders names were on the list - Austin, Harkness, Cocker, Kordes and Dickson among them - but all the roses had code names and there is no saying, at this stage, what JACPURR, COCJABBY or DICJOON will turn into.

THE ROYAL NATIONAL ROSE SOCIETY

International Rose Trials 1993 - List Of Awards

BEST ROSE BRED BY AN AMATEUR

BABY LOVE Floribunda. Buttercup yellow, single. Light scent. Medium height. Upright bushy growth with plentiful foliage.
Parentage: [Sweet Magic × (Sunblest × Coalite)] × [Sunblest × (Chinatown × *Rosa davidii* var. *elongata*)]

GOLD MEDAL

KORFULLWIND Floribunda. Medium pink, semi-double, clusters of several blooms. Little scent. Medium height. Growth spreading, with dense foliage.
Parentage: Surrey × Seedling
Raiser: Kordes

CERTIFICATES OF MERIT

SCRIVO Floribunda. Light pink, semi-double clusters of several blooms. Moderate scent. Medium height. Bushy habit.
Parentage: Seedling × Seedling
Raiser: L Scrivens

CHEWPIWITE Climbing Floribunda. Pale pink semi-double flowers in large clusters with beautiful yellow stamens. Good scent. Short, climbing habit, with small neat, plentiful foliage.
Parentage: Mary Sumner x Laura Ashley
Raiser: C Warner

CHEWPIXCEL Ground Cover Shrub. Pink with yellow centres, single; several blooms in a cluster. Light scent. Medium height, spreading habit, with small, dense foliage.
Parentage: Mary Sumner × Laura Ashley
Raiser: C Warner

TRIAL GROUND CERTIFICATES

POULMARI Floribunda Shrub. Deep pink, semi-double flowers with a yellow eye, several in a cluster. Light scent. Medium height, bushy with dark leathery foliage.
Parentage: Seedling × H C Andersen
Raiser: Poulsen

PEAVOODOO Floribunda. Salmon pink, double flowers, many in a cluster. Good scent. Medium height, bushy habit.
Parentage: Carol Ann × Seedling
Raiser: C Pearce

IDEM Hybrid Tea. Golden yellow, touched with red in the bud, double. Good scent. Tall and bushy, with large glossy foliage.
Parentage: Seedling × Freedom
Raiser: Interplant

CHRISTOPHER COLUMBUS Floribunda. Dark pink striped light pink, semi-double. Clusters of several blooms. Moderate scent, medium height. Spreading habit: bushy, with small, dense foliage.

Parentage: Seedling × Seedling
Raiser: Poulsen

KORDIALO Floribunda. Scarlet, pale reverse, semi-double. Clusters of several blooms. Light scent. Short and bushy.

Parentage: Regensberg × Seedling
Raiser: Kordes

FRYXOTIC Floribunda. Many salmon pink, double flowers in a clusters. Good scent. Tall, with upright growth.

Parentage: Pot o' Gold × (Seedling×Cheshire Life)
Raiser: Fryers

766-86 Floribunda. Light red, semi-double flowers, with many in a clusters. Good scent. Short and bushy, with plentiful foliage.

Parentage: Liebestraum - IGA Munchen - Liebestraum × Malindi.
Raiser: Noack

DICTOY Floribunda shrub. Many, dark red, semi-double, flowers in clusters. Little scent. Short and bushy, with small, dense foliage.

Parentage: Dicpretty × Seedling
Raiser: Dickson

CHEWMOREP Climbing floribunda. Semi-double flowers, light red, with a cream centre and light reverse. Several flowers in a cluster. Little scent. Medium height. Very thorny stems and small, dense foliage.

Parentage: Morgengruss × Eye Paint
Raiser: C Warner

CHEWSUNBEAM Miniature climber. Clusters of several double, golden yellow flowers with a good scent. A short climber.

Parentage: Anne Harkness × Laura Ford
Raiser: C Warner

TRIAL GROUND CERTIFICATES AWARDED AT THE END OF THE SECOND YEAR OF TRIALS

DICUMPTEEN Ground Cover Shrub. Double, pink flowers with a lighter reverse. The flowers tend to 'quarter' when fully open and are borne many in

a cluster. Moderate scent. Short, spreading habit and attractive, dense, medium green foliage.

Parentage: Unnamed Seedling × Grouse
Raiser: Dickson

1721-87 Ground Cover Shrub. Pink semi-double flowers, many in a cluster. Good scent. Short, spreading, habit: shiny, dense foliage.

Parentage: undisclosed
Raiser: Noack

THE ROYAL HORTICULTURAL SOCIETY

Permanent trials are conducted at Wisley with border carnations, early-flowering chrysanthemums, daffodils, dahlias, day-lilies, delphiniums, garden pinks, irises and sweet peas. Permanent trials of camellias are situated on nearby Battleston Hill. These trials continue from year to year with periodic replanting, at which time additions and removals are made. Results of trials are published in the horticultural press and in publications of the RHS available to members on request from the trials office at Wisley.

A good example is the current trial of hardy penstemons at Wisley. 151 entries were submitted by amateurs and professionals alike to the Trials Committee three years ago. Many of the plants were entered under the wrong name; there were instances where the same name was borne by more than one cultivar; plants of the same cultivar were also submitted under several different names; and some were entered without a name whatsoever. 'The penstemon trial provides a good illustration of the work of an RHS subcommittee and highlights the challenges which may be met with the naming of garden plants in general circulation' said a spokesman. The entries will be assessed for hardiness, floriferousness, vigour and other virtues, and some will receive awards of varying degree. The joy of such a trial is that eventually the names and naming are sorted out and the conclusions of the RHS's Floral A Committee filter out through *The Plant Finder* into the nursery catalogues of the trade.

The RHS's main system of awards has, however, been radically overhauled, following the publication last year of its new Award of Garden Merit [AGM]. This is the highest award that the Society can give a plant and in the past it was only bestowed irregularly. In practice, the earlier awards were often outclassed by later varieties and, once an award was given, there was no system for taking it away. Four years ago the RHS put the whole problem out to a series of committees whose task was to identify those ornamental plants, fruit and vegetables 'of the highest garden value, whether for cultivation in the open or under glass'. It was important that the plants should be reasonably widely available and carry a hardiness rating. The upshot is a list of 3,300 plants which are now designated carriers of the AGM.

The awards are not however intended as a selection. The criteria remain overall excellence, sound constitution and adaptability in cultivation. Nothing was excluded because there were others of equal quality and, as a result, the list contains nearly 200 roses, 73 camellias and 67 varieties of clematis. Nor did the committees put a premium on rarity: among the names are such common or garden trees as *Betula pendula*, *Fagus sylvatica* and *Fraxinus excelsior* · birch, beech and ash to you and me, and very good garden plants too. An innovative system of rolling awards has been instituted so that new plants can be added and fading stars deleted once they have reached the decline stage.

There follows a selection of the AGM awards made at the Wisley Trials during the course of 1993. Full details are available from the Royal Horticultural Society.

Marigolds, Dwarf French
(including crested and carnation flowered and F1 triploid types)
Aurora Light Yellow, Bonita Carmen, Boy O' Boy Orange, Caribbean Parade, Dainty Marietta (Tezier), Disco Yellow, Disco Orange, Fantasia, Gold Winner, Hero Orange, Honeycomb, Juliette, Mischief Orange/Red, Mischief Gold, Mischief Mahogany, Queen Sophia, Safari Mixture, Safari Scarlet, Safari Tangerine, Solar Sulphur, Sophia Classic, Tiger Eyes (King), Tiger Eyes (Marshall), Zenith Lemon Yellow.

Primrose and Polyanthus (under glass)
Belinda Red Shades, Charisma Pink, Danova Cream, Danova Purple/White Edge, Danova Rose, Ernst Benary Blue, Ernst Benary White, Europa Blue, Festival Orange Shades, Festival Primrose, Festival Yellow Shades, Festival Scarlet, Leda, Overture Mixed, Paloma Pink Shades, Paloma Rose Flame, Pirouette, Regency Pale Lemon, Regency Pink, Saga Pink, Saga Rose, Saga Scarlet, Saga White, Soprano

Rose Eye, Spectrum Golden Orange, Spectrum Golden Yellow, Spectrum Picottee, Spectrum Quasar, Spectrum Zenith, Tango.

Greigii and Kaufmanniana Tulips

Tulipa greigii:
China Lady, Corsage, Engadin, Toronto.

Tulipa kaufmanniana:
Early Harvest, Jeantine, Show Winner.

Border Carnations
Eileen O'Connor, Golden Sceptre.

Lupins
Anne Gregg, Deborah Woodfield, Esmerelder, Helen Sharman, Judy Harper, Kayleigh Ann Savage, Olive Tolley, Pope John Paul, Royal Parade, Troop the Colour.

Dahlias
(bedding types under 60cm/24" high)
Burnished Bronze, Diablo Mixed, Mignon Rosa Band, Rigoletto, Sunny Yellow (King).

Dahlias (others)
Butterball, Conway, Ellen Huston, Garden Party, Hamari Gold, Happy Hanny, Inca Metropolitan, Kathleen's Alliance, Kay Helen, Loud Applause, Piper's Pink, Walter Hardisty, Wandy, White Ballet, Wootton Cupid.

Pacific Coast Irises
Agnes James, Banbury Gem, Banbury Melody.

Hemerocallis
Beloved Returns, Berlin Lemon, Berlin Red, Berlin Red Velvet, Burning Daylight, Chief Sarcoxie, Green Flutter, Helle Berlinerin, Lemon Bells, Missenden, Nova.

Artemisia
Artemisia abrotanum, Artemisia absinthium 'Lambrook Mist', Artemisia alba 'Canescens', Artemisia caucasica, Artemisia frigida, Artemisia ludoviciana var. ludoviciana, Artemisia ludoviciana 'Silver Queen', Artemisia pontica, Seriphidium maritimum (syn. Artemisia maritima), Seriphidium vallesiacum (syn. Artemisia vallesiaca).

Chrysanthemums
(spray cultivars for garden decoration)
Bronze Enbee Wedding, Cameo, Cream Margaret, Gold Mine, Holly, Myss Angie, Orno, Payton Dale,

Payton Prince, Peach Enbee Wedding, Pennine Jude, Pennine Magic, Pennine Oriel, Pennine Silver, Pennine Tango, Pennine Twinkle, Pennine Sweetheart, Pink Margaret, Red Pennine Jade, Southway Sure.

(suitable as disbudded cultivars for garden decoration grown in the open without overhead protection at flowering time)
Creamist, Early Bird, Membury, Nora Brook, Rylands Gem, Yvonne Arnaud.

Tall Bearded Iris
Buckden Pike, Designer's Choice, Edale, Gay Parasol, Ice Dancer, Paradise, Pascoe, Snowy Owl, Tangerine Sunrise, Tintinara, Violet Icing, Warleggan.

Iris Sibirica Cultivars
Annemarie Troeger, Creme Chantilly, Likiang, Mikiko, Ruffles Plus.

Garden Pinks
Devon Glow, Devon Maid, Haytor White, Kesteven Kirkstead, Marg's Choice, Rhian's Choice, Suffolk Summer.

Chinese Cabbage
Kingdom, Mariko, Nerva, Spring Sun.

Beet
Action, Bikores, Bonel, Pablo, Regala, Wodan.

Onion
Centurion (Elsoms), Centurion (King), Centurion (Unwins), Jagro, Jetset (Elsoms), Sturon, Super Ailsa Craig, Turbo.

Peas
Edula, Honeypod, Mammoth Melting Sugarpod, Reuzensuiker, Sugar Snap.

Shallots
Atlantic (Unwins), Giant Yellow Improved, Pikant, Santé, Success.

Leeks
Abila, Autumn Giant - Cobra, Berdina, Giant Winter - Catalina, Ginka, Glorina, Herfstreuzen Enak, Longbow, Profina, Toledo, Verina, Winterreuzen - Granada.

Onion
Buffalo, Gion Festival, Imai Early Yellow, Juno.

Melon
Amber Nectar, Earlidawn, Earliqueen, Galoubet, Ogen (Marshall), Sweetheart.

Potato
Avalanche, Croft, Famosa, Maxine, Navan, Picasso, Stroma.

Bean
Algarve, Benefic, Cunera, Diamant, Eva, Hunter, Kwintus, Musica.

Lettuce
Delta, Liset, Becky.

HARLOW CARR

The Northern Horticultural Society carries out trials of flowers and vegetables at Harlow Carr in West Yorkshire, but these are less ambitious and rather more informal than the trials run by the Royal Horticultural Society at Wisley in Surrey.

One of the main trials of flower seeds in 1993 was of the hardy annual *Alyssum maritimum*. Thirty varieties were sown in mid-April and the flowering performance was examined at regular four-week intervals until the end of September. The best flowering varieties were 'Snow Crystals', 'Carpet of Snow', 'Snowcloth' and 'Snowdrift' - all traditional white flowering types. These were, moreover, the first varieties to produce complete flower cover during the last week in July. The best of the other colours were 'Easter Bonnet' (white, lavender, pale pink and purple), 'Creamery' and 'Purple Delight'. The coloured varieties came into flower later, reaching their peak during August.

Harlow Carr also has a *Fleuroselect* display garden where the four new Gold Medal winning varieties for 1994 were assessed alongside twenty-six past medal winners. According to the Northern Horticultural Society, the best of the 1994 introductions was undoubtedly the French-raised *Viola* 'Velour Blue', a mini-pansy with 3cm wide flowers. Plants are uniform, compact, 20cm high and covered in masses of light blue flowers, the lower petals being violet-blue with a distinct yellow eye. It outperformed all other pansies grown this year at Harlow Carr, including 'Imperial Gold Princess', 'Imperial Frosty Rose', 'Padparadja' and 'Jolly Joker'. The other two novelties tested at Harlow Carr were cornflowers in the 'Florence' series: 'Florence White' and 'Florence Pink'. These are considered a useful addition to the amateur's garden: unlike most cornflowers, they remain compact and sturdy, being only 30cm tall in mid-August.

Among older medal winners at Harlow Carr, the best were considered to be *Dianthus* 'Color Magician' and 'Telstar Crimson', together with the French marigolds 'Orange Jacket', 'Safari Tangerine', 'España Mix' and 'Disco Orange'. Disappointing were *Nierembergia* 'Mont Blanc', *Callistephus chinensis* 'Starlight Rose', *Limonium* 'Forever Gold' and *Gazania* 'Garden Sun'. These results differ considerably from those at Wisley, where *Nierembergia* 'Mont Blanc' made a good display, perhaps because of the warmer, drier weather in the south of England.

FLEUROSELECT

Current *Fleuroselect* Gold Medals
Begonia tuberosa 'Pin Up'
Bellis perennis 'Robella'
Callistephus chinensis 'Starlight Rose'

Centaurea cyanus 'Florence Pink'
Centaurea cyanus 'Florence White'
Cosmos bipinnatus 'Sonata'
Dianthus chinensis 'Raspberry Parfait'
Dianthus chinensis 'Strawberry Parfait'
Dianthus hybrida 'Color Magician'
Eschscholtzia californica 'Dalli'
Gazania splendens 'Garden Sun'
Impatiens walleriana 'Mega Orange Star'
Limonium sinuatum 'Forever Gold'
Nierembergia 'Mont Blanc'
Pelargonium × *hortorum* 'Orange Appeal'
Salvia coccinea 'Lady-in-Red'
Tagetes patula 'Safari Tangerine'
Verbena hybrida 'Peaches and Cream'
Verbena speciosa 'Imagination'
Viola 'Velour Blue'
Viola 'Imperial Frosty Rose'
Viola 'Imperial Gold Princess'
Viola 'Jolly Joker'
Viola 'Padparadja'

5

Latest Scientific Research

A vast corpus of horticultural research is undertaken by universities, institutes, nurserymen and enthusiasts worldwide and many of the results are published in obscure journals. Several organisations compile abstracts of these publications, so that students and researchers can know what is happening in their particular fields. By far the best is *Horticultural Abstracts*, C A B International Information Services, Wallingford, Oxfordshire, OX10 8DE. (Tel: 0491 832111. Fax: 0491 833508) and most of the articles which we summarise here have appeared, or will appear, in its pages, alongside more than 10,000 other horticultural abstracts every year. The amateur has something useful to learn from every one: we have added a comment at the end of each report to suggest what it might be.

'Rhododendron Propagation'. J L Harrington. *American Rhododendron Society Journal* (1990), pp.154-160 & pp.173-176.

This is a study of the factors which influence the rooting of rhododendron cuttings. Cuttings were taken of *Rhododendron catawbiense* 'Roseum Elegans', *Rh. catawbiense* 'Album' and *Rhododendron neriiflorum* ssp. *neriiflorum*. The rooting compost was 50:50 sphagnum peat and sand, which was carefully watered once a week and covered with clear polythene. The cuttings were taken in mid-July and trimmed down to two leaves. Four rooting hormones were used, each singly, or in various combinations. By 14th October, the survival rate was as follows: 78.8% 'Roseum Elegans'; 86.3%

'Album'; 90% *neriiflorum* ssp. *neriiflorum*. Survival was actually reduced by 2.5% by using a rooting hormone powder but, if the preparation was a dip, then the survival rate was slightly higher. In a separate experiment using just 'Roseum Elegans' the survival rate of cuttings was increased by 12.5% by wounding the base of the stem, 20% by using more mature growth for cuttings, and 22.5% by trimming the leaves. *Relevance to amateurs:* (1) rooting compounds are often unnecessary for woody cuttings (2) hedge your bets by experimenting with different methods in each batch of cuttings.

'The choice of Roses for growing as own-root plants'. J Zlebčík. (Růže vhodné pro výsadby jako pravokořenné rostliny). *Zahradnictví* (1992) pp.189 - 196. Výzkumný Ústav Okrásného Zahradnictví, 252 43 Průhonice, Czech Republic.

The Czech botanic garden at Průhonice trialled the propagation of roses from cuttings for many years, before the institute ended the project in 1992. These are the last in a long series of results from a wide variety of rose types. Plants were raised from single-node cuttings and judged for (i) percentage root-take (ii) vigour (iii) speed of growth to marketable size and (iv) overwintering in the first year after planting out. The following were considered suitable for growing on their own roots: 'Anne Cocker', 'Cantilena Bohemica', 'John S. Armstrong', 'Ludvik Vecera', 'Kořé', 'Margo Koster', 'Mount Shasta', 'New Dawn', *Rosa × paulii*, 'Pink Spray', 'Průhonice', 'Queen of Bermuda' and 'Westerland'. *Relev ance to amateurs:* (1) try taking cuttings from your rose prunings (2) look out for East European plant varieties which are now available to be tried in the West.

'Product development under the EC banner; changes in varieties and types'. W Bongartz. (Produktentwicklung im Zeichen der EG: Sortimente und Sorten im Wandel). *Gartnerbörse und Gartenwelt* (1992) pp.1829 - 1831.

This study is a good example of how the horticultural industry in another country is adjusting to the European Single Market. It concentrates upon German exports of cut flowers and the changes in image and packaging which are needed, as well as selecting new lines to appeal to consumers in different countries. It cites, among other examples, the experience of British companies with highly developed export markets and urges German nurserymen to learn from us. *Relevance to amateurs:* (1) look overseas to learn how others are doing things (2) the Dutch nursery trade is not the only horticultural competitor in Europe!

'Use of seed priming to bypass stratification requirements of three Aquilegia species'. T L Finnerty, J M Zajicek, M A Hussey. *HortScience* (1992) pp.310-313. Texas A&M University, College Station, TX 77843, USA.

This experiment compared the effect on germination of priming seeds of three species of *Aquilegia* by soaking them for periods of up to 72 hours in two media: distilled water and a solution of 50mM potassium phosphate. The chosen species were *AA. canadensis, caerulea* and *hinckleyana*, and each was immersed for 24, 48 or 72 hours. Some were then stratified and others sown immediately. There was no significant difference between the results for the two liquids. However, the soaking process had a measurable effect on the germination of *AA. canadensis* and *caerulea*. In the case of *A. caerulea*, soaked unstratified seed germinated as freely as unsoaked stratified seed: the same percentage germinated within 28 days of sowing. *A. canadensis* germinated better if it was both soaked and stratified but unsoaked stratified seed germinated better than soaked unstratified seed. 24 hours soaking produced the best results for *A. canadensis* and 72 hours for *A. caerulea*. Soaking had no measurable effect on *A. hinckleyana*. *Relevance to amateurs:* all seeds must first absorb enough water to start the process of germination. The effect of soaking varies from species to species, but it is a worthwhile process for experiment, at least in *Aquilegia*.

'Optimising nutrition and lighting for growing hothouse plants'. E Beel and P de Bruyn. (Optimalisatie voeding en assimilatiebelichting bij de teelt van warme kasplanten). *Verbondsnieuws voor de Belgische Sierteelt* (1991) pp.1141-1146.

In this Belgian trial, light timings and intensities were altered, and nutrient formulae varied, to test *Ficus benjamina, Schefflera* 'Trinetta' and *Dieffenbachia* 'Camille' for improved leaf formation and branching. Increased light intensity was more important than extended day length and resulted in the formation of a greater number of leaves in *Schefflera*, and increased branching in *Ficus. Dieffenbachia*, however, benefited from extra lighting during the latter part of the night (extending of the day length) rather than more intense lighting during the day. Changing the nutrient solution had no apparent effect on growth, except that the number of leaves on *Dieffenbachia* increased when a higher proportion of nitrate-N was used than ammonium-N. *Relevance to amateurs:* (1) all these houseplants would benefit from a position in good light (2) feeding with any general purpose houseplant fertiliser will probably provide optimal nutrition.

'Comparative evaluation of 'Golden Delicious' clones'. C Rapillard & A Dessimoz. (Essai comparatif de clones de 'Golden Delicious'). *Revue Suisse de Viticulture, d'Arboriculture et d'Horticulture* (1992) pp.231 - 234. Station Fédérale de Recherches Agronomiques de Changins, Centre d'Arboriculture et d'Horticulture des Fougères, 1964 Conthey, Switzerland.

This report summarises the results of a trial of eight different clones of 'Golden Delicious'. All were planted in 1979 on M9 rootstocks and studied over 11 years. They showed a yield variation of up to 15 kg/per tree per year. The highest yield of 391.54 kg per tree (cumulative over 11 years) was clone 'GD88'. 'Ed Gould' produced the highest proportion of first grade fruits at 78.6%. 'Belgolden' and 'Golden SR' were valuable because they matured about one week later than the others, although their yields were smaller: 'Golden SR' produced 39% less than 'GD88' and 'Belgolden' 33% less. These two lower yielding clones also showed some russeting, which is commercially less acceptable. *Relevance to ama-*

teurs: (1) the more widely a plant is grown, the more likely it is to produce sports that are suited to different conditions (2) it is important to buy the clone best suited to your circumstances (3) essential requirements for commercial production may not be primary considerations for the amateur.

'Cimicifuga L.: Ranunculaceae'. J Compton. *The Plantsman* (1992) pp.99 - 115.

A useful summary of the present state of our knowledge of this horticulturally popular genus. Compton recognises 12 species and sorts out the past taxonomic confusions. He gives a full botanical description, some horticultural comments, and an identification key. Compton's researches on *Cimicifuga* are continuing at Reading University.

'Breeding ornamental onions'. J B Van Duyvenbode. *The Plantsman* (1990) pp.152 - 156.

This article explores the horticultural potential for hybridising ornamental species of *Allium*. Three Asiatic species have particularly useful genes. *Allium aflatunense* has been developed by florists for its graceful long stem and lasting flowers. 'Purple Sensation', a darker form, is the best known selection to date. *A. elatum* (syn. *A. macleanii*), a strong-growing garden plant, has been crossed with other 16-chromosome species to produce 'Lucy Ball', 'Rien Poortvliet' and 'Gladiator'. Crossed with *A. christophii* it has given us the sterile hybrid 'Globemaster'. *A. christophii* is useful because it is strongly resistant to head rot (*Botrytis allii*). *Relevance to amateurs*: (1) further hybridisation will enormously improve alliums in the future (2) Asiatic species have qualities of disease resistance which may prove invaluable to such important European crops as onions, garlics and leeks (3) the Royal Horticultural Society is running a trial of *Allium* varieties at Wisley this year through to 1995.

'Competition effects of different tree strip widths on apple trees'. H J Van Hartingsveldt. *In IXe Colloque international sur la biologie des mauvaises herbes*, 16 - 18 Septembre 1992, Dijon, France. ANPP (1992) pp.147 - 152 Research Station for Fruit Growing, Brugstraat 51, 4475 AN Wilhelminadorp, Netherlands.

This report analysed results of trials on the effect of weed encroachment on productivity. Apples on M9 rootstocks were studied over a five-year period at two sites: 'Jonagold' on a sandy soil and 'Jonagold', 'Cox's Orange Pippin' and 'Golden Delicious' on clay. Trees were planted in rows 3 metres apart. 75 cm on either side of the rows was kept weed-free with residual herbicides, leaving a 1.5 m strip of grass down the middle. When the grass strips were allowed to extend close to the trunks of the apple trees, leaving only about 15 cm weed free around the base, the apple yields decreased cumulatively for the first three seasons. Then they began to increase again. The effect was more pronounced on sand than on clay. *Relevance to amateurs*: (1) the effect of competition for nutrients is more pronounced on hungry soils (2) roots will go in search of food.

'Evaluation of form and growth characteristics of Juniperus cultivars at the Secrest Arboretum'. K D Cockran. *Special Circular - Ohio Agricultural Research and Development Centre* (1992) No. 140. Secrest Arboretum, Ohio State University, OARDC, Wooster, Ohio, USA.

Junipers show considerable natural variation. This trial sought to evaluate some 65 cultivars of the following species: *JJ. chinensis, communis, conferta, davurica, horizontalis, procumbens, sabina, scopulorum, squamata* and *virginiana*. They were categorised by form (mounds, disks, ovoids, ellipsoids, pyramids, cones and spheres) and branching habit (horizontal, procumbent, ascending, arched, fastigiate and convergent). *Relevance to amateurs*: this kind of analysis is not uncommon, especially in USA. It is helpful when designing planting schemes to look at the shape of a plant and understand how it will grow in cultivation. There is a display of naturally occurring variations in *Juniperus communis* collected from samples across the UK at the Cambridge University Botanic Garden.

6

Current Restoration Projects

The rediscovery of the lost gardens at **Heligan**, Cornwall, was one of the hottest stories of 1993. The gardens belong to John Willis but have largely been restored by his archaeologist friend Tim Smit, who has been able to work out where long-lost plants once grew by using a metal detector to find their original labels. Some were introduced by no lesser plant collector than **Sir Joseph Hooker** whose expedition to the Himalaya from 1849 to 1851 brought many new species to England (he almost tripled the number of rhododendrons in cultivation). The accumulation of debris was formidable: the original pumps which were installed 100 years ago to water the gardens were only found after digging down through nearly 20ft of mud. In addition to the trees and shrubs which have survived the neglect of generations, a remarkable series of design features has been revealed and restored. These include an Italian garden where a simple summerhouse looks out over a formal rectangular pool, a 10 yard ravine strewn with rocks and planted with ferns, and an oval-shaped walled garden with hot frames for pine-apples.

The **Hampshire Gardens Trust** took part in the re-opening of the reconstructed Lily House at **Leigh Park** in Southampton. The original was built in 1853 as a tropical aquatic house and was among the first glasshouses where the giant Amazonian water lily *Victoria amazonica* flowered in cultivation. Now in the care of the local authority, the gardens of Leigh Park combine an educational facility with public amenity.

In February, it was announced that the famous gardens at **Probus** in Cornwall had been saved from closure following a decision by Cornwall College to take over their administration from Cornwall County Council. Probus was founded in 1971 and intended as an educational facility, both for professional horticulturists and for members of the public. Although developed as a teaching resource, the 7 acre gardens on an exposed site quickly became a valuable tourist attraction.

In March, **English Heritage** published details of an extensive restoration project for the gardens of **Osborne House** in the Isle of Wight. The changes are intended to take place steadily over a period of years and mark a return to Victorian ideas of maintenance and planting. One major feature of the restoration project will be the replanting of the kitchen garden and the reconstruction of its Victorian greenhouses. English Heritage has carried out extensive research to discover how it looked, which plants were grown, and how the paths were surfaced at the time when Queen Victoria knew it. The Mount has already been replanted and restored; the event was marked by an official planting on 21 April 1993.

Mindful of the popular song that associates Kew with lilac time, the Director of the **Royal Botanic Gardens** announced that a new lilac garden will be planted at Kew during the course of the next five years. A new hellebore collection will be made near Cumberland Gate and further alterations to the rock garden to improve the displays and increase public access. More dramatically, the contents of the Australian House will move to the Cycad House, to be replaced by a permanent exhibition which will show and interpret key stages of plant evolution: cycads will be among the specimens. Work has also begun on a new Sensory Garden, which will demonstrate how keen gardeners can respond positively to the problems of diminished mobility. It is hoped later to have a horticultural therapist on hand to offer practical advice on managing gardens to people with disabilities.

In May the National Trust announced that it had completed the purchase of the Gibside Estate in Tyne & Wear, the only Grade II* garden in the county. The Trust has immediately begun essential repairs to the Column of Liberty, a 140 ft high Doric column, erected in 1757, and a great landmark in the Derwent Valley.

On 28th May 1993 the National Trust launched an appeal to restore Prior Park, the famous eighteenth century landscape park on the hillside south of Bath. The appeal is for £400,000 and the restoration work is expected to take two years to complete. The first visitors will be admitted next year: 1995 is the National Trust's centenary year.

On 25 June the National Trust announced that it had completed its long-term master plan for the landscape gardens at Stowe. Its research draws upon approximately 60,000 documents, including photographs, engravings, drawings and plans. Transcripts are now being fed into a computer archive system which, among other tricks, will allow visitors to experience 'virtual reality' visions of the gardens in future.

After a ten year restoration project, the formal garden at Audley End was re-opened on 29 June by Sir Roy Strong. It is one of very few early 19th century examples to have been re-established in recent times. Designed to be seen from the house, and provide a link with the Capability Brown landscape beyond, the garden consists of 170 geometric segments cut out of the turf and planted with perennials.

At the end of June 1993, the European Commission named fifty-eight gardens which would receive financial assistance from the Commission's budget for European architectural conservation. The gardens to be chosen for this pilot scheme include Powerscourt in Ireland, Hanbury Hall in West Midlands, Padua Botanic Garden in Italy, Beloeil in Belgium and Lawrence Johnston's house near Menton, Serre de la Madone, the French 'Hidcote'. A full list of the gardens to benefit from this EC initiative is available from English Heritage.

During the summer, English Heritage launched a pilot grant scheme for restoration projects at gardens recognised as Grade I or Grade II* on the Register. Two of the grants were intended to complement funding from the European Commission: plans to finish the work of restoration at Painshill Park in Surrey in time for its full public opening this year; and the restoration of Sir Charles Barry's Italianate parterre at Harewood House in West Yorkshire. Other gardens to benefit from this first tranche of grants were Ham House, London; Lyme Park, Cheshire; and Farnborough Hall, Warwickshire.

In August it was confirmed that a grant of more than £22,000 had been made from the EC's Fund for the Conservation of Historic Gardens to Ruskin's garden at Brantwood in Cumbria. During his ownership, Ruskin created Italianate terraces and an azalea walk to the harbour on Coniston Water.

In the autumn, the Hampshire Gardens Trust revealed plans to develop a medieval style garden at King John's House, Romsey. This will include a 'herber' and flower garden. The Hampshire Gardens Trust has a distinguished record of garden restoration projects and has actively advised on replanting the Gertrude Jekyll garden at Manor House, Upton Grey, and restoring the nineteenth century garden at Rhinefield Park in the New Forest.

During November, the Edward James Foundation published details of its plans for the walled garden at West Dean near Chichester. The Foundation starts from the belief that the walled kitchen garden is an important expression of the social aspirations and the technological and horticultural achievements of the Victorian and Edwardian periods. Social and economic changes since 1918 have resulted in the almost complete disappearance of working walled gardens in Britain, most of which have either become derelict or been turned over to other uses. Jim Buckland, West Dean's garden manager, will supervise the restoration project and has carried out extensive research. One of the advisers was Peter Thoday, presenter of the success-ful BBC television series on the Victorian Kitchen Garden. Fortunately, most of the extensive garden structures at West Dean, including twelve glass-houses, survive in a repairable condition and are considered fine examples of their type. There is also much archival material available to draw upon. Res-toration is expected to be complete in 1995.

The Welsh Historic Gardens Trust gave fur-ther details of its active involvement in several restoration projects. One of the most important has been the Trust's new partnership with the owners of the Hafod Estate, which will lead to a series of conservation and re-instatement projects early this year. Hafod is important in the history of the land-scape movement in Wales. The Trust is also in-volved in negotiations to establish a botanic garden for Wales at Middleton Hall, Carmarthen, and a 'centre of horticultural excellence' at Dyffryn Gar-dens, the finest example of a grand Edwardian gar-den in Wales.

In December 1993 English Heritage an-nounced its intention to re-create a medieval monas-tic garden around the ruins of Mount Grace Priory, near Northallerton. The plantings will make use of flowers, vegetables and herbs which the monks employed medicinally: garlic, fennel, hyssop, rue, thyme and wormwood among others.

7

Weather
Records
1992–1993

We are publishing complete weather records for the twelve months September 1992 to August 1993. The data has been collected at the Meteorological Stations at five important gardens around the British Isles: the Royal Botanic Garden, Edinburgh; the Royal Horticultural Society's Gardens at Wisley, Surrey; the University of Liverpool's Ness Gardens, Cheshire and two National Trust properties: Trelissick in Cornwall and Rowallane in Northern Ireland.

The information is given on a day by day basis, without averaging, so that readers can see the fluctuations within any period of their choice. Close study reveals patterns that may help to explain plant growth and offer a general guide to seasonal variations.

Date 1992	Max (°C)	Min (°C)	Rainfall (mm)	Sunshine (hrs)	Date 1992	Max (°C)	Min (°C)	Rainfall (mm)	Sunshine (hrs)
Sept 1	15.6	9.9	4.0	7.8	Nov 1	10.3	5.7	15.3	5.2
2	12.9	9.0	2.7	0.0	2	9.7	5.3	3.9	0.0
3	15.0	8.4	0.0	9.6	3	9.5	4.9	0.0	5.8
4	15.9	7.5	0.0	8.8	4	13.2	5.6	1.5	0.0
5	15.2	6.9	6.7	7.5	5	15.4	7.0	0.0	5.6
6	17.4	5.8	4.3	0.0	6	13.6	11.4	0.7	0.4
7	15.7	6.0	3.4	9.2	7	9.7	6.7	0.0	5.8
8	14.3	8.8	0.0	5.5	8	12.3	0.1	1.1	1.4
9	16.5	11.1	0.0	4.3	9	12.4	3.6	3.8	0.0
10	16.1	12.9	0.8	0.2	10	8.9	2.8	1.2	4.1
11	17.6	11.5	2.7	5.4	11	7.7	4.5	0.2	4.2
12	15.0	8.1	14.9	9.5	12	7.1	2.8	0.0	5.6
13	14.0	7.1	4.6	8.7	13	5.6	0.1	0.0	6.0
14	16.2	9.4	1.7	7.9	14	6.0	-3.8	6.6	2.5
15	17.2	10.8	0.0	7.1	15	6.5	-0.5	2.7	0.1
16	14.7	6.2	0.3	8.2	16	6.4	0.9	0.2	0.0
17	17.0	10.6	2.3	0.3	17	8.9	0.8	0.0	5.7
18	16.0	11.8	0.1	0.4	18	9.1	1.6	1.0	1.7
19	14.4	11.0	6.9	0.0	19	6.7	2.9	0.0	5.3
20	16.9	11.2	3.6	2.9	20	6.9	1.7	1.2	2.8
21	12.9	3.1	18.3	7.9	21	3.7	0.0	7.7	0.0
22	12.1	7.1	1.8	0.0	22	14.3	0.1	5.3	0.0
23	15.4	8.6	0.3	4.0	23	13.9	3.1	0.0	0.4
24	13.7	7.7	10.6	0.1	24	10.7	5.9	4.0	2.5
25	12.4	9.4	0.1	0.3	25	8.4	5.0	2.8	2.5
26	12.7	5.8	2.9	0.0	26	9.0	3.4	1.8	0.4
27	12.9	8.5	0.5	0.0	27	9.9	3.3	9.7	0.0
28	14.0	10.6	0.2	0.0	28	7.2	3.4	0.0	4.1
29	17.7	11.3	4.2	3.6	29	12.3	-2.2	0.2	0.0
30	12.5	10.9	11.5	0.2	30	9.7	2.6	2.0	0.0
Oct 1	16.4	8.7	0.3	5.9	Dec 1	10.3	2.3	4.6	0.0
2	12.3	7.5	19.6	0.0	2	9.8	5.3	3.7	0.0
3	13.3	9.0	0.5	0.9	3	5.2	2.7	1.3	2.6
4	13.1	10.4	1.2	0.6	4	4.5	1.2	0.1	3.3
5	11.9	7.1	0.0	0.0	5	5.5	1.4	0.0	3.9
6	11.6	5.4	0.0	0.0	6	5.7	1.7	2.3	0.0
7	11.8	3.3	0.0	3.6	7	6.2	4.0	2.1	0.0
8	15.7	2.6	0.0	6.8	8	5.2	0.1	1.4	3.4
9	11.6	6.4	0.0	5.2	9	6.0	0.1	0.0	3.9
10	11.0	2.1	0.0	9.0	10	10.0	-1.3	0.7	0.2
11	10.5	2.5	0.0	0.0	11	7.9	3.7	0.3	0.0
12	12.5	5.1	0.0	2.5	12	9.9	3.0	0.0	2.6
13	12.0	5.9	0.0	2.6	13	11.3	4.0	0.0	0.0
14	9.4	7.7	0.7	1.9	14	11.5	9.2	0.0	4.5
15	8.4	2.3	0.0	1.9	15	11.7	9.5	2.6	1.7
16	8.4	4.2	0.0	1.8	16	5.8	2.2	2.4	0.0
17	8.0	3.6	1.8	0.2	17	9.5	-0.5	5.3	0.1
18	8.1	-1.4	0.1	2.4	18	5.6	4.1	0.4	0.0
19	9.0	1.2	0.4	5.1	19	2.6	0.1	0.8	2.3
20	10.1	2.0	0.0	3.0	20	0.1	-5.1	0.0	3.0
21	10.0	1.4	0.1	1.1	21	1.5	-5.7	2.3	0.2
22	8.5	1.1	0.2	0.2	22	2.1	-1.5	0.0	0.1
23	6.4	3.7	0.0	2.7	23	5.7	-2.1	0.0	0.7
24	7.5	2.3	0.0	7.0	24	6.7	-0.7	0.0	0.0
25	7.5	-1.1	0.5	1.3	25	7.0	1.2	1.9	2.4
26	8.0	-2.3	0.3	0.8	26	6.0	4.0	0.0	0.0
27	7.5	-0.2	7.6	2.1	27	4.6	2.9	0.0	0.1
28	6.6	2.7	5.1	0.0	28	2.0	-1.7	0.0	0.6
29	8.1	3.7	0.0	0.6	29	-0.4	-5.0	0.0	3.2
30	6.3	-2.7	1.1	0.1	30	4.8	-7.2	0.0	0.3
31	9.5	-1.2	2.9	1.1	31	7.9	-7.1	0.0	4.9

Date 1993	Max (°C)	Min (°C)	Rainfall (mm)	Sunshine (hrs)	Date 1993	Max (°C)	Min (°C)	Rainfall (mm)	Sunshine (hrs)
Jan 1	8.8	0.0	0.0	2.8	Mar 1	5.2	0.8	1.9	2.9
2	7.9	5.2	0.0	0.0	2	4.5	0.5	0.3	0.0
3	7.4	-1.5	5.1	0.3	3	3.6	1.9	3.1	0.1
4	10.1	2.1	2.3	3.5	4	8.0	-2.7	1.1	1.8
5	8.7	4.2	1.3	0.0	5	12.1	-0.2	0.0	4.0
6	7.6	3.2	0.0	1.8	6	11.6	4.7	0.0	8.7
7	9.3	3.2	2.0	1.9	7	7.9	4.4	0.0	0.0
8	10.4	1.7	6.9	4.6	8	11.0	4.8	0.0	6.2
9	7.9	1.9	3.2	1.6	9	6.8	4.1	0.0	3.7
10	10.5	4.0	4.5	0.0	10	6.2	0.3	2.9	1.1
11	2.9	-0.1	6.1	0.3	11	10.1	2.0	0.0	0.0
12	5.2	-0.8	4.3	0.2	12	12.0	3.0	4.2	4.5
13	5.2	0.9	6.7	0.0	13	14.7	6.4	0.0	0.1
14	11.6	0.4	5.9	1.4	14	12.7	3.7	0.0	0.9
15	11.5	1.5	5.7	2.2	15	12.6	8.3	1.6	1.7
16	13.9	1.9	4.6	0.0	16	12.5	4.8	0.0	1.6
17	5.0	3.6	6.9	0.6	17	14.4	6.3	0.8	4.0
18	6.7	0.6	1.9	2.8	18	8.7	5.3	0.2	7.6
19	10.0	2.5	1.7	0.0	19	8.8	3.8	0.1	3.3
20	10.6	2.8	8.7	1.1	20	10.0	7.2	0.6	0.2
21	12.0	2.5	10.7	0.0	21	10.5	6.8	0.0	6.7
22	7.0	4.6	4.9	0.3	22	8.6	4.1	6.7	5.4
23	11.4	2.1	16.5	0.0	23	6.9	0.5	0.2	8.0
24	6.2	2.6	3.9	4.1	24	9.5	1.4	0.0	9.2
25	5.8	0.5	0.0	4.4	25	8.0	-2.8	0.0	10.8
26	7.1	0.5	0.0	0.2	26	10.7	-3.4	0.0	10.7
27	8.0	-0.4	1.7	0.0	27	8.6	1.7	0.0	0.0
28	6.4	1.0	0.1	2.6	28	7.5	4.9	0.0	0.0
29	7.8	1.0	0.0	0.0	29	11.9	3.1	0.7	0.9
30	8.4	4.0	0.0	0.0	30	13.9	6.5	0.6	5.7
31	6.5	-1.5	0.0	6.3	31	13.5	2.1	0.9	8.6
Feb 1	7.6	-3.3	0.0	3.4	April 1	11.5	3.0	0.0	7.6
2	10.5	-3.6	0.0	1.2	2	10.9	0.5	0.0	8.5
3	11.0	7.1	0.0	0.7	3	11.5	0.7	0.0	0.5
4	9.8	8.5	0.0	0.0	4	11.4	3.7	2.9	8.8
5	10.9	7.7	0.0	0.0	5	11.5	3.0	2.5	3.8
6	11.8	7.8	0.0	1.1	6	12.5	4.8	0.0	4.0
7	12.1	9.3	0.0	3.1	7	10.8	6.5	0.0	4.4
8	7.1	5.6	0.0	0.0	8	9.0	6.0	6.4	0.0
9	10.2	5.9	0.0	0.4	9	9.5	6.6	10.4	0.0
10	6.1	4.5	0.0	0.0	10	13.0	5.8	0.0	6.4
11	6.7	4.3	0.0	0.0	11	8.2	4.2	0.3	0.2
12	7.7	0.0	0.0	0.2	12	7.5	4.2	1.2	0.0
13	9.1	1.1	0.0	0.0	13	7.8	5.4	0.0	0.0
14	12.7	3.6	0.2	5.2	14	10.0	-1.1	0.0	9.6
15	8.9	2.5	0.0	1.2	15	11.6	-0.1	0.0	0.7
16	11.0	4.4	0.0	0.0	16	13.3	8.6	0.1	0.3
17	12.5	7.0	0.1	7.5	17	11.9	5.6	10.2	7.6
18	8.8	6.5	0.0	3.0	18	7.4	4.6	13.5	0.0
19	9.1	3.5	0.0	5.6	19	11.6	5.0	1.0	0.0
20	10.6	2.0	0.0	2.1	20	13.1	5.9	2.0	4.2
21	5.9	2.2	0.3	3.7	21	13.0	7.5	0.0	5.1
22	7.2	2.8	1.1	2.1	22	12.5	9.3	1.3	0.0
23	8.7	0.5	0.0	1.7	23	14.7	6.2	0.9	2.0
24	10.4	5.0	0.0	0.6	24	12.5	6.5	0.0	2.7
25	10.4	6.6	2.0	1.2	25	8.7	6.0	9.9	0.0
26	6.2	1.1	0.0	1.8	26	8.3	6.5	0.0	0.0
27	3.5	-1.2	0.0	4.8	27	10.5	6.5	0.0	0.0
28	3.9	-1.2	0.0	0.5	28	11.4	6.1	0.0	11.9
					29	13.6	2.5	0.0	8.4
					30	14.9	6.3	0.0	7.2

Date 1993	Max (°C)	Min (°C)	Rainfall (mm)	Sunshine (hrs)	Date 1993	Max (°C)	Min (°C)	Rainfall (mm)	Sunshine (hrs)
May 1	14.4	7.4	5.5	8.5	July 1	19.5	11.5	0.0	9.2
2	11.5	4.5	0.0	3.0	2	17.5	12.4	0.0	1.2
3	12.1	0.9	0.0	10.3	3	18.5	13.9	0.1	1.4
4	14.4	0.4	0.2	3.2	4	17.8	13.1	0.0	9.2
5	14.7	9.1	0.0	0.1	5	17.8	8.8	0.0	7.8
6	15.1	8.2	0.0	5.1	6	18.0	11.0	0.0	8.4
7	16.1	7.6	6.0	4.3	7	19.0	10.9	0.0	5.4
8	11.5	7.3	0.0	2.4	8	18.4	13.6	2.5	4.2
9	11.6	6.9	0.0	5.4	9	15.3	7.4	4.8	10.1
10	11.9	7.4	2.0	0.6	10	14.2	7.6	0.0	4.9
11	12.5	8.4	0.0	11.9	11	15.5	8.5	0.8	6.7
12	9.4	7.0	0.4	0.0	12	17.2	6.9	0.0	7.2
13	6.6	6.2	26.2	0.0	13	18.5	7.5	1.2	6.8
14	6.8	3.0	29.8	0.0	14	15.6	11.8	3.1	0.0
15	9.8	3.3	1.6	5.9	15	19.6	12.0	4.6	0.9
16	14.8	4.5	11.3	5.8	16	18.5	13.1	32.6	0.8
17	18.8	7.7	1.2	1.4	17	18.2	13.9	0.0	6.4
18	15.1	9.4	0.0	12.5	18	18.9	8.9	0.0	8.1
19	12.9	7.7	3.5	1.2	19	18.6	12.0	2.4	4.5
20	13.0	2.8	2.6	5.4	20	19.2	10.8	0.0	5.6
21	12.5	8.2	0.0	0.0	21	17.5	10.7	0.0	5.0
22	17.0	3.8	0.5	6.0	22	18.9	10.8	1.7	2.5
23	16.0	6.9	0.0	1.9	23	20.1	13.9	0.0	5.2
24	14.5	5.8	0.0	11.4	24	17.9	11.5	0.0	9.4
25	10.6	7.3	0.0	0.6	25	16.0	10.4	0.0	5.8
26	9.5	7.1	0.0	0.1	26	17.1	10.7	0.0	7.5
27	10.4	7.2	0.0	0.1	27	17.9	5.9	0.4	0.6
28	15.7	6.3	0.2	6.9	28	19.0	12.2	1.7	8.6
29	17.0	9.0	5.8	3.7	29	20.7	10.5	0.0	9.7
30	16.5	9.8	6.0	1.3	30	17.5	10.1	0.6	7.4
31	16.6	11.0	0.0	4.3	31	16.8	10.6	0.0	7.6
June 1	12.2	8.5	13.1	0.8	Aug 1	18.4	11.3	0.0	1.6
2	11.2	8.5	3.6	0.0	2	19.5	13.6	0.5	3.7
3	16.1	7.8	0.0	0.0	3	17.6	12.0	0.5	5.9
4	17.8	8.8	0.0	0.5	4	18.9	12.4	6.7	6.0
5	17.6	8.2	0.0	10.2	5	16.9	11.9	0.2	0.6
6	20.3	10.2	0.0	2.3	6	17.4	7.9	0.0	3.2
7	19.3	13.2	0.0	8.3	7	18.8	14.1	0.0	4.9
8	22.0	12.5	0.0	10.8	8	16.7	10.2	4.0	0.7
9	18.4	10.8	4.0	5.0	9	18.0	12.4	0.0	7.4
10	13.2	11.5	8.9	0.0	10	16.9	8.6	6.4	10.2
11	14.6	10.9	25.9	0.0	11	12.4	9.6	4.1	0.0
12	13.4	9.3	0.2	6.5	12	15.6	8.4	0.0	9.5
13	14.1	7.3	3.6	8.2	13	18.1	7.9	0.0	8.3
14	13.2	7.5	0.0	6.5	14	15.7	11.6	4.4	0.0
15	18.0	4.9	0.0	1.0	15	16.1	11.4	1.5	6.4
16	17.7	11.2	0.1	6.2	16	17.0	10.3	0.3	6.8
17	19.0	11.6	7.4	3.4	17	18.4	6.6	0.0	6.7
18	17.4	11.0	0.5	3.0	18	19.8	10.5	0.7	0.8
19	17.4	9.1	8.6	4.3	19	17.9	9.3	0.0	5.0
20	17.3	9.9	0.0	5.8	20	17.1	11.6	0.0	3.3
21	16.1	10.0	0.0	2.5	21	17.5	10.7	3.3	10.7
22	14.2	11.2	1.5	2.8	22	14.9	9.1	0.1	6.6
23	16.1	9.4	3.0	6.2	23	16.1	6.8	1.3	2.7
24	15.4	7.4	0.0	2.9	24	14.3	6.8	0.3	1.8
25	15.9	7.4	6.9	0.0	25	16.8	10.8	0.0	2.8
26	18.6	11.0	0.0	8.5	26	17.8	8.8	0.0	10.0
27	21.4	10.5	0.0	15.3	27	19.4	10.6	0.0	3.3
28	19.1	9.6	0.0	9.4	28	20.6	9.6	0.0	9.1
29	20.6	12.0	0.6	6.2	29	18.8	14.2	0.0	6.1
30	15.0	13.9	0.0	0.0	30	19.1	7.0	0.0	3.3
					31	22.1	9.2	0.0	10.1

Date 1992	Max (°C)	Min (°C)	Rainfall (mm)	Sunshine (hrs)	Date 1992	Max (°C)	Min (°C)	Rainfall (mm)	Sunshine (hrs)
Sept 1	16.2	8.2	1.7	4.8	Nov 1	13.6	2.5	4.0	0.0
2	20.3	11.5	2.4	2.2	2	14.0	10.6	4.7	1.2
3	16.2	11.6	1.7	5.2	3	12.2	5.1	0.0	4.1
4	16.2	7.8	0.0	9.1	4	13.3	4.4	0.0	4.5
5	17.1	4.5	0.0	4.0	5	16.0	8.2	0.0	5.7
6	17.0	6.0	2.0	0.0	6	16.2	6.7	0.0	0.1
7	17.2	10.8	0.0	9.5	7	15.5	8.7	0.0	0.0
8	15.7	6.7	0.0	4.5	8	13.0	9.5	0.3	0.0
9	17.2	8.3	0.0	0.0	9	11.8	8.3	7.9	0.0
10	20.1	6.8	0.9	8.8	10	13.5	5.6	4.7	3.0
11	18.3	12.7	0.0	7.7	11	9.9	6.2	0.0	1.6
12	16.9	7.6	0.2	3.2	12	9.1	4.2	0.0	6.4
13	15.1	11.0	3.9	0.0	13	7.5	-0.5	0.0	6.2
14	18.4	7.0	0.0	5.6	14	9.3	-2.5	7.2	0.0
15	18.5	8.7	0.0	3.4	15	9.3	3.2	0.7	0.0
16	19.5	7.0	0.0	7.9	16	8.2	4.4	5.4	0.0
17	23.0	8.6	2.3	4.1	17	7.9	2.0	0.9	4.5
18	18.4	14.4	0.6	2.3	18	12.4	1.3	3.3	0.0
19	18.7	12.8	0.3	0.3	19	10.2	5.3	1.6	4.8
20	19.2	11.0	2.3	0.1	20	8.4	1.4	0.0	0.0
21	18.6	10.9	0.8	0.5	21	14.2	2.3	3.0	0.0
22	17.2	13.3	30.0	0.0	22	14.5	3.7	0.4	0.0
23	16.5	11.3	4.5	1.5	23	13.2	11.8	0.2	1.4
24	17.9	10.4	3.2	1.8	24	13.4	4.0	7.8	1.8
25	19.0	9.5	2.0	0.0	25	11.3	6.2	19.3	1.1
26	23.1	7.5	0.0	6.1	26	10.2	6.0	0.5	6.1
27	22.3	10.1	0.0	4.4	27	12.7	4.2	1.9	0.2
28	21.8	11.0	0.0	5.2	28	7.8	2.5	9.1	2.0
29	20.2	10.5	0.9	6.1	29	13.1	3.3	1.2	0.0
30	17.2	12.3	5.7	3.2	30	12.5	7.6	5.9	0.0
Oct 1	16.7	5.5	0.0	5.6	Dec 1	12.0	5.7	8.0	0.2
2	17.6	7.4	10.1	2.4	2	13.1	9.1	7.1	0.5
3	14.5	9.6	1.1	0.3	3	7.4	5.0	4.5	0.4
4	16.4	10.7	0.0	4.8	4	5.2	1.7	0.0	0.1
5	16.5	9.5	0.0	1.3	5	7.6	1.2	0.0	5.4
6	13.9	9.5	0.0	1.0	6	9.3	0.5	4.0	0.5
7	14.6	9.8	0.0	0.3	7	10.3	2.8	0.1	4.7
8	14.7	9.3	0.0	2.0	8	6.9	5.0	0.0	0.3
9	14.4	3.4	0.0	1.9	9	6.4	3.7	0.0	0.0
10	14.2	4.6	0.1	3.9	10	6.6	-0.8	0.0	0.0
11	12.4	4.5	0.1	0.0	11	11.8	0.0	1.0	0.0
12	13.4	8.7	0.0	1.9	12	8.0	4.3	0.0	3.2
13	13.7	-1.4	0.0	8.3	13	10.7	1.3	0.0	0.0
14	12.0	-1.0	2.5	0.3	14	10.0	4.9	0.0	0.0
15	9.7	1.1	0.0	7.8	15	9.9	8.0	1.3	0.0
16	10.1	-1.2	0.0	7.3	16	10.3	5.6	3.4	0.0
17	10.0	-3.2	0.0	6.9	17	10.2	-1.8	1.5	0.0
18	11.6	1.0	0.3	1.8	18	11.5	-1.1	10.7	0.0
19	10.2	1.6	22.1	0.0	19	6.6	4.5	5.5	0.0
20	10.0	6.1	4.5	1.2	20	6.0	2.0	0.0	0.0
21	11.3	2.9	0.8	4.5	21	6.0	-3.8	0.0	2.2
22	10.2	2.3	0.0	1.7	22	4.6	-2.7	0.0	3.7
23	11.2	4.4	0.0	5.4	23	1.8	-3.1	0.0	0.0
24	12.5	2.5	7.6	0.8	24	2.1	-2.0	0.0	0.0
25	12.6	5.0	0.1	1.4	25	4.6	-1.2	0.0	0.0
26	9.8	1.1	1.0	1.5	26	5.2	2.1	0.0	0.0
27	10.9	4.4	7.9	0.3	27	6.4	4.0	0.0	3.6
28	10.9	2.6	1.5	5.4	28	5.6	0.5	0.0	5.8
29	9.6	4.2	0.0	3.7	29	3.5	-5.5	0.0	5.4
30	9.6	-2.6	0.0	5.3	30	1.8	-7.5	0.0	0.0
31	10.7	-2.2	0.0	5.5	31	4.3	-6.1	0.0	0.0

Date 1993	Max (°C)	Min (°C)	Rainfall (mm)	Sunshine (hrs)	Date 1993	Max (°C)	Min (°C)	Rainfall (mm)	Sunshine (hrs)
Jan 1	4.8	1.2	0.0	1.1	Mar 1	4.3	-2.2	0.0	2.8
2	1.2	-2.8	0.0	1.3	2	3.9	0.4	0.0	0.0
3	2.6	-8.0	1.4	5.8	3	5.0	1.5	0.0	1.0
4	8.5	-4.8	0.1	0.0	4	4.4	1.3	0.0	0.9
5	12.0	2.0	2.4	0.0	5	9.5	-1.2	0.0	0.0
6	11.9	8.5	7.4	0.0	6	10.5	1.4	0.0	0.0
7	11.1	-0.4	0.4	0.0	7	9.3	3.7	0.0	0.1
8	12.0	-0.1	0.1	4.5	8	12.3	3.4	0.0	10.0
9	12.5	2.7	7.7	0.0	9	9.7	-1.2	0.0	9.6
10	12.4	7.7	12.1	0.0	10	12.2	-3.6	0.0	0.1
11	10.2	9.3	2.2	0.0	11	14.9	-1.3	0.0	5.6
12	7.8	3.3	0.4	4.6	12	15.4	0.7	0.0	4.9
13	13.3	3.7	9.7	0.0	13	16.2	3.9	0.0	8.7
14	11.6	4.3	3.0	6.0	14	16.5	5.1	0.0	5.5
15	13.3	5.1	0.6	1.5	15	19.2	3.3	0.0	8.7
16	13.0	9.3	0.0	0.0	16	12.0	6.5	0.0	0.0
17	11.2	9.9	0.1	0.0	17	16.5	7.1	0.0	6.9
18	9.7	2.8	0.1	5.6	18	15.0	7.2	0.0	3.0
19	11.3	3.8	0.5	2.4	19	12.8	-2.5	0.0	10.2
20	12.2	4.5	0.2	0.0	20	13.9	-3.1	0.0	8.5
21	12.7	7.1	1.1	0.0	21	13.9	4.0	6.6	1.0
22	9.1	8.5	5.6	0.0	22	12.6	7.8	0.1	3.8
23	12.6	5.0	1.4	0.0	23	11.1	1.0	0.0	8.1
24	10.1	7.8	0.0	0.8	24	11.1	-1.3	0.0	8.6
25	5.2	2.9	0.0	0.5	25	10.2	-1.9	0.0	8.1
26	10.4	-1.4	7.7	0.0	26	9.5	-5.1	0.0	4.8
27	9.5	1.6	1.4	0.0	27	7.9	-5.0	0.0	0.6
28	10.4	6.8	0.2	0.0	28	10.9	-1.4	0.0	4.8
29	10.2	6.5	0.0	1.1	29	12.2	2.7	0.0	3.5
30	8.0	4.5	0.0	0.3	30	14.0	6.4	4.2	1.4
31	7.6	0.7	0.2	0.0	31	11.5	1.9	13.8	0.0
Feb 1	6.9	2.3	0.0	7.4	April 1	7.8	5.8	28.0	0.0
2	11.0	2.6	0.0	4.5	2	12.4	0.1	0.0	8.6
3	4.9	2.4	0.2	0.0	3	10.6	-0.1	3.1	1.9
4	2.7	1.6	0.0	0.0	4	12.5	1.0	6.7	9.2
5	3.4	-1.2	0.0	0.0	5	13.3	4.1	0.5	4.7
6	10.0	-0.3	0.1	0.3	6	12.6	6.7	1.0	4.0
7	10.0	2.5	0.9	0.0	7	10.0	3.7	1.1	0.0
8	8.6	8.0	0.0	0.0	8	12.1	6.6	0.4	0.0
9	6.6	4.4	0.0	0.0	9	10.6	6.8	7.9	0.0
10	3.3	1.2	0.0	0.0	10	13.3	2.2	9.2	6.1
11	3.6	0.9	0.0	0.0	11	11.6	4.5	1.7	1.1
12	4.3	0.7	0.1	0.0	12	14.3	3.2	0.0	8.9
13	7.3	1.3	0.0	2.3	13	11.8	2.8	1.3	1.0
14	3.5	-1.4	0.0	0.0	14	12.0	4.0	0.0	3.4
15	8.5	-0.4	0.0	0.1	15	14.7	2.3	0.0	8.0
16	9.6	0.5	0.0	2.7	16	14.7	3.5	0.5	1.4
17	10.3	3.7	0.0	0.0	17	15.9	8.3	0.0	0.7
18	8.9	6.7	0.0	0.0	18	16.6	7.1	0.0	4.2
19	9.4	3.4	0.0	3.9	19	16.0	9.0	0.0	0.8
20	8.9	0.9	0.0	3.1	20	19.2	6.0	0.0	12.6
21	7.3	1.9	0.0	5.1	21	17.3	8.1	0.0	9.3
22	7.0	-1.2	0.0	1.5	22	14.4	5.2	0.6	1.9
23	7.6	-1.5	0.0	7.3	23	14.3	9.0	4.9	0.1
24	9.0	1.3	0.0	0.5	24	14.0	8.1	6.3	2.3
25	8.2	2.2	1.4	0.8	25	16.2	7.3	0.0	3.0
26	4.5	2.2	2.2	0.2	26	13.7	6.6	6.0	1.5
27	4.5	0.5	0.0	7.5	27	21.1	7.3	0.0	4.9
28	3.0	-3.9	0.0	1.0	28	16.8	5.3	0.0	10.6
					29	20.9	7.0	0.0	9.4
					30	22.0	5.7	0.0	7.0

Date 1993	Max (°C)	Min (°C)	Rainfall (mm)	Sunshine (hrs)	Date 1993	Max (°C)	Min (°C)	Rainfall (mm)	Sunshine (hrs)
May 1	19.6	8.1	0.0	4.9	July 1	24.2	9.6	0.0	9.1
2	14.5	7.0	0.0	1.4	2	25.4	13.6	0.0	7.3
3	13.9	2.5	0.0	1.3	3	26.8	12.5	0.0	8.9
4	16.0	0.5	0.0	9.2	4	27.3	14.2	0.0	10.5
5	14.7	-0.8	0.0	11.7	5	19.7	13.9	0.0	8.2
6	14.6	-1.3	0.0	12.3	6	23.3	7.5	0.0	13.2
7	16.3	4.6	0.0	11.5	7	22.6	7.7	0.0	12.8
8	18.0	5.5	0.2	5.6	8	21.8	11.3	0.0	4.3
9	17.7	6.8	1.1	1.5	9	17.7	14.6	7.8	0.8
10	20.9	8.2	0.0	6.0	10	17.9	6.1	0.6	9.2
11	24.7	9.6	1.0	9.3	11	18.3	4.5	0.0	5.4
12	18.6	8.9	0.0	0.9	12	17.8	5.6	0.0	4.3
13	17.0	6.9	0.0	5.3	13	18.7	5.9	5.5	0.0
14	15.1	8.2	0.8	1.2	14	23.9	13.2	1.9	3.2
15	13.9	2.9	2.2	8.9	15	20.2	13.9	9.3	0.0
16	17.4	4.8	0.6	1.7	16	20.8	15.0	0.0	1.5
17	21.5	9.7	7.1	3.8	17	21.4	13.7	0.9	8.1
18	18.0	6.1	0.0	11.9	18	19.5	7.9	0.1	3.2
19	17.8	7.0	0.0	12.3	19	20.9	11.5	0.8	6.7
20	12.6	5.8	14.7	0.2	20	19.6	13.0	0.1	3.1
21	17.3	6.7	0.0	9.2	21	17.9	12.4	0.0	0.3
22	19.6	3.9	0.0	5.8	22	21.7	10.1	0.0	8.5
23	23.2	9.9	0.0	7.3	23	24.9	14.5	0.2	3.0
24	24.7	11.4	0.0	5.9	24	19.1	15.7	0.0	0.1
25	18.9	9.8	2.8	0.0	25	19.3	9.8	0.2	6.9
26	15.5	10.6	10.5	0.0	26	18.5	10.6	2.8	2.2
27	14.6	10.5	0.5	0.0	27	20.2	13.8	2.9	0.8
28	17.9	8.6	0.4	5.9	28	23.3	15.0	0.0	4.8
29	16.4	5.5	0.9	4.8	29	19.9	17.0	0.3	0.4
30	16.2	12.5	0.1	6.4	30	21.0	13.3	0.0	5.0
31	17.6	9.9	0.0	6.5	31	19.5	10.5	0.0	6.4
June 1	19.4	11.0	2.3	9.1	Aug 1	21.3	8.4	0.0	8.0
2	18.2	10.0	0.7	2.2	2	21.8	12.6	0.0	7.1
3	18.7	12.1	0.0	0.5	3	20.9	12.6	0.0	5.5
4	21.9	7.4	0.0	9.4	4	18.8	12.6	1.1	1.4
5	23.8	10.5	0.0	10.1	5	20.3	14.2	0.0	8.1
6	24.9	7.6	0.0	12.2	6	21.1	7.6	0.0	4.1
7	25.4	10.6	0.0	13.2	7	23.4	12.6	0.0	9.3
8	27.2	9.9	0.0	13.6	8	21.5	13.0	0.0	4.8
9	26.5	12.2	0.5	2.2	9	22.3	13.8	0.2	1.2
10	22.7	14.3	4.5	1.2	10	18.6	12.4	0.0	7.5
11	18.6	14.6	5.2	1.1	11	20.6	9.6	16.5	1.3
12	18.5	11.1	2.2	0.1	12	19.5	14.3	0.0	8.9
13	18.6	12.0	3.5	4.1	13	21.0	5.6	0.0	11.3
14	18.9	10.8	4.4	0.5	14	25.1	7.0	0.0	7.8
15	20.3	8.7	3.6	13.7	15	22.6	14.0	0.0	5.2
16	17.4	12.2	15.5	0.0	16	22.4	11.8	0.0	7.3
17	20.9	11.1	0.2	8.6	17	22.6	6.7	0.0	9.7
18	17.6	13.2	0.2	0.2	18	23.3	7.9	0.0	8.8
19	18.0	12.0	0.0	2.3	19	25.2	9.0	0.0	6.0
20	20.8	8.7	0.0	10.2	20	25.4	14.0	0.0	11.3
21	19.0	6.3	0.0	12.0	21	24.6	11.4	13.0	5.4
22	19.3	5.8	0.0	5.2	22	17.0	12.0	0.3	1.6
23	19.2	8.6	0.0	5.0	23	17.7	9.6	0.0	7.4
24	20.5	6.7	0.0	6.9	24	17.4	5.9	0.0	10.4
25	21.5	6.9	0.0	10.1	25	18.3	3.2	0.2	5.7
26	23.1	12.9	0.0	2.8	26	18.6	6.3	0.0	5.5
27	25.0	14.2	0.0	12.3	27	18.1	7.3	0.0	6.3
28	24.0	10.4	0.0	14.1	28	20.2	6.2	0.0	10.0
29	23.7	7.9	0.0	13.3	29	22.2	3.7	0.0	8.7
30	26.8	13.9	0.0	12.6	30	23.3	13.8	0.0	5.0
					31	19.0	6.2	0.0	7.3

Date 1992	Max (°C)	Min (°C)	Rainfall (mm)	Sunshine (hrs)	Date 1992	Max (°C)	Min (°C)	Rainfall (mm)	Sunshine (hrs)
Sept 1	17.1	8.4	0.9	8.7	Nov 1	14.5	4.1	0.1	n/a
2	18.1	10.5	5.5	1.1	2	12.4	4.4	8.4	n/a
3	15.1	10.4	10.8	3.1	3	11.1	3.4	0.0	n/a
4	14.4	8.1	1.3	5.5	4	14.2	5.5	0.0	n/a
5	14.5	6.3	1.1	3.9	5	15.7	8.5	0.0	n/a
6	22.5	7.4	1.5	1.9	6	17.4	9.5	0.5	n/a
7	16.1	7.0	0.2	9.5	7	12.1	9.8	0.5	n/a
8	16.7	6.8	0.0	9.3	8	11.4	7.0	0.1	n/a
9	16.2	11.5	0.0	1.9	9	11.4	7.5	10.4	n/a
10	17.5	10.6	0.8	1.8	10	9.4	3.2	8.5	n/a
11	14.8	12.0	2.1	4.9	11	8.7	4.9	3.8	n/a
12	15.5	8.7	8.5	1.5	12	8.9	4.3	2.2	4.1
13	14.2	10.6	1.0	3.7	13	8.1	2.1	0.1	5.9
14	16.0	7.5	0.0	6.6	14	5.1	-0.9	5.3	0.0
15	19.4	10.5	0.0	5.5	15	6.0	2.1	2.2	0.0
16	17.1	11.6	0.6	4.0	16	7.4	3.3	8.1	0.4
17	17.7	10.7	2.0	0.0	17	8.5	3.5	7.6	1.0
18	19.3	12.8	0.9	2.5	18	11.9	1.7	0.8	0.0
19	17.8	11.1	5.9	0.1	19	8.9	5.2	1.2	3.3
20	17.4	11.0	0.0	6.5	20	10.9	1.9	0.9	4.0
21	15.4	7.6	8.1	0.2	21	13.1	3.3	9.0	0.0
22	16.1	11.3	1.2	1.7	22	14.0	4.0	7.0	0.0
23	14.5	11.4	0.0	5.4	23	14.1	9.9	0.9	0.0
24	16.7	8.5	0.0	4.0	24	11.1	3.7	2.3	1.6
25	16.3	6.3	0.0	6.5	25	9.3	3.9	0.6	1.5
26	15.1	8.5	0.7	0.0	26	9.4	3.1	0.0	3.6
27	20.6	11.0	0.1	3.1	27	10.4	2.3	1.0	0.0
28	21.3	13.0	0.0	4.3	28	6.6	2.8	0.0	0.3
29	17.4	11.3	2.5	1.4	29	11.6	0.0	8.1	0.0
30	13.5	7.9	2.6	0.8	30	11.5	4.1	7.8	0.0
Oct 1	16.8	7.1	0.9	n/a	Dec 1	11.8	3.9	4.2	0.0
2	13.9	9.3	11.9	n/a	2	11.4	8.6	11.8	0.0
3	12.1	9.4	3.3	n/a	3	6.6	2.3	0.4	1.9
4	15.7	7.8	0.0	n/a	4	5.7	0.4	0.7	3.4
5	12.1	8.6	0.0	n/a	5	7.1	1.1	0.1	3.5
6	12.4	9.6	0.0	n/a	6	7.0	1.2	5.3	0.0
7	12.1	8.5	0.0	n/a	7	8.2	2.5	2.3	0.1
8	12.7	6.5	1.5	n/a	8	7.5	3.7	0.8	4.1
9	13.0	8.6	0.0	n/a	9	7.3	2.6	0.3	0.3
10	10.7	7.6	0.0	n/a	10	10.2	2.9	0.3	3.2
11	12.6	5.0	0.0	n/a	11	11.9	2.8	8.8	0.0
12	11.1	8.0	0.0	n/a	12	9.4	5.2	0.0	0.8
13	12.6	7.8	0.5	n/a	13	11.6	4.7	0.0	1.2
14	10.7	8.7	6.7	n/a	14	12.3	4.8	0.0	1.3
15	9.2	5.4	1.6	n/a	15	10.0	8.5	6.7	0.0
16	8.6	3.2	0.0	n/a	16	6.0	5.1	0.2	0.4
17	10.4	1.3	8.5	n/a	17	8.9	-0.6	8.5	2.2
18	10.0	4.3	0.2	n/a	18	9.4	-0.3	10.7	0.0
19	7.8	0.1	0.0	n/a	19	5.4	0.3	0.0	1.1
20	9.9	0.3	0.8	n/a	20	2.6	-4.6	0.0	3.1
21	9.4	2.7	7.0	n/a	21	1.4	-4.7	0.0	0.6
22	10.3	5.1	7.0	n/a	22	2.4	-1.3	0.0	0.2
23	10.6	5.3	6.1	n/a	23	2.1	-3.2	0.0	3.1
24	10.1	3.3	27.1	n/a	24	2.1	-3.3	0.0	2.8
25	10.9	3.5	2.8	n/a	25	2.6	-3.6	0.0	3.8
26	8.3	3.5	3.5	n/a	26	4.6	-3.5	0.0	0.0
27	8.1	5.0	8.8	n/a	27	5.2	0.5	0.0	0.0
28	8.9	2.6	5.2	n/a	28	2.4	0.8	0.0	0.6
29	8.7	4.3	0.0	n/a	29	-0.5	-1.3	0.0	2.0
30	9.1	0.3	0.7	n/a	30	2.4	-4.2	0.0	0.2
31	10.3	1.1	0.3	n/a	31	6.7	-2.9	0.0	1.1

Date 1993	Max (°C)	Min (°C)	Rainfall (mm)	Sunshine (hrs)	Date 1993	Max (°C)	Min (°C)	Rainfall (mm)	Sunshine (hrs)
Jan 1	5.0	0.9	0.0	5.0	Mar 1	4.8	-0.5	0.2	4.4
2	0.4	-1.5	0.0	0.0	2	4.6	1.0	0.0	0.0
3	2.1	-2.1	3.2	0.8	3	4.9	2.9	0.0	0.2
4	10.4	-1.9	0.7	3.4	4	7.3	1.2	0.1	0.5
5	10.2	1.6	2.4	0.0	5	8.6	1.6	0.0	0.0
6	5.8	5.1	0.4	0.0	6	7.6	5.2	0.0	0.0
7	10.4	0.6	2.2	0.9	7	7.5	4.7	0.0	0.0
8	11.3	1.7	1.0	3.2	8	6.5	5.1	0.0	0.4
9	12.0	2.2	1.7	3.6	9	9.8	-1.4	0.0	7.1
10	12.3	4.6	6.5	0.2	10	10.2	1.0	1.4	0.6
11	5.6	2.5	0.5	3.6	11	12.8	6.1	0.0	3.4
12	7.7	1.1	1.5	3.1	12	12.3	3.9	0.0	1.5
13	6.2	2.1	6.0	0.0	13	17.1	5.7	0.0	8.3
14	13.1	2.0	8.0	4.3	14	15.6	5.8	0.0	4.2
15	13.3	4.0	0.1	1.6	15	16.8	5.7	1.3	8.0
16	13.6	6.9	0.4	0.1	16	10.7	6.4	1.4	0.0
17	8.1	6.8	0.0	5.5	17	13.6	6.3	2.3	6.3
18	9.5	0.6	1.0	2.8	18	8.1	6.5	0.1	2.8
19	11.5	2.1	2.0	0.0	19	10.9	2.1	0.0	1.9
20	13.4	2.7	0.3	4.0	20	10.8	4.3	0.0	0.9
21	13.1	5.3	0.0	0.0	21	11.1	6.5	1.1	0.0
22	7.6	6.8	2.2	1.5	22	11.9	5.7	0.3	6.1
23	12.7	3.0	2.7	0.0	23	10.3	1.0	0.1	9.4
24	8.4	4.4	2.2	0.5	24	8.9	1.7	0.0	8.9
25	4.7	1.9	0.2	3.7	25	9.6	0.7	0.0	10.0
26	9.9	0.6	6.5	0.0	26	10.8	-1.8	0.0	9.4
27	9.9	3.9	5.7	0.0	27	10.2	-0.3	0.1	4.8
28	12.5	5.7	1.0	1.1	28	11.1	4.1	0.0	0.3
29	8.4	7.4	1.1	0.0	29	12.3	3.5	0.0	0.2
30	8.8	5.1	1.0	0.0	30	14.4	5.7	0.0	6.7
31	7.6	5.1	0.0	1.9	31	10.4	1.0	1.4	1.7
Feb 1	7.3	3.6	0.0	0.4	Apr 1	8.8	2.9	0.0	3.1
2	11.7	2.3	0.0	4.5	2	11.1	1.0	3.0	3.4
3	10.9	5.1	0.0	6.8	3	9.1	1.4	4.3	0.2
4	9.1	2.3	0.0	5.9	4	11.0	1.2	4.9	7.7
5	9.2	2.5	0.0	6.9	5	12.1	5.8	0.6	8.6
6	9.5	3.0	0.3	0.0	6	12.4	6.4	0.6	8.8
7	9.3	7.6	0.8	0.0	7	10.1	6.2	0.1	0.0
8	9.3	6.7	0.0	0.0	8	10.6	7.9	5.9	0.0
9	7.0	6.5	0.6	0.0	9	13.3	6.9	4.6	0.2
10	5.0	3.8	0.0	0.0	10	14.2	4.9	0.0	4.4
11	3.9	2.6	0.0	0.0	11	11.1	4.8	0.9	0.0
12	6.3	2.0	0.0	0.3	12	13.6	5.4	0.2	8.3
13	7.4	2.1	0.0	1.3	13	10.4	4.8	0.0	0.0
14	5.7	1.8	2.2	0.0	14	11.4	3.6	0.0	9.0
15	7.9	1.7	0.0	1.2	15	15.0	1.1	0.0	8.4
16	9.3	5.2	0.0	0.0	16	14.1	8.5	1.6	1.3
17	8.2	6.8	0.2	0.0	17	12.7	8.3	2.9	7.6
18	11.2	6.5	1.0	1.1	18	13.4	8.1	1.0	0.0
19	8.4	5.0	0.0	4.9	19	14.0	10.1	0.0	0.0
20	8.7	4.4	0.7	1.4	20	14.7	8.0	0.5	5.1
21	6.1	4.7	0.0	6.2	21	14.1	8.6	0.0	2.5
22	7.1	1.2	0.3	0.0	22	12.7	8.4	2.4	0.0
23	7.9	-0.4	0.0	2.6	23	15.1	9.0	0.0	3.9
24	9.4	0.2	0.0	3.1	24	15.0	5.1	3.3	3.9
25	7.3	4.2	3.7	0.0	25	11.2	7.3	2.5	0.0
26	5.7	1.9	0.7	0.7	26	14.4	7.2	1.2	5.1
27	4.6	-1.6	0.0	4.1	27	17.7	6.8	0.0	4.1
28	3.1	-1.3	0.0	2.8	28	18.2	5.5	0.0	11.2
					29	18.0	5.8	0.0	9.4
					30	19.1	7.4	0.0	9.6

Date 1993	Max (°C)	Min (°C)	Rainfall (mm)	Sunshine (hrs)	Date 1993	Max (°C)	Min (°C)	Rainfall (mm)	Sunshine (hrs)
May 1	14.1	9.0	0.0	3.2	July 1	17.6	10.7	0.0	11.6
2	10.4	5.7	0.0	12.2	2	21.7	8.9	0.0	6.5
3	11.5	4.6	0.0	11.3	3	22.2	16.0	0.0	2.1
4	14.6	0.8	0.0	11.7	4	22.7	15.4	0.9	5.8
5	15.5	3.6	0.0	6.7	5	16.4	10.6	0.0	10.5
6	15.5	8.5	0.0	4.1	6	15.3	11.4	0.1	1.4
7	16.8	2.9	0.0	11.6	7	18.7	10.8	0.0	6.9
8	16.8	2.9	0.3	9.3	8	18.2	13.8	2.9	1.2
9	16.7	6.9	0.5	6.6	9	15.0	9.8	7.8	6.8
10	16.2	9.1	7.1	0.9	10	15.0	8.2	1.3	6.3
11	21.9	9.3	0.0	7.0	11	14.1	7.0	3.6	5.4
12	19.7	7.2	0.0	8.3	12	15.4	8.7	0.0	11.0
13	13.9	5.6	23.5	0.6	13	18.3	7.1	6.0	0.2
14	12.5	8.1	0.4	3.3	14	19.1	12.8	17.8	4.9
15	12.3	3.8	0.3	8.4	15	20.1	13.5	5.3	0.3
16	14.5	4.2	8.7	2.8	16	21.9	15.4	0.2	7.1
17	17.7	9.9	0.9	1.9	17	18.6	14.4	0.0	3.6
18	15.1	8.3	0.7	5.5	18	18.5	9.9	19.3	0.5
19	15.8	6.7	0.0	9.0	19	15.5	9.5	0.9	0.2
20	11.9	4.3	11.2	0.0	20	15.0	12.4	0.0	0.6
21	14.8	8.3	0.2	4.2	21	16.0	12.4	0.0	1.1
22	17.0	8.8	0.2	3.2	22	20.0	9.4	0.6	0.8
23	20.4	10.7	0.1	3.8	23	22.3	15.4	0.0	4.4
24	23.3	10.8	0.0	4.0	24	19.3	13.2	3.2	6.1
25	17.8	9.6	7.6	0.6	25	16.9	10.4	2.0	5.5
26	10.1	7.6	22.1	0.0	26	17.7	10.7	3.4	3.7
27	11.0	8.0	15.7	0.0	27	19.6	12.0	0.4	1.1
28	16.1	7.8	0.0	0.4	28	19.4	13.1	4.7	6.1
29	18.6	9.4	3.2	6.6	29	21.5	13.3	0.5	1.0
30	16.7	11.0	0.4	0.3	30	17.9	9.6	0.0	3.4
31	14.9	10.2	1.9	1.8	31	17.2	11.6	0.9	1.1
June 1	17.1	10.5	6.4	0.7	Aug 1	18.7	10.7	0.2	0.5
2	19.9	10.0	0.0	5.8	2	19.3	11.0	n/a	8.3
3	19.7	10.9	0.0	3.5	3	18.6	12.6	n/a	5.7
4	18.8	12.6	0.0	3.1	4	17.9	11.8	33.3	2.1
5	18.0	9.0	0.0	11.9	5	15.5	11.3	0.0	2.9
6	20.6	8.9	0.0	13.6	6	18.4	10.6	1.0	2.2
7	19.8	9.8	0.0	9.4	7	18.7	12.7	5.6	1.7
8	21.9	11.0	0.0	9.8	8	16.6	12.5	5.1	0.9
9	25.2	12.0	13.5	4.0	9	19.5	14.0	0.2	0.7
10	22.9	15.6	29.5	0.7	10	17.0	11.1	6.5	8.2
11	19.1	14.8	6.9	0.0	11	21.1	10.6	0.5	3.8
12	18.0	12.6	0.0	2.9	12	15.5	10.2	11.1	4.5
13	17.3	9.1	12.6	9.2	13	19.5	7.1	0.0	9.1
14	15.2	10.6	1.5	0.0	14	20.2	8.4	12.0	5.4
15	18.4	6.8	1.3	4.3	15	16.3	11.0	0.0	2.7
16	16.8	11.9	0.3	4.1	16	16.7	9.4	n/a	11.3
17	19.1	11.0	3.0	2.8	17	20.1	7.2	n/a	8.4
18	19.3	11.9	0.0	9.3	18	21.1	10.6	n/a	2.7
19	16.7	10.2	6.2	5.9	19	20.9	11.9	2.5	0.2
20	16.1	9.9	0.0	4.7	20	18.3	14.5	1.1	5.0
21	15.9	9.0	0.0	6.5	21	17.4	13.4	1.4	6.4
22	15.5	9.8	0.2	9.8	22	13.4	10.4	1.6	0.3
23	15.2	10.2	0.0	10.6	23	15.2	7.6	0.5	8.2
24	14.8	8.0	0.0	12.0	24	15.9	8.9	1.0	10.2
25	18.5	7.4	2.9	7.0	25	14.3	10.5	0.0	0.2
26	18.2	11.3	0.0	0.1	26	16.2	6.4	n/a	6.4
27	18.2	10.9	0.0	12.3	27	17.0	7.4	n/a	2.5
28	25.0	9.5	0.0	12.0	28	19.3	10.1	n/a	6.7
29	22.2	11.1	0.0	10.2	29	18.4	8.8	0.7	0.5
30	18.1	11.7	0.0	10.7	30	17.5	12.4	n/a	8.9
					31	23.1	8.7	n/a	10.5

Date 1992	Max (°C)	Min (°C)	Rainfall (mm)		Date 1992	Max (°C)	Min (°C)	Rainfall (mm)
Sept 1	18.3	10.2	18.0		Nov 1	13.8	2.9	18.1
2	19.6	11.7	0.3		2	13.5	10.9	0.9
3	17.6	11.4	1.8		3	14.0	2.9	0.0
4	15.9	10.9	0.0		4	13.8	4.6	0.2
5	16.8	6.2	10.5		5	13.1	7.0	0.3
6	16.5	10.6	5.5		6	12.9	7.9	0.0
7	17.1	12.4	0.9		7	13.7	9.4	0.5
8	17.3	7.7	0.0		8	13.0	10.7	2.4
9	17.4	10.2	0.0		9	12.6	10.6	10.6
10	17.4	12.5	6.2		10	14.4	6.7	12.3
11	16.4	10.6	0.4		11	11.5	8.0	1.5
12	17.3	10.4	1.2		12	11.2	6.3	0.4
13	15.7	12.7	7.0		13	12.0	1.3	13.7
14	17.8	10.6	0.1		14	12.8	3.0	7.6
15	17.7	8.7	0.0		15	13.2	2.2	3.6
16	16.3	11.6	0.0		16	13.2	4.1	1.9
17	16.7	13.2	0.0		17	12.7	3.4	13.7
18	17.0	11.4	0.0		18	13.6	5.2	4.8
19	19.1	11.8	1.2		19	13.0	6.4	0.3
20	17.8	11.6	2.1		20	12.8	3.4	7.3
21	16.4	11.7	21.2		21	13.9	5.3	5.1
22	15.3	9.6	2.6		22	13.9	12.2	1.3
23	15.6	9.4	8.4		23	13.5	11.2	2.3
24	15.5	10.9	0.2		24	12.6	2.4	7.8
25	15.0	5.9	0.6		25	12.0	6.0	17.2
26	16.9	7.3	3.3		26	11.8	6.1	0.4
27	18.5	11.6	1.1		27	13.2	6.3	11.4
28	16.6	13.5	2.0		28	11.7	1.3	21.8
29	15.7	10.4	3.3		29	14.0	3.7	30.1
30	17.2	7.9	0.9		30	12.3	10.7	5.7
Oct 1	14.9	6.1	14.4		Dec 1	13.7	4.4	27.3
2	14.4	11.5	1.5		2	12.9	10.4	11.9
3	15.6	10.6	1.2		3	8.1	4.8	5.6
4	16.7	11.2	0.0		4	7.5	3.4	8.5
5	14.7	12.4	0.0		5	10.2	2.8	1.8
6	13.5	9.8	0.0		6	10.6	1.6	10.0
7	15.7	9.9	0.0		7	10.4	6.7	5.8
8	15.6	6.7	0.0		8	10.9	7.8	1.3
9	14.0	3.0	0.0		9	10.4	6.9	0.0
10	14.0	4.1	0.0		10	10.5	0.6	0.0
11	14.7	3.2	0.0		11	12.0	1.2	2.5
12	15.8	7.9	0.0		12	10.8	4.9	0.2
13	14.1	5.0	0.0		13	10.7	4.3	0.1
14	13.6	1.8	2.8		14	11.0	8.6	0.4
15	11.6	6.4	5.9		15	12.4	9.0	6.7
16	11.5	-0.1	0.6		16	7.2	5.6	1.8
17	11.3	-0.3	3.4		17	11.7	-2.1	29.6
18	12.4	2.9	5.8		18	12.2	3.5	1.7
19	11.6	4.0	1.9		19	5.9	4.8	1.3
20	11.1	2.9	1.2		20	9.1	0.2	2.4
21	10.9	4.1	6.8		21	9.4	3.1	0.1
22	12.0	5.0	2.7		22	7.0	5.0	0.0
23	12.2	7.4	6.7		23	5.8	0.5	0.0
24	13.8	5.6	4.2		24	7.0	-2.6	0.0
25	12.7	8.9	0.9		25	7.4	-0.7	0.0
26	13.6	3.6	4.7		26	6.2	5.0	0.0
27	11.5	5.1	15.9		27	7.2	3.4	0.0
28	10.7	4.7	3.4		28	5.6	3.4	0.0
29	12.2	6.2	0.1		29	6.9	3.3	0.0
30	11.3	0.1	0.0		30	6.8	2.8	0.0
31	12.2	-1.4	2.0		31	10.4	0.4	0.0

Date 1993	Max (°C)	Min (°C)	Rainfall (mm)		Date 1993	Max (°C)	Min (°C)	Rainfall (mm)
Jan 1	10.4	-3.5	0.0		Mar 1	5.4	-2.7	0.0
2	8.8	-3.4	0.0		2	4.9	-1.0	0.0
3	9.8	2.2	9.8		3	6.7	2.7	0.0
4	12.3	2.7	2.1		4	6.4	-0.6	0.0
5	12.9	3.4	6.3		5	9.4	-3.1	0.1
6	12.2	10.4	6.1		6	9.4	3.4	0.0
7	11.9	4.9	2.0		7	9.7	6.5	0.0
8	12.2	1.9	5.8		8	9.4	6.8	0.0
9	12.4	2.7	27.6,		9	12.6	6.5	0.2
10	12.7	8.9	17.0		10	12.7	4.2	0.0
11	9.0	7.2	7.7		11	13.0	6.6	0.0
12	9.4	3.2	7.5		12	13.7	6.4	0.0
13	13.0	5.0	15.9		13	12.9	8.3	0.0
14	13.0	3.5	5.5		14	13.7	9.2	0.0
15	13.0	3.6	0.2		15	15.6	7.5	0.5
16	13.0	9.4	2.7		16	12.6	8.3	0.0
17	9.2	7.5	0.1		17	14.1	8.2	0.0
18	10.6	0.6	1.0		18	14.4	9.5	0.0
19	11.7	1.0	12.7		19	11.7	2.4	0.0
20	12.2	3.8	1.3		20	11.0	-1.4	0.0
21	12.4	7.6	10.8		21	11.9	4.5	12.2
22	10.7	8.4	5.0		22	12.6	7.2	0.6
23	12.8	5.9	0.4		23	11.2	3.3	0.0
24	11.3	5.9	0.3		24	11.0	-0.7	0.0
25	7.3	6.0	0.0		25	12.3	0.4	0.0
26	11.3	3.5	0.0		26	10.1	-0.5	0.0
27	11.9	5.8	1.4		27	10.7	3.8	0.2
28	11.4	9.2	2.4		28	10.7	7.3	4.7
29	13.1	8.7	0.2		29	12.5	4.7	3.1
30	12.1	7.3	0.0		30	14.2	9.8	1.3
31	12.3	5.9	0.0		31	13.6	3.7	4.7
Feb 1	9.1	5.4	0.0		April 1	11.1	6.0	1.7
2	10.6	5.4	0.0		2	12.1	2.9	8.2
3	8.6	7.0	0.0		3	10.5	7.4	3.2
4	7.3	3.8	0.0		4	12.4	2.4	23.2
5	7.1	3.8	0.0		5	12.8	8.2	0.2
6	8.8	-1.6	0.0		6	13.7	8.3	2.8
7	8.9	1.9	0.0		7	14.9	8.9	1.2
8	10.0	7.8	1.0		8	12.1	9.6	13.2
9	9.0	7.0	0.2		9	12.6	10.2	0.0
10	8.6	5.6	0.0		10	12.6	3.6	4.9
11	9.0	6.9	0.0		11	12.7	8.7	10.1
12	9.2	7.3	0.0		12	12.2	7.3	6.5
13	10.6	7.7	0.0		13	10.3	6.3	4.1
14	11.9	6.8	0.0		14	12.0	2.7	0.0
15	11.7	8.8	0.3		15	14.4	0.3	0.0
16	11.3	5.7	0.1		16	14.7	6.7	3.0
17	11.7	7.8	0.1		17	13.7	9.3	0.1
18	9.5	7.7	0.2		18	14.2	9.8	0.0
19	10.3	6.7	0.0		19	13.9	10.6	0.2
20	9.3	2.7	0.0		20	14.2	10.8	0.5
21	10.6	6.9	0.1		21	15.7	8.4	0.5
22	9.7	5.4	1.7		22	13.0	9.1	6.9
23	8.0	3.9	0.0		23	14.1	9.5	0.5
24	9.7	-2.0	0.0		24	14.1	3.8	0.0
25	9.4	-1.1	10.1		25	15.4	2.1	2.9
26	9.6	5.1	12.4		26	15.7	5.4	2.6
27	6.3	1.2	0.2		27	17.2	7.9	2.6
28	5.3	-1.3	0.0		28	21.3	7.4	0.0
					29	18.7	8.0	0.0
					30	17.9	7.7	0.0

Date 1993	Max (°C)	Min (°C)	Rainfall (mm)	Date 1993	Max (°C)	Min (°C)	Rainfall (mm)
May 1	17.9	9.6	0.0	July 1	19.3	13.9	0.0
2	12.9	4.7	0.0	2	20.4	12.2	0.0
3	14.6	1.0	0.0	3	21.6	15.2	0.0
4	14.3	1.8	0.0	4	17.4	13.7	0.0
5	14.1	3.0	0.0	5	18.1	13.1	0.0
6	13.6	2.7	0.0	6	18.2	7.5	0.0
7	14.2	2.3	0.0	7	19.7	8.4	0.0
8	16.6	3.9	1.9	8	19.1	8.5	0.2
9	11.8	6.8	0.6	9	14.8	11.7	7.7
10	17.1	8.5	1.2	10	16.1	9.1	7.0
11	22.1	6.8	1.4	11	16.3	7.9	0.6
12	15.7	11.5	0.0	12	17.6	9.4	7.5
13	14.8	11.1	5.0	13	17.2	10.8	4.4
14	11.6	8.6	1.5	14	20.2	15.5	14.0
15	13.6	3.9	6.7	15	18.2	15.6	20.3
16	13.8	6.7	14.9	16	20.9	15.6	0.0
17	15.7	11.8	1.0	17	19.5	12.1	6.6
18	15.0	8.0	17.8	18	17.9	10.5	11.8
19	14.4	5.5	0.0	19	17.4	12.6	2.1
20	15.8	2.5	0.0	20	17.7	13.4	0.0
21	14.8	3.4	9.4	21	18.1	12.4	0.0
22	13.9	10.3	1.0	22	18.6	10.5	0.4
23	16.6	10.4	12.7	23	17.3	15.2	1.6
24	16.8	12.6	8.4	24	18.3	12.2	3.8
25	15.8	10.2	46.9	25	18.0	11.2	0.1
26	16.9	12.4	1.1	26	17.9	11.6	9.6
27	17.6	9.6	0.0	27	19.0	14.5	3.8
28	18.0	8.4	0.0	28	19.7	15.4	2.7
29	14.7	8.4	16.5	29	18.6	15.9	0.6
30	15.7	11.2	0.9	30	18.7	10.7	0.5
31	15.9	10.1	1.6	31	18.5	13.0	0.0
June 1	n/a	12.0	1.8	Aug 1	19.2	12.2	1.7
2	n/a	12.0	0.5	2	19.3	12.9	0.3
3	n/a	9.7	0.0	3	19.0	11.2	1.6
4	n/a	8.2	0.0	4	18.1	11.2	1.5
5	n/a	7.5	0.0	5	17.7	11.4	0.0
6	n/a	9.7	0.0	6	18.4	8.8	0.0
7	n/a	9.2	0.0	7	20.3	8.7	0.5
8	n/a	6.7	21.2	8	18.0	12.2	0.2
9	20.3	14.6	2.8	9	18.7	15.3	0.3
10	17.9	14.7	5.7	10	17.8	14.0	0.8
11	14.3	12.4	14.9	11	18.8	13.7	17.1
12	12.9	9.9	11.9	12	17.1	11.2	0.0
13	16.2	10.8	6.6	13	17.8	5.4	0.0
14	16.1	12.6	0.7	14	20.1	9.4	0.3
15	18.2	12.0	19.5	15	19.4	13.9	0.0
16	17.2	13.5	1.0	16	19.7	10.0	0.0
17	18.6	12.3	2.4	17	18.7	8.3	0.0
18	16.8	13.8	0.2	18	20.5	10.4	0.0
19	17.3	11.6	0.0	19	23.3	12.8	0.0
20	18.5	9.1	0.0	20	21.8	12.2	0.0
21	18.2	8.4	0.0	21	21.2	11.8	0.6
22	18.5	8.6	0.0	22	17.3	13.3	0.0
23	18.0	8.8	0.0	23	16.7	10.7	0.0
24	18.7	6.8	0.0	24	17.8	5.4	0.0
25	18.4	4.9	0.0	25	18.5	7.1	0.0
26	18.8	10.2	0.0	26	18.2	10.5	0.0
27	21.3	14.1	0.0	27	18.1	6.9	0.0
28	19.8	11.3	0.0	28	19.0	9.2	0.0
29	20.1	12.8	0.0	29	19.6	6.2	1.1
30	20.7	14.1	0.0	30	19.4	14.8	0.3
				31	19.3	9.9	0.0

Date 1992	Max (°C)	Min (°C)	Rainfall (mm)	Date 1992	Max (°C)	Min (°C)	Rainfall (mm)
Sept 1	16.0	6.6	4.0	Nov 1	12.5	3.9	6.1
2	15.6	8.9	2.3	2	8.2	5.7	3.1
3	14.6	8.4	0.2	3	9.2	2.7	0.1
4	13.9	5.6	0.6	4	13.7	3.4	1.7
5	15.0	3.6	2.0	5	14.6	7.3	0.3
6	15.6	6.4	4.5	6	13.2	9.0	1.2
7	14.6	6.1	1.1	7	10.2	8.5	0.0
8	15.0	5.7	1.0	8	11.2	2.5	5.9
9	15.4	9.7	0.2	9	9.3	8.3	2.9
10	14.4	11.6	21.3	10	8.4	0.0	1.7
11	12.3	8.2	2.1	11	7.1	2.7	1.9
12	11.9	4.8	10.0	12	6.0	1.3	0.6
13	13.5	5.3	2.4	13	7.0	-2.3	0.0
14	15.1	7.9	0.6	14	8.0	-2.6	26.5
15	15.7	11.1	0.1	15	6.4	4.0	2.3
16	13.6	6.9	0.5	16	6.7	3.3	0.5
17	16.4	11.0	0.1	17	9.0	0.2	0.9
18	16.5	11.1	0.0	18	9.1	0.6	0.2
19	17.2	9.4	1.8	19	5.4	1.6	1.3
20	15.3	8.3	0.0	20	8.4	-0.1	0.6
21	14.4	8.1	0.0	21	10.7	-1.7	12.0
22	15.0	8.6	0.0	22	14.3	1.0	1.4
23	13.0	4.6	11.0	23	11.6	9.0	3.8
24	11.3	5.8	3.6	24	10.2	3.2	12.5
25	12.8	0.3	0.2	25	7.3	4.6	1.3
26	15.0	0.3	9.7	26	9.2	0.8	0.0
27	16.9	9.8	1.9	27	9.8	1.4	3.2
28	15.3	11.2	0.2	28	6.3	0.4	0.2
29	14.6	11.5	10.0	29	10.1	-1.6	2.6
30	13.3	4.7	0.1	30	9.1	5.7	7.0
Oct 1	15.8	3.8	10.5	Dec 1	9.6	1.6	9.3
2	12.3	9.6	3.9	2	9.0	3.6	1.0
3	14.4	6.8	0.0	3	4.3	0.7	0.0
4	14.6	6.7	0.0	4	4.5	-1.2	0.2
5	13.0	4.0	0.0	5	6.5	0.7	0.0
6	13.6	5.8	0.0	6	7.9	1.1	21.1
7	12.3	4.6	0.0	7	7.4	1.4	1.5
8	13.2	8.4	0.0	8	6.5	4.3	2.3
9	11.5	7.0	0.1	9	6.1	1.1	0.3
10	11.1	0.0	0.2	10	9.1	-1.6	1.7
11	13.3	5.4	0.0	11	7.4	-0.7	8.7
12	10.4	3.8	0.0	12	9.3	1.4	0.2
13	11.3	1.3	1.0	13	10.4	1.4	0.1
14	10.0	5.9	6.7	14	10.2	7.7	0.0
15	10.0	2.6	0.0	15	9.9	8.3	3.0
16	9.1	0.5	0.0	16	6.6	-0.1	0.1
17	9.0	0.8	1.6	17	8.9	-1.4	15.0
18	8.7	0.1	0.0	18	4.4	3.1	0.2
19	8.7	-1.1	3.5	19	2.0	-3.4	0.0
20	9.7	0.6	0.2	20	3.9	-6.5	3.3
21	9.5	1.6	2.4	21	5.2	-5.7	6.0
22	8.3	2.4	1.9	22	3.4	-1.3	0.1
23	6.6	2.7	0.8	23	4.5	-0.7	0.2
24	8.1	1.3	20.2	24	6.5	-1.6	0.0
25	6.3	1.6	0.5	25	7.7	0.0	1.1
26	7.4	-0.5	0.7	26	7.6	1.6	0.0
27	6.2	2.6	0.3	27	6.1	5.0	0.0
28	7.3	0.4	1.2	28	5.2	3.0	0.0
29	8.6	-0.2	0.1	29	2.1	-3.7	0.0
30	8.6	-2.5	0.0	30	4.1	-4.6	0.1
31	9.1	-1.2	2.5	31	7.5	-2.4	0.0

Date 1993	Max (°C)	Min (°C)	Rainfall (mm)	Date 1993	Max (°C)	Min (°C)	Rainfall (mm)
Jan 1	8.3	-0.4	0.0	Mar 1	5.6	-0.6	0.0
2	8.0	5.7	0.0	2	3.6	-0.1	0.0
3	7.1	4.1	13.4	3	6.3	-1.3	0.0
4	10.6	0.0	2.3	4	7.4	-5.4	0.2
5	7.7	0.6	0.0	5	9.4	-0.7	0.0
6	7.0	2.3	0.0	6	6.0	4.5	0.0
7	8.4	1.9	1.3	7	8.5	3.0	0.0
8	9.9	0.6	6.9	8	8.7	4.5	0.0
9	8.6	1.6	1.5	9	6.3	0.8	0.6
10	9.9	3.8	1.9	10	7.5	2.7	7.0
11	1.4	-0.6	0.5	11	9.6	3.9	0.1
12	4.6	-1.6	8.2	12	9.3	5.8	4.5
13	2.4	-0.1	1.3	13	11.6	6.9	0.2
14	12.3	0.0	8.3	14	10.2	6.6	0.0
15	13.2	0.4	2.5	15	13.4	4.6	2.2
16	13.6	4.0	3.0	16	11.6	2.9	1.9
17	4.9	2.3	0.1	17	12.1	5.0	1.5
18	6.7	0.3	5.5	18	7.9	4.2	0.1
19	10.7	0.6	0.1	19	10.3	1.8	0.0
20	10.3	1.3	0.7	20	9.0	4.3	0.5
21	12.0	3.9	0.7	21	10.4	4.6	0.0
22	6.3	4.4	3.4	22	8.6	0.3	0.4
23	12.1	0.7	9.6	23	8.3	0.3	0.3
24	6.1	2.9	1.1	24	10.0	0.1	0.4
25	3.7	0.2	3.2	25	11.1	-1.6	0.0
26	9.6	0.1	7.7	26	9.7	-1.1	0.0
27	9.9	2.5	2.0	27	6.8	4.7	9.1
28	10.9	5.8	9.1	28	10.3	-0.4	1.9
29	7.6	5.7	0.2	29	9.3	4.9	17.3
30	7.3	4.5	0.5	30	10.0	6.2	1.0
31	7.2	-1.7	0.0	31	9.2	0.1	6.7
Feb 1	7.7	-0.3	0.6	Apr 1	10.7	0.2	0.2
2	10.4	-0.1	0.1	2	9.3	-0.2	2.2
3	9.8	6.3	0.1	3	6.5	3.4	20.2
4	8.7	4.9	0.0	4	10.4	-0.7	21.3
5	10.0	2.8	0.0	5	11.3	2.0	1.1
6	10.7	4.5	0.0	6	12.7	4.8	3.0
7	10.6	8.3	0.0	7	8.8	4.2	1.8
8	7.8	5.8	0.0	8	9.2	6.6	15.3
9	7.4	5.9	1.3	9	10.1	6.9	8.6
10	5.3	3.6	0.4	10	12.2	2.6	0.0
11	6.5	3.3	0.0	11	11.2	0.3	1.0
12	8.8	4.6	0.0	12	8.0	4.4	0.8
13	7.6	5.7	0.5	13	10.7	1.9	0.0
14	8.4	6.4	1.2	14	11.3	4.3	0.0
15	8.3	-1.4	0.2	15	12.4	-0.4	0.5
16	10.3	0.2	0.2	16	13.2	7.7	1.3
17	9.3	6.9	0.1	17	13.3	5.2	4.1
18	9.2	4.6	1.1	18	13.7	7.5	7.5
19	8.9	3.7	0.2	19	11.1	9.2	6.0
20	8.4	1.8	1.5	20	12.3	6.7	1.2
21	7.9	3.4	0.1	21	14.2	4.7	0.2
22	10.2	4.3	0.0	22	11.8	7.5	4.2
23	8.1	0.6	0.0	23	11.8	5.3	1.4
24	8.0	4.6	3.8	24	13.0	4.5	0.0
25	10.6	5.3	3.2	25	11.6	0.9	12.0
26	6.3	1.7	0.6	26	11.8	6.6	0.1
27	5.1	-3.1	0.9	27	16.4	6.4	0.0
28	3.7	-1.9	0.0	28	15.1	7.2	0.0
				29	17.8	7.0	0.0
				30	16.2	6.1	0.0

Date 1993	Max (°C)	Min (°C)	Rainfall (mm)	Date 1993	Max (°C)	Min (°C)	Rainfall (mm)
May 1	12.2	4.3	0.0	July 1	17.9	4.3	0.0
2	10.6	-0.9	8.1	2	18.2	9.6	0.5
3	11.7	-1.3	0.0	3	20.3	13.0	1.5
4	13.3	1.4	0.0	4	18.0	13.4	0.0
5	15.6	1.3	0.0	5	15.5	6.9	0.0
6	15.4	5.5	0.0	6	17.2	9.5	0.1
7	17.4	3.2	0.0	7	19.9	12.0	2.2
8	13.7	5.7	0.0	8	17.5	6.3	0.0
9	13.8	4.4	0.0	9	14.0	6.0	8.6
10	14.2	5.5	5.7	10	13.4	7.2	2.0
11	18.8	6.9	2.0	11	14.0	7.6	1.9
12	16.2	6.2	0.1	12	16.3	6.0	0.0
13	11.4	3.6	30.4	13	13.7	5.0	18.8
14	5.5	0.1	26.5	14	19.9	9.8	3.0
15	11.1	1.8	1.7	15	19.4	12.5	7.0
16	13.6	1.9	15.4	16	21.7	11.6	1.5
17	12.2	6.6	8.9	17	17.9	12.0	0.8
18	13.1	5.0	5.0	18	13.6	6.2	16.0
19	13.4	1.8	4.5	19	17.4	11.3	0.4
20	15.2	1.1	1.6	20	15.0	9.9	0.1
21	14.5	6.5	3.5	21	16.5	10.0	1.3
22	14.2	8.4	0.0	22	17.1	8.9	0.7
23	17.3	6.5	1.5	23	19.1	13.7	7.4
24	15.9	9.1	11.9	24	17.9	8.9	6.8
25	14.3	9.0	3.8	25	15.4	9.0	3.3
26	11.0	6.3	3.8	26	17.1	8.4	3.8
27	11.1	5.9	9.2	27	18.1	11.7	0.8
28	13.6	5.9	2.4	28	17.7	11.9	0.2
29	15.2	7.2	30.4	29	17.2	12.1	0.1
30	16.4	9.4	10.8	30	17.3	8.6	1.4
31	15.0	9.5	0.6	31	14.7	9.6	3.4
June 1	13.0	6.8	9.9	Aug 1	18.3	11.1	2.8
2	15.3	8.9	0.1	2	17.4	10.4	4.2
3	17.2	9.3	0.0	3	17.8	10.6	1.8
4	16.2	9.1	0.4	4	19.2	7.7	7.1
5	17.7	3.1	0.0	5	18.0	7.7	0.4
6	19.6	4.3	0.0	6	18.3	9.2	0.3
7	19.7	11.4	0.0	7	15.5	12.7	0.1
8	17.0	9.0	0.0	8	17.5	10.4	12.9
9	18.2	9.8	1.9	9	17.7	12.1	1.3
10	17.9	12.8	5.2	10	16.3	8.4	13.0
11	13.2	12.3	22.4	11	14.3	8.6	2.5
12	14.0	10.5	1.0	12	15.0	5.3	0.5
13	12.2	7.4	5.9	13	17.5	3.9	1.4
14	14.6	8.2	0.3	14	15.1	10.5	7.1
15	16.3	6.1	4.1	15	16.6	5.9	0.0
16	18.8	10.0	0.0	16	16.9	6.6	0.0
17	17.5	10.2	7.5	17	19.2	4.2	0.0
18	17.5	10.4	2.1	18	18.6	9.9	0.0
19	16.6	8.6	7.5	19	17.7	9.3	0.0
20	14.6	8.2	0.0	20	16.9	9.6	0.2
21	15.6	8.9	0.0	21	15.9	9.9	0.0
22	16.7	10.1	0.0	22	14.6	7.8	0.5
23	15.3	4.6	0.0	23	16.8	4.6	0.4
24	15.6	5.3	0.0	24	16.1	5.2	0.0
25	17.7	2.2	4.7	25	15.4	8.8	0.0
26	19.6	11.1	0.1	26	15.7	7.3	0.0
27	21.0	8.4	0.0	27	19.0	4.3	0.0
28	20.6	9.2	0.0	28	19.4	7.0	0.2
29	21.5	11.6	0.1	29	16.7	8.2	0.3
30	18.5	11.5	0.0	30	20.6	1.5	0.0
				31	21.6	6.1	0.0

8

Societies

Specialist Societies

Alpine Garden Society

AGS Centre, Avon Bank, Pershore, Hereford &
Worcester WR10 3JP

☎ 0386 554790   📠 0386 554801

CONTACT   E. M. Upward (Secretary)
AIMS   To further knowledge of Alpine plants
MEMBERSHIP   13,000
SUBSCRIPTIONS   £13 individual, £16 joint
SERVICES   Lectures; seed scheme; library; publications; advice; awards; shows; journal; regional groups; outings

Founded in 1929. The AGS caters for anyone interested in rock gardening or alpine plants. You join the national organisation which entitles you to numerous benefits including free entry to the twenty or so shows, the bulletin, the seed exchange scheme, and the advisory service. If you wish you can also join one of the 60 local groups: there is a small additional subscription which varies from group to group. You have to be a member of the national AGS in order to join. Local groups organise their own busy programmes of events, including lectures, shows and visits. The *Quarterly Bulletin of the Alpine Garden Society* is an authoritative illustrated magazine which covers alpines in cultivation and in the wild. The AGS organises guided expeditions to many countries for its members, and these are both popular and respected. They also publish monographs and alpine titles (including the mammoth new alpine encyclopedia), and members can use the slide and postal book libraries. At local level, AGS groups are an excellent and informal way to learn and develop an interest in alpines. Some groups are more active than others: it depends on local demand. Many of the lecturers are acknowledged experts, as will be some of the group members. The dates for the national shows, and a number of group events, appear in our calendar. Most local groups allow members to bring guests and will usually admit visitors for a small charge, though if you expect to attend regularly then you should really sign up properly. AGS headquarters can put you in touch with your nearest group. Active groups include the following: Bedfordshire, Berkshire, Birmingham, Bristol, East Cheshire, Cleveland, Cotswold and Malvern, North Cumbria, Derby, East Dorset, North East England, Exeter, Epping Forest, Hertfordshire, South Humberside, Ipswich, East Kent, Kent Medway, East Lancashire, North Lancashire, Leicester, North London, Nottingham, Oxford, East Surrey, North Staffordshire, Southport, West Sussex, Ulster, North Wales, South Wales, Woking, East Yorkshire, West Yorkshire.

Botanical Society of Scotland

c/o Royal Botanic Garden, Edinburgh, Lothian
EH3 5LR

CONTACT   Hon. Secretary
AIMS   To promote the study of plants and exchange botanical information
SUBSCRIPTIONS   £7 basic; £14 including scientific publications
SERVICES   Lectures; publications; journal; regional groups; outings

Founded in 1836: formerly the Botanical Society of Edinburgh. Based in Edinburgh, with regional branches in Scotland, the society includes amateur and professional botanists. It holds regular lectures, conferences and field meetings. Its publications include a newsletter and a scientific journal.

Botanical Society of the British Isles

c/o Dept of Botany, The Natural History Museum,
Cromwell Road, London SW7 5BD

CONTACT   Hon. General Secretary
AIMS   The study of British and Irish flowering plants and ferns
MEMBERSHIP   2,500
SUBSCRIPTIONS   £15, reduced rate for junior members
SERVICES   Lectures; publications; advice; journal; outings;

This association of amateur and professional botanists traces its history back to 1836. Three regular publications cover the society's activities, articles on the taxonomy and distribution of plants in the British Isles, and an annual bibliography. The society also arranges conferences, exhibitions and study trips, and undertakes research projects and surveys. Members have access to a panel of experts on the British flora and can buy works on British botany at reduced prices.

British & European Geranium Society

Norwood Chine, 26 Crabtree Lane, Sheffield, South Yorkshire S5 7AY

☎ 0742 426200 📠 0742 425379

CONTACT Public Relations Office
AIMS To promote the Geranium (*Pelargonium*)
MEMBERSHIP 1,000
SUBSCRIPTIONS £5
SERVICES Lectures; library; publications; advice; awards; shows; journal; regional groups; outings; plant finder

The British & European Geranium Society is dedicated to growing, hybridising and exhibiting pelargoniums. The society is divided into regional groups, and they organise programmes of events including lectures and shows. There is an annual national show (on 18 June in the Sheffield area this year); every other year a conference is also staged. Members receive four newsletters and a Year Book. The society has other publications too. A new service is a computerised plant finder which has details of sources for any pelargonium which is available in Europe.

British Bonsai Association

c/o Inglenook, 36 McCarthy Way, Wokingham, Berkshire RG11 4UA

CONTACT J. White
AIMS To further interest and participation in bonsai
MEMBERSHIP 80
SUBSCRIPTIONS £12 full, £6 corresponding
SERVICES Lectures; library; advice; awards; journal

The British Bonsai Association is one of the leading bonsai clubs and exhibitors in the country. Those who cannot make the meetings in London (the first Tuesday of each month) can join as corresponding members. The meetings include lectures, demonstrations and competitions. Members can obtain expert advice and trees are sold at some meetings. There is a quarterly newsletter and a library of bonsai books and magazines.

British Clematis Society

The Tropical Bird Gardens, Rode, Bath, Avon BA3 6QW

☎ 0373 830326 📠 0373 831288

CONTACT Membership Secretary
AIMS To encourage and extend clematis cultivation, and to share knowledge with fellow members
MEMBERSHIP 500

SUBSCRIPTIONS £10 individual, £12 joint, £5 junior, £15 overseas, £17 overseas joint
SERVICES Lectures; seed scheme; advice; shows; journal; outings; plant sales; demonstrations;

A fast-growing society which organises meetings throughout the country and publishes a substantial illustrated journal, *The Clematis*, each year as well as supplements and newsletters. The society organises visits to gardens and nurseries. Members can obtain advice on clematis cultivation and join in the seed exchange programme. The society also produces a list of good clematis gardens and a list of clematis nurseries.

British Fuchsia Society

20 Brodawel, Llannon, Llanelli, Dyfed SA14 6BJ

CONTACT Hon. Secretary
AIMS To further interest in the cultivation of fuchsias
MEMBERSHIP 5,500
SUBSCRIPTIONS £5 individual, £7.50 joint
SERVICES Advice; shows; journal; special interest and regional groups; rooted cuttings

The British Fuchsia Society organises nine regional shows and a London show. Members receive the *Fuchsia Annual* and a twice yearly bulletin, as well as three free rooted cuttings. They can also obtain advice from the society's experts either by post or telephone. Special interest groups are devoted to old cultivars and hybridising. Some three hundred societies are affiliated to the national society, many of which organise programmes of events and festivals.

British Gladiolus Society

24 The Terrace, Mayfield, Ashbourne, Derbyshire DE6 2JL

CONTACT Hon. Secretary
AIMS To stimulate interest in and improve gladiolus growing
MEMBERSHIP 375
SUBSCRIPTIONS £8.50 individual
SERVICES Seed scheme; library; publications; advice; awards; shows; journal; regional groups

Founded in 1926 the British Gladiolus Society stages three major shows each year: the National, Southern and Northern. There are regional groups in Sussex and Buckinghamshire. Members keep in touch with society news through three bulletins and the yearbook, *The Gladiolus Annual*, which is published each spring. The society runs trials at three sites, and also has a book, slide and video library available for members and affiliated societies. Council members can advise on gladiolus cultivation, and the society raises money by distributing cormlets. A small range of booklets on showing and growing gladiolus is also available.

British Hosta & Hemerocallis Society

c/o Cleave House, Sticklepath, Okehampton, Devon
EX20 2NN

CONTACT Hon. Secretary
AIMS To foster interest in the cultivation of Hostas
and Hemerocallis
MEMBERSHIP 250
SUBSCRIPTIONS £8 individual, £10 joint
SERVICES Lectures; library; advice; awards; journal;
annual plant auction

Founded in 1981, the British Hosta & Hemerocallis
Society has members spread throughout the world. It
publishes an annual bulletin, and regular newsletters to
keep members informed of news and events. Garden
visits and lectures are arranged, and members can borrow by post from the society's specialist and comprehensive library. An annual award is presented to a hosta
and a hemerocallis. Expert advice is provided via the
secretary. There are eight relevant NCCPG National
Collections.

The British Iris Society

43 Sea Lane, Goring by Sea, West Sussex
BN12 4QD

CONTACT Hon. Secretary
AIMS To encourage and improve the cultivation of
irises
MEMBERSHIP 1,000
SUBSCRIPTIONS £9 individual
SERVICES Lectures; seed scheme; library; publications; advice; awards; shows; journal; special interest
and regional groups; plant sales scheme; lectures for
clubs and societies

The British Iris Society was founded in 1922 and caters
for all levels of interest in this varied genus. The illustrated *Iris Year Book* is supplemented by three newsletters. The society's programme includes three annual
shows and occasional lectures. There are regional
groups in Mercia and Kent, and special interest groups
for species, Japanese, Siberian and Pacific Coast irises.
Members can borrow from the reference library, and
the slide collection runs to some 5,000 items. As well
as a plant sales scheme there is also a seed distribution
scheme, and expert advice is available on request. New
hybrids are trialled at Wisley, and the Dykes Medal is
awarded to the best British bred hybrid in the trial.

British Ivy Society

Garden Cottage, Westgreen House, Thackham's
Lane, Hartley Whitney, Basingstoke, Hampshire
RG27 8JB

CONTACT Hon. Secretary
SERVICES Advice; journal

Members receive three copies of the journal each year,
and can obtain advice on *Hedera* cultivation. Further
details from the society.

The British National Carnation Society

3 Canberra Close, Hornchurch, Essex RM12 5TR

CONTACT Secretary
AIMS To improve the cultivation of the *Dianthus*
genus
MEMBERSHIP Under 1000
SUBSCRIPTIONS £8 individual
SERVICES Publications; advice; shows; journal; dis-
count coupon scheme

The British National Carnation Society organises three
London shows annually at the RHS Westminster Halls,
and another at the Great Autumn Show, Harrogate.
Members receive the illustrated *Carnation Year Book*
each year as well as two newsletters. New members can
also choose one of the society's cultural booklets when
they join. Medals and show cards are available for
affiliated societies, and together the society and its
affiliates hold area shows throughout the country. A
coupon in the autumn newsletter gives a discount on
plants from selected nurseries. A panel of experts can
be called on to answer questions. Other societies can
hire lectures: a fee is charged to non-affiliated societies.

The British Pelargonium & Geranium Society

134 Montrose Avenue, Welling, Kent DA16 2QY

CONTACT Carol and Ron Helyar
AIMS To promote interest in *Pelargonium*, *Gera-
nium* and other Geraniaceae
MEMBERSHIP 1,500
SUBSCRIPTIONS £6 individual
SERVICES Seed scheme; advice; shows; journal; bi-an-
nual conference; books on pelargoniums available by
post

The British Pelargonium & Geranium Society was
founded in 1951. It publishes a Year Book and three
issues of *Pelargonium News* annually. The society's
annual show, held in June, moves around the country,
and includes classes for beginners and flower arrangers.
Every other year a conference is held. Members can
take advantage of a postal advisory service, and free
seeds. They stage publicity and information stands at
Chelsea, Malvern and the RHS Westminster shows,
and encourage other societies to join as affiliated
members.

British Pteridological Society
16 Kirby Corner Road, Canley, Coventry, West Midlands CV4 8GD

CONTACT Hon. General Secretary
AIMS To promote the study and cultivation of ferns and fern allies
MEMBERSHIP 800
SUBSCRIPTIONS £15 individual, £12 optional, £8.50 student, £25 subscriber
SERVICES Lectures; seed scheme; publications; advice; journal; special interest and regional groups; outings; book sales service; plant exchange scheme

Now over 100 years old, this international society includes amateur and professional members. An annual *Bulletin* contains society news, whilst the *Pteridologist* prints articles and book reviews for the amateur enthusiast. The twice yearly *Fern Gazette* includes more scientific papers: members who do not wish to receive this journal pay the lower optional subscription rate. According to the season, activities include indoor meetings and field trips and garden visits. A spore exchange distributes fern spores from all over the world, whilst a plant exchange scheme helps members obtain rarely available or surplus plants. There are regional groups in south east England, the Midlands, Wessex and north east England. Members can obtain advice on fern cultivation through the Hon. General Secretary.

Carnivorous Plant Society
174 Baldwins Lane, Croxley Green, Hertfordshire WD3 3LQ

CONTACT Dudley Watts
AIMS To bring together all those interested in carnivorous plants
MEMBERSHIP 650
SUBSCRIPTIONS £9 individual, £10 Europe, £13 world
SERVICES Seed scheme; advice; shows; journal; outings; plant search service

The Carnivorous Plant Society publishes an annual colour journal and four newsletters. They organise a number of events including visits to nurseries, field trips and open days. A plant search scheme is run, and members have free access to the seed bank. The information officer can provide advice on all topics. The society attends the Chelsea Flower Show.

The Cottage Garden Society
5 Nixon Close, Thornhill, Dewsbury, West Yorkshire WF12 0JA

CONTACT Membership Secretary
AIMS To promote and conserve cottage garden plants and to encourage cottage-style gardens
SUBSCRIPTIONS £5 individual, £8 joint, £6 overseas, $20 USA
SERVICES Lectures; seed scheme; publications; shows; journal; regional groups; list of members' gardens which can be visited

The Cottage Garden Society promotes and conserves worthwhile old-fashioned garden plants, and encourages owners of small gardens to garden in the cottage style. Members receive a quarterly bulletin and can take part in the annual seed distribution. The society has a growing number of regional and county groups: each organises lectures, meetings, visits and other events. The society hires out slides to members. This year watch out for the National Plant Sale at Fetcham, Surrey on 4 June, and the society's new book, *The Cottage Gardener's Companion* (David & Charles).

The Cyclamen Society
Tile Barn House, Standen Street, Iden Green, Benenden, Kent TN17 4LB

CONTACT Peter Moore
AIMS To further interest in and scientific knowledge of cyclamen
MEMBERSHIP 1,200
SUBSCRIPTIONS £5 individual, £6 family, £7 overseas
SERVICES Lectures; seed scheme; library; advice; awards; shows; journal; annual weekend conference

The Cyclamen Society has an international membership but is based in Britain. Its work includes research and conservation, whilst members benefit from the twice yearly journal, a seed distribution scheme and access to expert advice through the society's advisory panel. It exhibits and stages shows, organises meetings and lectures, and maintains a specialist library of literature and slides on cyclamen.

The Delphinium Society
Takakkaw, Ice House Wood, Oxted, Surrey RH8 9DW

CONTACT Membership Secretary
AIMS To encourage and extend the culture of delphiniums
MEMBERSHIP 1,500
SUBSCRIPTIONS £4 individual, joint & overseas (1993)
SERVICES Seed scheme; publications: *Simply Delphiniums*, £2.50; advice; awards; shows; journal;

The Delphinium Society dates back to 1928. New members receive a mixed packet of seed when they join, and all members can buy the society's hand pollinated seeds of garden hybrids and species. The illustrated Year Book is a unique source of information about the genus. Two shows, at which cups are awarded, are held each year: in June at Westminster, and in July at Wisley. Members gain free entry to the shows, and can also take advantage of advice on cultivation and a number of social events.

Federation of British Bonsai Societies

Rivendale, 14 Somerville Road, Sutton Coldfield,
West Midlands B73 6JA

CONTACT   General Secretary
AIMS   To promote the art of Bonsai in the UK
MEMBERSHIP   67 societies
SUBSCRIPTIONS   £30 society, £5 individual, £18 commercial
SERVICES   Library; advice; shows; journal; regional
groups; list of lecturers

The Federation of Bonsai Societies is the national
bonsai organisation, and is a member of the European
Bonsai Association. It publishes a newsletter six times
a year giving members information on national and
worldwide bonsai events. Two national exhibitions are
held each year, and every other year up to 400 delegates
attend a major bonsai convention. FOBBS keeps a
library of slides, films and videos and can provide expert
advice through the secretary and chairman. The National Bonsai Collection is held at Birmingham Botanic
Gardens and Glasshouses.

The Garden History Society

5 The Knoll, Hereford, Hereford & Worcester
HR1 1RU

CONTACT   Membership Secretary
AIMS   To study garden history and preserve parks and
gardens
MEMBERSHIP   1,900
SUBSCRIPTIONS   £15
SERVICES   Lectures; journal; regional groups; outings;

Founded in 1965. Learned society which is concerned
with the study of garden and landscape history. They
are also actively involved in conservation and regularly
advise local authorities on such issues. The twice yearly
journal *Garden History* publishes new research, whilst
regular newsletters carry details of conservation matters and society events. These events include lectures
and garden visits, at home and abroad. All events are
limited to society members only.

Gladiolus Breeders Association

15 Guildhall Drive, Pinchbeck, Spalding, Lincolnshire
PE11 3RE

CONTACT   The Secretary
AIMS   To assist and encourage Gladiolus breeders
SERVICES   Advice; journal

A group for dedicated gladiolus fans and breeders.
Meant mainly for amateurs, it provides a meeting point
for mutual assistance and an exchange of views for
those who are interested in developing and showing the
flower. A newsletter is circulated irregularly, and much
of the contact is by correspondence.

The Hardy Plant Society

Little Orchard, Great Comberton, Pershore,
Hereford & Worcester WR10 3DP
☎ 0386 710317

CONTACT   Mrs Pam Adams (Adminstrator)
AIMS   To stimulate interest in growing hardy herbaceous plants
MEMBERSHIP   9,000
SUBSCRIPTIONS   £8.50 individual, £10 joint
SERVICES   Lectures; gardens; seed scheme; publications; advice; shows; journal; special interest and regional groups; outings; slide library

The Hardy Plant Society is based at the Pershore
College of Horticulture, where it also has its own
garden. Members join the national society and can then
choose to join one of the twenty six regional groups. In
addition there seven special interest groups (Grasses;
Dieramas; Hardy Geraniums; Half-hardy plants; Pulmonarias; Paeonies; and Variegated plants) and a correspondence group for those who cannot come to
meetings. Two journals are sent to members each year,
along with regular newsletters. The national society
attends Chelsea and the RHS Westminster shows,
whilst area groups patronise local shows and arrange
their own programmes of events. An annual seed distribution list is circulated to all members. Members
benefit from a horticultural advisory panel headed by
the society's vice president, and a slide library from
which they can borrow. The society is also involved in
conserving old cultivars and introducing new ones, and
has produced a number of useful publications. It has
grown very fast recently, and is currently undergoing
some structural changes. The local groups organise their
own busy programmes of meetings, trips and garden
visits: the additional cost of joining such a group is
usually very small. Full details of the local and specialist
groups are available from the national society: only HPS
members can join a local or specialist group. Because all
HPS events are for HPS members only they are not
included in our calendar. Regional groups exist for the
following areas: Berkshire; Buckinghamshire, Oxfordshire and Northamptonshire; Cambridgeshire and Bedfordshire; Cheshire; Cornwall; Devon; Essex;
Hampshire; Hereford & mid Wales; Hertfordshire;
Kent; Lincolnshire; Norfolk and Suffolk; North East
England; North London; North West England; Nottinghamshire; Shropshire; Somerset; Southern Counties;
South Wales; Western Counties; West Midlands;
West Yorkshire; Wiltshire and Avon.

The Heather Society

Denbeigh, All Saints Road, Creeting St Mary,
Ipswich, Suffolk IP6 8PJ

CONTACT   Administrator

AIMS To promote interest in heathers and provide a friendly meeting place for enthusiasts
MEMBERSHIP 1,000
SUBSCRIPTIONS £6 individual, £7 joint
SERVICES Publications; advice; shows; journal; regional groups; slide library

The Heather Society was founded in 1963. Members receive the society's authoritative *Year Book* and a twice yearly bulletin of news and events. Competitions are held through the RHS at Westminster. A slide library is maintained, and expert advice on cultivation and other technical queries is available. Regional groups arrange a series of local events, and an annual weekend conference, linked to the AGM, is held at a different location each year. The national reference collections are at Wisley, Surrey and Cherrybank, Perth.

Hebe Society
Rosemergy, Hain Walk, St Ives, Cornwall TR26 2AF

CONTACT Hon. Secretary
AIMS To encourage, conserve and extend the cultivation of *Hebe*, *Parahebe* and allied New Zealand plants
MEMBERSHIP 280
SUBSCRIPTIONS £6 individual, £7 joint, £10 professional
SERVICES Seed scheme: cuttings exchange; publications; advice; shows; journal; regional groups;

An international society, based in Britain. It was established in 1985, and has since expanded its brief to include other New Zealand plants. The society is affiliated to the New Zealand Alpine Garden Society. Quarterly issues of *Hebe News* keep members in touch with activities, and include botanical and horticultural articles. Local groups exist or are being formed in the north west of England, Cornwall and the Cotswolds. The society maintains a slide library, operates a cutting exchange service and produces booklets about hebes and parahebes. Society members can also obtain written advice on request. The area groups arrange shows; the AGM and Spring Visit will be held on 16 – 17 April this year at Rosewarne, Cornwall (the site of the national collection).

Henry Doubleday Research Association (HDRA)
National Centre for Organic Gardening, Ryton on Dunsmore, Coventry, West Midlands CV8 3LG
☎ 0203 303517   [FAX] 0203 639229

AIMS To promote and advise on organic gardening, growing and food
SUBSCRIPTIONS £14 individual, £17 joint; £6 additional for Heritage Seed

SERVICES Gardens; seed scheme; library; publications; advice; journal; regional groups; trials; product discounts

Europe's largest organic organisation. At the Ryton headquarters there is a ten acre garden, and a reference library which members can use. Members are kept up to date with HDRA events through a quarterly magazine. In addition there are over fifty local groups around the country. The society provides free advice on organic gardening to its members, and they receive discounts on HDRA products and books. They can also join the Heritage Seed programme for £6 (£12 for non-members): this scheme propagates and preserves vegetable varieties which have been squeezed out of commerce by current legislation. Since they are not allowed to be sold, the HDRA gives them away to subscribers. Hand in hand with this project is *The Vegetable Finder*. The HDRA also carries out scientific research, consultancy work for industry and public bodies, and worldwide research and agricultural aid projects.

Ichiyo School of Ikebana
4 Providence Way, Waterbeach, Cambridge, Cambridgeshire CB5 9QJ
☎ 0223 862470

CONTACT Mrs Eileen Gibson (President)
AIMS To introduce the art of Ikebana
MEMBERSHIP 60
SUBSCRIPTIONS £12.50
SERVICES Lectures; shows; journal

The School holds courses, workshops and demonstrations in Ikebana, and exhibits at major shows, including Chelsea and the RHS Westminster shows.

International Camellia Society
41 Galveston Road, East Putney, London SW15 2RZ

CONTACT UK Membership Representative
AIMS To foster the love of camellias and maintain and increase their popularity throughout the world
MEMBERSHIP 1,500
SUBSCRIPTIONS £8 individual; £11 joint
SERVICES Gardens; advice; shows; journal; regional groups; outings

Founded in 1962. There are now members in 34 countries, including 340 in the UK. The society has several trial grounds around the country; the national collection is at Mount Edgcumbe, Cornwall. Members receive the *International Camellia Journal* annually, and a UK newsletter twice a year. The society takes a stand at the main spring shows, and holds weekend meetings in spring and autumn (this year Wiltshire in April and the Lake District in October). Informal advice on camellias is available to members, as is a worldwide network of fellow enthusiasts.

International Dendrology Society

School House, Stannington, Morpeth,
Northumberland NE61 6HF

CONTACT Secretary
AIMS To promote the study and conservation of
trees, woody plants and shrubs
MEMBERSHIP 1,300
SUBSCRIPTIONS £16 individual, £200 life
SERVICES Lectures; seed scheme; publications; journal; regional groups; outings; conservation and research

This prestigious international society has a worldwide
membership. It encourages and helps fund conservation
and research projects by registered charities, and has
established a bursary to allow a dendrological student
from Eastern Europe to study in the UK for a few
months each year. The IDS holds a dendrological symposium every two years; members also receive the year
book and newsletters, and can take part in the seed
exchange scheme and the excellent botanical tours.
Membership is restricted, is at the invitation of existing
members only, and is subject to the approval of the
council.

International Violet Association

11 Myddlewood, Myddle, Shrewsbury, Shropshire
S04 3RY

CONTACT Membership Secretary
AIMS To bring together all those interested in the
violet and its near relations
MEMBERSHIP 130
SUBSCRIPTIONS £10 or $15
SERVICES Advice; journal

A new and growing international society which originated in the USA, though the president is British. The
society is still finding its feet in terms of activities, but
its aims include bringing the violet back into gardens,
assisting in the preservation of its natural habitats, and
recording and introducing new cultivars. Membership
is not limited to growers and collectors. A newsletter
is produced four times a year, and the president offers
an advisory service to European members.

International Water Lily Society

92 London Road, Stapeley, Nantwich, Cheshire
CW5 7LH

CONTACT Treasurer (IWLS Europe)
AIMS To further interest in all aspects of water gardening
MEMBERSHIP 930
SUBSCRIPTIONS £12.50 individual, £15 family
SERVICES Lectures; journal

The International Water Lily Society is based in the
USA but has members in 23 countries of the world.

The membership spans amateurs and professionals, and
the society carries out a range of research and educational work, including hybrid registration. Members
receive the quarterly journal. There are lectures at the
British branch AGM in October. This year the annual
International Symposium is being held in Britain at
Sparsholt, Hampshire in August. The National Collection of Water Lilies is held at Barnaby Hall, Yorkshire.

Japanese Garden Society

Tatton Park, Knutsford, Cheshire WA16 6QN
☎ 0565 750780

AIMS To record, conserve and encourage Japanese-style gardens
SUBSCRIPTIONS £10
SERVICES Lectures; library; journal

A new society which is devoted to gardens influenced
by the Japanese tradition of design. It aims to compile
a register of Japanese gardens in the UK, and to work
for the conservation of existing gardens and the creation of new ones. Since the society is new, its activities
are somewhat provisional.

The Mammillaria Society

26 Glenfield Road, Banstead, Surrey SM7 2DG

CONTACT Hon. Chairman
AIMS To promote interest in the genus *Mammillaria*
MEMBERSHIP 500
SUBSCRIPTIONS £6.50
SERVICES Seed scheme; publications; advice; journal

Founded in 1960. Its interests extend to *Coryphantha*
and allied genera as well as *Mammillaria*. Members
receive a quarterly illustrated bulletin, and have access
to specialised publications. There is an annual seed
scheme, and advice is available to any member. Lecturers can be provided for other societies.

Mesemb Study Group

Brenfield, Bolney Road, Ansty, West Sussex
RH17 5AW

AIMS To further the study and knowledge of *Mesembryanthemum* and related genera
MEMBERSHIP 450
SUBSCRIPTIONS £6 individual; £9 overseas, airmail
SERVICES Lectures; seed scheme; journal; research

Successor to the Mesembryanthemum Society. Aims to
operate 'informally but not inefficiently'. Members,
about a third of whom live overseas, receive a quarterly
bulletin and can take part in the annual seed list. Meetings are arranged irregularly, and announced in the
bulletin. A larger event, often including a show, takes
place every two or three years. Financial assistance is
also available for some research projects.

The National Association of Flower Arrangement Societies

21 Denbigh Street, London SW1V 2HF
☎ 071 828 5145

CONTACT National Secretary
AIMS To encourage a love of flowers and demonstrate their decorative value
MEMBERSHIP 103,000
SUBSCRIPTIONS Payable to local clubs
SERVICES Lectures; library; publications; awards; shows; journal; regional groups; outings; book service

Founded in 1959. NAFAS is the umbrella organisation for nearly 1,500 flower arrangement clubs: total membership exceeds 100,000. The Association is very active in training and teaching arrangers of all skill levels. Local clubs organise demonstrations and competitions, and area groups stage exhibits at NAFAS and local shows. Regular flower festivals are organised to raise money for charitable causes, and arrangements in hospitals are another important part of the NAFAS activity. They also co-ordinate the flowers at Westminster Abbey, and do the arrangements for major occasions including royal weddings. *The Flower Arranger* is circulated quarterly; members can use the book service, and there is a book and slide library at the London headquarters. Prospective members should write to headquarters in the first instance: they will put you in touch with a local club. Subscriptions to these clubs vary and are usually modest. All clubs are represented at area level: the twenty areas are as follows: East of England; South West; Scotland; North East; Three Counties and South Wales; London and Overseas; Surrey; Wessex and Jersey; Home Counties; Berks, Bucks and Oxon; Mercia and North Wales; North West; Kent; Sussex; North Midlands; South Midlands; Devon and Cornwall; Northumberland and Durham; Dorset and Guernsey; Cheshire. We have included details of a number of local and area events in our list of floral shows and in the calendar section.

National Auricula and Primula Society (Southern Section)

67 Warnham Court Road, Carshalton Beeches, Surrey SM5 3ND

CONTACT Hon. Secretary
AIMS To improve and encourage the cultivation of auriculas and hardy primroses
MEMBERSHIP 450
SUBSCRIPTIONS £7
SERVICES Seed scheme; advice; shows; journal; regional groups

Founded in 1876. Members receive a year book and an annual newsletter. Two shows are held: both usually in April. This year the Primula show is in Datchet on 2 April and the Auricula show is in Brompton Road, London on 30 April. Plants are for sale at the shows. Members can seek advice on all aspects of primula cultivation and exhibition. The society has corresponding sections serving the Midlands and the West (6 Lawson Close, Saltford, Bristol BS18 3LB) and the North (146 Queens Road, Cheadle Hulme, Cheshire SK8 5HY).

National Begonia Society

7 Springwood Close, Thurgoland, Sheffield, South Yorkshire S30 7AB

CONTACT Hon. Secretary
AIMS To promote and encourage the cultivation of all begonias
MEMBERSHIP 900
SUBSCRIPTIONS £3 individual; £4 joint; additional enrolment fee £4 single; £5 joint
SERVICES Lectures; publications; advice; awards; shows; journal; regional groups

Established in 1948. The society encourages the cultivation of all types of begonia. New members receive a cultural handbook, and the journal appears three times a year. Meetings are arranged through the regional groups, five of which also organise an annual area show. In addition there is a national show with 26 classes. New cultivars can be submitted for awards to the floral committee. An advisory service is available through the secretary.

National Bonsai Society

30 Dunbar Road, Southport PR8 4RD

CONTACT Tom Ball
AIMS To promote, educate and further interest in bonsai throughout the UK
MEMBERSHIP 700
SUBSCRIPTIONS £5 individual, £6.50 joint
SERVICES Lectures; library; publications; advice; awards; shows; journal

Members receive *The World of Bonsai* quarterly, and can take advantage of the society's library. The annual show takes place in Southport on the first Saturday in June. The National Bonsai Society meets on the third Tuesday of every month (except in December) at 7.45 pm in the Harry Livingstone Hall, Princes Street, Southport. Visitors are welcome at these meetings.

National Chrysanthemum Society

George Gray House, 8 Amber Business Village, Amber Close, Tamworth, Staffordshire B77 4RD

CONTACT Miss L. Morton
AIMS To promote the chrysanthemum and offer advice

MEMBERSHIP 4,500
SUBSCRIPTIONS £9.75
SERVICES Publications; advice; awards; shows; journal; regional groups

The National Chrysanthemum Society holds two national shows each year: in Bingley Hall, Stafford (September) and the RHS Halls, Westminster (November). The advisory bureau helps with queries about chrysanthemums and handles membership enquiries.

National Council for the Conservation of Plants and Gardens

The Pines, Wisley Garden, Woking, Surrey
GU23 6QB
☎ 0483 211465   📠 0483 211750
AIMS To encourage the conservation of plants and gardens
MEMBERSHIP 8,000
SERVICES Lectures; publications; shows; journal; regional groups; outings

Founded in 1978. The NCCPG is divided into local and county groups who organise their own programmes of events. The national body works to preserve individual plants and endangered gardens. The society's most successful innovation has been the establishment of National Collections of genera (and part genera). These gather together as many representatives of the genus as possible and form a unique resource. Many can be visited: full details appear in the 1994 *National Plant Collections Directory*, which is available from the NCCPG.

National Dahlia Society

19 Sunnybank, Marlow, Buckinghamshire SL7 3BL

CONTACT General Secretary
AIMS To promote the cultivation of dahlias
MEMBERSHIP 3,500
SUBSCRIPTIONS £10 individual, £8 OAPs, £11 affiliated society
SERVICES Lectures; library; publications; advice; awards; shows; journal; regional groups; judging examinations; classification of new varieties

The National Dahlia Society holds two main shows: in London at the RHS and at Harrogate during the Autumn Show. It runs trials at Bradford and Wisley, and gives an annual award for the best new British and new overseas seedlings. Members receive the society journal twice a year, and can take part in its annual conference and lecture programme. There are regional groups in the home counties and Lancashire, and affiliated societies can use the society's medals and certificates for their own shows. A range of books and pamphlets is available for members at reduced prices.

National Pot Leek Society

8 Nelson Avenue, Nelson Village, Cramlington, Northumberland NE23 9HG

CONTACT Hon. Secretary
AIMS To improve and encourage leek growing
MEMBERSHIP 1,000
SUBSCRIPTIONS £5
SERVICES Lectures; publications; advice; shows; journal; items for sale

The society produces a year book and two newsletters for its members. The annual members' show takes place on 17- 18 September this year. Advice can be provided by letter or phone, and the society produces a growing guide *Sound All Round*. Among the items on sale are measuring equipment and charts and a video.

National Society of Allotment and Leisure Gardeners

O'Dell House, Hunters Road, Corby, Northamptonshire NN17 1JE
☎ 0536 266576

CONTACT Geoff Stokes
AIMS To help all enjoy the recreation of gardening
MEMBERSHIP 98,000
SUBSCRIPTIONS £6.21 individual, £4 associate, 41p per member for societies; £30 local authority membership
SERVICES Seed scheme: Commercial seeds available at reduced prices; publications; advice; journal; regional groups; insurance

National society for allotment holders and other gardeners. Members can join individually or as part of a gardening association. In return they receive the journal and are able to take advantage of NSALG's many services. These include substantial discounts on seeds ordered through the society, and special insurance for allotment property. The society provides free advice on horticultural subjects, and in particular on the legal aspects of allotment gardening, including threatened loss of land and other disputes. It can also advise on suitable forms for leases, rents and agreements. A range of leaflets and fact sheets are available, along with show stationery and awards.

The National Sweet Pea Society

3 Chalk Farm Road, Stokenchurch, High Wycombe, Buckinghamshire HP14 3TB

CONTACT Hon. Secretary
AIMS To encourage the cultivation and improvement of the sweet pea
MEMBERSHIP 1,400
SUBSCRIPTIONS £12 individual, £10 affiliated society

SERVICES Lectures; advice; awards; shows; journal; regional groups; joint RHS/ NSPS trials

The National Sweet Pea Society was founded in 1900. The society's *Annual* appears every June, and further Bulletins appear in February and September. Its two major shows are held in July this year: the National in Salisbury and the Provincial in Market Bosworth. Each county has an area representative who arranges programmes for local members. The society actively promotes new varieties, and members can send their own seedlings to the trials at Wisley each year.

National Vegetable Society

56 Waun-y-Groes Avenue, Rhiwbina, Cardiff, South Glamorgan CF4 4SZ

MEMBERSHIP 3,500
SUBSCRIPTIONS £7 individual, £8.50 joint, £10 & £13 societies
SERVICES Seed scheme; library; publications; advice; awards; shows; journal; regional groups; lectures for hire

The National Vegetable Society was founded in 1960 and caters for individual members and societies. The latter can use the NVS medals and award cards. Membership spans the expert and the novice vegetable grower, and the annual *Handbook*, the National and the regional Bulletins that members receive contain advice on all aspects of growing and showing vegetables. The National Vegetable Championships are held at a different location each year (Wisley in 1994), and major awards are presented at it. There are regional branches.

National Viola and Pansy Society

c/o 28 Carisbrooke Road, Edgbaston, Birmingham, West Midlands B17 8NW

CONTACT Hon. Secretary
AIMS To encourage the cultivation, exhibition and improvement of violas and pansies
SUBSCRIPTIONS £2
SERVICES Library; shows; journal

Founded in 1911. The society encourages and popularises the growing of exhibition varieties, and helps its members with advice on propagation and cultivation. A newsletter is circulated irregularly, and there is an annual show in Handsworth, West Midlands at the end of July. Surplus cuttings and plants form the basis for occasional exchanges.

Northern Horticultural Society

Harlow Carr Botanical Gardens, Crag Lane, Harrogate, North Yorkshire HG3 1QB
☎ 0423 565418

CONTACT Barry S. Nuttall

AIMS To promote the science and practice of horticulture
MEMBERSHIP 11,000
SUBSCRIPTIONS £20
SERVICES Lectures; gardens; seed scheme; library; publications; advice; awards; journal; special interest groups

Founded in 1947, the Northern Horticultural Society is a particularly active group. Members receive free entrance to the Harlow Carr Botanical Gardens which are the society's headquarters. The annual programme includes a series of day and longer courses throughout the year at the garden. The garden also trials vegetable and flower varieties specifically for their suitability to northerly climates, and visitors can assess the new and unreleased varieties which are undergoing trial. An illustrated journal, *The Northern Gardener*, appears four times a year. Members can also take advantage of the seed scheme, the reference and lending library, and an advisory service (in writing only). There are special interest sections for alpines, bonsai, bulbs, delphiniums, ferns, rhododendrons and roses. A reciprocal arrangement with the Royal Horticultural Society allows free access to some of the RHS gardens. Many of the society's events are listed in our calendar.

Ohara School of Ikebana

Forresters, Sway Road, Lymington, Hampshire SO4 8LR

CONTACT Mrs A. Sawano
AIMS To teach and promote the art of Ikebana
SUBSCRIPTIONS £12
SERVICES Lectures; shows; journal

Teaches the Ohara style of Ikebana, the Japanese art of flower arranging. Three to four newsletters are produced each year, and members exhibit at flower, garden and Ikebana shows. Teachers are available throughout the UK and around the world.

Orchid Society of Great Britain

Athelney, 145 Binscombe Village, Godalming, Surrey GU7 3QL

CONTACT Hon. Secretary
AIMS To encourage amateur growers of orchids
MEMBERSHIP 1,200
SUBSCRIPTIONS £10 individual; £12 double; £5 joining fee
SERVICES Lectures; library; publications; advice; awards; shows; journal; regional groups; plant exchanges and sales

The nationwide orchid society. It produces an informative journal four times a year and stages two major shows annually. In addition there is a monthly meeting in the Napier Hall, London which may include a lecture and a show. The library lends books and slides, and members can obtain cultural advice in person or in writing from the Cultural Adviser. There is a plant exchange forum, and a sales table at most meetings. The society publishes a small booklet on orchid cultivation which is a useful introduction to the subject (£2.50).

The Royal Horticultural Society

P O Box 313, 80 Vincent Square, London
SW1P 2PE
☎ 071 834 4333; 071 828 1744 (Shows information); 071 821 3000 (Membership)

SUBSCRIPTIONS £23 individual, £12 student, £16 associate; £7 enrolment fee
SERVICES Lectures; gardens; seed scheme; library; publications; advice; awards; shows; journal; special interest groups; outings;

The premier horticultural society in the country and probably the world. Membership has grown steadily in recent years and the society's activities have expanded correspondingly. As well as the extensive gardens at Wisley in Surrey, there are now also regional gardens at Rosemoor, Devon and Hyde Hall, Essex and a regional centre at Pershore in the West Midlands. Reciprocal arrangements also give full and student members admission to Ness Botanic Gardens, Cheshire; the Sir Harold Hillier Gardens and Arboretum, Hampshire; and the Harlow Carr Botanical Gardens, North Yorkshire; as well as the National Trust's gardens at Hidcote Manor, Gloucestershire; Bodnant, Clwyd; Sheffield Park, East Sussex; and Nymans, West Sussex. There is a full range of courses, lectures and demonstrations at the RHS gardens and Pershore, and a wide variety of regional and London lectures each year. Members are admitted to these events at concessionary rates, and free of charge to most lectures: you should apply for tickets in writing. The show programme is formed around the so-called fortnightly shows in the RHS Halls in Westminster (see our calendar for dates). The halls are less full on Tuesday evenings and on Wednesdays. The RHS and specialist societies hold plant competitions at these shows, and members can bring along plants for exhibition or cultural awards. Schedules are available from the RHS. Members no longer receive free entrance to Chelsea, but they can buy tickets at reduced prices, and the Tuesday and Wednesday of Chelsea week are reserved for members. Members are entitled to reduced price admission to the increasing number of shows in which the RHS is now involved, including BBC Gardeners' World Live in Birmingham, the Hampton Court Palace Flower Show, and the established shows at Malvern and Harrogate. The illustrated RHS journal *The Garden* is sent free to members every month. Long a journal of record, the magazine is now back on form with a mixture of society news, horticultural and

botanical articles. Its sister title is *The New Plantsman*: aimed at the specialist, there is a separate subscription. A number of other publications are produced, and the society promotes a collection of gardening titles in association with commercial publishers. RHS members are entitled to technical advice from the society's experts: this service is accessible by post, at the society's own shows and a number of other major events which it attends, and in person at Wisley. Members may use and borrow from the Lindley Library in Vincent Square: its holdings are of world standing. A distribution of seed from the Wisley garden is made each year for a nominal charge. The new class of associate member coincides with changes which have been made to the membership privileges. Membership cards are no longer transferable, and the benefits now apply to the named holder only. Members can enrol up to three people who live at their address as associate members: they are entitled to all the normal benefits except free entry to those gardens which are not owned by the RHS; only one copy of the journal is sent to each address. There are some specialist sections (an additional subscription is payable) for Fruit, Lilies, and Rhododendrons, Magnolias and Camellias. Behind the scenes the RHS is involved in scientific and technical horticulture, including its regular trial programme. The trials can be viewed at Wisley (Portsmouth field). The society liaises with national and trade organisations in the interests of horticulture, and is increasingly active in the international arena too. Our calendar lists many events that are organised by the RHS. Up to date information, along with precise details of how to book, is published monthly in *The Garden* (which non-members can buy from newsagents). A recorded information line (071 828 1744) gives details of forthcoming flower shows for members and non-members. A new direct line has been established for membership and subscription enquiries: 071 821 3000.

The Royal National Rose Society

The Gardens of the Rose, Chiswell Green, St Albans, Hertfordshire AL2 3NR
☎ 0727 850461　　📠 0727 850360

CONTACT Reception
AIMS To promote the love of roses
MEMBERSHIP 20,000
SUBSCRIPTIONS £14.50 individual; £19.50 joint; £7.50 student; £5 extra for Historic Roses Group
SERVICES Lectures; gardens; library; publications; advice; awards; shows; journal; special interest and regional groups; outings

Founded in 1876. The world's largest specialist plant society has its headquarters near St Albans: the Gardens of the Rose display over 1,700 different roses. Members enter free. The society also maintains 12 regional rose gardens. An illustrated quarterly journal *The Rose* gives news of the society and the rose world, and there are regular shows including the British Rose Festival at the Hampton Court Palace Flower Show. The society always has hundreds of new roses on trial for awards at St Albans: the trial fields can be visited. There is a full advisory service for members and regular pruning demonstrations which anyone can attend (5 – 6 March and 15 – 16 October this year). There are regional groups in Yorkshire and the North West, and special interest sections for exhibitors and rose breeders (The Amateur Rose Breeders Association). For an additional £5 RNRS members can join the Historic Roses Group, which organises its own programme of events and visits.

The Saintpaulia & Houseplant Society

33 Church Road, Newbury Park, Ilford, Essex
IG2 7ET

CONTACT Hon. Secretary
AIMS To grow better and more beautiful houseplants, and to help the public to do the same
MEMBERSHIP 650
SUBSCRIPTIONS £4 individual, £5 joint
SERVICES Lectures; library; publications; shows; journal; regional groups; *Saintpaulia* leaf distribution

The society is affiliated to the Royal Horticultural Society, and holds regular Tuesday evening meetings at the RHS, usually to coincide with the Westminster shows. There are competitions at the meetings, and an annual show in August. Members receive the bulletin four times a year. The society arranges visits and also has three local groups with their own programmes. Members can borrow from the society's specialist library, and take part in the annual leaf distribution.

Scottish Rhododendron Society

Stron Ailne, Colintraive, Argyll, Strathclyde
PA22 3AS

CONTACT Hon. Secretary
AIMS To encourage the cultivation of rhododendrons
MEMBERSHIP 220
SUBSCRIPTIONS £19.50
SERVICES Lectures; gardens; seed scheme; publications; advice; awards; shows; journal; regional groups; outings; automatic membership of the American Rhododendron Society

The Scottish Rhododendron Society was founded just over ten years ago to provide a forum at which Scottish growers could meet and exhibit. Many of the best Scottish rhododendron gardens belong, but about a third of the members live outside Scotland. A newsletter is produced three times a year, and there are at least two meetings annually. Their national show, at a different venue each year, is probably the top show in Britain for rhododendrons. Members can purchase a range of books at reduced prices, seek specialist advice through the secretary, and gain free admission to Arduaine Gardens in Strathclyde. The society is also a chapter of the excellent American Rhododendron Society, and members automatically belong directly to the American society too. This gives them the scholarly quarterly journal, access to all the other ARS chapters (from Denmark and Holland to India), and the opportunity to raise seeds from the ARS seed bank.

Scottish Rock Garden Club

1 Hillcrest Road, Bearsden, Glasgow G61 2EB

CONTACT Mrs J. Thomlinson
AIMS To promote the cultivation of alpine and peat garden plants
MEMBERSHIP 4,500
SUBSCRIPTIONS £7 single, £1.50 additional family member or junior membership, £9 overseas
SERVICES Lectures; seed scheme; library; publications; advice; awards; shows: Organised by nine of the local groups; journal: Twice yearly; regional groups; slide library; annual conference

Founded in 1933 this is now the largest horticultural society in Scotland, with overseas members in thirty eight countries. There are regional groups in Ayr, Aberdeen, Belford, Dundee, Edinburgh, Glasgow, Inverness, Kircudbright, Newcastle, Oban, Penrith, Perth, Renfrew, Stirling, St Andrews and Thurso. Each local group is responsible for organising a programme of events including lectures, and some members also open their gardens. The society journal, *The Rock Garden*, appears twice a year: it is a well-produced and authoritative magazine which covers rock garden plants both in cultivation and in the wild. The seed exchange scheme is among the best of its kind.

The Sempervivum Society

11 Wingle Tye Road, Burgess Hill, West Sussex
RH15 9HR

CONTACT Peter J. Mitchell
AIMS The promotion and cultivation of sempervivums and allied plants
MEMBERSHIP 300
SUBSCRIPTIONS £2.50
SERVICES Library; publications; advice; journal

Members of the Sempervivum Society receive three newsletters or so a year. The society maintains a specialist library and produces a cultivar register for the genus. Specialist advice is available.

The Wild Flower Society

68 Outwoods Road, Loughborough, Leicestershire
LE11 3LY
AIMS To encourage field botany
MEMBERSHIP 1,000
SUBSCRIPTIONS £8 individual; £3.50 junior
SERVICES Publications; advice; journal; regional
groups; outings

Founded in 1886. Activity revolves around their *Field Botanists Diary* (£5), which contains lists of species. Members are encouraged to record their findings, and there are regular field meetings in summer. *The Wild Flower Magazine* is circulated three times a year. There is a branch structure, and branch secretaries help with and advise on recording and identification. Young people are particularly encouraged.

Regional Societies

Avon Gardens Trust

Station House, Church Lane, Wickwar, Wotton
under Edge, Gloucestershire GL12 8NB

CONTACT Avon Gardens Trust
SUBSCRIPTIONS £7.50 individual, £10 family
SERVICES Lectures; journal; outings

The trust works to conserve the county's gardens through monitoring planning applications and advising owners on surveys and restoration plans. Garden visits and other events are staged for their members.

BBONT

3 Church Cowley Road, Rose Hill, Oxford OX4 3JR
☎ 0865 775476
SUBSCRIPTIONS £12.50 individual, £18 joint
SERVICES Lectures; publications; advice; journal;
outings

Berkshire, Buckinghamshire and Oxfordshire Naturalists Trust has over ninety reserves across the three counties, including Bowdown Woods, Dancersend and the Warburg Reserve.

Cheshire Wildlife Trust

Grebe House, Reseheath, Nantwich, Cheshire
CW5 6DA
☎ 0270 610180
SUBSCRIPTIONS £16 individual, £18 joint
SERVICES Lectures; publications; advice; journal;
regional groups; outings

Formerly the Cheshire Conservation Trust, the trust manages 30 reserves including Red Rocks Marsh and Swettenham Meadows.

Cleveland Wildlife Trust

Bellamy House, Unit 2a, Brighouse Business Village,
Riverside Park, Middlesborough, Cleveland TS2 1RT
☎ 0642 253716
SUBSCRIPTIONS £12 individual, £15 joint
SERVICES Lectures; publications; advice; journal;
outings

Formed in 1979 to protect wildlife in the county. They have 13 reserves in hand, including the deciduous woodland of Saltburn Gill.

Cornwall Gardens Society

Liskeard Water Gardens, Pengover Road, Liskeard,
Cornwall PL14 3NL
☎ 0579 342278

CONTACT Hon. Secretary
AIMS To foster a love and knowledge of plants and
gardening
MEMBERSHIP 1,700
SUBSCRIPTIONS £8 individual
SERVICES Lectures; publications; advice; shows; journal; outings; garden openings

A scaled down model of the RHS, with an excellent magazine, good bulletins and a famous show in spring. They also organise a garden opening scheme.

Cornwall Gardens Trust

Sweet Thymes, Rose, Truro, Cornwall TR4 9PQ

CONTACT Membership Secretary
AIMS To preserve, enhance and recreate the gardens
of Cornwall
SUBSCRIPTIONS £8 individual and joint, £10 gardens
and schools
SERVICES Lectures; advice; journal; outings

Formed in 1988. Carries out conservation and preservation work, and organises special events and garden visits for its members.

Cornwall Trust for Nature Conservation

Five Acres, Allet, Truro, Cornwall TR4 9DJ
☎ 0872 73939
SUBSCRIPTIONS £10 individual, £1 each for additional
family members
SERVICES Lectures; publications; advice; journal;
outings

The trust has 36 nature reserves covering 3,000 acres. Good sites for botanists include Peters Wood and Ventongimps Moor.

Derbyshire Wildlife Trust
Elvaston Castle, Derby DE72 3EP
☎ 0332 756610

SUBSCRIPTIONS £12 individual, £15 family
SERVICES Lectures; publications; advice; journal; outings

The trust administers 49 reserves, including Cromford Canal and Spring Wood. DWT publishes Fran Hill's *Wildlife Gardening* (£4.50), and has a series of open gardens in the summer.

Devon Gardens Trust
Lucombe House, Devon County Council, County Hall, Exeter, Devon EX2 4QW
☎ 0884 253803

CONTACT Secretary
AIMS To preserve the gardens of Devon
SUBSCRIPTIONS £5 individual, £8 joint
SERVICES Lectures; advice; journal; outings

The trust surveys Devon gardens, and works to protect their future. Members benefit from special garden visits and seminars, and are kept informed of the trust's research and conservation work.

Dorset Perennial Group
Ivy Cottage, Aller Lane, Ansty, Dorchester, Dorset DT2 7PX

CONTACT Hon. Secretary
SUBSCRIPTIONS £1
SERVICES Lectures; journal; outings

Dorset-based society which used to be the local Hardy Plant Society group: they are no longer connected with the HPS. The programme includes garden visits and talks.

Dorset Trust for Nature Conservation
39 Christchurch Road, Bournemouth BH1 3NS
☎ 0202 554241

SUBSCRIPTIONS £12.50 individual, £6 each additional person
SERVICES Lectures; publications; advice; journal; special interest and regional groups; outings

The trust looks after 26 nature reserves including Fontmell Down and Kingcombe Meadows. A wildlife garden is being established at Preston near Weymouth.

Dyfed Wildlife Trust
7 Market Street, Haverfordwest, Dyfed SA61 1NF
☎ 0437 765462

SERVICES Lectures; publications; advice; journal; outings

The trust, the second oldest in the country, manages 65 reserves including the acid heath of Dowrog Common.

Essex Wildlife Trust
Fingringhoe Wick Nature Reserve, South Green Road, Fingringhoe, Colchester, Essex CO5 7DN
☎ 0206 729678
SUBSCRIPTIONS £15 individual, £18 joint
SERVICES Lectures; publications; advice; journal; outings

The trust manages 80 reserves and has 5 conservation centres. Its reserves include the Danbury complex and Fingringhoe Wick. The trust also sells organic compost and woodchips.

Federation of Edinburgh & District Allotments & Gardens
2 South House Avenue, Edinburgh EH17 8EA

CONTACT Secretary
AIMS To promote the interests of allotment and garden associations in Edinburgh
MEMBERSHIP 25 sites
SUBSCRIPTIONS £10 per site
SERVICES Seed scheme; advice; shows; journal

The Federation of Edinburgh & District Allotments and Gardens Associations represents about 1,300 individuals on 25 sites. Its main efforts recently have been directed at improving the management and facilities on council run sites, and at making allotments part of the city's leisure provisions. A newsletter is circulated about three times a year and members can obtain seed through the federation. The annual flower and vegetable show is held on the last Saturday in August. Informal advice is available through other members, and they are planning to extend the range of membership services offered.

Friends of Brogdale
The Brogdale Horticultural Trust, Brogdale Farm, Faversham, Kent ME13 8XS
☎ 0795 535286
AIMS Fruit research and conservation
SUBSCRIPTIONS £15 ordinary, £25 joint
SERVICES Lectures; advice; journal; orchard

The Brogdale Experimental Horticultural Station was bought from the government by the Brogdale Trust in 1991 to safeguard its work. It carries out commercial research and trialling, and maintains exceptional reference collections of fruit varieties, including over 2,300 different apples. Friends receive free entry to the site, priority booking for events, and access to a Friday afternoon information line. There is also a quarterly newsletter. The visitor centre opens from 10 am – 5 pm, Wednesday – Sunday, April to December.

Friends of the Royal Botanic Garden, Edinburgh

The Royal Botanic Garden, Inverleith Row,
Edinburgh, Lothian EH3 5LR
☎ 031 552 5339

CONTACT Hon. Secretary
AIMS To support the garden and raise funds for its activities
SUBSCRIPTIONS £15 individual; £20 joint
SERVICES Lectures; gardens; seed scheme; journal

The Friends raise funds for and promote the work of the Royal Botanic Garden Edinburgh. There is no admission charge to this great garden, but friends have free entry to the three regional gardens (Logan, Dawyck and Younger). There is a regular newsletter, and a series of lectures and other social events. Friends also have the chance to join in seed distributions and plant exchanges.

Friends of the Royal Botanic Gardens, Kew

Cambridge Cottage, Kew Green, Kew, Richmond,
Surrey TW9 3AB
☎ 081 332 5922   📠 081 332 5901

CONTACT Dianne Owens
AIMS Fund raising for Royal Botanic Gardens, Kew
MEMBERSHIP 17,000
SUBSCRIPTIONS £30 individual, £40 family, concessions for OAPs & students
SERVICES Lectures; gardens; shows; journal; discounts in Kew and Wakehurst Place shops; guest passes

The Friends of the Royal Botanic Gardens, Kew is a relatively new organisation: its aim is to raise funds for Kew's work, hence the highish subscription. That said, free entry to Kew and Wakehurst Place is a valuable benefit for regular visitors, and many will enjoy helping the scientific and conservation work which is carried out from Kew. The Friends' journal *Kew*, published three times a year, is colourful and outstandingly good. Lectures are given monthly throughout the year, and there is an annual plant auction in the autumn. Friends receive discounts on shop purchases, and six complimentary day passes to the gardens for their guests.

Glamorgan Wildlife Trust

Fountain Road, Tondu, Bridgend CF32 0EH
☎ 0656 724100

SUBSCRIPTIONS £12 joint
SERVICES Lectures; publications; advice; journal; regional groups; outings

The Glamorgan Wildlife Trust administers 47 reserves from woodland to coastal sites, including reserves on the Gower peninsula and Melincourt Falls.

Gloucestershire Gardens & Landscape Trust

Sunny Crest, Eden's Hill, Upleadon, Newent,
Gloucestershire GL18 9HA
☎ 0531 822433

CONTACT Secretary
AIMS To conserve gardens and landscape
SUBSCRIPTIONS £12 individual, £20 joint
SERVICES Lectures; advice; journal; outings

The trust exists to protect valuable gardens and landscapes. As well as conservation work it has a programme of lectures, garden visits and other events for members.

Gwent Wildlife Trust

16 White Swan Court, Monmouth, Gwent NP5 3NY
☎ 0600 715501

SUBSCRIPTIONS £12 individual, £16.50 joint
SERVICES Lectures; publications; advice; journal; outings

The trust was started in 1963 and now has over thirty reserves including Magor Marsh, its first purchase, and Cleddon Shoots.

Hampshire Gardens Trust

Jermyns House, Jermyns Lane, Ampfield, Romsey,
Hampshire SO51 0QA
☎ 0794 367752 (mornings) 📠 0794 368520

CONTACT Secretary
AIMS To care for Hampshire's gardens and parks
SUBSCRIPTIONS £10 individual, £15 joint
SERVICES Lectures; library; advice; journal; outings; research

The first of the county gardens trusts, formed with help from Hampshire county council in 1984. The trust is active in conservation and education work, and has a full programme of events for members also.

Herefordshire Nature Trust

25 Castle Street, Hereford HR1 2NW
☎ 0432 356872

SUBSCRIPTIONS £12 individual, £15 joint
SERVICES Publications; advice; journal; regional groups; outings

The trust manages over 40 reserves in the county, including those at Great Doward and the woods at Lea and Pagets.

Herts & Middlesex Wildlife Trust

Grebe House, St Michaels Street, St Albans,
Hertfordshire AL3 4SN
☎ 0727 858901

SUBSCRIPTIONS £14 individual, £18 joint
SERVICES Lectures; publications; advice; journal;
outings

The trust looks after some 44 reserves including Old
Park Wood and the old chalk downland of Therfield
Heath.

Isle of Wight Gardens Trust

Cassies, Billingham, Newport, Isle of Wight
PO30 3HD

CONTACT Membership Secretary
SUBSCRIPTIONS £5 individual, £7.50 joint
SERVICES Lectures; journal; outings

The trust helps to record the island's parks and gardens
and to assist in their conservation. Talks and garden
visits are staged for members, and they can also get
involved in conservation work.

Kent Trust for Nature Conservation

Tyland Barn, Sandling, Maidstone, Kent ME14 3BD
☎ 0622 662012

SUBSCRIPTIONS £18 individual, £22.50 joint
SERVICES Lectures; publications; advice; journal;
outings

The Kent Trust looks after more than 40 reserves
including Yockletts Bank, Sladden Wood, Park Gate
Down and Hothfield Common.

Leicestershire and Rutland Trust for Nature Conservation

1 West Street, Leicester LE1 6UU
☎ 0533 553904

SUBSCRIPTIONS £15 individual, £5 each additional
person
SERVICES Lectures; publications; advice; journal; regional groups; outings

The trust manages 37 reserves including Cribb's
Meadow and the woodland at Prior's Coppice.

The Lincolnshire Trust

Banovallum House, Manor House Street, Horncastle,
Lincolnshire LN9 5HF
☎ 0507 526667   FAX 0507 525732

SUBSCRIPTIONS £15 individual, £20 joint
SERVICES Lectures; publications; advice; journal;
regional groups; outings

The trust (one of the RSNC wildlife trusts) manages
over 100 sites including Little Scrubbs Meadow in the
Wolds and the dunes at Saltfleetby-Theddlethorpe.

Montgomeryshire Wildlife Trust

Collot House, 20 Severn Street, Welshpool,
Montgomeryshire SY21 7AD
☎ 0938 555654

SUBSCRIPTIONS £10 individual, £12 joint
SERVICES Lectures; publications; advice; journal;
regional groups; outings

The trust has 12 reserves under management including
Llyn Mawr, Roundton Hill and Dyfnant Meadows.

Norfolk Naturalists Trust

72 Cathedral Close, Norwich NR1 4DF
☎ 0603 625540

SUBSCRIPTIONS £16 individual, £20 joint
SERVICES Lectures; publications; advice; journal;
outings

The trust looks after 40 reserves across the county
including East Wretham Heath in the Breckland and
the pingos (glacial craters) of Thompsons Heath.

North of England Horticultural Society

4a South Park Road, Harrogate, North Yorkshire
HG1 5QU
☎ 0423 561049   FAX 0423 561049

CONTACT Mr A. Ravenscroft
AIMS The promotion of horticulture
MEMBERSHIP 65
SUBSCRIPTIONS £18
SERVICES Publications; shows;

The North of England Horticultural Society is the
organiser of the two annual shows in Harrogate. This
year the Spring Flower Show runs from 21 – 24 April,
and the Great Autumn Flower Show takes place on
16-17 September. The society publishes a show directory for each show. Many national, regional and amateur societies attend the shows and are able to provide
specialist advice on request.

The North of England Rose, Carnation and Sweet Pea Society

94 Hedgehope Road, Westerhope, Newcastle upon
Tyne NE5 4LA

CONTACT General Secretary
AIMS To further interest in the three named flowers,
and gardening in general
MEMBERSHIP 300
SUBSCRIPTIONS £2.50

SERVICES Lectures; library; advice; awards; shows; journal

The society – Rosecarpe, for short – was founded in 1938. Its interests extend beyond its three main flowers. Members can attend the regular meetings, usually on the first Monday of most months in the Civic Centre, Gateshead, for lectures or demonstrations. The four shows play an important part in the society's life, notably the Gateshead Spring and Summer Flower Shows organised in association with the Metropolitan Borough Council, and two Rosecarpe Flower Shows. Trophies are presented at all shows. An annual year book is produced, and members can also borrow the society's books and videos, and draw on the advice of the society's experts. Rosecarpe attends other shows and horticultural college events, and is affiliated to the national Rose, Carnation, Sweet Pea and Daffodil societies.

North Wales Wildlife Trust

376 High Street, Bangor, Gwynedd LL57 1YE
☎ 0248 351541

SUBSCRIPTIONS £12 individual, £17 joint
SERVICES Lectures; publications; advice; journal; outings

The trust has 33 reserves in North Wales including mixed woodland at Ddol Uchaf and the dunes of Morfa Bychan.

Northamptonshire Wildlife Trust

Lings House, Billing Lings, Northampton NN3 4BE
☎ 0604 405285

SUBSCRIPTIONS £12 individual, £16 joint
SERVICES Lectures; publications; advice; journal; outings

The trust looks after 1,500 acres spread over 40 sites. Reserves include High Wood and Meadow and Short Wood.

Nottinghamshire Wildlife Trust

310 Sneinton Dale, Nottingham NG3 7DN
☎ 0602 588242

SUBSCRIPTIONS £12 individual, £15 joint
SERVICES Lectures; publications; advice; journal; regional groups; outings

Formed in 1963. The trust looks after 50 reserves including Tresswell Wood and Eakring Meadows.

Radnorshire Wildlife Trust

Warwick House, High Street, Llandrindod Wells, Powys LD1 6AG
☎ 0597 823298

SUBSCRIPTIONS £12 individual, £15 joint

SERVICES Lectures; publications; advice; journal; regional groups; outings

In this sparsely populated county the trust manages reserves which include Bailey Einon and the newly acquired Pentrosfa Mire.

The Royal Caledonian Horticultural Society

21 Newbattle Abbey Crescent, Dalkeith, Lothian EH22 3LN

CONTACT Hon. Secretary
AIMS The improvement of horticulture in all its branches
MEMBERSHIP 750
SUBSCRIPTIONS £8 individual, £10 family
SERVICES Lectures; library; advice; awards; shows; journal; outings

The Royal Caledonian Horticultural Society publishes an annual journal, and a newsletter *Preview* three times a year. There is a regular lecture programme, fortnightly from October to April, whilst in the summer months a series of garden visits takes place. The society's president is the custodian of their library. Three annual shows are organised – spring, summer and autumn – and the society presents two prestigious awards: the Queen Elizabeth, the Queen Mother Medal, and the Scottish Horticultural Medal.

The Scottish Allotments and Gardens Society

14/1 Hoseasons Gardens, Edinburgh, Lothian EH4 7HQ

CONTACT The Secretary
AIMS To promote the interests of allotment holders
MEMBERSHIP 780
SUBSCRIPTIONS Individuals 75p; Sites 50p per plot
SERVICES Seed scheme; advice; journal; grants for gardeners

Long-established organisation which promotes the interests of allotment holders and societies. You can either join as an individual or as an entire site, in which case your subscription depends on the number of plots. There is a bi-monthly newsletter, and a discount seed scheme. SAGS also receives funds to assist needy gardeners with the upkeep of their plots.

Scottish National Sweet Pea, Rose & Carnation Society

72 West George Street, Coatbridge, Lanarkshire, Strathclyde ML5 2DD

CONTACT Secretary
AIMS To encourage the growing and showing of the named flowers in Scotland

MEMBERSHIP 100
SUBSCRIPTIONS £3
SERVICES Gardens; advice; awards; shows; journal

The Scottish National Sweet Pea, Rose & Carnation Society produces an annual Year Book in November, and holds a show in August (6 – 7 August this year). Some 28 trophies are awarded annually. Sweet Peas and roses are trialled in Glasgow, at Bellahouston Park and Tollcross Park respectively. There is an informal advisory service.

Scottish Wildlife Trust
Crammond House, Crammond Glebe Road, Edinburgh EH4 6NS
☎ 031 312 7765   FAX 031 312 8705
SUBSCRIPTIONS £15 individual, £25 joint
SERVICES Lectures; publications; advice; journal; regional groups; outings

Formed in 1964, the national wildlife conservation body in Scotland. They have over 80 reserves under management including Red Moss of Balerno, Rahoy Hills and Seaton Cliffs.

Somerset Gardens Trust
St Peter's Vicarage, 62 Eastwick Road, Taunton, Somerset TA2 7HD
CONTACT Membership Secretary
SUBSCRIPTIONS £10 individual, £15 joint
SERVICES Lectures; journal; outings

Works to conserve and protect Somerset's parks and gardens. As well as conservation and education work, talks and garden visits are arranged.

Somerset Trust for Nature Conservation
Fyne Court, Broomfield, Bridgwater, Somerset TA5 2EQ
☎ 0823 451587
SUBSCRIPTIONS £12 individual, £2 for additional members
SERVICES Lectures; publications; advice; journal; outings

The trust now has 60 reserves under management, including Greater Westhay in the Somerset Levels.

Staffordshire Gardens & Parks Trust
c/o Planning Department, South Staffordshire District Council, Wolverhampton Road, Codsall, Wolverhampton WV8 1PX
☎ 0902 846111
CONTACT Secretary
AIMS To record and encourage the conservation of parks and gardens

SUBSCRIPTIONS £7.50 individual, £10 joint
SERVICES Lectures; advice; journal; outings; training; exhibitions

The trust aims to record the county's most valuable gardens and work for their conservation. Members can assist in this task, and take part in study visits. Meetings and lectures are held in Stafford.

Staffordshire Wildlife Trust
Coutts House, Sandon, Stafford ST18 0DN
SUBSCRIPTIONS £12 individual, £15 joint
SERVICES Lectures; journal; outings

Part of the RSNC partnership. Over 1,100 acres of land in 30 reserves, including the wetland reserves Loynton Moss, Woodseaves and Branston Water Park.

Suffolk Wildlife Trust
Brooke House, The Green, Ashbocking, Ipswich, Suffolk IP6 9JY
☎ 0473 890089
SUBSCRIPTIONS £16 individual, £17 joint
SERVICES Publications; advice; journal; outings; education

The largest of the county wildlife trusts, with 75 reserves. A current concern is the effect of ground water levels on many of these reserves.

Surrey Gardens Trust
c/o Planning Department, Surrey County Council, County Hall, Kingston on Thames, Surrey KT1 2DT
☎ 081 541 9419
CONTACT Secretary
SUBSCRIPTIONS £8 individual, £10 joint
SERVICES Lectures; advice; journal; outings; research; restoration work

Members receive a twice yearly newsletter, and there is a programme of lectures and garden visits. Those wanting more active involvement may train as recorders, carry out archive research and assist on garden improvement projects.

Surrey Wildlife Trust
School Lane, Pirbright, Woking, Surrey GU24 0JN
☎ 0483 488055
SUBSCRIPTIONS £12.50 individual, £16 joint
SERVICES Lectures; publications; advice; journal; regional groups; outings

The Surrey Wildlife Trust looks after 24 nature reserves including Nower Wood and the Graeme Hendrey Wood.

Sussex Wildlife Trust

Woods Mill, Henfield, West Sussex BN5 9SD
☎ 0273 492630

SUBSCRIPTIONS £12 individual, £8.50 joint (each)
SERVICES Lectures; publications; advice; journal;
regional groups; outings

Formed in 1961, the trust now looks after 37 separate
nature reserves including The Mens. Among the attractions at the Woods Mill headquarters is managed hazel
coppice.

Urban Wildlife Trust, The West Midlands Wildlife Campaign

Unit 310 Jubilee Trades Centre, 130 Pershore Street,
Birmingham B5 6ND
☎ 021 666 7474

SUBSCRIPTIONS £11.50
SERVICES Publications; advice; nursery

Urban group which encourages and advises on the
formation of wildlife areas. They have an environmental
centre at Winson Green, and a wildflower nursery.

Wakefield & North of England Tulip Society

70 Wrenthorpe Lane, Wrenthorpe, Wakefield,
West Yorkshire WF2 0PT

CONTACT Hon. Secretary
AIMS The growing, breeding and showing of English
florist tulips
MEMBERSHIP 300
SUBSCRIPTIONS £4
SERVICES Seed scheme; publications; awards; shows;
journal; outings;

Long-established society devoted to florist tulips. They
publish an annual journal and hold two shows each
year: at Wrenthorpe on 7 May and at Normanton on
14 May this year. Other events include formal and
informal meetings and garden visits. Surplus bulbs are
distributed in October. *The English Tulip and its History* is available from the society, as are slide lectures.

Warwickshire Wildlife Trust

Brandon Marsh Nature Centre, Brandon Lane,
Coventry CV3 3GW
☎ 0203 302912

SUBSCRIPTIONS £15 individual, £19 joint
SERVICES Lectures; publications; advice; journal;
regional groups; outings

Formerly the Warwickshire Nature Conservation
Trust. They manage over 40 reserves including Ryton
Woods and Ufton Fields.

Welsh Historic Gardens Trust

Plas Tyllwyd, Tangroes, Cardigan SA43 2JD
☎ 0239 810432   FAX 0239 810432

CONTACT Trust Executive
AIMS To assist in and initiate conservation of gardens
and designed landscapes in Wales
SUBSCRIPTIONS £10 individuals, £15 joint
SERVICES Advice; journal; regional groups; outings

Through the trust office and local branches this organisation assists and initiates the conservation of important gardens, parks and landscapes. Members can
become involved in research, surveying and other conservation work which is carried out at branch level.

The Wildlife Trust Bedfordshire & Cambridgeshire

Enterprise House, Maris Lane, Trumpington,
Cambridge CB2 2LE
☎ 0223 846363

SUBSCRIPTIONS £13 individual, £16 joint
SERVICES Lectures; publications; advice; journal;
regional groups; outings

Nearly ninety reserves under management, including
Totternhoe Knolls and Hayley Wood. There are 15
local groups and other offices in Bedford and Luton.

Wildlife Trust for Bristol, Bath and Avon

Bristol Wildlife Centre, Jacob Wells Road, Bristol,
Avon BS8 1DR

SUBSCRIPTIONS £10 individual, £13 joint
SERVICES Lectures; publications; advice; journal;
outings

Formed in 1980, this is the new name for the Avon
Wildlife Trust. 28 nature reserves including Brown's
Folly above Bathford.

Wiltshire Gardens Trust

Treglisson, Crowe Lane, Freshford, Bath, Avon
BA3 6EB

CONTACT Hon. Secretary
SUBSCRIPTIONS Under revision
SERVICES Lectures; journal; special interest groups;
outings

This group doubles as the county gardens trust and (for
an additional subscription) as the Wiltshire branch of
the NCCPG. Their programme includes lectures and
garden visits, and the annual plant sale this year is on
10 July at Bradley House, Maiden Bradley.

Wiltshire Wildlife Trust
18 – 19 High Street, Devizes SN10 1AT
☎ 0380 725670

SUBSCRIPTIONS £13 individual, £16 joint
SERVICES Lectures; publications; advice; journal; outings

Formerly the Wiltshire Trust for Nature Conservation. They look after nearly 40 reserves including a fritillary meadow at Upper Waterhay (late April).

Yorkshire Wildlife Trust
10 Toft Green, York, North Yorkshire YO1 1JT
☎ 0904 659570

SUBSCRIPTIONS £15 individual, £22.50 joint
SERVICES Lectures; publications; advice; journal; regional groups; outings

Founded in 1946, and now managing 59 nature reserves. Sites of interest to botanists include Grass Wood and Spurn Head.

Overseas

American Camellia Society
One Massee Lane, Fort Valley, Georgia 31030, USA
SERVICES

UK representative: Westward, La Marquanderie, La Brelade, Jersey, Channel Islands.

American Hemerocallis Society
1454 Rebel Drive, Jackson, Mississippi 39211, USA

CONTACT Membership Secretary

American Hibiscus Society
P O Box 321540, Cocoa Beach, FL 32932-1540, USA

CONTACT Executive Secretary

American Horticultural Society
7931 East Boulevard Drive, Alexandria, VA 22308-1300, USA

American Hosta Society
7802 NE 63rd Street, Vancouver, WA 98662, USA

CONTACT Membership Secretary

American Iris Society
7414 East 60th, Tulsa, OK 74145-9317, USA

CONTACT The Secretary

American Orchid Society
6000 South Olive Avenue, West Palm Beach, Florida 33405, USA

American Rhododendron Society
P O Box 1380, Gloucester, VA 23061, USA

CONTACT Executive Director

American Rock Garden Society
P O Box 67, Millwood, NY 10546, USA

CONTACT Executive secretary

American Rose Society
P O Box 30000, 8877 Jefferson-Paige Road, Shreveport, LA 71130-0030, USA

CONTACT Membership Secretary

Australian Garden History Society
P O Box 972, Bowral, NSW 2576, Australia

CONTACT Executive Officer

Bonsai Clubs International
2636 W Mission Road, 277, Tallahassee, FL 32304, USA

CONTACT Virginia Ellerman

Botanical Society of South Africa
Kirstenbosch, Claremont, Cape Town 7735, South Africa

CONTACT Diana Peters

Cactus & Succulent Society of America
PO Box 35034, Desmoines, IA 50315-0301, USA

Cymbidium Society of America Inc
P O Box 2244, Orange, CA 92669, USA

CONTACT Membership Secretary

Gesellschaft der Heidefreunde
Tangstedter Landstr 276, 2000 Hamburg 62, Germany

CONTACT Herr Fritz Kircher

German Heather society.

Gesellschaft der Staudenfreunde
Meisenweg 1, 6234 Hattersheim 3, Germany

CONTACT Geschäftsführer (Secretary)

Perennial society.

Holly Society of America Inc
11318 West Murdock, Wichita, KS 67212-6609, USA

CONTACT   Hon. Secretary

International Aroid Society
P O Box 43-1853, Miami, FL 33143, USA

CONTACT   Bruce McManus

International Lilac Society
P O Box 315, Rumford, ME 04276, USA

CONTACT   Walter W. Oakes

International Palm Society
P O Box 368, Lawrence, KS 66044, USA

CONTACT   Mrs Lynn McKamey

The Magnolia Society Inc
907 South Chestnut Street, Hammond, LA 70403-5102, USA

CONTACT   Hon. Secretary

Nederlandse Heidervereniging 'Ericultura'
Esdoornstraat 54, 6681 ZM Bemmel, Netherlands

CONTACT   Mr J. Dahm

Dutch Heather society.

New Zealand Alpine Gardening Society
17 Courage Road, Amberley, Canterbury, New Zealand

New Zealand Fuchsia Society Inc
P O Box 11-082, Ellerslie, Auckland, New Zealand 5

CONTACT   Miss Joan Byres

New Zealand Gladiolus Council
13 Ramanui Avenue, Hawera, Taranaka, New Zealand

North American Heather Society
P O Box 101, Highland View, Alstead, New Hampshire 03602, USA

CONTACT   Hon. Secretary

North American Lily Society Inc
P O Box 272, Owatonna, MN 55060, USA

CONTACT   Hon. Secretary

The Rock Garden Club Prague
Mimonskà 12/639, 19000 Prague 9, Czech Republic

Rose Hybridizers Association
3245 Wheaton Road, Horsheads, NY 14845, USA

CONTACT   Larry D. Peterson

La Société Française des Roses
Parc de la Tête d'Or, 69459 Lyon, France

Société National d'Horticulture de France
84 rue de Grenelle, Paris 75007, France
☎ 010 331 45 48 81 00

More details in the Gardening in France section.

The Society for Growing Australian Plants
3 Currawang Place, Como West 2154, New South Wales, Australia

CONTACT   Hon. Secretary (NSW branch)

Verein Deutscher Rosenfreunde
Waldseestrasse 14, 76530 Baden-Baden, Germany

German rose society.

Western Horticultural Society
P O Box 60507, Palo Alto, CA 94306, USA

CONTACT   Robert Young

Local Gardening Clubs

If you have recently moved to a new area, and want to join a gardening club, it is sometimes difficult to know where to begin the search. Once you have found one, you discover that the character and interests of clubs differ enormously. One may be run for people who want to know how to grow vegetables that will win prizes at the Village Show, while a neighbouring club is exclusively concerned with how to acquire rare plants and grow them in artistic colour schemes.

The local library or information centre is most people's starting point: clubs usually send details of their programme of forthcoming events to such institutions. The local newspaper will also publish subsequent reports of those meetings. *Garden News* also includes club dates each week. If you encounter real problems in discovering a club locally, ask your County Horticultural College for help. The Royal Horticultural Society may also be willing to tell you the name of the nearest club among its affiliates.

Suppose you fail to find a satisfactory gardening club locally: you should consider starting your own with the help of a few like-minded friends. You will need to organise a regular time and venue for your events and you will have to think about such important matters as the constitution of the club, the costs and benefits of membership, and the need for third party insurance. That said, the greatest difficulty will be in finding good speakers at a reasonable price. Any reader who has been the secretary of a gardening club will know how difficult and time-consuming this task can be. One way to find good speakers is to ask among your friends for recommendations. Many people belong to more than one gardening club and will be able to recommend good speakers that they would like to hear again. The specialist plant societies such as the Alpine Garden Society can also find people local to your society who may be able to talk about their specialisation.

However, the whole problem of finding speakers has been enormously simplified in recent years by the *Horticultural Speakers' Register*, published first by Barbara Abbs and now by the Royal Horticultural Society. It lists over 450 speakers who offer a total of more than 1,800 different lectures, a Godsend for hard-pressed secretaries. Speakers are arranged alphabetically, rather than by subject, although it is quite easy to pick out the specialist experts. There are Bill Bossom, Ken Grapes and Colin Horner among others from the RNRS for example, and Bryan Stevens, Edward Stiff and Dick and Lorna Swinbank among the fuchsia experts. Lecture fees range from nil to £500. For £50 – £100 you can procure a lecturer of the distinction of James Compton, Brian Halliwell or Tony Lowe, but you might have to pay over £100 for Elizabeth Banks or Kay Sanecki, while Roy Lancaster will set you back twice that or more. The register gives full details of how far each is prepared to travel, when he is available, and the equipment he brings or needs. Every club secretary should have a copy.

Nurseries & Garden Centres

We have selected a range of nurseries from the very small and specialised to the largest of the garden centres. Between these extremes there should be several to suit most people's needs. There are three ways of finding them. In this section they are listed by county. We have used the post-1974 county names, and have adopted the regional divisions of Scotland. The English counties are followed by Wales, Scotland, Northern Ireland and the Republic of Ireland. Where possible the entries are placed in their geographical counties rather than by their postal address, to help plan a visit. The next section lists many of the nurseries by specialisation: the county names appear there to help you find the entry in the main listing. We have restricted this list to true specialists: those with an excellent but general range do not find a place. Finally, all the nurseries and garden centres are listed in the index alphabetically. Strict alphabetical order has been followed, so for example, the rose breeders R Harkness & Co are indexed under 'R' and not 'H'.

Mail order is an issue which splits the trade. Most garden centres will not offer this service, and nor will many traditional or smaller nurseries. We have indicated those which do. Buying by post, obviously, means you cannot inspect the plants first. You still have a right to expect healthy specimens. Remember that posted plants are likely to be smaller than normal to save on space and postage costs. Your order will probably be sent in the dormant season when the plants will be better able to cope with a journey through the postal system, and when the nurseryman is less busy. Trees are usually sent by road courier; roses travel cheaply in paper sacks; other plants need careful and time-consuming packing for which you will have to pay.

Some nurseries have demonstration and display gardens: these are mentioned. There are cross-references where necessary to the Gardens section. See also the publications of the National Gardens Scheme and Scotland's Garden Scheme: a number of nurseries open regularly for these charities. Where nurseries have indicated that they are holders of a NCCPG National Collection we have included this information: opening times and further details can be found in *The National Plant Collections Directory* which is available from the NCCPG, The Pines, Wisley Garden, Woking, Surrey GU23 6QB. Other useful publications are *The Plant Finder* for picking out stockists of individual genera and sources of a particular species; and a road atlas for tracking down the nursery site. Garden centres usually observe fixed opening times: traditional nurseries tend to open early and close at dusk; opening hours at smaller nurseries may depend on other commitments. Some small nurseries only operate by mail order: they do not open at all. If in doubt, phone first.

ENGLAND

AVON

A & A Phipps
62 Samuel White Road, Hanham, Bristol, Avon
BS15 3LX
☎ 0272 607591
CONTACT Alan Phipps
OPEN Phone first
SPECIALITIES Cacti and succulents
CATALOGUE SAE
MAIL ORDER Yes; smallish plants only

Cacti and succulent specialists with both a general and a collectors' range of species. Telephone first before calling. They also sell seed-grown cacti and succulents to retail and wholesale outlets. The mail order list is issued in April.

Arne Herbs

Limeburn Nurseries, Chew Magna, Bristol, Avon BS18 8QW
☎ 0275 333399
LOCATION 8 miles south of Bristol, just off B3130
OPEN 10 am – 5 pm, usually. Phone first
SPECIALITIES Herbs; wild flowers
CATALOGUE £1
MAIL ORDER Yes; no minimum order
DESIGN SERVICE Arne Herbs

Twin ranges of herbs and native species which can be used for conservation schemes. Fresh cut herbs available in season too. Advice service to customers. Consultancy for physic gardens.

Blackmore & Langdon

Stanton Nurseries, Pensford, Bristol, Avon BS18 4JL
☎ 0275 332300
CONTACT Mrs Rosemary Langdon
LOCATION 8 miles south of Bristol, off A37
OPEN 9 am – 5 pm, daily
SPECIALITIES Begonias; delphiniums
CATALOGUE SAE
MAIL ORDER Yes
SHOWS Chelsea; BBC GW Live; Hampton Court
GIFT TOKENS Own

This family business, started in 1901, is still run by the founder's grandchildren. Theirs is a long tradition of showy border plants, notably huge begonias and tall delphiniums. All plants are grown on site. A Chelsea preview and plant sale is held on the weekend of the 13 – 15 May.

Brackenwood Garden Centre

131 Nore Road, Portishead, Bristol, Avon BS20 8DU
☎ 0275 843484   FAX 0275 843484
CONTACT Manager
OPEN 9 am – 5 pm, Monday – Saturday; 10 am – 5 pm, Sundays. Closed over Christmas
MAIL ORDER No
REFRESHMENTS Tea room
GARDEN 6 acre Woodland Garden
GIFT TOKENS HTA

Garden centre with a wide and constantly changing all-round range. The Woodland Garden features in Jarrolds' *Beautiful Gardens of Britain* calendar this year. See also Brackenwood Nurseries.

Brackenwood Nurseries

Leigh Court Estate, Pill Road, Abbots Leigh, Bristol, Avon
☎ 0275 375292
CONTACT Manager
OPEN 10 am – 5 pm, spring and summer; 10 am – 4.30 pm, winter
MAIL ORDER No
GIFT TOKENS HTA

All-round stock. See their other site, Brackenwood Garden Centre, for more details.

C S Lockyer

70 Henfield Road, Coalpit Heath, Bristol, Avon BS17 2UZ
☎ 0454 772219
CONTACT C. S. Lockyer
OPEN Most days; phone first
SPECIALITIES Fuchsias
CATALOGUE 3 first class stamps
MAIL ORDER Yes
GARDEN Demonstration gardens
SHOWS Chelsea; Hampton Court
GIFT TOKENS Own

A specialist fuchsia grower, with young plants of both tender and hardy varieties. Regular talks and demonstrations are held at the nursery to pass on the experience of over 35 years in the business.

Hannays of Bath

Sydney Wharf Nursery, Bathwick, Bath, Avon BA2 4ES
☎ 0225 462230
CONTACT Spencer Hannay
OPEN 10 am – 5 pm, daily. Closed Tuesdays
SPECIALITIES Herbaceous perennials
NEW FOR 1994 *Albuca tortuosa*; *Sutherlandia microphylla*; *Geranium harveyi*; *Lavatera* 'Mary Hope'
CATALOGUE £1.40
MAIL ORDER No
GARDEN Display borders
GIFT TOKENS Own

A rich source of herbaceous plants and shrubs, mainly species. Recommended for both gardeners and collectors. Many plants are grown from seed collected by the Hannays, including *Dierama* species from South Africa. Keep an eye open for the results of trips to the Cape, Lesotho, Uganda, Spain and Nepal in 1993.

Hillier Garden Centre

Whiteway Road, Bath, Avon BA2 2RG
☎ 0225 421162
SPECIALITIES Climbers; conifers; trees

CATALOGUE   On request
MAIL ORDER   No
GIFT TOKENS   HTA

See Hillier Nurseries Ltd, Hampshire.

Jekka's Herb Farm

Rose Cottage, Shellards Lane, Alveston, Bristol,
Avon BS12 2SY
☎ 0454 418878   📠 0454 418878

CONTACT   Mrs J. McVicar
OPEN   Mail order only
SPECIALITIES   Herbs; wild flowers
CATALOGUE   SAE plus £1
MAIL ORDER   Yes; no minimum order
SHOWS   Chelsea; BBC GW Live; Hampton Court

A comprehensive and interesting range of herbs and
some wild flowers. The business is basically wholesale:
retail trade is mail order only.

John Sanday (Roses) Ltd

Over Lane, Almondsbury, Bristol, Avon BS12 4DA
☎ 0454 612195

CONTACT   Thomas Sanday
LOCATION   North of M5, J16 & J17
OPEN   9 am – 5 pm, Monday – Saturday; 10 am – 5 pm,
Sundays
SPECIALITIES   Roses
CATALOGUE   On request
MAIL ORDER   Yes
GARDEN   Rose gardens
GIFT TOKENS   Own

A wide choice of roses, both old and new varieties. The
rose gardens are open all year, and there are pruning
demonstrations in early spring and planting demonstrations in November.

Little Creek Nursery

39 Moor Road, Banwell, Weston super Mare, Avon
BS24 6EF
☎ 0934 823739

CONTACT   Rhys and Julie Adams
LOCATION   3 miles from M5, J21
OPEN   10.30 am – 4.30 pm, Thursday – Friday, March
to August. Phone first at other times
SPECIALITIES   Hellebores; cyclamen
CATALOGUE   3 first class stamps
MAIL ORDER   Yes; no minimum order

A small nursery which specialises in *Cyclamen* species
(raised from seed), and *Helleborus*, with some perennials too.

Misses I Allen and M J Huish

Quarry Farm, Wraxall, Bristol, Avon BS19 1LE

CONTACT   Misses I. Allen and M. J. Huish
OPEN   By appointment
SPECIALITIES   Asters
CATALOGUE   SAE plus 50p
MAIL ORDER   Yes
GARDEN   Private garden, open by appointment
NCCPG NATIONAL COLLECTIONS *Aster*

Quarry Farm is a private garden. The Misses Allen and
Huish hold the National Collection of Asters – some
300 varieties of Michaelmas daisies. Plants are for sale
as and when stocks are available.

Monocot Nursery

Jacklands, Jacklands Bridge, Tickenham, Clevedon,
Avon BS21 6SG

CONTACT   Mike Salmon
OPEN   10 am – 6 pm, by appointment
SPECIALITIES   Bulbs; seeds
CATALOGUE   SAE
MAIL ORDER   Yes

Specialist nursery with an amazing collection of bulbous plants (including tubers, rhizomes and corms). The
stock is mostly of species, and subspecies, grown from
seed, frequently from named collectors and sources. The
seed list appears in October. Nursery browsers will find
items which are not in the catalogue.

National Collection of Passiflora

Greenholm Nurseries Ltd, Kingston Seymour,
Clevedon, Avon BS21 6XS
☎ 0934 833350   📠 0934 838237

CONTACT   R. J. R. Vanderplank
LOCATION   Kingston Seymour
OPEN   9 am – 1 pm, 2 pm – 5 pm
SPECIALITIES   *Passiflora*
CATALOGUE   2 first class stamps
MAIL ORDER   Yes
GARDEN   Permanent display of passion flowers
SHOWS   Chelsea; BBC GW Live; Hampton Court
NCCPG NATIONAL COLLECTIONS *Passiflora*

Passion flowers only. A fascinating proposition for anyone in a position to grow them. The catalogue is detailed, and includes precise temperature requirements.

Park Garden Centre

Over Lane, Almondsbury, Bristol, Avon BS12 4BP
☎ 0454 612247   📠 0454 617559

CONTACT   Mr J. Billings (plants); Mrs J. Parrish (shop)
LOCATION   North of Bristol
OPEN   9 am – 6 pm, summer; 9 am – 5 pm, winter
SHOP   Garden machinery; conservatory; fish

REFRESHMENTS Coffee shop
GARDEN Demonstration rose garden and orchard
DESIGN SERVICE Park Garden Centre
GIFT TOKENS HTA; own

Garden centre with garden products. Agents for Hillier plants. Local delivery; design and landscaping services.

BEDFORDSHIRE

Bickerdike's Garden Centre
London Road, Sandy, Bedfordshire SG19 1DW
☎ 0767 680559   FAX 0767 680356

LOCATION On A1
OPEN 9 am – 5.30 pm, daily
SHOP Garden products
GARDEN Display gardens
GIFT TOKENS HTA

Garden centre under the same ownership as Brampton Garden Centre.

Walter Blom & Son Ltd
Coombelands Nurseries, Thurleigh Road, Milton Ernest, Bedfordshire MK44 1RQ
☎ 0234 782424   FAX 0234 782495

CONTACT Miss Samantha Papworth
OPEN 9 am – 5 pm, Monday – Friday. Also 9 am – 12 pm, Saturdays, September only
SPECIALITIES Bulbs
CATALOGUE On request
MAIL ORDER Yes
GARDEN Display at Chenies Manor, Buckinghamshire, see Gardens section
SHOWS Chelsea

Major bulb growers: their range covers hyacinth, daffodil, and tulip cultivars; they also have species and a wide selection of smaller bulbs.

Wyevale Garden Centre
Dunstable Road, Caddington, Luton, Bedfordshire LU1 4AN
☎ 0582 457313   FAX 0582 480716

BERKSHIRE

Bressingham Plant Centre
Dorney Court, Dorney, Windsor, Berkshire SL4 6QP
☎ 0628 669999   FAX 0628 669693

CONTACT Tim Baylis
LOCATION Dorney Court
OPEN 10 am – 5.30 pm, daily except Christmas and Boxing Day
SPECIALITIES Conifers; herbaceous perennials

CATALOGUE £2
MAIL ORDER See Bressingham Gardens, Norfolk
REFRESHMENTS Tea room
DESIGN SERVICE Bressingham Landscapes, Design & Build
SHOWS Chelsea; Hampton Court
GIFT TOKENS Own

Blooms' first plant centre to be opened away from Norfolk: Alan Bloom inaugurated it in March 1993. They carry the huge range of perennials and conifers for which the company is renowned. The quality is also outstanding. Talks are held at the plant centre. Mail order is available directly from Norfolk: see Bressingham Gardens Mail Order. Design and build service from Bressingham Landscapes.

Country Gardens
Turnpike Road, Thatcham, Berkshire RG13 3AN
☎ 0635 873700

LOCATION 22 sites in the south east and south Midlands

The head office of a chain of 22 garden centres in southern England.

Foxgrove Plants
Foxgrove, Enborne, Newbury, Berkshire RG14 6RE
☎ 0635 40554

CONTACT Louise Vockins
LOCATION West of Newbury
OPEN 10 am – 5 pm, Wednesday – Sunday, and Bank Holidays. Closed in August
SPECIALITIES Alpines; snowdrops
CATALOGUE 65p cheque
MAIL ORDER Yes
SHOWS RHS Westminster; Chelsea

This small nursery carries a pleasing range of hardy and cottage garden type plants. Their speciality is snowdrops: they have species, forms and hybrids.

Hare Hatch Nursery
London Road, Hare Hatch, Twyford, Reading, Berkshire RG10 9HW
☎ 0734 401600   FAX 0734 401600

CONTACT Curtis Leach
LOCATION Between Reading and Maidenhead on A4
OPEN 9 am – 5 pm, Saturdays and Sundays only. Phone for other times
SPECIALITIES Bedding plants
NEW FOR 1994 Mimulus 'Verity Purple'; Bacopa 'Snowflake'; Solenopsis axillaris and others
CATALOGUE SAE plus 2 first class stamps

The main lines here are plants for hanging baskets and tubs, and all year round bedding. Other ranges include cacti and succulents, and a general selection of other garden plants.

Henry Street
Swallowfield Road Nursery, Arborfield, Reading, Berkshire RG2 9JY
☎ 0734 761223 [FAX] 0734 761417

CONTACT Mr M. C. Goold
OPEN 9 am – 5.30 pm, daily
SPECIALITIES Bedding plants; roses
CATALOGUE On request
MAIL ORDER Yes; bare root only
GARDEN Rose fields open

Rose growers whose range covers all types, in mainly modern varieties. They also sell bedding plants, and carry a general stock at the garden centre.

Hillier Garden Centre
Priors Court Road, Hermitage, Newbury, Berkshire RG16 9TG
☎ 0635 200442

SPECIALITIES Climbers; conifers; trees
CATALOGUE On request
MAIL ORDER No
GIFT TOKENS HTA

See Hillier Nurseries Ltd, Hampshire.

Hollington Nurseries
Woolton Hill, Newbury, Berkshire RG15 9XT
☎ 0635 253903 [FAX] 0635 254990

CONTACT Judith and Simon Hopkinson
LOCATION 4 miles south of Newbury, off A343
OPEN 10 am – 5.30 pm, Monday – Saturday; 11 am – 5 pm, Sundays and Bank Holidays, March to September. 10 am – dusk, Monday – Saturday, October to December
SPECIALITIES Herbs
CATALOGUE SAE plus 50p
MAIL ORDER No
SHOP Herb products
REFRESHMENTS Tea room (summer only)
GARDEN Display gardens in walled garden
DESIGN SERVICE Hollington Nurseries

A large range of herbs and scented plants in containers, as well as roses to plant with them. Herb and wild flower seeds too. They run courses, and have a garden planning service.

M V Fletcher
70 South Street, Reading, Berkshire RG1 4RA
☎ 0734 571814

CONTACT M V Fletcher
OPEN Mail order only
SPECIALITIES Mosses

CATALOGUE 2 first class stamps
MAIL ORDER Yes

Something well outside the ambit of the horticultural trade. Mr Fletcher is a private collector who only sells mosses and hepatics (liverworts).

Wyevale Garden Centre
Forest Road, Binfield, Bracknell, Berkshire RG12 5ND
☎ 0344 869456 [FAX] 0344 869541

Wyevale Garden Centre
Heathlands Road, Wokingham, Berkshire RG11 3BG
☎ 0734 773055 [FAX] 0734 772949

BUCKINGHAMSHIRE

A J Palmer & Son
Denham Court Nursery, Denham Court Drive, Denham, Uxbridge, Buckinghamshire UB9 5PG
☎ 0895 832035

CONTACT Sheila or John Palmer
LOCATION Middle of New Buckinghamshire golf course, near Denham village
OPEN 9.30 am – 5 pm, during spring, early summer and autumn. Closed Sundays and January. See below
SPECIALITIES Roses
CATALOGUE On request
MAIL ORDER Yes; collection only for standards

Specialist rose growers with a range of mainly modern varieties. Opening times vary with the seasons and availability. Containerised plants are available from about March to June. From July to October the show field is open for viewing (near the Denham roundabout off the A40). Most of the stock is sold bare-rooted in November.

Buckingham Nurseries and Garden Centre
14 Tingewick Road, Buckingham, Buckinghamshire MK18 4AE
☎ 0280 813556 [FAX] 0280 815491

CONTACT Mrs P. L. Brown
LOCATION 1½ miles west of Buckingham, on A421
SPECIALITIES Hedging; shrubs; trees
NEW FOR 1994 Many new plants
CATALOGUE On request (September)
MAIL ORDER Yes
SHOP Retail garden shop
GIFT TOKENS HTA

The nursery produces bare-root hedging and tree plants for ornamental and forestry use. A selection of container plants, including ones not listed in the catalogue, is sold from the garden centre.

Butterfields Nursery

Harvest Hill, Bourne End, Buckinghamshire SL8 5JJ
☎ 0628 525455

SPECIALITIES Dahlias; orchids, pleiones
CATALOGUE SAE
MAIL ORDER Yes; pleiones only
SHOWS RHS Westminster; Chelsea
NCCPG NATIONAL COLLECTIONS *Pleione*

Butterfields has two main but very different specialities: pleiones and dahlias. The *Pleione* species are backed up by an impressive list of hybrids. The dahlia range consists of named varieties for showing, flower arranging and garden use.

The Conifer Garden

Hare Lane Nursery, Little Kingshill, Great Missenden, Buckinghamshire HP16 0EF
☎ 0494 890624

CONTACT Mr and Mrs M. P. S. Powell
OPEN 11 am – 4.30 pm, Tuesday – Saturday
SPECIALITIES Conifers
CATALOGUE 2 second class stamps
MAIL ORDER Yes

Specialists in conifers of all sizes. The stock is container-grown, and the choice is extensive (500).

East Midlands Cactus Nursery

Manor Close, Broughton, Milton Keynes, Buckinghamshire MK10 9AA
☎ 0908 665584

CONTACT M. and E. Watson
SPECIALITIES Cacti and succulents
CATALOGUE SAE or 1 first class stamp
MAIL ORDER Yes

Cacti and succulent specialists, with a good list of mammillarias in particular.

Great Gardens of England Ltd

Marlow Garden & Leisure Centre, Pump Lane South, Little Marlow, Buckinghamshire SL7 3RB
☎ 0628 482716 📠 0628 898135

CONTACT Les Brown (Manager)
LOCATION Off A404, between M4 and M40
OPEN 9 am – 5.30 pm
GIFT TOKENS HTA; own

Garden centre with a general range for indoor and outdoor gardening. Delivery service available.

Morehavens

28 Denham Lane, Gerrards Cross, Buckinghamshire SL9 0EX
☎ 0494 871563

CONTACT Ann Farmer
OPEN Collection by arrangement
CATALOGUE SAE
MAIL ORDER Yes; p & p included
GARDEN Gardens

Camomile lawns by post. Events and courses are also arranged.

Tamarisk Nurseries

Wing Road, Stewkley, Leighton Buzzard, Buckinghamshire LU7 0JB
☎ 0525 240747

CONTACT Alan Cupit
LOCATION North Buckinghamshire, between Wing and Stewkley
OPEN 12 – 5 pm, Monday – Friday; 10 am – 6 pm, Saturday – Sunday, and Bank Holidays
SPECIALITIES Air plants; carnivorous plants
MAIL ORDER Yes

The range here includes cacti and airplants, as well as orchids, carnivorous plants, alpines and perennials. You are advised to phone first during the show season.

Waddesdon Nursery

Queen Street, Waddesdon, Aylesbury, Buckinghamshire HP18 0JW
☎ 0296 658586 📠 0296 658852

CONTACT Mrs P. Wilson
LOCATION Between Aylesbury and Bicester on A41
OPEN 10 am – 5 pm, daily

Bedding plants, herbs and herbaceous perennials. No longer connected with the gardens: a name change is in the offing.

Wyevale Garden Centre

Junction Avebury Boulevard/ Secklow Gate, Milton Keynes, Buckinghamshire MK9 3BY
☎ 0908 604011 📠 0908 664678

Wyevale Garden Centre

Newport Road, Woburn Sands, Milton Keynes, Buckinghamshire MK17 8UF
☎ 0908 281161 📠 0908 281142

CAMBRIDGESHIRE

Arbor Exotica

The Estate Office, Hall Farm, Weston Colville,
Cambridgeshire CB1 5PE
☎ 0223 290328   FAX 0223 290650

CONTACT Mrs E. J. Capewell
LOCATION The nursery is at West Wratting Park,
West Wratting, Cambridge (0223 290316)
OPEN By appointment
SPECIALITIES Shrubs; trees
NEW FOR 1994 Several new trees and shrubs
CATALOGUE On request
MAIL ORDER Yes; handling charge plus 30p per kilo

Wholesale and retail tree and shrub nursery. The emphasis is on species trees, which are raised from seed (not grafted) and are container-grown. The main address and telephone number is for the Estate Office.

Ballerina Trees Ltd

Maris Lane, Trumpington, Cambridge,
Cambridgeshire CB2 2LQ
☎ 0223 840411   FAX 0223 842934

CONTACT Sean Gardner
OPEN Sold through garden centres
SPECIALITIES Fruit
CATALOGUE On request
MAIL ORDER Yes; bare-rooted trees in autumn only

Their only line is the new compact, columnar apple trees, now in six varieties, including a crab and a cooker. The price of £19.95 includes postage.

Brampton Garden Centre

Buckden Road, Brampton, Huntingdon,
Cambridgeshire PE18 8NF
☎ 0480 453048

CONTACT Peter Bates
LOCATION Opposite RAF Brampton
OPEN 9 am – 5.30 pm, Monday – Saturday; 10 am –
5.30 pm, Sundays and Bank Holidays
SHOP Garden sundries; garden furniture
REFRESHMENTS Coffee shop
GIFT TOKENS HTA

Medium-sized garden centre with a full range of garden products, indoor and outdoor plants, garden buildings and garden furniture. They can deliver locally.

Elsworth Herbs

Avenue Farm Cottage, 31 Smith Street, Elsworth,
Cambridge, Cambridgeshire CB3 8HY
☎ 0954 267414

CONTACT Dr J. Twibell

OPEN By appointment and on open days
SPECIALITIES Herbs; artemisias
NEW FOR 1994 New artemisias
CATALOGUE 2 first class stamps
MAIL ORDER Yes; minimum order £10
GARDEN Garden
NCCPG NATIONAL COLLECTIONS Artemisia,
Nerium oleander

Herbs and cottage garden plants are available, but artemisias are the main attraction. There will be talks on the genus during the collection open day, Sunday 19 June. They also hold the national collection of Nerium oleander.

John Drake Aquilegias

Hardwicke House, Fen Ditton, Cambridge,
Cambridgeshire CB5 8TF
☎ 0223 292246

CONTACT L. J. Drake
SPECIALITIES Aquilegias
CATALOGUE 70p
MAIL ORDER Yes; minimum order £10

Aquilegia species, hybrids and cultivars – and nothing else – from an enthusiast and collector.

Meadowcroft Fuchsias

Church St Nurseries, Woodhurst, Huntingdon,
Cambridgeshire PE17 3BN
☎ 0487 823333

CONTACT D. N. Pickard
LOCATION East of Huntingdon
OPEN 9 am – 6 pm, weekends and Bank Holidays
SPECIALITIES Fuchsias; pelargoniums
CATALOGUE 3 second class stamps
MAIL ORDER Yes
SHOWS RHS Westminster; Chelsea; Hampton
Court

Wholesale and retail fuchsia specialists, with thirty years experience. Their range includes regal, zonal and ivy leaf pelargoniums.

Monksilver Nursery

Oakington Road, Cottenham, Cambridgeshire
CB4 4TW

CONTACT Joe Sharman
OPEN 10 am – 4 pm, Friday – Saturday, April to June
and September
SPECIALITIES Herbaceous perennials
NEW FOR 1994 Nepeta reichenbachiana; Leucanthemum 'Aglaia'; Paradisea lusitanica and many others
CATALOGUE 6 first class stamps
MAIL ORDER Yes
GARDEN Display gardens

NCCPG NATIONAL COLLECTIONS *Lamium, Vinca, Galeobdolon, Lathyrus*

That overused word 'rare' applies here: Monksilver specialise in finding and rescuing some really rare plants. Much of the stock is herbaceous. Three National Collections are held by the nursery, and part of the *Lathyrus* collection is also on display.

Notcutts Garden Centre

Oundle Road, Orton Waterville, Peterborough, Cambridgeshire PE2 0UU
☎ 0733 234600

LOCATION Opposite Nene Park
OPEN 8.30 am – 5.30 pm, Monday – Saturday; 10 am – 5.30 pm, Sundays. Closes at 5 pm in winter
CATALOGUE £2.50
SHOP Sundries; furniture; buildings; conservatories
REFRESHMENTS Coffee shop
GIFT TOKENS HTA; own

See also Notcutts Nurseries, Suffolk.

Padlock Croft

19 Padlock Road, West Wratting, Cambridgeshire CB1 5LS
☎ 0223 290383

CONTACT Susan and Peter Lewis
OPEN 10 am – 6 pm, Tuesday – Saturday, April to October. Also open Bank Holiday Mondays and by appointment
SPECIALITIES Herbaceous perennials
CATALOGUE 4 second class stamps
MAIL ORDER No
GARDEN Padlock Croft, Cambridgeshire, see Gardens section
NCCPG NATIONAL COLLECTIONS *Campanula, Symphyandra, Adenophora, Platycodon*

This small nursery holds the National Collection of *Campanula*: a long list of species and cultivars forms the centre of their range. Other plants include different members of the Campanulaceae and border plants.

Scotsdale Nursery & Garden Centre

120 Cambridge Road, Great Shelford, Cambridge, Cambridgeshire CB2 5JT
☎ 0223 842777   ☏ 0223 844340

CONTACT Mrs Caroline Owen
LOCATION 4 miles south of Cambridge, on A1301
OPEN 9 am – 5.30 pm, daily
SHOP Garden sundries; furniture; fencing; gifts
REFRESHMENTS Tea room
DESIGN SERVICE Scotsdale Nursery & Garden Centre
GIFT TOKENS HTA

Large garden centre with plants and associated products. Garden design and delivery service.

Simply Plants

17 Duloe Brook, Eaton Socon, Cambridgeshire PE19 3DW
☎ 0480 475312

CONTACT Christine Dakin
LOCATION Near the A1
OPEN By appointment and on open days
SPECIALITIES Bamboos; grasses
CATALOGUE 2 first class stamps
MAIL ORDER No

The nursery specialises in grasses and bamboos, but has an increasing number of perennials also. Wholesale and retail.

CHESHIRE

Bents Garden Centre and Nurseries

Warrington Road, Glazebury, Leigh, Cheshire WA3 5NT
☎ 0942 262066   ☏ 0942 261960

CONTACT Ron Bent
LOCATION Near Leigh, just off A580 towards Warrington
OPEN 9 am – 8 pm, Monday to Friday; 9.30 am – 5 pm, Saturday – Sunday
SHOP Garden sundries; gifts and aquatics
REFRESHMENTS Café
GARDEN Demonstration gardens
GIFT TOKENS HTA

Garden centre with the usual range of ancillary products. The focus, however, is the 60 acre nursery which supplies hardy nursery stock.

Bridgemere Nurseries

Bridgemere, Nantwich, Cheshire CW5 7QB
☎ 09365 381

LOCATION West of M6, J15 and J16
OPEN 9 am – 8 pm, Monday – Saturday; 10 am – 8 pm, Sundays. Close at 5 pm in winter
MAIL ORDER No
SHOP Garden sundries; gifts; foods
REFRESHMENTS Coffee shop
GARDEN Bridgemere Garden World, Cheshire
GIFT TOKENS HTA

Astonishing 25 acre nursery *cum* garden theme park: the largest range of plants in the country including a 'Connoisseur's Corner'. The choice of houseplants is especially notable. Other attractions include five acres of gardens (£1 admission) and the Bridgemere Wildlife Park (09365 223).

C & K Jones

Goldenfield Nursery, Barrow Lane, Tarvin, Cheshire
CH3 8JF

☎ 0829 740663   📠 0829 741877

CONTACT Christine Slatcher and Paula Woolley
LOCATION Chester
OPEN 8.30 am – 5 pm, daily
SPECIALITIES Roses
NEW FOR 1994 Roses 'Isobel Derby'; 'Oranges and
Lemons'; 'Purple Tiger'; 'Glamis Castle'; 'Golden Cel-
ebration'; 'Charisma'; 'Avon'; 'Christopher Columbus';
'Daylight'; 'High Hopes'; 'Fellowship'; 'Dawn Chorus'
CATALOGUE £1
MAIL ORDER Yes
SHOWS RHS Westminster; Hampton Court; Harro-
gate (Autumn)

Specialist rose growers: the rose fields are at Halghton,
Clwyd. Their range includes all types, but they are
especially good for newer varieties and introductions.

Caddick's Clematis Nursery

Lymm Road, Thelwall, Warrington, Cheshire
WA13 0UF

☎ 0925 757196

CONTACT Mrs Caddick
OPEN 10 am – 5 pm, Tuesday – Sunday, & Bank
Holidays, February to mid December
SPECIALITIES Clematis
NEW FOR 1994 Clematis 'The Vagabond'
CATALOGUE £1
MAIL ORDER Yes

Obviously a clematis specialist. Their range of species
and cultivars is probably the largest in the country.

Cheshire Herbs

Fourfields, Forest Road, Little Budworth, Tarporley,
Cheshire CW6 9ES

☎ 0829 760578   📠 0829 760354

CONTACT Libby Riddell
LOCATION On A49, just north of A54 intersection
OPEN 10 am – 5 pm. Closed from Christmas to New
Year
SPECIALITIES Herbs; seeds
CATALOGUE On request
MAIL ORDER Seeds only
SHOP Herbal products
GARDEN Herb garden
SHOWS Chelsea; BBC GW Live

An extensive range of pot grown herbs are on sale,
retail and wholesale. The small shop sells associated
products, and seeds are available mail order. The nursery holds talks and courses.

Collinwood Nurseries

Mottram St Andrew, Macclesfield, Cheshire
SK10 4QR

CONTACT Anthony Wright
LOCATION In the middle of the village, 2 miles east of
Alderley Edge
OPEN 8.30 am – 6 pm, Monday – Saturday; 1 pm – 6 pm,
Sundays
SPECIALITIES Chrysanthemums
CATALOGUE On request; chrysanthemums only
MAIL ORDER Yes; no minimum order

In season general garden plants, bedding and cut
flowers are available. The main focus though is chrysanthemums (Dendranthema): Koreans, rubellums,
greenhouse and garden varieties. The catalogue and mail
order side deals only with this genus.

F Morrey & Son

Forest Nursery, Kelsall, Tarporley, Cheshire
CW6 0SW

☎ 0829 51342   📠 0829 52449

LOCATION 8 miles east of Chester on A54
OPEN 9 am – 5 pm, Monday – Saturday
SPECIALITIES Rhododendrons; shrubs; trees
CATALOGUE 20p
MAIL ORDER No
GIFT TOKENS HTA

A long-established family nursery. Their range includes
trees and shrubs of all kinds, as well as conifers,
heathers and roses. Notably good for rhododendrons
and azaleas.

The Firs Nursery

Chelford Road, Henbury, Macclesfield, Cheshire
SK10 3LH

☎ 0625 426422

CONTACT Mrs F. J. Bowling
LOCATION 2 miles west of Macclesfield on A537
OPEN 9.30 am – 5 pm, March to September. Closed
Wednesdays and Sundays
SPECIALITIES Alpines; herbaceous perennials
CATALOGUE 2 first class stamps
MAIL ORDER No

This small nursery specialises in herbaceous perennials.
It also stocks a range of hebes and alpines.

Gordale Nursery & Garden Centre

Chester High Road, Burton, South Wirral, Cheshire
L64 8TF

☎ 051 336 2116   📠 051 336 7818

CONTACT Jill Nicholson
LOCATION 8 miles west of Chester, on A540

OPEN 9 am – 5 pm, winter; 9 am – 6 pm, summer.
Open until 8 pm Thursdays
SHOP Sundries; gifts; garden furniture
REFRESHMENTS Coffee shop
GIFT TOKENS HTA

Garden centre with a general range of plants and garden products. Delivery service.

Harold Walker

Oakfield Nurseries, Huntington, Chester, Cheshire CH3 6EA
☎ 0244 320731   ☏ 0244 342372

CONTACT Barry Walker
LOCATION Chester
OPEN Daily, February to June
SPECIALITIES Chrysanthemums
CATALOGUE 1 first class stamp
MAIL ORDER Yes
SHOWS Malvern Spring; Chelsea

Chrysanthemum specialist, also selling fuchsias, bedding and basket plants too. The range of mums includes exhibition, garden, cut flower and greenhouse varieties.

Okell's Nurseries

Duddon Heath, Tarporley, Cheshire CW6 0EP
☎ 0829 741512   ☏ 0829 741587

CONTACT Donna Okell
OPEN 9 am – 5.30 pm, daily. Close at 7 pm, Saturday – Sunday, May and June
SPECIALITIES Heathers
CATALOGUE On request
MAIL ORDER No
SHOP Garden sundries

This wholesale nursery produces heathers in variety (150) and quantity (2.6 million). They also have a retail garden centre which stocks heathers and a general range of plants and sundries.

Phedar Nursery

Bunkers Hill, Romiley, Stockport, Cheshire SK6 3DS
☎ 061 430 3772   ☏ 061 430 3772

CONTACT Will McLewin
LOCATION 3 miles east of Stockport
OPEN By appointment only
SPECIALITIES Seeds; hellebores
NEW FOR 1994 Helleborus croaticus
CATALOGUE Large SAE (2 first class stamps)
MAIL ORDER Yes

A highly specialised source of authentic Helleborus species, which are only grown from collected material. They also offer fresh seed in August. Other plants from this research nursery include Paeonia, Erythronium and Dodecatheon.

Pilkington Garden Centre

Bold Heath, Widnes, Cheshire WA8 0UU
☎ 051 424 6264

CONTACT Ron Brooks
LOCATION 2 miles east of M62, J7 on A57
OPEN 9 am – 6 pm, Monday – Saturday; 10 am – 6 pm, Sundays
SHOP Garden sundries; furniture; gifts
REFRESHMENTS Café
GIFT TOKENS HTA

General garden centre with a full range of plants and products. Demonstrations held throughout the year.

Robinsons of Whaley Bridge

20 Vaughan Road, Whaley Bridge, Stockport, Cheshire SK12 7JT
☎ 0663 732991

CONTACT Mr J. E. Robinson
OPEN By appointment only
SPECIALITIES Iris; violas
NEW FOR 1994 Auriculas
CATALOGUE SAE
MAIL ORDER Yes

Very small and specialised. Their charming range consists of Viola odorata cultivars and dwarf bearded irises. They are adding some auriculas this year.

Stapeley Water Gardens Ltd

London Road, Stapeley, Nantwich, Cheshire CW5 7LH
☎ 0270 623868   ☏ 0270 624919

CONTACT Mr R G A Davis
LOCATION Near Nantwich, on the A51
OPEN 9 am – 6 pm, Monday to Friday; 10 am – 6 pm, Saturdays; 10 am – 7 pm, Sundays and Bank Holidays, summer; close at 5 pm, daily, winter
SPECIALITIES Aquatic plants; bog plants
NEW FOR 1994 New display gardens
CATALOGUE £1 cheque
MAIL ORDER Yes
SHOP Garden sundries; water equipment; furniture; gifts; books
REFRESHMENTS Restaurant
GARDEN Stapeley Water Gardens Ltd, Cheshire, see Gardens section
SHOWS Southport; Chelsea; BBC GW Live; Hampton Court
GIFT TOKENS Own
NCCPG NATIONAL COLLECTIONS Nymphaea

A water gardening centre, with aquatic plants, marginals and poolside varieties as well as equipment for ponds and pools. They hold the national water lily collection, here and at Burnby Hall, Humberside.

Weaver Vale Garden Centre

Winnington Lane, Winnington, Northwich,
Cheshire CW8 4EE
☎ 0606 79965   FAX 0606 784480

CONTACT Peter Jones
LOCATION 2 miles north west of Northwich on A533
OPEN 9 am – 6 pm, Monday – Saturday; 9.30 am – 6 pm,
Sundays. Closes at 5 pm in winter
SHOP Garden sundries; machinery; conservatories;
aquatics
REFRESHMENTS Coffee shop
GARDEN Demonstration gardens
DESIGN SERVICE Weaver Vale Garden Centre
GIFT TOKENS HTA

Garden centre with indoor and outdoor plants and
products. Landscaping and garden design service.

Wilmslow Garden Centre

Manchester Road, Wilmslow, Cheshire SK9 2JN
☎ 0625 525700   FAX 0625 539800

CONTACT Frank, Neil and Denise
LOCATION A34
OPEN 9 am – 6 pm, summer; 9 am – 5 pm, winter.
Open at 9.30 am on Sundays and Bank Holidays
SHOP Garden sundries; furniture; machinery; pets
REFRESHMENTS Restaurant, coffee shop
DESIGN SERVICE Wilmslow Garden Centre
GIFT TOKENS HTA

Garden centre selling plants and products. They have a
design and landscape capability, and a delivery service.

Wyevale Garden Centre

Otterspool, Dooley Lane, Marple, Stockport,
Cheshire SK6 7HE
☎ 061 427 7211   FAX 061 449 7636

CLEVELAND

Battersby Roses

Peartree Cottage, Old Battersby, Great Ayton,
Cleveland TS9 6LU
☎ 0642 723402

CONTACT Eric Stainthorpe
LOCATION Between Kildale and Ingleby Greenhow,
on the edge of the North Yorkshire moors
OPEN During flowering and planting season
SPECIALITIES Roses
NEW FOR 1994 Rose 'Worjackie'; Rose 'Rosecarpe'
CATALOGUE SAE
MAIL ORDER Yes

A family run specialist growing only roses. They are
mainly modern types, with a particular emphasis on

exhibition roses. Other interests include northern roses
– this year's introductions are no exception.

Peter Barratt's Garden Centres

Yarm Road, Stockton on Tees, Cleveland TS18 3SQ
☎ 0642 613433   FAX 0642 618185

CONTACT Keith Crackett
OPEN 9 am – 5.30 pm
SHOP Garden sundries; aquatics
REFRESHMENTS Refreshments
GARDEN Demonstration gardens
GIFT TOKENS HTA

General garden centre with garden and leisure products.
Delivery service.

Strikes Garden Centre

Urlay Nook Road, Eaglescliffe, Cleveland TS16 0PE
☎ 0642 780481

LOCATION Near Yarm
OPEN 9 am – 7 pm, Monday – Saturday; 10 am – 6 pm,
Sundays, spring, summer; 9 am – 6 pm, Monday –
Saturday; 10 am – 5 pm, Sundays, winter
SHOP Gifts
GIFT TOKENS HTA

Garden centre, with production nursery on the site.

Town Farm Nursery

Whitton, Stockton on Tees, Cleveland TS21 1LQ
☎ 0740 31079

CONTACT F. D. Baker
OPEN 10 am – 6 pm, Monday – Friday. Closed in
winter
SPECIALITIES Alpines; primulas
CATALOGUE SAE
MAIL ORDER Yes
GARDEN 1 acre display garden

A good selection of hardy alpines and perennials, as
well as some smaller shrubs. The display gardens are
open for nursery visitors.

CORNWALL

Bosvigo Plants

Bosvigo House, Bosvigo Lane, Truro, Cornwall
TR1 3NH
☎ 0872 75774

CONTACT Mrs Wendy Perry
LOCATION ¼ of a mile from Truro centre. Turn off
A390 at Highertown: then 500 metres down Dobbs Lane
OPEN 11 am – 6 pm, Wednesday – Saturday, March
to September
SPECIALITIES Herbaceous perennials

CATALOGUE 4 second class stamps
MAIL ORDER No
GARDEN Bosvigo House, Cornwall, see Gardens section

This small nursery concentrates on herbaceous perennials, including many geraniums and violas which can also be seen in the main garden.

Bregover Plants

Middlewood, Launceston, Cornwall PL15 7NN
☎ 0566 82661

CONTACT Jennifer Bousfield
LOCATION Between Launceston and Liskeard on B3254
OPEN 11 am -5 pm, Wednesday – Friday, mid March to mid October. Weekends and winter months by appointment.
SPECIALITIES Herbaceous perennials; primulas; violas
CATALOGUE 2 first class stamps
MAIL ORDER Yes; £2 minimum charge
GARDEN Cottage Garden and stock beds open by appointment

Mainly cottage garden, wild and woodland plants. Occasional lists of primulas and *Viola odorata* cultivars are produced: fellow collectors should peruse the offsets and divisions.

Brockings Exotics

Brockings Nursery, North Petherwin, Launceston, Cornwall PL15 8LW
☎ 0566 85533

CONTACT Ian Cooke
LOCATION Take signs to Otter Park, then continue into village centre
OPEN 2 – 6 pm, Monday – Saturday
SPECIALITIES Conservatory plants; cannas; coleus
NEW FOR 1994 New cannas introduced from France
CATALOGUE 3 first class stamps
MAIL ORDER Yes; £15 minimum order
SHOWS RHS Westminster; Hampton Court
NCCPG NATIONAL COLLECTIONS Canna; coleus

Brockings Exotics sell an outstanding collection of half-hardy perennials. Some are new, many are revived. Strengths include cannas, coleus (old named varieties) and argyranthemums (20).

Burncoose & South Down Nurseries

Gwennap, Redruth, Cornwall TR16 6BJ
☎ 0209 861112   ☎ 0209 860228

CONTACT C. H. Williams
LOCATION Between Redruth and Falmouth, on A393
OPEN 9 am – 5 pm, Monday – Saturday; 11 am – 5 pm, Sundays
SPECIALITIES Trees; magnolias

NEW FOR 1994 Around 250 additions
CATALOGUE £1
MAIL ORDER Yes
GARDEN Burncoose Gardens, beside the nursery
SHOWS RHS Westminster; International Spring Gardening Fair; Harrogate (Spring); Southport; Chelsea; BBC GW Live; Hampton Court
GIFT TOKENS HTA

A very large general range, particularly strong on flowering shrubs and trees, including magnolias. Some good tender and conservatory plants too. Look out for their masterly displays at horticultural shows.

Carnon Downs Garden Centre

Quenchwell Road, Carnon Downs, Truro, Cornwall TR3 4LN
☎ 0872 863058   ☎ 0872 862162

LOCATION Carnon Downs
OPEN 8 am – 5 pm, Monday – Friday; 9 am – 5 pm, Saturdays; 10 am – 5 pm, Sundays
SHOP Garden sundries; furniture and buildings; pets
REFRESHMENTS Licensed restaurant
GIFT TOKENS HTA; own

Garden centre with a large range of ancillary products including garden machinery. The plant centre includes a selection of plants suited to coastal conditions. They can deliver; on site there is also a working pottery and an adventure playground.

Duchy of Cornwall

Cott Road, Lostwithiel, Cornwall PL22 0BW
☎ 0208 872668   ☎ 0208 345672

CONTACT Andrew Carthew (Manager)
OPEN 9 am – 5 pm, Monday – Saturday; 10 am – 5 pm, Sundays. Closed Bank Holidays
NEW FOR 1994 Many new items
CATALOGUE £1 cheque
MAIL ORDER No
SHOP Garden sundries
GARDEN Woodland walk
GIFT TOKENS HTA; own

The nursery stocks an extensive general range of all types of plants as well as garden sundries. It is especially good on tender perennials. Set in woods, there is a woodland walk centred on the nursery.

Elizabeth Smith

Downside, Bowling Green, Constantine, Falmouth, Cornwall TR11 5AP
☎ 0326 40787

CONTACT Elizabeth Smith
OPEN Mail order only
SPECIALITIES Violets
CATALOGUE SAE; January

MAIL ORDER Yes

Mail order nursery devoted exclusively to scented violets: single, double and Parma.

Lanhydrock Gardens
The National Trust, Lanhydrock Gardens, Bodmin, Cornwall PL30 5AD
☎ 0208 72220

CONTACT Mr Teagle
OPEN 11 am – 5.30 pm, April to October
SPECIALITIES Rhododendrons; shrubs
CATALOGUE On request
MAIL ORDER No
GARDEN Lanhydrock, Cornwall, see Gardens section

There are some herbaceous plants here, but the best of the list is shrubs. You would expect rhododendrons and azaleas, but there are also attractive *Ceanothus* and *Deutzia*.

The Old Mill Herbary
Helland Bridge, Bodmin, Cornwall PL30 4QR
☎ 020884 206   ☎ 020884 206

CONTACT Mr and Mrs R. D. Whurr
LOCATION Helland Bridge: Map ref. 065717
OPEN 10 am – 5 pm, April to October
SPECIALITIES Herbs
CATALOGUE 6 first class stamps
MAIL ORDER No
GARDEN Terraced and water garden

The nursery sells a range of culinary and medicinal herbs. The garden, which includes herbs, bog plants and aquatics is open for different causes on 17 April (Mt Edgcumbe Hospice), 15 May (Arthritis and Rheumatism Council), 29 May (Children's Hospice), 26 June (Cornwall Garden Society) and 11 September (NGS).

Parkinson Herbs
Barras Moor Farm, Perran Ar Worthal, Truro, Cornwall TR3 7PE
☎ 0872 864380   ☎ 0872 864380

CONTACT Elizabeth Parkinson
SPECIALITIES Herbs
CATALOGUE On request
MAIL ORDER Yes

The nursery sells herbs and aromatic plants. Lectures and demonstrations within the county, by arrangement.

Porthpean House Gardens
Porthpean, St Austell, Cornwall PL26 6AX
☎ 0726 72888

CONTACT Mrs Petherick
LOCATION 1½ miles south east of St Austell
OPEN 9 am – 5 pm, Monday – Friday

SPECIALITIES Camellias
CATALOGUE On request
MAIL ORDER No

Camellia specialists, and regular award-winning camellia exhibitors.

Tomperrow Farm Nurseries
Threemilestone, Truro, Cornwall TR3 6BE
☎ 0872 560344

CONTACT Mrs Sandra Goodswen
LOCATION ½ mile south west of village, towards Hugus and Baldhu
OPEN Usually 10 am – 5 pm: phone first
SPECIALITIES Herbaceous perennials
NEW FOR 1994 About 20 new items
CATALOGUE 70p
MAIL ORDER Yes

Hardy herbaceous perennials: old favourites and some newer varieties.

Trewidden Estate Nursery
Trewidden, Penzance, Cornwall TR20 8TT
☎ 0736 62087   ☎ 0736 331470

CONTACT M. Snellgrove
LOCATION 2 miles west of Penzance on A30
OPEN 8 am – 1 pm, 2 – 5 pm, Monday – Saturday. Close at 4 pm, Fridays
SPECIALITIES Camellias
CATALOGUE 2 first class stamps
MAIL ORDER Yes; small plants only
GARDEN Trewidden, Cornwall, see Gardens section

A selection of trees and shrubs: their speciality is camellias. They also sell liners wholesale.

Trewithen Nurseries
Grampound Road, Truro, Cornwall TR2 4DD
☎ 0726 882764

CONTACT Mr M. Taylor
LOCATION Trewithen
OPEN 10 am – 5 pm, Monday – Saturday, March to September; 8 am – 4.30 pm, Monday – Friday, October to February
SPECIALITIES Camellias; climbers; rhododendrons; shrubs
CATALOGUE £1
MAIL ORDER No

Ornamental shrubs and climbers, especially those for acid soils and sheltered spots. A good choice of rhododendrons, camellias and magnolias.

Wall Cottage Nursery

Lockengate, Bugle, St Austell, Cornwall PL26 8RU
☎ 0208 831259

CONTACT   Mrs J. R. Clark
OPEN   8.30 am – 5 pm, Monday – Saturday. Closed
Sundays
SPECIALITIES   Rhododendrons
CATALOGUE   60p
MAIL ORDER   Yes; minimum order £15

Rhododendron and azalea specialist, with an extensive
range of species and hybrids.

Wyevale Garden Centre

Nut Lane, Hayle, Cornwall TR27 6LG
☎ 0736 753731   ☎ 0736 757331

CUMBRIA

Beechcroft Nurseries

Bongate, Appleby, Cumbria CA16 6UE
☎ 07683 51201

CONTACT   Roger Brown
OPEN   8 am – 6 pm, Monday – Saturday; 11 am – 6 pm,
Sundays. Closed Christmas and New Year's Day
SPECIALITIES   Shrubs; trees
CATALOGUE   £1.75; SAE only for list of field-grown
trees
MAIL ORDER   Field-grown trees, November to April
DESIGN SERVICE   Beechcroft Nurseries
GIFT TOKENS   HTA

A small nursery which specialises in trees and shrubs:
both container and field-grown. The rest of the selection is splendidly mixed, running from conifers to vegetables. Gardens designed and planted too.

Boonwood Garden Centre

Gosforth, Seascale, Cumbria CA20 1BP
☎ 0946 725330

CONTACT   Stanley Mossop
LOCATION   Off A595
OPEN   9 am – 5 pm, daily
SPECIALITIES   House plants; Achimenes
NEW FOR 1994   × Achimenantha hybrids
CATALOGUE   50p
MAIL ORDER   Yes
DESIGN SERVICE   Boonwood Garden Centre

Grower and hybridiser of Achimenes, with a selection
of new introductions and older varieties available. New
× Achimenantha hybrids are promised.

Brownthwaite Hardy Plants

Fell Yeat, Casterton, Kirkby Lonsdale, Cumbria
LA6 2JW
☎ 05242 71340

CONTACT   Chris Benson
LOCATION   Bull Pot Road in Casterton
OPEN   10 am – 5 pm, Tuesday – Sunday, April to
October
SPECIALITIES   Grasses; herbaceous perennials
CATALOGUE   3 first class stamps
MAIL ORDER   Yes
GARDEN   Garden opens for NGS

This Pennine nursery grows and stocks a range of hardy
perennials and grasses. The plants can be seen in a
garden setting.

Halecat Garden Nurseries

Witherslack, Grange over Sands, Cumbria
LA11 6RU
☎ 05395 52229

CONTACT   Mrs M. Stanley and Mrs Y. Langhorn
LOCATION   Between Grange and Levens, off A590
OPEN   9 am – 4.30 pm, Monday – Friday, all year;
2 – 4 pm, Sundays, Easter to October only
SPECIALITIES   Herbaceous perennials; Hydrangea
CATALOGUE   45p
MAIL ORDER   No

The owners specialise in species and cultivars of Hydrangea, and also stock a range of perennials for herbaceous and mixed borders.

Hartside Nursery Garden

Alston, Cumbria CA9 3BL
☎ 0434 381372

CONTACT   N. Huntley
LOCATION   1¼ miles south west of Alston on A686
OPEN   9 am – 5pm, Monday – Friday; 10 am – 4 pm,
Saturdays; 12.30 – 4 pm, Sundays; March to October.
Other months by appointment
SPECIALITIES   Alpines; ferns
NEW FOR 1994   More hardy ferns
CATALOGUE   £1 each; 3 annually
MAIL ORDER   Yes
GARDEN   12 acre wooded valley
SHOWS   Harrogate (Spring); Hampton Court; Harro-
gate (Autumn)
GIFT TOKENS   Own

The nursery specialises in alpines, dwarf shrubs and
conifers, and hardy ferns. The substantial gardens are
also open.

Hayes Gardenworld Ltd

Lake District Nurseries, Ambleside, Cumbria
LA22 0DW
☎ 05394 33434　📠 05394 34153

LOCATION　South of Ambleside on A591
OPEN　9 am – 6 pm, Monday – Saturday; 10 am – 6 pm,
Sundays
SHOP　Garden sundries; greenhouses; conservatories
REFRESHMENTS　Coffee lounge
DESIGN SERVICE　Hayes Gardenworld
GIFT TOKENS　HTA

Garden centre with a full range of garden products.
Landscaping and construction service.

Lingholm Gardens

Lingholm, Keswick, Cumbria CA12 5UA
☎ 07687 72003　📠 07687 75213

CONTACT　Mr M. J. Swift
LOCATION　2 miles from Keswick, on the west shore
of Derwentwater
OPEN　10 am – 5 pm, daily, April to October
MAIL ORDER　No
REFRESHMENTS　Tea room
GARDEN　Lingholm, Cumbria, see Gardens section

The plant centre attached to these Lakeland gardens
specialises in acid-loving plants.

Salley Gardens

Allergarth, Rowelton, Cumbria CA6 6JU

CONTACT　Richard Lewin
LOCATION　Remote
OPEN　By appointment only
SPECIALITIES　Herbaceous perennials; herbs; seeds
NEW FOR 1994　Many new items
CATALOGUE　On request
MAIL ORDER　Yes; no minimum order

Medicinal, aromatic and dye plants, with some culinary
herbs and perennial wild flowers. The business is
mainly mail order, and they also sell seeds.

Weasdale Nurseries

Newbiggin on Lune, Kirkby Stephen, Cumbria
CA17 4LX
☎ 05396 23246　📠 05396 23277

CONTACT　Andrew Forsyth
LOCATION　7 miles from M6, J38, off A685
OPEN　Collection only, by arrangement
SPECIALITIES　Hedging; shrubs; trees
CATALOGUE　£2.30 cheque
MAIL ORDER　Yes

Trees and shrubs by mail order, including ornamental,
hedging and woodland species. Forty years of mail order

experience: the high situation on the Fells promises
hardiness too.

Webbs Garden Centre

Burneside Road, Kendal, Cumbria LA9 4RT
☎ 0539 720068　📠 0539 727328

OPEN　9 am – 6 pm, Monday – Saturday; 11 am – 5 pm,
Sundays
CATALOGUE　General list
SHOP　Garden sundries; floristry
GIFT TOKENS　HTA; own

Garden centre with plants and garden products. Special
events, competitions and demonstrations are held
throughout the year. Delivery service.

DERBYSHIRE

Bluebell Nursery

Blackfordby, Swadlincote, Derbyshire DE11 8AJ
☎ 0283 222091

CONTACT　Robert Vernon
LOCATION　Off A50, behind Bluebell Inn in Black-
fordby
OPEN　Daily. Closed from Christmas Eve to 2 January
SPECIALITIES　Shrubs; trees
NEW FOR 1994　*Zelkova serrata* 'Variegata'; cultivars
of *Ilex verticillata*
CATALOGUE　50p plus 36p stamp
MAIL ORDER　Yes
SHOWS　RHS Westminster; Malvern Spring; Chelsea

An attractive mix of carefully chosen trees and shrubs,
both cultivars and species. Good on *Ilex*. Roy Lancaster
is lecturing here on 14 March: tickets from the nursery.

Burrows Roses

Meadowcroft, Spondon Road, Dale Abbey, Derby,
Derbyshire DE7 4PQ
☎ 0332 668289

CONTACT　Diane Burrows
OPEN　Mail order only
SPECIALITIES　Roses
NEW FOR 1994　Many new varieties
CATALOGUE　2 first class stamps
MAIL ORDER　Yes
SHOWS　Chelsea

Specialist rose growers. The range is mostly of the
modern types, especially hybrid teas of which they have
a large number. They are careful to select roses with
notably good scents.

Chatsworth Garden Centre

Calton Lees, Beeley, Matlock, Derbyshire DE4 2NX
☎ 0629 734004　　[FAX] 0629 580503

CONTACT　John Tarbatt
LOCATION　1 mile from Chatsworth House
OPEN　9 am – 5 pm, October – February; 9 am – 5.30 pm, March to September
SHOP　Garden sundries; gifts
REFRESHMENTS　Coffee shop
GIFT TOKENS　HTA

Garden centre with a range of indoor and outdoor plants, and related products. Delivery service within 20 mile radius.

DHE Plants

Darley House Estate, Darley Dale, Matlock, Derbyshire DE4 2QH
☎ 0629 732512

CONTACT　Peter M. Smith
OPEN　By appointment
SPECIALITIES　Alpines
CATALOGUE　3 first class stamps
MAIL ORDER　Yes; no minimum order

An alpine nursery whose stock includes particularly good choices of helianthemums (50), saxifrages (150) and sisyrinchiums (20).

Greenleaves Garden Centre Ltd

Birkin Lane, Wingerworth, Chesterfield, Derbyshire S42 6RD
☎ 0246 204214　　[FAX] 0629 580503

CONTACT　John Tarbatt
LOCATION　1 mile west of A61 Tupton roundabout
OPEN　9 am – 5 pm, October to February; 9 am – 5.30 pm, March to September, daily

Garden centre, with local delivery service. Closed between Christmas and New Year.

Highgates Nursery

166a Crich Lane, Belper, Derbyshire DE56 1EP
☎ 0773 822153

CONTACT　Mr and Mrs Straughan
OPEN　10 am – 4.30 pm, Monday – Saturday, early March to mid October
SPECIALITIES　Alpines; rhododendrons
CATALOGUE　2 first class stamps
MAIL ORDER　No

There are alpines in abundance at this specialist nursery, as well as a selection of dwarf rhododendrons.

Lea Gardens

Lea, Matlock, Derbyshire DE4 5GH
☎ 0629 534380　　[FAX] 0629 534260

CONTACT　Jon and Peter Tye
OPEN　10 am – 7 pm, mid March – July. Also 2 – 5 pm, Wednesdays and Sundays, in October and November
SPECIALITIES　Rhododendrons
CATALOGUE　SAE plus 30p
MAIL ORDER　Yes; minimum order £15
REFRESHMENTS　Refreshments
GARDEN　Lea Gardens, Derbyshire, see Gardens section

The plants on sale reflect those which grow in the garden, notably *Rhododendron*, azaleas and *Kalmia*, especially the dwarf or low-growing varieties.

Matlock Garden Centre Ltd

Nottingham Road, Tansley, Matlock, Derbyshire DE4 5FR
☎ 0629 580500　　[FAX] 0629 580503

CONTACT　John Tarbatt
LOCATION　7 miles from M1, J28
OPEN　9 am – 5 pm, October to February; 9 am – 5.30 pm, March to September. Closed between Christmas and New Year
SHOP　Aquatics
REFRESHMENTS　Restaurant
GIFT TOKENS　HTA

Garden centre with a hardy plant range. Delivery within 20 mile radius.

Riley's Chrysanthemums

Alfreton Nurseries, Ashover Road, Woolley Moor, Alfreton, Derbyshire DE55 6FF
☎ 0246 590320

CONTACT　Martin Riley
OPEN　Phone for details; nursery fields open 10 am – 4 pm, Sundays, September only
SPECIALITIES　Chrysanthemums
NEW FOR 1994　Six Early Bloom types; Eight Garden Spray types
CATALOGUE　40p; September, May
MAIL ORDER　Yes
GARDEN　Chrysanthemum fields
SHOWS　RHS Westminster; Harrogate (Autumn)

Trade and retail nursery devoted to chrysanthemums only. They come in all types, old and new, indoor and outdoor. Cut flowers in season. The fields are open for viewing on Sundays in September.

Wyevale Garden Centre

Burton Road, Findern, Derby, Derbyshire DE6 6BE
☎ 0322 514268　　[FAX] 0322 513128

DEVON

Altoona Nurseries
The Windmill, Tigley, Dartington, Totnes, Devon
TQ9 6DW
☎ 0803 868147

CONTACT   Paul Harber
LOCATION   1½ miles west of Totnes
OPEN   By appointment, any time
SPECIALITIES   Acers
CATALOGUE   SAE
MAIL ORDER   No

Specialists in Japanese acers, *Hamamelis* (witch hazels) and *Daphne*.

Ann & Roger Bowden
Hostas, Sticklepath, Okehampton, Devon EX20 2NN
☎ 083784 0481

CONTACT   Ann and Roger Bowden
OPEN   By appointment only
SPECIALITIES   Hostas
CATALOGUE   3 first class stamps
MAIL ORDER   Yes; no minimum order, low packing charges
GARDEN   National Collection of hybrid hostas
SHOWS   BBC GW Live; Hampton Court
NCCPG NATIONAL COLLECTIONS *Hosta* (hybrids)

Hostas only. They can be bought individually or as collections from very extensive range which includes some brightly coloured American hybrids.

Burnham Nurseries
Forches Cross, Newton Abbot, Devon TQ12 6PZ
☎ 0626 52233   📠 0626 62167

CONTACT   Brian and Ann Rittershausen
LOCATION   Forches Cross
OPEN   10 am – 4 pm, daily
SPECIALITIES   Orchids
CATALOGUE   £2 (£2 voucher enclosed)
MAIL ORDER   Yes
SHOP   Sundries
GARDEN   Visitor centre and display house
SHOWS   Chelsea

A very extensive range of orchid species and hybrids. Plants can be seen growing in the display house: current admission is £1.50 for adults.

Decorative Foliage
Higher Badworthy, South Brent, Devon TQ10 9EG
☎ 0364 72768

CONTACT   Amanda Morris
LOCATION   1½ miles from South Brent

OPEN   Phone first
SPECIALITIES   Foliage plants
NEW FOR 1994   Many new items
CATALOGUE   2 first class stamps
MAIL ORDER   Yes; no minimum order

A small nursery with an accent on perennials and shrubs that would be useful for flower arranging.

Endsleigh Garden Centre
Ivybridge, Devon PL21 9JL
☎ 0752 892254   📠 0752 690284

CONTACT   R. Taylor
LOCATION   On A38, Plymouth side of Ivybridge
OPEN   9 am – 5 pm (6 pm during BST), daily
SHOP   Garden machinery; buildings; pools; pets
REFRESHMENTS   Tea room
GARDEN   Demonstration gardens
DESIGN SERVICE   Endsleigh Garden Centre
GIFT TOKENS   HTA

Garden centre with separate departments for products. They have a garden design service and can deliver.

Glebe Cottage Plants
Pixie Lane, Warkleigh, Umberleigh, Devon
EX37 9DH
☎ 0769 540554

CONTACT   Carol Klein
LOCATION   5 miles south west of South Molton
OPEN   10 am – 5 pm, Wednesday – Sunday
SPECIALITIES   Herbaceous perennials
NEW FOR 1994   New *Corydalis*, *Helleborus*, *Pulmonaria* and *Omphalodes*
CATALOGUE   £1
MAIL ORDER   Yes; order by end of October
GARDEN   Garden
SHOWS   RHS Westminster; International Spring Gardening Fair; Malvern Spring; Harrogate (Spring); Southport; Chelsea; BBC GW Live; Hampton Court; Harrogate (Autumn); Courson

An exceptional list of perennials, with newly discovered species and promising cultivars. Carol Klein has a sharp eye for worthwhile new introductions, yet does not forget the reliable old classics.

Greenway Gardens
Churston Ferrers, Brixham, Devon TQ5 0ES
☎ 0803 842382

CONTACT   Roger Clark
OPEN   2 – 5 pm, Monday – Friday; 10 am – 12 pm, Saturdays
SPECIALITIES   Trees
CATALOGUE   3 second class stamps
MAIL ORDER   Yes

An interesting list of mainly trees and shrubs, though . ɔ sizes and prices. Specialities include South American species, and plants grown from wild collected seed.

H & S Wills

2 St Brannocks Park Road, Ilfracombe, Devon
EX34 8HU
☎ 0271 863949

CONTACT H. Wills
OPEN Mail order only
SPECIALITIES Sempervivums
CATALOGUE 3 first class stamps
MAIL ORDER Yes; minimum order £3

Small mail order only nursery with a large choice of *Sempervivum*, *Jovibarba* and *Rosularia*: both species and cultivars.

The High Garden

Courtwood, Newton Ferrers, Devon PL8 1BW
☎ 0752 872528

CONTACT F. Bennett
OPEN By appointment
SPECIALITIES Rhododendrons
CATALOGUE 60p
MAIL ORDER Yes

Young plants of *Rhododendron* species and hybrids, Japanese azaleas and *Pieris*.

Jack's Patch

Newton Road, Bishopsteignton, Teignmouth, Devon
TQ14 9PN
☎ 0626 776996

LOCATION Between Teignmouth and Newton Abbot on A381
OPEN 9 am – 5.30 pm, Monday – Saturday; 10 am – 5.30 pm, Sundays and Bank Holidays
SHOP Gifts
REFRESHMENTS Jack's Kitchen
GIFT TOKENS HTA; own

Garden centre providing bedding plants and plants for small gardens among a general range. Most of the stock is grown at its own nursery. The Devon Beekeeper's Annual Show is held at the nursery in October.

K & C Cacti

Fern Cottage, West Buckland, Barnstaple, Devon
EX32 0SF
☎ 0598 760393

CONTACT Keith and Jane Comer
OPEN Most days, but phone first
SPECIALITIES Cacti and succulents
CATALOGUE SAE
MAIL ORDER Yes

A good selection of cacti and succulents. Particularly strong on the *Mesembryanthemum* group and on *Haworthia*.

Kenwith Nursery

The Old Rectory, Littleham, Bideford, Devon
EX39 5HW
☎ 0237 473752

CONTACT Gordon C. Haddow
OPEN 10 am – 12 pm, 2 – 5 pm, Wednesday – Saturday. Other times by appointment
SPECIALITIES Conifers
CATALOGUE 3 first class stamps
MAIL ORDER Yes
GARDEN Display beds

Just conifers: a very interesting, extensive collection of dwarf and slow growing species and cultivars. They specialise in grafting. Recommended for enthusiasts.

Knightshayes Garden Trust

The Garden Office, Knightshayes, Tiverton, Devon
EX16 7RG
LOCATION Off A396 between Tiverton and Bampton
OPEN 10.30 am – 5.30 pm, daily, April to October
SPECIALITIES Bulbs; shrubs
CATALOGUE £2.50
MAIL ORDER No
SHOP National Trust shop
REFRESHMENTS Restaurant
GARDEN Knightshayes Court, Devon, see Gardens section

The nursery sells plants which look good in this National Trust garden, including bulbs and shrubs.

Lewdon Farm Alpine Nursery

Medland Lane, Cheriton Bishop, Exeter, Devon
EX6 6HF
☎ 0647 24283

CONTACT Betty Frampton
OPEN 9 am – 5.30 pm, daily, April to October
SPECIALITIES Alpines
CATALOGUE 2 second class stamps
MAIL ORDER Yes; alpines only
GARDEN Garden

A garden nursery with a selection of popular and more unusual alpines as well as some perennials.

Marwood Hill Gardens

Barnstaple, Devon EX31 4EB
☎ 0271 42528

CONTACT Dr J. A. Smart
OPEN 11 am – 1 pm, 2 – 5 pm, daily

SPECIALITIES Australian plants; bog plants; camellias; herbaceous perennials; New Zealand plants; shrubs; trees
CATALOGUE 70p
MAIL ORDER No
REFRESHMENTS Sundays, Bank Holidays (April to October)
GARDEN Marwood Hill Gardens, Devon, see Gardens section

A charmingly varied assortment of interesting trees, shrubs and perennials propagated from the garden. Look out for some new magnolias and the astilbes.

Nicky's Rock Garden Nursery

Hillcrest, Broadhayes, Stockland, Honiton, Devon EX14 9EH
☎ 0404 881213

CONTACT Bob and Di Dark
LOCATION 5 miles east of Honiton, off midpoint of north/south road between A30 and A35. Map ref. ST 236027
OPEN 9 am – dusk, daily. Phone first
SPECIALITIES Alpines
CATALOGUE 3 first class stamps
MAIL ORDER No
GARDEN Display gardens

This nursery has a wide and changing selection of alpines and perennials for rock garden planting. Visitors are advised to phone for directions in advance.

North Devon Garden Centre

Ashford, Barnstaple, Devon EX31 4BW
☎ 0271 42880   FAX 0271 23972

CONTACT Miss J. Dellow and Mr N. Robb
LOCATION Between Barnstaple and Braunton on A361
OPEN 9 am – 5 pm, Monday – Saturday; 10 am – 6 pm, Sundays
SHOP Garden sundries; conservatories; mowers; pools
REFRESHMENTS Tea room
GARDEN 2 acre show garden
DESIGN SERVICE North Devon Garden Centre
GIFT TOKENS HTA

General garden centre including all associated products. They have a landscaping department, and during the season a tropical butterfly house.

Otter Nurseries Ltd

Gosford Road, Ottery St Mary, Devon EX11 1LZ
☎ 0404 815815   FAX 0404 815816

CONTACT Mr S. Jones and Mr D. Knapman
LOCATION 400 yards from A30

OPEN 9 am – 5.30 pm, daily. Closed Christmas and Boxing Day
CATALOGUE On request
MAIL ORDER No
SHOP Garden sundries; conservatories; greenhouses; machinery
REFRESHMENTS Restaurant
DESIGN SERVICE Otter Nurseries Ltd

Large garden centre with a wide general range of plants and garden products. They also have a nursery, so many of the plants are home-produced.

Perrie Hale Forest Nursery

Northcote Hill, Honiton, Devon EX14 8TH
☎ 0404 43344   FAX 0404 47163

CONTACT Mrs Judith Davey
LOCATION 1 mile north of Honiton
OPEN Mid November to early April
SPECIALITIES Hedging; trees
CATALOGUE SAE
MAIL ORDER Yes

Forest trees and hedging plants. This wholesale nursery is happy to deal with the public. They prefer you to collect, but small orders (under 200 plants) can be sent by courier.

Peveril Clematis Nursery

Christow, Exeter, Devon EX6 7NG

CONTACT Barry Fretwell
OPEN 10 am – 1 pm, 2 – 5.30 pm, Monday – Saturday; 10 am – 1 pm, Sundays. Closed Thursdays
SPECIALITIES *Clematis*
CATALOGUE 2 first class stamps
MAIL ORDER No
GARDEN Clematis gardens

Clematis grower and hybridiser, with a host of interesting species and large and small-flowered varieties.

Plant World Botanic Gardens

St Marychurch Road, Newton Abbot, Devon TQ12 4SE
☎ 0803 872939

CONTACT Ray Brown
OPEN 9 am – 5.30 pm, daily. Closed over Christmas
SPECIALITIES Seeds
NEW FOR 1994 *Aquilegia* 'Mellow Yellow'; variegated *Viola* (true from seed)
CATALOGUE 3 second class stamps
MAIL ORDER Seeds only
GARDEN Gardens divided into world habitat zones
NCCPG NATIONAL COLLECTIONS *Primula (capitatae)*; *Primula (cortusoides)*; *Primula (farinosae)*

The nursery sells a selection of alpines, perennials and shrubs. There is an illustrated seed list with fresh material from the gardens and some collected species. They go collecting in Chile this year. The gardens are planted out as special habitat zones.

Pleasant View Nursery & Garden

Two Mile Oak, Denbury, Newton Abbot, Devon TQ12 6DG
☎ 0803 813388

CONTACT Mrs Christine Yeo
LOCATION Take A381 from Newton Abbot: right opposite Two Mile Oak garage. Nursery is ¾ mile on the left
OPEN 10 am – 5 pm, Wednesday – Saturday, 16 March to 29 October
SPECIALITIES Salvias
CATALOGUE 4 first class stamps
MAIL ORDER Yes; minimum order £20
GARDEN Garden open Wednesday and Friday afternoons, May to September
SHOWS RHS Westminster
NCCPG NATIONAL COLLECTIONS *Salvia*

The nursery carries a selection of rare trees for gardens and conservatories, and also a number of *Salvia* from the National Collection. The garden opens twice a week in season, and for the NGS on certain weekends. Groups and lectures by arrangement.

Pounsley Plants

Pounsley Combe, Spriddlestone, Brixton, Plymouth, Devon PL9 0DW
☎ 0752 402873

CONTACT Mrs Jane Hollow
OPEN By appointment
SPECIALITIES Herbaceous perennials
NEW FOR 1994 A few old roses
CATALOGUE SAE plus 2 first class stamps
MAIL ORDER Yes; October to February only
GARDEN Garden open

A small nursery with perennials for cottage garden plantings, and some clematis and old roses too.

R D Plants

Homelea Farm, Tytherleigh, Axminster, Devon EX13 7BG
☎ 0460 20206

CONTACT Mrs Lynda Windsor
LOCATION On A358, just inside the county boundary
OPEN 9 am – 1 pm, 2 – 5.30 pm, March to September. Phone first
SPECIALITIES Herbaceous perennials
NEW FOR 1994 *Tropaeolum sessilifolium*; *T. azureum*; *T. brachyceras*; *T. polyphyllum*

CATALOGUE 3 first class stamps
MAIL ORDER No

A good variety of perennials, pond and moisture-loving plants. There are some ferns, and the new *Tropaeolum* species, which are available in small quantities only, look interesting. Customers are asked to ring between 8.30 – 9.30 am and 5 – 6 pm only.

RHS Enterprises Ltd

RHS Garden, Rosemoor, Great Torrington, Devon EX38 8PH
☎ 0805 24067   FAX 0805 24717

CONTACT J. Gingell
OPEN 10 am – 6 pm, April to September; 10 am – 5 pm, March and October; 10 am – 3 pm, November to mid December
MAIL ORDER No
SHOP Books; gifts
REFRESHMENTS Restaurant (garden)
GARDEN RHS Garden, Rosemoor, Devon, see Gardens section
GIFT TOKENS HTA

There is an interesting selection of plants from the garden for sale here. Numerous walks and demonstrations are held here (and at Cannington College, Bridgwater). Both are open to non RHS members.

Rowden Gardens

Brentor, Tavistock, Devon PL19 0NG
☎ 0822 810275

CONTACT J. R. L. Carter
OPEN 10 am – 5 pm, Saturday – Sunday, and Bank Holiday Mondays. Other times by appointment
SPECIALITIES Aquatic plants; bog plants; *Iris*
CATALOGUE £1.50
MAIL ORDER Yes; minimum order £10
GARDEN Garden
SHOWS RHS Westminster; Chelsea; BBC GW Live; Hampton Court
NCCPG NATIONAL COLLECTIONS *Polygonum*

Mostly aquatic and moisture-loving plants. The choice of *Iris*, including *I. ensata* cultivars, is especially good.

Sampford Shrubs

Sampford Peverell, Tiverton, Devon EX16 7EW
☎ 0884 821164

CONTACT Martin Hughes-Jones and Sue Proud
LOCATION 1 mile from M5, J27 and Tiverton Parkway station
OPEN 9 am – 5 pm (dusk if earlier), Thursday – Sunday. Closed over Christmas and January
NEW FOR 1994 *Achillea millefolium* 'Lilac Beauty'; *Pandorea pandorana*; *Veronica spicata* 'Blue Fox'
CATALOGUE Long SAE

MAIL ORDER Yes; winter only

A mixed collection of herbaceous plants and trees and shrubs: the list is crammed with reliable varieties.

Scotts Clematis

Lee, Ilfracombe, Devon EX34 8LW
☎ 0271 863366   ▣ 0271 863366

CONTACT John Scott
LOCATION 3 miles west of Ilfracombe
OPEN 10 am – 5 pm, February to October. Closed Mondays and Saturdays
SPECIALITIES Clematis
CATALOGUE SAE
MAIL ORDER Yes; minimum order 3 plants

Clematis specialists, now producing in excess of 250 varieties at the nursery.

Southwick Country Herbs

Southwick Farm, Nomansland, Tiverton, Devon EX16 8NW
☎ 0884 861099

CONTACT Mrs Menist
OPEN 10 am – 5.30 pm, Monday – Saturday; 11 am – 5.30 pm, Sundays
SPECIALITIES Herbs
CATALOGUE SAE
MAIL ORDER Yes
SHOP Herb products
REFRESHMENTS Restaurant
GARDEN Elizabethan herb garden

Pot-grown herbs and wild flowers, as well as scented geraniums. Herb products, books and seeds also.

Stone Lane Gardens

Stone Farm, Chagford, Devon TQ13 8JU
☎ 0647 231311

CONTACT Kenneth Ashburner
LOCATION Between Whiddon Down and Drewsteignton
OPEN By appointment only
SPECIALITIES Trees
NEW FOR 1994 Alnus pendula; Betula utilis var. jacquemontii from Himalayan seed
CATALOGUE £2
MAIL ORDER Yes

Many rare species of Alnus and Betula, often of wild origin. Selected clones are available as grafted plants.

Thornhayes Nursery

Dulford, Cullompton, Devon EX15 2DF
☎ 08846 746   ▣ 08846 739

CONTACT Kevin Croucher
LOCATION 10 minutes from M5, J28

OPEN By appointment only
SPECIALITIES Fruit; trees
NEW FOR 1994 Fraxinus excelsior 'R. E. Davey'; Malus transitoria 'R. J. Fulcher'
CATALOGUE 4 first class stamps
MAIL ORDER Yes

A newish nursery, mainly wholesale. The stock is both open ground and container-grown, and covers a broad spectrum of ornamental and fruit trees, including west country apples (cider, cooking and eating). The Sorbus and Crataegus are also good: dendrophiles should take a closer look.

Tropicana Nursery

Westhill Avenue, Torquay, Devon TQ1 4LH
☎ 0803 312618

CONTACT Michael Eden
OPEN By appointment
SPECIALITIES Conservatory plants; house plants
NEW FOR 1994 About 20 new species
CATALOGUE 3 first class stamps
MAIL ORDER Yes; minimum order £15

Tropical and sub-tropical plants for the house and conservatory. The list includes daisies, showy climbers and a show stopper in Dichorisandra thyrsiflora (a blue ginger). Many of the plants are available as specimens.

Veryans Plants

Glebe, Coryton, Okehampton, Devon EX20 4PB
☎ 0566 83433

CONTACT Rebecca Miller
LOCATION 3 miles from A30
OPEN By appointment only
SPECIALITIES Herbaceous perennials
CATALOGUE 3 first class stamps
MAIL ORDER Yes
SHOWS Malvern Spring; Hampton Court

Young nursery with a selection of cottage garden plants including Primula cultivars and a good collection of penstemons.

Westfield Cacti

Kennford, Exeter, Devon EX6 7XD
☎ 0392 832921

CONTACT Ralph and Marina Northcott
OPEN 10 am – dusk, daily
SPECIALITIES Cacti and succulents; seeds
NEW FOR 1994 200 new items
CATALOGUE 4 first class stamps
MAIL ORDER Yes
SHOWS RHS Westminster; BBC GW Live

There is a huge choice of cacti and succulents at this retail and wholesale nursery. The stocks are also impressively large. Seeds and some books are also sold.

Withleigh Nurseries

Withleigh, Tiverton, Devon EX16 8JG
☎ 0884 253351

CONTACT C. S. Britton
LOCATION 3 miles west of Tiverton on B3137
OPEN 9 am – 5.30 pm, Tuesday – Saturday. Also open Mondays, July to February
MAIL ORDER No
GARDEN Garden

A retail nursery with a range of bedding, herbaceous perennials and shrubs. Visitors are usually allowed in the garden too.

Co. Durham

Beamish Clematis Nursery

Burntwood Cottage, Stoney Lane, Beamish, Co. Durham DH9 0SJ
☎ 091 370 0202

CONTACT C. Brown
OPEN 9 am – 5 pm, Monday – Saturday, February to October
SPECIALITIES Clematis; climbers
MAIL ORDER No

This retail nursery's main strength is clematis (over 300 varieties). Other ranges include *Lonicera* and *Hedera*.

Eggleston Hall Gardens

Eggleston Hall, Eggleston, Barnard Castle, Co. Durham DL12 0AG
☎ 0833 50378

CONTACT Mrs R. H. Gray and Mr Gordon Long
LOCATION Off the B6278: follow local signs
OPEN 10 am – 5 pm, daily
SPECIALITIES Foliage plants
CATALOGUE £1.50
MAIL ORDER No
GARDEN Garden open: 50p entrance charge (or £1 season ticket) covers nursery and garden

The gardens grow a varied selection of plants, with the emphasis on providing year round material for flower arranging. The wide choice in the plant centre reflects this balance.

Elly Hill Herbs

Elly Hill House, Barmpton, Darlington, Co. Durham DL1 3JF
☎ 0325 464682

CONTACT Mrs Nina Pagan
LOCATION 2 miles north east of Darlington
OPEN 9.30 am – 12.30 pm, 4 – 5.30 pm, daily, March to October. Phone first
SPECIALITIES Herbs
CATALOGUE Large SAE
MAIL ORDER Herb book only (£4.75)
GARDEN Herb garden

A herb nursery selling herb plants and products. They organise herb parties and give tours to groups. Their book, *Herbs and so on*, is available by post.

Equatorial Plant Co

7 Gray Lane, Barnard Castle, Co. Durham DL12 8PD
☎ 0833 690519   FAX 0833 690519

CONTACT Dr R. Warren
LOCATION South Durham
SPECIALITIES Orchids
CATALOGUE SAE
MAIL ORDER Yes
SHOWS RHS Westminster

They specialise in laboratory raised tropical orchids, which are sold at the right size for transplanting. They are active in conservation, including Brazil's coastal rain forest, where introductory tours can be arranged.

Rookhope Nurseries

Rookhope, Upper Weardale, Co. Durham DL13 2DD
☎ 0388 517272

LOCATION 5 miles west of Stanhope, off A689
OPEN 9 am – 5 pm, daily, mid March to September. Phone first in winter
SPECIALITIES Alpines; herbaceous perennials
CATALOGUE 3 first class stamps
MAIL ORDER No
GARDEN Display gardens

Hardy garden plants, alpines, perennials and shrubs: all in wide variety. The nursery is high up in the Pennines so the plants are selected for the northern climate.

Strikes Garden Centre

Woodlands Road, Cockerton, Darlington, Co. Durham DL3 9AA
☎ 0325 468474

LOCATION Near Cockerton Green
OPEN 9 am – 7 pm, Monday – Saturday; 10 am – 6 pm, Sundays, spring, summer; 9 am – 6 pm, Monday – Saturday; 10 am – 5 pm, Sundays, winter
SHOP Gifts
GIFT TOKENS HTA

DORSET

Abbey Plants

Chaffeymoor, Bourton, Gillingham, Dorset SP8 5BY
☎ 0747 840841

CONTACT   Mr K. R. Potts
LOCATION   3 miles east of Wincanton, off A303
OPEN   10 am – 1 pm, 2 – 5 pm, Tuesday to Saturday
MAIL ORDER   No
GARDEN   Chiffchaffs, Dorset, see Gardens section

The nursery sells a range of flowering shrubs including roses, and herbaceous and alpine plants.

Abbotsbury Gardens

Abbotsbury, Weymouth, Dorset DT3 4LA
☎ 0308 871412/ 871344

CONTACT   Mr D. Sutton
LOCATION   9 miles west of Weymouth, on the coast
OPEN   10 am – 6 pm, daily, March to October; 10 am – 3 pm, daily, November to March
SPECIALITIES   Shrubs; half-hardy plants; sub-tropical plants
CATALOGUE   £1 plus large SAE
MAIL ORDER   Yes; minimum order £10
SHOP   Garden shop and plant centre
REFRESHMENTS   Yes
GARDEN   Abbotsbury Sub-Tropical Gardens, Dorset, see Gardens section

Attached to these famous gardens, the plant centre naturally specialises in tender and sub-tropical plants, including penstemons and salvias, and in species which give a tropical effect.

Bennetts Water Lily Farm

Water Gardens, Putton Lane, Chickerell, Weymouth, Dorset DT3 4AF
☎ 0305 785150   ☎ 0305 781619

CONTACT   N. Bennett
OPEN   Tuesday – Sunday, April to September
SPECIALITIES   Aquatic plants; bog plants; water lilies
CATALOGUE   3 first class stamps
MAIL ORDER   Yes
REFRESHMENTS   Tea room
GIFT TOKENS   HTA

Water lilies, pond plants and marginals. They also have some tropical varieties to tempt conservatory owners.

C W Groves & Son

Nursery & Garden Centre, West Bay Road, Bridport, Dorset DT6 4BA
☎ 0308 22654   ☎ 0308 420888

OPEN   8.30 am – 5 pm, Monday – Saturday; 10 am – 5 pm, Sundays
SPECIALITIES   Violas
CATALOGUE   SAE
MAIL ORDER   Yes
REFRESHMENTS   Café
GIFT TOKENS   HTA

A traditional and family run nursery cum garden centre, with a good general range. In addition, they specialise in named violet cultivars: sold by mail order.

Cottage Garden Plants

Cox Cottage, Lower Street, East Morden, Wareham, Dorset BH20 7DL
☎ 0929 459496

CONTACT   Alex Brenton
LOCATION   8 miles west of Poole, off A35 and B3072
OPEN   Monday – Tuesday, March to July
CATALOGUE   2 first class stamps
MAIL ORDER   Yes; no minimum order
DESIGN SERVICE   Cottage Garden Plants

A small, part-time nursery with a selection of cottager's plants: violets, primroses and perennial wallflowers. Design and planting plans handled in the winter.

Cranborne Manor Garden Centre

Cranborne, Wimborne, Dorset BH21 5PP
☎ 0725 517248   ☎ 0725 517248

CONTACT   Miss Sandra Hewitt
LOCATION   10 miles north of Wimborne on B3078
OPEN   9 am – 5 pm, Tuesday – Saturday; 10 am – 5 pm, Sundays and Bank Holidays. Closed Mondays
SPECIALITIES   Roses; topiary
CATALOGUE   £1
MAIL ORDER   Roses only; November to February
SHOP   Pots and ornaments
GARDEN   Cranborne Manor, Dorset. Wednesdays only, March to September. See Gardens section
GIFT TOKENS   HTA

Among the general stock there is a good choice of herbaceous plants. The specialities, though, are old-fashioned roses and topiary specimens.

Global Orange Groves UK

PO Box 644, Poole, Dorset BH17 9YB
☎ 0202 691699

CONTACT   Mrs Oliver
LOCATION   Horton Heath, near Wimborne
OPEN   Weekends, when not exhibiting
SPECIALITIES   Citrus
NEW FOR 1994   Citrus care kit
CATALOGUE   SAE
MAIL ORDER   Yes
SHOWS   Malvern Spring; Hampton Court

Fruiting citrus trees in containers: they have 25 varieties, including lemons, mandarins and kumquats. Groups are offered a free talk and tour of the nursery. Their special summer and winter fertilisers are recommended for bedraggled and non-fruiting citrus.

Macpennys Nurseries

154 Burley Road, Bransgore, Christchurch, Dorset
BH23 8DB
☎ 0425 672348

CONTACT Mr T. M. Lowndes
LOCATION Between Christchurch and Burley
OPEN 9 am – 5 pm, Monday – Saturday; 2 – 5 pm, Sundays. Closed at Christmas and New Year
CATALOGUE SAE plus 50p
MAIL ORDER No
GARDEN 4 acre woodland garden
GIFT TOKENS Own

Long-established nursery with a reliable general range across the plant spectrum. The garden is open for the National Gardens Scheme at the same times. Talks and special openings can be arranged for groups.

Milton Garden Plants

Milton on Stour, Gillingham, Dorset SP8 5PX
☎ 0747 822484   📠 0747 822484

CONTACT Richard and Sue Cumming
OPEN 8.30 am – 5.30 pm, Tuesday – Saturday and Bank Holidays; 10 am – 5 pm, Sundays. Closed Mondays
CATALOGUE 3 first class stamps; perennials only
MAIL ORDER No
GARDEN Display gardens
GIFT TOKENS HTA; own

Family run plant centre, with a good general range, especially hardy perennials.

Naked Cross Nurseries

Waterloo Road, Corfe Mullen, Wimborne, Dorset
BH21 3SR
☎ 0202 693256

CONTACT Mr P. J. French and Mrs J. Paddon
OPEN 9 am – 5 pm, daily
SPECIALITIES Heathers; herbaceous perennials
CATALOGUE 50p
MAIL ORDER Yes

Family run nursery with a choice of heathers and herbaceous perennials.

Orchid Sundries Ltd & Hardy Orchids Ltd

New Gate Farm, Scotchey Lane, Stour Provost, Gillingham, Dorset SP8 5LT
☎ 0747 838368   📠 0747 838308

CONTACT N. J. Heywood
OPEN 8 am – 1 pm, 2 – 5 pm, Tuesday – Saturday
SPECIALITIES Orchids
CATALOGUE On request
MAIL ORDER Yes
SHOP Orchid books and sundries

The business is devoted to hardy orchids, old and new books about them, and the materials needed to grow them.

Rivendell Alpines

Horton Heath, Wimborne, Dorset BH21 7JN
☎ 0202 824013

CONTACT John and Claire Hornsey
OPEN 10 am – 5 pm, daily. Closed Fridays
SPECIALITIES Alpines
CATALOGUE SAE
MAIL ORDER No
SHOWS Malvern Spring; Hampton Court

An alpine nursery selling amongst other things spring bulbs, *Erythronium*, *Schizostylis* and *Rhodohypoxis*.

Three Counties Nurseries

Marshwood, Bridport, Dorset DT6 5QJ
☎ 0297 678257

CONTACT Mr and Mrs D. C. Hitchcock
OPEN Mail order only
SPECIALITIES *Dianthus*
CATALOGUE 2 second class stamps
MAIL ORDER Yes
SHOWS RHS Westminster; Chelsea; BBC GW Live; Hampton Court

Dianthus specialists, with a wide choice of garden pinks, including laced, old-fashioned and modern hybrids. They also have alpine *Dianthus* and a new selection of named *D. barbatus* (Sweet Williams). Lectures by arrangement.

Trehane Camellia Nursery

Stapehill Road, Hampreston, Wimborne, Dorset
BH21 7NE
☎ 0202 873490   📠 0202 873490

CONTACT Miss Jennifer Trehane
LOCATION Between Ferndown and Wimborne, off A31
OPEN 9 am – 4 pm, Monday – Friday, all year; 10 am – 4.30 pm, Saturday – Sunday, late February to October
SPECIALITIES Camellias; fruit
NEW FOR 1994 Several New Zealand bred camellias
CATALOGUE £1.50 handbook
MAIL ORDER Yes
GARDEN Display house
SHOWS RHS Westminster; International Spring Gardening Fair; Harrogate (Spring); Hampton Court

Wholesale and retail camellia growers. They have a wide choice of *Camellia* hybrids, and *Magnolia*, *Pieris* and azaleas. They also grow and sell blueberries and cranberries: there is an annual tasting in early August.

Wyevale Garden Centre
24 Wareham Road, Owermoigne, Dorchester, Dorset DT2 8BY
☎ 0305 852324   [FAX] 0305 854027

Wyevale Garden Centre
Van Dukes Garden Centre, 229-247 Wimborne Road West, Stapehill, Wimborne, Dorset BH21 2DN
☎ 0202 874208   [FAX] 0202 895335

ESSEX

B & H M Baker
Bourne Brook Nurseries, Greenstead Green, Halstead, Essex CO9 1RJ
☎ 0376 476369

CONTACT B. and H. M. Baker
LOCATION Halstead, Essex
OPEN 9 am – 4.30 pm, Monday – Friday; 9 am – 12 pm, 2 – 4.30 pm, Saturday – Sunday
SPECIALITIES Fuchsias
CATALOGUE 20p plus first class stamp
MAIL ORDER No

This fuchsia specialist carries a large range of old and new cultivars, and species. There are bedding plants and hanging baskets in season.

The Beth Chatto Gardens Ltd
Elmstead Market, Colchester, Essex CO7 7DB
☎ 0206 822007   [FAX] 0206 825933

LOCATION 7 miles east of Colchester on A133
OPEN 9 am – 5 pm, Monday – Saturday, March to October; 9 am – 4 pm, Monday to Friday, November to February
SPECIALITIES Herbaceous perennials
CATALOGUE £2.50
MAIL ORDER Yes; £20 minimum order
GARDEN Beth Chatto Gardens, Essex, see Gardens section
GIFT TOKENS Own

The nursery is a prime source for out of the ordinary plants. The selection bears the stamp of a plantswoman with a discerning eye for effective plant combinations.

Bypass Nurseries
72 Ipswich Road, Colchester, Essex CO1 2YF
☎ 0206 865500   [FAX] 0206 865810

CONTACT Bruce Ridgewell

OPEN 9 am – 5.30 pm, March to October; 9 am – 5 pm, winter
SHOP Conservatories; greenhouses; water and flowers
DESIGN SERVICE Bypass Nurseries
GIFT TOKENS HTA

A traditional garden centre supplying plants, and a range of garden products through franchises. Delivery and landscaping services available.

Cants of Colchester
Nayland Road, Mile End, Colchester, Essex CO4 5EB
☎ 0206 844008   [FAX] 0206 855371

CONTACT Miss Angela Pawsey
LOCATION North of Colchester, on A134
OPEN Times vary: phone first
SPECIALITIES Roses
NEW FOR 1994 Rose 'Sally's Rose'
CATALOGUE On request
MAIL ORDER Yes; fixed p & p rates
GARDEN Rose fields are open from the end of June to late September. Free entry, and no need to phone
SHOWS Chelsea
GIFT TOKENS HTA; own

Dynasty of rose breeders and growers, best known for 'Just Joey', one of the most popular roses of the century. The range is mostly of modern varieties. Callers can obtain containerised plants between April and August, and bare root from November to March: the nursery stresses the need to phone before visiting.

Copford Bulbs
Dorsetts, Birch Road, Copford, Colchester, Essex CO6 1DR
☎ 0206 330008

CONTACT D. J. Pearce
SPECIALITIES Daffodils
CATALOGUE 50p
MAIL ORDER Yes
SHOWS RHS Westminster; Harrogate (Spring); Chelsea; Hampton Court

Daffodils for exhibitors and enthusiasts. They also sell young plants of hardy cyclamen.

The Cottage Garden
Langham Road, Boxted, Colchester, Essex CO4 5HU
CONTACT Alison Smith
LOCATION 4 miles north of Colchester
OPEN 8 am – 6 pm, daily, March to June; 8 am – 6 pm, Thursday – Monday, July to February
MAIL ORDER No
SHOP Garden antiques; garden sundries
GIFT TOKENS Own

The nursery sells home grown plants in variety, including perennials and bulbs. Also on sale are garden sundries and garden antiques.

County Park Nursery
384 Wingletye Lane, Hornchurch, Essex RM11 3BU
☎ 0708 445205

CONTACT   Graham Hutchins
LOCATION   Essex Gardens, Hornchurch, Essex
OPEN   9 am – 6 pm, Monday – Saturday; 10 am – 5 pm, Sundays; from March to October. Closed Wednesdays. Open in winter by appointment only
SPECIALITIES   Australian plants; New Zealand plants
NEW FOR 1994   Several new items
CATALOGUE   3 first class stamps
MAIL ORDER   No
NCCPG NATIONAL COLLECTIONS   Coprosma

This small nursery specialises in Antipodean plants, many of them grown from native seed. Not all of them hardy. There are lots of hebes, as well as clematis, Coprosma and other genera. The main address is for postal enquiries only.

The Fens
Old Mill Road, Langham, Colchester, Essex CO4 5NU
☎ 0206 272259

CONTACT   Ann Lunn
LOCATION   5 miles north of Colchester, off A12
OPEN   10 am – 5 pm, Friday – Saturday; also, daily in April
SPECIALITIES   Primulas
CATALOGUE   3 first class stamps
MAIL ORDER   Yes
GARDEN   Garden opens for NGS

Mainly perennial plants for damp and woodland sites: a wide selection of primulas in particular.

Flora Exotica
Pasadena, South Green, Fingringhoe, Colchester, Essex CO5 7DR
☎ 0206 729414

CONTACT   Mr J. Beddoes
OPEN   Mail order only
SPECIALITIES   Carnivorous plants; seeds
NEW FOR 1994   New Pinguicula cultivars and species
CATALOGUE   SAE plus 2 first class stamps
MAIL ORDER   Yes

Insectivorous plants by mail order: Pinguicula, Utricularia and Nepenthe.

Frances Mount Perennial Plants
1 Steps Farm, Polstead, Colchester, Essex CO6 5AE
☎ 0206 262811

CONTACT   Frances Mount
LOCATION   8 miles from Colchester and Sudbury
OPEN   10 am – 5 pm, Tuesday, Wednesday, Saturday, Sunday; 2 pm – 6 pm, Fridays
SPECIALITIES   Herbaceous perennials
NEW FOR 1994   Salvia verticillata; Geranium × oxonianum 'Winscombe'; Geranium sanguineum 'Glenluce'
CATALOGUE   3 first class stamps
MAIL ORDER   Yes; minimum order £5

A small nursery whose stock includes hardy herbaceous perennials and over 50 varieties of geraniums.

Hull Farm Conifer Centre
John Fryer & Sons, Spring Valley Lane, Ardleigh, Colchester, Essex CO7 7SA
☎ 0206 230045

CONTACT   J. Fryer & Sons
OPEN   10 am – 4.30 pm, daily
SPECIALITIES   Conifers
CATALOGUE   SAE plus 70p
MAIL ORDER   No

Conifer specialists.

Ken Muir Nurseries
Honeypot Farm, Weeley Heath, Clacton on Sea, Essex CO16 9BJ
☎ 0255 830181   ℻ 0255 831534

CONTACT   Ken Muir
LOCATION   Between Colchester and Clacton, off A133
OPEN   10 am – 4 pm, daily. Closed Christmas and Boxing Day
SPECIALITIES   Fruit
NEW FOR 1994   Blackcurrant 'Ben Connan'
CATALOGUE   2 first class stamps
MAIL ORDER   Yes
SHOWS   RHS Westminster; International Spring Gardening Fair; Chelsea; BBC GW Live; Hampton Court

Fruit specialist with a substantial mail order business. If the lure of Honeypot Farm isn't enough in itself, then consider the wide range of strawberries, raspberries, other soft fruit and fruit trees. Some of the well known varieties are grown as slender columns, suitable for smaller gardens and tubs.

Langthorns Plantery
Little Canfield, Dunmow, Essex CM6 1TD
☎ 0371 872611   ℻ 0371 872611

CONTACT   D. N. Cannon

OPEN   10 am – 5 pm, daily. Closed Christmas to New
Year
SPECIALITIES   Herbaceous perennials; shrubs
CATALOGUE   £1
MAIL ORDER   No
GARDEN   Gardens
GIFT TOKENS   Own

Hardy plants of all kinds in a very varied range. The
herbaceous section is especially good, and there are
some interesting shrubs here too.

Mill Race Nursery

New Road, Aldham, Colchester, Essex CO6 3QT
☎ 0206 242324   ℻ 0206 241616

CONTACT   C. W. Matthews
LOCATION   Ford Street, Aldham, off A604
OPEN   9 am – 5.30 pm, daily
CATALOGUE   SAE
MAIL ORDER   No
REFRESHMENTS   Refreshments
GARDEN   Demonstration gardens
DESIGN SERVICE   Mill Race Landscapes Ltd
GIFT TOKENS   Own

A large nursery with a wide range of container grown
stock, sold both wholesale and retail. Plant types include conifers, climbers, trees, shrubs, perennials and
fruit trees and bushes.

Notcutts Garden Centre

Station Road, Ardleigh, Colchester, Essex CO7 7RT
☎ 0206 230271

LOCATION   On B1029
OPEN   8.30 am – 5.30 pm, Monday – Saturday; 10 am
– 5.30 pm, Sundays
CATALOGUE   £2.50
SHOP   Garden sundries; furniture
GARDEN   Landscaped gardens
GIFT TOKENS   HTA; own

See also Notcutts Nurseries, Suffolk.

Plantworld

Burnam Road, South Woodham Ferrers,
Chelmsford, Essex CM3 5QP
☎ 0245 320482

CONTACT   F. Waterworth
OPEN   10 am – 4 pm, Tuesday – Sunday. Closed
Mondays
SPECIALITIES   *Tropaeolum speciosum*
CATALOGUE   £2
MAIL ORDER   Yes

A range of hardy perennials, with a speciality in *Tropaeolum speciosum*: 3 plants cost £15 delivered.

Rhodes & Rockliffe

2 Nursery Road, Nazeing, Essex EN9 2JE
☎ 0992 463693   ℻ 0992 440673

CONTACT   David Rhodes
OPEN   By appointment only
SPECIALITIES   Begonias
CATALOGUE   Large SAE
MAIL ORDER   Yes; minimum order £2.50
SHOWS   RHS Westminster

Begonia specialists, with some out of the way species
and hybrids.

South Ockendon Garden Centre

South Road, South Ockendon, Essex RM15 6DU
☎ 0708 851991   ℻ 0708 859138

CONTACT   May Brisbane and Margaret Thomas
LOCATION   Near Lakeside Shopping Centre, on B186
OPEN   9 am – 6 pm, Monday – Saturday; 10 am – 6 pm,
Sundays
SHOP   Garden sundries; gifts; pets
REFRESHMENTS   Coffee shop
GIFT TOKENS   HTA

Garden centre with garden products. They have a good
record in the Chelsea hanging basket competition: demonstrations at the centre.

Trevor Scott Ornamental Grasses

Thorpe Park Cottage, Thorpe le Soken, Essex
CO16 0HN
☎ 0255 861308   ℻ 0255 861308

CONTACT   Trevor Scott
LOCATION   Thorpe le Soken
OPEN   By appointment only
SPECIALITIES   Grasses
CATALOGUE   5 first class stamps
MAIL ORDER   Yes; minimum order £10
GARDEN   Garden
DESIGN SERVICE   Designing with Plants

A very wide range of grasses for all purposes and
situations: there are some other interesting perennials
too. A design service, which aims for a natural effect,
is also available.

Whitehouse Ivies

Brookhill, Halstead Road, Fordham, Colchester,
Essex CO6 3LW
☎ 0206 240077

CONTACT   R. Whitehouse
OPEN   By appointment
SPECIALITIES   Ivies
CATALOGUE   £1
MAIL ORDER   Yes

The largest retail range of *Hedera* species and cultivars. About 220 are available, for climbing, trailing, topiary, ground cover and container use. Most of the business is mail order: the catalogue is fully illustrated.

Wyevale Garden Centre
Cressing Road, Braintree, Essex CM7 8DL
☎ 0376 553043   ⛶ 0376 553004

Wyevale Garden Centre
Homelands Retail Park, Cuton Hall Lane, Springfield, Chelmsford, Essex CM2 5PX
☎ 0245 466466   ⛶ 0245 451263

Wyevale Garden Centre
Cowdray Avenue, Colchester, Essex CO1 1DP
☎ 0206 575300   ⛶ 0206 48986

Wyevale Garden Centre
Eastwood Road, Rayleigh, Essex SS6 7QA
☎ 0702 527331   ⛶ 0702 421203

GLOUCESTERSHIRE

Andrew Norfield Trees & Seeds
Lower Meend, St Briavels, Gloucestershire
GL15 6RW
☎ 0594 530134   ⛶ 0594 530113

CONTACT Andrew Norfield
OPEN Mail order only
SPECIALITIES Acers; seeds; trees
CATALOGUE 1 first class stamp
MAIL ORDER Yes

The tree list sells young container-grown species including *Nothofagus* and *Stewartia*: the list is especially strong on *Acer* and *Betula*. The other side of the business supplies pre-germinated seed of trees, shrubs, houseplants, bulbs and herbaceous plants. Here you pay a premium on the ordinary seed price, but do not have to wait for lengthy or difficult germination conditions to be fulfilled.

Chris Pattison (Nurseryman)
Brookend, Pendock, Gloucestershire GL19 3PL
☎ 0531 650480

CONTACT Chris Pattison
LOCATION Gloucestershire, Worcestershire border
OPEN 9 am – 5 pm, Monday – Friday; at weekends, by appointment
SPECIALITIES Alpines; shrubs
NEW FOR 1994 *Daphne petraea* 'Alba'; many shrub cultivars
CATALOGUE 3 first class stamps
MAIL ORDER No

SHOWS Malvern Spring

Small retail and wholesale nursery offering alpines and shrubs, including dwarf *Daphne* cultivars, all container-grown at the nursery.

Cowcombe Farm Herbs
Gipsy Lane, Chalford, Stroud, Gloucestershire
GL6 8HP
☎ 0285 760544

CONTACT Caroline Barnett
LOCATION Between Stroud and Cirencester, near A419
OPEN 10 am – 5 pm, Wednesday – Saturday; 2 – 5 pm, Sundays; Easter to September
SPECIALITIES Herbs; seeds; wild flowers
CATALOGUE 2 second class stamps
MAIL ORDER No
GARDEN Cottage garden

Herbs and wild plants for sale. They are also the home of the Seed Bank and Exchange scheme.

Four Counties Nursery
Todenham, Moreton in Marsh, Gloucestershire
GL56 9PN
☎ 0608 650522   ⛶ 0608 650591

CONTACT Sandra Taylor
LOCATION Cotswolds
OPEN 9 am – 6 pm, daily, 25 March to 21 October; 9 am – 5 pm, daily, 22 October to 24 March
SPECIALITIES Citrus; conservatory plants; shrubs; trees
CATALOGUE £1 plus SAE
MAIL ORDER No
SHOP Farm shop; pick your own fruit
REFRESHMENTS Café (summer only)
GARDEN Demonstration gardens
GIFT TOKENS HTA

Four Counties have an extensive range of trees and shrubs. They also specialise in conservatory plants, including citrus trees.

Hoo House Nursery
Hoo House, Gloucester Road, Tewkesbury, Gloucestershire GL20 7DA
☎ 0684 293389

CONTACT Mrs Julie Ritchie
LOCATION 2 miles south of Tewkesbury on A38
OPEN 2 – 5 pm, Monday – Saturday
SPECIALITIES Alpines; herbaceous perennials
CATALOGUE 3 first class stamps
MAIL ORDER Yes; October to March only
NCCPG NATIONAL COLLECTIONS *Platycodon; Gentiana asclepiadea*

A mixed range of alpines and herbaceous plants. The nursery also holds two NCCPG National Collections.

Hunts Court Garden & Nursery

Hunts Court, North Nibley, Dursley, Gloucestershire
GL11 6DZ
☎ 0453 547440

CONTACT T. K. Marshall
OPEN 9 am – 5 pm, Tuesday – Saturday, Bank Holiday Mondays in spring. Closed August
SPECIALITIES Roses; shrubs
MAIL ORDER No
GARDEN Garden open 2 – 6 pm, Tuesday – Saturday (except August), and for NGS

The nursery has a large selection of old-fashioned, shrub, climbing and species roses, with shrubby potentillas, perennials and other shrubs too. The 2 acre rose garden has over 450 old varieties, and is recommended.

Hurrans Garden Centre Ltd

Cheltenham Road East, Churchdown, Gloucester, Gloucestershire GL3 1AB
☎ 0452 712232   FAX 0452 857369

CONTACT Miss L. Faulds
LOCATION Between Cheltenham and Gloucester on B4063
OPEN 9 am – 6 pm, Monday – Saturday; 10 am – 6 pm, Sundays
SHOP Garden products
GIFT TOKENS HTA; own

Garden centre selling plants and garden products only. Delivery service and trained staff.

Kiftsgate Court Gardens

Kiftsgate Court, Chipping Campden, Gloucestershire GL55 6LW
☎ 0386 438777

CONTACT Mr and Mrs Chambers
LOCATION Adjacent to Hidcote Manor
OPEN 2 – 6 pm, Wednesdays, Thursdays, Sundays, April to October; 2 – 6 pm; Saturdays and Bank Holidays, June and July only
CATALOGUE No
MAIL ORDER No
GARDEN Kiftsgate Court, Gloucestershire, see Gardens section

The nursery sells a seasonally varied range of plants propagated from this well-known garden.

Lechlade Garden Centre

Fairford Road, Lechlade, Gloucestershire GL7 3DP
☎ 0367 252372   FAX 0367 252782

CONTACT Mr M. Reed (plants); Mr P. Hodges (shop)
LOCATION North of Swindon

OPEN 9 am – 6 pm, summer; 9 am – 5 pm, winter
SHOP Garden machinery
REFRESHMENTS Coffee shop
DESIGN SERVICE Lechlade Garden Centre
GIFT TOKENS HTA; own

General garden centre with design and landscaping and delivery services. Agent for Hillier plants.

Marshall's Malmaisons

4 The Damsells, Tetbury, Gloucestershire GL8 8JA
☎ 0666 502589

CONTACT Jim Marshall
OPEN By appointment only
SPECIALITIES Carnations
CATALOGUE List on request
MAIL ORDER Yes
NCCPG NATIONAL COLLECTIONS *Dianthus* (Malmaison)

Not really a nursery: these are Malmaison carnations from the holder of the National Collection. These named varieties can be posted (though collection is preferred).

Mount Pleasant Trees

Rockhampton, Berkeley, Gloucestershire GL13 9DU
☎ 0454 260348

CONTACT G. Locke
LOCATION Mid way between Bristol and Gloucester
OPEN By appointment only
SPECIALITIES Hedging; trees
NEW FOR 1994 Many *Tiliae*, new to commerce
CATALOGUE 3 second class stamps
MAIL ORDER No

Mainly native trees for hedging and woodland use. In addition there is an eye-catching selection of specimen trees and shrubs for arboreta. The *Tilia* and *Ginkgo* collections are exceptional.

The Old Manor Nursery

Twyning, Gloucestershire GL20 6DB
☎ 0684 293516

CONTACT Mrs J. Wilder
OPEN 2 – 5 pm, Mondays, March to October
SPECIALITIES Alpines
NEW FOR 1994 A third of the list is new
CATALOGUE Large SAE plus 30p
MAIL ORDER No
REFRESHMENTS Teas on Bank Holidays
GARDEN Garden

Mainly alpines, but with a changing range of perennials, shrubs and trees also. All are propagated from the garden and can be seen in flower there at the appropriate seasons. Groups welcome by arrangement.

Priory Garden Nursery

The Priory, Kemerton, Tewkesbury, Gloucestershire
GL20 7JN
☎ 0386 725258

CONTACT Mrs Healing
OPEN 2 – 7 pm, Thursdays only
SPECIALITIES Herbaceous perennials; shrubs
MAIL ORDER No
GARDEN The Priory, Gloucestershire, see Gardens
section

Small nursery selling plants from this Gloucestershire
garden which is famous for its late summer borders.

St Annes Vineyard

Wain House, Oxenhall, Newent, Gloucestershire
GL18 1RW
☎ 0989 82313

CONTACT B. R. Edwards
LOCATION West Gloucestershire
OPEN 2 – 7 pm, Wednesday – Sunday
SPECIALITIES Vines
CATALOGUE SAE
MAIL ORDER Yes
SHOP Wine

Specialist grower of vines for dessert and table wines:
they claim to have the largest choice in the United
Kingdom. Most of the business is mail order: there are
some vines but more wine at the premises.

Wyevale Garden Centre

Shurdington Road, Brockworth, Gloucestershire
GL3 4PU
☎ 0452 862334   ⊞ 0452 864839

Wyevale Garden Centre

Milbury Heath, Wotton under Edge, Gloucestershire
GL12 8QH
☎ 0454 412247   ⊞ 0454 281502

GREATER
MANCHESTER

Daisy Nook Garden Centre

Daisy Nook, Failsworth, Manchester, Greater
Manchester M35 9WJ
☎ 061 681 4245   ⊞ 061 688 0822

CONTACT Mr P. Tyler
SHOP Landscape materials
REFRESHMENTS Café
GIFT TOKENS HTA

Garden centre including a fish centre.

Fairy Lane Nurseries

Fairy Lane, Sale, Greater Manchester M33 2JT
☎ 061 905 1137

CONTACT John B. Coxon
LOCATION In the Mersey valley, close to M63, J8
OPEN 9.30 am – 5.30 pm, Monday to Saturday; 10
am – 5.30 pm, Sundays. Closed over New Year from
19 December
NEW FOR 1994 100 new perennials
MAIL ORDER No
SHOP Garden sundries
GARDEN Herb garden
GIFT TOKENS HTA

A nursery and garden centre which makes an effort to
stock more than just the obvious varieties across its
general range. Informal design advice is usually available, and courses are sometimes run.

The Vicarage Gardens

Carrington, Urmston, Greater Manchester M31 4AG
☎ 061 775 2750   ⊞ 061 775 3679

CONTACT M. Zugor
LOCATION Greater Manchester
OPEN 10 am – 5.30 pm, daily, April to September; 10
am – 5 pm, daily, October to March. Closed Thursdays
all year, and 12.30 – 1.30 pm, weekdays for lunch
CATALOGUE 5 first class stamps
MAIL ORDER Yes; minimum order 5 plants
SHOP Gifts
REFRESHMENTS Tea room
GARDEN 5 acre garden
SHOWS RHS Westminster; Chelsea

Large garden in the hands of a charitable trust. The
nursery sells old-fashioned herbaceous plants and
alpines. Teas and gifts.

Worsley Hall Nurseries & Garden Centre

Leigh Road, Boothstown, Worsley, Greater
Manchester M28 4LJ
☎ 061 790 8792
LOCATION Near M62, J13
OPEN 8 am – 5.30 pm, summer. Closes at dusk in
winter
SHOP Garden sundries
REFRESHMENTS Café
GIFT TOKENS HTA

Garden centre and nurseries with a general range of
plants and products, including fruit trees and hedging.
Delivery service.

HAMPSHIRE

Agars Nursery

Agars Lane, Hordle, Lymington, Hampshire
SO41 0FL
☎ 0590 683703

CONTACT   George and Diane Tombs
OPEN   10 am – 5 pm, March to October; 10 am – 4 pm,
February and November. December and January by
appointment. Phone first. Closed Thursdays
SPECIALITIES   Irises
CATALOGUE   3 first class stamps
MAIL ORDER   Yes; minimum order £10
DESIGN SERVICE   Agars Nursery

A family-run nursery which is strong on *Iris*, osteospermums, penstemons and salvias. They also stock a range
of hardy trees and shrubs.

Apple Court

Hordle Lane, Hordle, Lymington, Hampshire
SO41 0HU
☎ 0590 642130   📠 0590 642130

CONTACT   Diana Grenfell or Roger Grounds
LOCATION   New Forest
OPEN   9.30 am – 1 pm, 2 – 5.30 pm, Thursday –
Monday, February to November. Closed last week in
August
SPECIALITIES   Ferns; grasses, hostas
NEW FOR 1994   Many new American *Hemerocallis*
CATALOGUE   3 first class stamps
MAIL ORDER   Yes; spring & autumn
GARDEN   Display gardens
DESIGN SERVICE   Apple Court
NCCPG NATIONAL COLLECTIONS   *Hosta*   (small
leaved), *Camassia*, *Woodwardia*, *Rohdea japonica*

Their main specialisations are hostas and hemerocallis:
they have over eighty of each. There is also an interesting selection of ferns and grasses, and a collection of
plants for white gardens.

Blackthorn Nursery

Kilmeston, Alresford, Hampshire SO24 0NL
☎ 0962 771796

CONTACT   Mrs S. B. White
LOCATION   1 mile south of Cheriton, off A272
OPEN   9 am – 5 pm, Friday and Saturday only, March
to October
SPECIALITIES   Alpines; herbaceous perennials
NEW FOR 1994   *Incarvillea lutea*; *Viola cazorlensis*
CATALOGUE   3 first class stamps
MAIL ORDER   No
SHOWS   RHS Westminster

Their specialities are daphnes and hellebores (see them
at Vincent Square in January). Otherwise, there is a
good range of alpine and rock plants, and a covetable,
changing selection of other plants grown at the nursery.

Christopher Fairweather Ltd

The Garden Centre, High Street, Beaulieu,
Hampshire SO42 7YR
☎ 0590 612307   📠 0590 612615

CONTACT   Christopher Fairweather
LOCATION   Beaulieu village
OPEN   8.45 am – 5.30 pm, daily
NEW FOR 1994   *Lavatera* 'Pink Frills'; *Pelargonium*
'Silver Cascade'
CATALOGUE   Wholesale catalogue only
MAIL ORDER   No
REFRESHMENTS   Refreshments
GIFT TOKENS   HTA

General garden centre in an attractive old building.
They specialise in shrubs, and also organise talks and
demonstrations on the premises.

D J Case

Higher End Nursery, Hale, Fordingbridge, Hampshire
SP6 2RA
☎ 0725 22243
LOCATION   Hampshire, Wiltshire border
OPEN   10 am – 5 pm, Tuesday – Saturday; 2 – 5 pm,
Sundays; April to August
SPECIALITIES   Aquatic plants; herbaceous perennials
CATALOGUE   2 first class stamps
MAIL ORDER   Yes

Water lilies and aquatics are the main specialities, but
there is a good choice of hardy perennials too.

Denmead Geranium Nurseries

Hambledon Road, Denmead, Waterlooville,
Hampshire PO7 6PS
☎ 0705 240081

CONTACT   Ivan H. Chance or Mrs K. J. Churcher-
Brown
LOCATION   2 miles west of A3, on B2150
OPEN   9 am – 5 pm, Monday – Friday; 9 am – 12.30 pm,
Saturdays. Open Saturday afternoons and Sundays in
April and May also. Closed Saturdays in August
SPECIALITIES   Pelargoniums
CATALOGUE   3 second class stamps
MAIL ORDER   Yes; minimum order 6 plants

Specialist growers of pelargoniums, including the following classes: zonal, coloured leaf, ivy leaf, Swiss
balcony, miniatures, stellars, angels and regals.

Drysdale Exotics

Bowerwood Road, Fordingbridge, Hampshire
SP6 1BN
☎ 0425 653010

CONTACT David Crampton
OPEN 9.30 am – 5.30 pm, Wednesday – Friday; 10 am
– 5.30 pm, Sundays
SPECIALITIES Bamboos; foliage plants; Mediterranean
plants
CATALOGUE 3 first class stamps
MAIL ORDER Yes
GARDEN Bamboo garden
NCCPG NATIONAL COLLECTIONS Bamboos

The plants here are chosen for their dramatic foliage
and for use in Mediterranean plantings. The bamboo
collection is reflected in the number of species available
from the nursery.

Exbury Enterprises Ltd

Exbury, Southampton, Hampshire SO4 1AZ
☎ 0703 898625

OPEN 10 am – 5.30 pm, daily
SPECIALITIES Rhododendrons
CATALOGUE SAE
MAIL ORDER Yes
REFRESHMENTS Restaurant
GARDEN Exbury Gardens, Hampshire, see Gardens
section
GIFT TOKENS HTA

Plant centre attached to this famous garden: unsurpris-
ingly they specialise in rhododendrons.

Family Trees

P O Box 3, Botley, Hampshire SO3 2EA
☎ 0329 834812

CONTACT Philip House
LOCATION 1 mile from Botley
OPEN 9 am – 12 pm, Wednesday and Saturday, No-
vember to April
SPECIALITIES Fruit
NEW FOR 1994 Dual fan trained apples and pears
CATALOGUE On request
MAIL ORDER Yes; minimum order £30

Many varieties of dessert apples, pears, plums and
peaches. They are available as bushes or trained. They
also have old roses, hedging and woodland trees. They
can graft to order.

Hardy's Cottage Garden Plants

The Walled Garden, Laverstoke Park, Laverstoke,
Whitchurch, Hampshire RG28 7NT
☎ 0256 896533

CONTACT Mr and Mrs R. K. Hardy

OPEN 9 am – 5.30 pm, Monday – Saturday, March to
October
SPECIALITIES Herbaceous perennials
CATALOGUE SAE or 50p
MAIL ORDER No
DESIGN SERVICE Hardy's Cottage Garden Plants
SHOWS RHS Westminster; Malvern Spring; Chel-
sea; BBC GW Live; Hampton Court

A family-run nursery with a large range of pretty cottage garden perennials and flowering shrubs. Watch
out for their attractive exhibits at shows. They also
offer a design and construction service.

Hillier Garden Centre

Botley Road, Romsey, Hampshire SO51 8ZL
☎ 0794 513459
SPECIALITIES Climbers; conifers; trees
CATALOGUE On request
MAIL ORDER No
GIFT TOKENS HTA

See Hillier Nurseries Ltd, Hampshire.

Hillier Garden Centre

Farnham Road, Liss, Hampshire GU33 6LJ
☎ 0730 892196

SPECIALITIES Climbers; conifers; trees
CATALOGUE On request
MAIL ORDER No
GIFT TOKENS HTA

See Hillier Nurseries Ltd, Hampshire.

Hillier Garden Centre

Romsey Road, Winchester, Hampshire SO22 5DL
☎ 0962 842288

SPECIALITIES Climbers; conifers; trees
CATALOGUE On request
MAIL ORDER No
GIFT TOKENS HTA

See Hillier Nurseries Ltd, Hampshire.

Hillier Garden Centre

Woodhouse Lane, Botley, Southampton, Hampshire
SO3 2EZ
☎ 0489 782306

SPECIALITIES Climbers; conifers; trees
CATALOGUE On request
MAIL ORDER No
GIFT TOKENS HTA

See Hillier Nurseries Ltd, Hampshire.

Hillier Nurseries Ltd

Ampfield House, Ampfield, Romsey, Hampshire
SO51 9PA
☎ 0794 368733   FAX 0794 368813

CONTACT   Sheila Pack
LOCATION   Hampshire based: see below
SPECIALITIES   Climbers; conifers; shrubs; trees
NEW FOR 1994   Azalea 'Salmon Leap'
CATALOGUE   On request or from stockists
MAIL ORDER   No
SHOP   Nine garden centres
GARDEN   Sir Harold Hillier Gardens and Arboretum,
Hampshire   See Gardens section
SHOWS   Chelsea
GIFT TOKENS   HTA

Celebrated and long-established wholesale and retail nurseries, best known for their wide range of trees and shrubs, available container or field-grown in large sizes. They have nine garden centres in southern England. The old mail order list has been replaced by the Hillier Premier Plant Service: the choice of plants has been cut back but distribution has been expanded. Nationwide Hillier stockists now give much wider access to the new, restricted list. Hampshire County Council now runs the arboretum built up by Harold Hillier: the Sir Harold Hillier Gardens and Arboretum, Hampshire. There is a free gardening club which produces a mgazine with details of events and product discount vouchers (0794 368966). The nine Hillier garden centres are at Bath, Newbury, Romsey, Liss, Winchester, Botley, Ampfield, Windlesham and Horsham.

Hillier Plant Centre

Jermyns Lane, Ampfield, Romsey, Hampshire
SO5 0QA
☎ 0794 368407
CATALOGUE   On request
GIFT TOKENS   HTA

See Hillier Nurseries Ltd, Hampshire.

Langley Boxwood Nursery

Rake, Liss, Hampshire GU33 7JL
☎ 0730 894467   FAX 0730 894703

CONTACT   Elizabeth Braimbridge
LOCATION   Near Petersfield
OPEN   By appointment only
SPECIALITIES   Hedging; boxwood
CATALOGUE   4 first class stamps
MAIL ORDER   Yes
NCCPG NATIONAL COLLECTIONS   Buxus

Specialist growers of box with a comprehensive range for hedging, topiary and as specimens. There are over 50 varieties of Buxus here, and some Taxus also.

Little Brook Fuchsias

Ash Green Lane West, Ash Green, Aldershot,
Hampshire GU12 6HL
☎ 0252 29731

CONTACT   Carol Gubler
LOCATION   1 mile from A31
OPEN   9 am – 5 pm, Wednesday – Sunday and Bank Holidays, 1 January to 1 July. Closed Mondays and Tuesdays
SPECIALITIES   Fuchsias
NEW FOR 1994   Fuchsia 'Popsie Girl'; 'Rose Fantasia'; 'Whickam Beauty'
CATALOGUE   SAE plus 25p
MAIL ORDER   No

Old and new Fuchsia varieties.

Longstock Park Nursery

Longstock, Stockbridge, Hampshire SO20 6EH
☎ 0264 810894   FAX 0264 810439

CONTACT   Mr D. Stuart
OPEN   8.30 am – 4.30 pm, Monday – Saturday; 2 – 5 pm, Sundays
SPECIALITIES   Aquatic plants; bog plants; herbaceous perennials; primulas; shrubs
CATALOGUE   £1.50
MAIL ORDER   No
GARDEN   Longstock Water Gardens, Hampshire, see Gardens section
DESIGN SERVICE   Longstock Park Nursery

A good range of conifers, ferns, perennials and shrubs. The nursery is recommended for its aquatic, moisture-loving and marginal plants, many of which are propagated from the adjacent water gardens. Excellent selection of primulas. The gardens, also owned by the John Lewis Partnership, open 2 – 4.30 pm on the third Sunday of the month, April to September.

Nine Springs Nursery

24 Winchester Street, Whitchurch, Hampshire
RG28 7AL
☎ 0256 892837   FAX 0256 892837

CONTACT   Gillian Anderson
OPEN   By appointment
SPECIALITIES   Aquatic plants
CATALOGUE   1 first class stamp
MAIL ORDER   Yes

Retail and wholesale aquatic plant nursery: small plants by post, and larger sizes on site. They can supply plants in a fibre roll to minimise erosion and wildfowl damage. See also Artscapes, Professional Services.

Oakleigh Nurseries

Petersfield Road, Monkwood, Alresford, Hampshire
SO24 0HB

☎ 0962 773344   📠 0962 772622

CONTACT Miss Sally Smith
OPEN 10 am – 1 pm, 2 – 4.30 pm, Monday – Friday,
April to July; 10.30 am – 1 pm, 2 – 4 pm, Sundays, April
to June
SPECIALITIES Cacti and succulents; fuchsias; pelargoniums
CATALOGUE 3 first class stamps
MAIL ORDER Yes
SHOWS Chelsea

Specialists for fuchsias (specimens, bush and standards)
and pelargoniums (zonal, regal and ivy leaf). They also
have a range of Christmas cacti hybrids and *Epiphyllum*. They publish a number of books, and Periwinkle Productions have filmed videos at the nursery.

Peter Trenear Nurseries

Chequers Lane, Eversley Cross, Hampshire
RG27 0NX

☎ 0734 732300

CONTACT Peter Trenear
LOCATION Between Reading and Camberley
OPEN 9 am – 4.30 pm. Closed Sundays
SPECIALITIES Trees
CATALOGUE 1 first class stamp
MAIL ORDER Yes; no minimum order

Here is a list of young trees and shrubs, including
conifers. They can either be planted out in the garden
or cultivated as bonsai specimens.

Pound Lane Nurseries

Ampfield, Romsey, Hampshire SO5 9BL

☎ 0703 739685   📠 0703 740300

CONTACT T. A. Holmes
LOCATION Between North Baddesley and Ampfield
OPEN 8.30 am – 5.30 pm, Monday – Friday; 9.30 am –
5.30 pm, Saturday – Sunday
MAIL ORDER No

Wholesale and retail working nursery offering hardy
container-grown stock, including trees, shrubs and
heathers.

Southview Nurseries

Chequers Lane, Eversley Cross, Basingstoke,
Hampshire RG27 0NT

☎ 0734 732206

CONTACT Elaine and Mark Trenear
LOCATION Between Camberley and Reading, off
B3272

OPEN 9 am – 4.30 pm, Thursday – Saturday. Closed
November to January
SPECIALITIES *Dianthus*; herbaceous perennials
CATALOGUE On request
MAIL ORDER Yes; September to May
GARDEN Garden open

Specialists for older varieties of named pinks and herbaceous perennials: they can help with historical plantings. Their own garden opens for the National Gardens
Scheme for the first time this year.

Spinners

Boldre, Lymington, Hampshire SO41 5QE
LOCATION Off A337
OPEN 10 am – 5 pm, daily, 20 April to 1 September.
Closed Mondays and Tuesdays after 1 July
SPECIALITIES Herbaceous perennials; shrubs; trees
CATALOGUE 4 first class stamps
MAIL ORDER No
GARDEN Spinners, Hampshire, see Gardens section

There is always plenty of interest at this nursery,
attached to a plantsman's garden. The herbaceous plants
are particularly strong.

Steven Bailey

Silver Street, Sway, Lymington, Hampshire
SO41 8ZA

☎ 0590 682227   📠 0590 683765

CONTACT S. E. Bailey and Ian Perry (Manager)
LOCATION Near Hordle: not Sway village
OPEN 8 am – 4.30 pm, Monday – Friday; 9 am – 4.30 pm,
Saturdays. Also 10 am – 4.30 pm, Sundays, March to
June only
SPECIALITIES Bedding plants; *Dianthus*
CATALOGUE 2 first class stamps
MAIL ORDER Yes
SHOWS RHS Westminster; International Spring Gardening Fair; Malvern Spring; Harrogate (Spring);
Southport; Chelsea; BBC GW Live; Hampton Court

Specialists for carnations, pinks and alstromerias. Active on the show circuit, so look out for them. The
nursery shop also has a selection of bedding and summer
pot plants.

Water Meadow Nursery and Herb Farm

Cheriton, Alresford, Hampshire SO24 0JT

☎ 0962 771895

CONTACT Mrs Sandy Worth
OPEN 9 am – 5 pm, Friday – Saturday, and Bank
Holidays; 2 – 5 pm, Sundays. March to November
SPECIALITIES Aquatic plants; bog plants; herbaceous
perennials; herbs
NEW FOR 1994 15 more water lilies

CATALOGUE 2 first class stamps
MAIL ORDER Yes
DESIGN SERVICE Water Meadow Nursery & Herb Farm

There is an extensive range of herbs and perennials here, but the main speciality is in plants that grow near water. Strong on *Nymphaea* (70). Other services include design and landscaping, and wholesale.

HEREFORD & WORCESTER

Abbey Dore Court Garden

Abbey Dore, Hereford, Hereford & Worcester HR2 0AD
☎ 0981 240419   [FAX] 0981 240279

CONTACT Charis Ward
LOCATION Between Hereford and Abergavenny, 3 miles west of A465
OPEN 11 am – 6 pm, Thursday – Tuesday, from third Saturday in March to third Sunday in October
SPECIALITIES Clematis
MAIL ORDER No
SHOP Country Gift Gallery
REFRESHMENTS Licensed restaurant, homemade food
GARDEN Abbey Dore Court Garden, Hereford & Worcester, see Gardens section

A small nursery attached to the garden: it is particularly good for perennials and clematis. To see the hellebores before the garden season, telephone for an appointment.

Baker Straw Partnership

Perhill Nurseries, Worcester Road, Great Witley, Hereford & Worcester WR6 6JT
☎ 0299 896329   [FAX] 0299 896990

CONTACT Mr D. Straw and Mr J. Baker
LOCATION At Great Witley, on A443
OPEN 9 am – 6 pm, daily
SPECIALITIES Alpines; herbaceous perennials; herbs
NEW FOR 1994 *Penstemon* 'Knightwick'; *Veronica wormskjoldii* 'Alba'
CATALOGUE SAE
MAIL ORDER No
SHOWS BBC GW Live

The retail nursery stocks over two thousand different alpines, herbs and perennials. Notable collections include *Dianthus* (100), thymes (40), penstemons (150) and salvias (90). They also operate a wholesale cash and carry business and deliver to local garden centres.

Bouts Cottage Nurseries

Bouts Lane, Inkberrow, Hereford & Worcester WR7 4HP
☎ 0386 792923

CONTACT Mark Roberts
OPEN Not open to the public
SPECIALITIES Violas
CATALOGUE SAE
MAIL ORDER Yes; no minimum order
SHOWS Malvern Spring; Chelsea; BBC GW Live

Mail order nursery devoted to old-fashioned violas. The plants can be seen at shows, but the nursery is not open for visiting.

Caves Folly Nurseries

Evendine Lane, Colwall, Malvern, Hereford & Worcester WR13 6DU
☎ 0684 40631

CONTACT B. Evans and W. Leaper
LOCATION Near Malvern
OPEN 10 am – 5 pm, Tuesday – Saturday
SPECIALITIES Alpines; herbaceous perennials
CATALOGUE On request
GARDEN Garden opens under the NGS from 2 pm – 6 pm, on 22 May, 26 June, 24 July and 28 August
DESIGN SERVICE Caves Folly Nurseries

The nursery sells alpine and herbaceous plants, all of which are organically grown in peat-free compost. A landscaping and garden maintenance service is also offered.

Cotswold Garden Flowers

1 Waterside, Evesham, Hereford & Worcester WR11 6BS
☎ 0386 47337

CONTACT Bob Brown
LOCATION Sands Lane, Badsey, Evesham. Continue ⅓ of a mile after tarmac runs out
OPEN 8 am – 4.30 pm, Monday – Friday. Weekends by appointment
SPECIALITIES Herbaceous perennials
NEW FOR 1994 Many new items
CATALOGUE On request
MAIL ORDER No
GARDEN 1 acre herbaceous display gardens

The nursery stocks a wide selection of herbaceous perennials, all of which have been chosen on the basis of their garden worthiness. There is no phone at the nursery, and garden visitors are advised to bring wellingtons when it's wet.

The Cottage Herbery

Mill House, Boraston, Tenbury Wells, Hereford &
Worcester WR15 8LZ

☎ 0584 79575   ☎ 0299 266216

CONTACT K. and R. Hurst
OPEN 10 am – 6 pm, Sundays only; weekdays by
appointment
SPECIALITIES Herbs
CATALOGUE 4 first class stamps
MAIL ORDER No
GARDEN Garden opens every Sunday
SHOWS Malvern Spring

A small, specialist nursery whose stock includes herbs
and aromatic plants, including *Symphytum*, *Pulmonaria*
and *Monarda*. The plants are organically grown in peat-
free compost. They will open specially for groups.

Cranesbill Nursery

White Cottage, Earls Common Road, Stock Green,
Redditch, Hereford & Worcester B96 6SZ

☎ 0386 792414

CONTACT Mrs J. Bates
LOCATION 9 miles west of Worcester, 1½ miles
north of A422
OPEN 10 am – 5 pm, Friday – Wednesday
SPECIALITIES Herbaceous perennials
CATALOGUE 4 first class stamps
MAIL ORDER Yes
SHOP Coneybury Plant Centre
GARDEN Customers can visit the 2 acre garden, open
under the NGS

Hardy geraniums are the speciality here – hardly surprising given the name. Yet there is a good selection of
other perennials, and some interesting shrubs too. They
also run Coneybury Plant Centre, nearby at Dormston.

D & M Everett

Greenacres Nursery, Bringsty, Worcester, Hereford
& Worcester WR6 5TA

☎ 0885 482206   ☎ 0885 488160

CONTACT Daphne Everett
OPEN By appointment
SPECIALITIES Heathers
CATALOGUE On request; separate wholesale and
retail lists
MAIL ORDER No
GARDEN Owners' garden opens for NGS

A heather specialist, with a mainly wholesale business
though a retail list is available. There are upwards of
200 containerised varieties.

Eastgrove Cottage Garden Nursery

Sankyns Green, Shrawley, Little Witley, Hereford &
Worcester WR6 6LQ

☎ 0299 896389

LOCATION On minor road between Shrawley and
Great Witley
OPEN 2 – 5 pm, Thursday – Monday, 1 April to July
31; 2 – 5 pm, Thursday – Saturday, 1 September to 15
October. Closed August
SPECIALITIES Herbaceous perennials
CATALOGUE SAE plus 5 second class stamps
MAIL ORDER No
GARDEN Eastgrove Cottage Garden, Hereford &
Worcester, see Gardens section

A large and varied range of interesting plants, all of them
propagated from the garden. They are mainly perenials,
but there is a smaller collection of half-hardy plants too.

Frank P Matthews Ltd

Berrington Court, Tenbury Wells, Hereford &
Worcester WR15 8RS

☎ 0584 810214   ☎ 0584 811830

CONTACT Janet Powell and Susan Bowen
LOCATION Tenbury Wells
OPEN By appointment only, for collection
SPECIALITIES Fruit; trees
NEW FOR 1994 *Malus* 'White Star'
CATALOGUE On request
MAIL ORDER No

The nursery is mainly a wholesale business, but serious
amateurs who are interested in the fruit and ornamental
tree ranges are encouraged. The plants are open ground
and container-grown. Order by phone in advance and
arrange to collect from the nursery.

Grange Farm Nursery

Guarlford, Malvern, Hereford & Worcester
WR13 6NY

☎ 0684 562544

CONTACT Mrs C. Nicholls
LOCATION Malvern
OPEN 9 am – 5.30 pm, summer; 9 am – dusk, winter.
Closed over Christmas and New Year
SPECIALITIES Shrubs; trees
MAIL ORDER No
GIFT TOKENS HTA

An all round range, with the emphasis on well-grown
trees and shrubs, sold from the retail plant centre.

Hayloft Plants

The Hayloft, Cooks Hill, Wick, Pershore, Hereford
& Worcester WR10 3PA

☎ 0386 561235

CONTACT Yvonne Walker
OPEN Mail order only
SPECIALITIES Half-hardy plants
CATALOGUE £1
MAIL ORDER Yes
SHOWS International Spring Gardening Fair

A new nursery with mainly half-hardy stock – penstemons, osteospermums and gazanias for example.

Helen Ballard
Old Country Farm, Mathon, Malvern, Hereford &
Worcester WR13 5PS
☎ 0886 880215

CONTACT Helen Ballard
OPEN By appointment
SPECIALITIES Hellebores
CATALOGUE SAE
MAIL ORDER Yes

Specialist source of hellebore hybrids.

International Acers
Acer Place, Coalash Lane, Hanbury, Bromsgrove,
Hereford & Worcester B60 4EY
☎ 0527 821774

CONTACT D. L. Horton
LOCATION South of Bromsgrove: ask for map
OPEN 9 am – 5.30 pm, weekends. Other times by
appointment
SPECIALITIES Acers
CATALOGUE SAE
MAIL ORDER No
DESIGN SERVICE International Acers

They specialise in maples, with good lists of species and
Acer palmatum cultivars. Worth keeping an eye on.

Jungle Giants
Plough Farm, Wigmore, Leominster, Hereford &
Worcester HR6 9UW
☎ 0568 86708   📠 0568 86383

CONTACT Michael Brisbane
LOCATION North Herefordshire, Welsh borders
OPEN By appointment only
SPECIALITIES Bamboos
CATALOGUE Bamboo information pack £5.75
MAIL ORDER Yes

Specialist growers of bamboos and other plants which
provide a tropical effect. They also sell large diameter
canes.

Marley Bank Nursery
Whitbourne, Hereford & Worcester WR6 5RU
☎ 0886 21576

CONTACT Roger Norman

OPEN By appointment all year
SPECIALITIES Alpines
CATALOGUE SAE
MAIL ORDER No
GARDEN Garden opens for NGS and by appointment

Small, specialist alpine nursery. The garden is open for
the NGS from April to September on the first and third
Sundays of the month (except 3 July).

Marston Exotics
Brampton Lane, Madley, Hereford, Hereford &
Worcester HR2 9LX
☎ 0981 251140   📠 0432 274023

CONTACT Paul Gardner
OPEN 8 am – 4.30 pm, Monday – Friday, all year; 1 –
5 pm, Saturday – Sunday, March to October
SPECIALITIES Carnivorous plants
CATALOGUE £1 guide; list is free
MAIL ORDER Yes; worldwide
REFRESHMENTS Refreshments
GARDEN National Collection of *Sarracenia* open
SHOWS RHS Westminster; International Spring Gardening Fair; Southport; Chelsea; Hampton Court
GIFT TOKENS Own
NCCPG NATIONAL COLLECTIONS *Sarracenia*

A formidable choice of carnivorous plants – the largest
public collection in Europe they claim. Their range
includes species for the house, greenhouse and garden,
as well as appropriate accessories. The National Collection of *Sarracenia* is open for the first time this year.

Old Court Nurseries
Walwyn Road, Colwall, Malvern, Hereford &
Worcester WR13 6QE
☎ 0684 40416

CONTACT Meriel Picton
LOCATION B4218 in Colwall Stone
OPEN 10 am – 1 pm, 2.15 – 5.30 pm, Wednesday –
Sunday, April to October
SPECIALITIES Herbaceous perennials; Michaelmas
daisies
CATALOGUE 2 first class stamps
MAIL ORDER Yes; asters only
GARDEN Picton Garden
NCCPG NATIONAL COLLECTIONS *Aster*

Holders of National Collection of Michaelmas daisies.
This is their speciality and there is a very extensive
collection of them. There are also many other interesting perennials and cottage garden type plants here.

Paul Jasper Trees
The Lighthouse, Bridge Street, Leominster, Hereford
& Worcester HR6 8DU
☎ 0568 611540   📠 0568 616499

CONTACT Paul Jasper
OPEN By appointment only
SPECIALITIES Fruit
CATALOGUE On request
MAIL ORDER Yes

Trade and retail fruit specialist with over 100 traditional apple varieties among other fruiting and ornamental trees. Roses no longer sold.

R F Beeston

294 Ombersley Road, Worcester, Hereford &
Worcester WR3 7HD
☎ 0905 53245

CONTACT R. F. Beeston
LOCATION Bevere Nurseries, Bevere, Worcester
OPEN 10 am – 1 pm, 2 – 5 pm, Wednesday – Friday,
March to October. Other times by appointment
SPECIALITIES Alpines; primulas
CATALOGUE SAE
MAIL ORDER Yes

Alpine specialist with an emphasis on smaller plants for use in alpine houses, alpine beds and troughs. Strengths include European *Primula* species, *Androsace* and *Dionysia*.

Rickard's Hardy Ferns Ltd

Kyre Park, Tenbury Wells, Hereford & Worcester
WR15 8RP
☎ 0885 410282

CONTACT Hazel and Martin Rickard
LOCATION Off Bromyard road, from Tenbury Wells
OPEN By appointment: phone first
SPECIALITIES Ferns
CATALOGUE SAE
MAIL ORDER Yes
SHOWS Malvern Spring; Chelsea

Specialists in hardy ferns. They have a great number for sale, and over 900 different varieties in their own collection. Half-hardy tree ferns are also sold.

Rosemary Spreckley

Hailey House, Great Comberton, Pershore, Hereford
& Worcester WR10 3DS
☎ 0386 710733

CONTACT Rosemary Spreckley
OPEN By appointment only
SPECIALITIES Penstemons
CATALOGUE SAE

Devoted solely to *Penstemon* species and cultivars. Mail order may be possible this year.

Rushfields of Ledbury

Ross Road, Ledbury, Hereford & Worcester
HR8 2LP
☎ 0531 632004

CONTACT Mr B. Homewood
LOCATION ½ mile south west of Ledbury on A449
OPEN 11 am – 5 pm, Wednesday – Saturday
SPECIALITIES Herbaceous perennials
NEW FOR 1994 Mildew resistant *Monarda* varieties
CATALOGUE Large SAE (29p) plus £1
MAIL ORDER Yes; their collections only
SHOWS Harrogate (Spring); Southport; Chelsea;
Hampton Court

A good choice of perennials, including geraniums, hardy osteospermums and hostas. Mail order is restricted to their collections.

S & E Bond

Gardener's Cottage, Letton, Hereford, Hereford &
Worcester HR3 6DH
☎ 0544 328422

CONTACT Sarah Bond
OPEN 10 am – 6 pm, Wednesday – Saturday and
Bank Holidays; 1 – 5 pm, Sundays. Open March to
October only.
SPECIALITIES Herbaceous perennials
CATALOGUE 3 first class stamps
MAIL ORDER Yes
GARDEN Walled garden
SHOWS Malvern Spring

Just herbaceous perennials, and an excellent choice of them too. There is a bias towards shade-lovers. Worth a visit to see what did not make it into the catalogue.

Stone House Cottage Nurseries

Stone, Kidderminster, Hereford & Worcester
DY10 4BG
☎ 0562 69902

CONTACT J. F. Arbuthnott
LOCATION 2 miles south east of Kidderminster, on
A448
OPEN 10 am – 6 pm, Wednesday – Saturday, March
to October. Also Sundays, May – June only
SPECIALITIES Climbers
CATALOGUE SAE
MAIL ORDER No
GARDEN Walled garden with towers

Wall shrubs and climbers are the speciality here, but there are also some interesting shrubs, old roses (on their own roots) and a constantly changing list of herbaceous plants.

Sunnybank House Nursery

Sunnybank House, Little Birch, Hereford, Hereford
& Worcester HR2 8BB
☎ 0981 540684

CONTACT Mrs Pat Jones
LOCATION 5 miles south of Hereford, near A49
OPEN By appointment only
CATALOGUE 2 first class stamps
MAIL ORDER Yes; minimum order £6
GARDEN Farmhouse garden
SHOWS Malvern Spring

A range of herbs and cottage garden type perennials.
The plants are raised organically, and can be seen in the
old farmhouse garden.

Toad Hall Produce

Frogmore, Weston under Penyard, Hereford &
Worcester HR9 5TQ
☎ 0989 750214

CONTACT S. V. North
LOCATION 4 miles south east of Ross on Wye
OPEN 10 am – 6 pm, Mondays, April to September
SPECIALITIES Herbaceous perennials
NEW FOR 1994 New geraniums
CATALOGUE SAE
MAIL ORDER Yes
GARDEN 2 acre garden

This small nursery specialises in hardy geraniums, all of
which can be seen in the garden. They have other
ground cover and herbaceous plants too.

Treasures of Tenbury Ltd

Burford House Gardens, Tenbury Wells, Worcester,
Hereford & Worcester WR15 8HQ
☎ 0584 810777

CONTACT Mr Hall
LOCATION A456 between Tenbury Wells and Ludlow
OPEN 10 am – 5 pm, daily
SPECIALITIES Clematis
CATALOGUE Yes
MAIL ORDER Yes
REFRESHMENTS Tea room
GARDEN Burford House Gardens, Hereford & Wor-
cester, see Gardens section
GIFT TOKENS HTA

The nursery specialises in herbaceous plants and especially the clematis which characterise the garden. Mail
order is restricted to clematis plants.

Webbs of Wychbold

Wychbold, Droitwich, Hereford & Worcester
WR9 0DG
☎ 0527 861777   📠 0527 861284

CONTACT John Grunsell
LOCATION 1 mile north of M5, J5 on A38
OPEN 9 am – 5.45 pm, Monday to Saturday; 10 am –
5 pm, Sundays and Bank Holidays. Close at 5 pm in
winter and have some late night openings in summer
NEW FOR 1994 New herbaceous plants
CATALOGUE £1
MAIL ORDER No
SHOP Garden sundries
REFRESHMENTS Restaurant
GARDEN Demonstration gardens
DESIGN SERVICE Webbs of Wychbold
SHOWS Malvern Spring
GIFT TOKENS HTA
NCCPG NATIONAL COLLECTIONS Forsythia;
·Potentilla fruticosa

Forward looking garden centre and nursery, with an
extensive range of good plants and all sorts of sundries
and equipment. Design and landscaping service.

Wintergreen Nurseries

Bringsty, Worcester, Hereford & Worcester
WR6 5UJ
☎ 0886 21858

CONTACT Stephen Dodd
LOCATION 3 miles east of Bromyard, on A44
OPEN 10 am – 5.30 pm, Wednesday – Sunday, March
to October
SPECIALITIES Alpines; herbaceous perennials
CATALOGUE 2 second class stamps
MAIL ORDER Yes
SHOWS Malvern Spring

A small nursery which specialises in alpines and perennials: there are also some shrubs.

Wyevale Garden Centre

Kings Acre Road, Hereford, Hereford & Worcester
HR4 0SE
☎ 0432 266261   📠 0432 341863

Wyevale Garden Centres plc

Kings Acre Road, Hereford, Hereford & Worcester
HR4 0SE
☎ 0432 276568   📠 0432 263289

CONTACT Stephen Morgan
OPEN 9 am – 6 pm, summer; 9 am – 5.30 pm, winter
CATALOGUE 99p plant guide
MAIL ORDER No
GIFT TOKENS HTA

The country's largest garden centre chain, with 41
centres and another 5 shops. Facilities vary, but all sell
the company's illustrated Good Plant Guide which
covers the Wyevale range. They offer over 2,500 var-

ieties of trees and shrubs, backed by a substantial wholesale nursery business. In addition the chain operates a plant finding service for a £5 deposit. Many of the centres also have pet shops and restaurants.

HERTFORDSHIRE

The Abbots House Garden
10 High Street, Abbots Langley, Hertfordshire
WD5 0AR
☎ 0923 264946

CONTACT   Dr Peter Tomson and Mrs Joan Gentry
OPEN   9 am – 1 pm, 2 – 4 pm, Saturdays, March to October; 9 am – 1 pm, Saturdays, November to December
SPECIALITIES   Conservatory plants
CATALOGUE   3 second class stamps
MAIL ORDER   Yes

A small nursery with a pleasantly mixed range, including shrubs, perennials, half-hardy and conservatory plants. Normally only open Saturdays, but visitors welcome on other days by arrangement.

Aylett Nurseries Ltd
North Orbital Road, London Colney, St Albans,
Hertfordshire AL2 1DH
☎ 0727 822255   ℻ 0727 823024

CONTACT   Mr R. S. Aylett
LOCATION   On A414
OPEN   8.30 am – 5.30 pm, Monday – Friday; 8.30 am – 5.30 pm, Saturdays; 9.30 am – 5 pm, Sundays and Bank Holidays
SPECIALITIES   Dahlias
SHOP   Garden sundries
GARDEN   Trial grounds
DESIGN SERVICE   Aylett Nurseries Ltd

A general garden centre, including a design service and delivery. Their award winning speciality is dahlias: they have a large selection of all types.

Chenies Garden Centre
Chenies, Rickmansworth, Hertfordshire WD3 6EN
☎ 0494 764545   ℻ 0494 762216

LOCATION   Between Rickmansworth and Amersham, on A404
OPEN   9 am – 5.30 pm, daily
SHOP   Garden buildings; fencing; paving; sundries
GIFT TOKENS   HTA

General garden centre, with a particularly large display of garden buildings. A design service is available through their sister company, Chenies Landscapes (see entry in Services).

Godly's Roses
Redbourn, St Albans, Hertfordshire AL3 7PS
☎ 0582 792255   ℻ 0582 794267

CONTACT   Colin and Andy Godly
LOCATION   A5183, ½ a mile south of M1, J9
OPEN   9 am – 6 pm, daily
SPECIALITIES   Roses
CATALOGUE   On request
MAIL ORDER   Yes; local orders only for standards
GARDEN   Rose fields

Rose growers with a selection of popular modern varieties. A general range of plants is carried in the garden centre.

Great Gardens of England Ltd
Chandlers Cross Garden Centre, Fir Tree Hill,
Chandlers Cross, Hertfordshire WD3 4LZ
☎ 0923 260488   ℻ 0923 261010

CONTACT   Mrs Jenny Welch
LOCATION   2 miles south of Kings Langley, off A41
OPEN   9 am – 5.30 pm
GIFT TOKENS   HTA; own

General garden centre with full indoor and outdoor stock. Delivery available.

Great Gardens of England Ltd
Chipperfield Home & Garden Centre, Tower Hill,
Chipperfield, Hertfordshire WD4 9LH
☎ 0442 834364   ℻ 0442 834259

CONTACT   Caroline Snow
LOCATION   2 miles west of Kings Langley, off A41
OPEN   9 am – 5.30 pm
GIFT TOKENS   HTA; own

General garden centre, with a range of stock for indoor and outdoor gardening. Delivery service available. The chain has other centres nearby at Chandlers Cross, and at Marlow and Syon Park.

Growing Carpets
Christmas Tree House, High Street, Guilden
Morden, Royston, Hertfordshire SG8 0JP
☎ 0763 852705

CONTACT   Mrs Eileen Moore
OPEN   10 am – dusk, Monday – Saturday; 2 pm – dusk, Sundays
SPECIALITIES   Ground cover plants
CATALOGUE   £1
MAIL ORDER   Yes; from October
GARDEN   Garden, including the whole nursery range

This ground cover nursery has recently changed hands: the above details are correct. The plants are container-grown, and include spreading perennials and prostrate shrubs.

Hopleys Plants Ltd

High Street, Much Hadham, Hertfordshire SG10 6BU
☎ 0279 842509   FAX 0279 843784

CONTACT Mr A. D. Barker
OPEN 9 am – 5 pm, daily; 2 – 5pm, Sundays. Closed Tuesdays, and January and August
SPECIALITIES Herbaceous perennials; shrubs
NEW FOR 1994 *Verbena* 'Pink Parfait'
CATALOGUE 4 first class stamps
MAIL ORDER Yes; autumn only
SHOWS RHS Westminster; International Spring Gardening Fair; Harrogate (Spring); Chelsea; Hampton Court
GIFT TOKENS Own

An extensive choice of hardy shrubs and perennials, with many half-hardy varieties too. Strong on penstemons and salvias. Over the last quarter of a century the nursery has been responsible for numerous introductions, the most famous being *Lavatera* 'Barnsley' and *Potentilla fruticosa* 'Red Ace'.

Maydencroft Aquatic Nurseries

Maydencroft Lane, Gosmore, Hitchin, Hertfordshire SG4 7QD
☎ 0462 456020   FAX 0462 422652

CONTACT Mr P. Bromfield
LOCATION 1 mile from Hitchin
OPEN Mail order only; collection by arrangement
SPECIALITIES Aquatic plants; bog plants
CATALOGUE 50p
MAIL ORDER Yes
SHOP Pond products; paving
GARDEN Demonstration gardens
GIFT TOKENS HTA; own

Aquatic, marginal and water-loving plants, available individually or as collections. There is a good choice of water lilies, and a range of associated pond and landscaping products.

Notcutts Garden Centre

Hatfield Road, Smallford, St Albans, Herts AL4 0BR
☎ 0727 53224

LOCATION On A1057
OPEN 8.30 am – 5.30 pm, Monday – Saturday; 10 am – 5 pm, Sundays. Closes at 5 pm in winter
CATALOGUE £2.50
SHOP Garden sundries; furniture
GIFT TOKENS HTA; own

See also Notcutts Nurseries, Suffolk.

R Harkness & Co Ltd

The Rose Gardens, Cambridge Road, Hitchin, Hertfordshire SG4 0JT
☎ 0462 420402   FAX 0462 422170

CONTACT Sales Office
OPEN 9 am – 5.30 pm, Monday – Friday; 10.30 am – 5.30 pm, Saturday – Sunday
SPECIALITIES Roses
NEW FOR 1994 Roses 'Renaissance'; 'Mrs Iris Clow'; 'Julie 'Y'', 'Della Balfour'; 'City Girl'
CATALOGUE On request
MAIL ORDER Yes; winter despatch
SHOP Garden centre
REFRESHMENTS Restaurant
SHOWS Chelsea
GIFT TOKENS HTA

Rose breeders and growers with a range dominated by Hybrid Teas, Cluster Flowered and low growing varieties. There are also climbers and shrub roses on the list. There is a garden centre on the site too with a wide range of bulbs, herbaceous plants, shrubs and trees.

The Van Hage Garden Company

Great Amwell, Ware, Hertfordshire SG12 9RP
☎ 0920 870811   FAX 0920 871861

CONTACT Miss Sandra Cronin
LOCATION Off A10
OPEN 9 am – 6 pm, daily. Opens 9.30 am, Mondays
SPECIALITIES Seeds
CATALOGUE Seeds only
MAIL ORDER Yes
SHOP Houseplants; furniture; machinery; wholefoods
REFRESHMENTS Coffee house
GARDEN Display gardens
SHOWS Chelsea

Long-established and award winning garden centre and seed merchants. The garden centre is strong on houseplants, and has a large choice of plants and related products. The seed catalogue covers flowers and vegetables, and includes the record-breaking Carrot 'Flak' as well as some untreated seed which is suitable for organic gardeners.

Wards Nurseries (Sarratt) Ltd

Dawes Lane, Sarratt, Rickmansworth, Hertfordshire WD3 6BQ
☎ 0923 263237

CONTACT T. Davis
LOCATION Turn opposite The Boot, in Sarratt
OPEN 8 am – 5 pm, Monday – Saturday; 9 am – 5 pm, Sundays and Bank Holidays
CATALOGUE On request
MAIL ORDER No

A mixed range which covers shrubs, conifers, herbaceous and scented plants.

Wyevale Garden Centre

Broadwater Garden Centre, Great Gaddesden,
Hemel Hempstead, Hertfordshire HP2 3BW
☎ 0442 231284 📠 0442 68987

HUMBERSIDE

California Gardens

Howden, Goole, Humberside DN14 7TF
☎ 0430 430824 📠 0430 432023

LOCATION On A614, near M62, J37
OPEN 9 am – 5 pm, daily
MAIL ORDER No
SHOP Greenhouses; garden buildings; sundries
REFRESHMENTS Coffee lounge
GIFT TOKENS HTA; own

This garden centre carries an all-round range of plants and sundries. It stocks Blooms' perennials, and organises demonstrations and garden workshop days. The National Vegetable Society's Northern Championships takes place at California Gardens this year on 9 October.

Mendle Nursery

Holme, Scunthorpe, Humberside DN16 3RF
☎ 0724 850864

CONTACT Mrs A. Earnshaw
LOCATION Holme
OPEN 10 am – 6 pm, daily
SPECIALITIES Alpines; sempervivums
CATALOGUE 2 first class stamps
MAIL ORDER Yes; no minimum order

A broad range of alpines, including primulas and lots of sempervivums.

Pennell & Sons Ltd

Garden Centre, Humberston Road, Grimsby,
Humberside DN36 4RW
☎ 0472 694272 📠 0472 694272

CONTACT Mr J. R. Cousins
LOCATION Outskirts of Grimsby
OPEN 8.30 am – 5.30 pm, Monday – Saturday;
10 am – 5.30 pm, Sundays and Bank Holidays
SHOP Garden sundries
GIFT TOKENS HTA

Garden centre with a full range. Delivery available.

Stephen H Smith's Garden & Leisure

Trent Valley, Doncaster Road, Scunthorpe,
Humberside DN15 8TE
☎ 0724 848950 📠 0724 848950

CONTACT Neil Parker

LOCATION On A18, ½ mile east of M181 junction
OPEN 9 am – 6 pm, summer; 9 am – 5.30 pm, winter
SHOP Garden sundries; furniture; gifts; aquatics
REFRESHMENTS Coffee shop
GIFT TOKENS HTA

Garden centre with plants and garden products. Delivery service.

White Cottage Alpines

Eastgate, Rudston, Driffield, Humberside YO25 0UX
☎ 0262 420668

CONTACT Mrs S. E. Cummins
LOCATION Just off B1253 (Bridlington to York: the scenic route)
OPEN 10 am – 5 pm, Thursday – Sunday, and Bank Holiday Mondays. Closed December and January
SPECIALITIES Alpines
CATALOGUE 2 first class stamps
MAIL ORDER Yes
GARDEN Display troughs

There is an interesting range to be found at this alpine nursery. Among the plants for alpine houses and rock gardens are some American species.

ISLE OF WIGHT

Deacons Nursery

Moor View, Godshill, Isle of Wight PO38 3HW
☎ 0983 840750/ 522243

CONTACT G. D. Deacon
SPECIALITIES Fruit
CATALOGUE SAE (29p stamp)
MAIL ORDER Yes; no minimum order

Fruit specialist, with tree and soft fruit of every size and variety. The very comprehensive list includes over 250 apple cultivars. All rootstocks are of virus free origin

KENT

Alan C Smith

127 Leaves Green Road, Keston, Kent BR2 6DG
☎ 0959 572531

CONTACT Alan C. Smith
OPEN By appointment only
SPECIALITIES Sempervivums
CATALOGUE 50p
MAIL ORDER Yes
SHOWS RHS Westminster

An amazing range of sempervivums and jovibarbas, including species, hybrids and cultivars: there are about one thousand on offer. A small selection is also available at Westerham Heights Garden Centre, Hawley Corner, Westerham Hill, Westerham TN16 2AW.

Ashenden Nursery

Cranbrook Road, Benenden, Cranbrook, Kent
TN17 4ET
☎ 0580 241792

CONTACT   Kevin McGarry
OPEN   10 am – 4.30 pm, Monday – Saturday. Phone first
SPECIALITIES   Alpines
NEW FOR 1994   Several *Hemerocallis* and *Campanula* cultivars
CATALOGUE   SAE
MAIL ORDER   Yes

Stocks a range of plants for rock gardens. They exhibit at specialist and local shows.

Brenda Hyatt

1 Toddington Crescent, Bluebell Hill, Chatham, Kent
ME5 9QT
☎ 0634 863251

CONTACT   Brenda Hyatt
OPEN   Thursdays only: by appointment
SPECIALITIES   Primulas
CATALOGUE   SAE plus 50p
MAIL ORDER   Yes
SHOWS   RHS Westminster; Malvern Spring; Chelsea
NCCPG NATIONAL COLLECTIONS   *Primula auricula* (show)

Auricula specialist – and National Collection holder. The superb range includes stripes, doubles, selfs and alpine specimens. Among the show types available are white-edged, green and grey flowered plants. Orders are dealt with in rotation, subject to availability.

Bybrook Barn Garden & Produce Centre

Canterbury Road, Kennington, Ashford, Kent
TN24 9JZ
☎ 0233 631959   ✆ 0233 635642

OPEN   9 am – 5.30 pm, Monday – Saturday; 9.30 am – 5 pm, Sundays
SHOP   Garden sundries; gifts; furniture
REFRESHMENTS   Refreshments
DESIGN SERVICE   Bybrook Barn Garden & Produce Centre
GIFT TOKENS   HTA

Garden centre stocking garden requirements and indoor plants. They have a delivery service and a design capability. A gardening club is run from the premises.

Church Hill Cottage Gardens

Charing Heath, Ashford, Kent TN27 0BU
☎ 0233 712522

CONTACT   Mr and Mrs Metianu
OPEN   10 am – 5 pm, Tuesday – Sunday, and Bank Holidays. Closed Mondays, and 1 -15 September, 20 October – 31 January
SPECIALITIES   *Dianthus*; herbaceous perennials
CATALOGUE   3 first class stamps
MAIL ORDER   No
GARDEN   1½ acre garden open with nursery: entrance £1.50

The nursery specialises in hardy herbaceous perennials, but there are many *Dianthus*, alpines and shrubs to choose from too. The garden opens too: park in the nearby pub.

Coblands Nursery

Trench Road, Tonbridge, Kent TN10 3HQ
☎ 0732 770999   ✆ 0732 770271
LOCATION   Tonbridge
SPECIALITIES   Bamboos; climbers; conifers; ferns; grasses; herbaceous perennials; shrubs; trees
CATALOGUE   Wholesale catalogue only
MAIL ORDER   No

A large wholesale nursery which carries a comprehensive range of all types of plants for landscapers and garden centres. They also supply their own garden centres at Dartford (0474 704888), Tunbridge Wells (0892 515234), and a plant centre at Ightham (0732 780816).

Connoisseurs' Cacti

51 Chelsfield Lane, Orpington, Kent BR5 4HG
☎ 0689 837781

CONTACT   John Pilbeam
LOCATION   Woodlands Farm, Shire Lane, Farnborough, Kent
OPEN   Phone first
SPECIALITIES   Cacti and succulents
CATALOGUE   SAE
MAIL ORDER   Yes; UK and EC only
SHOP   Books on cacti
SHOWS   Chelsea; Hampton Court

An extensive range of cacti and succulents (over 20,000 specimens in stock), as well as books on cacti. Particularly strong on *Gymnocalycium*, *Mammillaria*, *Rebutia* and *Sulcorebutia*. The main address is for postal enquiries only.

Forward Nurseries

Borough Green Road, Ightham, Kent TN15 9JA
☎ 0732 884726   ✆ 0732 884726

CONTACT Paul van Leeuwen
LOCATION A25 and A227 roundabout at Borough Green
OPEN 8 am – 5 pm, daily
SPECIALITIES Hedging
CATALOGUE Trade catalogue; retail mail order list
MAIL ORDER Yes

This mainly wholesale nursery carries a general range. Their retail section specialises in hedging plants (which are available mail order) and containerised ivy plants.

The Fruit Garden

Mulberry Farm, Woodnesborough, Sandwich, Kent CT13 0PT
☎ 0304 813454   ℻ 0304 813454

CONTACT Patricia and Peter Dodd
OPEN By appointment only, for collection
SPECIALITIES Fruit
CATALOGUE On request
MAIL ORDER Yes
DESIGN SERVICE The Fruit Garden

A tempting list of fruit trees, with the emphasis on older varieties. They can design fruit gardens, and will bud or graft to order. This service can be done with your own scion wood: a way to propagate a favourite tree.

Hazeldene Nursery

Dean Street, East Farleigh, Maidstone, Kent ME15 0PS
☎ 0622 726248

CONTACT Mrs J. Adams
LOCATION 2½ miles south west of Maidstone
OPEN 10 am – 3 pm, Tuesday – Saturday, March to September
SPECIALITIES Seeds; violas
CATALOGUE 2 first class stamps
MAIL ORDER Yes
SHOWS RHS Westminster; International Spring Gardening Fair; Malvern Spring; Harrogate (Spring); Southport; Chelsea; Hampton Court; Harrogate (Autumn)

Many kinds of pansies, violas, violets and violettas. These are often available as seed as well as plants. The nursery has amassed five gold medals at Chelsea.

High Banks Nurseries

Slip Mill Road, Hawkhurst, Kent TN18 5AD
☎ 0580 753031

CONTACT Jeremy Homewood
OPEN 8 am – 4.30 pm, winter; 8.30 am – 5 pm, spring and summer
NEW FOR 1994 Cedrus deodara 'Roman Candle'; Choisya ternata 'Moonbeam'
CATALOGUE Large SAE

MAIL ORDER No

The nursery carries a full, general range of plants.

Iden Croft Herbs

Frittenden Road, Staplehurst, Kent TN12 0DH
☎ 0580 891432   ℻ 0580 892416

CONTACT Rosemary Titterington and Marion Browne
OPEN 9 am – 5 pm, Monday – Saturday, all year; 11 am – 5 pm, Sundays and Bank Holidays, March to September only
SPECIALITIES Herbs
NEW FOR 1994 New items each year
CATALOGUE SAE for list; £2.50 full catalogue
MAIL ORDER Yes
SHOP Herb products; seeds; books
REFRESHMENTS Tea room
GARDEN Herb gardens
GIFT TOKENS HTA
NCCPG NATIONAL COLLECTIONS Origanum; Mentha

Call themselves a 'total herb centre' with some justification. The range of herbs and aromatic plants is both impressive and extensive. Other herb products are on sale too. The main catalogue is very helpful and informative. They hold tours, workshops and other events. The gardens are designed for disabled access.

J Bradshaw & Son

Busheyfields Nursery, Herne, Herne Bay, Kent CT6 7LJ
☎ 0227 375415   ℻ 0227 375415

CONTACT Denis Bradshaw
LOCATION On A291, 2 miles south of A299 junction
OPEN By appointment only. Orders can be collected 9 am – 5 pm, Monday – Friday
SPECIALITIES Clematis; climbers
CATALOGUE SAE
MAIL ORDER No
GARDEN Stock fields of Clematis and Lonicera open by appointment, £1
NCCPG NATIONAL COLLECTIONS Lonicera (climbing)

Family nursery. The business is mainly wholesale but retail orders can be collected from the premises. They specialise in clematis, Lonicera and other climbers. The stock fields, with over 100 Lonicera species and 250 clematis are open by appointment. There are special terms for NCCPG and British Clematis Society members.

Keepers Nursery

446 Wateringbury Road, East Malling, Kent ME19 6JJ
☎ 0622 813008

CONTACT Anne and Mike Cook
LOCATION 5 miles west of Maidstone, between M20 and A26
OPEN By appointment at all reasonable times
SPECIALITIES Fruit
NEW FOR 1994 50 new varieties
CATALOGUE SAE
MAIL ORDER Yes
DESIGN SERVICE Keepers Nursery

A very lengthy list of fruit trees, including some lovely names, and a good choice of nuts and soft fruit too. An idea of the scope: over 360 apples, 70 plums, 40 cherries, not to mention medlars, pears and quinces. They will design fruit gardens and orchards, and can advise on maintenance within their area. The grafting service offers to propagate known and unknown varieties for customers. They also hold workshops.

Layham Garden Centre

Lower Road, Staple, Canterbury, Kent CT3 1LH
☎ 0304 813267   📠 0304 615349

CONTACT Andrew Marshall (manager)
LOCATION 8 miles south of Canterbury
OPEN 9 am – 5 pm, Monday – Saturday; 10 am – 5 pm, Sundays
SPECIALITIES Roses
NEW FOR 1994 Several new roses
CATALOGUE Rose list on request
MAIL ORDER Yes
REFRESHMENTS Refreshments
GIFT TOKENS HTA

The garden centre carries a general range of plants with a particular accent on roses: the business is backed by its own wholesale nursery, Layham Nurseries (0304 611380).

Longacre Nursery

Longacre, Perry Wood, Selling, Faversham, Kent ME13 9SE
☎ 0227 752254

CONTACT Dr G. Thomas
LOCATION East of Selling village
OPEN 2 – 5 pm
SPECIALITIES Herbaceous perennials
CATALOGUE SAE
MAIL ORDER No
GARDEN Garden opens under NGS and by appointment
DESIGN SERVICE Longacre Nursery

The nursery sells a wide variety of hardy perennials. The garden can be visited, and the Thomases offer garden design (especially for borders) and lectures. Groups welcome by appointment.

Madrona Nursery

Harden Road, Lydd, Kent TN29 9LT
☎ 0679 20868

CONTACT Mr Liam MacKenzie
OPEN Check with nursery
SPECIALITIES Bamboos; grasses; shrubs; trees
CATALOGUE £1
MAIL ORDER Yes; minimum carriage charge £10
SHOWS RHS Westminster; Hampton Court; Courson

The emphasis is on attractive trees and shrubs, but there are also perennials, ferns, grasses and bamboos.

Marle Place Gardens & Nursery

Marle Place Road, Brenchley, Tonbridge, Kent TN12 7HS   📠 0892 724099

CONTACT Mrs Williams
LOCATION West Kent
OPEN 10 am – 5.30 pm
SPECIALITIES Herbs
CATALOGUE SAE
MAIL ORDER Yes
GARDEN Marle Place Gardens
NCCPG NATIONAL COLLECTIONS *Calamintha; Santolina*

The nursery grows herbs, aromatic and scented plants in containers. This year more plants from the garden are being introduced. Courses, talks and tours can be arranged.

Notcutts Garden Centre

Newnham Court, Bearstead Road, Maidstone, Kent ME14 5LH
☎ 0622 39944

LOCATION Near M20, J7
OPEN 9 am – 5.45 pm, Monday – Saturday; 10 am – 5.30 pm, Sundays
CATALOGUE £2.50
SHOP Garden sundries; furniture; buildings; pets
REFRESHMENTS Restaurant
GIFT TOKENS HTA; own

See also Notcutts Nurseries, Suffolk.

Notcutts Garden Centre

Tonbridge Road, Pembury, Tunbridge Wells, Kent TN2 4QN
☎ 0892 822636

OPEN 8.30 am – 5.30 pm, Monday – Saturday; 10 am – 5 pm, Sundays. Closes at 5 pm in winter
CATALOGUE £2.50
SHOP Garden sundries; furniture; buildings; landscape materials
DESIGN SERVICE Nottcutts Landscapes

GIFT TOKENS HTA; own

See also Notcutts Nurseries, Suffolk.

Oldbury Nurseries

Brissenden Green, Bethersden, Ashford, Kent
TN26 3BJ
☎ 0233 820416

CONTACT Wendy and Peter Dresman
LOCATION 7 miles south west of Ashford, off A28
OPEN 9.30 am – 5 pm, daily, February to June
SPECIALITIES Fuchsias
CATALOGUE 2 first class stamps
MAIL ORDER No
SHOWS Chelsea; Hampton Court

Oldbury Nurseries are specialist fuchsia growers with
an extensive range. Some pelargoniums too.

P De Jager & Sons Ltd

Staplehurst Road, Marden, Kent TN12 9BP
☎ 0622 831235   FAX 0622 832416

LOCATION Between Maidstone and Staplehurst on
A229
OPEN 9 am – 5 pm, Monday – Friday; 9 am – 12 pm,
Saturdays
SPECIALITIES Bulbs; daffodils
CATALOGUE On request; December, May
MAIL ORDER Yes
GIFT TOKENS Own

Bulbs of all kinds, ranging from well known *Narcissus*
and *Tulipa* varieties to some rare specimen bulbs.

P H Kellett

Laurels Nursery, Benenden, Cranbrook, Kent
TN17 4JU
☎ 0580 240463

CONTACT Mr P. H. Kellett
LOCATION ¾ mile off Benenden to Rolvenden road,
towards Dingleden
OPEN 8 am – 5 pm, Monday – Thursday; 8 am – 4 pm,
Fridays; 8.30 am – 12 pm, Saturdays. Other times by
appointment
SPECIALITIES Shrubs; trees
NEW FOR 1994 New rose varieties
CATALOGUE On request
MAIL ORDER No
DESIGN SERVICE P H Kellett
GIFT TOKENS HTA

A traditional nursery growing a varied range of trees
and shrubs, including roses, conifers, fruit trees and
climbers. Plants are both open ground and container-
grown: browsers can inspect stock for autumn lifting.
Border planning and advice available also.

Pete & Ken Cactus Nursery

Saunders Lane, Ash, Canterbury, Kent CT3 2BX
☎ 0304 812170

CONTACT Ken Burke
LOCATION 10 miles east of Canterbury, off A257
OPEN 9 am – 6 pm, daily
SPECIALITIES Cacti and succulents
CATALOGUE Large SAE
MAIL ORDER Yes

Cacti and succulents specialists, with a particularly
good choice of *Lithops*. They also sell some alpines,
fuchsias and shrubs.

Plaxtol Nurseries

The Spoute, Plaxtol, Sevenoaks, Kent TN15 0QR
☎ 0732 810550

CONTACT Tessa and Jenny Forbes
LOCATION On the east side of Plaxtol, off A227
OPEN 10 am – 5 pm, daily. Closed for a fortnight at
Christmas
SPECIALITIES Foliage plants
NEW FOR 1994 *Jasminum nudiflorum* 'Mystique';
Cotinus 'Grace'; *Garrya* x *issaquahensis* 'Glasnevin
Wine'
CATALOGUE 2 first class stamps
MAIL ORDER Yes; November to March
GARDEN Garden open
DESIGN SERVICE Plaxtol Nurseries
GIFT TOKENS Own

Trees, shrubs, heathers, conifers and herbaceous plants
which have been chosen with the flower arranger in
mind. Talks by arrangement. They design and construct
Japanese gardens, and their own garden is open to
customers.

Richard G M Cawthorne

Lower Daltons Nursery, Swanley Village, Swanley,
Kent BR8 7NU

CONTACT R. G. M. Cawthorne
OPEN Mail order only
SPECIALITIES Violas
NEW FOR 1994 *Viola* 'Astrid'; *V.* 'Kinvarna';
V. 'Colette'
CATALOGUE 70p
MAIL ORDER Yes
SHOWS Chelsea
NCCPG NATIONAL COLLECTIONS *Viola*

The *Viola* and violetta specialist, with a collection of
550 named varieties and species. The majority of these
have been bred by Mr Cawthorne, whose outdoor
displays are a familiar sight at Chelsea each year. Mixed
viola seed is sent airmail to overseas customers only.

Rumwood Nurseries

Langley, Maidstone, Kent ME17 3ND
☎ 0622 861477 ⚫ 0622 863123

CONTACT James Fermor
LOCATION On A274
OPEN 9 am – 5 pm, Monday – Saturday; 10 am – 5 pm, Sundays
SPECIALITIES Roses
CATALOGUE SAE
MAIL ORDER Yes
GARDEN Rose fields
GIFT TOKENS HTA

A family-run retail and wholesale nursery. They specialise in roses, of which they grow an all-round range, and other hardy nursery stock.

Ruxley Manor Garden Centre Ltd

Maidstone Road, Sidcup, Kent DA14 5BQ
☎ 081 300 0084 ⚫ 081 302 3879

CONTACT John Owen
SHOP Garden sundries; furniture; conservatories; pools
SHOWS Chelsea
GIFT TOKENS HTA

Starborough Nursery

Starborough Road, Marsh Green, Edenbridge, Kent TN8 5RB
☎ 0732 865614

CONTACT Mrs P. Kindley and Colin Tomlin
LOCATION Between Edenbridge and Lingfield on B2028
OPEN 10 am – 4.30 pm, Thursday – Monday. Closed Tuesdays, Wednesdays and in January and July
SPECIALITIES Rhododendrons; shrubs; trees
NEW FOR 1994 Azalea 'Salmon's Leap'
CATALOGUE £1.50
MAIL ORDER Yes
SHOWS RHS Westminster; Chelsea

Recently joined forces with G. Reuthe Ltd. They now issue a single catalogue, combining Starborough's trees and shrubs with Reuthe's rhododendrons and azaleas.

Tile Barn Nursery

Standen Street, Iden Green, Benenden, Kent TN17 4LB
☎ 0580 240221

CONTACT Peter Moore
OPEN 9 am – 5 pm, Wednesday – Saturday
SPECIALITIES Cyclamen
CATALOGUE SAE
MAIL ORDER Yes

Mail order is restricted to their speciality – *Cyclamen* species. Nursery visitors will also find some species *Crocus, Fritillaria, Leucojum* and *Narcissus*.

Tim Ingram

Copton Ash Gardens, 105 Ashford Road, Faversham, Kent ME13 8XW
☎ 0795 535919

CONTACT Tim Ingram
LOCATION On A251, opposite M2 eastbound exit
OPEN 2 – 6 pm, Tuesday – Thursday, Saturday – Sunday, March to October. Other times by appointment
SPECIALITIES Alpines; fruit; herbaceous perennials
NEW FOR 1994 New Proteaceae
CATALOGUE 4 first class stamps
MAIL ORDER Yes: fruit trees only
GARDEN 1½ acre garden

The nursery carries a range of alpine and perennial plants. The emphasis is on those suited to the drier climate of the south east. Mail order is restricted to bare root fruit trees. The garden is also open.

Westwood Nursery

65 Yorkland Avenue, Welling, Kent DA16 2LE
☎ 081 301 0886

CONTACT Mr S. Edwards
OPEN Mail order only
SPECIALITIES Orchids; pleiones
CATALOGUE SAE; summer, winter
MAIL ORDER Yes

Hardy orchids and pleiones: suitable for the garden and frost free greenhouse. Some orchid books too.

Wyevale Garden Centre

Romney Marsh Garden Centre, Hamstreet, Ashford, Kent TN26 2Q
☎ 0233 732988 ⚫ 0233 733703

Wyevale Garden Centre

Oakley Road, Keston Mark, Bromley, Kent BR2 6BY
☎ 0689 859419 ⚫ 0689 862359

LANCASHIRE

Auldene Nurseries Ltd

338 Southport Road, Ulnes Walton, Leyland, Lancashire PR5 3LQ
☎ 0772 600271 ⚫ 0772 601483

CONTACT Richard Iddon
LOCATION 3 miles south of Leyland, on A581
OPEN 9 am – 8 pm (or dusk if earlier), daily
SHOP Books; gifts and sundries
REFRESHMENTS Coffee shop

DESIGN SERVICE Auldene Nurseries Ltd
GIFT TOKENS HTA

Family run garden centre which stocks plants and shrubs, aquatics, seeds, sundries and conservatories. They have a design and landscaping capability, and deliver free locally. Monthly gardening seminars are held, and they run their own gardening club.

Barkers Primrose Nurseries

Whalley Road, Clitheroe, Lancashire BB7 1HT
☎ 0200 23521   ☎ 0200 28160

CONTACT Philip Bradley
LOCATION Ribble Valley: from M6, J31 follow A59 to Clitheroe
OPEN 9 am – 5.30 pm, Monday – Saturday; 10 am – 5 pm, Sundays and Bank Holidays
SPECIALITIES Acers; aquatic plants
CATALOGUE SAE; trees, roses and shrubs
MAIL ORDER No
GIFT TOKENS HTA

Nursery and garden centre with a large and varied range of plants, including aquatics and marginals, Japanese acers, trees, shrubs and perennials. Named after the area: they are not *Primula* specialists.

Barton Grange Garden Centre

Wigan Road, Bolton, Lancashire BL3 4RD
☎ 0204 660660   ☎ 0204 62525

CONTACT Shane Harper
LOCATION ½ a mile from M61, J 5, on A58 to Bolton
OPEN 9 am – 5.30 pm, Monday – Saturday (until 8 pm Tuesdays); 10 am – 5.30 pm Sundays
SHOP Garden sundries; gifts
REFRESHMENTS Café
DESIGN SERVICE Barton Grange Garden Centre
GIFT TOKENS HTA

Large garden centre with a full range of plants and associated garden products. They are stockists for the Hillier Premier Plant Collection. Landscaping and garden maintenance service.

Barton Grange Garden Centre

Garstang Road, Barton, Preston, Lancashire PR3 5AA
☎ 0772 864242   ☎ 0772 862863

CONTACT Mrs P. Heavyside
LOCATION Off A6 Garstang road
OPEN 9 am – 5.30 pm, Monday – Saturday; 10 am – 5.30 pm, Sundays
SHOP Garden sundries; gifts; furniture; conservatories
REFRESHMENTS Café
DESIGN SERVICE Barton Grange Landscapes
GIFT TOKENS HTA

Large garden centre with a full range of plants and products. They have a Halls Conservatory Showcase (0772 865861), and a landscaping and maintenance arm, Barton Grange Landscapes (0772 864242). Weekly talks and demonstrations. They also have a wholesale nursery.

Catforth Gardens

Roots Lane, Catforth, Preston, Lancashire PR4 0JB
☎ 0772 690561/ 690269

CONTACT Judith Bradshaw and Chris Moore
OPEN 19 March – 18 September
SPECIALITIES Herbaceous perennials
CATALOGUE £1 by post
MAIL ORDER No
GARDEN Two gardens: admission £1
NCCPG NATIONAL COLLECTIONS *Geranium*

The nursery is sandwiched between two gardens which are open at the same time. The list is strongest on hardy geraniums (species and cultivars). Many other herbaceous perennials are also on offer.

Craig House Cacti

94 King Street, Southport, Lancashire PR8 1LG
☎ 0704 545077

CONTACT George A. McCleod
OPEN Mail order only
SPECIALITIES Cacti and succulents
CATALOGUE On request
MAIL ORDER Yes
SHOWS RHS Westminster; Chelsea; BBC GW Live; Hampton Court

Mail order specialists selling cacti, succulents and cycads including Madagascan caudiciform succulents (swollen stemmed). They also exhibit widely, so look out for them at shows.

Croston Cactus

43 Southport Road, Eccleston, Chorley, Lancashire PR7 6ET
☎ 0257 452555

CONTACT John L. Henshaw
OPEN Saturday – Sunday only
SPECIALITIES Cacti and succulents
CATALOGUE 2 first class stamps; spring & summer
MAIL ORDER Yes; no minimum order

Cacti and succulents aimed chiefly at the enthusiast: many mammillarias and some interesting haworthias. Bromeliads (including tillandsias) are available at the nursery.

Eversley Nurseries
10 Granville Avenue, Hesketh Bank, Preston,
Lancashire PR4 6AH
☎ 0772 812538

CONTACT   Stan Crabtree
OPEN   By appointment, at any time
SPECIALITIES   Heathers
NEW FOR 1994   *Calluna vulgaris* 'Jill'
CATALOGUE   SAE
MAIL ORDER   Yes
SHOWS   International Spring Gardening Fair; Harrogate (Spring); Southport; BBC GW Live; Hampton Court; Harrogate (Autumn)

Specialist growers and exhibitors of heathers (and other ericaceous plants). The large range (over 250 heather varieties) is matched by scale (¼ million grown).

Holden Clough Nursery
Holden, Bolton by Bowland, Clitheroe, Lancashire
BB7 4PF
☎ 0200 447615

CONTACT   Mr P. Foley
LOCATION   8 miles north east of Clitheroe, off A59
OPEN   1 – 5 pm, Monday – Thursday; 9 am – 5 pm, Saturdays; 2 – 5pm, Sundays (April and May only)
SPECIALITIES   Alpines; conifers; ferns; grasses; herbaceous perennials; shrubs
NEW FOR 1994   *Heuchera* 'Pewter Moon'; *Coreopsis* 'American Dream'
CATALOGUE   £1.20
MAIL ORDER   Yes; October to March
SHOWS   RHS Westminster; Harrogate (Spring); Southport; BBC GW Live; Hampton Court; Harrogate (Autumn)

A long-established working nursery, with a large and very hardy range of interesting alpines, perennials, dwarf conifers, shrubs, ferns and grasses. Please note that this Pennine nursery only opens for Sundays in April and May, and that the last admission on all days is at 4.30 pm.

Pinks & Carnations
22 Chetwyn Avenue, Bromley Cross, Bolton,
Lancashire BL7 9BN
☎ 0204 306273

CONTACT   Tom Gillies
OPEN   By appointment only
SPECIALITIES   *Dianthus*
CATALOGUE   1 first class stamp
MAIL ORDER   Yes

This wholesale and retail nursery supplies garden pinks, and perpetual flowering and border carnations. Some

Malmaison carnations will be available in spring. A sideline is model wooden cars.

Reginald Kaye Ltd
Waithman Nurseries, Silverdale, Carnforth,
Lancashire LA5 0TY
☎ 0524 701252

CONTACT   Mrs Kaye
LOCATION   4 miles north west of Carnforth
OPEN   9 am – 5 pm, Monday – Saturday; 2.30 – 5 pm Sundays
SPECIALITIES   Alpines; ferns; herbaceous perennials
NEW FOR 1994   New ferns
CATALOGUE   60p
MAIL ORDER   No
GARDEN   New rock garden

Alpine and fern specialists: the list of ferns is being increased this year, and there is a new rock garden.

Sellet Hall Gardens
Sellet Hall, Kirkby Lonsdale, Carnforth, Lancashire
LA6 2QF
☎ 05242 71865   ✆ 05242 72208

CONTACT   Mrs Judy Gray
LOCATION   1 mile from Kirkby Lonsdale, off A65
OPEN   10 am – 5 pm, daily
SPECIALITIES   Acers
CATALOGUE   SAE
MAIL ORDER   Yes; October to March
REFRESHMENTS   Tea room
GARDEN   Display gardens
DESIGN SERVICE   Sellet Hall Gardens

There are herbs and herbaceous plants here. The main speciality though is Japanese Acers, many of which also grow in the gardens.

Wyevale Garden Centre
Preston New Road, Westby, Kirkham, Lancashire
PR4 3PE
☎ 0772 684129   ✆ 0772 671770

LEICESTERSHIRE

A & A Thorp
Bungalow No 5, Main Street, Theddingworth,
Lutterworth, Leicestershire LE17 6QZ
☎ 0858 880496

CONTACT   Anita Thorp
LOCATION   Between Market Harborough and Lutterworth, on A427
OPEN   9 am – 6 pm (dusk in winter)
SPECIALITIES   Alpines
CATALOGUE   SAE plus 50p

MAIL ORDER No

A small nursery which stocks alpine and herbaceous plants in small quantities. The range is large, though. Personal service rather than help yourself.

Fosse Alpines
33 Leicester Road, Countesthorpe, Leicestershire
LE8 3QU
☎ 0533 778237

CONTACT Mr T. West
OPEN By appointment only
SPECIALITIES Alpines
CATALOGUE 30p
MAIL ORDER Yes; minimum order £8

This small nursery is recommended for its range of rare and unusual alpines.

Gandy's Roses Ltd
North Kilworth, Lutterworth, Leicestershire
LE17 6HZ
☎ 0858 880398

CONTACT Mr D. Gandy, Mrs E. Gandy, Miss R. Gandy and Mrs M. Spence
OPEN Office hours: 9 am – 5 pm, Monday – Saturday; 2 – 5 pm, Sundays
SPECIALITIES Roses
CATALOGUE On request
MAIL ORDER Yes
GARDEN Rose fields open, July – September

Rose growers covering the whole spectrum (600), with a particularly interesting choice of climbers. The nursery also sells shrubs, fruit trees and conifers. Items need to be ordered in advance for winter collection and mail order.

Goscote Nurseries Ltd
Syston Road, Cossington, Leicestershire LE7 4UZ
☎ 0509 812121

CONTACT D. C. Cox and R. Plant
LOCATION 5 miles north of Leicester, on B5328
OPEN 8 am – 5 pm (4.30 pm in winter), Monday – Friday; 9 am – 5 pm, Saturdays; 10 am – 5 pm, Sundays
SPECIALITIES Conifers; heathers; shrubs; trees
CATALOGUE 4 second class stamps
MAIL ORDER Yes; minimum order £10
GARDEN Display gardens
DESIGN SERVICE Goscote Nurseries Ltd

Many varieties of trees, shrubs and conifers, acers and azaleas, are available here from the open ground. The nursery centre also stocks container plants.

John Smith & Son
Hilltop Nurseries, Thornton, Coalville, Leicestershire
LE67 1AN
☎ 0530 230331

CONTACT N. Smith
LOCATION 3 miles from M1, J22
OPEN 8 am – 5.30 pm
SPECIALITIES Fuchsias
CATALOGUE SAE
MAIL ORDER Yes

In addition to a general range, the nursery specialises in rooted fuchsia cuttings, including American and other named varieties.

Laburnum Nurseries
6 Manor House Gardens, Main Street, Humberstone Village, Leicester, Leicestershire LE5 1AF
☎ 0533 766522

CONTACT Mr W. M. Johnson
OPEN 9.15 am – 12 pm, 2 – 4.30 pm, Monday – Friday; 9 am – 12 pm, Saturday – Sunday
SPECIALITIES Fuchsias
NEW FOR 1994 *Fuchsia* 'Firefox'; 'Martha Brown'; 'William's Lass'; 'Pa's Princess'; 'Obsession'; 'Pure Magic'
CATALOGUE On request
MAIL ORDER Yes

Growers and breeders of *Fuchsia* cultivars: the six introductions planned for this year are listed above.

Linda Gascoigne Wild Flowers
17 Imperial Road, Kibworth Beauchamp, Leicester, Leicestershire LE8 0HR
☎ 0533 793959

CONTACT Linda Gascoigne
LOCATION Between Leicester and Market Harborough, off A6
OPEN By appointment
SPECIALITIES Wild flowers
CATALOGUE 3 first class stamps
MAIL ORDER Yes; minimum order £5

A small nursery with a selection of native flowers and plants which attract wildlife. Linda Gascoigne is also a wildlife artist.

Philip Tivey & Son
28 Wanlip Road, Syston, Leicestershire LE7 8PA
☎ 0533 692968

OPEN 9 am – 5 pm, Monday – Friday; 9 am – 3 pm, Saturdays
SPECIALITIES Chrysanthemums; dahlias
CATALOGUE SAE plus 25p
MAIL ORDER Yes; minimum order £8.50

SHOWS RHS Westminster; Southport; Chelsea; Hampton Court; Harrogate (Autumn)

Specialist growers of dahlias, with mixed collections of chrysanthemums, including Korean and hardy border types, available too.

S & S Perennials

24 Main Street, Normanton le Heath, Leicestershire LE6 1TB
☎ 0530 262250

OPEN Afternoons and weekends
SPECIALITIES Irises; lilies
CATALOGUE SAE
MAIL ORDER Yes

This small nursery sells *Cyclamen, Erythronium, Fritillaria* and *Lilium* species, plus a number of *Iris* cultivars.

Ulverscroft Unusual Plants

Ulverscroft Grange Nursery, Priory Lane, Ulverscroft, Markfield, Leicester, Leicestershire LE67 9PB
☎ 0530 243635

CONTACT Ted Brown
LOCATION Near M1, J22
OPEN From 10 am – 5.30 pm, Wednesday – Sunday, March to November. Other times by appointment
SPECIALITIES Bamboos; grasses; herbaceous perennials
MAIL ORDER No

A wide choice of perennials, grasses and bamboos: specialities include *Bergenia* and *Pulmonaria*.

Wyevale Garden Centre

1665 Melton Road, East Goscote, Leicester, Leicestershire LE7 8YQ
☎ 0533 605515   📠 0533 695122

LINCOLNSHIRE

Baytree Nurseries

High Road, Weston, Spalding, Lincolnshire PE12 6JU
☎ 0406 370242   📠 0406 371665

CONTACT Peter Wayman
LOCATION 1½ miles east of Spalding, on A151
OPEN 9 am – 6 pm, summer; 9 am – 5.30 pm, winter
MAIL ORDER No
SHOP Garden sundries; machinery; crafts
REFRESHMENTS Restaurant
GARDEN Demonstration gardens
GIFT TOKENS HTA; own

Large, award-winning garden centre. They produce much of their stock themselves, and are especially good

on trees and shrubs, roses and bulbs. Venue for the UK Giant Fruit, Vegetable and Flower Championships in 1993. The Baytree Owl Centre is on the same site.

C E & D M Nurseries

The Walnuts, 36 Main Street, Baston, Peterborough, Lincolnshire PE6 9PB

CONTACT Colin Fletcher
LOCATION South of Bourne, on A15
OPEN 10 am – 5 pm, Friday – Tuesday. Closed Christmas & Boxing Day
SPECIALITIES Herbaceous perennials
CATALOGUE 2 first class stamps
MAIL ORDER Yes; no minimum order
GARDEN Demonstration gardens

This fenland nursery stocks a dependable selection of hardy herbaceous perennials.

Clive Simms

Woodhurst, Essendine, Stamford, Lincolnshire PE9 4LQ
☎ 0780 55615

CONTACT Clive Simms
OPEN Mail order only
SPECIALITIES Fruit
CATALOGUE 2 first class stamps
MAIL ORDER Yes

Nut trees and uncommon edible fruits. There are all sorts of wonderful curiosities on offer here.

Cottage Nurseries

Thoresthorpe, Alford, Lincolnshire LN13 0HX
☎ 0507 466968

CONTACT W. H. Denbigh
LOCATION 1 mile from Alford on A1104 Mablethorpe road
OPEN 9 am – 5 pm, daily
SPECIALITIES Herbaceous perennials
CATALOGUE 3 first class stamps
MAIL ORDER Yes
GARDEN Demonstration gardens
DESIGN SERVICE Cottage Nurseries

A good choice of hardy (and some tender) perennials, as well as shrubs and alpines. Most of the range would be at home in a cottage type garden.

Donington Plants

Main Road, Wrangle, Boston, Lincolnshire PE22 9AT
☎ 0205 870015

CONTACT Derek Salt
LOCATION North east of Boston on A52; north end of Wrangle, on the left

OPEN By appointment only. Contact the nursery for details of open week
SPECIALITIES Primulas
NEW FOR 1994 6 new double auriculas
CATALOGUE No
MAIL ORDER No
NCCPG NATIONAL COLLECTIONS *Primula auricula*

As holder of the National Collection of double auriculas, they are the major attraction here. There are other primulas and auriculas too. The plants can be seen at Primula Society shows.

Foliage & Unusual Plants

The Dingle Nursery, Pilsgate, Stamford, Lincolnshire PE9 3HW
☎ 0780 740775 📠 0780 740838

CONTACT Margaret Handley
LOCATION Less than a mile from Burghley House, on B1443
OPEN 10 am – 6 pm, 1 March to 14 November
SPECIALITIES Foliage plants; herbaceous perennials
CATALOGUE 3 first class stamps
MAIL ORDER Yes; minimum order £10
REFRESHMENTS Picnics welcomed
GARDEN Gardens

The range includes hardy shrubs, perennials, alpines, grasses and conifers. Most are chosen for their coloured or variegated foliage. Group and evening visits are welcome by prior arrangement.

Glenhirst Cactus Nursery

Station Road, Swineshead, Boston, Lincs PE20 3NX
☎ 0205 820314

CONTACT N. C. and S. A. Bell
LOCATION Just off A17, near Boston
OPEN 10 am – 5 pm, Thursdays, Fridays and Sundays, April to October. By appointment at other times
SPECIALITIES Cacti and succulents; seeds
NEW FOR 1994 Extended range of hardy and half-hardy cacti and succulents
CATALOGUE 2 first class stamps
MAIL ORDER Yes
SHOP Books; sundries
GARDEN Scree garden

An extensive range of cacti and succulents, including epiphyllums. More succulents and half-hardy cacti are being added this year. They also sell books, seeds and sundries, and are happy to advise on cultivation and display.

Hall Farm Nursery

Hall Farm, Harpswell, Gainsborough, Lincolnshire DN21 5UU
☎ 0427 668412

CONTACT Pam and Mark Tatam
LOCATION 7 miles east of Gainsborough on A631
OPEN Open daily. Closed weekends, December to February
SPECIALITIES Herbaceous perennials; shrubs
NEW FOR 1994 Many new items
CATALOGUE Large SAE
MAIL ORDER No

A small nursery with an interesting and expanding range of hardy roses, shrubs and perennials. The *Nepeta* species and cultivars are worth looking out for.

J Walkers Bulbs

Washway House Farm, Holbeach, Spalding, Lincolnshire PE12 7PP
☎ 0406 26216 📠 0406 25468

CONTACT J. W. Walkers
OPEN Mail order only
SPECIALITIES Bulbs; daffodils
CATALOGUE 2 first class stamps
MAIL ORDER Yes
SHOWS International Spring Gardening Fair; Harrogate (Spring); Chelsea

Specialists in daffodil bulbs of all kinds, including exhibition varieties. They also sell some fritillaries.

Judy's Country Garden

The Villa, Louth Road, South Somercotes, Louth, Lincolnshire LN11 7BW
☎ 0507 358487

CONTACT Judy Harry
LOCATION 8 miles east of Louth
SPECIALITIES Herbaceous perennials; herbs
CATALOGUE 3 first class stamps
MAIL ORDER No
GARDEN Garden is open for nursery visitors
DESIGN SERVICE Judy's Country Garden
GIFT TOKENS Own

A small, garden nursery with a range of herbs and perennials, especially the older varieties. Courses, talks and group visits are held.

Kathleen Muncaster Fuchsias

18 Field Lane, Morton, Gainsborough, Lincolnshire DN21 3BY
☎ 0427 612329

CONTACT Kathleen Muncaster
OPEN 10 am – dusk, February to mid July. Phone first at other times
SPECIALITIES Fuchsias
CATALOGUE 2 first class stamps
MAIL ORDER Limited mail order
GARDEN Garden and stock plants on display

Fuchsia specialist with an extensive range of species, hardy fuchsias and other varieties. The hardy fuchsias can be seen in the garden. They also sell other plants for hanging baskets.

Martin Nest Nurseries

Grange Cottage, Hemswell, Gainsborough, Lincolnshire DN21 5UP

☎ 0427 668369   🖷 0427 668080

CONTACT M. A. Robinson
LOCATION 6 miles east of Gainsborough on A631
OPEN 10 am – 5 pm, daily
SPECIALITIES Alpines
CATALOGUE 3 second class stamps
MAIL ORDER Yes
GARDEN Demonstration garden

A good businesslike range of tough pot-grown hardy alpine plants (including primulas, auriculas and saxifrages) for garden centres and individuals.

Orchard Nurseries

Tow Lane, Foston, Grantham, Lincolnshire NG32 2LE

☎ 0400 81354   🖷 0400 81354

CONTACT R. and J. Blenkinship
LOCATION Near A1
OPEN 10 am – 6 pm, daily, 1 March to 1 October
SPECIALITIES Clematis; herbaceous perennials
NEW FOR 1994 *Lavatera* 'Pink Ice'; *L.* 'Pink Velvet'; *Osteospermum* 'Orchard White'; *O.* 'Calypso'
CATALOGUE £1
MAIL ORDER No
GARDEN Garden opens from 1 May to 1 September for NGS
DESIGN SERVICE Orchard Nurseries
GIFT TOKENS Own

The nursery has a good range of the smaller-flowered *Clematis* hybrids, and other climbers, as well as many, many herbaceous plants. The garden is open daily from May to the beginning of September, and they offer garden design.

The Plant Lovers

Candlesby House, Candlesby, Spilsby, Lincolnshire PE23 5RU

☎ 0754 85256

CONTACT Tim Wilson
LOCATION 8 miles west of Skegness on A158
OPEN Phone first
SPECIALITIES Cacti and succulents; seeds; sempervivums
MAIL ORDER Limited
GARDEN Display house
SHOWS Malvern Spring

Wholesale and retail cacti and succulent specialists. They have a wide selection of reliable varieties and species. The nursery is open most days but you are asked to phone first.

Potterton and Martin

The Cottage Nursery, Moortown Road, Nettleton, Caistor, Lincolnshire LN7 6HX

☎ 0472 851792

CONTACT Mr and Mrs Potterton
LOCATION On B1205: leave A46 at Nettleton
OPEN 9 am – 5 pm, daily
SPECIALITIES Alpines; bulbs; carnivorous plants; seeds
NEW FOR 1994 *Diascia* 'Appleby Apricot'; *D.* 'Jacqueline's Joy'; *D.* 'Joyce's Choice'; *Phlox subulata* 'Surprise, Surprise'
CATALOGUE £1
MAIL ORDER Yes
GARDEN Display gardens
SHOWS International Spring Gardening Fair; Harrogate (Spring); Chelsea; BBC GW Live

Alpine and rock plant specialist with an interesting and extensive range, running from the easy to the unusual. Bulbs and seeds too. The nursery holds five Chelsea gold medals, and has won the RHS Farrer Trophy (best alpine display) on several occasions.

Southfield Nurseries

Bourne Road, Morton, Bourne, Lincolnshire PE10 0RH

☎ 0778 570168

CONTACT Mr and Mrs B. Goodey
OPEN 10 am – 5 pm, daily
SPECIALITIES Cacti and succulents; seeds
CATALOGUE 1 first class stamp
MAIL ORDER Yes
SHOWS RHS Westminster; International Spring Gardening Fair; Harrogate (Spring); Chelsea; Hampton Court

Cacti and succulent specialist with an extensive choice of plants, all raised from seed at the nursery. Various sizes, including some specimens. There is also a small seed list.

LONDON

Derek Lloyd Dean

8 Lynwood Close, South Harrow, London HA2 9PR

☎ 081 864 0899

CONTACT Derek Lloyd Dean
OPEN Mail order only
SPECIALITIES Pelargoniums

CATALOGUE 2 first class stamps
MAIL ORDER Yes; minimum order 6 plants
SHOWS RHS Westminster; Chelsea

A pelargonium specialist with an extensive range of rooted cuttings available by mail order only. The list is good on new introductions.

The Garden Centre at Hounslow Heath

Staines Road, Hounslow, London TW4 5DS
☎ 081 572 3211   📠 081 572 5623

CONTACT Barry Sutherns
OPEN 9 am – 6 pm, daily
SHOP Garden sundries; gifts
REFRESHMENTS Coffee shop

Garden centre, with plants and sundries. They have a delivery service, and there is a water life centre also on the site.

Great Gardens of England (Syon) Ltd

The Garden Centre, Syon Park, Brentford, London TW8 8JG
☎ 081 568 3908   📠 081 847 3865

CONTACT Alan Chapman (Manager)
LOCATION 8 miles west of London on A4
OPEN 9 am – 5.30 pm, Monday – Friday (8 pm Wednesdays); 9.30 am – 6 pm, Saturday – Sunday
DESIGN SERVICE See Syon Courtyard
GIFT TOKENS HTA; own

Garden centre with a general stock for indoor and outdoor gardening. A delivery service is available, and they offer landscaping through Syon Courtyard. There are other branches of Great Gardens of England at Marlow, Chandlers Cross and Chipperfield.

Jacques Amand Ltd

The Nurseries, Clamp Hill, Stanmore, London HA7 3JS
☎ 081 954 8138   📠 081 954 6784

CONTACT Matthew Downes
OPEN 8.30 am – 5 pm, Monday – Friday; 8.30 am – 1 pm, Saturdays; 9 am – 1 pm, Sundays
SPECIALITIES Bulbs
CATALOGUE On request
MAIL ORDER Yes
SHOWS Harrogate (Spring); Chelsea; Hampton Court

Celebrated bulb specialists, whose range includes flower bulbs of all types. Look out for their displays at shows.

Marks and Spencer plc

47 Baker Street, London W1A 1DN
☎ 071 935 4422   📠 071 268 2655

CONTACT Food Customer Services Department
LOCATION Nationwide
OPEN Normally 9 am – 5.30 pm

Most stores carry a range of dormant shrubs, with roses and bulbs in season. The new garden shops carry a wider choice (currently at Camberley, Culverhouse Cross, Pinner, Shoreham by Sea and Cheshunt).

The Palm Centre

563 Upper Richmond Road West, London SW14 7ED
☎ 081 876 3223   📠 081 876 6888

CONTACT Martin Gibbons
OPEN 10 am – 6 pm, daily
SPECIALITIES Palms
CATALOGUE £1.95, palms; £1.85, cycads
MAIL ORDER Yes

Specialist in ornamental palms, both hardy and indoor varieties. They come in all sizes from seedlings to specimens. There is also a range of cycads.

Syon Courtyard

Great Gardens of England (Syon) Ltd, Syon Courtyard, Syon Park, Brentford, London TW8 8JG
☎ 081 568 3114   📠 081 847 3865

CONTACT Karl Lawrence
LOCATION 8 miles west of London on A4
OPEN 9 am – 5.30 pm, Monday – Friday; 9.30 am – 6 pm, Saturday – Sunday
SHOP Sheds; paving; fencing
DESIGN SERVICE Syon Courtyard
GIFT TOKENS HTA; own

Attached to the Great Gardens of England garden centre at Syon Park. Supplies landscaping materials and offers a design and landscaping service.

Wolden Nurseries & Garden Centre

Cattlegate Road, Crews Hill, Enfield, London EN2 9DW
☎ 081 363 7003   📠 081 366 2705

CONTACT Vic Barnard
OPEN 8.30 am – 5.30 pm, Monday – Friday; 8 am – 5 pm, Saturday – Sunday
GARDEN Seasonal displays
GIFT TOKENS HTA

North London garden centre. Free advice.

Wyevale Garden Centre
Cattlegate Road, Crews Hill, Enfield, London
EN2 9DX
☎ 081 367 0422   📠 081 366 3810

Wyevale Garden Centre
Headstone Lane, Harrow, London HA2 6NB
☎ 081 428 3408   📠 081 420 1833

MERSEYSIDE

Landlife Wildflowers Ltd
The Old Police Station, Lark Lane, Liverpool,
Merseyside L17 8UU
☎ 051 728 7011   📠 051 728 8413

CONTACT Gillian Watson
SPECIALITIES Seeds; wild flowers
NEW FOR 1994 'Queen Anne's Lace' mixed
CATALOGUE Large SAE (35p stamp)
MAIL ORDER Yes

This small nursery sells a range of native wild flowers
as seeds, small plants and bulbs. All profits go to the
environmental charity Landlife.

Porter's Fuchsias
12 Hazel Grove, Southport, Merseyside PR8 6AX
☎ 0704 533902   📠 0704 832196

CONTACT John Porter
OPEN 10.30 am – 4 pm, Thursday – Sunday, January
to 2 May
SPECIALITIES Fuchsias
NEW FOR 1994 Fuchsia 'Popsie Girl'; 'Rose Fanta-
sia'; 'Whickham Beauty'
CATALOGUE 2 first class stamps
MAIL ORDER Yes; January to May only
SHOWS Southport

A fuchsia specialist, concentrating mainly on modern
cultivars, and on show varieties in particular. Mr Porter
also lectures nationwide.

NORFOLK

African Violet Centre
Station Road, Terrington St Clement, Kings Lynn,
Norfolk PE34 4PL
☎ 0553 828374   📠 0553 827520

CONTACT Mrs Maggie Garford
OPEN 10 am – 5 pm, March to October
SPECIALITIES African violets; house plants
CATALOGUE On request: phone 0553 827281
MAIL ORDER Yes
REFRESHMENTS Tearoom, Easter to September

SHOWS Chelsea; Hampton Court

The specialists for saintpaulias, with a huge selection
on offer. Other house and garden plants are available in
season too.

Bawdeswell Garden Centre
Bawdeswell, Dereham, Norfolk NR20 4SJ
☎ 036288 387   📠 036288 504

CONTACT Peter Underwood
LOCATION Between Norwich and Fakenham on
A1067
OPEN 8 am – 5.30 pm, summer; 8 am – 5 pm, winter
CATALOGUE Plant guide 50p
SHOP Garden sundries; gifts
REFRESHMENTS Coffee shop
GIFT TOKENS HTA

General garden centre, including conservatories and
greenhouses. They operate a design and landscaping
service.

Bressingham Gardens Mail Order
Bressingham, Diss, Norfolk IP22 2AB

CONTACT Sara O'Hara
OPEN Mail order only
CATALOGUE £2; also available from plant centres
MAIL ORDER Yes
GIFT TOKENS Own

The mail order section of Bressinghams. It is run separately from the retail plant centres at Bressingham and
Dorney Court. The range is similar: an excellent choice
of hardy perennials and alpines, and the trademark small
conifers and heathers.

Bressingham Plant Centre
Bressingham, Diss, Norfolk IP22 2AB
☎ 0379 888133   📠 0379 888289/ 888034

CONTACT Tony Fry
OPEN 10 am – 5.30 am daily, except Christmas and
Boxing Day
SPECIALITIES Alpines; conifers; herbaceous peren-
nials
CATALOGUE £2 for Bressingham Gardens Mail Order
catalogue
MAIL ORDER See Bressingham Gardens Mail Order
GARDEN Bressingham Gardens, Norfolk, see Gardens
section
DESIGN SERVICE Bressingham Landscapes, Design &
Build
SHOWS Chelsea; Hampton Court
GIFT TOKENS Own

The plant centre here at Bressingham is a model of its
type: there is another at Dorney Court, Berkshire. The
mail order side is called Bressingham Gardens and is run

separately. The retail range is strong on hardy perennials and alpines, conifers and heathers. Good quality stock. Pick your own fruit also, in season. Bressingham Landscapes offers design and build.

Chris Bowers & Son

Whispering Trees Nursery, Wimbotsham, Norfolk
PE34 8QB
☎ 0366 388752

CONTACT   Chris Bowers
LOCATION   North of Downham Market
OPEN   9 am – 5 pm
SPECIALITIES   Fruit; shrubs
CATALOGUE   £2
MAIL ORDER   Yes
SHOWS   RHS Westminster; Chelsea

Although many types of plants are stocked the attraction here is the fruit. The excellent selection includes purple raspberries, blueberries and cranberries, and rhubarb cultivars from the National Collection, as well as tree fruits and nuts.

Croftacre Hardy Plants

Croftacre, Ellingham Road, Scoulton, Norfolk
NR9 4NT
☎ 0953 850599   FAX 0953 851399

CONTACT   Mrs Veronica Allen
LOCATION   Off the B1108, between Hingham and Watton
OPEN   By appointment only: phone first
SPECIALITIES   Herbaceous perennials
CATALOGUE   3 first class stamps
MAIL ORDER   Yes; no minimum order; spring and winter only

A good selection of genuinely uncommon perennials. Species predominate, but the nursery is, for instance, strong on *Platycodon* cultivars.

Daphne ffiske Herbs

Rosemary Cottage, The Street, Bramerton, Norwich, Norfolk NR13 7DW
☎ 0508 538187

CONTACT   Daphne ffiske
LOCATION   4 miles south east of Norwich, off A146
OPEN   10 am – 4 pm, Thursday – Sunday, March to September
SPECIALITIES   Herbs
CATALOGUE   SAE
MAIL ORDER   Yes

The nursery stocks a selection of herbs and medicinal plants, including those which are attractive to bees.

Four Seasons

Forncett St Mary, Norwich, Norfolk NR16 1JT
☎ 0508 418344   FAX 0508 418478

CONTACT   J. P. Metcalf and Richard Ball
OPEN   Mail order only
SPECIALITIES   Herbaceous perennials
CATALOGUE   £1
MAIL ORDER   Yes; autumn and spring despatch
SHOWS   RHS Westminster; Chelsea

An outstanding range of herbaceous perennials, both cultivars and species. Highlights include the asters and *Monarda*. The nursery only trades mail order, but exhibits regularly at the RHS shows in Vincent Square, Westminster.

Hoecroft Plants

Severals Grange, Wood Norton, Dereham, Norfolk
NR20 5BL
☎ 0362 844206/ 860179

CONTACT   Miss Jane M. Lister
LOCATION   2 miles north of Guist on B1110
OPEN   10 am – 4 pm, Wednesdays and Saturdays
SPECIALITIES   Foliage plants; grasses
CATALOGUE   £1
MAIL ORDER   Yes; no minimum order
SHOWS   Chelsea; Hampton Court

A large and attractive range of plants with variegated and coloured leaves, and of decorative grasses. A good source for admirers of variegated foliage.

Jenny Burgess' Alpine Nursery

Alpine Nursery, Sisland, Norwich, Norfolk
NR14 6EF
☎ 0508 20724

CONTACT   Jenny Burgess
OPEN   By appointment only
SPECIALITIES   Alpines
CATALOGUE   2 first class stamps
MAIL ORDER   Yes; sisyrinchiums only
NCCPG NATIONAL COLLECTIONS   *Sisyrinchium*

An alpine grower, with a strong list of sisyrinchiums, and many campanulas too.

Norfolk Lavender Ltd

Caley Mill, Heacham, Kings Lynn, Norfolk PE31 7JE
☎ 0485 70384   FAX 0485 71176

CONTACT   Teresa Melton
LOCATION   North of Kings Lynn on A149
OPEN   9.30 am – 6 pm, summer; 10.30 am – 4 pm, winter. Closed 23 December to 8 January
SPECIALITIES   Lavenders
CATALOGUE   On request
MAIL ORDER   Yes; minimum order 6 plants

SHOP Lavender products
GARDEN Lavender collection
NCCPG NATIONAL COLLECTIONS *Lavandula*

They grow and sell hardy and tender *Lavandula*, bare root and in containers respectively. Lavender products are for sale, and the national collection is on display.

Norwich Heather and Conifer Centre
54a Yarmouth Road, Thorpe St Andrew, Norwich, Norfolk NR7 0HE
☎ 0603 39434

CONTACT Mr B. Hipperson
LOCATION 2 miles east of Norwich
OPEN 9 am – 5 pm, Monday – Saturday; 2 – 5 pm, Sundays. Closed Thursdays
SPECIALITIES Conifers; heathers
CATALOGUE 40p
MAIL ORDER Yes

Just heathers and conifers, but with about 500 varieties of each the range is very extensive.

Notcutts Garden Centre
Daniels Road, Norwich, Norfolk NR4 6QP
☎ 0603 53155

OPEN 8.30 am – 5.30 pm, Monday – Saturday; 10 am – 5.30 pm, Sundays
CATALOGUE £2.50
SHOP Garden sundries; furniture; pools; pets
REFRESHMENTS Coffee shop
DESIGN SERVICE Notcutts Landscapes
GIFT TOKENS HTA; own

See also Notcutts Nurseries, Suffolk.

P W Plants
Sunnyside, Heath Road, Kenninghall, Norfolk NR16 2DS
☎ 0953 888212

CONTACT Paul Whittaker
LOCATION South west Norfolk
OPEN Fridays, and last Saturday of the month. Phone first
SPECIALITIES Bamboos; foliage plants; grasses
NEW FOR 1994 Many new species
CATALOGUE £1.50
MAIL ORDER Yes; September to April only
GARDEN Display gardens
DESIGN SERVICE P W Plants
SHOWS RHS Westminster; Chelsea; Hampton Court

A general range, with the emphasis on interesting foliage, including bamboos and grasses. Extensive display gardens. Garden design within the region.

Peter Beales Roses
London Road, Attleborough, Norfolk NR17 1AY
☎ 0953 454707   FAX 0953 456845

LOCATION 2 miles south of Attleborough, off A11
OPEN 9 am – 5 pm, Monday – Friday; 9 am – 4.30 pm, Saturdays; 10 am – 4 pm, Sundays
SPECIALITIES Roses
CATALOGUE On request
MAIL ORDER Yes; no minimum order
GARDEN Rose garden
DESIGN SERVICE Peter Beales Roses
SHOWS Chelsea; Hampton Court
GIFT TOKENS Own

Specialist grower and collector of older and classic roses. The extensive list has over 1,000 species and varieties, many not available elsewhere. Among the popular and rare items, there is also an interesting selection of early Hybrid Teas. They will design rose gardens, and their own fields can be visited.

Raveningham Gardens
Estate Office, Raveningham Hall, Raveningham, Norwich, Norfolk NR14 6NS
☎ 050846 222   FAX 050846 8958

CONTACT Alison Bowell
LOCATION 15 miles south east of Norwich
OPEN 9 am – 5.30 pm, Monday – Saturday, April to October; 9 am – 4 pm, Monday – Friday, November – March. Also 2 – 5.30 pm, Sundays and Bank Holidays, late March to mid September
SPECIALITIES Herbaceous perennials; shrubs
CATALOGUE 3 first class stamps
MAIL ORDER Yes
GARDEN Raveningham Hall, Norfolk, see Gardens section

An interesting list of shrubs and herbaceous perennials, with a bias towards those with good foliage, berries or bark. Look out for *Galanthus* and *Pulmonaria* too. The garden opens with the nursery on Sunday afternoons.

Reads Nursery
Hales Hall, Loddon, Norfolk NR14 6QW
☎ 050846 395   FAX 050846 395

CONTACT Judy Read
OPEN 10 am – 1 pm, 2 – 5 pm, Tuesday – Saturday
SPECIALITIES Climbers; conservatory plants; citrus
CATALOGUE 4 first class stamps
MAIL ORDER Yes
NCCPG NATIONAL COLLECTIONS *Citrus*; *Vitis vinifera*; *Ficus*

Long-established family nursery which specialises in citrus and conservatory plants. The mouth-watering list includes excellent collections of both of these, with vines, figs and topiary also.

The Romantic Garden Nursery

Swannington, Norwich, Norfolk NR9 5NW
☎ 0603 261488   ▣ 0603 871668

CONTACT   John Powles
LOCATION   7 miles north west of Norwich
OPEN   10 am – 5 pm, Wednesdays, Fridays, Saturdays
SPECIALITIES   Topiary
CATALOGUE   4 first class stamps
MAIL ORDER   Yes
REFRESHMENTS   Refreshments
DESIGN SERVICE   The Romantic Garden Nursery

Ornamental standards, bobbles and pyramids in *Cupressus* and *Ilex*, as well as box in animal and other shapes. Clematis and half-hardy plants are also available. They can design and sell topiary packages which include a layout and the necessary plants.

Simpsons Nursery

The Plant Centre, High Street, Marsham, Norwich, Norfolk NR10 5QA
☎ 0263 733432

CONTACT   Gillian and Jonathan Simpson
LOCATION   2 miles south of Aylsham, off A140
OPEN   Daily, summer; Wednesday – Sunday and Bank Holidays, winter
CATALOGUE   Ask for details
MAIL ORDER   No
DESIGN SERVICE   Simpsons Nursery

Nursery and plant centre which stocks home-grown plants, notably conifers and shrubs. They also have a landscaping and tree surgery department.

Thorncroft Clematis Nursery

The Lings, Reymerston, Norwich, Norfolk NR9 4QG
☎ 0953 850407

CONTACT   Mrs Ruth P. Gooch and Mrs Dorothy Turner
LOCATION   Between Dereham and Wymondham on B1135
OPEN   10 am – 5 pm, daily, March to October. Closed Wednesdays. By appointment only in winter
SPECIALITIES   *Clematis*
CATALOGUE   2 first class stamps
MAIL ORDER   No
GARDEN   Display garden

There is a good range of species and cultivars at this *Clematis* specialist. Free pruning demonstrations take place in February and March: phone for details.

Trevor White Old Fashioned Roses

Chelt Hurst, Sewell Road, Norwich, Norfolk NR3 4BP
☎ 0603 418240   ▣ 0603 482967

CONTACT   Trevor and Vanessa White
OPEN   Mail order only
SPECIALITIES   Roses
CATALOGUE   On request
MAIL ORDER   Yes

Mainly wholesale. An interesting choice of old and species shrub and climbing roses. Good quality plants.

The Wild Flower Centre

Church Farm, Sisland, Norwich, Norfolk NR14 6EF
☎ 0508 520235

CONTACT   Mrs D. Corne
OPEN   9 am – 5 pm. Other times by appointment
SPECIALITIES   Wild flowers
CATALOGUE   30p
MAIL ORDER   Yes

This small centre grows a selection of native and naturalised wild flowers.

Waveney Fish Farm

Park Road, Diss, Norfolk IP22 3AS
☎ 0379 642697   ▣ 0379 651315

LOCATION   Near Diss town centre, on A1066
OPEN   10 am – 1 pm, 2 – 5 pm, daily
SPECIALITIES   Aquatic plants
CATALOGUE   On request
MAIL ORDER   Yes; minimum order £10
SHOP   Fish and animals
GARDEN   Display gardens

Aquatic plants for sale: the display gardens are open from March to October.

Wyevale Garden Centre

Blue Boar Lane, Sprowston, Norwich, Norfolk NR7 8RJ
☎ 0603 412239   ▣ 0603 402949

NORTHAMPTONSHIRE

E L F Plants, Cramden Nursery Ltd

Harborough Road North, Northampton, Northamptonshire NN2 8LU
☎ 0604 846246

LOCATION   Leave A508 at Kingsthorpe cemetery
OPEN   10 am – 5 pm, Thursday – Saturday. Closed December and January
SPECIALITIES   Conifers; shrubs
CATALOGUE   50p plus stamp

MAIL ORDER No
GARDEN Garden
SHOWS RHS Westminster; International Spring Gardening Fair; Chelsea; BBC GW Live

This small nursery specialises in dwarf and small shrubs and conifers that are suitable for rock gardens and borders. Some alpines and heathers too. It's advisable to phone first (evenings only). Garden clubs welcome at any time by arrangement.

Podington Garden Centre

High Street, Podington, Wellingborough, Northamptonshire NN9 7HS
☎ 0933 53656 📠 0933 410332

CONTACT Colin Read
LOCATION 2 miles west of A6
OPEN 9 am – 6.30 pm, summer; 9 am – 5.30 pm, winter
SHOP Garden sundries; paving; fencing
REFRESHMENTS Gnomes Kitchen
GIFT TOKENS HTA

Plants and garden products. Local delivery.

Ravensthorpe Nursery

6 East Haddon Road, Ravensthorpe, Northamptonshire NN6 8ES
☎ 0604 770548

CONTACT Jean and Richard Wiseman
LOCATION Between Rugby and Northampton, near M1, J18
OPEN 10 am – 6 pm, Tuesday – Sunday, and Bank Holiday Mondays
CATALOGUE 4 first class stamps
MAIL ORDER Yes; no minimum order
GARDEN Display garden being made

This nursery has a sound all-round range of plants, much of the material being home-grown.

Wyevale Garden Centre

Newport Pagnell Road, Wootton, Northampton, Northamptonshire NN4 6HP
☎ 0604 765725 📠 0604 700492

NORTHUMBERLAND

Halls of Heddon

West Heddon Nurseries, Heddon on the Wall, Newcastle upon Tyne, Northumberland NE15 0JS
☎ 0661 852445

CONTACT Mrs J. A. Lockey
OPEN 9 am – 5 pm, Monday – Saturday; 10 am – 5 pm, Sundays
SPECIALITIES Chrysanthemums; dahlias
CATALOGUE 2 second class stamps

MAIL ORDER Dahlias and chrysanthemums only
GARDEN Herbaceous borders
SHOWS Harrogate (Autumn)
GIFT TOKENS HTA

Specialists in dahlias and chrysanthemums of all types for showing, the garden and as cut flowers. The garden centre has a general range of plants.

Heighley Gate Garden Centre

Morpeth, Northumberland NE61 3DA
☎ 0670 513416 📠 0670 510013
LOCATION 3 miles north of Morpeth on A697
OPEN 9 am – 5 pm, Monday – Friday; 9.30 am – 5 pm, Saturday – Sunday
SHOP Gardens sundries; gifts; conservatories
REFRESHMENTS Coffee shop
DESIGN SERVICE Heighley Gate Garden Centre
GIFT TOKENS HTA

All round range of plants and garden sundries, including home-grown bedding, houseplants and pansies.

Herterton House Gardens & Nursery

Hartington, Cambo, Morpeth, Northumberland NE61 4BN
☎ 067074 278

CONTACT Frank Lawley
LOCATION 2 miles north of Cambo, off B6342
OPEN 1.30 – 5.30 pm, daily, April to September, and by appointment. Closed Tuesdays and Thursdays
MAIL ORDER No
GARDEN Herterton House Gardens & Nursery, Northumberland, see Gardens section

The nursery stocks a range of herbaceous perennials and some herbs. The garden, which is open at the same times, was featured in *The Englishman's Garden*.

Hexham Herbs

Chesters Walled Garden, Chollerford, Hexham, Northumberland NE46 4BQ
☎ 0434 681483

CONTACT Mrs S. White
LOCATION 6 miles north of Hexham, next to Chesters Roman fort
OPEN 10 am – 5 pm, Easter to October. Shorter hours in winter
SPECIALITIES Herbs
CATALOGUE £1.50 cheque
MAIL ORDER No
SHOP Pots; gifts
GARDEN Hexham Herbs, Northumberland, see Gardens section
NCCPG NATIONAL COLLECTIONS *Thymus*; *Origanum* (marjoram)

Specialist herb nursery with a wide range of herbs as plants and freshly cut for cooking. They also stock old roses and wild flowers, and dried flowers and gifts.

Northumbria Nurseries

Castle Gardens, Ford, Berwick upon Tweed, Northumberland TD15 2PZ
☎ 0890 820379 [FAX] 0890 820594

CONTACT H. M. Huddleston
OPEN 9 am – 6 pm, Monday – Friday, all year; 10 am – 6 pm, Saturdays and Sundays from March to October
SPECIALITIES Herbaceous perennials
CATALOGUE £2.25 cheque
MAIL ORDER Yes
GARDEN Display gardens
DESIGN SERVICE Hazel M. Huddleston

A wide range of container-grown hardy shrubs and perennials. A design and advisory service is also available. The nursery can be visited at other times by appointment: it closes before 6 pm if it's dark.

Ryal Nursery

East Farm Cottage, Ryal, Northumberland NE20 0SA
☎ 0661 886562

CONTACT R. F. Hadden
OPEN 1 – 5 pm, Tuesdays; 10 am – 5 pm, Sundays, March to July. Other times by appointment
SPECIALITIES Alpines; primulas
CATALOGUE SAE
MAIL ORDER Yes

The nursery grows a range of woodland plants, with auriculas and alpines too.

NOTTINGHAMSHIRE

Brinkley Nurseries

Fiskerton Road, Southwell, Nottinghamshire NG24 0TP
☎ 0636 814501

CONTACT Mrs C. Steven
OPEN 10 am – 5 pm, summer; 10 am – 4 pm, winter
SPECIALITIES Shrubs; trees
CATALOGUE £1.95
MAIL ORDER Yes; £10 minimum order
GARDEN Garden opens under the NGS, or by arrangement. Admission £1

Containerised trees and shrubs, both retail and wholesale. The choice is large and interesting. They also stock herbaceous plants.

Field House Alpines

Leake Road, Gotham, Nottingham, Nottinghamshire NG11 0JN
☎ 0602 830278

CONTACT Doug Lochhead and Val Woolley
OPEN 9 am – 5 pm, Friday – Wednesday
SPECIALITIES Alpines; primulas; seeds
CATALOGUE 4 second class stamps
MAIL ORDER Yes; primulas and seeds
GARDEN Auricula Theatre at Calke Abbey, Derbyshire, see Gardens section

A good range of alpines, both as plants and seed. They are particularly strong on primulas and auriculas. As well as maintaining the auricula theatre at Calke Abbey, Derbyshire they are also organising a specialist plant sale there on 24 April.

Hewthorn Herbs & Wild Flowers

Simkins Farm, Adbolton Lane, West Bridgford, Nottinghamshire NG2 5AS
☎ 0602 812861

CONTACT Julie Scott
OPEN Weekdays during termtime, and some weekends. Phone first
SPECIALITIES Herbs; wild flowers
CATALOGUE 3 first class stamps
MAIL ORDER Yes; no minimum order
SHOP Cards
GARDEN Garden open for groups by arrangement

The nursery sells native and naturalised wild flowers, herbs, medicinal, culinary and dye plants. The garden is open for groups by arrangement: talks are also possible.

Mill Hill Plants

Mill Hill House, Elston Lane, East Stoke, Newark, Nottinghamshire NG23 5QJ
☎ 0636 525460

CONTACT G. M. Gregory
LOCATION 5 miles south west of Newark. Leave A46 at East Stoke, for Elston. Nursery is ½ mile down, on right
OPEN 10 am – 6 pm, Wednesday – Sunday, and Bank Holiday Mondays, March to October. Closed Monday – Tuesday, and from November to February
SPECIALITIES Herbaceous perennials; irises
CATALOGUE 3 first class stamps
MAIL ORDER Yes; irises only
GARDEN Garden opens under NGS
NCCPG NATIONAL COLLECTIONS Berberis

The nursery stocks a range of hardy perennials. The speciality is bearded irises, which are available by mail order also. Groups welcome by appointment.

Wheatcroft Ltd
Landmere Lane, Edwalton, Nottingham,
Nottinghamshire NG12 4DE
☎ 0602 216060   ▣ 0602 841247

OPEN 9 am – 6 pm
SPECIALITIES Roses
REFRESHMENTS Refreshments
GIFT TOKENS HTA

Wholesale rose growers with a retail range of roses and
hardy shrubs sold from their own garden centre.

OXFORDSHIRE

Broadstone Nurseries
13 The Nursery, High Street, Sutton Courtenay,
Abingdon, Oxfordshire OX14 4UA
☎ 0235 847557

CONTACT Broadstone Nurseries
OPEN 4 – 7 pm, Fridays; 3 – 7 pm; Saturdays. Advis-
able to phone first. Other times by appointment only
SPECIALITIES Alpines
NEW FOR 1994 Three new campanulas
CATALOGUE 3 first class stamps
MAIL ORDER No
DESIGN SERVICE Broadstone Nurseries

An alpine nursery, with plants for troughs, sinks and
screes, as well as a range of perennials. They have a
design service, and also supply specialist potting and
planting mixtures.

Burford Garden Centre
Shilton Road, Burford, Oxfordshire OX18 4PA
☎ 0993 823117   ▣ 0993 823529

LOCATION Near A40, on B4020 at Burford
OPEN 9 am – 5.45 pm, Monday to Friday; 9.30 am –
6 pm, Saturday – Sunday
CATALOGUE Suppliers' catalogues available
SHOP Furniture; fencing; stoneware; Neal's Yard
Wholefoods; gifts and pets
REFRESHMENTS Restaurant
GIFT TOKENS HTA

Large garden centre with indoor and outdoor plants,
and an extensive clutch of associated product suppliers.
Local delivery available; children's play area, and wheelchairs on site.

Mattock Roses
Nuneham Courtenay, Oxford, Oxfordshire
OX44 9PY
☎ 0865 343265   ▣ 0865 343267

CONTACT Mark W. Mattock

OPEN 9 am – 5.30 pm, Monday – Saturday; 10.30 am –
5.30 pm, Sundays. Close at 5 pm in winter
SPECIALITIES Roses
CATALOGUE On request
MAIL ORDER Yes
SHOP Garden sundries; furniture
REFRESHMENTS Restaurant
GARDEN Rose fields
SHOWS RHS Westminster; Chelsea; Hampton
Court; Harrogate (Autumn)
GIFT TOKENS HTA; own

A large choice of all kinds of roses. They are particularly
good on ground cover varieties and their own 'County'
roses. They are part of Notcutts, and are attached to a
Notcutts Garden Centre (0865 343454).

Newington Nurseries
Newington, Wallingford, Oxfordshire OX10 7AW
☎ 0865 891401   ▣ 0865 891766

OPEN 10 am – 4 pm, Monday – Friday. Closed 1 – 2 pm
for lunch. Weekends by appointment
SPECIALITIES Conservatory plants
CATALOGUE £1.50
MAIL ORDER Yes

Specialises in plants for greenhouses and conservatories only, including tropical and sub-tropical species.
Particularly strong on *Hoya*. They can advise on
regimes for conservatory plants, and sell special diets
for *Plumeria* and *Citrus*.

Waterperry Gardens Ltd
Waterperry, Wheatley, Oxfordshire OX33 1JZ
☎ 0844 339226

LOCATION Near M40, J8
OPEN 10 am – 5.30 pm, Monday – Friday; 10 am – 6 pm,
Saturday – Sunday. Close at 5 pm in winter
SPECIALITIES Saxifrages
CATALOGUE Lists
MAIL ORDER No
SHOP Garden sundries
REFRESHMENTS Tea shop
GARDEN Waterperry Gardens, Oxfordshire, see
Gardens section
GIFT TOKENS HTA

Among a general stock there are good alpines, notably
the saxifrages, and a useful choice of fruit trees.

The Wildlife Gardening Centre
Witney Road, Kingston Bagpuize, Abingdon,
Oxfordshire OX13 5AN
☎ 0865 821660

CONTACT Jennifer Steel
OPEN Phone for details

SPECIALITIES Herbs; seeds; shrubs; wild flowers; native trees and shrubs
NEW FOR 1994 Increased range of British natives
CATALOGUE 1 first class stamp plus 50p
MAIL ORDER Yes; no minimum order
GARDEN Wildlife garden

Plants which have been selected for their ability to attract bees and butterflies. The trees and shrubs are not available mail order.

Wyevale Garden Centre

Old London Road, Wheatley, Oxfordshire OX9 1XJ
☎ 08677 3057   [FAX] 08677 5321

SHROPSHIRE

Barbara Molesworth

Byeways, Daisy Lane, Whittington, Oswestry, Shropshire SY11 4EA
☎ 0691 659539

CONTACT Barbara Molesworth
LOCATION Whittington, Oswestry
OPEN Mondays only, by appointment
SPECIALITIES Herbaceous perennials
NEW FOR 1994 *Geranium pratense* 'Striatum'; *Aster pringlei* 'Monte Cassino'
CATALOGUE SAE plus 1 second class stamp
MAIL ORDER No
SHOP Market stall in Newtown, Powys (Tuesday), and Oswestry (Wednesday)

A small nursery with a varied selection of hardy herbaceous plants. Strong on asters and geraniums. Barbara Molesworth also runs day courses at Oswestry Community College.

Fron Nursery

Fron Issa, Rhiwlas, Oswestry, Shropshire SY10 7JH
☎ 0691 76605

CONTACT Thoby Miller
LOCATION Clwyd, Shropshire border
OPEN By appointment only
SPECIALITIES Conifers; shrubs; trees
NEW FOR 1994 Several Himalayan species unique to Fron
CATALOGUE SAE
MAIL ORDER Yes; £20 minimum order
GARDEN 2 acre woodland garden

An interesting selection of hardy trees and shrubs, including conifers: the smaller sizes are mostly containerised, the larger, open ground. The more choice offerings include *Abies amabilis* and *Taxodium mucronatum*. The setting, 1,000 feet up, promises good

views as well as hardiness, and many specimens can be seen growing in the woodland planting.

Hall Farm Nursery

Kinnerley, Oswestry, Shropshire SY10 8DH
☎ 0691 682219

CONTACT Christine Ffoulkes Jones
OPEN 10 am – 5 pm, Tuesday – Sunday, March to October
SPECIALITIES Alpines; carnivorous plants; herbaceous perennials
CATALOGUE 4 first class stamps
MAIL ORDER No
GARDEN Garden open by appointment
SHOWS Malvern Spring; BBC GW Live

The nursery carries a good range of herbaceous perennials, including a great number of geraniums. Alpines and carnivorous plants are the other specialities. Talks, demonstrations and a garden tour are offered by arrangement for groups.

Hillview Hardy Plants

Worfield, Bridgnorth, Shropshire WV15 5NT
☎ 07464 454

CONTACT Ingrid Millington
LOCATION Between Worfield and Albrighton, off B4176
OPEN 10 am – 5 pm, Monday – Saturday
SPECIALITIES Alpines; herbaceous perennials; primulas
NEW FOR 1994 *Aquilegia* 'Woodside'
CATALOGUE 4 second class stamps
MAIL ORDER Yes
SHOWS Malvern Spring; Harrogate (Spring); Harrogate (Autumn)

Twin ranges of alpines and hardy perennials. There are many different primulas and auriculas too.

Lingen Alpine Nursery

Lingen, Bucknell, Shropshire SY7 0DY
☎ 0544 267720

CONTACT Kim W. Davis
OPEN 10 am – 6 pm, February to October
SPECIALITIES Alpines; herbaceous perennials
CATALOGUE SAE
MAIL ORDER Yes; p & p from £3.50
GARDEN Garden open
SHOWS Malvern Spring

There is a promising herbaceous range developing at this specialist alpine and rock garden nursery. Its traditional strengths include plants for alpine houses, screes and troughs.

Llanbrook Alpine & Wildflower Nursery

3 Llanbrook, Hopton Castle, Clunton, Shropshire
SY7 0QG
☎ 05474 298

CONTACT John Clayfield
OPEN By appointment, phone first
SPECIALITIES Alpines; wild flowers
MAIL ORDER No
SHOWS Malvern Spring; Southport

Alpines, wild flowers and other hardy plants – all grown in peat-free compost.

Nordybank Nurseries

Clee St Margaret, Craven Arms, Shropshire SY7 9ET
☎ 058475 322

CONTACT Polly Bolton
OPEN Mondays, Wednesdays, Sundays, Easter to mid October
SPECIALITIES Herbaceous perennials; herbs; wild flowers
CATALOGUE Large SAE plus 50p
MAIL ORDER No
REFRESHMENTS Teas
GARDEN 1 acre display garden opens for NGS

A choice of hardy herbaceous plants, with herbs and wild flowers also.

Oak Cottage Herb Garden

Nesscliffe, Shrewsbury, Shropshire SY4 1DB
☎ 0743 81262   [FAX] 0743 81262

CONTACT Edward and Jane Bygott
LOCATION Halfway between Shrewsbury and Oswestry on A5
OPEN Usually 10.30 am – 6 pm, daily
SPECIALITIES Herbs; wild flowers
NEW FOR 1994 Many new items
CATALOGUE SAE plus 2 first class stamps
MAIL ORDER Yes
SHOP Herb products; books; seeds
GARDEN Herb garden
DESIGN SERVICE Oak Cottage Herb Garden

A small nursery propagating and selling wild flowers, herbs and cottage garden plants. Small quantities only, but larger orders by arrangement. There's also a small shop, and they offer design advice.

Perrybrook Nursery

Brook Cottage, Wykey, Ruyton XI Towns, Shrewsbury, Shropshire SY4 1JA
☎ 0939 261120

CONTACT Mrs G. Williams
LOCATION North Shropshire

OPEN By appointment
SPECIALITIES Herbaceous perennials
CATALOGUE 3 first class stamps
MAIL ORDER No

Specialist wholesale and retail nursery with a range of hardy perennials, notably primulas. There is also a display of agricultural machinery, including a working threshing drum.

SOMERSET

Avon Bulbs

Burnt House Farm, Mid-Lambrook, South Petherton, Somerset TA13 5HE
☎ 0460 242177

CONTACT Mr C. Ireland-Jones
LOCATION 3 miles north west of South Petherton, off A303
OPEN 9 am – 4.30 pm, Thursday – Saturday, mid February to end March, and mid September to end October
SPECIALITIES Bulbs
CATALOGUE 4 second class stamps
MAIL ORDER Yes
SHOWS RHS Westminster; Malvern Spring; Harrogate (Spring); Chelsea

An impressive variety of bulbs (and close relatives) covering all sizes, seasons and shapes. Opening hours are limited because of the seasonal nature of the business and their show commitments. It is a good idea to check with them before visiting. The striking show exhibits are recommended. Botanical prints, from the catalogue cover, also available.

Bradley Batch Cactus Nursery

64 Bath Road, Ashcott, Bridgwater, Somerset TA7 9QJ
☎ 0458 210256

CONTACT Mr J. E. White
LOCATION 5 miles from Glastonbury, on A39
OPEN 10 am – 6 pm, Tuesday – Saturday. Closed Mondays. Ring first during summer show season
SPECIALITIES Cacti and succulents
NEW FOR 1994 Crassula 'Buddha's Temple'; Echeveria 'Topsy-Turvy'; Mammillaria duwei
MAIL ORDER No

Cacti, of course, and a wide choice of succulents including Hoya, Epiphyllum and Crassula. They sell mixed cacti seed. They welcome group visits, by appointment, and offer B & B all year round.

Broadleigh Gardens

Bishops Hull, Taunton, Somerset TA4 1AE
☎ 0823 286231   📠 0823 323646

OPEN   9 am – 4 pm, Monday – Friday. Viewing only,
and collection by prior arrangement
SPECIALITIES   Bulbs; daffodils; tulip species
CATALOGUE   2 first class stamps; spring, autumn
MAIL ORDER   Yes
GARDEN   Gardens open
SHOWS   RHS Westminster; Chelsea
GIFT TOKENS   Own

The nursery specialises in all kinds of small bulbs, and
a few perennials. Look out for the snowdrops, the many
miniature narcissus and species tulips, and a double
green *Muscari*. Open for viewing only. Prior arrangement is essential if you want to collect from the nursery.

Cannington College

Cannington, Bridgwater, Somerset TA5 2LS
☎ 0278 652226

CONTACT   Mr S. J. Rudhall
OPEN   2 – 5 pm, daily, Easter to October
SPECIALITIES   Half-hardy perennials
CATALOGUE   On request
MAIL ORDER   Yes
GARDEN   Extensive gardens
SHOWS   Malvern Spring; Hampton Court
NCCPG NATIONAL COLLECTIONS *Abutilon; Argy-
ranthemum; Ceanothus; Cordyline; Osteospermum;
Phormium; Wisteria; Yucca*

The Somerset county agricultural college at Cannington
sells a range of plants propagated at the college. They
are known particularly for tender perennials including
new *Osteospermum* cultivars. The college holds no less
than eight National Collections.

Clapton Court Plant Centre

Clapton Court Gardens, Crewkerne, Somerset
TA18 8PT
☎ 0460 73220/ 72200

CONTACT   Capt. S. Loder
LOCATION   3 miles south of Crewkerne
OPEN   10.30 am – 5 pm, Monday – Friday;
CATALOGUE   Yes
MAIL ORDER   No
REFRESHMENTS   Refreshments
GARDEN   Clapton Court Gardens, see Gardens section

The plant centre, which is attached to the gardens,
carries an interesting selection of containerised plants,
including trees and shrubs, roses, climbers, perennials
and hardy fuchsias.

Elworthy Cottage Garden Plants

Elworthy Cottage, Elworthy, Lydeard St Lawrence,
Taunton, Somerset TA4 3PX
☎ 0984 56427

CONTACT   J. M. Spiller
LOCATION   10 miles north west of Taunton, on B3188
in village centre
OPEN   2 – 5 pm, Tuesdays and Thursdays only, mid
March to mid October
SPECIALITIES   Herbaceous perennials
CATALOGUE   3 second class stamps
MAIL ORDER   No
GARDEN   Garden opens same times for NGS

A pleasant selection of perennials and cottage garden
plants. Strong on geraniums, with over 120 varieties.

Hadspen Garden

Hadspen Garden, Castle Cary, Somerset BA7 7NG
☎ 0963 350939

CONTACT   Nori Pope
LOCATION   Castle Cary
OPEN   9 am – 6 pm, Thursday – Sunday, and Bank
Holidays
SPECIALITIES   Herbaceous perennials
CATALOGUE   2 first class stamps
MAIL ORDER   No
REFRESHMENTS   Lunch (Bonds Hotel)
GARDEN   Hadspen House, Somerset, see Gardens
section
NCCPG NATIONAL COLLECTIONS *Rodgersia*

The nursery, which is attached to this well known
garden, sells the larger garden-worthy herbaceous
plants, such as hostas and rodgersias, as well as clematis
and old roses (many of which are on their own roots).

Kelways Nurseries Ltd

Barrymore Farm, Langport, Somerset TA10 9EZ
☎ 0458 250521   📠 0458 253351

CONTACT   Carmen T. Duell
LOCATION   10 miles east of Taunton
OPEN   9 am – 5 pm, Monday – Friday; 10 am – 4 pm,
Saturday – Sunday
SPECIALITIES   Irises; paeonies
NEW FOR 1994   New paeonies, bearded and beard-
less irises, and daylilies. Also *Corydalis flexuosa* 'China
Blue'; *C. flexuosa* 'Père David'; *Nepeta subsessile*
CATALOGUE   On request (retail and wholesale)
MAIL ORDER   Yes
GARDEN   Demonstration gardens
DESIGN SERVICE   Kelways Nurseries Ltd
SHOWS   Chelsea; Hampton Court

Long famous for their herbaceous and tree paeonies,
Kelways also has a large range of irises and day lilies,

and an expanding perennial section. A selection of their plants are now also available through some 150 garden centres.

Lower Severalls Herb Nursery
Crewkerne, Somerset TA18 7NX
☎ 0460 73234   🖷 0460 76105

CONTACT   Mary R. Cooper
LOCATION   1 mile east of Crewkerne
OPEN   10 am – 5 pm, Monday – Saturday; 2 – 5pm, Sundays. Closed Thursdays
SPECIALITIES   Herbaceous perennials; herbs
CATALOGUE   3 first class stamps
MAIL ORDER   Yes; minimum order £7 plus p & p
GARDEN   2 acre garden

Herbs of all kinds, as you would expect. Other good selections include the hardy geraniums and the salvias.

Mallet Court Nursery
Curry Mallet, Taunton, Somerset TA3 6SY
☎ 0823 480748   🖷 0823 481009

CONTACT   David Williamson
OPEN   9 am – 1 pm, 2 – 5 pm, Mondays to Fridays. Other days by appointment
SPECIALITIES   Trees
NEW FOR 1994   *Quercus dentata* 'Pinnatifida'; *Quercus rysophylla*; *Acer palmatum* cultivars from J. D. Vertree's collection
CATALOGUE   Large SAE (37p stamp)
MAIL ORDER   Yes
SHOWS   RHS Westminster; Hampton Court; Courson

Specialist tree nursery with an excellent list of unusual trees. Particularly good for *Quercus* and *Acer*, and also strong on species from China and Korea.

Margery Fish Plant Nursery
East Lambrook Manor, East Lambrook, South Petherton, Somerset TA13 5HL
☎ 0460 240328   🖷 0460 242344

CONTACT   Mark Stainer
LOCATION   Signed from A303 at South Petherton
OPEN   10 am – 5 pm, Monday – Saturday, March to October; 10 am – 5 pm, Monday – Friday, November to February
SPECIALITIES   Herbaceous perennials
NEW FOR 1994   New *Geranium* cultivars and hybrids
CATALOGUE   4 first class stamps
MAIL ORDER   Yes
REFRESHMENTS   Refreshments
GARDEN   East Lambrook Manor, Somerset, see Gardens section
GIFT TOKENS   Own

NCCPG NATIONAL COLLECTIONS *Geranium*

A wide and attractive range mainly devoted to hardy herbaceous perennials. Good for *Artemisia*, *Euphorbia* and *Lavandula*: the *Geranium* list is exceptional. The late Margery Fish's garden needs no recommendation.

Mill Cottage Plants
The Mill, Henley Lane, Wookey, Somerset BA5 1AP
☎ 0749 676966

CONTACT   Mrs Sally Gregson
LOCATION   2 miles from Wells: ring for directions
OPEN   10 am – 6 pm, Wednesdays, March to September
CATALOGUE   2 first class stamps
MAIL ORDER   Yes; minimum order £5; October to March
GARDEN   Garden open for groups

The nursery grows a selection of cottage garden type plants. Talks and workshops can be arranged, as can design and planting advice.

Monkton Elm Garden Centre
Monkton Heathfield, Taunton, Somerset TA2 8QN
☎ 0823 412381   🖷 0823 412745

CONTACT   Mr M. Valuks
LOCATION   2½ miles north east of Taunton
OPEN   9.30 am – 5.30 pm
SHOP   Garden sundries; greenhouses; buildings; aquatics
REFRESHMENTS   Restaurant
DESIGN SERVICE   Monkton Elm Garden Centre

Garden centre with a complete range of plants and products. They have a design service and can deliver.

Otter's Court Heathers
West Camel, Yeovil, Somerset BA22 7QF
☎ 0935 850285

CONTACT   Mrs D. H. Jones
OPEN   9 am – 5.30 pm, Wednesday – Sunday. Closed Mondays and Tuesdays
SPECIALITIES   Conifers; heathers
CATALOGUE   3 first class stamps
MAIL ORDER   Yes
GARDEN   Display gardens
DESIGN SERVICE   Otter's Court Heathers

This nursery stocks a selection of hardy, lime-tolerant heathers, and some conifers to plant with them. They offer a design service and can draw up planting plans.

P M A Plant Specialities
Lower Mead, West Hatch, Taunton, Somerset TA3 5RN
☎ 0823 480774   🖷 0823 481046

CONTACT   Karan Junker

OPEN Collection only: by appointment
SPECIALITIES Acers; shrubs; trees
NEW FOR 1994 *Acer campestre* 'Carnival'; *Cornus nuttallii* 'Colrigo Giant'; *Fothergilla gardenii* 'Blue Mist'; *Acer palmatum* 'Corallinum'
CATALOGUE 4 second class stamps
MAIL ORDER Yes; no minimum order
DESIGN SERVICE PMA Plant Specialities

Wholesale growers (with retail trade by mail order) of some interesting container-grown trees and shrubs. Strong on Japanese and snakebark acers, and on tree species of *Cornus*. They also offer design and a specialist pruning service.

Scotts Nurseries Ltd
Merriott, Somerset TA16 5PL
☎ 0460 72306   ▦ 0460 77433

CONTACT Mark and Michael Wallis
OPEN 9 am – 5 pm
SPECIALITIES Fruit; roses; shrubs
CATALOGUE £1.50 (shrubs and perennials); Roses and fruit, on request
MAIL ORDER Yes
SHOP Garden sundries
SHOWS Chelsea; BBC GW Live
GIFT TOKENS HTA

Large nurseries with a very extensive range of field and container-grown plants of all kinds. The garden centre carries container stock, and is strong on fruit trees and shrubs.

Shepton Nursery Garden
Old Wells Road, Shepton Mallet, Somerset BA4 5XN
☎ 0749 343630

CONTACT P. W. Boughton
OPEN 9.30 am – 5.30 pm, Tuesday – Saturday
SPECIALITIES Shrubs
CATALOGUE 4 second class stamps
MAIL ORDER No

A mixed stock which includes alpines, herbaceous perennials and many shrubs. The nursery is strongest on *Chaenomeles*.

West Somerset Garden Centre
Mart Road, Minehead, Somerset TA24 5BJ
☎ 0643 703812   ▦ 0643 706470

CONTACT Mrs J. Shoulders
LOCATION Just outside Minehead
OPEN 8 am – 5 pm, Monday – Saturday; 11 am – 5 pm, Sundays. Some winter variation
SPECIALITIES Bedding plants; shrubs
CATALOGUE On request; roses and fruit, autumn
MAIL ORDER Yes

Bedding plants produced at the nursery, and a good selection of shrubs stand out in a general range. Monthly availability lists are produced.

Wyevale Garden Centre
Pen Elm, Norton Fitzwarren, Taunton, Somerset TA2 6PE
☎ 0823 323777   ▦ 0823 323773

YSJ Seeds
Kingsfield Conservation Nursery, Broadenham Lane, Winsham, Chard, Somerset TA20 4JF
☎ 0460 30070   ▦ 0460 30070

CONTACT Mrs Margaret White
OPEN Phone first
SPECIALITIES Seeds; trees; wild flowers
CATALOGUE 1 second class stamp
MAIL ORDER Yes
GIFT TOKENS Own

The nursery specialises in British native trees and shrubs (of British provenance) either open ground or container-grown. Wild flowers are sold as plugs or as seed. Advice or consultations are available, as are tours for groups.

STAFFORDSHIRE

Barncroft Nurseries
Dunwood Lane, Longsdon, Leek, Stoke on Trent, Staffordshire ST9 9QW
☎ 0538 384310

CONTACT Mr S. Warner
LOCATION 3 miles west of Leek, off A53
OPEN 9 am – dusk (latest 8 pm), Friday – Sunday
SPECIALITIES Conifers; heathers; rhododendrons; shrubs
MAIL ORDER No
GARDEN Display gardens with 400 heather varieties

This wholesale nursery is open on Fridays and weekends for retail customers. Many varieties of heathers (400), conifers (400), shrubs (500), rhododendrons, trees and some alpines are available. The display gardens open at the same time. Wholesale only, Monday to Thursday.

Bretby Nurseries
Bretby Lane, Burton on Trent, Staffordshire DE15 0Qs
☎ 0283 703355   ▦ 0283 704035

CONTACT David Cartwright
OPEN 9 am – 5 pm, daily
SPECIALITIES Shrubs
CATALOGUE None

MAIL ORDER No
SHOP Gift shop
REFRESHMENTS Tea room
GIFT TOKENS HTA

Retail garden centre and wholesale nursery (Barn Farm Nurseries) which specialise in shrubs.

Byrkley Park Centre

Rangemore, Burton on Trent, Staffordshire
DE13 9RN
☎ 0283 716467   ☏ 0283 716594

CONTACT Information Desk
LOCATION 5 miles west of Burton on Trent; leave A38 at Branston
OPEN 9 am – 5 pm, daily, September to March; 9 am – 6 pm (until 9 pm Thursdays, Fridays, Saturdays), April to August
CATALOGUE Leaflets
SHOP Garden products
REFRESHMENTS Tea room and carvery
DESIGN SERVICE Byrkley Park Centre
GIFT TOKENS HTA

Garden centre which has been developed inside a Victorian walled garden. Services include delivery, design and landscaping, play area and farm animals. The Annual Flower Show is on the August Bank Holiday weekend.

Jackson's Nurseries

Clifton Campville, Tamworth, Staffordshire B79 0AP
☎ 0827 373307

CONTACT Mrs N. Jackson
LOCATION 3 miles from M42, J11
OPEN 9 am – 5.30 pm, Mondays, Wednesday – Saturday; 10 am – 5 pm, Sundays. Closed Tuesdays
SPECIALITIES Fuchsias
NEW FOR 1994 Fuchsia 'Sailor'; Fuchsia 'Cancun'
CATALOGUE 2 first class stamps
MAIL ORDER No

Fuchsia specialists, with many cultivars available between March and June. They also have pelargoniums and vegetables, bedding and pot plants in season.

Planters Garden Centre

Woodlands Farm, Freasley, Tamworth, Staffordshire
B78 2EY
☎ 0827 251511   ☏ 0827 251511

CONTACT Gerald Ingram, Christine Raynor and Stewart Milligan
LOCATION 1 mile from M42, J10
OPEN 9 am – 6 pm, daily
SHOP Garden sundries; greenhouses; gifts; pets
REFRESHMENTS Restaurant, coffee shop
GIFT TOKENS HTA

Garden centre with outdoor and indoor plant ranges, garden products, fish and a toy shop. Delivery service.

Wyevale Garden Centre

Wolseley Bridge, Stafford, Staffordshire ST17 0YA
☎ 0889 574884   ☏ 0889 574881

SUFFOLK

Brian Sulman Pelargoniums

54 Kingsway, Mildenhall, Bury St Edmunds, Suffolk
IP28 7HR
☎ 0638 712297

CONTACT Brian Sulman
LOCATION Mildenhall
OPEN Open weekend 11 – 12 June
SPECIALITIES Pelargoniums
CATALOGUE 1 first class stamp
MAIL ORDER Yes; 6 plants minimum
SHOWS RHS Westminster

A new venture specialising in pelargoniums, especially regals. The nursery is only open at the June open weekend. Trades from the same address as Pearl Sulman (dwarfs and miniatures): the business is distinct.

Crown Vegetables

Marward House, Stock Corner Farm, Beck Row, Bury St Edmunds, Suffolk IP28 8DW
☎ 0638 712779

CONTACT Trevor Sore
OPEN Mail order only
SPECIALITIES Vegetables
NEW FOR 1994 Dried flowers
MAIL ORDER Yes

Specialist vegetables by post, including asparagus crowns, artichokes and horseradish.

Denbeigh Heathers

All Saints Road, Creeting St Mary, Ipswich, Suffolk
IP6 8PJ
☎ 0449 711220

CONTACT D. J. Small
LOCATION Creeting St Mary
OPEN Phone first
SPECIALITIES Heathers
CATALOGUE On request
MAIL ORDER Yes

Wholesale and retail hardy heathers, sold as rooted cuttings, mini plants and some larger sizes. There are over 1,000 species and cultivars here: they claim to have the largest range in the world.

Goldbrook Plants

Hoxne, Eye, Suffolk IP21 5AN
☎ 0379 668770

CONTACT Sandra Bond
OPEN 10.30 am – 6 pm, Thursday to Sunday. Other
days by appointment. Closed January
SPECIALITIES Hostas
NEW FOR 1994 *Hosta* 'Fragrant Bouquet'; *H.* 'El
Capitan', and others
CATALOGUE 4 first class stamps
MAIL ORDER Yes; winter and spring dispatch
SHOWS RHS Westminster; Chelsea; Hampton
Court

An exceptional collection of *Hosta* (over 500), with a
good choice of *Hemerocallis* and shade loving plants
too. As exhibitors they have an impressive run of
Chelsea gold medals for each of the last six years.

Goulding's Fuchsias

Link Lane, Bentley, Ipswich, Suffolk IP9 2DP
☎ 0473 310058

CONTACT Mr T. J. Goulding
OPEN 10 am – 5 pm, daily, 8 January to 3 July
SPECIALITIES Fuchsias
NEW FOR 1994 See catalogue
CATALOGUE 3 first class stamps; December
MAIL ORDER Yes

Specialist fuchsia growers. The following categories are
sold: basket, upright, hardy, encliandras and triphyllas.
They welcome coach parties, and can help with the
naming of varieties.

Home Meadows Nursery Ltd

Top Street, Martlesham, Woodbridge, Suffolk
IP12 4RD
☎ 0394 382419

CONTACT S. Denis O'Brien Baker
OPEN 8 am – 5 pm, Monday – Saturday. Closed
Sundays
SPECIALITIES Chrysanthemums
CATALOGUE SAE
MAIL ORDER Yes
SHOWS RHS Westminster; Chelsea
NCCPG NATIONAL COLLECTIONS Chrysanthemums

As well as a general selection of bedding and herbaceous plants, the main specialities here are Korean and
spray chrysanthemums, and Iceland poppies.

Mickfield Fish and Watergarden Centre

Debenham Road, Mickfield, Stowmarket, Suffolk
IP14 5LP
☎ 0449 711336   ⊠ 0449 711018

CONTACT Robert Davis
OPEN 9 am – 5 pm, daily. Closed Christmas, Boxing
Day and New Year's Day
SPECIALITIES Aquatic plants; bog plants
NEW FOR 1994 American water lilies
CATALOGUE 50p
MAIL ORDER Yes
SHOP Pond products; fish
REFRESHMENTS Tea room (weekends)
GARDEN 2 acre display gardens
DESIGN SERVICE Mickfield Fish and Watergarden
Centre

Plants for in and around water – aquatic, marginal and
moisture-loving species. They also sell liners, pumps,
rock and fish.

Mills Farm Plants and Gardens

Norwich Road, Mendlesham, Suffolk IP14 5NQ
☎ 0449 766425

CONTACT Sue and Peter Russell
OPEN 9 am – 5.30 pm, daily. Closed Tuesdays, and all
January
SPECIALITIES *Dianthus*; roses
CATALOGUE 2 second class stamps
MAIL ORDER Yes; pinks and roses only
SHOWS RHS Westminster

Mills Farm specialise in *Dianthus* (new and old hybrids,
species and rock garden types) and roses: there is a list
for each genus. The roses are mostly old-fashioned
varieties, in a well-chosen selection. Gardening courses
are also held at the nursery, but advice is free.

Mrs S Robinson

21 Bederic Close, Bury St Edmunds, Suffolk
IP32 7DR
☎ 0284 764310

CONTACT Mrs S. Robinson
OPEN By appointment
MAIL ORDER No
DESIGN SERVICE Sue's Garden Designs

Plants on wheels: Sue Robinson lectures to clubs and
societies and brings plants to sell with her. Garden
design and plant supply also.

Nareys Garden Centre

Bury Road, Stowmarket, Suffolk IP14 3QD
☎ 0449 612559

CONTACT J. B. Narey, F. Narey and E. Hicks
LOCATION West of Stowmarket on A45
OPEN 8.30 am – 5.30 pm, summer; 8.30 am – 5 pm,
winter
SHOP Garden sundries; above ground swimming
pools
DESIGN SERVICE Nareys Garden Centre

GIFT TOKENS HTA

General garden centre, producing its own bedding and pot plants. Some landscaping, and pool and building installation. Delivery service.

Notcutts Nurseries
Woodbridge, Suffolk IP12 4AF
☎ 0394 383344   ☏ 0394 385460

CONTACT Notcutts Nurseries
LOCATION Woodbridge, and ten other garden centres
SPECIALITIES Roses; shrubs; trees
CATALOGUE £3.25 by post; £2.50 from garden centres
MAIL ORDER Yes
SHOP Garden sundries
GARDEN Demonstration gardens
DESIGN SERVICE Notcutts Landscapes
SHOWS RHS Westminster; Chelsea; Hampton Court
GIFT TOKENS HTA; own

Large wholesale nurseries with a garden centre chain. They are strongest on flowering shrubs and trees, including roses, but they have more or less everything else too. Quality is first class. They have a design capability through Nottcutts Landscapes who are listed in our Services section.

Paradise Centre
Twinstead Road, Lamarsh, Bures, Suffolk CO8 5EX
☎ 0787 269449   ☏ 0787 269449

CONTACT Hedy J. Stapel-Valk
LOCATION Near Bures
OPEN 10 am – 5 pm, Saturday – Sunday, and Bank Holidays. By appointment at other times
SPECIALITIES Bulbs
CATALOGUE 4 first class stamps
MAIL ORDER Yes
GARDEN Gardens
DESIGN SERVICE Garden Scents
SHOWS Chelsea; Hampton Court
GIFT TOKENS Own

A garden nursery which specialises in bulbous plants and shade lovers, all grown at the nursery. They have in-house design and build through Garden Scents, run by Writtle-trained Alan Mitchell (0206 865040).

Park Green Nurseries
Wetheringsett, Stowmarket, Suffolk IP14 5QH
☎ 0728 860139

CONTACT Richard and Mary Ford
LOCATION 6 miles north east of Stowmarket
OPEN 10 am – 5.30 pm, Thursday – Sunday, March to November
SPECIALITIES Herbaceous perennials

NEW FOR 1994 New *Hosta* cultivars
CATALOGUE 2 first class stamps
MAIL ORDER Yes; no minimum order
SHOWS Malvern Spring; Southport; BBC GW Live

This nursery specialises in *Hosta* and *Hemerocallis*, with new cultivars each year. Other plants include astilbes.

Pearl Sulman
54 Kingsway, Mildenhall, Bury St Edmunds, Suffolk IP28 7HR
☎ 0638 712297

CONTACT Pearl Sulman
OPEN Mail order only, except for Open weekend, 11 – 12 June
SPECIALITIES Pelargoniums
NEW FOR 1994 6 new miniature *Pelargonium* raised by the late Ray Bidwell
CATALOGUE 3 first class stamps
MAIL ORDER Yes
SHOWS Chelsea; BBC GW Live; Hampton Court

A small nursery which specialises in dwarf and miniature pelargoniums (500). Trades from the same address as Brian Sulman, but is a separate business.

Siskin Plants
Davey Lane, Charsfield, Woodbridge, Suffolk IP13 7QG
☎ 0473 37567

CONTACT Chris and Valerie Wheeler
OPEN 10 am – 5 pm, Tuesday – Saturday, and Bank Holidays. By appointment November to February
SPECIALITIES Alpines
CATALOGUE £1
MAIL ORDER Yes
SHOWS BBC GW Live; Hampton Court

Alpines and dwarf shrubs, particularly those which are suited to sinks and troughs. A good choice of hebes.

Smallscapes Nursery
3 Hundon Close, Stradishall, Newmarket, Suffolk CB8 9YF
☎ 0440 820336

CONTACT Stephen and Leigh Sage
LOCATION 6 miles north east of Haverhill on A143
OPEN By appointment: phone first
SPECIALITIES Rooted cuttings
NEW FOR 1994 *Heuchera* 'Pewter Dome'; *Hosta* 'Sum and Substance'
CATALOGUE 4 first class stamps
MAIL ORDER Yes; no minimum order
GARDEN Garden

This nursery specialises in rooted cuttings and young plants, all in containers, for safe mail order. The list includes alpines, perennials, climbers, trees and shrubs. Larger plants are available at the nursery.

Wyevale Garden Centre
Rougham Road, Bury St Edmunds, Suffolk IP33 2RN
☎ 0284 755818   📠 0284 706184

Wyevale Garden Centre
Newton Road, Chilton, Sudbury, Suffolk CO10 0PZ
☎ 0787 373628   📠 0787 373714

Wyevale Garden Centre
Grundisburgh Road, Woodbridge, Suffolk IP13 6HX
☎ 0394 380022   📠 0394 380740

SURREY

Beechcroft Nursery
127 Reigate Road, Ewell, Surrey KT17 3DE
☎ 081 393 4265

CONTACT C. Kimber
OPEN 10 am – 5 pm, summer; 10 am – 4 pm, winter, and Sundays and Bank Holidays
SPECIALITIES Alpines; conifers
CATALOGUE On request
MAIL ORDER No

A mainly wholesale nursery specialising in the supply of alpines and conifers to nurseries and garden centres. Some retail trade also, and they have bedding plants in season.

Brian Hiley
25 Little Woodcote Estate, Wallington, Surrey SM5 4AU
☎ 081 647 9679

CONTACT Brian and Heather Hiley
OPEN 9 am – 5 pm, Wednesday – Saturday
SPECIALITIES Herbaceous pèrennials, half-hardy plants
CATALOGUE 3 first class stamps
MAIL ORDER Yes; £10 minimum order
GARDEN Display gardens
SHOWS Chelsea; BBC GW Live; Hampton Court

An interesting collection of tender perennials and shrubs: the salvias are particularly good. Among the hardy perennials the penstemons stand out.

Clay Lane Nursery
3 Clay Lane, South Nutfield, Redhill, Surrey RH1 4EG
☎ 0737 823307

CONTACT K. W. Belton
OPEN 9 am – 6 pm, Tuesday – Sunday, and Bank Holidays
SPECIALITIES Fuchsias
CATALOGUE 2 first class stamps
MAIL ORDER No

This fuchsia specialist sells a wide range of cultivars and species, incuding hardy varieties and varieties which are suitable for baskets. They also have pelargoniums.

Constable Daffodils
45 Weydon Hill Road, Farnham, Surrey GU9 8NX
☎ 0252 721062

CONTACT Peter Fenn
OPEN Mail order only
SPECIALITIES Daffodils
CATALOGUE On request
MAIL ORDER Yes; local orders delivered
SHOWS International Spring Gardening Fair

Specialist bulb grower with a list of *Narcissus* and daffodils in all divisions of the genus. This mail order business caters for both the gardener and exhibitor.

D N Bromage & Co Ltd
St Mary's Gardens, Worplesdon, Guildford, Surrey GU3 3RS
☎ 0483 232893

CONTACT D. N. Bromage amd Mrs R. A. Hughes
OPEN 10 am – 4 pm, daily
SPECIALITIES Bonsai
CATALOGUE On request
MAIL ORDER Yes
SHOP Bonsai accessories
SHOWS Chelsea

Bonsai trees and all accessories. Other services include offering a holiday home, hospital and repotting.

Foliage Scented & Herb Plants
Walton Poor Cottage, Ranmore Common, Dorking, Surrey RH5 6SX
☎ 0483 282273

CONTACT Mrs Prudence Calvert
LOCATION From A246 take Greendene Shere turning, near Ranmore Arms pub; then left into Crocknorth Road
OPEN Wednesday – Sunday, and Bank Holidays, March to September
SPECIALITIES Herbs
MAIL ORDER No

GARDEN Herb garden and new potager

The nursery stocks a range of aromatic herbs and shrubs. As well as the herb and display gardens, a potager is planned for this year. The 2 acre private gardens are also open by appointment.

Garson Farm

Thompson Bros (Esher) Ltd, Garson Farm, Winterdown Road, Esher, Surrey KT10 8LS
☎ 0372 460181 📠 0372 470410

CONTACT Garson Farm
OPEN 9 am – 5 pm, Monday – Friday; 10 am – 5 pm, Sundays. Extended hours in summer
SHOP Conservatories; pools
REFRESHMENTS Restaurant
GIFT TOKENS HTA

A garden centre, with plants and garden products, and a pick your own farm, including a farm shop.

Green Farm Plants

Bentley, Farnham, Surrey GU10 5JX
☎ 0420 23202

CONTACT John Coke and Marina Christopher
LOCATION North east Hampshire
OPEN 10 am – 6 pm, Wednesday – Saturday, mid March to mid October
SPECIALITIES Herbaceous perennials
CATALOGUE 3 first class stamps
MAIL ORDER No
SHOWS RHS Westminster

This nursery is full of interesting plants, including the results of recent collecting trips. The main groups are hardy and half-hardy perennials, with an increasing number of woodland plants and sun-loving shrubs.

Herons Bonsai Ltd

Herons Bonsai Nursery, Wire Mill Lane, Newchapel, Lingfield, Surrey RH7 6HJ
☎ 0342 832657 📠 0342 832025

CONTACT Peter and Dawn Chan
LOCATION Newchapel
OPEN 9 am – 6 pm, daily
SPECIALITIES Bonsai
NEW FOR 1994 Large Japanese acers from Japan
CATALOGUE SAE plus £1
MAIL ORDER Yes
SHOP Bonsai accessories; Japanese items
SHOWS Chelsea; Hampton Court

Bonsai nursery, with a string of nine Chelsea golds. As well as trees for indoors and outdoors, there are pots, tools and accessories (retail and wholesale). Bonsai classes and design available.

Hillier Garden Centre

London Road, Windlesham, Surrey GU20 6LN
☎ 0344 23166

SPECIALITIES Climbers; conifers; trees
CATALOGUE On request
MAIL ORDER No
GIFT TOKENS HTA

See Hillier Nurseries Ltd, Hampshire.

Hydon Nurseries

Clock Barn Lane, Hydon Heath, Godalming, Surrey GU8 4AZ
☎ 0483 860252 📠 0483 419937

CONTACT A. F. George
LOCATION 2 miles east of A3, Milford exit. Near Cheshire Home
OPEN 8 am – 5 pm, Monday to Friday, and Saturdays in season. Closed for lunch 12.45 – 2 pm
SPECIALITIES Rhododendrons
CATALOGUE £1.50
MAIL ORDER Yes; p & p at cost
DESIGN SERVICE Hydon Nurseries
SHOWS Chelsea
GIFT TOKENS HTA

Rhododendron and azalea specialists. The extensive range covers all types – among them some tender species and their own *Rhododendron yakushimanum* hybrids. They also stock companion trees and shrubs. They can advise on design and planting. The annual open weekend for enthusiasts is from 30 April to 2 May this year.

Knap Hill Nursery Ltd

Barrs Lane, Knaphill, Woking, Surrey GU21 2JW
☎ 0483 481212 📠 0483 797261

CONTACT Miss Daphne Buckle
LOCATION 2½ miles west of Woking, off A322
OPEN 9 am – 5 pm, Monday – Saturday; 10 am – 5 pm, Sundays
SPECIALITIES Rhododendrons
CATALOGUE 50p
MAIL ORDER Yes
SHOP Garden centre
REFRESHMENTS Coffee shop
SHOWS Chelsea

Garden and nursery which specialises in rhododendrons and azaleas. Their extensive list includes hybrids, dwarf, semi-dwarf and *R. yakushimanum* cultivars, as well as deciduous and evergreen azaleas.

Knights Garden Centre

Limpsfield Road, Chelsham, Surrey CR6 9DZ
☎ 0883 622340 📠 0883 627252

OPEN 8 am – 5.30 pm, Monday – Saturday; 9 am –
5 pm, Sundays
REFRESHMENTS Yes
GIFT TOKENS HTA; own

One of three Knights garden centres: the others are at
Woldingham and Godstone.

Knights Garden Centre
Nag's Hall Nursery, Godstone, Surrey RH9 8DB
☎ 0883 742275   📠 0883 744429

OPEN 8 am – 5.30 pm, Monday – Saturday; 9 am –
5 pm, Sundays
REFRESHMENTS Yes
GIFT TOKENS HTA; own

General garden centre.

Knights Garden Centre
Rosedene Nursery, Woldingham Road,
Woldingham, Surrey CR3 7LA
☎ 0883 653142   📠 0883 652221

OPEN 8 am – 5.30 pm, Monday – Saturday; 9 am – 5 pm,
Sundays
REFRESHMENTS Yes
GARDEN Woldingham Dene
GIFT TOKENS HTA; own

One of three Surrey garden centres in the Knights chain.

Merrist Wood College Plant Shop
Merrist Wood College, Worplesdon, Guildford,
Surrey GU3 3PE
☎ 0483 232424   📠 0483 236518

CONTACT Danny O'Shaughnessy
LOCATION On campus, off A322
OPEN 8 am – 5 pm, Monday – Friday. Selected week-
ends too: phone first
MAIL ORDER No
SHOWS Chelsea; Hampton Court

Plants of all descriptions, from bedding to semi-mature
trees. Most of it is produced by the students as part of
their training.

Millais Nurseries
Crosswater Lane, Churt, Farnham, Surrey GU10 2JN
☎ 0252 792698   📠 0252 792526

CONTACT David Millais
OPEN 10 am – 1 pm, 2 – 5 pm, Tuesday – Saturday.
Also daily, May to mid June
SPECIALITIES Rhododendrons
NEW FOR 1994 30 new varieties
CATALOGUE 5 second class stamps
MAIL ORDER Yes; minimum order £20; October to
March
REFRESHMENTS NGS days only

GARDEN 10 acre woodland garden
GIFT TOKENS Own

A rhododendron and azalea specialist. The extensive
range of species and hybrids includes some new Himalayan species. The garden is open in May and early June,
with a NGS weekend from 28 – 30 May.

Nettletons Nursery
Ivy Mill Lane, Godstone, Surrey RH9 8NF
☎ 0883 742426

CONTACT Jonathan Nettleton
OPEN 8.30 am – 1 pm, 2 – 5.30 pm, Monday –
Saturday. Also 10 am – 1 pm, Sundays from March to
early June. Closed Wednesdays
SPECIALITIES Acers
CATALOGUE 2 first class stamps
MAIL ORDER No

Acers in great variety (100), as well as many wisterias
(15). There are other good trees and shrubs here too, all
produced at the nursery.

Notcutts Garden Centre
Waterers Nurseries, London Road, Bagshot, Surrey
GU19 5DG
☎ 0276 72288

LOCATION On A30
OPEN 9 am – 5.30 pm, Monday – Saturday; 10 am –
5.30 pm, Sundays. Closes at 5 pm in winter
CATALOGUE £2.50
SHOP Garden sundries; furniture; pools; aquatics
REFRESHMENTS Restaurant
GIFT TOKENS HTA; own

Famous old nursery (including a wholesale division).
Now part of the Notcutts empire.

Notcutts Garden Centre
Guildford Road, Cranleigh, Surrey GU6 8LT
☎ 0483 274222

LOCATION On B2128
OPEN 9 am – 5.30 pm, Monday – Saturday; 10 am –
5.30 pm, Sundays. Closes at 5 pm in winter
CATALOGUE £2.50
SHOP Garden sundries; furniture; machinery
GIFT TOKENS HTA; own

See also Notcutts Nurseries, Suffolk.

Pantiles Plant & Garden Centre
Almners Road, Lyne, Chertsey, Surrey KT16 0BJ
☎ 0932 872195   📠 0932 874030

CONTACT Brendan Gallagher
OPEN 8.30 am – 5.30 pm, Monday – Saturday; 9 am –
5 pm, Sundays

SPECIALITIES Aquatic plants; bedding plants; large specimen trees
CATALOGUE SAE for availability list
MAIL ORDER No
DESIGN SERVICE Pantiles Plant & Garden Centre
GIFT TOKENS HTA

The nursery specialises in outsize container-grown specimens (up to 8 metres), including *Dicksonia antarctica* (tree fern). There is also a good bedding range and an aquatic centre. Full landscaping service also available.

Rupert Bowlby
Gatton, Reigate, Surrey RH2 0TA
☎ 0737 642221   ℻ 0737 642221

CONTACT Rupert Bowlby
OPEN Saturdays and Sunday afternoons, March, September and October. By appointment at other times
SPECIALITIES Bulbs
CATALOGUE 2 first class stamps
MAIL ORDER Yes
SHOWS RHS Westminster; Chelsea

Bulb specialist, including *Narcissus, Tulipa* and *Fritillaria*. He has some greenhouse species, and an excellent choice of *Allium* which formed a striking display at Chelsea last year.

Secretts Garden Centre
Old Portsmouth Road, Milford, Godalming, Surrey GU8 5HL
☎ 0483 426633   ℻ 0483 426855

OPEN 9 am – 5.30 pm, Monday – Saturday; 10 am – 5 pm, Sundays and Bank Holidays
SHOP Farm shop; flowers; pick your own
GIFT TOKENS HTA

Plant orientated garden centre, including a flower nursery and pick your own farm.

Surrey Primroses
Merriewood, Sandy Lane, Milford, Godalming, Surrey GU8 5BJ
☎ 0483 416747

CONTACT G. J. E. Yates
OPEN Mail order only
SPECIALITIES Primulas
CATALOGUE SAE
MAIL ORDER Yes; no minimum order

Specialist source of old, named single primrose and polyanthus cultivars. Many delightful and garden-worthy survivors.

V H Humphrey
Westlees Farm, Logmore Lane, Westcott, Dorking, Surrey RH4 3JN
☎ 0306 889827

CONTACT Mrs P. J. Brown
OPEN By appointment only, and at May open days
SPECIALITIES Irises
NEW FOR 1994 New tall bearded iris and sibiricas
CATALOGUE Large SAE
MAIL ORDER Yes
SHOWS RHS Westminster; Chelsea

Irises only, and in abundance. Most of this list consists of bearded iris, but there are also species, pacific coast hybrids, *spuria* and *sibirica* cultivars too. The business is mainly mail order, but there are two open days in May, at flowering time.

The Vernon Geranium Nursery
Cuddington Way, Cheam, Sutton, Surrey SM2 7JB
☎ 081 393 7616   ℻ 081 786 7437

OPEN 9.30 am – 5.30 pm, Monday – Saturday; 10 am – 4 pm, Sundays, February to August
SPECIALITIES Pelargoniums
NEW FOR 1994 *Pelargonium* 'Pac Unity'; 'John's Chamaeleon'; 'John's Wishy Washy'; 'Winford Winnie'; 'Brookside Astra'; 'Brookside Abigale'; 'Brookside Arundel'
CATALOGUE £1.50
MAIL ORDER Yes; no minimum order
SHOWS International Spring Gardening Fair; Southport; Hampton Court

Specialist growers of pelargoniums (1,100) and fuchsias (100). Plants are available as rooted cuttings by post, and pot-grown plants can be had from the nursery or at shows. The number of pelargonium varieties speaks for itself: there are even too many categories for us to list here.

Wisley Plant Centre
RHS Garden, Wisley, Woking, Surrey GU23 6QB
☎ 0483 211113

LOCATION RHS Garden, Wisley near M3, A3 intersection
OPEN 10 am – 6.30 pm, summer; 10 am – 5.30 pm, winter
CATALOGUE No
MAIL ORDER No
SHOP Garden sundries; seeds; books
REFRESHMENTS Restaurants
GARDEN RHS Garden, Wisley, Surrey, see Gardens section
GIFT TOKENS HTA

Wisley's plant centre carries a very wide and interesting selection of most kinds of plants. You need a strong will if you are to prevent your visit proving expensive.

Wyevale Garden Centre

Lower Morden Lane, Morden, Surrey SM4 4SJ
☎ 081 337 7781   📠 081 335 3326

EAST SUSSEX

Axletree Nursery

Starvecrow Lane, Peasmarsh, Rye, East Sussex
TN31 6XL
☎ 0797 230470

CONTACT   Dr D. J. Hibberd
LOCATION   2 miles south west of Peasmarsh, off A268. Send SAE for map and directions
OPEN   10 am – 5 pm, Wednesday – Saturday, mid March to September
SPECIALITIES   Herbaceous perennials; hardy geraniums
NEW FOR 1994   New *Geranium* cultivars
CATALOGUE   4 first class stamps
MAIL ORDER   No

Best known for their substantial list of hardy geraniums: more cultivars are being introduced this year. There is a good range of other herbaceous perennials.

Coghurst Nursery

Ivy House Lane, Three Oaks, Hastings, East Sussex
TN35 4NP
☎ 0424 425371/ 437657

CONTACT   Mrs J. Farnfield
LOCATION   Near Hastings
OPEN   12 – 4.30 pm, Monday – Friday; 10 am – 4.30 pm, Sundays. Closed Saturdays
SPECIALITIES   Camellias; rhododendrons
NEW FOR 1994   Sasanqua camellias
CATALOGUE   2 first class stamps
MAIL ORDER   Yes; no minimum order
SHOWS   RHS Westminster

Camellia and *Rhododendron* specialists. They stock all types of camellias and rhododendrons, and have a good selection of hydrangeas, eucryphias and other shrubs.

Great Dixter Nurseries

Great Dixter, Northiam, Rye, East Sussex TN31 6PH
☎ 0797 753107

CONTACT   Mrs K. Leighton
LOCATION   Off A28, ½ a mile north of Northiam
OPEN   9 am – 12.30 pm, 1.30 – 5.00 pm, Monday – Friday; 9 am – 12 pm, Saturdays
SPECIALITIES   Clematis
CATALOGUE   60p
MAIL ORDER   Yes; minimum order £10; not in May to July
SHOP   Books

REFRESHMENTS   Refreshments
GARDEN   Great Dixter, East Sussex, see Gardens section

The nursery is attached to Christopher Lloyd's famous garden, and copies of his books are on sale here. The nursery specialises in clematis, but the rest of the general range includes many other plants which can be seen in the garden.

Harvest Nurseries

Harvest Cottage, Boonshill Farm, Iden, Rye, East Sussex TN31 7QA
☎ 0797 280493

CONTACT   Mr D. A. Smith
OPEN   Mail order only
SPECIALITIES   Cacti and succulents
NEW FOR 1994   New *Epiphyllum* hybrids
CATALOGUE   2 first class stamps
MAIL ORDER   Yes; no minimum order

A mail order only cacti and succulent nursery. They specialise in *Epiphyllum* hybrids. All the plants are propagated at the nursery.

Just Roses

Beales Lane, Northiam, Rye, East Sussex TN31 6QY
☎ 0797 252355

CONTACT   Mr J. H. Banham
OPEN   9 am – 5 pm, Monday – Friday; 10 am – 4 pm, Saturday – Sunday
SPECIALITIES   Roses
CATALOGUE   On request
MAIL ORDER   Yes; November to February

Specialist rose growers, covering the whole spectrum of the genus. Container roses can be bought from April, while stocks last. Most of the business is bare root, from November on.

Kent Street Nurseries

Sedlescombe, Battle, East Sussex TN33 0SF
☎ 0424 751134

CONTACT   P. Stapley and Mrs D. Downey
OPEN   9 am – dusk, daily
SPECIALITIES   Bedding plants; fuchsias; pelargoniums
CATALOGUE   SAE plus 2 first class stamps per list
MAIL ORDER   Yes

A general plant range is complemented by over 800 *Fuchsia* and *Pelargonium* varieties, including some older ones. They have separate lists for fuchsias and pelargoniums: specify which one you want.

Lime Cross Nursery

Herstmonceux, Hailsham, East Sussex BN27 4RS
☎ 0323 833229

CONTACT J. A. Tate
OPEN 8.30 am – 5 pm, Monday – Saturday; 9.30 am – 5 pm, Sundays
SPECIALITIES Conifers
CATALOGUE On request
MAIL ORDER No

Specialist conifer growers with some 300 varieties and more. There is also a good choice of trees and shrubs among a general plant range.

Long Man Gardens

Lewes Road, Wilmington, Polegate, East Sussex BN26 5RS
☎ 0323 870816

CONTACT O. Menzel
OPEN 9 am – 12 pm, 2.30 – 5 pm, Tuesday – Sunday. Phone first
SPECIALITIES Conservatory plants
CATALOGUE On request
MAIL ORDER Yes

The nursery specialises in plants for conservatory and greenhouse culture, including *Hoya* and *Bougainvillea*. They will do mail order, but recommend a visit.

Merriments Gardens

Hawkhurst Road, Hurst Green, East Sussex TN19 7RA
☎ 0580 860666   FAX 0580 860324

CONTACT David Weeks
OPEN 10 am – 5.30 pm, daily
CATALOGUE 75p
MAIL ORDER No
SHOP Garden sundries
REFRESHMENTS Tea room
GARDEN Show garden
DESIGN SERVICE Merriments Gardens

Retail nursery growing a range of hardy plants. They also sell garden products, offer a design and landscaping service, and have their own garden club.

Norman Bonsai

3 Westdene Drive, Brighton, East Sussex BN1 5HE
☎ 0273 506476

CONTACT Ken Norman
LOCATION Brighton, and Leonardslee Gardens, West Sussex
OPEN 10.30 am – 6 pm, mid April to October, at Leonardslee Gardens
SPECIALITIES Bonsai
MAIL ORDER No

SHOP Bonsai accessories
GARDEN Leonardslee Gardens, see Gardens section
SHOWS Chelsea

Imported and British-grown bonsai trees and accessories. There is a permanent display at Leonardslee Gardens of part of Mr Norman's personal bonsai collection. Demonstrations and tuition can be arranged.

Perryhill Nurseries

Hartfield, East Sussex TN7 4JP
☎ 0892 770377   FAX 0892 770929

CONTACT Peter Chapman
LOCATION 1 mile north of Hartfield on B2026
OPEN 9 am – 5 pm, March to October; 9 am – 4.30 pm, November to February
SPECIALITIES Rhododendrons; roses; shrubs; trees
CATALOGUE £1.65
MAIL ORDER No; delivery for large orders
DESIGN SERVICE Perryhill Nurseries
GIFT TOKENS HTA; own

No real specialities, except for the extent of the range. Trees, shrubs, herbaceous perennials and roses are all available in quantity, and the varieties are well-chosen. A design and landscaping service is available. The Perryhill Sackville Garden Workshop holds learning days here, often with gardening personalities.

Stuart Ogg

Hopton, Fletching Street, Mayfield, East Sussex TN20 6TL
☎ 0435 873322

CONTACT Stuart Ogg
OPEN By appointment only
SPECIALITIES Delphiniums
CATALOGUE SAE
MAIL ORDER Yes

Specialist delphinium nursery.

Usual & Unusual Plants

Onslow House, Magham Down, Hailsham, East Sussex BN27 1PL
☎ 0323 840967   FAX 0323 840967

CONTACT Mrs Jennie Maillard
OPEN 9.30 am – 5.30 pm, daily. Closed August
SPECIALITIES Herbaceous perennials
CATALOGUE SAE plus 1 first class stamp
MAIL ORDER No

Small herbaceous nursery: plants include hardy geraniums and euphorbias.

Wyevale Garden Centre

Newhaven Road, Kingston, Lewes, East Sussex BN7 3NE
☎ 0273 473510   FAX 0273 477135

WEST SUSSEX

Allwood Bros

Mill Nursery, Hassocks, West Sussex BN6 9NB
☎ 0273 844229

CONTACT W. Rickaby
OPEN 9 am – 4 pm, Monday – Friday
SPECIALITIES *Dianthus*
CATALOGUE 2 first class stamps
MAIL ORDER Yes
SHOWS International Spring Gardening Fair; Malvern Spring; Chelsea

Allwood Bros sell *Dianthus*, carnations and pinks of all kinds, and at all stages of the plants' development – as seed, plants or cut flowers. Their original postal carnation service started in 1910. A booklet, *Allwoods Guide to Perpetual Flowering Carnations*, is available for £2 by post.

Anthony Archer-Wills Ltd

Broadford Bridge Road, West Chiltington, West Sussex RH20 2LF
☎ 0798 813204   ☎ 0798 815080

OPEN By appointment
SPECIALITIES Aquatic plants; bog plants
CATALOGUE On request
MAIL ORDER Yes
DESIGN SERVICE Anthony Archer-Wills Ltd
SHOWS Chelsea

Water nursery belonging to a garden designer: see his entry in Horticultural Services for more details. The nursery stocks aquatic, marginal and waterside plants. They also sell liners and pumps.

Apuldram Roses

Apuldram Lane, Dell Quay, Chichester, West Sussex PO20 7EF
☎ 0243 785769   ☎ 0243 536973

CONTACT Mrs D. Sawday
LOCATION 1 mile south west of Chichester
OPEN 9 am – 5 pm, Monday – Saturday; 10.30 am – 4.30 pm, Sundays and Bank Holidays
SPECIALITIES Roses
CATALOGUE On request
MAIL ORDER Yes
GARDEN Rose fields

Apuldram sell a mixed range of mainly modern roses. They hold an open evening in the rose fields during the season.

Architectural Plants

Cooks Farm, Nuthurst, Horsham, West Sussex RH13 6LH
☎ 0403 891772   ☎ 0403 891056

CONTACT Angus White and Christine Shaw
LOCATION 3 miles south of Horsham, behind the Black Horse pub in Nuthurst
OPEN 9 am – 5 pm, Monday – Saturday
SPECIALITIES Aromatic and scented plants; Australian plants; conservatory plants; ferns; foliage plants; Mediterranean plants; New Zealand plants; South American plants
CATALOGUE On request
MAIL ORDER Yes; minimum carriage £13
GARDEN Display garden

The catalogue is breezily written and easy to use. They offer a wide choice of mainly evergreen plants which have been chosen for their shape and texture. Large sizes are available for immediate impact. They deliver anywhere, and also sell terracotta pots and wheelbarrows of their own design.

Cheals Garden Centre

Horsham Road, Crawley, West Sussex RH11 8LY
☎ 0293 522101   ☎ 0293 524255

LOCATION Junction of A264 with A23
OPEN 9 am – 5.30 pm, Monday – Saturday; 10 am – 5.30 pm, Sundays
SHOP Garden sundries
GIFT TOKENS HTA

General garden centre.

Cottage Garden Plants

Mytten Twitten, High Street, Cuckfield, West Sussex RH17 5EN
☎ 0444 456067   ☎ 0444 456067

CONTACT David and Pat Clarke
LOCATION Cuckfield
OPEN Times under revision: phone first
SPECIALITIES Herbaceous perennials
CATALOGUE 3 first class stamps
MAIL ORDER Yes; starting this autumn
SHOWS RHS Westminster; International Spring Gardening Fair; Hampton Court

An appropriately named nursery. Their range is mostly herbaceous, but they sell shrubs and climbers too.

Croftway Nursery

Yapton Road, Barnham, Bognor Regis, West Sussex PO22 0BH
☎ 0243 552121

CONTACT Graham Spencer
LOCATION Between Yapton and Barnham, on B2233

OPEN 9 am – 5.30 pm, daily. Closed Wednesdays from November to February, and over Christmas
SPECIALITIES Herbaceous perennials; irises
NEW FOR 1994 New *Geranium*
CATALOGUE £1
MAIL ORDER Yes; bearded irises sent August, other plants in November
GARDEN Display garden and iris fields

This family business specialises in bearded irises, of which they have a very large selection. But they also sell other *Iris* types, and herbaceous perennials. The display fields are best seen in late May, early June.

Denmans Garden Plant Centre

Clock House, Denmans, Fontwell, Arundel, West Sussex BN18 0SU
☎ 0243 542808   📠 0243 544064

CONTACT Pamela Wilson
LOCATION 6 miles east of Chichester, just off westbound A27
OPEN 9 am – 5 pm, daily
SPECIALITIES Shrubs
CATALOGUE £2.50
REFRESHMENTS Café
GARDEN Denmans, West Sussex, see Gardens section
DESIGN SERVICE Denmans Ltd

Part of this 1940s garden which is now under designer John Brookes's care. The plant centre, which can be visited separately, sells a good choice of shrubs and other plants, many of them propagated from the garden.

Hillier Garden Centre

Brighton Road, Horsham, West Sussex RH13 6QA
☎ 0403 210113

SPECIALITIES Climbers; conifers; trees
CATALOGUE On request
MAIL ORDER No
GIFT TOKENS HTA

See Hillier Nurseries Ltd, Hampshire.

Holly Gate Cactus Nursery

Billingshurst Road, Ashington, West Sussex RH20 3BA
☎ 0903 892930

CONTACT Mr T. M. Hewitt
OPEN 9 am – 5 pm, daily. Closed 25 – 26 December
SPECIALITIES Cacti and succulents; seeds
CATALOGUE 4 second class stamps
MAIL ORDER Yes
SHOP Garden sundries
REFRESHMENTS Refreshments
GARDEN Cactus garden
SHOWS International Spring Gardening Fair

One of the largest of the cacti and succulent specialists. The extensive retail and wholesale business includes all types of cacti, with over 50,000 specimens in stock. There is a cactus garden, and monthly special events are held in the spring and summer. They also issue an extensive seed list, and supplementary plant lists: £2 covers all mailings.

Houghton Farm Plants

Houghton Farm, Arundel, West Sussex BN18 9LW
☎ 0798 831100   📠 0798 831183

CONTACT R. Lock
LOCATION In Houghton village, on B2139
OPEN 10 am – 5 pm, Monday – Friday; 2 – 5.30 pm, Sundays, March to October. Closed Saturdays
SPECIALITIES Herbaceous perennials
CATALOGUE 3 first class stamps
MAIL ORDER Yes

An interesting mixed range of good hardy perennials with some shrubs and variegated plants too.

Leonardslee Gardens Nurseries

1 Mill Lane, Lower Beeding, West Sussex RH13 6PX
☎ 0403 891412

CONTACT Mr and Mrs Clark
LOCATION 3 miles south east of Horsham
OPEN By appointment only
SPECIALITIES Rhododendrons
CATALOGUE £2
MAIL ORDER Yes; minimum order £20
GARDEN Leonardslee Gardens, West Sussex, see Gardens section

Rhododendrons and azaleas are the speciality at this nursery, as at the famous gardens to which it is attached. Beyond these groups there is a selection of small trees and shrubs which are also suited to acid soil.

Mary & Peter Mitchell

11 Wingle Tye Road, Burgess Hill, West Sussex RH15 9HR
☎ 0444 236848

CONTACT Peter Mitchell
OPEN By appointment only
SPECIALITIES Sempervivums
CATALOGUE 1 first class stamp
MAIL ORDER Yes

Specialist growers of *Sempervivum*, *Jovibarba* and *Rosularia*.

Mrs J Sadler

Ingrams Cottage, Wisborough Green, Billingshurst, West Sussex RH14 0ER
☎ 0403 700234

CONTACT   Mrs Sadler
OPEN   Phone first
CATALOGUE   SAE
MAIL ORDER   No

A small nursery whose range includes primulas, lavenders, *Lathyrus* and species pelargoniums.

Roundstone Garden Centre Ltd
Roundstone Bypass, Angmering, West Sussex
BN16 4BD
☎ 0903 776481   📠 0903 785433

CONTACT   Ivan D. Turner (General Manager)
LOCATION   On A259 at Angmering
OPEN   8.30 am – 5.30 pm, summer and weekends;
9 am – 5 pm, winter
CATALOGUE   On request
SHOP   Garden sundries; buildings; machinery; gifts;
aquatics
REFRESHMENTS   Coffee shop
GIFT TOKENS   HTA

Garden hypermarket with a large choice of plants, garden and more general products including foods. Delivery service.

The Geranium Nursery
Chapel Lane, West Wittering, West Sussex
PO20 8QG
☎ 0860 586256

CONTACT   Mr and Mrs F. W. Mepham
LOCATION   6 miles south of Chichester
OPEN   10 am – 5 pm, Good Friday to mid June. Closed
Mondays, except Bank Holidays
SPECIALITIES   Pelargoniums

The nursery specialises in dwarf, fancy leaf and scented pelargoniums, but carries many other members of the genus too.

Vesutor Airplants
The Bromeliad Nursery, Marringdean Road,
Billingshurst, West Sussex RH14 9EH
☎ 0403 784028   📠 0403 785373

CONTACT   Liam O'Rourke
OPEN   By appointment. 9 am – 3 pm, Monday – Friday
SPECIALITIES   Air plants; bromeliads
CATALOGUE   £1 handbook; SAE for list
MAIL ORDER   Yes

Specialist grower and retailer of bromeliads, with an outstanding range of *Tillandsia*. They also have orchids and some carnivorous plants ('Microplants'). Their wholesale business supplies these plants to many garden centres.

W E Th. Ingwersen Ltd
Birch Farm Nursery, Gravetye, East Grinstead, West
Sussex RH19 4LE
☎ 0342 810236

CONTACT   Mr M. P. Ingwersen
LOCATION   Sussex, Surrey borders
OPEN   9 am – 1 pm, 1.30 – 4 pm, daily, March to
October. Closed Saturdays and Sundays from November to February
SPECIALITIES   Alpines; conifers; bulbs
CATALOGUE   5 first class stamps
MAIL ORDER   Yes; spring and autumn despatch
SHOWS   RHS Westminster; Chelsea; BBC GW Live;
Hampton Court

Long-established alpine nursery with an excellent range of popular and less common rock garden plants, including dwarf shrubs and conifers. There is an annual plant sale in late September, and the nursery is worth a browse.

Wyevale Garden Centre
Copthorne Road, Felbridge, West Sussex RH19 2PD
☎ 0342 328881   📠 0342 317184

TYNE & WEAR

Birkheads Cottage Garden Nursery
Birkheads Lane, Sunniside, Newcastle upon Tyne,
Tyne & Wear NE16 5EL
☎ 0207 232262   📠 0207 232262

CONTACT   Christine Lyddle
LOCATION   5 miles from A1(M) Birtley Services: ½ a
mile south of Tanfield Steam Railway on A6076
OPEN   10 am – 5 pm, Saturday – Sunday and Bank
Holidays, March to mid October; other times by appointment
SPECIALITIES   Herbaceous perennials
MAIL ORDER   No
GARDEN   Display gardens
DESIGN SERVICE   Birkheads Cottage Garden Nursery

Small nursery with a varied and informed selection of cultivar and species alpines, perennials and shrubs. Worth a browsing visit. A professional design service is available, and plants can also be supplied from stock.

Cowells Garden Centre
Main Road, Woolsington, Newcastle upon Tyne,
Tyne & Wear NE13 8BW
☎ 091 286 3403   📠 091 271 2597

CONTACT   George Richardson
LOCATION   1 mile south of Newcastle airport
OPEN   9 am – 6 pm, summer; 9 am – 5 pm, winter
GARDEN   Demonstration gardens

GIFT TOKENS   HTA

Award-winning garden centre, which stocks Blooms of Bressingham plants and is also a Hillier Premier Plant stockist. They have a special emphasis on hanging baskets, in season.

Peter Barratt's Garden Centres
Gosforth Park, Newcastle upon Tyne, Tyne & Wear NE3 5EN
☎ 091 236 7111   📠 091 236 5496

CONTACT   Sheila Caisley
OPEN   9 am – 5.30 pm
SHOP   Garden sundries; aquatics
REFRESHMENTS   Refreshments
GARDEN   Demonstration gardens
GIFT TOKENS   HTA

Garden centre with a range of garden and leisure products. Delivery service.

Peter Barratt's Garden Centres
The Peel Centre, District 10, Washington, Tyne & Wear NE37 2PA
☎ 091 417 7777   📠 091 415 4787

CONTACT   Grahame Darling
OPEN   9 am – 5.30 pm
SHOP   Garden products; aquatics
REFRESHMENTS   Refreshments
GARDEN   Demonstration gardens
GIFT TOKENS   HTA

General garden centre with a range of garden and leisure products. Delivery service.

WARWICKSHIRE

A D & N Wheeler
Pye Court, Willoughby, Rugby, Warwickshire CV23 8BZ
☎ 0788 890341

CONTACT   Tony Wheeler
OPEN   10 am – 4.30 pm, daily, January to June. Phone first at other times
SPECIALITIES   Fuchsias; Pelargoniums
NEW FOR 1994   Pelargonium 'Mr Henry Apps'
CATALOGUE   2 first class stamps
MAIL ORDER   Yes
SHOWS   Southport; BBC GW Live

Fuchsia and Pelargonium specialists, with a good range of each.

Bernhard's Rugby Garden & Leisure Centre
Bilton Road, Rugby, Warwickshire CV22 7DT
☎ 0788 811500   📠 0788 816803

CONTACT   Alan Plumtree, Garden Centre Manager
LOCATION   Close to Rugby town centre, on A4071
OPEN   9.30 am – 6 pm, daily
SHOP   Garden sundries; gifts; furniture
REFRESHMENTS   Coffee lounge
DESIGN SERVICE   O. Lawson
GIFT TOKENS   HTA

The retail nursery stocks a wide range of indoor and outdoor plants. Lectures and demonstrations are held regularly. Design and construction is available through their horticultural consultant, O. Lawson. The associated large wholesale nursery (175 acres) operates nationwide, supplying the trade and local authority markets. They will quote for complete planting schemes.

Diana Hull
Fog Cottages, 178 Lower Street, Hillmorton, Rugby, Warwickshire CV21 4NX
☎ 0788 536574

CONTACT   Diana Hull
OPEN   By appointment only
SPECIALITIES   Pelargoniums
CATALOGUE   SAE
MAIL ORDER   Yes

This small and very specialised nursery concentrates on species pelargoniums. Some new hybrids may also be available.

Fibrex Nurseries Ltd
Honeybourne Road, Pebworth, Stratford upon Avon, Warwickshire CV37 8XT
☎ 0789 720788   📠 0789 721162

CONTACT   Mr R. L. Godard-Key
OPEN   12 – 5pm, Monday – Friday, January to March, September to November; 12 – 5 pm, Tuesday – Sunday, April to August
SPECIALITIES   Ferns; pelargoniums; ivy
CATALOGUE   2 first class stamps
MAIL ORDER   Yes
GARDEN   Pelargonium collection open April to August
SHOWS   International Spring Gardening Fair; Harrogate (Spring); Chelsea; Hampton Court
NCCPG NATIONAL COLLECTIONS   Pelargonium

Specialists for pelargoniums. They hold the national collection, but plants are for sale from April to August only. Hardy ferns and Hedera are available all year round.

John Beach (Nursery) Ltd

9 Grange Gardens, Wellesbourne, Warwickshire
CV35 9RL
☎ 0926 624173

CONTACT John Beach
LOCATION Case Lane, Shrewley, Warwickshire
OPEN 10 am – 4 pm
SPECIALITIES Clematis; fruit; shrubs; trees
NEW FOR 1994 Horticultural sundries
CATALOGUE 6 second class stamps
MAIL ORDER Yes; minimum order 2 plants

Species, small and large-flowered *Clematis*, as well as fruit trees and bushes, and ornamental trees and shrubs. Some specimen sizes are available for impatient gardeners.

Preston-Mafham Collection

2 Willoughby Close, King's Coughton, Alcester,
Warwickshire B49 5QJ
☎ 0789 762938   📠 0789 762938

CONTACT Jean Preston-Mafham
LOCATION 6 miles west of Stratford upon Avon, on A435
OPEN 10 am – 5.30 pm, Monday – Friday, April to October. Other times by appointment
SPECIALITIES Cacti and succulents
MAIL ORDER No
GARDEN Cacti collection

A large range of cacti and succulents is available at this retail nursery. The owners also write about the subject, and their private collection is open for viewing.

Tollgate Cottage Nursery

Ladbrooke, Leamington Spa, Warwickshire
CV33 0BY
☎ 0926 814020

CONTACT Brenda Timms
OPEN 11 am – 5 pm, Friday – Sunday and Bank Holidays, Easter to mid October. Closed 21 August to 11 September.
SPECIALITIES Herbaceous perennials
CATALOGUE 3 first class stamps
MAIL ORDER Yes; no minimum order

A selection of pretty plants for cottage type gardens. They no longer sell herbs. It is best to phone first before visiting.

Woodfield Bros

Wood End, Clifford Chambers, Stratford on Avon,
Warwickshire CV37 8HR
☎ 0789 205618

CONTACT Brian Woodfield

OPEN 9.30 am – 4.30 pm, daily. Closed Sunday afternoons
SPECIALITIES Delphiniums; exhibition carnations
CATALOGUE SAE
MAIL ORDER Yes: carnations only
SHOWS RHS Westminster; Chelsea

They specialise in perpetual flowering carnations, dahlias and lupins. *Phlox*, *Hosta* and *Begonia* cultivars are usually available also. Mail order is restricted to carnations.

WEST MIDLANDS

Ashwood Nurseries

Greensforge, Kingswinford, West Midlands
DY6 0AE
☎ 0384 401996   📠 0384 401108

CONTACT Mr P. D. Baulk
LOCATION 2 miles west of Kingswinford, near A449
OPEN 9 am – 6 pm, Monday – Saturday; 9.30 am – 6 pm, Sundays. Closed 25 & 26 December
SPECIALITIES Seeds, *Lewisia*, *Cyclamen*, *Helleborus*
CATALOGUE 2 first class stamps
MAIL ORDER Seeds only
SHOP Gift shop
REFRESHMENTS Tea room
GARDEN Display gardens
SHOWS RHS Westminster
NCCPG NATIONAL COLLECTIONS *Lewisia*

This large nursery carries a wide general range as well as a particularly good selection of hardy cyclamen and hellebores. Lewisias are for sale from the National Collection.

David Austin Roses

Bowling Green Lane, Albrighton, Wolverhampton,
West Midlands WV7 3HB
☎ 0902 373931   📠 0902 372142

CONTACT Nursery Manager
LOCATION South of M54, J3
OPEN 9 am – 6 pm, Monday – Friday; 10 am – 6 pm, Saturday – Sunday. Close at dusk in winter
SPECIALITIES Roses
NEW FOR 1994 5 new roses
CATALOGUE On request
MAIL ORDER Yes
REFRESHMENTS Refreshments
GARDEN Rose gardens
SHOWS Chelsea; BBC GW Live; Hampton Court
GIFT TOKENS Own

Rose grower and breeder, best known for his popular English Roses strain which combines modern performance standards of flowering with an old-fashioned shape.

H Woolman (Dorridge) Ltd

Grange Road, Dorridge, Solihull, West Midlands B93 8QB
☎ 0564 776283   ☏ 0564 770830

OPEN 8 am – 4.15 pm, Monday – Friday
SPECIALITIES Chrysanthemums
CATALOGUE On request; September
MAIL ORDER Yes
SHOWS Chelsea

Long-established specialist grower of garden and greenhouse chrysanthemum cultivars.

Notcutts Garden Centre

Stratford Road, Shirley, Solihull, West Midlands B90 4EN
☎ 021 744 4501

LOCATION Near M42, J4
OPEN 9 am – 6 pm, Monday – Saturday; 10 am – 6 pm, Sundays. Closes at 8 pm, Thursdays and Fridays in spring and summer; 5.30 pm closing in winter
CATALOGUE £2.50
SHOP Garden sundries; buildings; furniture
REFRESHMENTS Restaurant
DESIGN SERVICE Notcutts Landscapes
GIFT TOKENS HTA; own

See also Notcutts Nurseries, Suffolk.

Plantables

The Old Orchard, Hall Lane, Hurst Hill, Coseley, West Midlands WV14 9RJ
☎ 0902 662647

CONTACT Alan Rumble
LOCATION Between Dudley and Wolverhampton
OPEN Mail order only: collection by appointment
SPECIALITIES Alpines; herbaceous perennials; rhododendrons
CATALOGUE 2 first class stamps
MAIL ORDER Yes; no minimum value

The nursery focuses on plants for small features or for use in small gardens. Types include dwarf rhododendrons and other shrubs, alpines and herbaceous perennials.

Wyevale Garden Centre

Hampton Road, Eastcote, Hampton in Arden, Solihull, West Midlands B92 0JJ
☎ 0675 442031   ☏ 0675 443859

WILTSHIRE

Barters Farm Nurseries Ltd

Chapmanslade, Westbury, Wiltshire BA13 4AL
☎ 0373 832294   ☏ 0373 832677

LOCATION At the Westbury end of the village, on A3098
OPEN 9 am – 5 pm, Monday – Saturday; 10 am – 5 pm, Sundays and Bank Holidays
SPECIALITIES Ferns; hedging; trees
CATALOGUE Wholesale catalogue only
MAIL ORDER No
GARDEN Demonstration gardens
SHOWS International Spring Gardening Fair; Malvern Spring
GIFT TOKENS HTA

A retail plant centre operates in conjunction with a wholesale nursery. The range runs from trees, conifers and shrubs (mostly container-grown) to half-hardy and ground cover plants. There are many ferns on offer. Open weekends are held in May, for container gardening, and in September, when the nurseries are opened.

Botanic Nursery

Cottles Lane, Atworth, Melksham, Wiltshire SN12 8NU
☎ 0225 706597

CONTACT Terence and Mary Baker
LOCATION On A365 in Atworth, behind the clock tower
OPEN 10 am – 5 pm, daily. Closed for lunch 1 – 2 pm, and all of January
SPECIALITIES Herbaceous perennials
CATALOGUE £1
MAIL ORDER Limited
DESIGN SERVICE The Botanic Nursery
SHOWS RHS Westminster; Courson
NCCPG NATIONAL COLLECTIONS Digitalis

Specialists for lime tolerant plants, including foxgloves, of which they have the National Collection. There is much else of interest here. Limited mail order, but you can arrange to collect from shows. The landscape company offers design and construction services for larger gardens in southern England.

Bowood Garden Centre

Bowood Estate, Calne, Wiltshire SN11 0LZ
☎ 0249 816828

CONTACT Charlotte
LOCATION Between Chippenham and Calne, on A4
OPEN 10 am – 6 pm, April to October; 10 am – 5 pm, November to March. Closed between Christmas and New Year

SPECIALITIES Rhododendrons; roses; shrubs
CATALOGUE SAE plus 20p: roses only
MAIL ORDER No
SHOP Gifts and garden sundries
GARDEN Bowood House, Wiltshire, see Gardens section

Attached to the famous landscape gardens, the garden centre stocks a good range of containerised old-fashioned roses, rhododendrons, shrubs and perennials. Local delivery is available.

Broadleas Gardens Charitable Trust Ltd

Broadleas, Devizes, Wiltshire SN10 5JQ
☎ 0380 722035

CONTACT Lady Anne Cowdray
LOCATION 1½ miles south west of Devizes, on A360
OPEN 2 – 6 pm, Wednesday – Thursday, Sunday, April to October
SPECIALITIES Salvias; *Euonymus*
MAIL ORDER No
GARDEN Broadleas, Wiltshire, see Gardens section
NCCPG NATIONAL COLLECTIONS *Euonymus*

The nursery sells a varied selection of plants propagated from this plantswoman's garden. The emphasis is on salvias and shrubby *Euonymus* species and cultivars.

Corsley Mill, Brigid Quest-Ritson

Highfield House, Shrewton, Salisbury, Wiltshire SP3 4BU

LOCATION 4 miles from Stonehenge, 1 mile north of A303
OPEN By appointment for collection
SPECIALITIES Roses
CATALOGUE 2 first class stamps
MAIL ORDER Yes; no minimum order
NCCPG NATIONAL COLLECTIONS Primula (European), *Pyrus*

A small nursery which specialises in roses grown on their own roots: species, shrubs, old-fashioned and climbing.

Landford Trees

Landford Lodge, Landford, Salisbury, Wiltshire SP5 2EH
☎ 0794 390808   📠 0794 390037

CONTACT Mr C. D. Pilkington
OPEN 8 am – 5 pm, Monday – Friday
SPECIALITIES Hedging; trees
CATALOGUE On request
MAIL ORDER Yes; minimum order £15
SHOWS Courson

An interesting range of ornamental deciduous field-grown trees. In addition many species are now available

in containers, and they stock hedging and conifers too. On a different tack they sell stone urns. Group visits by arrangement.

Longhall Nursery

Stockton, Warminster, Wiltshire BA12 0SE
☎ 0985 50914

CONTACT Helen and James Dooley
LOCATION 14 miles north west of Salisbury on A36
OPEN 9.30 am – 6 pm, Wednesday – Sunday, 23 March to 2 October. Other times by appointment
CATALOGUE Large SAE
MAIL ORDER Yes
GARDEN Longhall Gardens

Formerly Green City Plants, now joining forces with Longhall Gardens. There's a good choice of lime tolerant plants, many propagated from the garden.

Special Plants

Laurels Farm, Upper Wraxall, Chippenham, Wiltshire SN14 7AG
☎ 0225 891686

CONTACT Ms Derry Watkins
LOCATION Near Bath
OPEN Most days: phone first
SPECIALITIES Conservatory plants
NEW FOR 1994 *Salvia greggii* 'Peach'; *Bacopa* 'Snowflake'; *Scutellaria origanifolia*
CATALOGUE 3 second class stamps
MAIL ORDER Yes; October to February
SHOWS RHS Westminster; Hampton Court

Special Plants concentrates on tender perennials, including *Felicia*, *Osteospermum* and *Scaevola*, and on conservatory climbers and small shrubs. One day courses are held at the nursery, and Ms Watkins organises specialist plant sales, including the London Rare Plant Fair.

The Mead Nursery

Brokerswood, Westbury, Wiltshire BA13 4EG
☎ 0373 859990

CONTACT Emma Lewis-Dale
LOCATION Near Rudge, off A36 or A361
OPEN 9 am – 5 pm, Wednesday – Saturday, and Bank Holiday Mondays; 12 – 6 pm, Sundays, 2 February to 30 October
SPECIALITIES Alpines; herbaceous perennials
CATALOGUE 4 first class stamps
MAIL ORDER No
GARDEN Display gardens
GIFT TOKENS Own

A mixed range of alpines and herbaceous perennials, including varieties suitable for trough and tufa plantings. Ready planted troughs and tufa are also on sale.

Walter T Ware Ltd

Woodborough Garden Centre & Nurseries, Nursery Farm, Woodborough, Pewsey, Wiltshire SN9 5PF
☎ 0672 851249

CONTACT Mrs Els Brewin
LOCATION 3 miles west of Pewsey
OPEN 9 am – 5 pm
MAIL ORDER No
GARDEN Demonstration gardens
GIFT TOKENS HTA

A garden centre on a large daffodil farm, and old flower nursery – Daffodil 'Fortune' was bred here. The garden centre specialises in clematis and spring bulbs. Pick your own fruit, vegetables and flowers.

West Kington Nurseries Ltd

West Kington, Chippenham, Wiltshire SN14 7JG
☎ 0249 782822   FAX 0249 782953

CONTACT Mrs Barbara Ellis
OPEN 10 am – 5 pm, Wednesday – Sunday
SPECIALITIES Alpines; herbaceous perennials; roses
NEW FOR 1994 Melianthus major
CATALOGUE On request (wholesale)
GARDEN Garden opens for NGS
DESIGN SERVICE West Kington Nurseries Ltd
SHOWS Malvern Spring

Wholesale nursery which deals in alpine and herbaceous plants. The attached retail plant centre also has a selection of old-fashioned and English roses, and topiary plants. They offer garden design and run courses.

Whitehall Garden Centre

Lacock, Chippenham, Wiltshire SN15 2LZ
☎ 0249 730204   FAX 0249 730755

LOCATION Between Chippenham and Melksham on A350
OPEN 9 am – 6 pm, daily
SHOP Garden sundries; conservatories; pools; gifts
REFRESHMENTS Restaurant
GARDEN 5 acre gardens
DESIGN SERVICE Whitehall Garden Centre
GIFT TOKENS HTA; own

Large family-run garden centre with plants and garden products. Extensive landscaped gardens, and a landscaping service in association with a local landscaping firm.

NORTH YORKSHIRE

Cruck Cottage Cacti

Cruck Cottage, Cliff Road, Wrelton, Pickering, North Yorkshire YO18 8PJ
☎ 0751 72042

CONTACT Ronald and Dorothy Wood
SPECIALITIES Cacti and succulents
MAIL ORDER No
GARDEN Display area

The nursery sells both large and small specimens of cacti and succulents, and has special collections for beginners. Advice is on hand from the owners, and the nursery is accessible for disabled visitors.

Daleside Nurseries

Ripon Road, Killinghall, Harrogate, North Yorkshire HG3 2AY
☎ 0423 506450   FAX 0423 527872

LOCATION 4 miles north of Harrogate
OPEN 9 am – 5 pm, Monday – Saturday; 10 am – 12 pm, 1.30 – 4.30 pm, Sundays
MAIL ORDER No
GIFT TOKENS HTA

A general plant range, including clematis, conifers and shrubs. They are happy to provide free advice on garden planning.

Deanswood Plants

Deanswood, Potteries Lane, Littlethorpe, Ripon, North Yorkshire HG4 3LF
☎ 0765 603441

CONTACT Jacky Barber
OPEN 10 am – 5 pm, April to September. Closed Mondays
SPECIALITIES Bog plants; flower arranging
CATALOGUE £1.30; list only, 40p
MAIL ORDER No
GARDEN 2 acre garden opens for NGS and Northern Horticultural Society

A nursery in a streamside garden, specialising in moisture loving plants. Open in the summer only. Also a flower arranging service with trained florists.

Gardenscape

Fairview, Smelthouses, Summerbridge, Harrogate, North Yorkshire HG3 4DH
☎ 0423 780291

CONTACT Michael D. Myers
LOCATION 12 miles north of Harrogate
OPEN By appointment only
SPECIALITIES Primulas
CATALOGUE 3 second class stamps
MAIL ORDER Yes
GARDEN Garden opens under NGS and by appointment
NCCPG NATIONAL COLLECTIONS Hepatica; Anemone nemorosa; Primula marginata

This specialist nursery is based around the three national collections held: *Anemone nemorosa*, *Primula marginata* and *Hepatica*. There are other interesting plants here too, though. They also sell hand made stone troughs and ornaments.

Hippopottering Nursery

Orchard House, Brackenhill Road, East Lound, Haxey, Doncaster, North Yorkshire DN9 2LR
☎ 0427 752185

CONTACT John and Margaret Gibbons
OPEN By appointment only
SPECIALITIES Acers
NEW FOR 1994 *Acer palmatum* 'Orange Dream'; high worked patio plants
CATALOGUE 2 first class stamps
MAIL ORDER Yes; after leaf fall
SHOWS Malvern Spring; Harrogate (Spring); BBC GW Live; Hampton Court; Harrogate (Autumn)

True specialists in Japanese maples: they sell nothing else. The list goes from selected colourful seedlings and bonsai material to mature specimens. Cultivars are selected from their collection of over 100; they also sell rootstocks. Phone between 8.30 am and 6.30 pm only.

Norden Alpine Nursery

Hirst Road, Carlton, Selby, North Yorkshire DN14 9PX
☎ 0405 861348

CONTACT Mrs N. Walton
OPEN Weekends and Bank Holidays, March – September
SPECIALITIES Alpines
MAIL ORDER No

A large range of alpines, including *Campanula*, *Oxalis*, *Primula* and *Saxifraga*. Bed and Breakfast is available at the nursery if you fancy a closer look.

Oak Tree Nursery

Mill Lane, Barlow, Selby, North Yorkshire YO8 8EY
☎ 0757 618409

CONTACT C. G. and G. M. Plowes
LOCATION 14 miles south of York
OPEN 10 am – 4.30 pm, Tuesday – Sunday. Closed Mondays
SPECIALITIES Herbaceous perennials
CATALOGUE 2 first class stamps
MAIL ORDER No

A range of cottage garden type plants, mainly herbaceous perennials.

Orchard House Nursery

Orchard House, Wormald Green, Harrogate, North Yorkshire HG3 3PX
☎ 0765 677541

CONTACT Brian Corner
LOCATION 4 miles south of Ripon on A61
OPEN 8.30 am – 5 pm, Monday – Saturday; 2 – 5 pm, Sundays. Closed Wednesdays
SPECIALITIES Herbaceous perennials
NEW FOR 1994 Many new plants
CATALOGUE 4 first class stamps
MAIL ORDER No
SHOWS Harrogate (Spring); Harrogate (Autumn)

A fairly new nursery with a mixed range of hardy perennials and cottage garden type plants.

Perry's Plants

River Garden, Sleights, Whitby, North Yorkshire YO21 1RR
☎ 0947 810329

CONTACT Mrs Patricia Perry
LOCATION 2 miles south west of Whitby, on B1410 (near A169)
OPEN 10 am – 5 pm, daily, Easter to October
SPECIALITIES Herbaceous perennials
NEW FOR 1994 *Erysimum* 'Perry's Peculiar'; *E.* 'Perry's Pumpkin'
CATALOGUE SAE
MAIL ORDER No
REFRESHMENTS Licensed café
GARDEN Riverside gardens

Herbaceous plants, including their own new cultivars and others which originated here (including *Osteospermum* 'Stardust'). Boats, putting and croquet in the old Victorian gardens.

R V Roger Ltd

The Nurseries, Pickering, North Yorkshire YO18 7HG
☎ 0751 72226   FAX 0751 76749

CONTACT Ian Roger
LOCATION 1 mile south of Pickering, on A169
OPEN 9 am – 5 pm, Monday – Saturday; 1 – 5 pm, Sundays
SPECIALITIES Fruit
CATALOGUE £1
MAIL ORDER Yes
SHOWS Southport; Chelsea; Hampton Court; Harrogate (Autumn)
GIFT TOKENS HTA
NCCPG NATIONAL COLLECTIONS *Erodium*

The nurseries have a good all-round range including alpines, bulbs, conifers, perennials, roses, and trees and shrubs. They are especially good on fruit trees and bushes, including apples and gooseberries.

Rarer Plants

Ashfield House, Austfield Lane, Monk Fryston, Leeds, North Yorkshire LS25 5EH
☎ 0977 682263

CONTACT Anne Watson and Mandy Nicholls
LOCATION 2½ miles from A1, A63 intersection
OPEN 9.30 am – 3.30 pm, Mondays, Fridays; 9.30 am – 5 pm, Saturday – Sunday, Easter to 13 September
SPECIALITIES Herbaceous perennials
NEW FOR 1994 *Iris sibirica* 'Clementine'
CATALOGUE SAE
MAIL ORDER No

A small nursery with an agreeably mixed stock which includes *Penstemon* hybrids and Ballard strain *Helleborus* hybrids. The nursery is specially open on Sundays from February to Easter for hellebores.

Rivendell Nursery

Menagerie Farm, Skipwith Road, Escrick, York, North Yorkshire YO4 6EH
☎ 0904 728690

CONTACT Dave Fryer and Gareth Hughes
LOCATION 6 miles south of York: phone for directions
OPEN 10 am – 5 pm, Sundays. Other times by appointment
NEW FOR 1994 Heathers
CATALOGUE 2 second class stamps
MAIL ORDER No

A small wholesale nursery which opens for retail customers on Sundays. The range includes alpines, conifers, heathers and shrubs. The nursery is run organically.

Stillingfleet Lodge Nurseries

Stillingfleet, North Yorkshire YO4 6HW
☎ 0904 728506   FAX 0904 728506

CONTACT Vanessa Cook
LOCATION 7 miles south of York: turn opposite the church
OPEN 10 am – 4 pm, Tuesday – Wednesday, Friday – Saturday, 1 April to 18 October
SPECIALITIES Herbaceous perennials
CATALOGUE 5 first class stamps
MAIL ORDER Yes; winter only
GARDEN Garden opens under NGS
NCCPG NATIONAL COLLECTIONS *Pulmonaria*

Small nursery with an interesting and extensive range of hardy perennials: good on grey foliage and pulmonarias. The garden is open on the second and fourth Wednesdays of May and June from 1 – 4 pm.

Strikes Garden Centre

York Road, Knaresborough, North Yorkshire HG5 0SP
☎ 0423 865351

LOCATION ½ mile east of Knaresborough
OPEN 9 am – 7 pm, Monday – Saturday; 10 am – 6 pm, Sundays, spring, summer; 9 am – 6 pm, Monday – Saturday; 10 am – 5 pm, Sundays, winter
SHOP Gifts
GIFT TOKENS HTA

Strikes Garden Centre

Boroughbridge Road, Northallerton, North Yorkshire DL7 8BN
☎ 0609 773694

LOCATION 1 mile from town centre, beyond the station
OPEN 9 am – 7 pm, Monday – Saturday; 10 am – 6 pm, Sundays, spring, summer; 9 am – 6 pm, Monday – Saturday; 10 am – 5 pm, Sundays, winter
SHOP Gifts
GIFT TOKENS HTA

Strikes Garden Centre

Meadowfields, Stokesley, North Yorkshire TS9 5HJ
☎ 0642 710419

OPEN 9 am – 7 pm, Monday – Saturday; 10 am – 6 pm, Sundays, spring, summer; 9 am – 6 pm, Monday – Saturday; 10 am – 5 pm, Sundays, winter
SHOP Gifts

Whitestone Gardens Ltd

Sutton under Whitestone Cliffe, Thirsk, North Yorkshire YO7 2PZ
☎ 0845 597467   FAX 0845 597467

CONTACT Roy Mottram
LOCATION 4 miles east of Thirsk on A170
OPEN Dawn till dusk, daily. Closed Fridays
SPECIALITIES Cacti and succulents
CATALOGUE 4 second class stamps
MAIL ORDER Yes
SHOP Books; sundries

A lengthy list of cacti and succulents is available at this specialist nursery. They also sell relevant books and sundries.

Wytherstone Nurseries

The Estate Office, Pockley, York, North Yorkshire YO6 5TE
☎ 0439 70012

CONTACT Ian Powell
LOCATION 3 miles from Helmsley, off A170
OPEN 10 am – 5 pm, Wednesday – Sunday, April to October
SPECIALITIES Pelargoniums

CATALOGUE 2 first class stamps
MAIL ORDER Yes: pelargoniums only

They specialise in pelargoniums, of which they have a large range. Also available at the nursery, but not by mail order, are other greenhouse and conservatory plants, hardy perennials and some shrubs. Duncombe Sawmill, under the same ownership, makes arches, troughs and seats.

SOUTH YORKSHIRE

Brambling House Alpines
119 Sheffield Road, Warmsworth, Doncaster, South Yorkshire DN4 9QX
☎ 0302 850730

CONTACT Jane McDonagh
LOCATION West of Doncaster on A630; near A1M Rotherham exit
OPEN 10 am – 6 pm. Closed Mondays except Bank Holidays
SPECIALITIES Alpines; sempervivums
NEW FOR 1994 New diascias and *Nemesia denticulata*
CATALOGUE SAE
MAIL ORDER Yes; spring and autumn

A small nursery concentrating on alpines. Look out for their saxifrages and a wide range of *Sempervivum* species and cultivars.

Chris Rodgerson
35 Lydgate Hall Crescent, Crosspool, Sheffield, South Yorkshire S10 5NE
☎ 0742 685533

CONTACT Chris Rodgerson
OPEN Mail order only
SPECIALITIES Cacti and succulents
CATALOGUE SAE; outside UK send 2 international reply coupons
MAIL ORDER Yes

This specialist nursery concentrates on *Conophytum* (as rooted or unrooted cuttings) and *Adromischus* (unrooted leaves). Much of the material is propagated from wild collected material, for which full data is available.

Ferndale Nursery and Garden Centre Ltd
Dyche Lane, Coal Aston, Sheffield, South Yorkshire S18 6AB
☎ 0246 412763

CONTACT Kevin Daniels
LOCATION On Sheffield's southern boundary, off the A61

OPEN 9 am – 5.30 pm (6 pm, March to September), daily
SHOP Florists; conservatories; greenhouses and garden buildings
REFRESHMENTS Coffee shop
DESIGN SERVICE Ferndale Nursery and Garden Centre Ltd
GIFT TOKENS HTA

A garden centre with a wide general range: stockists of both Hillier's and Blooms' plants. They have a garden design service, and can advise on plant ailments too. Talks, demonstrations and classes are also held.

WEST YORKSHIRE

Armitage's Garden Centre
Pennine Garden Centre, Huddersfield Road, Shelley, Huddersfield, West Yorkshire HD8 8LG
☎ 0484 607248   📠 0484 608673

CONTACT A. Harper
LOCATION Between Shelley and Skelmanthorpe on the B6116
OPEN 9 am – 5.30 pm, daily. Closes at 8 pm in the summer
SHOP Garden sundries; cut flowers
REFRESHMENTS Café

Long-established garden centre, stocking trees and shrubs, alpines, house plants, aquatics, greenhouses and garden machinery. Their specialist garden machinery outlet Mower World, is at the garden centre in Birchencliffe (off the A629).

Cravens Nursery
1 Foulds Terrace, Bingley, West Yorkshire BD16 4LZ
☎ 0274 561412

CONTACT Mr and Mrs Craven
OPEN Mail order only
SPECIALITIES *Dianthus*; primulas; seeds
CATALOGUE £1 each; £1.50 both (seed & plant)
MAIL ORDER Yes
SHOWS RHS Westminster; Malvern Spring; Harrogate (Spring); Chelsea

Their specialities are primroses and auriculas, and pinks, old and new. They also issue a separate seed catalogue devoted to primulas.

Greenslacks Nurseries
Ocot Lane, Scammonden, Huddersfield, West Yorkshire HD3 3FR
☎ 0484 842584

CONTACT Mrs V. K. Tuton

OPEN 10 am – 4 pm, March to October. Closed Mondays and Tuesdays
SPECIALITIES Alpines; primulas; sempervivums
CATALOGUE £1
MAIL ORDER Yes

An impressive and interesting list of alpines and hardy succulents. Strengths include saxifrages and sempervivums. Their ready made collections are good value.

Mansell & Hatcher Ltd

Cragg Wood Nurseries, Woodlands Drive, Rawdon, Leeds, West Yorkshire LS19 6LQ
☎ 0532 502016

CONTACT Allan Long
LOCATION Leave A658 at Apperley Bridge: follow signs to Woodlands Hospital
OPEN 9 am – 5 pm, Monday – Friday. Closed Bank Holidays. Open some weekends: phone for details
SPECIALITIES Orchids
CATALOGUE On request
MAIL ORDER Yes

Long-established orchid growers and hybridisers, with a large range of many genera, species and cultivars, including *Odontoglossum* and *Masdevallia*.

Newton Hill Alpines

335 Leeds Road, Newton Hill, Wakefield, West Yorkshire WF1 2JH
☎ 0924 377056

CONTACT Mrs Sheena Vigors
LOCATION 3 miles east of M1, J41
OPEN 9 am – 5 pm, daily. Closed Thursdays
SPECIALITIES Alpines
CATALOGUE 75p by post
MAIL ORDER No

This mainly wholesale alpine nursery welcomes retail customers too. They are good for saxifrages especially, and also have dwarf conifers and heathers.

Stephen H Smith's Garden & Leisure

Wharfe Valley, Pool Road, Otley, West Yorkshire LS21 1DY
☎ 0943 462195   FAX 0943 850074

CONTACT Peter Scott
LOCATION 1 mile east of Otley on A659
OPEN 9 am – 6 pm, summer; 9 am – 5.30 pm, winter
SHOP Garden sundries; furniture; aquatics; gifts
REFRESHMENTS Coffee shop
GIFT TOKENS HTA

Garden centre with indoor and outdoor plants and garden products. Delivery service.

Stephen H Smith's Garden & Leisure

Aire Valley, Wilsden Road, Harden, Bingley, West Yorkshire BD16 1BL
☎ 0535 274653   FAX 0535 274691

CONTACT Richard Coggill
LOCATION Take Wilsden road from B6429 in Harden
OPEN 9 am – 6 pm, summer; 9 am – 5.30 pm, winter
SHOP Garden sundries; furniture; aquatics; gifts
REFRESHMENTS Coffee shop
GIFT TOKENS HTA

Garden centre with plants and garden products. Delivery service.

Strikes Garden Centre

Red Hall Lane, Wellington Hill, Leeds, West Yorkshire LS17 8NA
☎ 0532 657839

LOCATION Wetherby Road, Leeds
OPEN 9 am – 7 pm, Monday – Saturday; 10 am – 6 pm, Sundays, spring, summer; 9 am – 6 pm, Monday – Saturday; 10 am – 5 pm, Sundays, winter
SHOP Gifts
GIFT TOKENS HTA

Strikes Garden Centre

Selby Road, Swillington Common, Leeds, West Yorkshire LS15 4LQ
☎ 0532 862981

LOCATION Between Leeds and Selby
OPEN 9 am – 7 pm, Monday – Saturday; 10 am – 6 pm, Sundays, spring, summer; 9 am – 6 pm, Monday – Saturday; 10 am – 5 pm, Sundays, winter
SHOP Gifts
GIFT TOKENS HTA

Totties Nursery

Greenhill Bank Road, Totties, Holmfirth, Huddersfield, West Yorkshire HD7 1UN
☎ 0484 683363   FAX 0484 688129

CONTACT David A. Shires
LOCATION On the edge of the Pennines
OPEN 9 am – 5 pm, daily
MAIL ORDER No
GIFT TOKENS HTA

The wide range here includes shrubs, conifers, alpines and herbaceous plants.

Zephyrwude Irises

48 Blacker Lane, Crigglestone, Wakefield, West Yorkshire WF4 3EW
☎ 0924 252101

CONTACT Richard L. Brook
LOCATION 1 mile south west of M1, J39, off A636

OPEN For collection, by appointment in August and September
SPECIALITIES Irises
NEW FOR 1994 New imports every year
CATALOGUE 1 first class stamp (between April and September)
MAIL ORDER Yes; minimum order £10
GARDEN Trial fields

Specialist growers and importers of modern bearded irises. The range concentrates on miniature and standard dwarf, intermediate, and miniature tall types. There is a selection of border and tall bearded irises too. The list appears in April, for collection or despatch in August and September. The trial fields are open in May and June, 9 am till dusk, but check first.

WALES

CLWYD

Aberconwy Nursery

Graig, Glan Conwy, Colwyn Bay, Clwyd LL28 5TL
☎ 0492 580875

CONTACT K. G. or R. Lever
LOCATION South of Glan Conwy, 2nd right off A470. Turn right at top of hill: nursery is on the right
OPEN 9 am – 5 pm, Tuesday – Sunday. Closed Mondays, except Bank Holidays
SPECIALITIES Alpines
NEW FOR 1994 *Gentiana* 'Shot Silk'; *Gentiana* 'Indigo'; *Helianthemum* 'Silvery Salmon'; *Helianthemum* 'Firegold'; *Cistus salviifolius* 'Avalanche'
CATALOGUE 2 second class stamps
MAIL ORDER No
GARDEN Their own garden, Bryn Meifod, opens under the National Gardens Scheme: 2 – 5 pm, Thursdays (May, September), Sundays (June, August)

Mainly alpines, including some interesting primroses, but there are also trees, shrubs and herbaceous plants. They exhibit at several Alpine Garden Society Shows.

Bodnant Garden Nursery Ltd

Tal-y-Cafn, Colwyn Bay, Clwyd LL29 6DG
☎ 0492 650460 📠 0492 650448

CONTACT Mrs A. Harvey
LOCATION Next to Bodnant Garden, near A55
OPEN 9.30 am – 5 pm, daily
SPECIALITIES Camellias; rhododendrons; shrubs; trees
CATALOGUE 3 second class stamps
MAIL ORDER Yes; £10 minimum order

GARDEN Bodnant Gardens, Clwyd, see Gardens section

The nursery specialises in those plants for which the garden is renowned – rhododendrons, azaleas, magnolias and camellias. There is much else of interest in the wide choice of trees and shrubs here.

C & K Jones

Halghton Nursery, Whitchurch Road, Halghton, Bangor on Dee, Clwyd SY14 7LX
☎ 094874 685

CONTACT Richard Parker
LOCATION Between Whitchurch and Bangor on Dee, on A525
OPEN 9 am – 5 pm, daily
SPECIALITIES Roses
CATALOGUE £1
MAIL ORDER Yes

C & K Jones's new plant centre. The rose crop is produced here. There are shrubs and conifers on sale too. See C & K Jones, Cheshire for more details.

Celyn Vale Nurseries

Allt-y-Celyn, Carrog, Corwen, Clwyd LL21 9LD
☎ 0490 83671 📠 0490 83671

CONTACT Andrew McConnell
LOCATION 3 miles east of Corwen, near A5
OPEN 9 am – 5.30 pm, Monday – Friday
SPECIALITIES Trees; *Eucalyptus*; acacias
CATALOGUE 1 first class stamp
MAIL ORDER Yes; minimum order 3 plants; p & p is included

Specialist growers of *Eucalyptus* and acacias: they use seed from high altitude specimens to maximise hardiness.

Dibleys

Efenechtyd Nurseries, Llanelidan, Ruthin, Clwyd LL15 2LG
☎ 0978 88677

OPEN 9 am – 5 pm, daily, April to September
SPECIALITIES Begonias; house plants; *Streptocarpus*
CATALOGUE SAE
MAIL ORDER Yes
SHOWS Malvern Spring; Southport; Chelsea; Hampton Court

Varieties and species of *Streptocarpus* are the main speciality here, but the choice extends to other gesneriads and foliage begonias. Active on the show circuit: they attend more than 50 each year.

Paul Christian Rare Plants

P O Box 468, Wrexham, Clwyd LL13 9XR
☎ 0978 366399   📠 0978 366399

CONTACT Dr P. J. Christian
OPEN Mail order only
SPECIALITIES Bulbs
NEW FOR 1994 List changes constantly
CATALOGUE 3 first class stamps; May, December
MAIL ORDER Yes

Bulb, corm and tuber specialist. An exciting range of
rare and enticing small, hardy bulbs and greenhouse
subjects. The list changes annually according to the
availability of new and rediscovered items. An illustrated book going into more detail than the catalogues
is newly published.

DYFED

Cilwern Plants

Cilwern, Talley, Llandeilo, Dyfed SA19 7YH
☎ 0558 685526

CONTACT Anne Knatchbull-Hugessen
LOCATION 6 miles north of Llandeilo on B4302, be-
fore Talley village
OPEN 11 am – 6 pm, daily. Closed Fridays
SPECIALITIES Herbaceous perennials
CATALOGUE 2 first class stamps
MAIL ORDER Yes; minimum order £10
GARDEN 2 acre garden being created from scrubland

The nursery sells a range of hardy perennials, including
geraniums. There are also shrubs and conifers. A demonstration garden is being formed from the surrounding
scrub and swamp.

Wyevale Garden Centre

Myrtle Hill, Pensarn, Camarthen, Dyfed SA31 2NG
☎ 0267 221363   📠 0267 221316

Wyevale Garden Centre

Bynea, Llanelli, Dyfed SA14 9ST
☎ 0554 772189   📠 0554 777938

MID GLAMORGAN

Wyevale Garden Centre

Village Farm Industrial Estate, Pyle, Mid Glamorgan
CF33 6NU
☎ 0656 741443   📠 0656 744693

WEST GLAMORGAN

Wyevale Garden Centre

Valley Way, Swansea Enterprise Park, Morriston,
Swansea, West Glamorgan SA6 8QP
☎ 0792 310052   📠 0792 310608

GWENT

Waterwheel Nursery

Bully Hole Bottom, Shirenewton, Chepstow, Gwent
NP6 6SA
☎ 0291 641577

CONTACT Desmond and Charlotte Evans
LOCATION Turn off B4235 (Chepstow to Usk road)
OPEN 9 am – 6 pm, Monday – Saturday
SPECIALITIES Climbers; herbaceous perennials;
shrubs; trees
CATALOGUE 2 first class stamps
MAIL ORDER Yes; winter only
GARDEN Garden around mill buildings

A wide and interesting choice of perennials, trees and
shrubs for different situations. Most of the plants can
be seen in the garden. You are advised to phone first if
you are travelling far.

Wye Valley Herbs

The Nurtons, Tintern, Gwent NP6 7NX
☎ 0291 689253

CONTACT A. and E. Wood
LOCATION 7 miles north of M4, J22 Opposite 'Old
Station Tintern' on A466
OPEN 10.30 am – 5 pm, daily
SPECIALITIES Herbs
NEW FOR 1994 Many new items
CATALOGUE 3 first class stamps
MAIL ORDER No
GARDEN Herb garden

A large collection of organically grown herbs, with
some perennials and shrubs. All carry the Soil Association symbol.

Wyevale Garden Centre

Newport Road, Castleton, Cardiff, Gwent CF3 8UQ
☎ 0633 680002   📠 0633 680769

GWYNEDD

Crûg Farm Plants

Griffith's Crossing, Caernarfon, Gwynedd LL55 1TU
☎ 0248 670232   📠 0248 670232

CONTACT Bleddyn Wynn-Jones
LOCATION 2 miles north east of Caernarfon, off A487
OPEN 10 am – 6 pm, Thursday – Sunday, and Bank Holidays
SPECIALITIES Shade loving plants
NEW FOR 1994 Many new items
CATALOGUE SAE plus 1 second class stamp
MAIL ORDER No
GARDEN Garden opens for NGS

The nursery is unusual in specialising in plants for shade: perennials, shrubs and climbers. Watch out for the fruits of recent collecting expeditions to Korea and Taiwan.

Gwydir Plants

Plas Muriau, Betws-y-coed, Gwynedd LL24 0HD
☎ 0690 710201   ⟨FAX⟩ 0690 6379

CONTACT Mrs D. Southgate and Mrs L. Schärer
LOCATION ¼ mile north of Waterloo Bridge, towards Llanrwst on A470
OPEN 11 am – 6 pm, Tuesday – Sunday, and Bank Holidays, March to October
SPECIALITIES Herbs; wild flowers
CATALOGUE 2 first class stamps
MAIL ORDER No
GARDEN Plas Muriau garden is open under the NGS at the same times

This small nursery specialises in herbs, wild flowers and cottage garden plants. They can supply collections for school projects.

Henllys Lodge Plants

Henllys Lodge, Beaumaris, Anglesey, Gwynedd LL58 8HU
☎ 0248 810106

CONTACT Mrs E. Lane
OPEN 11 am – 5 pm, daily. Closed Tuesdays and Thursdays
SPECIALITIES Herbaceous perennials
CATALOGUE 2 first class stamps
MAIL ORDER No
GARDEN Woodland garden open under National Gardens Scheme (18 – 19 June) and by appointment

The nursery stocks a selection of cottage garden type perennials including hardy geraniums and plants for shade. They run half day workshops for small groups on planning and planting a garden, and their own garden is also open.

Holland Arms Garden Centre

Gaerwen, Anglesey, Gwynedd LL60 6LA
☎ 0248 421655

CONTACT Miss Susan Knock
LOCATION On A5 in central Anglesey

OPEN 9 am – 5.30 pm, Monday – Saturday; 10 am – 5.30 pm, Sundays and Bank Holidays
REFRESHMENTS Restaurant
GARDEN Demonstration gardens
GIFT TOKENS HTA

Large, family run garden centre, with indoor and outdoor plants. Hillier Premier Collection agent. The very large Christmas display includes a bilingual Santa.

Ty'r Orsaf Nursery

Maentwrog Road Station, Ty Nant, Gellilydan, Gwynedd LL41 4RB
☎ 076685 233

CONTACT Tony and Molly Faulkner
LOCATION Between Trawsfynydd and Ffestiniog on A470
OPEN 10 am – 7 pm, summer; 10 am – dusk, winter
SPECIALITIES Alpines; herbaceous perennials
CATALOGUE 5 second class stamps
MAIL ORDER Yes; no minimum charge

A pleasantly mixed collection of garden-worthy alpines, hardy perennials and shrubs.

SCOTLAND

BORDERS

Pringle Plants

Groom's Cottage, Kirklands, Ancrum, Jedburgh, Borders TD8 6UJ
☎ 08353 354

CONTACT Dr Jan Boyd
LOCATION Scottish borders
OPEN By appointment only
SPECIALITIES Alpines
CATALOGUE 2 second class stamps
MAIL ORDER Yes; no minimum order

A small nursery which concentrates on dwarf forms of shrubs, conifers, bulbs, alpines and herbaceous plants. Orders can be collected from shows (including the Royal Highland and the Great Yorkshire) by arrangement.

CENTRAL

Blairhoyle Nursery

East Lodge, Blairhoyle, Port of Menteith, Stirling, Central FK8 3LF
☎ 0877 385669

CONTACT Mrs B. A. Cartwright

OPEN 10 am – 5.30 pm, Monday, Thursday, Friday, Saturday; 12 – 5 pm, Wednesday, Sunday. Closed Tuesdays
SPECIALITIES Alpines; heathers
CATALOGUE SAE
MAIL ORDER No
GARDEN Demonstration gardens
DESIGN SERVICE Blairhoyle Nursery

They grow a range of alpines and dwarf conifers, with an emphasis on heathers (200). A design service is available.

DUMFRIES & GALLOWAY

British Wild Plants

Stockerton Nursery, Kirkcudbright, Galloway, Dumfries & Galloway DG6 4XS
☎ 0557 31226

CONTACT Martin Gould
SPECIALITIES Wild flowers
CATALOGUE 3 first class stamps for guide to garden use of plants
MAIL ORDER Yes

A small nursery with a range of native wild plants for a variety of habitats, including aquatic, coastal, meadow and hedgerow, and woodland. Their stock includes bulbs, trees and shrubs.

Cally Gardens

Gatehouse of Fleet, Castle Douglas, Dumfries & Galloway DG7 2DJ

CONTACT Michael Wickenden
LOCATION 12 miles west of Castle Douglas, on A75
OPEN 10 am – 5.30 pm, Saturday – Sunday only, Easter to mid October
SPECIALITIES Herbaceous perennials
NEW FOR 1994 Each catalogue is substantially different
CATALOGUE 3 first class stamps; November
MAIL ORDER Yes; £10 minimum order; spring despatch
GARDEN Eighteenth century walled garden opens for SGS

A nursery for the horticultural avant-garde. It specialises in perennials from collected and botanic garden seed. Culled from a collection of over 3,000 varieties, the catalogue changes by as much as half each year.

Charter House Hardy Plant Nursery

2 Nunwood, Dumfries DG2 0HX
☎ 0387 720363

CONTACT John Ross
OPEN 10 am – 5 pm, Saturday – Sunday. Also in Scottish school holidays and by appointment
SPECIALITIES Herbaceous perennials
NEW FOR 1994 *Geranium shikokianum* ssp. *yoshianum*; *Geranium gymnocaulon*; *Erodium* 'Helen'
CATALOGUE 3 first class stamps
MAIL ORDER Yes
GARDEN Demonstration gardens partly built
NCCPG NATIONAL COLLECTIONS *Erodium*

Here are hardy geraniums and erodiums in abundance, plus a selection of other herbaceous and alpine plants.

Craigieburn Classic Plants

Craigieburn House, By Moffat, Dumfriesshire, Dumfries & Galloway DG10 9LF
☎ 0683 21250

CONTACT Janet Wheatcroft and Bill Chudziak
LOCATION 2 miles east of Moffat, near A74
OPEN 12.30 – 8 pm, Easter to October
SPECIALITIES Herbaceous perennials; primulas
NEW FOR 1994 Many new varieties
CATALOGUE 4 first class stamps; October
MAIL ORDER Yes; minimum order £15; spring only
GARDEN Craigieburn Woodland Garden, admission £1.50

Set in the garden, the nursery carries an attractive range of perennials, with an emphasis on woodlanders. *Meconopsis* and primulas are among the specialities.

J Tweedie Fruit Trees

Maryfield Road Nursery, Maryfield, Terregles, Dumfries & Galloway DG2 9TX
☎ 0387 720880

CONTACT John Tweedie
LOCATION 3 miles from Dumfries, between Newbridge and Terregles
OPEN 9.30 am – 2.30 pm, Saturdays, October to March. Other times by appointment
SPECIALITIES Fruit
NEW FOR 1994 Blackcurrant 'Ben Connan'
CATALOGUE SAE
MAIL ORDER Yes

A good choice of fruit trees and bushes in new varieties, with some old ones also in the list. During the season fresh soft fruit can be bought.

Whitehills Nurseries

Minnigaff, Newton Stewart, Dumfries & Galloway DG8 6SL
☎ 0671 402049   FAX 0671 403106

CONTACT Tony Weston
LOCATION 1 mile north of Creebridge, towards Wood of Cree

OPEN 8.30 am – 4.30 pm, Monday – Friday. Other times by appointment
SPECIALITIES Rhododendrons
CATALOGUE 50p
MAIL ORDER Yes; minimum order £10
GARDEN Woodland and water garden open for SGS

Specialists for rhododendrons and azaleas: they have a wide choice of other trees and shrubs also. The garden admission of £1.50 is refundable against nursery purchases.

FIFE

Dalgety Bay Garden Centre
Western Approach Road, Dalgety Bay, Fife KY11 5XP
☎ 0383 823841

CONTACT Laura Hastie
GIFT TOKENS HTA

A Dobbies garden centre.

Roots Garden Centre Ltd
1 Caskieberran Road, Glenrothes, Fife KY6 2NR
☎ 0592 756407   ✆ 0592 758973

CONTACT Andrew Butchart (Manager)
LOCATION Opposite Saltire Centre
OPEN 8.30 am – 5.30 pm, Monday – Friday; 9 am – 5.30 pm, Saturdays; 10 am – 5.30 pm, Sundays
SHOP Garden sundries; furniture; buildings; florist
DESIGN SERVICE Roots Garden Centre Ltd
GIFT TOKENS HTA

Garden centre with a full range of plants and products. They offer design and landscaping (interior and exterior) and daily delivery.

GRAMPIAN

Ben Reid & Co
Pinewood Park Nurseries, Countesswells Road, Aberdeen, Grampian AB9 2QL
☎ 0224 318744   ✆ 0224 310104

CONTACT Mr Shand
LOCATION Aberdeen
OPEN Garden Centre open 9 am – 5 pm, Monday – Saturday; 10 am – 5 pm, Sundays
SPECIALITIES Hedging; shrubs; trees
CATALOGUE On request
MAIL ORDER Yes; £10 minimum order
GIFT TOKENS HTA

Large wholesale nursery which specialises in coniferous and deciduous forest trees, hedging, ornamental

trees and shrubs. Their retail plant centre carries a good general range.

Findlay Clark (Aberdeen)
Hazeldene Road, Hazlehead, Aberdeen, Grampian AB9 2QU
☎ 0224 318658   ✆ 0224 325029

CONTACT Henry Brown
LOCATION Off Queen's Road
OPEN 9 am – 5.30 pm, daily
SHOP Gifts; floral art
GIFT TOKENS HTA

A Findlay Clark garden centre. Delivery is available.

James Cocker & Sons
Whitemyres, Lang Stracht, Aberdeen, Grampian AB9 2XH
☎ 0224 313261   ✆ 0224 312531

OPEN 9 am – 5 pm, daily
SPECIALITIES Roses
NEW FOR 1994 3 new roses
CATALOGUE On request; May
MAIL ORDER Yes; no minimum order
SHOP Garden centre
REFRESHMENTS Refreshments
SHOWS RHS Westminster
GIFT TOKENS HTA

Rose breeders and growers, with a garden centre too. They have an all-round range of roses, but the emphasis is on the modern, shorter varieties. The firm holds a royal warrant.

T & W Christie (Forres) Ltd
The Nurseries and Garden Centre, Forres, Moray, Grampian IV36 0EA
☎ 0309 672633   ✆ 0309 676846

CONTACT Mr Williamson (advice); Mrs Maclachlan, Mrs Jenkins (orders)
LOCATION Invererne Road, Forres
OPEN 8 am – 5 pm, Monday – Friday; 8 am – 12 pm, Saturdays. Closed Sundays
SPECIALITIES Hedging; shrubs; trees
CATALOGUE On request
MAIL ORDER Yes
GIFT TOKENS HTA

Large and long-established nursery and garden centre. A wide range of trees and shrubs, from woodland and hedging species to ornamental varieties. Some fruit trees also.

Tough Alpine Nursery
Westhaybogs, Tough, Alford, Aberdeenshire, Grampian AB33 8DU
☎ 09755 62783   ✆ 09755 62783

CONTACT   Fred Carrie
OPEN   10 am – 5 pm, February to October
SPECIALITIES   Alpines
CATALOGUE   3 second class stamps
MAIL ORDER   Yes; minimum order £10

Retail and wholesale alpine nursery producing a wide range of very hardy alpines in this chilly area.

HIGHLAND

Abriachan Gardens & Nursery

Abriachan Nurseries, Loch Ness Side,
Inverness-shire, Highland IV3 6LA
☎ 046386 232

CONTACT   Mrs & Mrs Davidson
LOCATION   9 miles south of Inverness, on A82
OPEN   9 am – 7 pm, daily
SPECIALITIES   Herbaceous perennials; primulas
CATALOGUE   4 first class stamps
MAIL ORDER   Yes; no minimum order
GARDEN   Large garden open under SGS

Mainly perennials, with a large choice of primroses, particularly the Barnhaven strains. Other interesting ranges including helianthemums and hebes.

Arivegaig Nursery

Acharacle, Argyll, Highland PH36 4LE
☎ 096785 331

CONTACT   Mr E. Stewart
LOCATION   Ardnamurchan peninsula, Argyll
OPEN   9 am – 5 pm (or dusk if earlier), daily, Easter to October
SPECIALITIES   Half-hardy plants
CATALOGUE   4 first class stamps
MAIL ORDER   Yes; p & p at cost

The nursery stocks a general range of all plant types, with a particular emphasis on those which flourish in the milder west coast climate.

Evelix Daffodils

Aird Asaig, Evelix, Dornoch, Sutherland, Highland
IV25 3NG
☎ 0862 810715

CONTACT   D. C. MacArthur
LOCATION   Off A9 at Evelix filling station
OPEN   By appointment
SPECIALITIES   Daffodils
NEW FOR 1994   Ask in May
CATALOGUE   3 first class stamps
MAIL ORDER   Yes; minimum order £5

Daffodil breeder with an interesting small range of novelty, exhibition and garden varieties. The 1994 introductions, part of an extensive breeding programme, will be registered in May. Sutherland Soil Services operates from the same address.

Garden Cottage Nursery

Tournaig, Poolewe, Achnasheen, Ross-shire,
Highland IV22 2LH
☎ 044586 339

CONTACT   Ron and Lesley Rushbrooke
LOCATION   1½ miles north of Inverewe Gardens
OPEN   12 pm – 7 pm, Monday – Saturday, March to October
SPECIALITIES   Alpines; heathers; herbaceous perennials; shrubs
NEW FOR 1994   Many new items
CATALOGUE   3 first class stamps; September
MAIL ORDER   Yes; minimum order £10
GARDEN   Rocky garden surrounds the nursery

This small nursery carries a general range, and specialises in those plants which thrive in the mild, moist climate. Mature specimens from the list can be seen in the garden.

Jack Drake

Inshriach Alpine Nursery, Aviemore, Inverness-shire, Highland PH22 1QS
☎ 0540 651287   📠 0540 651656

CONTACT   J. C. Lawson
OPEN   9 am – 5 pm Monday – Friday; 9 am – 4 pm, Saturdays. Closed Sundays
SPECIALITIES   Alpines; seeds
CATALOGUE   £1
MAIL ORDER   Yes; no minimum order
GIFT TOKENS   HTA

Highland nursery devoted to alpine and rock garden plants, including species for wild and bog gardens. A seed list is also available, with about 300 items.

Poyntzfield Herb Nursery

Black Isle, Dingwall, Ross-shire, Highland IV7 8LX
☎ 0381 610352   📠 0381 610352

CONTACT   Duncan Ross
OPEN   1 – 5 pm, Monday – Friday
SPECIALITIES   Herbs
CATALOGUE   SAE plus 3 first class stamps
MAIL ORDER   Yes

This range of herbs and aromatic plants from the north of Scotland is grown with an eye on hardiness and vigour as well as scent and flavour.

Speyside Heather Centre

Dulnain Bridge, Inverness-shire, Highland PH26 3PA
☎ 047985 359   📠 047985 396

CONTACT   David and Betty Lambie
LOCATION   Between Aviemore and Grantown on Spey, off A95
OPEN   9 am – 6 pm, Monday – Saturday; 10 am – 5.30 pm, Sundays
SPECIALITIES   Heathers
CATALOGUE   £2.25 booklet
MAIL ORDER   Yes
SHOP   Crafts; garden sundries
REFRESHMENTS   Tea room
GARDEN   Gardens
GIFT TOKENS   Own

Garden centre which specialises in heathers and heather gardening. They have other plants, sundries, crafts and a tearoom with dumplings as its speciality.

Uzumara Orchids
9 Port Henderson, Gairloch, Ross-shire, Highland IV21 2AS
☎ 044583 228

CONTACT   Mrs I. F. La Croix
LOCATION   8 miles south west of Gairloch
OPEN   By appointment
SPECIALITIES   Orchids; *Streptocarpus*
CATALOGUE   SAE
MAIL ORDER   Yes

A highly specialised nursery offering species orchids from Africa and Madagascar, most of them seed raised. They also have an exceptional choice of *Streptocarpus* species. Still quite new: the range will expand.

LOTHIAN

Belwood Nurseries Ltd
Mauricewood Mains, Penicuik, Midlothian, Lothian EH26 0NJ
☎ 0968 673621   📠 0968 678354

CONTACT   Ron Low (Sales Manager)
LOCATION   Penicuik and Meigle, Tayside
OPEN   By appointment only
SPECIALITIES   Conifers; trees
CATALOGUE   On request
MAIL ORDER   Yes

A large wholesale nursery, with some 300 acres under production. Retail customers must make as appointment before visiting. The main production site is at Meigle. Trees, shrubs and conifers are available rootballed or container-grown. They specialise in semimature specimens.

Bonsai
81 Bruntsfield Place, Edinburgh, Lothian EH10 4HG
☎ 031 229 0539   📠 0337 30218

CONTACT   Andrew McLennan
OPEN   9 am – 5.30 pm
SPECIALITIES   Bonsai
CATALOGUE   On request
SHOP   Five shops

A chain of five shops which sell bonsai specimens and bonsai accessories. Contact head office for details.

Dobbie & Co Ltd, Melville Garden Centre
Melville Nursery, Lasswade, Midlothian, Lothian EH18 1AZ
☎ 031 663 1941   📠 031 654 2548

CONTACT   J. H. Trotter
LOCATION   Dalkeith
OPEN   8.30 am – 5 pm, Monday – Friday; 9 am – 5 pm, Saturdays; 10 am – 5 pm, Sundays
CATALOGUE   No
SHOP   Garden sundries; buildings; machinery; landscape materials
REFRESHMENTS   Tea room
GARDEN   Demonstration gardens
DESIGN SERVICE   Dobbies Landscape Ltd
GIFT TOKENS   HTA

Large garden centre, part of the Dobbies chain. As well as hardy nursery stock and associated garden products, the site includes a bird of prey centre and a butterfly and insect exhibition.

Melville Nurseries
Lasswade, Midlothian, Lothian EH18 1AZ
☎ 031 663 1944   📠 031 654 2548

CONTACT   J. D. K. Barnes
LOCATION   Dalkeith
OPEN   8.30 am – 5.30 pm, Monday – Friday
SPECIALITIES   Conifers; Rhododendrons
CATALOGUE   Yes

Wholesale only. Large nursery which specialises in deciduous azaleas and rhododendrons. Specimen shrubs and conifers are available in containers from 20 to 130 litres.

STRATHCLYDE

Ardencaple Garden Centre
Rhu Road Higher, Helensburgh, Strathclyde G84 8JT
☎ 0436 71202

CONTACT   The Manager
GIFT TOKENS   HTA

A Dobbies garden centre.

Ballagan Nursery

Gartocharn Road, Alexandria, Dunbartonshire,
Strathclyde G83 8NB
☎ 0389 52947   📠 0389 52947

CONTACT   Mr Stephenson
LOCATION   Between Balloch and Gartocharn on
A811
OPEN   9 am – 6 pm, daily
SPECIALITIES   Trees
SHOP   Garden centre
GIFT TOKENS   HTA

Garden centre and nursery dealing in bedding plants,
unusual hardy shrubs and trees (including feathered
specimens).

Chatelherault Garden Centre

Chatelherault Country Park, Ferniegair, Hamilton,
Lanarkshire, Strathclyde ML3 7UE
☎ 0698 457700

CONTACT   The Manager
GIFT TOKENS   HTA

A Dobbies garden centre.

Duncans of Milngavie

Flower & Garden Centre, 101 Main Street,
Milngavie, Glasgow, Strathclyde G62 6JJ
☎ 041 956 2377   📠 041 956 6649

CONTACT   Andrew N. Duncan
OPEN   8.30 am – 5.30 pm, Monday – Saturday; 10 am
– 5 pm, Sundays
SHOP   Florist; garden sundries and furniture
REFRESHMENTS   Tea room
GIFT TOKENS   HTA

Garden centre with a comprehensive choice of indoor
and outdoor plants and associated products. Daily delivery. Annual Christmas event in late November, including a Bavarian band.

Findlay Clark Limited

Boclair Road, Milngavie, Glasgow, Strathclyde
G62 6EP
☎ 0360 620721   📠 0360 622833

CONTACT   Mr David Monaghan
LOCATION   At Allander Toll roundabout, on B8049
OPEN   9 am – 9 pm, summer; 9 am – 6 pm, winter
SHOP   Gifts; floral art
GIFT TOKENS   HTA

A Findlay Clark garden centre. Delivery is available.

Kinlochlaich House Gardens

Appin, Argyll, Strathclyde PA38 4BD
☎ 063173 342   📠 063173 482

CONTACT   D. E. Hutchison MIHort.
OPEN   9 am – 5.30 pm, summer; 9 am – 4.45 pm, winter
CATALOGUE   No
MAIL ORDER   No
GARDEN   Kinlochlaich House Gardens
DESIGN SERVICE   Kinlochlaich House Gardens
GIFT TOKENS   Own

A garden centre which prides itself on its enormous
range of hardy garden plants across the whole spectrum
from alpines to trees.

P A Jordan

Kittoch Mill, Carmunnock, Glasgow, Strathclyde
G76 9BJ
☎ 041 644 4712

CONTACT   P. A. Jordan
LOCATION   Off Busby to Carmunnock road
OPEN   By appointment only: phone first
SPECIALITIES   Herbaceous perennials
NEW FOR 1994   New American *Hosta*
MAIL ORDER   No
GARDEN   Display gardens
NCCPG NATIONAL COLLECTIONS   *Hosta*

They specialise in hostas, with new American cultivars
coming soon. Some other perennials too. The annual
open day for garden and nursery is 12 June, and recommended viewing times are between late May and late
July.

Westerwood Garden Centre

Eastfield Road, Westerwood, Cumbernauld,
Strathclyde G68 0EB
☎ 0236 736100

CONTACT   Colin Watt
GIFT TOKENS   HTA

A Dobbies garden centre.

TAYSIDE

Angus Heathers

10 Guthrie Street, Letham, Tayside DD8 2PS
☎ 0307 818504

CONTACT   David Sturrock
LOCATION   Forfar, by Dundee
OPEN   9 am – 5 pm, daily
SPECIALITIES   Heathers; gentians
MAIL ORDER   No
GARDEN   Demonstration garden

As well as heathers they stock a range of gentians, and a number of dwarf and slow-growing conifers which make good companions for heathers.

Bonhard Nursery
Murrayshall Road, Scone, Perth, Tayside PH2 7PQ
☎ 0738 52791   📠 0738 52791

CONTACT   Mr C. and Mrs P. Hickman
LOCATION   Between Perth and New Scone. Turn right off A94; continue for 1 mile
OPEN   10 am – 6 pm (or dusk if sooner)
SPECIALITIES   Fruit; roses
CATALOGUE   Rose and fruit tree lists only
MAIL ORDER   No; but ask for shrub roses
REFRESHMENTS   Tea room
GIFT TOKENS   Own

Just outside Perth, this nursery stocks a general range of plants, with the emphasis on old shrub roses and fruit trees.

Glendoick Gardens Ltd
Glendoick, Perth, Tayside PH2 7NS
☎ 073886 205/ 073886 260   📠 073886 735
LOCATION   7 miles from Perth, on A85
OPEN   9 am – 5 pm, winter; 9 am – 6 pm, summer
SPECIALITIES   Primulas; rhododendrons
NEW FOR 1994   New rhododendrons and azaleas
CATALOGUE   £1 in stamps
MAIL ORDER   Yes
GARDEN   Glendoick Gardens, Tayside, see Gardens section
GIFT TOKENS   HTA

The garden centre is open daily at the times shown: the gardens open on four Sundays in May. Glendoick are specialist growers of rhododendrons and other ericaceous shrubs, with a large and impressive collection, including new hybrids. Among the short list of other plants there are a number of interesting Asiatic primulas from collected seed.

Kinross Garden Centre and Butterfly House
Turfhills, Kinross, Tayside KY13 7NQ
☎ 0577 863327   📠 0577 863442

CONTACT   Stephen Cowan
LOCATION   Off M9, J6
OPEN   9 am – 5.30 pm, daily
SHOP   Gifts; floral art
GIFT TOKENS   HTA

A Findlay Clark garden centre. Delivery is available.

Perth Garden Centre
Crieff Road, Perth, Tayside PH1 2NR
☎ 0738 38555

CONTACT   Alastair Brown
GIFT TOKENS   HTA

A Dobbies garden centre.

NORTHERN IRELAND

CO. ANTRIM

Carncairn Daffodils
Carncairn Grange, Brouhghshane, Ballymena, Co. Antrim BT43 7HF
☎ 0266 861216

CONTACT   Mrs R. H. Reade
LOCATION   5 miles from Ballymena, just outside Broughshane
SPECIALITIES   Daffodils
CATALOGUE   On request; March
MAIL ORDER   Yes

Raisers and growers of daffodils for exhibition use and garden display. Present at the Belfast Show and most other Northern Ireland shows.

Colemans Nurseries
6 Old Ballyclare Road, Templepatrick, Ballyclare, Co. Antrim BT39 0BJ
☎ 0849 432513   📠 0849 432151

CONTACT   The Manager
LOCATION   Templepatrick; also at Bangor, Ballymoney and Larne
OPEN   9 am – 8 pm, Monday – Saturday; 12 pm – 5.30 pm, Sundays; spring; 9 am – 5.30 pm, Monday – Saturday; 2 pm – 5.30 pm, Sundays; summer
NEW FOR 1994   Hanging basket plants
CATALOGUE   Yes
MAIL ORDER   Yes
SHOP   Garden sundries
GIFT TOKENS   HTA

Nursery and garden centre (the head office is Templepatrick). As well as a general range of plants and sundries they sell cuttings and young plants.

Landscape Centre
24 Donegore Hill, Dunadry, Co. Antrim BT41 2QU
☎ 0849 432175   📠 0849 432051

CONTACT   Mark Davis and Kaye Campbell

OPEN   9 am – 5 pm, Monday – Saturday; 2 – 5 pm, Sundays. Late closing, 8 pm, Wednesdays and Thursdays, April to August
SHOP   Sundries; gifts
REFRESHMENTS   Coffee shop
GARDEN   Demonstration gardens
DESIGN SERVICE   Landscape Centre
GIFT TOKENS   HTA; own

General garden centre with a range of plants and garden products. Run in conjunction with a landscape design office: see Services section.

Co. Down

Ballydorn Bulb Farm
Ballydorn Hill, Killinchy, Newtownards, Co. Down BT23 6QB
☎ 0238 541250

CONTACT   N. P. Harrison
SPECIALITIES   Daffodils
NEW FOR 1994   New *Narcissus* cultivars, awaiting RHS naming approval, including 'Drumlin', 'Barleywine', 'Kirkcubbin' and 'Ballygowan'
CATALOGUE   £1
MAIL ORDER   Yes

Narcissus breeders and hybridisers since 1946. The unique collection consists solely of their own cultivars, bred for either the show bench or the garden. They were awarded a gold medal in 1993 by the American Daffodil Society for hybridising.

Ballyrogan Nurseries
The Grange, Ballyrogan, Newtownards, Co. Down BT23 4SD
☎ 0247 810451

CONTACT   Gary Dunlop
OPEN   Collection only, by prior arrangement
SPECIALITIES   Herbaceous perennials
CATALOGUE   2 first class stamps
MAIL ORDER   Yes; £10 minimum order

A small part-time nursery selling stock derived from their own large collections. The plants are mostly herbaceous: the crocosmias and euphorbias look particularly interesting.

Daisy Hill Nurseries Ltd
Hospital Road, Newry, Co. Down BT35 8PN
☎ 0693 62474

CONTACT   Alan Grills
LOCATION   On Newry's western boundary
OPEN   9 am – 5 pm, Monday – Friday
SPECIALITIES   Rhododendrons; shrubs; trees
CATALOGUE   On request

MAIL ORDER   Yes; £5 minimum order
DESIGN SERVICE   Daisy Hill Nurseries Ltd
GIFT TOKENS   Own

The nursery sells alpines and heathers, shrubs and trees. Strengths include small-flowered and dwarf rhododendrons. They offer a landscaping service within a 25 mile radius.

Dickson Nurseries Ltd
Milecross Road, Newtownards, Co. Down BT23 4SS
☎ 0247 812206   FAX 0247 813366

CONTACT   Linda Stewart
OPEN   8 am – 12.30 pm, 1.15 – 5 pm, Monday – Thursday; 8 am – 1 pm, Fridays. Closed Saturdays and Sundays
SPECIALITIES   Roses
NEW FOR 1994   Rose 'Shine On'; 'Party Trick'; 'Lovely Fairy'; 'Leslie's Dream'; 'Our Molly'
CATALOGUE   On request
MAIL ORDER   Yes
SHOWS   Chelsea

Modern rose breeders, with some distinguished introductions to their credit. They only sell their own roses, and those of Jackson & Perkins and Interplant.

Donaghadee Garden Centre
34 Stockbridge Road, Donaghadee, Co. Down BT21 0PN
☎ 0247 883603   FAX 0247 883030

LOCATION   Between Bangor and Donaghadee, off B21
OPEN   9.30 am – 5.30 pm, Monday – Saturday; 12.30 – 5.30 pm Sundays
SHOP   Gifts
REFRESHMENTS   Coffee shop
DESIGN SERVICE   Donaghadee Garden Centre
GIFT TOKENS   HTA; own

Garden centre with a range of hardy plants. They offer a landscaping and design service, and can deliver. There is also a customer club and discount scheme.

Lisdoonan Herbs
98 Belfast Road, Saintfield, Co. Down BT24 7HF
☎ 0232 813624

CONTACT   Barbara Pilcher
LOCATION   Between Carryduff and Saintfield, 6 miles south of Belfast on A7
OPEN   By appointment
SPECIALITIES   Herbs
CATALOGUE   SAE
MAIL ORDER   No
GARDEN   Demonstration gardens

The nursery sells culinary herbs and salad plants, as well as cut herbs. One day workshops and visits to the garden can be arranged.

Seaforde Gardens

Seaforde, Downpatrick, Co. Down BT30 8PG
☎ 0396 811225   📠 0396 811370

CONTACT   Patrick Forde
LOCATION   Between Belfast and Newcastle
OPEN   10 am – 5 pm, Monday – Saturday; 2 – 6 pm, Sundays. Open Monday – Friday only, November to February
SPECIALITIES   Rhododendrons; shrubs; trees
CATALOGUE   On request
MAIL ORDER   Yes
GARDEN   Gardens
NCCPG NATIONAL COLLECTIONS   Eucryphia

An interesting collection of trees and shrubs, including some for sheltered spots only. Particularly good for *Rhododendron* and *Eucryphia*. There are also gardens and a tropical butterfly house.

Timpany Nurseries

77 Magheratimpany Road, Ballynahinch, Co. Down BT24 8PA
☎ 0238 562812

CONTACT   Susan Tindall
LOCATION   2 miles from Ballynahinch, in Drumlin country
OPEN   10 am – 6 pm, Monday – Saturday. Closed Sundays and Mondays during winter
SPECIALITIES   Alpines; primulas
CATALOGUE   50p
MAIL ORDER   Yes
GARDEN   Garden

A selection of alpine and rock garden plants, including specimens raised from collected seed. Strong on *Primula* and *Helichrysum*. The garden is open to groups by arrangement.

Co. TYRONE

Baronscourt Nurseries

Abercorn Estates, Newtownstewart, Co. Tyrone BT78 4EZ
☎ 06626 61683   📠 06626 62059

CONTACT   Neville Mooney
OPEN   10 am – 5 pm, Monday – Saturday; 2 – 5 pm, Sundays (Garden centre times)
SPECIALITIES   Shrubs; trees
NEW FOR 1994   Meconopsis 'Slieve Donard'; *Fascicularia bicolor*
CATALOGUE   Trade catalogues only

MAIL ORDER   No
SHOP   Garden centre
REFRESHMENTS   Coffee shop
DESIGN SERVICE   Baronscourt Nurseries

Retail garden centre and a wholesale nursery. They specialise in large trees, and container-grown conifers and shrubs. Landscaping service is available.

CHANNEL ISLANDS

Jersey Lavender Ltd

Rue du Pont Marquet, St Brelade, Jersey, Channel Islands JE3 8DS
☎ 0534 42933   📠 0534 45613

CONTACT   David Christie
LOCATION   Between St Aubin's Bay and Red Houses, on B25
OPEN   10 am – 5 pm, Monday – Saturday, 23 May to 24 September
SPECIALITIES   Herbs; lavender
CATALOGUE   On request
MAIL ORDER   Products only: not plants
SHOP   Lavender products
REFRESHMENTS   Tea room
GARDEN   Herb garden and lavender farm
NCCPG NATIONAL COLLECTIONS   Lavandula

Jersey Lavender is a working lavender farm, growing and distilling lavender and rosemary. The distillery and bottling room can be visited. A range of *Lavandula* species and cultivars is also for sale.

Martel's Garden World

Route des Blicqs, St Andrews, Guernsey, Channel Islands GY6 8YD
☎ 0481 36888   📠 0481 35542

CONTACT   Mrs D. de la Rue
OPEN   9 am – 6 pm, daily
SHOP   General garden centre
REFRESHMENTS   Refreshments
GIFT TOKENS   HTA

General garden centre.

Ransoms Garden Centre

St Martin, Jersey, Channel Islands JE3 6EB
☎ 0534 856699   📠 0534 853779

CONTACT   B. Webb
LOCATION   East end of island, near Gorey
OPEN   8.30 am – 6 pm, Monday – Saturday
REFRESHMENTS   Restaurant
GIFT TOKENS   HTA

Garden centre with licensed restaurant.

St Peters Garden Centre

Airport Road, St Peter, Jersey, Channel Islands
JE3 7BP

☎ 0534 45903   📠 0534 46774

CONTACT   Mark Beresford
OPEN   8.30 am – 6 pm, summer; 8.30 am – 5.30 pm,
winter

Garden centre. Free delivery service.

EIRE

CO. CORK

Deelish Garden Centre

Deelish, Skibbereen, Co. Cork

☎ 010 353 28 21374   📠 010 353 28 63187

CONTACT   Rain Chase
LOCATION   West Cork
OPEN   10 am – 1 pm, 2 – 6 pm, Monday – Saturday;
2 – 6 pm, Sundays
CATALOGUE   Yes: specialist range only

The nursery carries a general range of most types of
plants, and some more unusual varieties as well.

Hosford's Geraniums & Garden Centre

Cappa, Enniskeane, Co. Cork

☎ 010 353 23 39159   📠 010 353 23 39300

CONTACT   John and David Hosford
LOCATION   5 miles west of Bandon; 1 mile off N71
OPEN   9 am – 6 pm, Monday – Saturday, and Holidays,
all year; 2 – 5.30 pm, Sundays, March to June, mid
September to Christmas only
SPECIALITIES   Pelargoniums; roses
NEW FOR 1994   New pelargoniums and roses
CATALOGUE   Lists for pelargoniums, roses, perennials,
hedging etc.
MAIL ORDER   Yes; credit cards accepted
GIFT TOKENS   Own

A general garden centre which also makes a speciality
of pelargoniums. The rose list is good, and there are
regular talks and demonstrations: the programmes appear in February and September.

CO. DONEGAL

Crocknafeola Nursery

Killybegs, Co. Donegal

☎ 010 353 73 51018

CONTACT   Andy McKenna

LOCATION   3 miles from Killybegs
OPEN   9 am – 8 pm, Monday – Saturday; 12 – 6 pm,
Sundays
MAIL ORDER   No

The nursery produces a range of hardy plants which are
particularly suitable for exposed positions. All stock is
properly hardened off before sale.

CO. DUBLIN

Fernhill Nursery

Fernhill, Sandyford, Co. Dublin

☎ 010 353 1 295 6158

CONTACT   Robert Walker
LOCATION   Towards Enniskerry
OPEN   11 am – 5 pm, Tuesday – Saturday; 2 – 5 pm,
Sundays. Closed Sundays, November to March
SPECIALITIES   Herbaceous perennials
CATALOGUE   No
MAIL ORDER   No
GARDEN   Fernhill, Co. Dublin, see Gardens section

The nursery is open at the same time as the garden, and
sells a mainly herbaceous range.

Flower Centre

754 Howth Road, Blackbanks, Dublin 5, Co. Dublin

☎ 010 353 1 324047   📠 010 353 1 327251

CONTACT   Eugene Higgins
LOCATION   5 miles east of Dublin
OPEN   10 am – 1 pm, 2.30 pm – 6 pm
MAIL ORDER   No
SHOP   Garden sundries

Garden centre with a full range of plants.

Mackey's Garden Centre

Castlepark Road, Sandycove, Co. Dublin

☎ 010 353 280 7385   📠 010 353 284 1922

CONTACT   Breda Roseingrave
LOCATION   5 miles south of Dublin
OPEN   9 am – 5.30 pm, Monday – Saturday; 2 – 5.30
pm, Sundays and Holidays
SPECIALITIES   Australian plants; seeds
CATALOGUE   On request: bulbs, seeds, old roses, mod-
ern roses
MAIL ORDER   Yes
SHOP   Garden centre and city shop
GARDEN   Demonstration gardens
GIFT TOKENS   Own

The garden centre outlet of a famous old seed merchant
(founded in 1777). There are many interesting plants in
the all-round range, most notably the Australian collection. Mackey's Seed Ltd is at 22 St Mary Street, Dublin.

Malahide Nurseries Ltd

Mabestown, Malahide, Co. Dublin

☎ 010 353 845 0110 📠 010 353 845 0872

CONTACT Miss Ann Nutty
LOCATION 7 miles north of Dublin
OPEN 9.30 am – 1 pm, 2 – 5.30 pm, Monday – Friday; 9.30 am – 5.30 pm, Saturdays; 2 – 5.30 pm, Sundays
SPECIALITIES Aquatic plants
NEW FOR 1994 15 new rose varieties
MAIL ORDER Yes
SHOP Garden products; seeds
GARDEN 2 model gardens
GIFT TOKENS Own

This nursery, trading from a thatched building, carries a general range of plants and sundries. The aquatic plants are home grown.

Co. GALWAY

Seaside Nursery and Garden Centre

Claddaghduff, Co. Galway

☎ 010 353 95 44687 📠 010 353 95 44687

CONTACT Charles Dÿck
LOCATION Claddaghduff
OPEN 9 am – 1 pm, 2 – 6 pm, Monday – Saturday; 2 – 6 pm, Sundays
SPECIALITIES Coastal plants
NEW FOR 1994 Many new items
CATALOGUE I£1
MAIL ORDER No
SHOP Pots

The nursery specialises in plants for seaside locations, and in plants for containers. They import and sell Italian pots also.

Co. KERRY

Muckross Garden Centre

Muckross, Killarney, Co. Kerry

☎ 010 353 64 34044

CONTACT John Fuller
LOCATION 3 miles from Killarney, on Kenmare road
OPEN 10 am – 6 pm, Tuesday – Saturday; 2 – 6 pm, Sundays. Closed Mondays
MAIL ORDER No
DESIGN SERVICE Muckross Garden Centre

Garden centre with a general range: a new shrub nursery is being developed. They have a design and main-tenance capacity. The garden centre is opposite the Killarney National Park (accommodation available).

Co. LEITRIM

Eden Plants

Rossinver, Co. Leitrim

☎ 010 353 72 54122

CONTACT Rod Alston
LOCATION 25 miles north east of Sligo
OPEN 2 – 6 pm, daily
SPECIALITIES Herbs
CATALOGUE I£1 plus SAE
MAIL ORDER Yes; SAE for price list
GARDEN Herb garden

An organic herb nursery: all stock is grown at the nursery under organic conditions.

Co. TIPPERARY

Clonmel Garden Centre

Glenconnor House, Clonmel, Co. Tipperary

☎ 010 353 52 23294

CONTACT Beth and Terry Hanna
OPEN 10 am – 6 pm, Monday – Saturday; 2 – 6 pm, Sundays and Bank Holidays
SPECIALITIES Trees
MAIL ORDER No
GARDEN Surrounding gardens
DESIGN SERVICE Clonmel Garden Centre

This garden centre is set in the grounds of a country house: there are also antique showrooms on the site. The emphasis is on trees and shrubs.

Co. WATERFORD

Orchardstown Nurseries

Cork Road, Waterford, Co. Waterford

☎ 010 353 51 84273 📠 010 353 51 84422

CONTACT Ron Dool
LOCATION 4 miles from Waterford, towards Cork
OPEN 9 am – 6 pm
SPECIALITIES Shrubs; trees
CATALOGUE I£1.50
MAIL ORDER Yes; minimum order I£50

Irish nursery, with a varied choice of trees and shrubs, including climbers and rhododendrons.

Nursery Specialities

ACERS
Altoona Nurseries, Devon
Andrew Norfield Trees & Seeds, Gloucestershire
Barkers Primrose Nurseries, Lancashire
Hippopottering Nursery, North Yorkshire
International Acers, Hereford & Worcester
Nettletons Nursery, Surrey
P M A Plant Specialities, Somerset
Sellet Hall Gardens, Lancashire

AFRICAN VIOLETS
African Violet Centre, Norfolk

AIR PLANTS
Tamarisk Nurseries, Buckinghamshire
Vesutor Airplants, West Sussex

ALPINES
A & A Thorp, Leicestershire
Aberconwy Nursery, Clwyd
Ashenden Nursery, Kent
Baker Straw Partnership, Hereford & Worcester
Beechcroft Nursery, Surrey
Blackthorn Nursery, Hampshire
Blairhoyle Nursery, Central
Brambling House Alpines, South Yorkshire
Bressingham Plant Centre, Norfolk
Broadstone Nurseries, Oxfordshire
Caves Folly Nurseries, Hereford & Worcester
Chris Pattison (Nurseryman), Gloucestershire
DHE Plants, Derbyshire
Field House Alpines, Nottinghamshire
The Firs Nursery, Cheshire
Fosse Alpines, Leicestershire
Foxgrove Plants, Berkshire
Garden Cottage Nursery, Highland
Greenslacks Nurseries, West Yorkshire

Hall Farm Nursery, Shropshire
Hartside Nursery Garden, Cumbria
Highgates Nursery, Derbyshire
Hillview Hardy Plants, Shropshire
Holden Clough Nursery, Lancashire
Hoo House Nursery, Gloucestershire
Jack Drake, Highland
Jenny Burgess' Alpine Nursery, Norfolk
Lewdon Farm Alpine Nursery, Devon
Lingen Alpine Nursery, Shropshire
Llanbrook Alpine & Wildflower Nursery,
   Shropshire
Marley Bank Nursery, Hereford & Worcester
Martin Nest Nurseries, Lincolnshire
The Mead Nursery, Wiltshire
Mendle Nursery, Humberside
Newton Hill Alpines, West Yorkshire
Nicky's Rock Garden Nursery, Devon
Norden Alpine Nursery, North Yorkshire
The Old Manor Nursery, Gloucestershire
Plantables, West Midlands
Potterton and Martin, Lincolnshire
Pringle Plants, Borders
R F Beeston, Hereford & Worcester
Reginald Kaye Ltd, Lancashire
Rivendell Alpines, Dorset
Rookhope Nurseries, Co. Durham
Ryal Nursery, Northumberland
Siskin Plants, Suffolk
Tim Ingram, Kent
Timpany Nurseries, Co. Down
Tough Alpine Nursery, Grampian
Town Farm Nursery, Cleveland
Ty'r Orsaf Nursery, Gwynedd
W E Th. Ingwersen Ltd, West Sussex
West Kington Nurseries Ltd, Wiltshire

White Cottage Alpines, Humberside
Wintergreen Nurseries, Hereford & Worcester

AQUATIC PLANTS
Anthony Archer-Wills Ltd, West Sussex
Barkers Primrose Nurseries, Lancashire
Bennetts Water Lily Farm, Dorset
D J Case, Hampshire
Longstock Park Nursery, Hampshire
Malahide Nurseries Ltd, Co. Dublin
Maydencroft Aquatic Nurseries, Hertfordshire
Mickfield Fish and Watergarden Centre, Suffolk
Nine Springs Nursery, Hampshire
Pantiles Plant & Garden Centre, Surrey
Rowden Gardens, Devon
Stapeley Water Gardens Ltd, Cheshire
Water Meadow Nursery and Herb Farm,
  Hampshire
Waveney Fish Farm, Norfolk

ASTERS
Misses I Allen and M J Huish, Avon
Old Court Nurseries, Hereford & Worcester

AUSTRALIAN PLANTS
Architectural Plants, West Sussex
County Park Nursery, Essex
Mackey's Garden Centre, Co. Dublin
Marwood Hill Gardens, Devon
The Seed House, Hampshire

BAMBOOS
Coblands Nursery, Kent
Drysdale Exotics, Hampshire
Jungle Giants, Hereford & Worcester
Madrona Nursery, Kent
P W Plants, Norfolk
Simply Plants, Cambridgeshire
Ulverscroft Unusual Plants, Leicestershire

BEDDING PLANTS
Hare Hatch Nursery, Berkshire
Henry Street, Berkshire
Kent Street Nurseries, East Sussex
Pantiles Plant & Garden Centre, Surrey
Steven Bailey, Hampshire
West Somerset Garden Centre, Somerset

BEGONIAS
Blackmore & Langdon, Avon
Dibleys, Clwyd
Rhodes & Rockliffe, Essex

BOG PLANTS
Anthony Archer-Wills Ltd, West Sussex
Bennetts Water Lily Farm, Dorset
Deanswood Plants, North Yorkshire
Longstock Park Nursery, Hampshire
Marwood Hill Gardens, Devon
Maydencroft Aquatic Nurseries, Hertfordshire
Mickfield Fish and Watergarden Centre, Suffolk
Rowden Gardens, Devon
Stapeley Water Gardens Ltd, Cheshire
Water Meadow Nursery and Herb Farm,
  Hampshire

BONSAI
Bonsai, Lothian
D N Bromage & Co Ltd, Surrey
Herons Bonsai Ltd, Surrey
Norman Bonsai, East Sussex

BROMELIADS
Vesutor Airplants, West Sussex

BULBS
Avon Bulbs, Somerset
Broadleigh Gardens, Somerset
J Walkers Bulbs, Lincolnshire
Jacques Amand Ltd, London
Knightshayes Garden Trust, Devon
Monocot Nursery, Avon
P De Jager & Sons Ltd, Kent
Paradise Centre, Suffolk
Paul Christian Rare Plants, Clwyd
Potterton and Martin, Lincolnshire
Rupert Bowlby, Surrey
Walter Blom & Son Ltd, Bedfordshire

CACTI AND SUCCULENTS
A & A Phipps, Avon
Bradley Batch Cactus Nursery, Somerset
Chris Rodgerson, South Yorkshire
Connoisseurs' Cacti, Kent
Craig House Cacti, Lancashire
Croston Cactus, Lancashire
Cruck Cottage Cacti, North Yorkshire
East Midlands Cactus Nursery, Buckinghamshire
Glenhirst Cactus Nursery, Lincolnshire
Harvest Nurseries, East Sussex
Holly Gate Cactus Nursery, West Sussex
K & C Cacti, Devon
Oakleigh Nurseries, Hampshire
Pete & Ken Cactus Nursery, Kent

The Plant Lovers, Lincolnshire
Preston-Mafham Collection, Warwickshire
Southfield Nurseries, Lincolnshire
Westfield Cacti, Devon
Whitestone Gardens Ltd, North Yorkshire

CAMELLIAS
Bodnant Garden Nursery Ltd, Clwyd
Coghurst Nursery, East Sussex
Marwood Hill Gardens, Devon
Porthpean House Gardens, Cornwall
Trehane Camellia Nursery, Dorset
Trewidden Estate Nursery, Cornwall
Trewithen Nurseries, Cornwall

CARNIVOROUS PLANTS
Flora Exotica, Essex
Hall Farm Nursery, Shropshire
Marston Exotics, Hereford & Worcester
Potterton and Martin, Lincolnshire
Tamarisk Nurseries, Buckinghamshire

CHRYSANTHEMUMS
Collinwood Nurseries, Cheshire
H Woolman (Dorridge) Ltd, West Midlands
Halls of Heddon, Northumberland
Harold Walker, Cheshire
Home Meadows Nursery Ltd, Suffolk
Philip Tivey & Son, Leicestershire
Riley's Chrysanthemums, Derbyshire

CLEMATIS
Abbey Dore Court Garden, Hereford & Worcester
Beamish Clematis Nursery, Co. Durham
Caddick's Clematis Nursery, Cheshire
Great Dixter Nurseries, East Sussex
J Bradshaw & Son, Kent
John Beach (Nursery) Ltd, Warwickshire
Orchard Nurseries, Lincolnshire
Peveril Clematis Nursery, Devon
Scotts Clematis, Devon
Thorncroft Clematis Nursery, Norfolk
Treasures of Tenbury Ltd, Hereford & Worcester

CLIMBERS
Beamish Clematis Nursery, Co. Durham
Coblands Nursery, Kent
Hillier Nurseries Ltd, Hampshire
J Bradshaw & Son, Kent
Reads Nursery, Norfolk
Stone House Cottage Nurseries, Hereford & Worcester

Trewithen Nurseries, Cornwall
Waterwheel Nursery, Gwent

CONIFERS
Barncroft Nurseries, Staffordshire
Beechcroft Nursery, Surrey
Belwood Nurseries Ltd, Lothian
Bressingham Plant Centre, Norfolk
Bressingham Plant Centre, Berkshire
Coblands Nursery, Kent
The Conifer Garden, Buckinghamshire
E L F Plants, Cramden Nursery Ltd, Northamptonshire
Fron Nursery, Shropshire
Goscote Nurseries Ltd, Leicestershire
Hillier Nurseries Ltd, Hampshire
Holden Clough Nursery, Lancashire
Hull Farm Conifer Centre, Essex
Kenwith Nursery, Devon
Lime Cross Nursery, East Sussex
Melville Nurseries, Lothian
Norwich Heather and Conifer Centre, Norfolk
Otter's Court Heathers, Somerset
W E Th. Ingwersen Ltd, West Sussex

CONSERVATORY PLANTS
The Abbots House Garden, Hertfordshire
Architectural Plants, West Sussex
Brockings Exotics, Cornwall
Four Counties Nursery, Gloucestershire
Long Man Gardens, East Sussex
Newington Nurseries, Oxfordshire
Reads Nursery, Norfolk
Special Plants, Wiltshire
Tropicana Nursery, Devon

DAFFODILS
Ballydorn Bulb Farm, Co. Down
Broadleigh Gardens, Somerset
Carncairn Daffodils, Co. Antrim
Constable Daffodils, Surrey
Copford Bulbs, Essex
Evelix Daffodils, Highland
J Walkers Bulbs, Lincolnshire
P De Jager & Sons Ltd, Kent

DAHLIAS
Aylett Nurseries Ltd, Hertfordshire
Butterfields Nursery, Buckinghamshire
Halls of Heddon, Northumberland
Philip Tivey & Son, Leicestershire

DELPHINIUMS
Blackmore & Langdon, Avon
Stuart Ogg, East Sussex
Woodfield Bros, Warwickshire

DIANTHUS
Allwood Bros, West Sussex
Church Hill Cottage Gardens, Kent
Cravens Nursery, West Yorkshire
Mills Farm Plants and Gardens, Suffolk
Pinks & Carnations, Lancashire
Southview Nurseries, Hampshire
Steven Bailey, Hampshire
Three Counties Nurseries, Dorset

FERNS
Apple Court, Hampshire
Architectural Plants, West Sussex
Barters Farm Nurseries Ltd, Wiltshire
Coblands Nursery, Kent
Fibrex Nurseries Ltd, Warwickshire
Hartside Nursery Garden, Cumbria
Holden Clough Nursery, Lancashire
Reginald Kaye Ltd, Lancashire
Rickard's Hardy Ferns Ltd, Hereford & Worcester

FOLIAGE PLANTS
Architectural Plants, West Sussex
Decorative Foliage, Devon
Drysdale Exotics, Hampshire
Eggleston Hall Gardens, Co. Durham
Foliage & Unusual Plants, Lincolnshire
Hoecroft Plants, Norfolk
P W Plants, Norfolk
Plaxtol Nurseries, Kent

FRUIT
Ballerina Trees Ltd, Cambridgeshire
Bonhard Nursery, Tayside
Chris Bowers & Son, Norfolk
Clive Simms, Lincolnshire
Deacons Nursery, Isle of Wight
Family Trees, Hampshire
Frank P Matthews Ltd, Hereford & Worcester
The Fruit Garden, Kent
J Tweedie Fruit Trees, Dumfries & Galloway
John Beach (Nursery) Ltd, Warwickshire
Keepers Nursery, Kent
Ken Muir Nurseries, Essex
Paul Jasper Trees, Hereford & Worcester
R V Roger Ltd, North Yorkshire
Scotts Nurseries Ltd, Somerset

Thornhayes Nursery, Devon
Tim Ingram, Kent
Trehane Camellia Nursery, Dorset

FUCHSIAS
A D & N Wheeler, Warwickshire
B & H M Baker, Essex
C S Lockyer, Avon
Clay Lane Nursery, Surrey
Goulding's Fuchsias, Suffolk
Jackson's Nurseries, Staffordshire
John Smith & Son, Leicestershire
Kathleen Muncaster Fuchsias, Lincolnshire
Kent Street Nurseries, East Sussex
Laburnum Nurseries, Leicestershire
Little Brook Fuchsias, Hampshire
Meadowcroft Fuchsias, Cambridgeshire
Oakleigh Nurseries, Hampshire
Oldbury Nurseries, Kent
Porter's Fuchsias, Merseyside

GRASSES
Apple Court, Hampshire
Brownthwaite Hardy Plants, Cumbria
Coblands Nursery, Kent
Hoecroft Plants, Norfolk
Holden Clough Nursery, Lancashire
Madrona Nursery, Kent
P W Plants, Norfolk
Simply Plants, Cambridgeshire
Trevor Scott Ornamental Grasses, Essex
Ulverscroft Unusual Plants, Leicestershire

GROUND COVER PLANTS
Growing Carpets, Hertfordshire

HEATHERS
Angus Heathers, Tayside
Barncroft Nurseries, Staffordshire
Blairhoyle Nursery, Central
D & M Everett, Hereford & Worcester
Denbeigh Heathers, Suffolk
Eversley Nurseries, Lancashire
Garden Cottage Nursery, Highland
Goscote Nurseries Ltd, Leicestershire
Naked Cross Nurseries, Dorset
Norwich Heather and Conifer Centre, Norfolk
Okell's Nurseries, Cheshire
Otter's Court Heathers, Somerset
Speyside Heather Centre, Highland

HEDGING
Barters Farm Nurseries Ltd, Wiltshire

Ben Reid & Co, Grampian
Buckingham Nurseries and Garden Centre, Buckinghamshire
Forward Nurseries, Kent
Landford Trees, Wiltshire
Langley Boxwood Nursery, Hampshire
Mount Pleasant Trees, Gloucestershire
Perrie Hale Forest Nursery, Devon
T & W Christie (Forres) Ltd, Grampian
Weasdale Nurseries, Cumbria

HERBACEOUS PERENNIALS
Abriachan Gardens & Nursery, Highland
Axletree Nursery, East Sussex
Baker Straw Partnership, Hereford & Worcester
Ballyrogan Nurseries, Co. Down
Barbara Molesworth, Shropshire
The Beth Chatto Gardens Ltd, Essex
Birkheads Cottage Garden Nursery, Tyne & Wear
Blackthorn Nursery, Hampshire
Bosvigo Plants, Cornwall
Botanic Nursery, Wiltshire
Bregover Plants, Cornwall
Bressingham Plant Centre, Norfolk
Bressingham Plant Centre, Berkshire
Brian Hiley, Surrey
Brownthwaite Hardy Plants, Cumbria
C E & D M Nurseries, Lincolnshire
Cally Gardens, Dumfries & Galloway
Catforth Gardens, Lancashire
Caves Folly Nurseries, Hereford & Worcester
Charter House Hardy Plant Nursery, Dumfries & Galloway
Church Hill Cottage Gardens, Kent
Cilwern Plants, Dyfed
Coblands Nursery, Kent
Cotswold Garden Flowers, Hereford & Worcester
Cottage Garden Plants, West Sussex
Cottage Nurseries, Lincolnshire
Craigieburn Classic Plants, Dumfries & Galloway
Cranesbill Nursery, Hereford & Worcester
Croftacre Hardy Plants, Norfolk
Croftway Nursery, West Sussex
D J Case, Hampshire
Eastgrove Cottage Garden Nursery, Hereford & Worcester
Elworthy Cottage Garden Plants, Somerset
Fernhill Nursery, Co. Dublin
The Firs Nursery, Cheshire
Foliage & Unusual Plants, Lincolnshire

Four Seasons, Norfolk
Frances Mount Perennial Plants, Essex
Garden Cottage Nursery, Highland
Glebe Cottage Plants, Devon
Green Farm Plants, Surrey
Hadspen Garden, Somerset
Halecat Garden Nurseries, Cumbria
Hall Farm Nursery, Lincolnshire
Hall Farm Nursery, Shropshire
Hannays of Bath, Avon
Hardy's Cottage Garden Plants, Hampshire
Henllys Lodge Plants, Gwynedd
Hillview Hardy Plants, Shropshire
Holden Clough Nursery, Lancashire
Hoo House Nursery, Gloucestershire
Hopleys Plants Ltd, Hertfordshire
Houghton Farm Plants, West Sussex
Judy's Country Garden, Lincolnshire
Langthorns Plantery, Essex
Lingen Alpine Nursery, Shropshire
Longacre Nursery, Kent
Longstock Park Nursery, Hampshire
Lower Severalls Herb Nursery, Somerset
Margery Fish Plant Nursery, Somerset
Marwood Hill Gardens, Devon
The Mead Nursery, Wiltshire
Mill Hill Plants, Nottinghamshire
Monksilver Nursery, Cambridgeshire
Naked Cross Nurseries, Dorset
Nordybank Nurseries, Shropshire
Northumbria Nurseries, Northumberland
Oak Tree Nursery, North Yorkshire
Old Court Nurseries, Hereford & Worcester
Orchard House Nursery, North Yorkshire
Orchard Nurseries, Lincolnshire
P A Jordan, Strathclyde
Padlock Croft, Cambridgeshire
Park Green Nurseries, Suffolk
Perry's Plants, North Yorkshire
Perrybrook Nursery, Shropshire
Plantables, West Midlands
Pounsley Plants, Devon
Priory Garden Nursery, Gloucestershire
R D Plants, Devon
Rarer Plants, North Yorkshire
Raveningham Gardens, Norfolk
Reginald Kaye Ltd, Lancashire
Rookhope Nurseries, Co. Durham
Rushfields of Ledbury, Hereford & Worcester
S & E Bond, Hereford & Worcester

Salley Gardens, Cumbria
Southview Nurseries, Hampshire
Spinners, Hampshire
Stillingfleet Lodge Nurseries, North Yorkshire
Tim Ingram, Kent
Toad Hall Produce, Hereford & Worcester
Tollgate Cottage Nursery, Warwickshire
Tomperrow Farm Nurseries, Cornwall
Ty'r Orsaf Nursery, Gwynedd
Ulverscroft Unusual Plants, Leicestershire
Usual & Unusual Plants, East Sussex
Veryans Plants, Devon
Water Meadow Nursery and Herb Farm,
  Hampshire
Waterwheel Nursery, Gwent
West Kington Nurseries Ltd, Wiltshire
Wintergreen Nurseries, Hereford & Worcester

HERBS

Arne Herbs, Avon
Baker Straw Partnership, Hereford & Worcester
Cheshire Herbs, Cheshire
The Cottage Herbery, Hereford & Worcester
Cowcombe Farm Herbs, Gloucestershire
Daphne ffiske Herbs, Norfolk
Eden Plants, Co. Leitrim
Elly Hill Herbs, Co. Durham
Elsworth Herbs, Cambridgeshire
Foliage Scented & Herb Plants, Surrey
Gwydir Plants, Gwynedd
Hewthorn Herbs & Wild Flowers,
  Nottinghamshire
Hexham Herbs, Northumberland
Hollington Nurseries, Berkshire
Iden Croft Herbs, Kent
Jekka's Herb Farm, Avon
Jersey Lavender Ltd, Channel Islands
Judy's Country Garden, Lincolnshire
Lisdoonan Herbs, Co. Down
Lower Severalls Herb Nursery, Somerset
Marle Place Gardens & Nursery, Kent
Nordybank Nurseries, Shropshire
Oak Cottage Herb Garden, Shropshire
The Old Mill Herbary, Cornwall
Parkinson Herbs, Cornwall
Poyntzfield Herb Nursery, Highland
Salley Gardens, Cumbria
Southwick Country Herbs, Devon
Water Meadow Nursery and Herb Farm,
  Hampshire

The Wildlife Gardening Centre, Oxfordshire
Wye Valley Herbs, Gwent

HOUSE PLANTS

African Violet Centre, Norfolk
Boonwood Garden Centre, Cumbria
Dibleys, Clwyd
Tropicana Nursery, Devon

IRIS

Agars Nursery, Hampshire
Croftway Nursery, West Sussex
Kelways Nurseries Ltd, Somerset
Mill Hill Plants, Nottinghamshire
Robinsons of Whaley Bridge, Cheshire
Rowden Gardens, Devon
S & S Perennials, Leicestershire
V H Humphrey, Surrey
Zephyrwude Irises, West Yorkshire

LILIES

S & S Perennials, Leicestershire

MEDITERRANEAN PLANTS

Architectural Plants, West Sussex
Drysdale Exotics, Hampshire

NEW ZEALAND PLANTS

Architectural Plants, West Sussex
County Park Nursery, Essex
Marwood Hill Gardens, Devon

ORCHIDS

Burnham Nurseries, Devon
Butterfields Nursery, Buckinghamshire
Equatorial Plant Co, Co. Durham
Mansell & Hatcher Ltd, West Yorkshire
Orchid Sundries Ltd & Hardy Orchids Ltd, Dorset
Uzumara Orchids, Highland
Westwood Nursery, Kent

PAEONIES

Kelways Nurseries Ltd, Somerset

PALMS

The Palm Centre, London

PELARGONIUMS

A D & N Wheeler, Warwickshire
Brian Sulman Pelargoniums, Suffolk
Denmead Geranium Nurseries, Hampshire
Derek Lloyd Dean, London
Diana Hull, Warwickshire
Fibrex Nurseries Ltd, Warwickshire

The Geranium Nursery, West Sussex
Hosford's Geraniums & Garden Centre, Co. Cork
Kent Street Nurseries, East Sussex
Meadowcroft Fuchsias, Cambridgeshire
Oakleigh Nurseries, Hampshire
Pearl Sulman, Suffolk
The Vernon Geranium Nursery, Surrey
Wytherstone Nurseries, North Yorkshire

PRIMULAS
Abriachan Gardens & Nursery, Highland
Bregover Plants, Cornwall
Brenda Hyatt, Kent
Craigieburn Classic Plants, Dumfries & Galloway
Cravens Nursery, West Yorkshire
Donington Plants, Lincolnshire
The Fens, Essex
Field House Alpines, Nottinghamshire
Gardenscape, North Yorkshire
Glendoick Gardens Ltd, Tayside
Greenslacks Nurseries, West Yorkshire
Hillview Hardy Plants, Shropshire
Lingen Alpine Nursery, Shropshire
Longstock Park Nursery, Hampshire
R F Beeston, Hereford & Worcester
Ryal Nursery, Northumberland
Surrey Primroses, Surrey
Timpany Nurseries, Co. Down
Town Farm Nursery, Cleveland

RHODODENDRONS
Barncroft Nurseries, Staffordshire
Bodnant Garden Nursery Ltd, Clwyd
Bowood Garden Centre, Wiltshire
Coghurst Nursery, East Sussex
Daisy Hill Nurseries Ltd, Co. Down
Exbury Enterprises Ltd, Hampshire
F Morrey & Son, Cheshire
Glendoick Gardens Ltd, Tayside
The High Garden, Devon
Highgates Nursery, Derbyshire
Hydon Nurseries, Surrey
Knap Hill Nursery Ltd, Surrey
Lanhydrock Gardens, Cornwall
Lea Gardens, Derbyshire
Leonardslee Gardens Nurseries, West Sussex
Millais Nurseries, Surrey
Perryhill Nurseries, East Sussex
Plantables, West Midlands
Seaforde Gardens, Co. Down
Starborough Nursery, Kent

Trewithen Nurseries, Cornwall
Wall Cottage Nursery, Cornwall
Whitehills Nurseries, Dumfries & Galloway

ROSES
A J Palmer & Son, Buckinghamshire
Apuldram Roses, West Sussex
Battersby Roses, Cleveland
Bonhard Nursery, Tayside
Bowood Garden Centre, Wiltshire
Burrows Roses, Derbyshire
C & K Jones, Cheshire
C & K Jones, Clwyd
Cants of Colchester, Essex
Corsley Mill, Brigid Quest-Ritson, Wiltshire
Cranborne Manor Garden Centre, Dorset
David Austin Roses, West Midlands
Dickson Nurseries Ltd, Co. Down
Gandy's Roses Ltd, Leicestershire
Godly's Roses, Hertfordshire
Henry Street, Berkshire
Hosford's Geraniums & Garden Centre, Co. Cork
Hunts Court Garden & Nursery, Gloucestershire
James Cocker & Sons, Grampian
John Sanday (Roses) Ltd, Avon
Just Roses, East Sussex
Layham Garden Centre, Kent
Mattock Roses, Oxfordshire
Mills Farm Plants and Gardens, Suffolk
Notcutts Nurseries, Suffolk
Perryhill Nurseries, East Sussex
Peter Beales Roses, Norfolk
R Harkness & Co Ltd, Hertfordshire
Rumwood Nurseries, Kent
Scotts Nurseries Ltd, Somerset
Trevor White Old Fashioned Roses, Norfolk
West Kington Nurseries Ltd, Wiltshire
Wheatcroft Ltd, Nottinghamshire

SEMPERVIVUMS
Alan C Smith, Kent
Brambling House Alpines, South Yorkshire
Greenslacks Nurseries, West Yorkshire
H & S Wills, Devon
Mary & Peter Mitchell, West Sussex
Mendle Nursery, Humberside
The Plant Lovers, Lincolnshire

SHRUBS
Abbotsbury Gardens, Dorset
Arbor Exotica, Cambridgeshire

Barncroft Nurseries, Staffordshire
Baronscourt Nurseries, Co. Tyrone
Beechcroft Nurseries, Cumbria
Ben Reid & Co, Grampian
Bluebell Nursery, Derbyshire
Bodnant Garden Nursery Ltd, Clwyd
Bowood Garden Centre, Wiltshire
Bretby Nurseries, Staffordshire
Brinkley Nurseries, Nottinghamshire
Buckingham Nurseries and Garden Centre,
  Buckinghamshire
Chris Bowers & Son, Norfolk
Chris Pattison (Nurseryman), Gloucestershire
Coblands Nursery, Kent
Daisy Hill Nurseries Ltd, Co. Down
Denmans Garden Plant Centre, West Sussex
E L F Plants, Cramden Nursery Ltd,
  Northamptonshire
F Morrey & Son, Cheshire
Four Counties Nursery, Gloucestershire
Fron Nursery, Shropshire
Garden Cottage Nursery, Highland
Goscote Nurseries Ltd, Leicestershire
Grange Farm Nursery, Hereford & Worcester
Hall Farm Nursery, Lincolnshire
Hillier Nurseries Ltd, Hampshire
Holden Clough Nursery, Lancashire
Hopleys Plants Ltd, Hertfordshire
Hunts Court Garden & Nursery, Gloucestershire
John Beach (Nursery) Ltd, Warwickshire
Knightshayes Garden Trust, Devon
Langthorns Plantery, Essex
Lanhydrock Gardens, Cornwall
Longstock Park Nursery, Hampshire
Madrona Nursery, Kent
Marwood Hill Gardens, Devon
Notcutts Nurseries, Suffolk
Orchardstown Nurseries, Co. Waterford
P H Kellett, Kent
P M A Plant Specialities, Somerset
Perryhill Nurseries, East Sussex
Priory Garden Nursery, Gloucestershire
Raveningham Gardens, Norfolk
Scotts Nurseries Ltd, Somerset
Seaforde Gardens, Co. Down
Shepton Nursery Garden, Somerset
Spinners, Hampshire
Starborough Nursery, Kent
T & W Christie (Forres) Ltd, Grampian
Trewithen Nurseries, Cornwall

Waterwheel Nursery, Gwent
Weasdale Nurseries, Cumbria
West Somerset Garden Centre, Somerset
The Wildlife Gardening Centre, Oxfordshire

SOUTH AMERICAN PLANTS
Architectural Plants, West Sussex

SWEET PEAS
S & N Brackley, Buckinghamshire

TOPIARY
Cranborne Manor Garden Centre, Dorset
The Romantic Garden Nursery, Norfolk
Langley Boxwood Nursery, Hampshire

TREES
Andrew Norfield Trees & Seeds, Gloucestershire
Arbor Exotica, Cambridgeshire
Ballagan Nursery, Strathclyde
Baronscourt Nurseries, Co. Tyrone
Barters Farm Nurseries Ltd, Wiltshire
Beechcroft Nurseries, Cumbria
Belwood Nurseries Ltd, Lothian
Ben Reid & Co, Grampian
Bluebell Nursery, Derbyshire
Bodnant Garden Nursery Ltd, Clwyd
Brinkley Nurseries, Nottinghamshire
Buckingham Nurseries and Garden Centre,
  Buckinghamshire
Burncoose & South Down Nurseries, Cornwall
Celyn Vale Nurseries, Clwyd
Clonmel Garden Centre, Co. Tipperary
Coblands Nursery, Kent
Daisy Hill Nurseries Ltd, Co. Down
F Morrey & Son, Cheshire
Four Counties Nursery, Gloucestershire
Frank P Matthews Ltd, Hereford & Worcester
Fron Nursery, Shropshire
Goscote Nurseries Ltd, Leicestershire
Grange Farm Nursery, Hereford & Worcester
Greenway Gardens, Devon
Hillier Nurseries Ltd, Hampshire
John Beach (Nursery) Ltd, Warwickshire
Landford Trees, Wiltshire
Madrona Nursery, Kent
Mallet Court Nursery, Somerset
Marwood Hill Gardens, Devon
Mount Pleasant Trees, Gloucestershire
Notcutts Nurseries, Suffolk
Orchardstown Nurseries, Co. Waterford
P H Kellett, Kent

P M A Plant Specialities, Somerset
Perrie Hale Forest Nursery, Devon
Perryhill Nurseries, East Sussex
Peter Trenear Nurseries, Hampshire
Seaforde Gardens, Co. Down
Spinners, Hampshire
Starborough Nursery, Kent
Stone Lane Gardens, Devon
T & W Christie (Forres) Ltd, Grampian
Thornhayes Nursery, Devon
Waterwheel Nursery, Gwent
Weasdale Nurseries, Cumbria
YSJ Seeds, Somerset

VIOLAS
Bouts Cottage Nurseries, Hereford & Worcester
Bregover Plants, Cornwall
C W Groves & Son, Dorset
Hazeldene Nursery, Kent
Richard G M Cawthorne, Kent
Robinsons of Whaley Bridge, Cheshire

WILD FLOWERS
Arne Herbs, Avon
British Wild Plants, Dumfries & Galloway
CN Seeds, Cambridgeshire
Cowcombe Farm Herbs, Gloucestershire
Gwydir Plants, Gwynedd
Hewthorn Herbs & Wild Flowers,
  Nottinghamshire
Jekka's Herb Farm, Avon
John Chambers Wild Flower Seeds,
  Northamptonshire
Landlife Wildflowers Ltd, Merseyside
Linda Gascoigne Wild Flowers, Leicestershire
Llanbrook Alpine & Wildflower Nursery,
  Shropshire
Nordybank Nurseries, Shropshire
Oak Cottage Herb Garden, Shropshire
Sawyers Seeds, Suffolk
The Wild Flower Centre, Norfolk
Wild Seeds, Gwynedd
The Wildlife Gardening Centre, Oxfordshire
YSJ Seeds, Somerset

12

Importing & Exporting Plants

CITES

Before considering the import and export of plants, it is necessary to understand the growing importance of the Convention on International Trade in Endangered Species of Wild Fauna and Flora (CITES). It regulates all the trade in wild plants which are listed in its schedules, and the UK is among its 120 signatories. 'Trade' is not limited to commerce: any movement of specimens across international frontiers constitutes trade for CITES purposes. A plant bought by you on holiday abroad falls within CITES if it is of a species included in one of the appendices to the Convention. Failure to comply with the rules is a criminal offence.

CITES has several appendices. The first is a list of species which can only be traded if they are artificially propagated and carry a licence: it includes seriously endangered species like *Mammillaria pectinifera* and *Vanda coerulea*. The second list is of plants which may be traded only if they are licensed: it permits trade in wild collected material and seed. The principal genera protected by CITES are *Aloe*, *Cyclamen*, *Galanthus*, *Nepenthes* and all Orchidaceae, cacti and cycads, but it is essential that anyone wishing to buy, sell or collect plants should know what is protected and what is not. That said, you can assume that any plant offered by a reputable nurseryman may legitimately be bought.

The Law of Import & Export

The basis of all the rules about importing and exporting plants is *The Plant Health (Great Britain) Order 1993* (S.I. No.1993/1320). It is a fiendishly complicated piece of legislation, partly because it consists of old British regulations which have had European Community directives grafted onto them, and partly because it reads as a list of prohibitions to which exceptions have been wrung only with difficulty. In fact, those exceptions are of great importance to most of us: they represent a significant loosening up of the old restrictions on the import and export of plants.

The Plant Health (Great Britain) Order 1993 'seeks to implement a new system of controls on the movement of plants, plant products and other objects arising from the establishment of the single market within the European Community'. It divides the world into three zones. First there is the European Community. Within the EC the rules are all the same and comparatively lax. Second, there is the rest of the world from Switzerland to Vanuatu: by and large these countries get second-class treatment. The keen gardener in Munich can bring plants back from the wildest parts of Sicily or Crete but may not pop across the border to buy them from nurseries in Salzburg or Basle. Finally there are the 'protected zones' within the countries of the EC. These are areas of Europe where stricter regulations apply.

The EC and the Rest of the World

The background to the EC's relations with the rest of the world sometimes appears to be a story of protectionism masquerading as sound phytosanitary practice. The argument is that the import and export of plants have to be controlled to ensure that pests and diseases are not spread. The key was the phytosanitary certificate. Government scientists inspected produce to ensure that it was free from contamination. Armed with a certificate, plants could travel anywhere in the world.

Phytosanitary certificates are still needed for the export of a large number of types of plants to many countries and for their import into the EC. The Schedules to *The Plant Health (Great Britain) Order 1993* list in great detail the plants, and plant products such as forest bark, which cannot be imported into the EC, and those which can come into the EC provided they have been inspected in the country of origin or consignor country, and are accompanied by phytosanitary certificates. Anyone who needs to know the exact extent of the legislation, should buy a copy and study it carefully.

The rules are most readily relaxed for those countries nearest to us. (1) *Austria & Switzerland* enjoy one unique concession: they suffer from no restrictions on the export of seed potatoes (varieties of *Solanum tuberosum*) to the EC. (2) The following genera can be imported into the EC from *all non-EC European countries*: *Abies* (firs), *Castanea* (sweet chestnuts), *Cedrus* (cedars); *Chaenomeles* (Japanese quinces), *Chamaecyparis* (false cypresses); *Cydonia* (true quinces); *Juniperus* (junipers); *Larix* (larches); *Malus* (apples); *Photinia*; *Picea* (spruces); *Pinus* (pines); *Prunus* (plums, cherries, peaches, almonds & apricots), *Pseudotsuga* (Douglas firs), *Pyrus* (pears); *Quercus* (oaks), *Rosa* (roses) and *Tsuga* (hemlock trees). There is still an absolute ban on their import from outside Europe, subject to certain concessions: *Cydonia, Malus, Prunus* and *Pyrus* can be imported from *all Mediterranean countries, Australia, New Zealand, Canada and the continental states of the USA*, while strawberry plants (*Fragaria*) can be brought in from those countries but NOT from the rest of Europe. (3) Some types of plants are, however, banned from entering the EC from whatever source. These include two major economic genera: *Vitis* (grape vines) and *Citrus*. (4) Finally, there are some oddities. Palm trees of the genus *Phoenix* are prohibited from entering the EC from Algeria and Morocco; poplars (*Populus*) may not be imported from any part of North America.

Personal Allowances

How does this all affect the holidaymaker who wants to bring a hibiscus back from his holiday in Tenerife? Or fancies the anemones growing in the woods around his Tuscan villa? There is no distinc-tion between wild and cultivated plants so far as the international conservation controls are concerned.

The guiding principle for collecting plants is this: do not touch anything unless (i) you are sure it is not protected and (ii) you have the permission of the owner. Moreover, you should never endanger the plant community from which you collect, nor collect material which you will not be able to grow or use. That said, most people would like to know what they can bring back from their holidays abroad. First you must be certain that there are no legal restrictions in the country you visit. Then you need to know the regulations which apply in Great Britain.

Never smuggle anything home in your sponge-bag. Find out what the British authorities allow, and keep within the rules. The basic principle - contrary to widespread belief - is that *individuals are free to bring back small quantities of plants and propagating material from anywhere in the world.* 'Small quantities' means:

(i) up to 2kg of fruit and raw vegetables (although potatoes are not permitted)
(ii) one bouquet of cut flowers
(iii) five packets of seed

These can be imported from *any part of the world, provided that they are only for your personal household use, exhibit no sign of pests or diseases, and accompany you home as part of your personal baggage.*

More can be imported from the 'non-EC countries of the Euro-Mediterranean area': this means all European countries, plus Algeria, Cyprus, Egypt, Israel, Jordan, Lebanon, Libya, Malta, Morocco, Tunisia and Turkey. The allowance from these countries is increased to permit two additional items:

(i) 2kg of bulbs, corms tubers and/or rhizomes
(ii) five plants

Once again, there is a proviso that they should be only for your personal household use, exhibit no sign of pests or diseases, and accompany you home as part of your personal baggage.

All these allowances apply to children as well as to adults. The regulations make no distinction between wild-collected and cultivated plants. Nor is there any restriction on the import of flower seeds from any part of the world: the 'five packets' rule therefore applies only to non-flower seeds.

These rules and concessions apply only to Great Britain, not to Northern Ireland or to any other country. Similar regulations apply within each member-state of the EC, but travellers wishing to take plants abroad should check the local requirements before departure. This is important: there may be some nasty surprises for the unwary. For example, many countries ban the import of apples, pears and plums from Great Britain, because of the widespread incidence of fireblight here.

Further advice on personal allowances is available from the Plant Health Division, MAFF, Whitehall Place (East Block), London SW1A 2HH. MAFF also publishes a leaflet entitled 'Traveller's Guide to Bringing Plants Back From Abroad (Including Wild Plants)'.

Moving Plants within the EC

The really crucial regulation to understand is that, as a general rule, *there are no restrictions on private individuals buying plants for their personal use anywhere in the EC*. The only exception is that people who live in protected zones will have to comply with the higher plant health standards which exist there. Regulations govern the movement of *wholesale* material through the EC but the essence of those regulations is that *free movement is permitted* provided plants have been inspected at the place of production and are accompanied by a plant passport.

Plant passports are effectively phytosanitary certificates for internal EC use only. They are needed even within a single member state, for any sale or transport of certain economic plants: hops, potatoes, vines, citrus fruits and all those pomaceous fruit trees or berried ornamentals which are members of the *Rosaceae* and susceptible to fireblight - *Amelanchier*, *Chaenomeles* (Japanese quince), *Cotoneaster*, *Crataegus*, *Cydonia* (common quince), *Eriobotrya* (loquat), *Malus* (apple), *Mespilus* (medlar), *Prunus* (plum, cherry, peach, almond & apricot), *Pyracantha*, *Pyrus* (pear), *Sorbus* and *Stransvaesia*. These genera require a plant passport at all stages down to the retailer.

But there is also a much wider category of plants which require a plant passport unless, as is usually the case, they are intended and ready for immediate retail sale. Those plants include the following genera: *Argyranthemum* (chrysanthemums), *Aster*, *Brassica*, *Castanea* (chestnuts), *Cucumis* (cucumbers), *Dendranthema* (more chrysanthemums), *Dianthus*,

Exacum, *Fragaria* (strawberries), *Gerbera*, *Gypsophila*, *Impatiens*, *Lactuca* (lettuces), *Larix* (larches), *Leucanthemum* (yet more chrysanthemums), *Lupinus*, *Pelargonium*, *Picea* (spruces), *Pinus* (pines), *Platanus* (plane trees), *Populus* (poplars), *Pseudotsuga* (Douglas firs), *Quercus* (oaks), *Rubus* (blackberries & raspberries), *Spinacia* (spinach), *Tanacetum* (tansy), *Tsuga* (hemlock trees) and *Verbena*. To these should be added bulbs and corms of: *Camassia*, *Chionodoxa*, *Crocus flava*, *Galanthus*, *Galtonia candicans*, *Gladiolus*, *Hyacinthus*, *Iris*, *Ismene*, *Muscari*, *Narcissus*, *Ornithogalum*, *Puschkinia*, *Scilla*, *Tigridia* and *Tulipa*.

But that is not all. The same regulations apply to a ragbag of plants including all members of the Solanaceae (apart from potatoes), all *Persea* species (avocado pears) and all members of the Araceae, Marantaceae, Musaceae and Strelitzaceae unless their roots have been cut off; and bulbs (and seeds too, rather an unusual stipulation) of onions, leeks and chives. All these require a plant passport unless 'they are intended for immediate retail sale'.

What is new about the changes that came into effect last year is that these plant passports are issued by the selling nursery and the procedures are easily accommodated within the routines of a well-run nursery. Any nursery may apply to MAFF for authority to issue plant passports. If it complies with their requirements, MAFF appoints a member of the nursery's staff to implement the correct procedures. This person's responsibility is to inspect plants in the nursery, keep records and liaise with MAFF. Detailed information and assistance is available from MAFF offices.

Protected Zones

Protected zones are exceptions to the One Nation Europe policy which have been negotiated by individual member states. They are areas (usually countries) which are substantially free from a particular harmful pest or disease and where, as a result, a higher level of plant health control is required to keep them free. In practice the regulations mean, for example, that a Belgian nurseryman needs to know that no tomato plants may be sent to Denmark unless they are free from spotted wilt virus, and he must be careful to note that, if he wishes to sell his poinsettias in Great Britain, he will need to issue a passport, but not if they are exported to France or Germany.

13

Seedsmen

Andrew Norfield Trees & Seeds
See Gloucestershire, Nurseries section

Ashwood Nurseries
See West Midlands, Nurseries section

B & T World Seeds
Whitnell House, Fiddington, Bridgwater, Somerset
TA5 1JE
☎ 0278 733209   📠 0278 733209

CONTACT David Sleigh
OPEN Mail order only
SPECIALITIES Seeds
CATALOGUE Master list £10 (£14 beyond Europe);
sub lists 50p
MAIL ORDER Yes

Specialists in exotic seeds supplied from (and to) most
of the world. The system is based on a computerised
master list, and 150 specialist lists (say Californian
natives or Salt tolerant) derived from it. Seed lists don't
come any longer than this one: the range is phenomenal.
Be aware that many species will be ordered specially
for you and that this may take time.

Bakker Holland
P O Box 111, Spalding, Lincolnshire PE12 6EL
☎ 0775 711411

OPEN Mail order only
SPECIALITIES Seeds
CATALOGUE On request: seeds; spring; autumn
MAIL ORDER Yes

Bright and lively vegetable and flower seed catalogues
from this Dutch firm. Bakker also produces a well-
stocked spring and autumn catalogue of plants and bulbs.

Carters Tested Seeds Ltd
Hele Road, Torquay, Devon TQ2 7QJ
☎ 0803 616156   📠 0803 615747

OPEN Mail order only
SPECIALITIES Seeds
CATALOGUE On request
MAIL ORDER Yes, and from stockists

Long-established seed company in the Suttons group.
The flower and vegetable range is sold through garden
centres and some supermarkets. Details of stockists
(and mail order if necessary) from the company.

Cheshire Herbs
See Cheshire, Nurseries section

Chiltern Seeds
Bortree Stile, Ulverston, Cumbria LA12 7PB
☎ 0229 581137   📠 0229 584549

CONTACT Mrs P. A. Burns
OPEN Mail order only
SPECIALITIES Seeds
NEW FOR 1994 Hundreds of new items
CATALOGUE On request
MAIL ORDER Yes

The distinctive long, tall catalogue lists thousands of
species and cultivars from around the world including
garden flowers and vegetables. Always something to
interest the adventurous or the armchair gardener. The
careful descriptions make it useful for reference too.

Chris Chadwell - Freelance Botanist
81 Parlaunt Road, Slough, Berkshire SL3 8DE

CONTACT Chris Chadwell
OPEN Mail order only
SPECIALITIES Seeds
CATALOGUE See below
MAIL ORDER Yes

Himalayan plant seeds. You pay for a share in a seed
collecting expedition and the fruits of the trip are then
distributed to the shareholders along with collecting
notes.

CN Seeds
Denmark House, Pymoor, Ely, Cambridgeshire
CB6 2EG
☎ 0353 699413   📠 0353 698806

CONTACT Chris Nye
SPECIALITIES Seeds; wild flowers
CATALOGUE On request
MAIL ORDER Yes

Specialist herb and flower seed merchants. Aimed at the trade, but retail customers welcome. Prices are quoted by weight, and the quantities are usually larger than retail packets. Now incorporates the herb list of Sawyers Seeds. Can you resist thirteen different varieties of Basil, for example?

Cowcombe Farm Herbs
See Gloucestershire, Nurseries section

Cravens Nursery
See West Yorkshire, Nurseries section

D T Brown & Co Ltd
Station Road, Poulton le Fylde, Lancashire FY6 7HX
☎ 0253 882371   ☎ 0253 890923

CONTACT Mr David N. Whittam
OPEN Mail order only
SPECIALITIES Seeds
NEW FOR 1994 Pansy 'Chalon Mixed'; *Nicotiana* 'F1 Domino Salmon Pink'; and many others
CATALOGUE On request
MAIL ORDER Yes
GIFT TOKENS Own

Flower and vegetable seed merchants, with some young plants, grass seed and horticultural sundries. A large range is sold from their clear and concise catalogue. They issue a separate seed catalogue for commercial growers and florists.

Edwin Tucker & Sons
Brewery Meadow, Stonepark, Ashburton, Devon TQ13 7DG
☎ 0364 52403   ☎ 0364 54300

LOCATION Asburton and Crediton
SPECIALITIES Seeds
NEW FOR 1994 Runner Bean 'Scarlet Emperor'; Tomato 'Totem F1 Hybrid'; *Brachycome iberidifolia*; Potato 'Samba'; Potato 'Linzer Delicatesse'
CATALOGUE On request
MAIL ORDER Yes
SHOP Seeds; garden sundries; plants
GIFT TOKENS HTA

Long-established seed merchants, with a retail and agricultural catalogue. They have over 50 seed potatoes as well as vegetables and garden flowers. Some garden products are also available mail order. There is a country store at the above address and at Commercial Road, Crediton (0363 772202). Their working malthouse (near Newton Abbot railway station) can be visited daily, except Saturdays, from Easter to October (0626 334734).

Emorsgate
Terrington Court, Popes Lane, Terrington St Clement, King's Lynn, Norfolk PE34 4NT
☎ 0553 829028   ☎ 0553 829028

CONTACT Donald MacIntyre
OPEN Mail order only
SPECIALITIES Seeds
CATALOGUE On request
MAIL ORDER Yes

Wild flowers, wild grasses and mixtures for retail and wholesale customers. The seed stocks are based on native collected seed which is then grown at the farm: the source county is given and stocks are regularly replenished. A good choice of wild and amenity grasses. Flower and grass mixtures are available for different soil types, and some are derived (with permission) from specified nature reserves.

Field House Alpines
See Nottinghamshire, Nurseries section

Flora Exotica
See Essex, Nurseries section

Glenhirst Cactus Nursery
See Lincolnshire, Nurseries section

Hazeldene Nursery
See Kent, Nurseries section

Holly Gate Cactus Nursery
See West Sussex, Nurseries section

J E Martin
4 Church Street, Market Harborough, Leicestershire LE16 7AA
☎ 0858 462751   ☎ 0858 434544

OPEN Mail order
SPECIALITIES Seeds
CATALOGUE On request
MAIL ORDER Yes

35 varieties of potatoes including 'Pink Fir Apple' and 'Stroma'. Mainly wholesale: they operate in the Midlands.

J W Boyce
Bush Pasture, Lower Carter Street, Fordham, Ely, Cambridgeshire CB7 5JU
☎ 0638 721158

CONTACT Roger Morley
OPEN 9 am - 1 pm, 2 - 5 pm, Monday - Friday (and Saturdays from January to April); 10 am - 1 pm, 2 - 5 pm, Sundays, January to April. Closed Saturday afternoons and Sundays, May to December

SPECIALITIES Seeds
NEW FOR 1994 Cabbage 'F1 Tundra'; Winter Cauliflower 'Janus'; Sweet Peas 'Pink Pearl'; 'Red Pearl', 'White Pearl'; and six old-fashioned Sweet Pea varieties
CATALOGUE On request
MAIL ORDER Yes
GIFT TOKENS Own

Specialists for Pansy seed, including their Soham Surprise strain (developed over the last 80 years). Many other fresh flower and vegetable seeds, which are sold packeted and by weight. Free help and advice.

Jack Drake
See Highland, Scotland, Nurseries section

James Henderson & Sons
Kingholm Quay, Dumfries, Dumfries & Galloway DG1 4SU
☎ 0387 52234   FAX 0387 62302

CONTACT Richard J. Henderson
OPEN Mail order only
SPECIALITIES Seeds
CATALOGUE On request
MAIL ORDER Yes

Seed potato merchants with a wholesale and retail business. They supply many garden centres but you can also order direct. This family firm currently lists 36 varieties including 'Pink Fir Apple', and a special potato fertiliser.

Jim & Jenny Archibald
Bryn Collen, Ffostrasol, Llandysul, Dyfed SA44 5SB

CONTACT Jim and Jenny Archibald
OPEN Mail order only
SPECIALITIES Seeds
CATALOGUE On request
MAIL ORDER Yes

Serious alpine seed list for serious alpine enthusiasts. The Archibalds are professional collectors, and the list is based on their extensive trips. It includes detailed collection, cultivation and historical notes. Many species will be unavailable elsewhere. This year's list will concentrate on South American species.

John Chambers Wild Flower Seeds
15 Westleigh Road, Barton Seagrave, Kettering, Northamptonshire NN15 5AJ
☎ 0933 652562   FAX 0933 652576
OPEN Mail order only
SPECIALITIES Seeds; wild flowers
CATALOGUE On request
MAIL ORDER Yes
SHOP Books

SHOWS International Spring Gardening Fair; Malvern Spring; Chelsea; BBC GW Live
GIFT TOKENS Own

Biggest and best known of the wild flower merchants, with everything from British natives and butterfly plants to mixtures and grass seeds. There's also a good choice of books in the somewhat frenetic catalogue. Keep an eye out for their Chelsea displays: they hit the jackpot with best in show last year for their controversial Seaside Garden.

Johnsons Seeds
W W Johnson & Sons Ltd, London Road, Boston, Lincolnshire PE21 8AD
☎ 0205 365051   FAX 0205 310148

CONTACT Richard Johnson
OPEN Mail order and nationwide stockists
SPECIALITIES Seeds
NEW FOR 1994 *Salvia coccinea* 'Coral Nymph'; Stock 'Cinderella Mixed'; *Impatiens* 'Super Elfin Pastel Mixed F1 Hybrid'; *Oenothera caespitosa*; *Calceolaria* 'Sunset Mixed F1 Hybrid'; Tomato 'Typhoon'
CATALOGUE 50p
MAIL ORDER Yes

Founded in 1820 and still run by the Johnson family. Large collection of general flower and vegetable seed available by post. Flower packets contain an illustrated plastic label for the first time this year. The company's products, including its grass seed range, are also sold in shops and garden centres. There's also a wholesale division.

Kings Crown of Kelvedon
Monks Farm, Pantlings Lane, Coggeshall Road, Kelvedon, Essex CO5 9PG
☎ 0376 570000
OPEN Mail order only
SPECIALITIES Seeds
CATALOGUE On request
MAIL ORDER Yes

Good value retail seed list: all the seed is untreated. Strong on herbs and sweet peas. They also have a large wholesale flower and vegetable seed business aimed at growers.

Landlife Wildflowers Ltd
See Merseyside, Nurseries section

Mackey's Garden Centre
See Co. Dublin, Eire, Nurseries section

Marshalls

S E Marshall & Co Ltd, Wisbech, Cambridgeshire
PE13 2RF

☎ 0945 583407   📠 0945 588235

CONTACT   Val Green
OPEN   Mail order
SPECIALITIES   Seeds
NEW FOR 1994   Potato 'Kestrel'; Potato 'Samba'; Lettuce 'Tiger'; Lettuce 'Raisa'; Beetroot 'Action'; Beetroot 'Lola'; Carrot 'Lisa'; Sweet Corn 'Honey and Cream'; Cauliflower 'Limelight'; Celery 'Victoria'; Pansy 'Romeo and Juliet'; African Marigold 'Excel Orange'
CATALOGUE   On request
MAIL ORDER   Yes
GIFT TOKENS   Own

Fenland seed company which specialises in vegetables and seed potatoes: they have a range of popular flowers too, and own Elm House Nursery (which supplies young plants). Like the other major seed firms they place great emphasis on looking after their customers: there are free seeds for larger orders. Regular opportunities to trial (and report) on varieties before they are properly introduced.

Monocot Nursery

See Avon, Nurseries section

Mr Fothergill's Seeds Ltd

Gazeley Road, Kentford, Newmarket, Suffolk
CB8 7QB

☎ 0638 751887

CONTACT   Customer services
OPEN   Mail order only
SPECIALITIES   Seeds
NEW FOR 1994   Carrot 'Newmarket F1 hybrid'; Onion 'Rijnsburger 2 Sito'; Lettuce 'Action'; *Impatiens* 'Tempo Jazz F1 hybrid'; Sweet Pea 'Fantasia'; Pansy 'Romeo and Juliet'; Pansy 'Armado Mixed S1 hybrid'
CATALOGUE   On request
MAIL ORDER   Yes
GIFT TOKENS   Own

General seed company selling flowers, vegetables and some sundries from a colourful catalogue. High standard of service and information.

Northside Seeds

323 Norwood Road, London SE24 9AQ
☎ 081 671 2654

CONTACT   Nicholas Turland
OPEN   Mail order
SPECIALITIES   Seeds
CATALOGUE   See below
MAIL ORDER   Yes

Seed collector who is an expert on the Greek flora. You subscribe to a share in the trip: the seed is then distributed proportionally.

Peter Grayson - Sweet Pea Seedsman

34 Glenthorne Close, Brampton, Chesterfield,
Derbyshire S40 3AR
☎ 0246 278503

CONTACT   Peter Grayson
OPEN   Mail order only
SPECIALITIES   Seeds
CATALOGUE   On request
MAIL ORDER   Yes

A short but enticing list which includes unrivalled collections of *Lathyrus* species, and pre-Spencer Grandifloras (or Heirlooms), and some of Mr Grayson's introductions. Seed is produced on site. Two booklets, on cultivating sweet peas (£2.50), and on raising new varieties (£5), will be available shortly.

Phedar Nursery

See Cheshire, Nurseries section

The Plant Lovers

See Lincolnshire, Nurseries section

Plant World Botanic Gardens

See Devon, Nurseries section

Potterton and Martin

See Lincolnshire, Nurseries section

Roy Young Seeds

23 Westland Chase, West Winch, Kings Lynn,
Norfolk PE33 0QH
☎ 0553 840867

CONTACT   Roy Young
OPEN   Mail order only
SPECIALITIES   Seeds
CATALOGUE   On request (retail and wholesale)
MAIL ORDER   Yes

Cacti and succulent seeds by post, for retail and wholesale customers. Much of the seed is harvested from their own plants. The *Lithops* range is especially notable. Many items are in short supply, and so telephone orders are not accepted.

S & N Brackley

117 Winslow Road, Wingrave, Aylesbury,
Buckinghamshire HP22 4QB
☎ 0296 681384

CONTACT   Mrs S. Brackley
OPEN   For collection in April only
SPECIALITIES   Seeds; sweet peas; vegetables

NEW FOR 1994   Sweet Pea 'Anne Gregg'; Sweet Pea 'Balmoral'
CATALOGUE   On request
MAIL ORDER   Yes
SHOWS   RHS Westminster; Chelsea; BBC GW Live; Hampton Court

Sweet pea specialists, both as seeds and as young plants: garden and exhibition varieties. They also produce exhibition vegetable seeds, with leek and onion plants available in April.

S M McArd

39 West Road, Pointon, Sleaford, Lincolnshire NG34 0NA
☎ 0529 240765   ℻ 0529 240765

CONTACT   S. McArd
OPEN   Mail order only
SPECIALITIES   Seeds
CATALOGUE   On request
MAIL ORDER   Yes

Carefully chosen vegetable seeds divided into such headings as unusual and oriental vegetables, and 'economical F1s'. Some bulbs and flower seeds too.

Salley Gardens

See Cumbria, Nurseries section

Samuel Dobie & Son Ltd

Broomhill Way, Torquay, Devon TQ2 7QW
☎ 0803 616281

OPEN   Mail order only
SPECIALITIES   Seeds
CATALOGUE   On request
MAIL ORDER   Yes
GIFT TOKENS   Own

General seed company with a catalogue of flower and vegetable varieties. They specialise in young annual plants also, and have a decent range of garden equipment too.

Sawyers Seeds

Sawyers Farm Ltd, Little Cornard, Sudbury, Suffolk CO10 0NY
☎ 0787 228498   ℻ 0787 227258

CONTACT   John and Caroline Stevens
SPECIALITIES   Seeds; wild flowers
CATALOGUE   On request
MAIL ORDER   Yes

This seed firm has recently stopped supplying herbs: they now concentrate on wild flower seed and mixed grass and flower seed for conservation use. Mainly trade: you buy by weight. Economical for large quantities.

The Seed House

9a Widley Road, Cosham, Portsmouth, Hampshire PO6 2DS
☎ 0705 325639

CONTACT   Richard Spearing
OPEN   Mail order only
SPECIALITIES   Australian plants; seeds
CATALOGUE   On request
MAIL ORDER   Yes; £5 minimum order

Interesting list of Australian native plants, including *Callistemon* and *Eucalyptus* as well as less common genera. The species are chosen with regard to suitability for a European climate.

Seeds-by-Size

45 Crouchfield, Boxmoor, Hemel Hempstead, Hertfordshire HP1 1PA
☎ 0442 251458

CONTACT   John Robert Size
OPEN   Mail order only
SPECIALITIES   Seeds
CATALOGUE   On request
MAIL ORDER   Yes

Over 1,250 vegetable strains, and around 3,000 flower varieties. Seeds are sold by weight in any quantity from ½ gram up: the pricing system looks more daunting than it really is. Mr Size is good source for many old and hard to obtain varieties.

Southfield Nurseries

See Lincolnshire, Nurseries section

Stewarts (Nottm) Ltd

3 George Street, Nottingham, Nottinghamshire NG1 3BH
☎ 0602 476338

CONTACT   Brenda Lochhead
OPEN   9 am - 5.30 pm
SPECIALITIES   Seeds
CATALOGUE   On request
MAIL ORDER   Yes
SHOP   Seeds and bulbs; chemicals; fertilisers; sundries
GIFT TOKENS   HTA

Long-established seed and bulb merchant. Seeds and bulbs, including potatoes and their own grass seed mixtures. Their Economy collections of flowers and vegetables are packaged by them.

Suttons Seeds

Hele Road, Torquay, Devon TQ2 7QJ
☎ 0803 614455

OPEN   Mail order only
SPECIALITIES   Seeds

CATALOGUE On request
MAIL ORDER Yes
GIFT TOKENS Own

Famous old seed house with a strong catalogue of flowers and vegetable varieties as well as a useful range of garden sundries and plants.

Thompson & Morgan
Poplar Lane, Ipswich, Suffolk IP8 3BU
☎ 0473 688821   📠 0473 680199

SPECIALITIES Seeds
NEW FOR 1994 *Nemophila atromaria* 'Snowstorm; *Nicotiana* 'Domino Salmon-Pink F1 hybrid'; *Impatiens* 'Spectra Salmon Shades'; *Phacelia parryi* 'Royal Admiral'; *Ipomoea hirsuta* 'Mini Sky-Blue'; *Potentilla atrosanguinea*; *Catanache caerulea* 'Bicolor'; Runner Bean 'Red Rum'; Carrot 'Fly Away' F1 hybrid; Snap Pea 'Sugar Gem'
CATALOGUE On request
MAIL ORDER Yes
GIFT TOKENS Own

Established in 1855. The T & M list is the world's largest illustrated seed catalogue. It combines a tradition of good new introductions with a wide choice of less easily attainable plants. This year, for instance, they are selling pre-germinated seed of the spotted orchid, *Dactylorrhiza maculata*. Like all the major seed companies they pride themselves on their service to customers.

Unwins Seeds Ltd
Histon, Cambridge, Cambridgeshire CB4 4LE
☎ 0223 236236   📠 0223 237437

CONTACT Order Department
OPEN Mail order and retailers nationwide
SPECIALITIES Seeds
NEW FOR 1994 Buzy Lizzie 'Cherry Ripple'; French Marigold 'Royal King'; *Helichrysum* 'Sombrero'; Cornflower 'Florence'; Ornamental Tobacco 'Domino Salmon Pink'; Autumn Broccoli 'Trixie'; Squash 'Unwins Butternut'; Lettuce 'Lumina'; Melon 'No Name'; Broad Bean 'Red Epicure'; Carnation 'Monarch'
CATALOGUE On request; October

MAIL ORDER Yes

Long famous as breeders of sweet peas. Unwins also has a full choice of flowers and vegetables, including mixtures, new introductions and established varieties.

The Van Hage Garden Company
See Hertfordshire, Nurseries section

W Robinson & Sons Ltd
Sunny Bank, Forton, Preston, Lancashire PR3 0BN
☎ 0524 79121033

LOCATION 17 miles north of Preston on A6
OPEN Phone first
SPECIALITIES Seeds
CATALOGUE On request
MAIL ORDER Yes

Home of the 'Mammoth' seed strain: exhibition and garden vegetable seeds, including the 'Mammoth Improved Onion'. Seedlings and small plants are also available.

Westfield Cacti
See Devon, Nurseries section

Wild Seeds
Branas, Llandderfel, Gwynedd LL23 7RF

CONTACT Mike Thorne
OPEN Mail order only
SPECIALITIES Seeds; wild flowers
CATALOGUE On request
MAIL ORDER Yes

Native plants, including bulbs and trees, available as seed and as plants. All are available in quantity. Special flower mixtures for different habitats.

The Wildlife Gardening Centre
See Oxfordshire, Nurseries section

YSJ Seeds
See Somerset, Nurseries section

14

Seed Exchange Schemes

Many of the specialist and general societies run a seed exchange. Sometimes participation is free, sometimes there is a charge. These schemes are usually an excellent way of obtaining interesting and unusual species. Some general points: supply and demand rarely balance out, so the popular items will be in short supply. You ought to respond very promptly, and accept that your application may be scaled down considerably. Be aware that naming may not always be accurate, and that many forms and most hybrids will not come true from seed. The seed is also likely to be open-pollinated, so there is a chance of further hybridisation too. If you sow seed from a hybrid with a cultivar name (e.g., *Aster* × *frikartii* 'Mönch') it is important that you do not give the seedlings you raise the cultivar name. Failure to follow this simple rule is the cause of more wrong naming in the horticulture industry than any other factor, and it can lead to the eventual extinction of the original plant. These seed schemes are very labour intensive, so be patient with the organisers, many of whom are working on a voluntary basis. If you can, consider contributing seed yourself. Often this will bring you a higher allocation, and the schemes depend upon people putting material in as well as taking it out. Serious seed raisers may find it worth their while to join one of the American or international societies, many of whom have excellent schemes. We suggest you consult *Gardening by Mail* (Tusker Press, 1990) for more information. Every year the organisers of seed schemes are driven to distraction by people applying for schemes which they are not entitled to take part in, and by people who ignore the stated procedures. Do not apply if you are not a member. If you are interested in the seeds, then think about joining the society itself through the usual channels. Non-members who try to take advantage are unlikely to receive a sympathetic response. It is only courtesy to follow the rules for taking part in any distribution: you should not contact the seed officers except as requested.

Alpine Garden Society

AGS Centre, Avon Bank, Pershore, Hereford & Worcester WR10 3JP

CONTACT Seed Distribution Manager
See the Societies, specialist section
SCOPE Alpine and rock garden plants mostly, but some herbaceous plants, trees and shrubs
VARIETIES 10,000
COST 15 packets for £2.50; 5p a packet for surplus seed
LIST DESPATCHED Request list in January
CONTRIBUTIONS Before November

An excellent list. The scheme has a long lead time: you have to request the list well in advance. The booklet includes material from members' gardens and species from named collectors and sites. Some items are scarce and sell out very quickly: you are asked to give alternatives. Even prompt responses will normally find that their allocation has had to be scaled down. The lottery packets (20 varieties of their choice) are a bargain for the adventurous.

British Clematis Society

See the Societies, specialist section
SCOPE *Clematis* species and hybrids
VARIETIES Over 100
COST Approximately £1 per packet; five free packets for donors
LIST DESPATCHED Early spring; updated late summer
CONTRIBUTIONS Seed to BCS Seed Exchange before year end

A list of collected seeds, with details of donors, is circulated in the spring. Members indicate preferences. The list is a mixture of species and hybrids, so it should appeal to those who want to experiment. Donors receive five packets free. Left over seed is then sold at society meetings and events, including the Malvern Spring Show.

The British Gladiolus Society
7 Kingston Lane, Southwick, Brighton, East Sussex BN42 4SJ

CONTACT Distribution Officer
See the Societies, specialist section
SCOPE *Gladiolus* varieties
VARIETIES Between 100 to 150
COST Sold to the public at shows; available on request to members
LIST DESPATCHED No list: stock varies
CONTRIBUTIONS Spare cormlets should be sent to the distribution officer

The system relies upon members sending in varieties, so the number of varieties available changes constantly. The sale of cormlets is an important source of revenue for the society: look out for the publicity stand at shows.

British Iris Society
5 Storeys Lane, Burgh le Marsh, Skegness, Lincolnshire PE24 5LR

CONTACT Seed Distribution Officer
See the Societies, specialist section
SCOPE *Iris* species, hybrids and other irids
VARIETIES Over 300
COST Members only: details from the British Iris Society
LIST DESPATCHED January
CONTRIBUTIONS Material can be sent at any time to the seed distribution officer

Restricted to members only: the society has an international membership so there are always unusual species collected in the wild and a good selection of the latest hybrids. The list includes most of the species *Iris*, with self crosses and crosses between known hybrids (with breeding potential). There are also up to forty other irids, ranging from *Anomatheca* to *Watsonia*. The society also has a substantial Plant Sales List including species, classic bearded and beardless irises, and new hybrids.

British Pteridological Society
201 Chesterton Road, Cambridge, Cambridgeshire CB4 1AH

CONTACT Organiser, Spore Exchange Scheme
See the Societies, specialist section

SCOPE Fern species and varieties from all over the world
VARIETIES Over 750
COST Members only; 20 packets free each year
LIST DESPATCHED January
CONTRIBUTIONS Fresh spores, labelled with botanical name, collector, source and collection date should be sent to the organiser

Restricted to society members only. A new list of fern varieties and species is published every January. Members can apply for 20 packets of free spores each year. The list includes spores of garden origin and wild collected spores. Contributors should make sure that such spores are fully labelled, with the exact collection location for wild spores in particular. Further details from the organiser.

The Cottage Garden Society
See the Societies, specialist section

SCOPE Cottage garden style seeds, both species and named varieties
COST 15 packets per member; £2 handling charge
LIST DESPATCHED January
CONTRIBUTIONS By mid October

The Cyclamen Society
CONTACT Hon. Seed Distribution Manager
See the Societies, specialist section
SCOPE *Cyclamen* species and cultivars
VARIETIES Approx 50
COST Several packets free; small charge for extra quantities
LIST DESPATCHED Application form appears with donation form in June
CONTRIBUTIONS Requested in June via *Cyclamen* journal

Members of the society only. Each member receives about four packets free, with an extra free allowance going to donors. Seed is distributed promptly to ensure freshness. The scheme anticipates what will be contributed, so you apply at the same time as you send in donations. Seed from Cyclamen Society Collecting Expeditions is also often available: in 1993 this cost £2 per packet.

The Delphinium Society
5 Woodfield Avenue, Carshalton Beeches, Surrey SM5 3JB

CONTACT Hon. Secretary
See the Societies, specialist section
SCOPE Hand crosses, cultivars and open pollinated delphinium seed
VARIETIES See October list

COST Hand crossed and scarce items are reserved for members; open pollinated seed is sold to the public at shows
LIST DESPATCHED October
CONTRIBUTIONS Contact the Seed Manager

Mainly for members, but see below. A list is circulated in October of the available varieties. The named cultivars and hand crosses are usually in short supply and members have priority. The open pollinated seed is more widely available, and the public can buy it from the society's stands at Chelsea, RHS Westminster shows or their Wisley shows. The seed manager monitors contributions, including open pollinated seeds, to ensure that only good cultivars are used as sources. Seed should not be sent to the secretary: see the society bulletin for further details.

The Mammillaria Society
See the Societies, specialist section

Mesemb Study Group
See the Societies, specialist section

SCOPE *Mesembryanthemum* and related genera
LIST DESPATCHED January edition of bulletin

Some of the seed is collected in the wild, and the organisers also draw on hand pollinated cultivated material and commercial sources. Collection data and numbers are available. The list is circulated to group members in the January bulletin.

Northern Horticultural Society
See the Societies, specialist section
SCOPE Seeds of all types from the garden, including those from National Collections
VARIETIES Over 1,000
COST £4 donation requested
LIST DESPATCHED January or February

Restricted to members of the Northern Horticultural Society only.

The Royal Horticultural Society
RHS Garden, Wisley, Woking, Surrey GU23 6QB

CONTACT Director of Horticulture (Seed application)
See the Societies, specialist section
VARIETIES 800 species
COST Members only: not available to affiliated societies
LIST DESPATCHED October

Members need to send a large sae to the above address (with their membership number): orders have to be returned by the end of December. Overseas members receive the list automatically. A respectable list, but not of the highest interest, and helpings are seldom generous.

The Saintpaulia & Houseplant Society
33 Church Road, Newbury Park, Ilford, Essex IG2 7ET

CONTACT Hon. Secretary
See the Societies, specialist section
SCOPE Named *Saintpaulia* leaves
VARIETIES Around 140
COST 3 to 4 leaves per applicant; a small charge is made
LIST DESPATCHED List is published in the April bulletin
CONTRIBUTIONS Details appear in the January bulletin

Restricted to society members. An annual appeal is published for named leaves: these are sorted and stored and a list of available varieties then appears in the society's April bulletin. The leaves are posted to members in small boxes in late May. The nature of the material means this is a time consuming and delicate process. Would-be contributors should follow the instructions in the January bulletin: leaves should not be sent to the secretary.

The Scottish Rock Garden Club
1 Wallace Road, Dunblane, Perthshire, Central FK15 9HY

CONTACT Seed Reception Manager
See the Societies, specialist section
SCOPE Plants and bulbs for rock, peat and woodland gardens
VARIETIES 4,000
COST Approx. £2 per allocation
LIST DESPATCHED Christmas
CONTRIBUTIONS Contributions to Seed Reception Manager before November

Seeds are collected by their worldwide membership and distributed in time for spring sowing. One of the best schemes, and a reason in itself for joining the society. The list usually contains many otherwise unobtainable species. Donors have priority over non-donors, and applications are dealt with in rotation. Alpine gardeners say they usually have a better chance of getting what they want from this list than from similar schemes.

Wakefield and North of England Tulip Society
See the Societies, specialist section
SCOPE Spare bulbs of English florist tulips
LIST DESPATCHED October

15

Overgrown & Undergrown

This is the editors' personal choice of plants which deserve to be more or less grown. They are arranged genus by genus from A to Z with one absence. We challenge any reader to produce a pair from a genus beginning with X. Some we consider overrated, and some underrated. There are no other value judgments attached: this not a list of Ins and Outs, just of plants which are overgrown and undergrown.

Overgrown

Artemisia absinthium 'Lambrook Silver'
Berberis thunbergii
Choisya ternata ' Sundance'
Deutzia scabra 'Candidissima'
Epilobium canum 'Albiflorum'
Forsythia 'Beatrix Farrand'
Geranium endressii
Hebe × franciscana 'Variegata'
Ilex aquifolium 'Silver Queen'
Jasminum beesianum
Kniphofia 'Maid of Orleans'
Ligustrum ovalifolium 'Argenteum'
Magnolia kobus
Nepeta cataria
Oenothera acaulis
Philadelphus 'Manteau d'Hermine'
Quercus rubra
Ribes alpinum
Symphytum × uplandicum
Tradescantia × andersoniana 'Isis'
Ulmus × hollandica 'Jacqueline Hillier'
Viburnum × bodnantense 'Dawn'
Wisteria sinensis 'Alba'
Yucca filamentosa
Zantedeschia aethiopica 'Crowborough'

Undergrown

Artemisia 'Powis Castle'
Berberis temolaica
Choisya 'Aztec Pearl'
Deutzia corymbosa
Epilobium canum ssp. latifolium
Forsythia viridissima
Geranium wlassovianum
Hebe salicifolia 'Variegata'
Ilex aquifolium 'Silver Milkmaid'
Jasminum × stephanense
Kniphofia 'Little Maid'
Ligustrum lucidum 'Excelsum Superbum'
Magnolia 'Wada's Memory'
Nepeta clarkei
Oenothera caespitosa
Philadelphus microphyllus
Quercus palustris
Ribes × gordonianum
Symphytum caucasicum
Tradescantia × andersoniana 'Blue Stone'
Ulmus parvifolia 'Frosty'
Viburnum × bodnantense 'Charles Lamont'
Wisteria venusta
Yucca whipplei
Zantedeschia aethiopica 'Green Goddess'

16

Gardens

This section recommends gardens in Great Britain and Ireland. Our aim is to supply sufficient detail to enable readers to decide whether and when to plan a visit. The list is not exhaustive. It offers a selection of the different types of garden which are open to the public: ancient and modern, large and small, public and private. The editors welcome suggestions for additions, deletions or alterations to entries.

Gardens are listed by county or region (for Scotland), and then alphabetically by name. The order is England, Wales, Scotland, Northern Ireland and Eire. This section also serves as a reference source for the rest of the book, where gardens are referred to only by their name, followed by their county, as in Marwood Hill, Devon, and Rowallane, Co. Down. All the counties of Sussex and Yorkshire appear under 'S' and 'Y', respectively.

The basis for all the practical information about directions, open times, admission charges, parking, loos, disabled facilities, shops and refreshments has been the owners or their staff, backed up by our own enquiries, where applicable. The accuracy of these details is not guaranteed, but is believed to be correct at the time of going to press. We have taken the unusual step of listing the telephone and fax numbers to which enquiries should be directed about a garden. In many cases this is the private telephone line of the owners: readers are strongly urged to respect their privacy. Some owners were unable to tell us their 1994 admission charges and, in those cases, we have indicated that the prices quoted are for 1993. All entrance fees are, in any event, liable to be changed: visitors should always take more money than they think they will need.

The guide indicates whether parking is available: this may be at the garden itself or on a public road very close to it. In the case of refreshments, however, we have referred only to what is offered within the garden itself, and not to restaurants, tea-rooms and public houses nearby. It is often a condition of visiting a garden that no photographs taken there may be used for sale or public reproduction without the consent of the garden's owner. Visitors should also remember that most gardens only accept dogs if they are kept on leads.

Information about outsize trees is taken from a fascinating small publication *Champion Trees in the British Isles* by A F Mitchell, V E Hallett and J E J White (3rd Edition 1990, HMSO £3.80). There are two ways of measuring trees: height and girth. Sometimes the tallest specimen will also have the thickest trunk – but not always. Both the tallest and the biggest can claim to be the champion tree, and we have made this distinction when noting record breakers in gardens. Tree measurements can never be fully up to date: some records have not been verified since the great gales of 1987 and 1990, but *Champion Trees in the British Isles* clearly indicates where to find the best collections of trees – for example, Westonbirt Arboretum in Gloucestershire and Hergest Croft in Hereford & Worcester.

A note on the choice of gardens is appropriate. Our aim is to be comprehensive but realistic. All major gardens which are open regularly are listed as a matter of course. These include many gardens of the National Trust as well as botanic and public gardens and those attached to stately homes. But many gardens do not open to visitors regularly: the National Gardens Scheme lists over three thousand. We have found space for a selection of these gardens which open only once a year or by appointment. Some guides would omit them on the grounds that it is not worthwhile to give publicity to gardens which so few people can visit. We take the view that, if a good garden is seldom open, it is all the more important to know when the opportunity will arise to see it.

The starting point for garden visiting must be the 'Yellow Book' which the National Gardens Scheme publishes annually in February under the full title

Gardens of England & Wales Open to the Public.
It is wonderfully comprehensive and totally undis-
criminating. The owners write their own garden
entries, with the result that a really good garden may
come across as self-deprecatingly boring, while an
exciting description can often lead to a disappointment. Beware of self-publicists: you can usually spot
the hype.

The Yellow Book suffers from another irritating
shortcoming: the National Gardens Scheme is reluctant to accept some of the boundary changes which
took effect in 1974. East Sussex and West Sussex
are still treated as one; Merseyside and Greater
Manchester are lumped in with Lancashire; Oxfordshire incorporates the whole of the Vale of the
White Horse, at the expense of Berkshire; and
Rutland is still named as a separate county. The
Yellow Book has a further disadvantage: it does not
mention that some gardens are open at other times,
not for the benefit of the National Gardens Scheme.
Indeed, some open for the National Gardens Scheme
only one day a year, and for their own funds for the
other 364 days. But, for all this, the Yellow Book is
the single most important guide to visiting gardens
in England and Wales, and the least expensive.
Scotland has its own Yellow Book called *The Gardens of Scotland*. This is available from Scotland's
Gardens Scheme, 31 Castle Terrace, Edinburgh EH1
2EL, and lists over 300 gardens throughout Scotland. Unfortunately, it divides the country into dis-
tricts and areas which do not correspond with either
the old counties or new regions. The list of gardens
is, however, given alphabetically, and the openings
are separately listed in calendar order, so it is not
difficult to follow. *The Gardens of Scotland* is
essential reading for anyone who wishes to know
about the many wonderful Scottish gardens which
are seldom open to the public. We strongly recommend Graham Rose's *The Good Gardens Guide*,
which comes out every autumn: the 1994 edition is
published by Vermilion and costs £12.99. Its quality
is inevitably somewhat uneven because the entries
are written by many different hands and the standard of its judgements varies. Nevertheless, it has
unearthed many good gardens and described them
in the detail which is not available elsewhere. Above
all, it sorts out and evaluates the thousands of gardens in the Yellow Book. *The Good Gardens Guide
1994* itself lists over one thousand gardens, some
across the Channel within a day's driving distance

of the Tunnel. It saves so much time and money –
not to mention humour – which would otherwise
be lost driving many miles to a disappointing garden,
that *The Good Gardens Guide 1994* must be
worth every penny of its price.

Patrick Taylor's *The 1994 Gardener's Guide to
Britain* (Pavilion, £10.99) is beautifully laid out and
illustrated – its author is a publisher. It is also
elegantly written and sound in its judgements. It
describes rather too few gardens and nurseries, and
their geographic spread is sometimes too thin to
make it really useful. It is, however, recommended
as a point of first reference and its judgements cannot
be faulted – accurate, observant and intelligent.

The Good Gardens Guide and *The Good Gardener's Guide to Britain* are especially valuable
because they include a substantial number of public
parks where entry is free and unrestricted. These
may not be gardens in the popular sense, but they
are of great potential interest to garden visitors. Both
books also list good nurseries – Patrick Taylor in
particular recognises that visiting new nurseries is
just as enjoyable and important to a keen gardener
as seeing other people's gardens.

British Leisure Publications produces an illustrated annual paperback guide *Historic Houses,
Castles and Gardens in Great Britain and Ireland*.
It lists about 1,500 historic properties in the United
Kingdom and Ireland, including many of the grander
gardens in this section. This large, well-illustrated
handbook is most useful as a reference source for
planning a trip: the garden descriptions tend to be
short and uninformative. You could not say the same
about *The Blue Guide to Gardens of England*
(£14.99). Its scope is limited to about 300 gardens,
all in England, but they are described in great detail
and often illustrated with drawings and plans of
garden layouts.

The National Trust Gardens Handbook describes fully about 130 gardens. Most are attached
to historic houses. Some are little known, and deservedly so. We have included only those which we
believe our readers will find worth visiting. The
handbook is excellent; its detail includes the altitude
and terrain of a garden, and how many gardeners are
employed there. It also lists such special features as
NCCPG collections and garden architecture, suggests the best time to visit a garden and, most
usefully, tells you when to avoid it. In its detail *The
National Trust Gardens Handbook* is a model guide

to gardens, although it is limited to National Trust properties and its scope does not extend to Scotland or Eire: a snip at £3.95. English Heritage publishes a *Guide to English Heritage Properties 1994*, which is issued to all members. Although many of the properties which it owns are ancient monuments, most notably castles and abbeys, English Heritage does own a number of good gardens, including Belsay Hall, Northumberland, and Chiswick House, London. In Scotland, historic gardens are maintained by Historic Scotland and include such important gardens as Edzell Castle. There are no gardens of importance maintained by the Welsh Historic Monuments Commission. The Ulster Gardens Scheme raises funds every year for work in National Trust Gardens which would not otherwise be possible. It is run by the Northern Ireland region of the National Trust at Rowallane House, Saintfield, Ballynahinch, Co Down, BT24 7LH (Tel: 0238 510721; Fax: 0238 511242). It usually lists about a dozen gardens, mainly in Down, Armagh and Derry, and each opens only once. All are smallish private gardens made by the present owners: the Ulster Gardens Scheme eschews the big gardens of the stately homes and the National Trust itself.

Not all genera are the subject of a National Collection: there are still some horticulturally important groups of plants which have not yet been seriously collected and studied under the auspices of the NCCPG. Other genera have been split into a number of different collections. This is particularly necessary in the case of such a large genus as *Rhododendron* or one which requires a great variety of growing conditions, as *Euphorbia* does. Moreover, the NCCPG has wisely introduced a number of duplicate collections so that plants are grown in two or more gardens. The need to maintain duplicate collections and split large genera explains why certain names occur several times in our list of National Collections. That list is not comprehensive. We have only included those of which we have received notice. A full list is available from the NCCPG and a 1994 edition will be published during the course of the year.

ENGLAND

AVON

The American Museum
Claverton Manor, Bath, Avon BA2 7BD
☎ 0225 460503   ⊞ 0225 480726

OWNER Trustees of the American Museum in Britain
LOCATION Off A36 south of Bath
OPEN 1 pm – 6 pm, Tuesday – Friday; 12 noon – 6 pm, Saturdays, Sundays and Bank Holiday Mondays; 31 March to 31 October
ADMISSION Adults £1.50; Children £1.00
FACILITIES Parking; dogs permitted; loos; access for the disabled; plants for sale; book shop, herb shop and country store; light lunches at weekends; tea, coffee and American cookies
FEATURES Good collection of trees; herbaceous borders; fine conifers; fruit and vegetables of special interest; herbs; old roses and climbers; good topiary; woodland garden
ENGLISH HERITAGE GRADE II
FRIENDS Apply to Membership Secretary (0225 460503)

15 immaculate acres devoted to elements of American gardening, including a Colonial herb garden ('Colonial' = pre-1778), old roses (best in June) and a pastiche of Mount Vernon. But some say it is *all* a pastiche, a chunk of American folksiness slightly incongruous in the Avon Valley.

Badminton
Chipping Sodbury, Avon GL9 1DB
☎ 0454 218346

OWNER The Duke of Beaufort
LOCATION 5 miles east of Chipping Sodbury
OPEN 2 pm – 6 pm; 25 June
ADMISSION Adults £1.50; Senior Citizens £1.00; Children under 10 free
FACILITIES Parking; dogs permitted; loos; access for the disabled; plants for sale; tea, lemonade, cakes & scones
FEATURES Herbaceous borders; glasshouses to visit; old roses and climbers; sub-tropical plants
ENGLISH HERITAGE GRADE I

Since moving to Badminton ten years ago, the Duchess has begun a series of small formal gardens to the side of the house, which do not interfere with the grand 18th century vistas across three counties. These modern gardens run into each other like the rooms of the house and are each different in character. Work continues.

Bath Botanic Gardens

Royal Victoria Park, Bath, Avon
☎ 0225 448433   📠 0225 480072

OWNER Bath City Council
LOCATION West of city centre by Upper Bristol Road
OPEN Dawn – dusk; daily; all year
ADMISSION Free
FACILITIES Parking; dogs permitted; facilities for the disabled
FEATURES Good collection of trees; herbaceous borders; fine conifers; rock garden; old roses and climbers; water features; autumn colour; fine bedding displays; tallest tree of heaven *Ailanthus altissima* in England (and nine other record trees)
NCCPG NATIONAL COLLECTIONS *Scilla*
FRIENDS Newly formed – telephone 0225 448433 for details. Quarterly newsletter; lectures all through the year

9 acres of trees, shrubs, borders, limestone-loving plants and scented walks. Essentially a 'closed' collection and now run by the Parks Department as a public amenity. Standards are high, maintenance is good, and the seasonal highlights of bulbs and bedding are among the best. Some splendid old trees recall the garden's origin as a private collection.

Crowe Hall

Widcombe Hill, Bath, Avon BA2 6AR
☎ 0225 310322

OWNER John Barratt
LOCATION Off A36 up Widcombe Hill
OPEN 2 pm – 6 pm; 20 March, 24 April, 15 May, 5 & 26 June, 14 August
ADMISSION Adults £1.50; Children 30p
FACILITIES Parking; dogs permitted; loos; plants for sale; teas
FEATURES Follies and garden buildings; rock garden; old roses and climbers
ENGLISH HERITAGE GRADE II

One of the most extraordinary gardens we know. It looks straight out at the Capability Brown landscape at Prior Park, and 'borrows' it. Below the house is an Italianate terrace, which leads to a ferny rock garden (real rocky outcrops here) and down into a modern garden in the woodland.

Dyrham Park

near Chippenham, Avon SN14 8ER
☎ 0272 372501

OWNER The National Trust
LOCATION On A46, 8 miles north of Bath
OPEN 12 noon – 5.30 pm; Saturday – Wednesday; 3 April to 31 October
ADMISSION £4.70 house & garden; £1.50 park

FACILITIES Parking; loos; tea room
FEATURES Herbaceous borders; landscape designed by Humphry Repton; deer park; handsome conservatory;
ENGLISH HERITAGE GRADE II*

Fascinating for garden historians, who can study the Kip plan and trace the lines of the 17th century formal garden which Humphry Repton turned into classic English parkland. But pretty boring for the dedicated plantsman.

Essex House

Badminton, Chipping Sodbury, Avon GL9 1DD
☎ 0454 218288

OWNER Mr & Mrs James Lees-Milne
LOCATION Far end of Badminton village
OPEN By appointment, preferably groups
ADMISSION £2.00 for Macmillan nurses appeal
FACILITIES Parking; dogs permitted
FEATURES Old roses and climbers; good topiary; pretty parterres; unusual plants; weeping pears

A small garden made by the distinguished garden writer Alvilde Lees-Milne. The formal design uses box edging, topiary, silver foliage and soft colours to create a sense of space and quiet enchantment.

Goldney Hall

Lower Clifton Hill, Clifton, Bristol, Avon BS8 1BH
☎ 0272 265698   📠 0272 293414

OWNER The University of Bristol
LOCATION Top of Constitution Hill
OPEN 2 pm – 6 pm, Sunday 1 May & 15 May
ADMISSION Adults £1.50; Senior Citizens, Students & Children 75p
FACILITIES Loos; cream teas in the Orangery
FEATURES Herbaceous borders; follies and garden buildings; fruit and vegetables of special interest; glasshouses to visit; herbs; garden sculpture; interesting for children; holm oak hedge; many varieties of fruit; the *Chronicles of Narnia* were filmed in the grotto
ENGLISH HERITAGE GRADE II*

A Bristol merchant's extravagance, nearly 300 years ago. Ten acres in the middle of the City, with an elegant orangery, a gothic folly tower and the gorgeous Goldney Grotto, which sparkles with crystalline rocks among the shells.

The Manor House, Walton-in-Gordano

Walton-in-Gordano, Clevedon, Bristol, Avon BS21 7AN
☎ 0275 872067

OWNER Simon & Philippa Wills

LOCATION   North side of B3124 on Clevedon side of Walton-in-Gardano
OPEN   10 am – 4 pm; Wednesdays and Thursdays; 13 April to 15 September and 19 October to 3 November, plus some Sundays and Bank holidays for the NGS
ADMISSION   £1.50, accompanied children free
FACILITIES   Parking; loos; access for the disabled; plants for sale; teas on Sundays & Bank Holidays only
FEATURES   Herbaceous borders; fine conifers; fruit and vegetables of special interest; gravel or scree garden; herbs; plantsman's garden; rock garden; modern roses; old roses and climbers; water features; woodland garden; particularly good in July-August
NCCPG NATIONAL COLLECTIONS Dodecatheon

A really interesting plantsman's garden on a substantial scale, offering something for every taste, from autumn-flowering bulbs to rare conifers. The range of the Wills' interests is breath-taking and there is always much for the visitor to learn and enjoy, whatever the season. Beautifully maintained, too.

Sherborne Garden
Pear Tree House, Litton, Avon BA3 4PP
☎ 0761 241220

OWNER   Mr & Mrs John Southwell
LOCATION   ½ mile west of Litton village
OPEN   11 am – 6.30 pm; Mondays & Sundays; 6 June to 26 September, plus 3 April, 1 May, 5 June, 2 October. Other times by appointment. Parties by arrangement
ADMISSION   £1.50, children free
FACILITIES   Parking; dogs permitted; loos; access for the disabled; plants for sale; tea/coffee all times; teas 5 June & 2 October
FEATURES   Fine conifers; ecological interest; gravel or scree garden; herbs; plantsman's garden; rock garden; modern roses; old roses and climbers; water features; woodland garden; collection of hollies (180 varieties)

Plantsman's garden, started in a modest way in 1964 on ¾ acre but now extending to nearly 4 acres. Thickly planted, and wild at the edges. The owners are particularly interested in trees and plant them closely in groups for comparison: hence the holly wood, the larch wood and the salicetum (Salix = willow). But there is much more than trees and it is a garden to dawdle in and learn from.

University of Bristol Botanic Garden
Bracken Hill, North Road, Leigh Woods, Bristol, Avon BS8 3PF
☎ 0272 733682   FAX 0272 733682

OWNER   University of Bristol
LOCATION   Take M5 J17 towards Clifton, left into North Road before suspension bridge
OPEN   9 am – 5 pm; Monday – Friday; all year

ADMISSION   None (only on NGS open days)
FACILITIES   Parking; loos
FEATURES   Good collection of trees; herbaceous borders; fine conifers; ecological interest; glasshouses to visit; gravel or scree garden; herbs; plantsman's garden; rock garden; cistus; hebes; sempervivums; paeonies; aeoniums; salvias
FRIENDS   Good programme and privileges (e.g. seed list). Details from Nicholas Wray on 0272 733682

An educational and accessible garden that bridges the gap between botany and horticulture. Because of the climatic conditions in its unusual position above the Avon gorge, it has a particularly fine collection of South African and New Zealand plants. And of course there is the rare endemic Sorbus bristoliensis.

Vine House
Henbury, Bristol, Avon BS10 7AD
☎ 0272 503573

OWNER   Professor and Mrs T F Hewer
LOCATION   On Henbury Road, opposite Crow Lane
OPEN   2 pm – 7 pm; 3 & 4 April, 29 & 30 May, and by appointment
ADMISSION   £1; Senior Citizens and children 50p
FACILITIES   Dogs permitted; loos
FEATURES   Fine conifers; gravel or scree garden; plantsman's garden; old roses and climbers; water features; woodland garden; rare trees and shrubs; collected plants; shady 'cliff' garden

The garden of a great plant collector – Tom Hewer's trips to Iran and Afghanistan in the 1960s and 1970s introduced endless good novelties to our gardens. Some are here at Vine House, but much of the garden is a flowing plantsman's paradise, with good forms of trees and shrubs the main theme: Ribes × gordonianum and a huge Hydrangea sargentiana, for instance, often underplanted by naturalised bulbs.

BEDFORDSHIRE

Luton Hoo
The Mansion House, Luton, Bedfordshire LU1 3TQ
☎ 0582 22955   FAX 0582 34437

OWNER   Trustees of Luton Hoo Foundation
LOCATION   Signposted from J10 of M1
OPEN   12 noon – 5 pm; Friday – Sunday and Bank Holiday Mondays; 6 April to 17 October
ADMISSION   Adults £2.50; Senior Citizens & Students £2.25
FACILITIES   Parking; loos; access for the disabled; plants for sale; cafeteria
FEATURES   Herbaceous borders; landscape designed by Capability Brown; fine conifers; gravel or scree

garden; rock garden; modern roses; garden sculpture; water features; fine cedars

ENGLISH HERITAGE GRADE   II*

The grand Italianate formal gardens include a large rose garden stuffed with colour. But there is a a classic early rock garden (c.1900) and a Capability Brown park too.

Odell Castle

Odell, Bedfordshire MK43 7BB

☎ 0234 720240

OWNER   Lord Luke

LOCATION   North west of Bedford

OPEN   2 pm – 6 pm; 15 May and 19 June

ADMISSION   Adults £1.00, Children free

FACILITIES   Parking; dogs permitted; tea & biscuits

FEATURES   Herbaceous borders; fine conifers; modern roses; old roses and climbers

A new garden for a new castle, built in 1962, but drawing on an old landscape with grand old trees. The site is magnificent, with views down to the Ouse valley, and the modern gardens around the house are secondary to it. There are splendid herbaceous borders and a pretty rose garden.

The Swiss Garden

Old Warden, Biggleswade, Bedfordshire

☎ 0767 627666   FAX 0234 228921

OWNER   Shuttleworth Trust

LOCATION   1½ miles west of Biggleswade

OPEN   10 am – 6 pm, but 11 am – 6 pm on Sundays and Bank Holiday Mondays; daily except Tuesday; 1 April to 31 October. 11.00 am – 3.00 pm; daily except Tuesday; 1 January to 31 March

ADMISSION   Adults £2.00, Senior Citizenss £1.00, Children 75p

FACILITIES   Parking; loos; facilities for the disabled; publications and souvenirs shop; restaurant at neighbouring Shuttleworth collection

FEATURES   Fine conifers; follies and garden buildings; garden sculpture; water features; woodland garden; interesting for children; daffodils; rhododendrons; azaleas; Pulhamite grotto; fernery; Swiss cottage

ENGLISH HERITAGE GRADE   II*

FRIENDS   Details available at the entrance

A rustic, gothic landscape garden from c.1830, now maintained as a public amenity. Winding paths, little bridges across streams, picturesque huts and kiosks, vast conifers and cheerful rhododendrons make a unique experience. Great fun to visit.

Woburn Abbey

Woburn, Bedfordshire MK43 0TP

☎ 0525 290666   FAX 0525 290271

OWNER   The Marquess of Tavistock

LOCATION   1½ miles from Woburn on A4012

OPEN   10 am – 5 pm; daily; 27 March to 30 October. Private gardens open for NGS: 17 April, 12 June. Hornbeam Maze: 17 July & 21 August

ADMISSION   Park: £5 per car: NGS extra

FACILITIES   Parking; loos; two shops; coffee shop (teas & light meals)

FEATURES   Landscape designed by Capability Brown; fine conifers; water features; woodland garden; interesting for children; deer park

ENGLISH HERITAGE GRADE   I

Not a gardener's garden, though the park has many rare trees: the best way to see the famous redwood avenue is from the cable car. The private gardens are simple and formal, mainly 19th century and Italianate, but they include the hornbeam maze which has a Chinese pavilion in the centre.

Wrest Park

Silsoe, Bedfordshire MK45 4HS

☎ 0525 860152

OWNER   English Heritage

LOCATION   ¾ mile east of Silsoe

OPEN   10 am – 6 pm; Saturdays, Sundays and Bank Holiday Mondays; 1 April to 26 September

ADMISSION   Adults £1.70; Concessions £1.30; Children 85p

FACILITIES   Parking; dogs permitted; loos; gift shop; light refreshments

FEATURES   Landscape designed by Capability Brown; follies and garden buildings; garden sculpture; water features; grand parterres; long vistas

ENGLISH HERITAGE GRADE   I

The 'English Versailles', dominated by a graceful long canal which runs down to the classical domed pavilion built by Thomas Archer in 1710. Capability Brown came here later, but worked around the earlier design. The house came later still, in the 1830s. A garden of grandeur.

BERKSHIRE

Folly Farm

Sulhamstead, Reading, Berkshire RG7 4DF

☎ 0734 303098

OWNER   The Hon. Hugh Astor

LOCATION   On Sulhampstead road from Theale

OPEN   2 pm – 6 pm; 17 April, 30 May, 26 June. Private bookings on written application.

ADMISSION   £1.50 on open days, otherwise £2.50, for charity

FACILITIES   Parking; loos; teas; home-made cakes; biscuits

FEATURES Fruit and vegetables of special interest;
designed by Lutyens; modern roses; old roses and
climbers; good topiary; water features; lavender; lilies;
paeonies; iris; lupins; delphiniums
ENGLISH HERITAGE GRADE   II*

One of the most enchanting gardens to come from the
partnership between Sir Edwin Lutyens and Gertrude
Jekyll, the structure of Folly Farm is intact. The most
famous incidents are the canal garden, running up to a
double-gabled wing of the house, and the sunken rose
garden, where a cruciform bed of lavender rises from a
tank of waterlilies. The plantings have been adapted to
modern conditions and to the owners' taste for floribunda roses. Folly Farm is particularly lovely in spring
when drifts of anemones flower under cherries and
crabs.

Foxgrove Farm

Enborne, Newbury, Berkshire RG14 6RE
☎ 0635 40554

OWNER   Miss Audrey Vockins
LOCATION   On edge of village
OPEN   2 pm – 6 pm; 13 March, 10 April, 12 June, 2
October
ADMISSION   Adults £1.00, children free
FACILITIES   Parking; loos; facilities for the disabled;
plants for sale; tea & cakes
FEATURES   Herbaceous borders; gravel or scree gar-
den; primulas; spring and autumn bulbs

A plantsman's garden, linked to Louise Vockins' nursery next door (see Foxgrove Plants, Berkshire). Bulbs,
alpines and herbaceous plants are Audrey Vockins'
great interest. The hellebores, crocus and snowdrops
give a great display in March; colchicums are the main
reason to visit in October. There are good shrubs, roses
and handsome small trees too.

The Harris Garden

Plant Sciences Laboratory, University of Reading,
Whiteknights, Reading, Berkshire RG4 9EY
☎ 0734 318071   FAX 0734 750630

OWNER   University of Reading
LOCATION   On A327, 1 mile south east of Reading
OPEN   2 pm – 6 pm; 15 May; 10 July; 18 September
ADMISSION   Adults £1.00, Children free
FACILITIES   Parking; loos; facilities for the disabled; teas
FEATURES   Good collection of trees; herbaceous borders; fine conifers; ecological interest; fruit and vegetables of special interest; glasshouses to visit; gravel or
scree garden; herbs; plantsman's garden; rock garden;
modern roses; old roses and climbers; sub-tropical
plants; water features; woodland garden; particularly
interesting in winter; Mediterranean shrubs; hardy annuals; heathers; primula dell

NCCPG NATIONAL COLLECTIONS Iris
FRIENDS   The Friends of the Harris garden has an
active programme of events and gives members free
access to the garden. Ring Dr David Collett (0734
318024) in Department of Applied Statistics

This is the new botanic garden attached to Reading
University, which is the leading centre for teaching
economic and amenity horticulture. Started in 1988,
there is already much to see and to learn. Visit it now,
in the early years, and return as it matures.

Hazelby House

North End, Newbury, Berkshire RG15 0AZ
☎ 0635 253544   FAX 0635 254960

OWNER   Mr & Mrs Martin Lane Fox
LOCATION   6 miles south west of Newbury, right off
A343 to Ball Hill, ¼ mile on left
OPEN   By written appointment
ADMISSION   £2.00
FACILITIES   Parking; loos; plants for sale
FEATURES   Herbaceous borders; plantsman's garden;
old roses and climbers; water features; young garden

We have not seen this newish garden, made by Robin
Lane Fox's brother, but it has received such universal
praise for its tight design and luscious planting that we
include in The Gardener's Yearbook nevertheless.

Old Rectory Cottage

Tidmarsh, Pangbourne, Berkshire RG8 8ER
☎ 0734 843241

OWNER   Mr & Mrs A W A Baker
LOCATION   Small lane on right 200 yards north of
Tidmarsh village
OPEN   2 pm – 6 pm; 27 February, 10 April, 8 May,
12 June, 3 July
ADMISSION   £1.00
FACILITIES   Parking; loos; plants for sale
FEATURES   Good collection of trees; herbaceous borders; fine conifers; ecological interest; gravel or scree
garden; herbs; plantsman's garden; rock garden; modern
roses; old roses and climbers; water features; woodland
garden; particularly good in July-August; cyclamen;
colchicums; hardy geraniums; snowdrops; plants collected in the wild; small lake; collection of birds; wonderful
lilies;

This is the marvellous garden of a great plantsman who
has collected in all four corners of the world – the
introducer of such staples as Geranium palustre and
Symphytum caucasicum. The garden is a treasure house
of unusual species, forms and home-made hybrids.
Snowdrops, crocus, cyclamen, hellebores and winter
stem colours justify a visit in February. Lilies are a
special interest in early July – Bill Baker breeds them in
thousands.

The Old Rectory, Burghfield

Burghfield, Berkshire RG3 3TH
☎ 0734 833200

OWNER Mr & Mrs R Merton
LOCATION Right at Hatch Gate Inn and first entrance on right
OPEN 11 am – 4 pm; last Wednesday in month; February to October. Plus 11 June, for roses
ADMISSION Adults £1.00, Children 50p
FACILITIES Parking; loos; facilities for the disabled; plants for sale; teas
FEATURES Herbaceous borders; gravel or scree garden; herbs; plantsman's garden; rock garden; modern roses; water features; woodland garden; stone troughs; exotic displays in tubs; hellebores; lilies;

Highly acclaimed garden, whose main *tour de force* is a double herbaceous border where plants build up their impact through repetition, backed by yew hedges which get taller towards the end, to cheat the perspective. It leads to a pool framed by dense plantings of strong foliage – ferns, hostas, maples. Would that this delicious garden were open more often.

BUCKINGHAMSHIRE

Ascott

Wing, Buckinghamshire LU7 0PS
☎ 0296 688242

OWNER The National Trust
LOCATION ½ mile east of Wing
OPEN 2 pm – 6 pm. Tuesday – Sunday; 4 April, 6 April to 2 May, 4 to 8 May, 1 to 30 September. Also Wednesdays and last Sundays in month; 11 May to 31 August
ADMISSION £3 adults; £1.50 children
FACILITIES Parking; loos
FEATURES Herbaceous borders; fine conifers; garden sculpture; good topiary; water features; woodland garden; spring bulbs; Dutch garden; tallest *Cedrus atlantica* 'Aurea' in the British Isles
ENGLISH HERITAGE GRADE II
NCCPG NATIONAL COLLECTIONS *Canna*

Opulent late Victorian extravaganza. Tremendous set piece fountains by Story, grand terraces, magnificent trees and a giant sundial of box and golden yew. Almost too good to be true.

Chenies Manor

Chenies, Rickmansworth, Buckinghamshire
WD3 6ER

OWNER Mrs A MacLeod Matthews
LOCATION Centre of Chenies village

OPEN 2 pm – 5 pm, Wednesdays, Thursdays and Bank Holidays, 1 April to 30 October
ADMISSION £1.75 garden only ; £3.50 house & garden
FACILITIES Parking; loos; access for the disabled; herbs for sale; tea, coffee, home-made cakes
FEATURES Herbaceous borders; fruit and vegetables of special interest; herbs; good topiary; physic garden; award-winning maze

Three acres of tightly designed gardens full of variety. A Tudor bulb garden, modelled on Hampton Court; a Physic garden for herbs; Edwardian skittle alley; grass labyrinth; beautiful old lawns, yew hedges and walls alive with clever modern colour-conscious planting. Ethereally English.

Chicheley Hall

Chicheley, Newport Pagnell, Buckinghamshire
MK16 9JJ
☎ 0234 391252   FAX 0234 391388

OWNER Mrs John Nutting
LOCATION 2 miles from Newport Pagnell on A422
OPEN 2.30 pm – 5 pm; Sundays; April, May and August
ADMISSION £1.50
FACILITIES Parking; loos; tea room
FEATURES Modern roses; old roses and climbers; water features; woodland garden; historic landscape; spring daffodils
ENGLISH HERITAGE GRADE II*

Not a plantsman's garden, but a historic landscape which includes a formal lake in the French style c.1700 and a modern replanting of an old lime avenue.

Cliveden

Taplow, Maidenhead, Buckinghamshire SL6 0JA
☎ 0628 605069   FAX 0628 669461

OWNER The National Trust
LOCATION 2 miles north of Taplow, M4 J7
OPEN 11 am – 6 pm, March to October; 11 am – 4 pm; November to December
ADMISSION Adults (Grounds) £3.80; (House) £1.00; Children half price
FACILITIES Parking; dogs permitted; loos; facilities for the disabled; National Trust shop, Wednesday – Sunday; light refreshments and meals, Wednesday – Sunday
FEATURES Herbaceous borders; plantings by Graham Thomas; fine conifers; garden sculpture; woodland garden; modern roses
ENGLISH HERITAGE GRADE I
NCCPG NATIONAL COLLECTIONS *Catalpa*, *Anemone nemorosa*, *Convallaria*

A vast landscape garden, just stuffed with whatever money could buy: balustrading from the Villa Borghese in Rome, the dramatic 'Fountain of Love' and a huge parterre below the house, now dully planted by the National Trust. The best bits are the Arcadian ilex wood, quite magical, and newly restored rose garden, originally made by Geoffrey Jellicoe in 1932.

Great Barfield

Bradenham, High Wycombe, Buckinghamshire
UP14 4UP
☎ 0494 563741

OWNER   Richard Nutt
OPEN   2 pm – 5 pm; 20 February. 2 pm – 6 pm, 24 April and 3 July. 2 pm – 5 pm; 18 September. And by appointment
ADMISSION   £1.00.
FACILITIES   Access for the disabled; plants for sale; home-made teas
FEATURES   Herbaceous borders; plantsman's garden; rock garden; old roses and climbers; woodland garden; particularly interesting in winter; plants, plants, plants!; wonderful hellebores and snowdrops in February
NCCPG NATIONAL COLLECTIONS *Iris unguicularis, Ranunculus ficaria, Leucojum*

One of the best modern plantsman's gardens in southern England, not least because it is beautifully designed, labelled and maintained. Whatever the season, Great Barfield amazes the visitor by the number and variety of plants in flower and their thoughtful placing.

Hughenden Manor

High Wycombe, Buckinghamshire HP14 4LA
☎ 0494 532580

OWNER   The National Trust
LOCATION   1½ miles north of High Wycombe
OPEN   2 pm – 6 pm; Saturday & Sunday; March. 2 pm – 6 pm; Wednesday & Saturday; 1 April to 31 October. Sundays & Bank Holiday Monday 12 noon – 6 pm.
ADMISSION   £3.30; parties must book
FACILITIES   Parking; loos; facilities for the disabled; National Trust shop;
FEATURES   Herbaceous borders; formal Victorian parterres; rolling parkland;
ENGLISH HERITAGE GRADE   II

Not a great garden, but interesting for its association with Disraeli. The garden was made by his wife c.1860 and is a classic formal design of its period. Recently restored, using photographs taken in 1881, the parterre is once again planted with Victorian bedding.

The Manor House, Bledlow

Bledlow, Princes Risborough, Buckinghamshire
HP27 9PB

OWNER   Lord & Lady Carrington
LOCATION   Off B4009

OPEN   2 pm – 6 pm; 1 May & 19 June & by appointment
ADMISSION   £3.00
FACILITIES   Parking; loos; access for the disabled
FEATURES   Herbaceous borders; fruit and vegetables of special interest; modern roses; old roses and climbers; garden sculpture; water features

Designer garden, prettily planted and well maintained. The kitchen garden is particularly well laid out, with a gazebo in the middle. Fun collection of modern sculptures.

Stowe Landscape Gardens

Stowe, Buckingham, Buckinghamshire MK18 5EH
☎ 0280 822850

OWNER   The National Trust
LOCATION   1½ miles north of Buckingham
OPEN   10 am – 6 pm or dusk; daily; 26 March to 17 April, 3 July to 4 September, 21 to 31 October; 18 to 23 & 27 to 31 December. Also 10 am – 5 pm, Monday, Wednesday & Friday only, 18 April to 1 July; 5 September to 19 October
ADMISSION   £3.50; Family ticket £9.00; NT members £2.00
FACILITIES   Parking; dogs permitted; loos; light snacks
FEATURES   Landscape designed by Capability Brown; Vanburgh and Bridgeman
ENGLISH HERITAGE GRADE   I

Mega landscape, considered by some the most important in the history of gardens. The National Trust acquired control from the boys' public school five years ago, and the restoration will take many years. Go if you have not been already, and go again if you have. Stowe is not obvious: stomp round slowly, and try to appreciate the historic and symbolic significance of each feature. Read the National Trust's excellent guide and then go round again, this year, next year, every year, and commune with the *genius loci*.

Turn End

Townside, Haddenham, Aylesbury, Buckinghamshire
HP17 8BG
☎ 0844 291383

OWNER   Mr & Mrs Peter Aldington
LOCATION   Rising Sun turning, in Haddenham
OPEN   2 pm – 6 pm; 9 April, 16 May, 27 June, 12 September; groups by appointment
ADMISSION   Adults £1.20; Children 40p
FACILITIES   Loos; plants for sale; home-made teas
FEATURES   Plantsman's garden; rock garden; old roses and climbers; ferns; grasses; brilliant design

Only one acre, but never was space so used to create an illusion of size. A brilliant series of enclosed gardens, sunken or raised, sunny or shady, each different and yet harmonious, contrasts with lawns, borders and glades. Much featured in the glossies, and deservedly.

Waddesdon Manor

Aylesbury, Buckinghamshire HP18 0JH
☎ 0296 651282   ⊠ 0296 651293

OWNER The National Trust
LOCATION A41 Bicester & Aylesbury
OPEN 11 am – 5 pm; Wednesday – Sunday & public
holidays; 1 March to 24 December
ADMISSION Adults: £3; Children (5 – 17) £1.50;
under 5 free
FACILITIES Parking; loos; shop; tea room
FEATURES Herbaceous borders; water features
ENGLISH HERITAGE GRADE II*

A grand park, splendid formal gardens, a rococo aviary
and extravagant bedding are the first fruits of restoring
the grounds of this amazing Rothschild palace. An
exciting addition to the National Trust's portfolio of
historic gardens.

West Wycombe Park

West Wycombe, Buckinghamshire HP14 3AJ
☎ 0494 524411

OWNER The National Trust
LOCATION West end of West Wycombe on Oxford
road
OPEN 2 pm – 6 pm; Sunday – Thursday; 1 June to 31
August, also Sundays, Wednesdays and Bank Holi-
days, 2 April to 31 May
ADMISSION £2.50 Adults
FACILITIES Parking
FEATURES Follies and garden buildings; garden sculp-
ture; water features
ENGLISH HERITAGE GRADE I

Early landscape park, with a lake in the shape of a swan.
Classical temples and follies, plus three modern eye-
catchers designed by Quinlan Terry.

CAMBRIDGESHIRE

Abbots Ripton Hall

Abbots Ripton, Cambridgeshire
☎ 04873 555   ⊠ 04873 545

OWNER Lord De Ramsey
LOCATION Off B1090
OPEN 2 pm – 6 pm; six days (details to be announced),
May to August
ADMISSION Adults £2.00; reduction for Senior
Citizens
FACILITIES Parking; loos; plants for sale; teas
FEATURES Herbaceous borders; follies and garden
buildings; plantsman's garden; rock garden; modern
roses; old roses and climbers; water features; irises; grey
border; Chinese bridge; trellis work
ENGLISH HERITAGE GRADE II

Humphrey Waterfield, Lanning Roper and Jim Russell
all worked here, and few garden owners have had so
many gardening friends as Lord & Lady De Ramsey,
who made and remade this garden over more than 50
years. The result is a garden of stylish individuality – as
witness the gothic trellis work and the bobbles of
yellow *Philadelphus* – but also of great unity: pure
enchantment.

Anglesey Abbey

Lode, Cambridgeshire CB5 9EJ
☎ 0223 811200

OWNER The National Trust
LOCATION Off B1102
OPEN 11 am – 5.30 pm; Wednesday – Sunday; April
to October
ADMISSION £3 Wednesday – Saturday; £3.50 Sun-
days.
FACILITIES Parking; loos; facilities for the disabled;
plants for sale; National Trust shop; licensed restaurant;
picnic area
FEATURES Herbaceous borders; garden sculpture;
landscaping on the grandest scale; long avenues of trees
ENGLISH HERITAGE GRADE II*

Sixty years old, no more, but the grounds at Anglesey
already deserve to be famous, for they are the grandest
made in England this century. Majestic avenues are the
stuff of it: visit Anglesey when the horse chestnuts are
out and tulips glow in the grass. Large formal gardens,
carved out of the flat site by yew hedges, house Lord
Fairhaven's collection of homoerotic sculpture. Then
there are smaller gardens, said to be more intimate,
where thousands of dahlias and hyacinths hit the eye:
glorious or vainglorious, Anglesey has no match.

Bury Farm

Meldreth, Roston, Cambridgeshire SG8 6NT
☎ 0763 260475

OWNER Mr & Mrs T D Lynch
LOCATION Opposite Meldreth Church
OPEN 1st Sunday in the month; April to July
ADMISSION £1.00
FACILITIES Parking; loos; access for the disabled;
plants for sale
FEATURES Herbaceous borders; plantsman's garden

This amazing plantsman's garden combines collectoma-
nia with scholarship and artistry. Margaret Lynch is a
leading expert on herbaceous plants (her monograph on
Campanula was published in 1992 but she uses all
plants as elements of design – Bury Farm has a pastel
border and a grey border, exciting contrasts and drifts
of irises. Quite remarkable.

Cambridge University Botanic Garden

Trumpington Road, Cambridge, Cambridgeshire
CB2 1JF
☎ 0223 336265   📠 0223 336278

OWNER   University of Cambridge
LOCATION   ¼ mile to the south of the City Centre
OPEN   10 am – 6 pm (4 pm in winter); daily
ADMISSION   Adults £1.50 Senior Citizens £1.00;
Children £1.00
FACILITIES   Loos; facilities for the disabled; plants for
sale; light refreshments
FEATURES   Good collection of trees; herbaceous borders; fine conifers; ecological interest; glasshouses to visit; gravel or scree garden; herbs; rock garden; modern roses; old roses and climbers; sub-tropical plants; water features; woodland garden; particularly good in July-August; particularly interesting in winter; tallest *Maclura pomifera* in the British Isles (and six other record trees)
NCCPG NATIONAL COLLECTIONS *Alchemilla, Bergenia, Fritillaria, Geranium, Lonicera, Ribes, Ruscus, Saxifraga, Tulipa*
FRIENDS   A very active association – contact the Friends Administrator, c/o Cory Lodge.

One of the best botanic gardens in the world for the way it matches amenity and public recreation to education, research, conservation, ecology, systematic taxonomy and horticultural excellence. The two rock gardens, one limestone and the other sandstone, are particularly successful and alone worth a long journey. For all-round interest, Cambridge BG runs close to Kew, Wisley and Edinburgh.

Crossing House Garden

Meldreth Road, Shepreth, Royston, Cambridgeshire
SG8 6PS
☎ 0763 261071

OWNER   Mr & Mrs D G Fuller
LOCATION   8 miles south of Cambridge off A10
OPEN   Dawn – dusk, daily.
ADMISSION   Collection box for NGS
FACILITIES   Dogs permitted; access for the disabled
FEATURES   Plantsman's garden

One of the wonders of modern gardening, the Crossing House celebrates the achievements of its makers over the last 30 years, on an unpropitious site right beside the main railway line to Cambridge. It contains over 5,000 varieties of plant, densely planted in the cottage style. Peat beds, screes, arches, topiary, pools and raised beds are some of the features which add variety to the most intensely and intensively planted small garden in England.

Docwra's Manor

Shepreth, Royston, Cambridgeshire SG8 6PS
☎ 0763 260235

OWNER   Mrs John Raven
LOCATION   Off A10 to Shepreth
OPEN   10 am – 4 pm; Monday, Wednesday and Friday; all year; 2 pm – 5 pm, first Sundays of April to October; 10 am – 5 pm, Bank Holiday Mondays. And by appointment
ADMISSION   £1.50
FACILITIES   Facilities for the disabled; plants for sale; teas for NGS openings on 15 May and 2 September
FEATURES   Herbaceous borders; ecological interest; fruit and vegetables of special interest; plantsman's garden; modern roses; old roses and climbers; Mediterranean plants

Very much a plantsman's garden, whose lush profusion defies the dry, cold site. Docwra's Manor is a series of small gardens – walled, wild, paved and so on – each brimming with rarities. Unstructured and informal, and yet the garden *works*. Do read John Raven's charming and erudite *The Botanist's Garden*, now in print again.

Elton Hall

Peterborough, Cambridgeshire PE8 6SH
☎ 0832 280223/280468   📠 0832 280584

OWNER   Mr & Mrs William Proby
LOCATION   A605 near Oundle
OPEN   2 pm – 5 pm; Wednesday and Sunday; July and August. Also Thursdays in August, plus Bank Holiday Sundays and Mondays
ADMISSION   House and Garden: Adults £3.80, Children £1.90 Garden: Adults £1.80, Children 90p
FACILITIES   Parking; loos; tea room
FEATURES   Good collection of trees; herbaceous borders; modern roses; old roses and climbers; garden sculpture; good topiary; handsome hedges; good colour plantings
ENGLISH HERITAGE GRADE   II*

The house is a castellated monstrosity, but the Victorian gardens have been energetically restored in recent years and make Elton highly visitable. The knot garden and the collection of old roses are the high spots, best in June.

Hardwicke House

High Ditch Road, Fen Ditton, Cambridge,
Cambridgeshire CB5 8TF
☎ 0223 292246

OWNER   John Drake
LOCATION   ¼ mile from village crossroad
OPEN   For NGS and by appointment
ADMISSION   £1.50
FACILITIES   Parking; plants for sale

FEATURES Herbaceous borders; plantsman's garden; bulbs

NCCPG NATIONAL COLLECTIONS *Aquilegia, Semiaquilegia*

Essentially a plantsman's garden with an emphasis on herbaceous plants, roses and bulbs. The owner has a particular interest in Asia Minor, as witness an area devoted to Turkish bulbs.

North End House

Grantchester, Cambridge, Cambridgeshire CB3 9NQ
☎ 0223 84023   FAX 071 437 3736

OWNER Lady Nourse
LOCATION 2 miles south west of Cambridge
OPEN 2 pm – 6 pm; 26 June
ADMISSION £1.50
FACILITIES Parking; facilities for the disabled; plants for sale; home-made teas in village
FEATURES Herbaceous borders; rock garden; old roses and climbers; water features; young garden
NCCPG NATIONAL COLLECTIONS *Geranium*

A good example of what can be done by discriminating plantsmen in a few years. Interesting too for its National Collection of hardy Geraniums.

Padlock Croft

West Wratting, Cambridgeshire CB1 5LS
☎ 0223 290383

OWNER Peter & Susan Lewis
LOCATION Turn of A604 between Linton & Horseath
OPEN 10 am – 6 pm; Tuesday to Saturday; April to October or by appointment. Open Bank Holiday Mondays
ADMISSION Donation box
FACILITIES Parking; loos; plants for sale; tea & biscuits by prior arrangement
NCCPG NATIONAL COLLECTIONS *Adenophora; Campanula; Platycodon; Symphyandra*
FEATURES Herbaceous borders; plantsman's garden; rock garden

One acre of plantsmanship, 'interesting' rather than 'exquisite' say the owners. But they do themselves an injustice, because this is a fascinating garden. Plants are crammed in, growing where they will do best. Not only are there four National Collections, but a nursery as well, specialising in *Campanulaceae*.

Peckover House

North Brink, Wisbech, Cambridgeshire PE13 1JR
☎ 0945 583463

OWNER National Trust
LOCATION Signposted from Wisbech

OPEN House & Garden: Sunday & Wednesday; Garden: Saturday, Monday & Tuesday; 1 April to 31 October
ADMISSION House & Garden: £2.40; Garden only £1.00 (1993)
FACILITIES Parking; loos; facilities for the disabled
FEATURES Herbaceous borders; glasshouses to visit; Victorian shrubberies; orangery; fernery; Malmaison carnations; tallest *Acer negundo* in the British Isles
ENGLISH HERITAGE GRADE II

Charming example of a not-too-grand Victorian garden, complete with monkey puzzle, fernery and spotted laurel shrubberies. One of the orange trees in the conservatory is 200 years old.

Wimpole Hall

Arrington, Royston, Cambridgeshire SG8 0BW
☎ 0223 207257   FAX 0223 207838

OWNER The National Trust
LOCATION On A603, south west of Cambridge
OPEN 1 pm – 5 pm; Tuesday – Thursday, Saturday & Sunday; 26 March to 30 October. Bank Holiday Sundays & Mondays 11am – 5pm
ADMISSION £4.50 (house and garden); park only, free
FACILITIES Parking; dogs permitted; loos; facilities for the disabled; National Trust shop; restaurant & tea room
FEATURES landscape designed by Capability Brown and Humphry Repton; old roses and climbers; interesting for children; Chinese bridge; daffodils; parterres
ENGLISH HERITAGE GRADE I

A classical 18th century landscape where Bridgeman, Brown and Repton have all left their mark. The Victorian parterres and pleasure gardens are being restored but remain grand and simple for the present. Not a flower garden, but a joy to lovers of the landscape style.

CHESHIRE

Adlington Hall

Macclesfield, Cheshire SK10 4LF
☎ 0625 829206   FAX 0625 828756

OWNER Mrs A S Barnett Legh
LOCATION 5 miles north of Macclesfield off A523
OPEN 2 pm – 5.30 pm; Sundays and Bank Holidays; 1 April to 2 October
ADMISSION Gardens only, £1
FACILITIES Parking; dogs permitted; loos; plants for sale; gift shop and home produce; tea room, home made cakes, scones
FEATURES Follies and garden buildings; woodland garden
ENGLISH HERITAGE GRADE II*

An old avenue of lime trees, planted in 1688 to celebrate accession of William and Mary, leads to a woodland 'wilderness' with follies. These include a Shell Cottage, a Temple to Diana, a Chinese bridge and a Hermitage. The new owners are restoring these buildings, and have plans for further developments.

Arley Hall

Great Budworth, Northwich, Cheshire CW9 6NA
☎ 0565 777353

OWNER The Hon Michael Flower
LOCATION 5 miles west of Knutsford
OPEN 12 noon – 5 pm; Tuesday – Sunday; 27 March to 2 October
ADMISSION Adults £2.60 (1993)
FACILITIES Parking; dogs permitted; loos; access for the disabled; plants for sale; shop; lunches & light refreshments
FEATURES Herbaceous borders; plantsman's garden; old roses and climbers; good topiary; water features; woodland garden; HHA/Christie's Garden of the Year in 1987
ENGLISH HERITAGE GRADE II*

Arley has pleached limes, red *Primula florindae*, clipped ilex cylinders (30 feet high) and pretty old roses. But its claim to fame is the double herbaceous border, backed and buttressed by yew hedges, one of the oldest and still one of the best in England.

Bridgemere Garden World

Bridgemere, Nantwich, Cheshire CW5 7QB

OWNER J Ravenscroft
LOCATION On A51 south of Nantwich
OPEN 10 am – 6 pm (4 pm in winter); daily
ADMISSION £1
FACILITIES Parking; loos; access for the disabled; plants for sale; several shops, as well as the famous garden centre; refreshments
FEATURES Herbaceous borders; fruit and vegetables of special interest; glasshouses to visit; gravel or scree garden; herbs; plantsman's garden; rock garden; modern roses; old roses and climbers; water features; woodland garden; young garden; particularly good in July-August

Lots of immaculate show gardens in different styles: too numerous to list, but definitely worth a visit, whatever the season.

Capesthorne Hall

Siddington, Macclesfield, Cheshire SK11 9JY
☎ 0625 861221   ☏ 0625 861619

OWNER W Bromley-Davenport
LOCATION 3 miles south of Alderley Edge

OPEN 12 noon – 6 pm; Sundays, April to September; plus Wednesdays in May, August and September; plus Tuesdays and Thursdays in June and July
ADMISSION Adults £2.25, Children £1
FACILITIES Parking; loos; facilities for the disabled; small gift shop; tea rooms
FEATURES Good collection of trees; water features; woodland garden; historic park

Classic English landscape, with some pretty modern planting by Vernon Russell-Smith by the lakes, a 19th century arboretum and formal gardens.

Cholmondeley Castle Gardens

Malpas, Cheshire SY14 8AH
☎ 0829 720383   ☏ 0829 720519

OWNER The Marchioness of Cholmondeley
LOCATION Off A49 Tarporley/ Whitchurch road
OPEN 12.30 pm – 5 pm, Wednesday & Thursday, 3 April to 2 October; 12 noon – 5.30 pm, Sundays, Bank Holidays and other days by prior arrangement
ADMISSION Adults £2.50, Senior Citizens £1.50, Children 75p
FACILITIES Parking; dogs permitted; loos; facilities for the disabled; plants for sale; gift shop; tea room; light lunches; home-made teas
FEATURES Good collection of trees; herbaceous borders; fine conifers; follies and garden buildings; rock garden; modern roses; old roses and climbers; water features; woodland garden; Japanese cherry walk; climbing roses; rhododendrons; daffodils & bluebells
ENGLISH HERITAGE GRADE II
FRIENDS Friends of Cholmondeley season ticket

Handsome early 19th century castle in rolling parkland, redeveloped since 1960s with horticultural advice from Jim Russell. The results include drifts of modern rhododendrons and azaleas, a very pretty rose garden, tender plants along the terraces, a restored rock garden, good waterside plantings and a great variety of shrubs and underplantings. Highly recommended.

Dorfold Hall

Nantwich, Cheshire CW5 8LD
☎ 0270 625245   ☏ 0270 628723

OWNER R C Roundell
LOCATION 1 mile west of Nantwich on A534
OPEN 2 pm – 5 pm, Tuesdays and Bank Holiday Mondays, 1 April to 31 October
ADMISSION House and gardens: Adults £3.00, Children £1.50
FACILITIES Parking; loos
FEATURES Water features; woodland garden; 1,000 year old Spanish Chestnut tree; rhododendrons; formal gardens
ENGLISH HERITAGE GRADE II

William Nesfield designed the formal approach but the main reason for visiting the gardens is the new woodland garden of rhododendrons and other shrubs, leading down to a stream.

Granada Arboretum

Jodrell Bank, Macclesfield, Cheshire SK11 9DL
☎ 0477 71339   FAX 0477 71695

OWNER Manchester University
LOCATION On A535 between Holmes Chapel and Chelford
OPEN 10.30 am – 5.30 pm; daily; 19 March to 30 October: 11 am – 4.30 pm; Saturdays & Sundays; 31 October to 18 March
ADMISSION Grounds, Science Centre & Planetarium: Adults £3.50, Senior Citizens £2.50, Children £1.90, Family £10.50
FACILITIES Parking; loos; shop; self-service cafeteria
FEATURES Good collection of trees; modern roses; old roses and climbers; water features; Heather Society's *Calluna* collection

Better known as the Jodrell Bank Arboretum, and founded by Sir Bernard Lovell in 1971, this arboretum specialises in alders, birches, crab apples, pine and *Sorbus*. Long straight drives lead out from the new visitor centre, known as the Environmental Discovery Centre, by way of large collections of heaths (*Erica*), heathers (*Calluna*) and old fashioned roses. The huge radio telescope dominates the site: an awesome presence.

Hare Hill Garden

Garden Lodge, Over Alderly, Macclesfield, Cheshire SK10 4QB
☎ 0625 828981

OWNER The National Trust
LOCATION Between Alderley Edge and Prestbury
OPEN 10 am – 5.30 pm; Wednesday, Thursday, Saturday, Sunday and Bank Holiday Mondays; 1 April to 31 October
ADMISSION Adults £2.50, Children £1.25
FACILITIES Parking; loos
FEATURES Herbaceous borders; plantsman's garden; rock garden; old roses and climbers; garden sculpture; woodland garden

Basically a woodland garden, thickly planted with trees and underplanted with rhododendrons, azaleas and shrubs by Jim Russell in the 1960s. In the middle is a walled garden which has been developed as a flower garden with a pergola, arbour and tender plants against the walls. Best in May but there are still some rhododendrons to flower with the roses in July.

Little Moreton Hall

Congleton, Cheshire CW12 4SD
☎ 0260 272018

OWNER The National Trust
LOCATION 4 miles south of Congleton on A34
OPEN 12 noon – 5.30 pm, Wednesday – Sunday (closed Good Friday), 26 March to 30 September; 11 am – 5.30 pm Bank Holiday Mondays; 12 noon – 5.30 pm, Saturday & Sunday; October
ADMISSION Weekdays £2.80, Weekends and Bank Holiday Mondays £3.60
FACILITIES Parking; loos; plants for sale; restaurant – lunches, coffee, teas
FEATURES Herbaceous borders; fruit and vegetables of special interest; herbs; plantings by Graham Thomas; Graham Thomas knot garden
ENGLISH HERITAGE GRADE I

Little Moreton Hall is the handsomest timber-framed house in England. When the National Trust asked Graham Thomas to design and plant a suitable period garden, he specified box-edged parterres with yew topiary and gravel infilling – and very fine they are too. In the kitchen garden, a speciality has been made of old varieties of fruit and vegetables. Peaceful, charming and orderly.

Lyme Park

Disley, Cheshire SK12 2NX
☎ 0663 762100   FAX 0663 765035

OWNER The National Trust
LOCATION 6½ miles south east of Stockport on A6, just west of Disley
OPEN 11 am – 4.45 pm, 24 March to 19 October; otherwise 11 am – 4 pm. Closed on Christmas Day and Boxing Day
ADMISSION Car £3.20, motorcycle £2.20, pedestrians free
FACILITIES Parking; dogs permitted; loos; facilities for the disabled; shop; light refreshments from Easter to October
FEATURES Herbaceous borders; follies and garden buildings; glasshouses to visit; old roses and climbers; water features; spring bulbs; bedding out
ENGLISH HERITAGE GRADE II*

There is much of horticultural interest at Lyme, as well as the razzmatazz of a country park: traditional bedding out, two enormous camellias in the conservatory, and a Jekyll-type herbaceous border whose colours run from orange to deepest purple. Best of all is the sunken Dutch garden whose looping box and ivy parterres contain the most extravagant bedding displays.

Ness Botanic Gardens

Neston, South Wirral, Cheshire L64 4AY

☎ 051 336 7769/2135 [FAX] 051 353 1004

OWNER University of Liverpool

LOCATION Signed off A540, Chester to Hoylake

OPEN 9.30 am – 4.00 pm; daily; 1 November to 28 February: 9.30 am – dusk; daily; 1 March – 31 October

ADMISSION Adults £3.00; Senior Citizens £2.00; Children under 10 free

FACILITIES Parking; loos; facilities for the disabled; plants for sale; two restaurants

FEATURES Good collection of trees; herbaceous borders; fine conifers; glasshouses to visit; gravel or scree garden; herbs; rock garden; old roses and climbers; water features; woodland garden

ENGLISH HERITAGE GRADE II

FRIENDS Season ticket for gardens £13.50 adults, £10 Senior Citizens, £22.50 families. Membership of the 7,500-strong Friends of Ness Gardens gives lectures, a newsletter, and a seed list (max 10 pkts). Contact Dr Joanna Sharples

Ness was started by A K Bulley, who sponsored George Forrest the plant collector, and it was here that many Chinese plants were first grown in Europe – notably candelabra primulas. It retains the sense of being a private garden not a botanic one. The borders and shrubberies teem with interesting plants: rhododendrons, *Sorbus*, lilies, willows, roses, heathers and conifers – including a magnificent *Sequoia sempervirens* 'Adpressa'. The rock garden is particularly well planted, and the mild climate and acid soil allow a wide variety of different plants to flourish. Ness is one of those gardens where you tend to spend much longer than you intended.

Norton Priory Museum & Gardens

Tudor Road, Runcorn, Cheshire WA7 1SX

☎ 0928 569895

OWNER Norton Priory Museum Trust (Cheshire County Council)

LOCATION Well signposted locally

OPEN 12 pm – 5 pm; weekdays; 1 April – 31 October: 12 pm – 6 pm, weekends and Bank Holidays

ADMISSION Adults £2.40; Senior Citizens £1.20

FACILITIES Parking; loos; facilities for the disabled; plants for sale; garden produce shop; refreshments at museum site

FEATURES Herbaceous borders; fruit and vegetables of special interest; herbs; rock garden; modern roses; old roses and climbers; collection of *Cydonia* varieties

A new layout in the old walled garden, modelled on 18th century precedents and intended to instruct and please modern visitors. A cottage garden border, medicinal herb garden and orchard rub shoulders with

colour borders, children's gardens and a scented garden. Beyond are 16 acres of woodland garden with Georgian summerhouses and glades by the stream.

Penn

Macclesfield Road, Alderley Edge, Cheshire SK9 7BT

☎ 0625 583334

OWNER R W Baldwin

LOCATION ¼ mile east of Alderley village on B5087

OPEN 2 pm – 5 pm; 24 April to 2 May, 29 & 30 May

ADMISSION Adults £2.00, Senior Citizens £1.25, Children 50p

FACILITIES Parking; loos; plants for sale; light refreshments

FEATURES Herbaceous borders; fine conifers; woodland garden; rhododendrons & azaleas; magnolias; camellias; embothriums

Penn is famous for its rhododendrons, thickly planted in the woods above the house and the wide views across the lawns to the valley. But the range of good plants is very wide, and the collections of magnolias and camellias also comprehensive.

Peover Hall

Over Peover, Knutsford, Cheshire

OWNER R Brooks Ltd

LOCATION 3 miles south of Knutsford

OPEN 2 pm – 4.30 pm; Mondays & Thursdays; 1 May to 30 September

ADMISSION Adults, £1.50; children, 50p

FACILITIES Parking; loos; access for the disabled; refreshments on Mondays only

FEATURES Herbs; old roses and climbers; good topiary; walled garden; landscaped park; rhododendrons

ENGLISH HERITAGE GRADE II

First a classic 18th century parkland, then an Edwardian overlay of formal gardens – yew hedges and brick paths. Now Peover has modern plantings too – borders in colour combinations, a herb garden, and a rhododendron dell in the woods.

Rode Hall

Church Lane, Scholar Green, Stoke on Trent, Cheshire ST7 3QP

☎ 0270 882961 [FAX] 0270 882962

OWNER Sir Richard Baker Wilbraham

LOCATION 5 miles south west of Congleton between A34 and A50

OPEN 2 pm – 5 pm; Wednesdays and Bank Holidays; 1 April to 30 September

ADMISSION Garden £2.00

FACILITIES Parking; dogs permitted; loos; plants for sale; garden produce

FEATURES Landscape designed by Humphry Repton; fine conifers; follies and garden buildings; fruit and vegetables of special interest; old roses and climbers; good topiary; woodland garden; ice house; rhododendrons; grotto

ENGLISH HERITAGE GRADE II

Landscaped by Repton c.1790 and given a formal garden by Nesfield in 1860, the main horticultural interest comes from the massed banks of azaleas and rhododendrons in the late Victorian 'Wild Garden'.

Stapeley Water Gardens Ltd

London Road, Stapeley, Nantwich, Cheshire CW5 7LH

☎ 0270 623868　　📠 0270 624919

OWNER R G A Davies

LOCATION A51 south of Nantwich

OPEN 9 am – 5 pm; all year

ADMISSION Palms Tropical Oasis: Adults £2.90, Senior Citizens £1.95, Children £1.45

FACILITIES Parking; facilities for the disabled; plants for sale; cafeteria & terrace restaurant

FEATURES Glasshouses to visit; sub-tropical plants; water features; interesting for children; particularly interesting in winter; collection of hardy water lilies; *Victoria regia*, the giant water lily

NCCPG NATIONAL COLLECTIONS *Nymphaea*

Part entertainment, part nursery and part display garden, the Palms Tropical Oasis is worth a visit in its own right. A long rectangular pool in the Moorish style is flanked by tall palms, strelitzias and other showy tropical flowers. Visit in winter.

Tatton Park

Knutsford, Cheshire

☎ 0565 750780　　📠 0565 650179

OWNER The National Trust (managed by Cheshire County Council)

LOCATION Off M6 J19 and M56 J 7 – well signposted

OPEN 10.30 am – 5 pm; daily except Mondays; 1 April to 23 October. 11 am – 3 pm; daily except Mondays; 24 October to 31 March

ADMISSION Adults £2.50, Children £1.70, Family ticket £7.50

FACILITIES Parking; loos; facilities for the disabled; plants for sale; shop; hot meals and snacks (summer only)

FEATURES Good collection of trees; herbaceous borders; landscape designed by Humphry Repton; follies and garden buildings; glasshouses to visit; oriental features; modern roses; water features; rhododendrons & azaleas in May; fernery; current holder of Sandford Award

ENGLISH HERITAGE GRADE II*

NCCPG NATIONAL COLLECTIONS *Adiantum, Inula*

Humphry Repton laid out the parkland. Joseph Paxton designed both the formal Italian garden and the exquisite fernery; it claims to be the finest in the United Kingdom. Later came a Japanese garden and Shinto temple, such follies as the African hut, and the mass plantings of rhododendrons and azaleas. Tatton Park is wonderfully well organised for visitors, and gets better every year.

Tirley Garth Trust

Utkinton, Tarporley, Cheshire CW6 0LZ

☎ 0829 732301　　📠 0829 732265

OWNER The Tirley Garth Trust

LOCATION 2½ miles north of Tarporley, just north of village of Utkinton on road to Kelsall

OPEN 2 pm – 6 pm; 15, 21, 22, 29, 30 May

ADMISSION Adults £2.50, Children 50p

FACILITIES Parking; dogs permitted; loos; home baking; home-made ices

FEATURES Herbaceous borders; rock garden; modern roses; woodland garden

ENGLISH HERITAGE GRADE II

FRIENDS Friends of Tirley Garth: details available from the gardens

Famous example of Thomas Mawson's work: wonderful terraces, paths, retaining walks and garden buildings. Good rhododendrons and azaleas in the woodland below.

CORNWALL

Antony House

Torpoint, Cornwall PL11 2QA

☎ 0752 812364

OWNER The National Trust

LOCATION 5 miles west of Plymouth, 2 miles north west of Torpoint

OPEN 1.30 am – 5.30 pm; Tuesday, Thursday & Bank Holidays; April to August; also Sundays in June & August

ADMISSION Adults £3.40, Children £1.70

FACILITIES Parking; loos; access for the disabled; tea room

FEATURES Herbaceous borders; fine conifers; good topiary; water features; woodland garden; magnolias; yew hedges; tallest Japanese loquat *Eriobotrya japonica* in the British Isles

ENGLISH HERITAGE GRADE II

NCCPG NATIONAL COLLECTIONS *Hemerocallis*

A classic 18th century landscape, influenced by Humphry Repton, in a superb position above the Tamar estuary. Yew hedges nearer the house enclose modern plantings while the kitchen garden houses the vast National Collection of *Hemerocallis* or day lilies.

Antony Woodland Garden

Antony House, Torpoint, Cornwall PL11 2QA
☎ 0752 812364

OWNER   The Carew Pole Garden Trust
LOCATION   5 miles west of Plymouth, 2 miles north west of Torpoint
OPEN   11 am – 5.30 pm; daily; 15 March – 30 October
ADMISSION   Adult £1.50, Children 50p
FACILITIES   Parking; loos; tea room
FEATURES   Fine conifers; plantsman's garden; water features; woodland garden; camellias; magnolias; rhododendrons & azaleas

This is the 'Cornish' part of the grounds at Antony, still controlled by the Carew Pole family rather than the National Trust. They have planted it with the best modern forms of rhododendrons, azaleas, magnolias, camellias and other trees.

Bosvigo House

Bosvigo Lane, Truro, Cornwall TR1 3NH
☎ 0872 75774

OWNER   Wendy and Michael Perry
LOCATION   A390 to Redruth, at Highertown right into Dobbs Lane, 500 yds on left
OPEN   11 am – 6 pm; Wednesday – Saturday; 1 March to 30 September
ADMISSION   Adults £1.50, Children 50p
FACILITIES   Parking; loos; plants for sale
FEATURES   Herbaceous borders; plantsman's garden; woodland garden; young garden; unusual perennials; Victorian conservatory; colour borders

Not a typical Cornish garden, the emphasis at Bosvigo is upon herbaceous plants, chosen for all their qualities and planted in fine colour combinations. Many are rare: some for sale.

Caerhays Castle

Gorran, St. Austell, Cornwall PL26 6LY
☎ 0872 501310   FAX 0872 501870

OWNER   F J Williams
LOCATION   In Caerhays village
OPEN   11 am – 4 pm; Monday – Friday; 21 March – 6 June. Charity opening: 3 April, 24 April, 9 May
ADMISSION   Adults £2.50, Children (under 14) £1.50
FACILITIES   Parking; dogs permitted; loos; plants for sale; tea rooms & beach shop/cafe in car park
FEATURES   Good collection of trees; fine conifers; plantsman's garden; woodland garden; camellias; magnolias; rhododendrons; tallest specimen of *Emmenopterys henryi* in the British Isles, and twelve further record-breaking tree species

ENGLISH HERITAGE GRADE   II*

The Williams family subscribed to many of the great plant collecting expeditions and the fruits of their labours flourish at Caerhays. Wilson and Forrest are represented by thousands of trees and shrubs, and one of the joys of Caerhays is to stumble upon magnificent old specimens deep in its 100 acres of woodland. There are splendid collections of *Nothofagus* and *Lithocarpus* as well as the three genera for which Caerhays is famous – magnolias, camellias and rhododendrons. The original × *williamsii* camellias still flourish, including 'J.C. Williams', 'Mary Christian' and 'St. Ewe'. There is much to discover at Caerhays: allow plenty of time.

Carclew Gardens

Perran-ar-Worthal, Truro, Cornwall TR3 7PB
☎ 0872 864070

OWNER   Mrs Robert Chope
LOCATION   A39 east at Perran-ar-Worthal, 1 mile to garden
OPEN   2 pm – 5.30 pm; 15, 22 & 29 May
ADMISSION   Adults £1.50; Children 50p
FACILITIES   Parking; loos; home-made teas
FEATURES   Herbaceous borders; follies and garden buildings; garden sculpture; water features; rhododendrons; tallest *Pseudolarix amabilis* in the British Isles

The gardens first opened to the public in 1927 and have continued to do so for charity every year since then. Vast hummocks of old rhododendrons, some grown from Sir Joseph Hooker's Himalayan collections nearly 150 years ago. Good trees, including a *Quercus* × *hispanica* which is *not* 'Lucombeana'.

Carwinion

Mawnan Smith, Falmouth, Cornwall TR11 5JA
☎ 0326 250258

OWNER   Anthony Rogers
LOCATION   From Mawnan Smith, turn off at Red Lion, 500 yds up hill on right
OPEN   10.00 am – 5.30 pm; daily or by appointment
ADMISSION   £1.00
FACILITIES   Parking; dogs permitted; loos; plants for sale; cream teas 2 pm – 5.30 pm
FEATURES   Fine conifers; ecological interest; sub-tropical plants; water features; woodland garden; 100 species of bamboo; tree ferns; gunnera; bluebells

10 acres of Cornish jungle, exotically thick with rhododendrons, camellias, *Drimys* and the largest collection of bamboos in the south west.

Chyverton

Zelah, Truro, Cornwall TR4 9HD
☎ 0872 540324

OWNER   Mr & Mrs Nigel Holman

LOCATION 1 mile south west of Zelah on A30
OPEN By appointment; March to June
ADMISSION Adults £2.50, Children (under 16) free
FACILITIES Parking; dogs permitted
FEATURES Fine conifers; plantsman's garden; water features; woodland garden; magnolias; nothofagus
ENGLISH HERITAGE GRADE II

The garden of a distinguished writer on gardening who is both a keen plantsman and a landscaper with plants. Magnolias are a special interest: several Chyverton seedlings now bear cultivar names. Many other established plants have also been grown from seed: rhododendron hybrids from Brodick, for instance, and *Eucalyptus nicholii* from a wild collection. But there is much more to interest the plantsman. A large *Berberidopsis corallina* and a lanky red-stemmed hedge of *Luma apiculata* below the house are both outstanding. And the planting continues.

Cotehele

St Dominick, Saltash, Cornwall PL12 6TA
☎ 0579 50909

OWNER The National Trust
LOCATION 14 miles from Plymouth via Saltash
OPEN 11 am – 5.30 pm (dusk if earlier); daily; all year
ADMISSION 1 April – 31 October £2.50, rest of year free
FACILITIES Parking; loos; facilities for the disabled; plants for sale; refreshments 1 April – 31 October
FEATURES Good collection of trees; fine conifers; modern roses; good topiary; water features; woodland garden; palms; ferns; pretty dovecote; daffodils
ENGLISH HERITAGE GRADE II

Broad Victorian terraces below the house support many tender climbers such as *Jasminum mesnyi* while the beds beneath have wallflowers and roses. Down the wooded valley are camellias, rhododendrons and shade-loving plants which thrive in an ancient woodland, kept damp by a small stream.

Glendurgan Gardens

Helford River, Mawnan Smith, Falmouth, Cornwall TR11 5JZ
☎ 0326 250906

OWNER The National Trust
LOCATION 1 mile west of Mawnan Smith, next to Trebah
OPEN 10 am – 5.30 pm (last admission 4.30 pm); Tuesday – Saturday, 1 March to 31 October. Open Bank Holiday Mondays, but closed Good Friday
ADMISSION £2.60
FACILITIES Parking; loos; plants for sale; small shop; light refreshments

FEATURES Fine conifers; sub-tropical plants; water features; woodland garden; laurel maze; wild flowers; huge tulip tree
ENGLISH HERITAGE GRADE II

A steep, sub-tropical valley garden on the Helford River with a good collection of old rhododendrons and camellias. Glendurgan also boasts an extraordinary 1830s maze of clipped cherry laurel, which the National Trust has recently restored. A lovely garden, almost best when just viewed from the top – but the temptation to wander down and into it is irresistible!

Heligan Manor Gardens

Pentewan, St Austell, Cornwall PL26 6EW
☎ 0726 844157 / 843566 [FAX] 0726 843023

OWNER The Heligan Manor Gardens Project
LOCATION St. Austell to Mevagissey Road, following brown tourist signs
OPEN 10.00 am – 4.30 pm (last ticket)
ADMISSION Adults £2.50, Senior Citizens £2.20, Children £1.50, Family tickets £7.00
FACILITIES Parking; dogs permitted; loos; facilities for the disabled; plants for sale; tea room with sandwiches, salads, etc.
FEATURES Herbaceous borders; follies and garden buildings; fruit and vegetables of special interest; rock garden; sub-tropical plants; water features; woodland garden; restoration work; Italian garden
ENGLISH HERITAGE GRADE II
FRIENDS Friends subscription £15.00 includes newsletters

Heligan is one of the 'lost' gardens of Cornwall, which has been rediscovered under the debris of many years' growth. To date the restoration team has uncovered the Italian garden, the Crystal Grotto, the wishing well, the Bee Boles, a Melon Garden, the Sundial Garden and other authentic features. The enthusiasm of the restorers is infectious and their achievements are already substantial. They are also brilliant at getting financial support and publicity. Visit Heligan now, while the Sleeping Beauty awakes.

Ken Caro

Bicton, Pensilva, Liskeard, Cornwall PL14 5RF
☎ 0579 62446

OWNER Mr & Mrs K R Willcock
LOCATION 1 mile north east of Gang
OPEN 2 pm – 6 pm; Monday – Wednesday & Sundays; 10 April to 30 June; Tuesday and Wednesday in July & August
ADMISSION £2.00
FACILITIES Parking; plants for sale
FEATURES Herbaceous borders; fine conifers; oriental features; plantsman's garden; aviary and waterfowl

Started in 1970 as two acres of intensely planted formal gardens in different styles, and extended in 1993 by taking in a further 2 acres. Very much a plantsman's garden with good herbaceous plants and shrubs, not at all a typical Cornish garden. The owners are flower arrangers: look for architectural plants and original combinations.

Lamorran House

Upper Castle Road, St Mawes, Cornwall TR2 5BZ
☎ 0326 270800   📠 0326 270801

OWNER   Mr & Mrs Robert Dudley-Smith
LOCATION   ½ mile from village centre
OPEN   27 March, 10 April, 1 & 22 May, 19 June, and by appointment
ADMISSION   £2
FACILITIES   Parking; loos; plants for sale
FEATURES   Good collection of trees; herbaceous borders; fine conifers; follies and garden buildings; oriental features; plantsman's garden; sub-tropical plants; water features; young garden

Made since 1980 on a steep site above the sea and tightly designed in the Italian style, but also full of unusual plants. An English Mediterranean Garden in Cornwall, say the owners.

Lanhydrock

Bodmin, Cornwall PL30 5AD
☎ 0208 73320

OWNER   The National Trust
LOCATION   2½ miles south east of Bodmin
OPEN   11 am – 5.30 pm; daily except Mondays; 30 March to 31 October
ADMISSION   House and grounds £5.00, grounds £2.50
FACILITIES   Parking; loos; plants for sale; National Trust shop; restaurant & bar, cream teas
FEATURES   Herbaceous borders; modern roses; good topiary; woodland garden; Victorian parterres; collection of magnolias;
ENGLISH HERITAGE GRADE   II*
NCCPG NATIONAL COLLECTIONS   *Crocosmia*

A grand mansion, mainly 19th century, with one of the best formal gardens in Cornwall – clipped yews, box parterres and bedding out, as well as large herbaceous borders which contain the National Collection of crocosmias. The woodlands behind are impressive for their size and colourful rhododendrons in spring. But it is the magnolias which impress the visitor most: 140 different species and cultivars.

Mount Edgcumbe Gardens

Cremyll, Torpoint, Cornwall PL10 1HZ
☎ 0752 822236   📠 0752 822199

OWNER   Cornwall County Council & Plymouth City Council
LOCATION   At the end of the B3247, or by ferry from Plymouth
OPEN   Dawn to dusk; all year
ADMISSION   Free
FACILITIES   Parking; dogs permitted; loos; facilities for the disabled; gift and book shops; orangery restaurant in formal gardens
FEATURES   Good collection of trees; herbaceous borders; fine conifers; follies and garden buildings; glasshouses to visit; modern roses; sub-tropical plants; water features; woodland garden; summer bedding; deer park; formal gardens; fern dell; tallest cork oak *Quercus suber* in the British Isles
ENGLISH HERITAGE GRADE   I
NCCPG NATIONAL COLLECTIONS   *Camellia*
FRIENDS   Contact Mrs. C. Gaskell Brown (0752 822236)

A long, stately grass drive runs down from the house to Plymouth Sound, through woods which contain extraordinarily large specimen trees. Here is the National Collection of Camellias which will eventually hold all 32,000 known varieties. The formal gardens are right down on the waterside, protected by a clipped ilex hedge 30 feet high. There are no less than ten acres of gardens, including an Italian garden (c.1790), a French garden (early Victorian), an American garden, a New Zealand garden complete with geyser, Milton's Temple, an orangery, a conservatory and the fern dell. A restaurant and other amenity features contribute enormously to the visitor's enjoyment.

Pencarrow

Washaway, Bodmin, Cornwall PL30 3AG
☎ 020 884 369

OWNER   The Trustees of the Molesworth-St Aubyn Family
LOCATION   4 miles north west of Bodmin – signed off the A389 at Washaway
OPEN   1.30 pm – 5 pm, 3 April to 15 October except Friday and Saturday; 11 am – 5 pm, 1 June to 10 September and Bank Holiday Mondays
ADMISSION   House and Garden: Adults £3.50, Children £1.50 Garden only: Adults £1.50, Children free
FACILITIES   Parking; dogs permitted; loos; facilities for the disabled; plants for sale; craft centre; light lunches, cream teas
FEATURES   Fine conifers; fruit and vegetables of special interest; rock garden; old roses and climbers; water features; woodland garden; Italian garden; rhododendrons; camellias;
ENGLISH HERITAGE GRADE   II

A long drive through rhododendrons and vast conifers leads to the pretty Anglo-Palladian house. Below is an

Italian garden, laid out in the 1830s, and next to it a great granite rock garden where boulders from Bodmin Moor lie strewn among the trees and shrubs. Pencarrow is famous for its conifers: an ancestor planted one of every known variety in the mid 19th century and the survivors are so venerable that the great Alan Mitchell wrote a guide to them. Recent plantings have concentrated upon rhododendrons (many hundreds of the best modern varieties) and adding new conifers to the old. It is good to see the fortunes of such a distinguished garden revived.

Penjerrick

Budock, Falmouth, Cornwall TR11 5ED
☎ 0326 250074 / 0872 870105

OWNER   Mrs Rachel Morin
LOCATION   3 miles south west of Falmouth, entrance at junction of lanes opposite Penmoruah Manor Hotel
OPEN   1.30 pm – 4.30 pm; Wednesdays and Sundays; 1 March to 30 September
ADMISSION   Adults £1.00, Children 50p
FACILITIES   Parking; dogs permitted
FEATURES   Arboreteum; conifers; water features; woodland garden; rhododendrons; camellias; tree ferns
ENGLISH HERITAGE GRADE   II

Famous for the Barclayi and Penjerrick hybrid rhododendrons and now a mature woodland garden recovering well from a period of neglect. Very Cornish.

Pine Lodge

Cuddra, St Austell, Cornwall PL25 3RQ
☎ 0726 73500

OWNER   Mr & Mrs Raymond Clemo
LOCATION   East of St Austell between Holmbush and Tregrehan
OPEN   1 pm – 5 pm; 29 May & 26 June for charity, and by appointment for parties of 20 or more
ADMISSION   Groups £3.00 each, Charity days £2.00
FACILITIES   Parking; loos; access for the disabled; plants for sale; cream teas on charity days
FEATURES   Good collection of trees; herbaceous borders; fine conifers; plantsman's garden; garden sculpture; water features; woodland garden; bog gardens
NCCPG NATIONAL COLLECTIONS   *Grevillea*

A modern garden, rather different from the typical Cornish garden. There are rhododendrons and azaleas, of course, but they are planted and underplanted with other shrubs and herbaceous plants to create lasting colour effects. Interesting.

St Michael's Mount

Marazion, Cornwall TR17 OHT
☎ 0736 710507   ☎ 0736 711544

OWNER   Lord St Levan and The National Trust

LOCATION   1 mile south of Marazion
OPEN   10.30 am – 5.30 pm; Monday – Friday, 1 April to 31 May (plus some weekends during the summer)
ADMISSION   £1.50
FACILITIES   Loos; plants for sale; refreshments
FEATURES   Herbaceous borders; ecological interest; rock garden; sub-tropical plants; woodland garden; wild narcissus; naturalised kniphofias and agapanthus
ENGLISH HERITAGE GRADE   II

A triumph of man's ingenuity in the face of Atlantic gales, salt spray and bare rock with sand for a garden soil. Careful experiment over the generations has enabled the owners to plant a remarkable garden of plants which resist the elements: *Luma apiculata*, rugosa roses, correas, nerines, Hottentot figs and naturalised agapanthus. On the north side, a sparse wood of sycamores and pines gives protection to camellias, azaleas and hydrangeas. There is nothing rare about the plants: the wonder is that they grow at all.

Trebah Garden Trust

Mawnan Smith, Falmouth, Cornwall TR11 5JZ
☎ 0326 250448   ☎ 0326 250781

OWNER   The Trebah Garden Trust
LOCATION   6 miles south west of Falmouth, signposted from Mawnan Smith
OPEN   10.30 am – 5.00 pm (last admission); all year
ADMISSION   Adults £2.50, Children (5 – 15 yrs) £1, disabled visitors £1; Under 5 years free
FACILITIES   Parking; dogs permitted; loos; plants for sale; light refreshments, hot and cold drinks
FEATURES   Good collection of trees; herbaceous borders; fine conifers; plantsman's garden; sub-tropical plants; water features; woodland garden; interesting for children; particularly interesting in winter; Tarzan camp and Tarzan trails for children; access to private beach; tallest hornbeam *Carpinus betulus* in the British Isles and two other tree records
ENGLISH HERITAGE GRADE   II
FRIENDS   The Trebah Trust is a registered charity which aims to preserve the gardens for posterity: details from 0326 250448

Wonderful Trebah! This lost garden has been vigorously restored and succesfully improved since the Hibberts bought it in 1980. The view from the top is magical – a secret valley which runs right down to the Helford estuary. Vast trees, natural and exotic, line the steep sides, while the central point is held by a group of elegant palms: one is the tallest in the British Isles. Trebah is popular with children, whose curiosity is aroused by trails, quizzes and educational games.

Tregrehan

Par, Cornwall PL24 2SJ
☎ 0726 812438

OWNER T C Hudson
LOCATION 1 mile west of St. Blazey on A390
OPEN 10.30 am – 5 pm; daily except Good Friday;
mid-March to June, then September
ADMISSION Adults £2.00, Children 50p
FACILITIES Parking; loos; facilities for the disabled;
plants for sale; teas
FEATURES Good collection of trees; fine conifers;
glasshouses to visit; plantsman's garden; woodland garden; camellias; pinetum; walled garden; sunken garden
ENGLISH HERITAGE GRADE II*

An old Cornish garden whose 20 acres include a fine range of Victorian conservatories, tall conifers and lanky rhododendrons. But Tregrehan is best known for the camellias bred there by the late Gillian Carlyon, especially 'Jennifer Carlyon' which won her the Reginald Cory Memorial Cup from the Royal Horticultural Society.

Trehane

Probus, Truro, Cornwall TR2 4JG
☎ 0872 520270

OWNER David & Simon Trehane
LOCATION Signposted from A39
OPEN 2 pm – 5 pm; 20 March, 3 & 17 April, 1, 15 & 29 May; 19 June; 17 July; 7 August
ADMISSION Adults £1.00, Children 50p
FACILITIES Parking; dogs permitted; loos; access for the disabled; plants for sale; teas
FEATURES Herbaceous borders; fine conifers; plantsman's garden; good topiary; woodland garden; bluebells

You would expect camellias from anyone called Trehane, and their eponymous garden has a fine collection. There is, however, no limit to their interests and there are many other good things here, especially herbaceous plants.

Trelissick (Feock)

Feock, Truro, Cornwall TR3 6QL
☎ 0872 862090

OWNER The National Trust
LOCATION Take B3289 off main Truro – Falmouth Road
OPEN 10.30 am – 5.30 pm, Monday – Saturday;
12.30pm – 5.30pm, Sunday; 1 March to 31 October;
March and October closes at 5 pm
ADMISSION Adult £3.00, Children £1.50
FACILITIES Parking; loos; facilities for the disabled;
gift and plant shop; refreshments
FEATURES Fine conifers; fruit and vegetables of special interest; plantsman's garden; woodland garden; particularly good in July-August; aromatic plant garden; fig garden; hydrangeas
ENGLISH HERITAGE GRADE II

Once famous for its fig garden, still maintained by the National Trust, Trelissick is particularly colourful in August and September when the hydrangeas are in full flower. There are over 100 varieties, some in a special walk. But venerable conifers and tender plants are also features: *Rosa bracteata* and *Yucca whipplei* are among the many good things to admire in summer, not to mention the rhododendrons and camellias in spring.

Trengwainton Gardens

Madron, Penzance, Cornwall TR20 8RZ
☎ 0736 63148

OWNER Lt Col E T Bolitho & The National Trust
LOCATION 2 miles north west of Penzance, ½ mile west of Heamoor
OPEN 10.30 am – 5.30 pm (5 pm in March & October); Wednesday – Saturday & Bank Holidays;
1 March to 31 October
ADMISSION Adults £2.50, Children £1.25
FACILITIES Parking; dogs permitted; loos; facilities for the disabled; plants for sale; small shop; coffee, snacks, teas
FEATURES Fruit and vegetables of special interest; modern roses; old roses and climbers; sub-tropical plants; water features; woodland garden; lilies; acacias *Myosotidium hortensia*; tree ferns
ENGLISH HERITAGE GRADE II

Trengwainton has the best collection of tender plants on the Cornish mainland, all thanks to the Bolitho family who started planting seriously only in 1925. Much came from original seed from such collectors as Kingdon Ward: some rhododendrons flowered here for the first time in the British Isles, among them *R.R. macabeanum, elliottii* and *taggianum*. The plants in many Cornish gardens are past their best. Not so at Trengwainton, where so many are in their prime. It is a garden to wander through slowly, giving yourself as much time as you need to enjoy its riches.

Trerice

Newquay, Cornwall TR8 4PG
☎ 0637 875404

OWNER The National Trust
LOCATION 3 miles south east of Newquay – turn right at Kestle Mill
OPEN 11 am – 5.30pm (5 pm in October); daily except Tuesday; 1 April to 31 October
ADMISSION House £3.60, Garden free
FACILITIES Parking; loos; plants for sale; National Trust shop; restaurant & tea room

FEATURES Herbaceous borders; fruit and vegetables of special interest; oriental features; modern roses; colour borders

A perfect West Country manor house with pretty Dutch gables, Trerice is unusual among Cornish gardens. It is small and comparatively formal: the design and herbaceous plantings are its best points. It is not surrounded by swirling rhododendron woodland. There is a perfect harmony between the Jacobean architecture and the gardens. Somewhat anomalously, it boasts the largest collection of mid-Victorian to modern lawn mowers in the country. They are both interesting and fun.

Tresco Abbey

Isles of Scilly, Cornwall TR24 0QQ
☎ 0720 22849   ☒ 0720 22807

OWNER Robert Dorrien Smith
LOCATION Direct helicopter flight from Penzance
OPEN 10 am – 4 pm; daily
ADMISSION Adults £3.00, Children under 14 £1.00
FACILITIES Dogs permitted; loos; facilities for the disabled; plants for sale; shop; light refreshments
FEATURES Herbaceous borders; fine conifers; follies and garden buildings; plantsman's garden; rock garden; sub-tropical plants; water features; woodland garden; interesting for children; particularly good in July-August; particularly interesting in winter; cacti; succulents; South African, Australian and New Zealand plants; tallest *Luma apiculata* in the British Isles
ENGLISH HERITAGE GRADE I
NCCPG NATIONAL COLLECTIONS *Acacia*

Tresco has recovered brilliantly from the arctic weather of January 1987 and the hurricane of January 1990. Kew donated hundreds of plants and English Heritage helped to plant new shelter belts. The amazing profusion of exotica is intact. The helicopter service makes access easier than ever, but it does distract you while actually visiting the garden.

Trewidden

Penzance, Cornwall
☎ 0726 882414

OWNER Captain A R Bolitho
LOCATION On A390 between Truro and St. Austell
OPEN 10 am – 4.30 pm; Monday – Saturday; 1 March to 30 September
ADMISSION £1.50 adults, 75p children
FACILITIES Parking; dogs permitted; loos; plants for sale
FEATURES Good collection of trees; fine conifers; water features; woodland garden; walled gardens with camellias; rhododendrons; magnolias

Trewidden is as much a nursery as a garden, but there are fine specimen trees in the woods, notably a copse of tree ferns.

Trewithen

Grampound Road, Truro, Cornwall TR2 4DD
☎ 0726 882763   ☒ 0726 882301

OWNER A M J Galsworthy
LOCATION A390 between Probus and Grampound
OPEN 10 am – 4.30 pm; Monday – Saturday; 1 March to 30 September
ADMISSION March – June, Adults £2.00, Children £1.00; July – September, Adults £1.75, Children £1.00
FACILITIES Parking; dogs permitted; loos; facilities for the disabled; garden shop; tea room with light refreshments
FEATURES Good collection of trees; herbaceous borders; fine conifers; plantsman's garden; woodland garden; camellias; rhododendrons; magnolias; trees and shrubs from collected seed; tallest *Eucryphia cordifolia* in the British Isles and four more record-breaking tree species
ENGLISH HERITAGE GRADE II*

Trewithen's setting is magnificent. Instead of the steep terraces of most Cornish gardens, there is a long flat lawn that stretches 200 yards into the distance, with gentle banks of rhododendrons, magnolias and rare shrubs on all sides. It sets the tone for the garden's grandeur, which was entirely the work of George Johnstone in the first half of this century. Johnstone was a great plantsman. He subscribed to plant hunting expeditions, such as those of Frank Kingdon Ward. He also had an eye for how to place good plants to great advantage. As a breeder, he gave us *Rhododendron* 'Alison Johnstone', *Ceanothus* 'Trewithen Blue' and *Camellia saluensis* 'Trewithen White'. All are still grown at Trewithen, a garden of infinite attractions. The Michelin Guide gives it their top award of three stars – *vaut le voyage!*

CUMBRIA

Acorn Bank Garden

Acorn Bank, Temple Sowerby, Penrith, Cumbria CA10 1SP
☎ 07683 61893/61281

OWNER The National Trust
LOCATION North of Temple Sowerby, 6 miles east of Penrith on A66
OPEN 10 am – 5.30 pm; 1 April to 31 October;
ADMISSION Adult £1.50; Child 80p (1993 prices)
FACILITIES Parking; loos; facilities for the disabled; plants for sale; National Trust shop; light refreshments

FEATURES Herbaceous borders; ecological interest; fruit and vegetables of special interest; glasshouses to visit; herbs; old roses and climbers; woodland garden; spring bulbs; woodland walk past Mill

Acorn Bank boasts the largest collection (250 varieties) of culinary and medicinal plants in the north, but it is almost better visited in spring when thousands and thousands of daffodils fill the woodland slopes, and the fruit trees flower in the old walled garden. Best of all is the huge quince tree, a wondrous sight in flower or fruit.

Brantwood
Coniston, Cumbria LA21 8AD
☎ 05394 41396

OWNER Brantwood Educational Trust
LOCATION East side of Coniston Water, 2½ miles from Coniston, 4 miles from Hawkshead
OPEN 11 am – 5.30 pm; daily; mid-March to mid-November. 11 am – 4 pm; Wednesday to Sunday; winter season
ADMISSION House, garden and trails: £3
FACILITIES Parking; dogs permitted; loos; bookshop & craft gallery; meals, light refreshments & drinks all day
FEATURES Water features; woodland garden
FRIENDS Friends of Brantwood, very active, currently restoring fern garden. Ring 05394 41396 for details

Most interesting for being the home of John Ruskin, whose garden is being restored with a grant from the European Community. Rhododendron woodland and wonderful views across Coniston Water.

Dalemain
Penrith, Cumbria CA11 0HB

OWNER R Hasell-McCosh
LOCATION M6 (J40), A66 (West 1m), A592
OPEN 11.15 am – 5.00 pm; Thursday – Sunday
ADMISSION House and garden £4.00, Gardens only £3.00
FACILITIES Parking; loos; facilities for the disabled; gift shop; small plant centre; morning coffee, light lunches, afternoon teas
FEATURES Fruit and vegetables of special interest; herbs; old roses and climbers; woodland garden; interesting for children; meconopsis; old flower and fruit varieties; adventure playground
ENGLISH HERITAGE GRADE II*

This historic garden has a 16th century terrace, and 17th century parterre, and a kitchen garden with fruit trees planted 250 years ago. All have been beautifully restored and replanted with period flowers. Charming and not at all self-conscious.

Graythwaite Hall
Ulverston, Hawkshead, Cumbria LA12 8BA
☎ 05395 31248   📠 05395 30060

OWNER Graythwaite Estate Co
LOCATION Between Newby Bridge and Hawkshead
OPEN 10 am to 6 pm; daily; 1 April to 30 June
ADMISSION Adults £2; Children free
FACILITIES Parking; dogs permitted; loos
FEATURES Good collection of trees; herbaceous borders; rock garden; modern roses; old roses and climbers; good topiary

Thomas Mawson on home ground and at his best. Formal gardens by the house drop down to sweeping lawns; beyond the stream is a woodland with rhododendrons and azaleas.

Holehird
Patterdale Road, Windermere, Cumbria LA23 1NP
☎ 0539 446008

OWNER Lakeland Horticultural Society
LOCATION 1½ miles north of Windermere town, off A592
OPEN Dawn – dusk, all year
ADMISSION By donation – minimum £1.00 per adult
FACILITIES Parking; loos; access for the disabled
FEATURES Herbaceous borders; glasshouses to visit; herbs; rock garden; modern roses; old roses and climbers; water features; woodland garden; heathers; hostas; ferns; Victorian garden; walled garden
FRIENDS The Lakeland Horticultural Society is a registered charity: details from the Secretary

A demonstration and trial garden, maintained almost entirely by local volunteers to promote appropriate horticultural practices for the Lake District. Particularly good to see what flourishes in a cool damp climate: alpines, azaleas, heathers, ferns and much, much more.

Holker Hall
Cark-in-Cartmel, Grange-over-Sands, Cumbria LA11 7PL
☎ 05395 58328   📠 05395 58776

OWNER Lord Cavendish of Furness
LOCATION Junction 36 off M6, follow brown and white tourist signs
OPEN 10.30 am – 6.00 pm; Fridays – Sundays; 1 April to 30 October. Last admission 4.30 pm
ADMISSION 1993 prices Adult £2.90; Child £1.65 (under 6 FOC); Family ticket £8.50
FACILITIES Parking; loos; facilities for the disabled; plants for sale; shop; clocktower cafeteria (licenced)
FEATURES Modern roses; water features; woodland garden; rhododendrons; formal gardens; HHA/Christie's Garden of the Year in 1991 and current holder of Sandford Award

ENGLISH HERITAGE GRADE II*

19th century formal gardens below the house with scrumptious herbaceous borders. The woodland has rhododendrons and splendid trees: Joseph Paxton planted a monkey puzzle and Lord George Cavendish the cedars grown from the seeds he brought back from the Holy Land.

Hutton-in-the-Forest

Skelton, Penrith, Cumbria CA11 9TH
☎ 07684 84449   📠 07684 84571

OWNER   Lord Inglewood
LOCATION   3 miles from Exit 41 of M6 on B5305
OPEN   House: 1 pm – 4 pm; 3 April to 3 October. Gardens: 11 am – 5 pm; all year except Saturdays and Christmas Day
ADMISSION   House and Gardens: Adults £3.00, Children 7 – 16 £1.00, Gardens: Adults £1.50, Children free
FACILITIES   Parking; dogs permitted; loos; refreshments: 1 pm – 4 pm; Thurs, Fri & Sun; 1 May – 30 Sept
FEATURES   Herbaceous borders; good topiary; woodland garden; rhododendrons; herbaceous borders in the walled garden
ENGLISH HERITAGE GRADE   II

Handsomely sited house with high Victorian terraces and grand views across the valley. Romantic parkland and good modern plantings. A garden to watch.

Levens Hall

Kendal, Cumbria LA8 0PD
☎ 05395 60321

OWNER   C H Bagot
LOCATION   5 miles south of Kendal on A6
OPEN   11 am – 5 pm; Thursday – Sunday; 1 April to 30 September
ADMISSION   House and Garden, Adults £3.80, Children £2.20, Garden only, Adults £2.50, Children £1.50
FACILITIES   Parking; loos; access for the disabled; gift shop and plant centre; light lunches & teas
FEATURES   Good topiary; summer bedding
ENGLISH HERITAGE GRADE   I

Levens means topiary, huge overgrown chunks of box and yew left over from a simple formal parterre and supplemented by golden yews in the 19th century. Laid out in 1694, so this is its 300th anniversary. The yew hedges are spangled with *Tropaeolum speciosum* and the modern parterres are planted annually with 15,000 plants, which makes Levens one of the best places to study the expensive art of bedding out.

Lingholm

Keswick, Cumbria CA12 5UA
☎ 0768 772003   📠 0768 775213

OWNER   Viscount Rochdale

LOCATION   Follow signs from Portinscale village
OPEN   10 am – 5 pm; daily; 1 April to 31 October
ADMISSION   Adults £2.60, (accompanied) Children free, Groups (20 minimum) £2.10
FACILITIES   Parking; loos; facilities for the disabled; plants for sale; tea room for morning coffee, light lunches, teas
FEATURES   Fine conifers; old roses and climbers; rhododendrons; azaleas; daffodils

Set on the hillside above Derwentwater, the main feature of Lingholm is its rhododendron and azalea woodland. The trees include fine conifers yet the overall impression is of naturalness and peace.

Muncaster Castle

Ravenglass, Cumbria CA18 1RQ
☎ 0229 717614/203   📠 0229 717010

OWNER   Mrs P R Gordon-Duff-Pennington
LOCATION   A595 1 mile east of Ravenglass on west coast of Cumbria
OPEN   11 am – 5 pm; daily; all year
ADMISSION   Adults £2.90, Children £1.60, Family (2+2) £8.00
FACILITIES   Parking; dogs permitted; loos; facilities for the disabled; plants for sale; two gift shops; snacks and full meals
FEATURES   Fine conifers; plantsman's garden; woodland garden; rhododendrons; camellias; maples; tallest *Acer palmatum*, *Nothofagus dombeyi* and *Nothofagus obliqua* in the British Isles
ENGLISH HERITAGE GRADE   II*

Visit Muncaster in May, when the rhododendrons are at their peak. Many are grown from the original seed introduced by such plant hunters as Forrest and Kingdon Ward in the 1920s and 1930s. The castle was revamped 150 years ago: its steep slopes and the lakeland hills behind create an intensely romantic landscape.

Rydal Mount

Ambleside, Cumbria LA22 9LU
☎ 05394 33002

OWNER   Rydal Mount Trust (Wordsworth family)
LOCATION   1½ miles north of Ambleside on A591, turn up Rydal Hill
OPEN   9.30 am – 5.00 pm, 1 March to 31 October; 10.00 am – 4.00 pm, 1 November to 28 February
ADMISSION   Adults £2.00, Children 80p, Group (min 10) £1.70
FACILITIES   Parking; dogs permitted; loos
FEATURES   Water features; trees; rhododendrons
ENGLISH HERITAGE GRADE   II

Kept very much as it was in the poet's day, the garden at Rydal Mount is a memorial to William Wordsworth. He believed that a garden should be informal in its design, harmonise with the country and keep its views open.

Sizergh Castle

Kendal, Cumbria LA8 8AE
☎ 05396 60070

OWNER The National Trust
LOCATION 3½ miles south of Kendal
OPEN 12.30 pm – 5.30 pm; Thursday – Sunday;
1 April to 31 October
ADMISSION Castle and Garden £3.30, Garden £1.70
FACILITIES Parking; loos; facilities for the disabled; tea room from 1.30pm
FEATURES Herbaceous borders; fine conifers; rock garden; old roses and climbers; garden sculpture; water features; hardy geraniums; autumn colour; wildflower meadow
ENGLISH HERITAGE GRADE II*

One of the best National Trust gardens, with lots of interest from daffodils and alpines in April to hydrangeas and a hot half-hardy border in September. Best of all is the 1920s rock garden made of local stone, whose dwarf maples and conifers have grown to great size.

DERBYSHIRE

Calke Abbey

Ticknall, Derbyshire DE7 1LE
☎ 0332 863822

OWNER The National Trust
LOCATION 10 miles south of Derby in village of Ticknall
OPEN 11 am – 5 pm; Wednesday – Saturday
ADMISSION £2.00
FACILITIES Parking; loos; facilities for the disabled; National Trust Gift Shop; restaurant
FEATURES Herbaceous borders; fruit and vegetables of special interest; dahlias; good Victorian-style bedding
ENGLISH HERITAGE GRADE II*

The 'sleeping beauty' house is not really matched by its garden, but when funds are available it will be replanted in the early 19th century style, with period ornamental and fruit varieties, a physic garden and an orangery. In the walled garden is the only surviving Auricula Theatre, originally built to display the perfection of these beautiful 'florist's' plants.

Chatsworth

Bakewell, Derbyshire DE4 1PP
☎ 0246 582204   📠 0246 583536

OWNER Chatsworth House Trust
LOCATION 8 miles north of Matlock off B6012. 16 miles from M1 J29 (Chesterfield). 36 miles M6 J19.

OPEN 11 am – 5 pm; 21 March to 31st October
ADMISSION Adult £3.00, Senior Citizens £2.50, Children £1.50, Family ticket £8.00
FACILITIES Parking; dogs permitted; loos; facilities for the disabled; plants for sale in Potting Shed Shop, in Orangery; self-service restaurant, licensed
FEATURES Good collection of trees; fine conifers; rock garden; modern roses; garden sculpture; good topiary; water features; woodland garden; interesting for children; pinetum; rhododendrons; azaleas; maze; tulip tree avenue; adventure playground; tallest *Nyssa sylvatica* and *Pinus strobus* in the British Isles
ENGLISH HERITAGE GRADE I
FRIENDS Season ticket available, ring 0264 582204

Everyone knows of Chatsworth: 105 acres of Capability Brown, a 'conservative wall' to keep the heat and ripen fruit trees, Paxton's rockeries (huge boulders surrounded by conifers), a serpentine hedge with yews of different hues, enormous *Camellia reticulata* 'Captain Rawes' with trunks 80 cms thick, and of course the famous long cascade. But there is so much more: well run and fun for all the family. New maze and kitchen garden opening in 1994.

Darley House

Darley Dale, Matlock, Derbyshire DE4 3BP
☎ 0629 733341

OWNER Mr & Mrs G H Briscoe
LOCATION On A6, 2 miles north of Matlock
OPEN 1 May – 30 September, by appointment
ADMISSION Adults £1.00, Children free
FACILITIES Parking; loos; plants for sale; tea, coffee & biscuits
FEATURES Herbaceous borders; plantsman's garden; water features

Basically a modern, plantsman's garden, just over an acre, but planted with good colour sense and commendable restraint. Interesting too because it belonged to Sir Joseph Paxton in the 1840s and his layout still gives the whole garden its structure.

Elvaston Castle County Park

Borrowash Road, Elvaston, Derbyshire DE72 3EP
☎ 0332 571342

OWNER Derbyshire County Council
LOCATION 5 miles south east of Derby. Signed from A6 and A52
OPEN Dawn – dusk (except Old English Garden 9.00 am – 5.00 pm), all year
ADMISSION Gardens free. Car park 60p midweek, £1.20 weekends, coaches £6.00
FACILITIES Parking; dogs permitted; loos; facilities for the disabled; gift shop and light meals: Easter – 31 Oct, 11.00 am – 4.30 pm

FEATURES Herbaceous borders; old roses and climbers; good topiary; water features; particularly interesting in winter
ENGLISH HERITAGE GRADE II*

A historic garden, once famous for its topiary, and saved from oblivion by Derby County Council 25 years ago. The parterres have been replaced and the walled garden replanted with roses and herbaceous plants, and renamed the Old English Garden.

Haddon Hall

Bakewell, Derbyshire DE4 1LA
☎ 0629 812855   FAX 0629 814379

OWNER The Duke of Rutland
LOCATION 1½ miles south of Bakewell on A6
OPEN 11 am – 6 pm, closed Mondays; closed Sundays in July and August; 1 April to 30 September
ADMISSION Adult £4.00, Senior Citizens £3.00, Children £2.50, Groups (20 min) £3.00
FACILITIES Parking; loos; coffee, lunch, afternoon teas
FEATURES Herbaceous borders; modern roses; old roses and climbers; clematis; delphiniums
ENGLISH HERITAGE GRADE I

Terraced neo-Tudor gardens to complement a castellated Elizabethan prodigy house. Fine balustrading and old yews, spring bulbs and herbaceous borders but, above all, roses, roses, roses.

Hardwick Hall

Doe Lea, Chesterfield, Derbyshire S44 5QJ

OWNER The National Trust
LOCATION Signposted from J29 of M1
OPEN 12 noon – 5.30 pm; daily; 1 April – 31 October
ADMISSION £5 adults; £2.50 children (1993 prices)
FACILITIES Parking; loos; facilities for the disabled; weekend plant sales only; refreshments Wed/Thurs/Sat/Sun when Hall is open
FEATURES Herbaceous borders; herbs; old roses and climbers; daffodils; fine hedges; mulberry walk; hollies
ENGLISH HERITAGE GRADE I
NCCPG NATIONAL COLLECTIONS *Scabiosa caucasica*

The formal gardens are extensive: avenues of hornbeam and yew and a new 'Elizabethan' herb garden (lavender and eglantine) in the kitchen garden. Wonderful old fruit trees, mulberries, old roses and borders. In the park, fine cedars and Hungarian oaks.

Lea Gardens

Lea, Matlock, Derbyshire DE4 5GH
☎ 0629 534380   FAX 0629 534260

OWNER Mr & Mrs J Tye
LOCATION 3 miles south east of Matlock
OPEN 10 am – 7 pm; 20 March to 30 June

ADMISSION Adults £2, Children 50p, Season ticket £3, Wheelchair bound free
FACILITIES Parking; dogs permitted; loos; plants for sale; light refreshments
FEATURES Rhododendrons & azaleas

This is the garden of a rhododendron lover: over 650 varieties as well as kalmias, magnolias, maples and dwarf conifers. Best in May, when it is frankly spectacular.

Melbourne Hall

Melbourne, Derbyshire D73 1EN
☎ 0332 862502

OWNER Lord Ralph Kerr
LOCATION 8 miles south of Derby
OPEN 2 pm – 5 pm; 1 – 31 August
ADMISSION Adults £2
FACILITIES Parking; loos; access for the disabled; shop; refreshments
FEATURES Herbaceous borders; garden sculpture; water features; turf terracing; grand avenues
ENGLISH HERITAGE GRADE I

Near-perfect example of an early 18th century garden, influenced by Le Nôtre. Statues, gravel, *bassins* and the famous yew tunnel.

Renishaw Hall

Renishaw, Sheffield, Derbyshire S31 9WB
☎ 0246 432042 / 0777 860755

OWNER Sir Reresby Sitwell
LOCATION 2½ miles from M1 (exit 30)
OPEN 12 noon – 5 pm; 3 & 4 April, 1 & 2, 29 & 30 May, 28 & 29 August, Sundays in June, July & August
ADMISSION Adults £3.00, Senior Citizens £2.00, Children £1.00
FACILITIES Parking; dogs permitted; loos; access for the disabled; plants for sale; small tea rooms open from 12 noon – 5 pm
FEATURES Herbaceous borders; fine conifers; modern roses; old roses and climbers; water features; woodland garden; daffodils; Italian garden
ENGLISH HERITAGE GRADE II*

Lots of horticultural interest, including a good collection of shrub roses, but best for the formal Italian garden laid out by Sir George Sitwell c.1900, and at last appreciated as a meticulous and scholarly creation.

DEVON

Arlington Court

Arlington, Barnstaple, Devon EX31 4LP
☎ 0271 850296

OWNER The National Trust

LOCATION 8 miles north of Barnstable on A39
OPEN 11 am – 5.30 pm; closed Saturday; 1 April to 31 October
ADMISSION Adults £2.40; Children £1.20; (1993)
FACILITIES Parking; dogs permitted; loos; facilities for the disabled; plants for sale; National Trust shop; restaurant & tea rooms
FEATURES Fine conifers; huge old rhododendrons
ENGLISH HERITAGE GRADE II
NCCPG NATIONAL COLLECTIONS Fraxinus

Mature parkland on a dead flat site in front of a fine Georgian house. Pretty Victorian formal garden and conservatory. Peacocks.

Bicton Park Gardens

East Budleigh, Budleigh Salterton, Devon EX9 7DP
☎ 0395 68465

OWNER Bicton Park Trust Co
LOCATION On B3178 north of Budleigh Salterton
OPEN 10 am – 6 pm; daily; April to September
ADMISSION Adults £3.75
FACILITIES Parking; dogs permitted; loos; facilities for the disabled; shop; self-service restaurant; licensed bar
FEATURES Good collection of trees; herbaceous borders; fine conifers; glasshouses to visit; oriental features; plantsman's garden; modern roses; old roses and climbers; water features; woodland garden; interesting for children; play area; miniature railway
ENGLISH HERITAGE GRADE I

60 acres, beautifully maintained by the college nearby. Italian garden; important trees; oriental garden; American garden; collection of dwarf conifers; more than 2000 heathers; an avenue of monkey puzzles; a hermitage; and the finest pre-Paxton palm house built 1815-20 from thousands of tiny panes of glass. Allow lots of time.

Castle Drogo

Drewsteignton, Devon EX6 6PB
☎ 0647 433306   [FAX] 0647 433186

OWNER The National Trust
LOCATION Drewsteignton village; signs from A30 & Exeter-Okehampton Road.
OPEN 10 am – 5.30 pm; Daily; 1 April to October
ADMISSION £2.00; Children £1.00 (1993)
FACILITIES Parking; loos; facilities for the disabled; plants for sale; National Trust shop; self-service tea-room, waitress-service restaurant
FEATURES Herbaceous borders; designed by Lutyens; rock garden; modern roses; old roses and climbers; woodland garden; interesting for children
ENGLISH HERITAGE GRADE II*

Major 1920s garden high on the edge of Dartmoor. Handsome yew hedges; formal design; rich and spacious herbaceous borders, contrasting with the austere castle on its windy bluff. Weather-beaten, lichen-heavy Prunus and acers on the slopes below. All on a vast scale.

Coleton Fishacre Garden

Coleton, Kingswear, Dartmouth, Devon TQ6 0EQ
☎ 0803 752466

OWNER The National Trust
LOCATION 2 miles from Kingswear off Lower-Ferry Road
OPEN 10.30am – 5.30pm; Wednesday – Friday & Sunday; 1 April to 31 October plus Sundays in March 2 pm – 5 pm.
ADMISSION Adults £2.60; Children £1.30 (1993)
FACILITIES Parking; loos; plants for sale; tea-hut, snacks & ice creams
FEATURES Herbaceous borders; plantsman's garden; sub-tropical plants; woodland garden; rhododendrons; rare trees;
ENGLISH HERITAGE GRADE II

Twenty acres of rhododendron and camellia woodland crashing down a secret valley to the sea. Almost frost-free, the range and size of Southern Hemisphere trees and shrubs is astounding. Rare bulbs in the warm terraces around the Lutyensesque house.

Dartington Hall

Dartington, Totnes, Devon TQ9 6EL
☎ 0803 862271

OWNER Dartington Hall Trust
LOCATION 2 miles north west of Totnes
OPEN Daily; dawn to dusk
ADMISSION Donation
FACILITIES Parking; loos
FEATURES Herbaceous borders; garden sculpture; good topiary; water features; woodland garden; magnolias; rhododendrons; camellias; tilt-yard
ENGLISH HERITAGE GRADE II*

Grand mid-20th century garden with some famous associations. Beatrix Farrand designed the terraces, including the so-called tilt-yard, and Percy Cane built the long staircase and spring plantings on either side. Henry Moore deposited a reclining woman. Some consider the garden grandiose and cold: we think it is magnificent, and wholly appropriate to the scale of house and landscape.

Docton Mill

Lymebridge, Hartland, Devon EX39 6EA
☎ 0237 441369   [FAX] 0237 441681

OWNER N S & I D Pugh
LOCATION Hartland Village – Stoke, turn left. Follow signposts towards Elmscott

OPEN   10 am – 5 pm; daily; 1 March to 30 September
ADMISSION   Adults £1.50; under 16 free
FACILITIES   Parking; dogs permitted; refreshments at nearby Hartland Quay Hotel
FEATURES   Fruit and vegetables of special interest; water features; woodland garden; apple orchards

The main attraction is a working water mill, but the garden is developing quickly and the owners are keen plantsmen. Worth watching.

Exeter University Gardens

Exeter, Devon EX4 4PX
☎ 0392 263059   📠 0392 264547

OWNER   The University of Exeter
LOCATION   3 miles north of City Centre
OPEN   All year round
ADMISSION   Free
FACILITIES   Parking; dogs permitted
FEATURES   Fine conifers; tender plants; heathers; rhododendrons; summer bedding
NCCPG NATIONAL COLLECTIONS Azara

One of the best University campuses, the gardens are educational, attractive and important. Based on the 19th century Veitch collections of exotic trees, the plantings were supplemented by Chinese species collected 80 years ago by E H Wilson.

The Garden House

Buckland Monachorum, Yelverton, Devon PL20 7LQ
☎ 0822 854769

OWNER   Fortescue Garden Trust
LOCATION   Signed off A386 on Plymouth side of Yelverton
OPEN   10.30 am – 5 pm; daily; 1 March to 30 October
ADMISSION   Adults £2.50; Senior Citizens £2.25; Children 50p
FACILITIES   Parking; loos; plants for sale; tea room open in season with light lunches
FEATURES   Herbaceous borders; gravel or scree garden; plantsman's garden; rock garden; old roses and climbers; woodland garden; alpine bank; flowering cherries; wisterias

A plantsman's garden, made by the late Lionel Fortescue, who insisted on planting only the best forms of plants. The setting is awesome: a ruined abbey on the edge of Dartmoor. Much of the effect is achieved through rigorous cultivation. Plants are well fed and firmly controlled: they flourish on the treatment.

Gidleigh Park Hotel

Chagford, Devon TQ13 8HH
☎ 0647 432367   📠 0647 432574

OWNER   Paul Henderson

LOCATION   15 miles west of Exeter. Turn off in Chagford: do not go to Gidleigh
OPEN   9 am – 6 pm; Monday – Friday only
ADMISSION   50p to National Garden Scheme
FACILITIES   Parking; dogs permitted; loos; delicious food in Hotel
FEATURES   Water features; woodland garden

45 acres of woodland on the edge of Dartmoor with a 1920s garden round the Tudorised house. Nothing very rare or special, but the position is stupendous and the sense of space, even grandeur, is enhanced by immaculate maintenance. Innumerable awards for the hotel & restaurant over the last 11 years.

Hill House Garden

Landscove, Ashburton, Newton Abbot, Devon TQ13 7LY
☎ 0803 762273

OWNER   R & V A Hubbard
LOCATION   Off A34 follow signs for Landscove
OPEN   11 am – 5 pm; daily
ADMISSION   Free
FACILITIES   Parking; dogs permitted; loos; facilities for the disabled; plants for sale; garden shop; Mother Hubbards Tea Room
FEATURES   Fine conifers; glasshouses to visit; particularly interesting in winter; daffodils; garden temple; cyclamen and snowdrops

Victorian Old Vicarage made famous by Edward Hyams' An Englishman's Garden. Now the centre of an ambitious young nursery.

Killerton

Broadclyst, Exeter, Devon EX5 3LE
☎ 0392 881345

OWNER   The National Trust
LOCATION   West side of B3181, Exeter to Cullompton Road
OPEN   11 am – 5.30 pm, daily, April to October; daylight hours in winter
ADMISSION   £2.80; winter rate £1.00
FACILITIES   Parking; loos; facilities for the disabled; plants for sale; National Trust shop; waitress-service restaurant and self-service tea room
FEATURES   Good collection of trees; herbaceous borders; fine conifers; follies and garden buildings; rock garden; woodland garden; particularly interesting in winter; magnolias; rhododendrons; herbaceous borders by William Robinson
ENGLISH HERITAGE GRADE   II*

A historic giant among gardens, whose long connections with Veitch's Nursery have made it one of the greatest tree collections in the world. Innumerable record-breaking specimens, many from collectors' seed.

Knightshayes Court

Tiverton, Devon EX16 7RH
☎ 0884 253264

OWNER The National Trust
LOCATION Off A396 Tiverton – Bampton Road
OPEN 10.30 am – 5.30 pm; 1 April to 31 October
ADMISSION Garden only £2.80
FACILITIES Parking; loos; plants for sale; National Trust shop; licensed restaurant; coffee, lunch & teas
FEATURES Herbaceous borders; good topiary; woodland garden; plantings by Graham Thomas; hellebores; cyclamen; bulbs; peat beds
ENGLISH HERITAGE GRADE II*

Brilliant herbaceous plantings and stunning formal gardens, but Knightshayes is above all a garden in a wood, delightful at all seasons and notable for its high standard of maintenance. The shop has particularly interesting plants for sale. Good new plantings by the adventurous head gardener.

Marwood Hill Gardens

Barnstaple, Devon EX31 4EB
☎ 0271 42528

OWNER Dr J A Smart
LOCATION Signed from A361 Barnstaple & Braunton Road
OPEN Dawn to dusk; daily; all year except Christmas Day
ADMISSION Adults £2.00; Senior Citizens £1.50.
FACILITIES Parking; dogs permitted; loos; plants for sale; teas, April – September, Sundays & Bank Holidays only
FEATURES Gravel or scree garden; plantsman's garden; water features; particularly interesting in winter; birches; *Eucalyptus*; camellias; hebes; plants, more plants & yet more plants
NCCPG NATIONAL COLLECTIONS *Astilbe*, *Tulbaghia*, *Iris ensata*

An extraordinary plantsman's garden on a grand scale with masses to look at all through the year. Exciting for its scale, variety, and the energy of its owner.

Paignton Zoo & Botanical Gardens

Totnes Road, Paignton, Devon TQ4 7EU
☎ 0803 557479   0803 523457

OWNER Whitley Wildlife Conservation Trust
LOCATION On A385 Totnes Road, 1 mile from Paignton
OPEN 10 am – 6 pm (5pm in winter); daily
ADMISSION Adults £5.50; Senior Citizens £4.50; Children £3.50
FACILITIES Parking; loos; plants for sale; shops; large self-service restaurant

FEATURES Good collection of trees; herbaceous borders; fine conifers; glasshouses to visit; rock garden; interesting for children; glasshouses with tropical plants
NCCPG NATIONAL COLLECTIONS *Buddleja*, *Sorbaria*

Once a private garden devoted to blue-flowered & blue-leaved plants, now an inspiring combination of zoo, botanic collection, public park and holiday entertainment.

Powderham Castle

Exeter, Devon EX6 8JQ
☎ 0626 890243   0626 890729

OWNER Lord & Lady Courtenay
LOCATION Off A379 Dawlish to Exeter Road at Kenton
OPEN 10 am – 5.30 pm; Easter to 31 October
ADMISSION Adults £3.95; Senior Citizens £3.75; Children £2.95. Charges include guided tour of Castle
FACILITIES Parking; loos; plants for sale; light lunches & cream teas
FEATURES Modern roses; woodland garden
ENGLISH HERITAGE GRADE II

Not a major garden, but the 18th century landscaped park is serenely English and there is a cheerful modern rose garden all along the front of the house.

RHS Garden, Rosemoor

Rosemoor, Great Torrington, Devon EX38 8PH
☎ 0805 24067   0805 24717

OWNER The Royal Horticultural Society
LOCATION 1 mile south of Torrington on B3220
OPEN 10 am – 6 pm (5 pm, March & October; 4 pm, Nov – Feb); all year
ADMISSION £2.50; children 50p. RHS members free.
FACILITIES Parking; loos; facilities for the disabled; plants for sale; good range of book & gifts; licensed restaurant
FEATURES Fine conifers; fruit and vegetables of special interest; herbs; plantsman's garden; modern roses; old roses and climbers; water features; woodland garden; young garden; particularly interesting in winter; large collection of dwarf conifers
NCCPG NATIONAL COLLECTIONS *Cornus*, *Ilex*

A competent, if uninspired, garden by Lady Anne Palmer which the RHS has made its West Country flagship by pouring money into developing and improving it. Although still young, the new Rosemoor is worth a visit at any season, but please note that the sales and food facilities are open March to October only.

Tapeley Park
Instow, Devon EX39 4NT
☎ 0271 860528

OWNER Hector & Kirsty Christie
LOCATION Off A39 between Barnstaple & Bideford
OPEN 10.30 am – 6pm ; Easter to 31 October except Saturdays
ADMISSION Adults £2.00; Senior Citizens £1.60; Children £1.00
FACILITIES Parking; dogs permitted; loos; facilities for the disabled; plants for sale; gift shop; licensed lunches & cream teas
FEATURES Follies and garden buildings; fruit and vegetables of special interest; glasshouses to visit; water features; woodland garden; interesting for children; British Jousting Centre
ENGLISH HERITAGE GRADE II*

Fine Italianate formal garden laid out on several levels c.1900 and planted with tender plants (*Sophora tetraptera* and *Myrtus communis* 'Tarentina'). Beyond are palm trees and a rhododendron woodland: worth getting to know.

Wylmington Hayes Gardens
Wilmington, Honiton, Devon EX14 9JZ
☎ 0404 831751   FAX 0404 831826

OWNER Mr & Mrs P Saunders
LOCATION 5½ miles north of Honiton on A30, right to Stockland then right before TV mast
OPEN 2 pm – 5 pm; Good Friday to Easter Monday; then Sundays and Bank Holiday Mondays to 30 June
ADMISSION Adults £2.50; Children £1; Wheelchair occupants £1
FACILITIES Parking; loos; facilities for the disabled; plants for sale; gift stand; home-made refreshments & cream teas
FEATURES Good collection of trees; good topiary; water features; woodland garden

An Edwardian house in the Tudor style, with a formal Italian garden and ornamental woodland planted with rhododendrons, azaleas, camellias, acers and magnolias.

DORSET

Abbotsbury Sub-Tropical Gardens
Abbotsbury, Weymouth, Dorset DT3 4LA
☎ 0305 871387

OWNER Ilchester Estates
LOCATION On coast, in village
OPEN 10 am – 5 pm; daily all year, but closed on Mondays November to February
ADMISSION Adults £2.80

FACILITIES Parking; dogs permitted; loos; plants for sale; shop; refreshments
FEATURES Good collection of trees; plantsman's garden; woodland garden; rhododendrons; camellias; magnolias; candelabra primulas; biggest English oak *Quercus robur* in the British Isles; three other record trees
ENGLISH HERITAGE GRADE I

A woodland garden of splendid specimens and trees of great rarity. Abbotsbury is making great efforts to become more visitor-friendly.

Athelhampton
Puddletown, Dorchester, Dorset DT2 7LG
☎ 0305 848363   FAX 0305 848135

OWNER Patrick Cooke
LOCATION 1 mile east of Puddletown on A35
OPEN 12 pm – 5 pm; Wednesdays, Thursdays, Sundays and Bank Holiday Mondays; Easter to 31 October. Plus Tuesdays, May to September and Mondays, July and August
ADMISSION House & Garden £4.20; Garden £2.10
FACILITIES Parking; loos; plants for sale; shop; refreshments
FEATURES Good topiary; water features; gazebos; beautiful walls and hedges
ENGLISH HERITAGE GRADE I

Inigo Thomas designed this about 100 years ago as the perfect garden for the perfect manor house. Sharply cut pyramids of yew, a long canal with water lilies, and rambling roses in early summer.

Broadlands
Hazelbury Bryan, Sturminster Newton, Dorset DT10 2EE
☎ 0258 817374

OWNER Mr & Mrs Michael Smith
LOCATION 4 miles south of Sturminster Newton
OPEN 2 pm – 5.30 pm; 4 & 24 April, 8 & 22 May, Wednesdays from June to August
ADMISSION Adults £1.50
FACILITIES Loos; access for the disabled; plants for sale; refreshments on Wednesdays only
FEATURES Plantsman's garden; old roses and climbers; woodland garden; young garden

An excellent and highly instructive modern garden. There is an infinity of character within its two acres, and good plants a-plenty. Island bedding and narrow paths are used to slow down your progress and increase your sense of space, yet there are always glimpses of the prospects to come. Ingenious.

Chiffchaffs

Chaffeymoor, Bourton, Gillingham, Dorset SP8 5BY
☎ 0747 840841

OWNER Mr & Mrs K R Potts
LOCATION At Wincanton end of Bourton
OPEN 2 pm – 5.30 pm; Sundays, Wednesdays &
Thursdays; April to September (but closed on 10 April,
8 May, and first Sundays from June – September)
ADMISSION £1.50
FACILITIES Parking; plants for sale; teas on last Sunday in month & Bank Holidays
FEATURES Plantsman's garden; old roses and climbers; woodland garden; spring bulbs; dwarf rhododendrons

A thatched cottage, with a promising small nursery attached, and just off the A303. Only fifteen years old, the garden has a flowing design, exploits a great variety of habitats and burgeons with good plants.

Compton Acres Gardens

Canford Cliffs Road, Poole, Dorset BH13 7ES
☎ 0202 700778   [FAX] 0202 707537

OWNER L Green
LOCATION Well signposted locally
OPEN 10.30 am – 6.30 pm; daily; March to October
ADMISSION Adults £3.50; Senior Citizens £2.50;
Children £1.00
FACILITIES Parking; loos; facilities for the disabled; plants for sale; several shops; tea rooms & crêperie
FEATURES Fine conifers; follies and garden buildings; oriental features; garden sculpture; sub-tropical plants; water features; woodland garden
ENGLISH HERITAGE GRADE II*

Very touristy, very Bournemouth, and very 1920s. Compton Acres has a ten totally unconnected gardens in different styles, joined by tarmac paths. Best are the Italian garden, the palm court, the white azaleas in the chine which runs down to the harbour, and the stupendous Japanese garden. There is opulence, vulgarity, overcrowding and blatant commercialism, but the standards are among the highest in any garden: no visitor could fail to be cheered up by the bravura of it all.

Cranborne Manor

Cranborne, Wimborne, Dorset BH21 5PP
☎ 0725 517248   [FAX] 0725 517248 (same)

OWNER Viscount Cranborne
LOCATION 10 miles north of Wimborne on B3078
OPEN 9 am – 5 pm; Wednesdays; 1 March to 30
September
ADMISSION £2.50 adults; £2 Senior Citizens & students; 50p children under 16
FACILITIES Parking; loos; garden centre

FEATURES Herbaceous borders; old roses and climbers; good topiary; parterres; Jacobean mount
ENGLISH HERITAGE GRADE II*

The garden at Cranborne is modern, but employs Elizabethan elements. Most successful are the parterres: long, low and prettily planted. The mixed borders in the charming courtyard are good too. Very 1970s.

Dean's Court

Wimborne, Dorset BH21 1EE

OWNER Sir Michael & Lady Hanham
LOCATION 2 mins walk from central Wimborne
OPEN 10 am – 6 pm, Bank Holidays; 2 pm – 6 pm,
preceding Sundays; 2 pm – 6 pm, 12 June, 10 July, 2
October; 2 pm – 6 pm, Tuesday and Thursday, 1 April
to 30 September
ADMISSION Adults £1.50; Children 70p
FACILITIES Parking; loos; plants for sale; organic herb plants and vegetables; wholefood refreshments, June – September
FEATURES Herbs; plantsman's garden; rock garden; old roses and climbers; water features; monastery fishpond; good trees; all organic; tallest *Catalpa bignonioides* in the British Isles

A very wholesome garden: everything, including 150 different herb varieties, is grown without artificial fertilisers, pesticides or herbicides.

Edmondsham House

Edmondsham, Wimborne, Dorset BH21 5RE
☎ 0725 517207

OWNER Mrs Julia E Smith
LOCATION Off B3081 between Cranborne & Verwood
OPEN 2 pm – 5 pm; Wednesdays & Sundays; 1 April
to 31 October
ADMISSION Adults £1; Children 50p
FACILITIES Parking; dogs permitted; loos; access for the disabled; plants for sale
FEATURES Herbaceous borders; fruit and vegetables of special interest; glasshouses to visit; herbs; old roses and climbers; organic kitchen garden

The walled garden is maintained organically, with borders round the sides. It is intensively cultivated and brims with interesting vegetables. Fine trees in the park.

Forde Abbey

Chard, Dorset TA20 4LU
☎ 0460 20231   [FAX] 0460 20296

OWNER The Trustees of the E Roper settlement
LOCATION 4 miles south of Chard
OPEN 10 am – 4.30 pm; daily; all year
ADMISSION Adults £3.00; Senior Citizens £2.60.

FACILITIES Parking; dogs permitted; loos; facilities for the disabled; plants for sale; shop; cafeteria

FEATURES Good collection of trees; herbaceous borders; fine conifers; fruit and vegetables of special interest; gravel or scree garden; rock garden; water features; rock garden planted by Jack Drake; HHA/Christie's Garden of the Year in 1992; biggest limetree *Tilia cordata* in U.K.

ENGLISH HERITAGE GRADE II*

A garden of great variety around the rambling house, part Jacobean, part Gothick. The planting is modern, and includes rhododendrons, azaleas, acers, magnolias, irises, meconopsis and candelabra primulas. But there are also mature Victorian conifers (*Sequoia sempervirens*, *Calocedrus decurrens*), lakes, ponds, streams, cascades, bogs and such oddities as the Beech House.

Ivy Cottage

Aller Lane, Ansty, Dorchester, Dorset DT2 7PX
☎ 0258 880053

OWNER Anne & Alan Stevens
LOCATION Midway between Blandford & Dorchester
OPEN 10 am – 5 pm; Thursdays; April to October. Also for NGS
ADMISSION Adults £1.50; Children 30.
FACILITIES Parking; plants for sale
FEATURES Herbaceous borders; plantsman's garden
NCCPG NATIONAL COLLECTIONS *Trollius, Lobelia*

1½ acres of cottage garden made by the present owners over the last 30 years and crammed with interesting things, particularly herbaceous plants and bulbs. Springs and streams, combined with greensand soil, multiply the possibilities – drifts of marsh marigolds and candelabra primulas.

Kingston Lacy

Wimborne Minster, Dorset BH21 4EA

OWNER The National Trust
LOCATION 1½ miles from Wimborne on B3082 to Blandford
OPEN 11.30 am – 6 pm; Saturday – Wednesday; 1 April to 31 October
ADMISSION £2 adults, £1 children (1993 prices)
FACILITIES Parking; loos; access for the disabled; lunches & teas
FEATURES Fine conifers; garden sculpture; Victorian fernery; snowdrops; Dutch parterre; huge cedars of Lebanon planted by visiting royalty; current holder of Sandford Award

ENGLISH HERITAGE GRADE II

250 acres of classic 18th century parkland, still undergoing restoration by the National Trust, with a cedar avenue, Egyptian obelisk and laurel walk dating from Victorian times.

Kingston Maurward Gardens

Dorset College of Ag & Hort, Dorchester, Dorset DT2 8PY
☎ 0305 264738   📠 0305 250059

OWNER Kingston Maurward College
LOCATION 1 mile east of Dorchester from A35
OPEN 1 pm – 5 pm; Good Friday to 30 September
ADMISSION Adults £2.50; Children £1.50
FACILITIES Parking; loos; facilities for the disabled; plants for sale; cakes & drinks
FEATURES Herbaceous borders; oriental features; good topiary; water features
ENGLISH HERITAGE GRADE II*
NCCPG NATIONAL COLLECTIONS *Salvia Penstemon*

Kingston Maurwood belonged to the Hanbury family who owned La Mortola on the Riviera, and laid out the formal garden here in the Italian style (c.1920). It is being restored in the country house style with herbaceous borders and old-fashioned roses, but the old kitchen garden is a splendid modern teaching garden with innumerable demonstrations of what can be grown in Dorset. Highly instructive.

Minterne

Minterne Magna, Dorchester, Dorset DT 7AU
☎ 0300 341370   📠 0300 341747

OWNER Lord Digby
LOCATION On A352 Dorchester to Sherborne Road
OPEN 10 am – 7 pm; daily; 1 April to 31 October
ADMISSION Adults £2.00; accompanied children free
FACILITIES Parking; dogs permitted; loos
FEATURES Woodland garden; rhododendrons; azaleas; cherries; tallest *Chamaecyparis pisifera* 'Filifera' in British Isles – 26 metres high
ENGLISH HERITAGE GRADE II

A spring garden, planted by the late Lord Digby and still reflecting his interest in trees and shrubs. Pretty woodland walks and some outstanding specimens.

Parnham House

Beaminster, Dorset DT8 3NA
☎ 0308 862204   📠 0308 863494

OWNER Mr & Mrs J Makepeace
LOCATION On A3066 north of Bridport
OPEN 10 am – 5 pm; Sundays, Wednesdays and Bank Holidays; April to 28 October; and groups by appointment
ADMISSION Adults £4.00; Children over 10 £2.00, includes House, Garden & Workshop

FACILITIES Parking; dogs permitted; loos; facilities for the disabled; woodware & contemporary crafts; tea, coffee, hot & cold lunches
FEATURES Herbaceous borders; old roses and climbers; good topiary; water features
ENGLISH HERITAGE GRADE II*

A handsome Jacobean mansion, approached by a courtyard, with formal terraces running down to lakes and bluebell woods. The gardens have been restored and imaginatively replanted with mixed borders and, above all, roses. But Parnham offers much more beside: iris borders, a meadow of fritillaries, an Italian garden, topiary, gazebos, rhododendrons and splendid modern sculptures including a larger-than-life Morecambe and Wise.

Sticky Wicket
Buckland Newton, Dorchester, Dorset DT2 7BY
☎ 0300 345476

OWNER Peter & Pam Lewis
LOCATION 11 miles from Dorchester & Sherborne
OPEN 10.30 am – 8 pm; Thursdays; June to September
ADMISSION Adults £1.50; Children 75p
FACILITIES Parking; loos; plants for sale; tea, coffee & home-made cakes
FEATURES Ecological interest; plantsman's garden; young garden; made since 1987

An original garden, worth watching. The owners are both designers and conservationists, and their devotion to ecology guides their garden-making. A scented garden, a white garden and a colour wheel are secondary to the need to attract birds, insects and other wild life. The garden is still and expanding: worth seeing now in its youth, and returning to in later years.

CO. DURHAM

Barningham Park
Richmond, Co. Durham DL11 7DW
☎ 0833 21202   ☎ 0833 21298

OWNER Sir Anthony Milbank Bt
LOCATION 10 miles north west of Scotch Corner off A66
OPEN 2 pm – 6 pm; 29 May, 5 June, 25 September
ADMISSION Adults £1.50, Children 50p
FACILITIES Parking; dogs permitted; loos; plants for sale; home-made teas
FEATURES Herbaceous borders; rock garden; water features; terraced gardens; rhododendrons

Terraced early 18th century landscape, leading up to the old bowling green and down to the skating pond. Reworked by keen horticultural Milbanks in the 1920s.

Unknown and perhaps underrated, if Barningham were in the Home Counties everyone would rave about it.

The Bowes Museum Garden & Park
Barnard Castle, Co. Durham DL12 8NP
☎ 0833 690606   ☎ 0833 37163

OWNER Durham County Council
LOCATION ½ mile west of Barnard Castle town
OPEN 10 am – 4 pm, Monday – Saturday; 2 pm – 4 pm, Sunday; November to February. 10 am – 5 pm, Monday – Saturday; 2 pm – 5 pm, Sunday; March, April and October. 10 am – 5.30 pm, Monday – Saturday, 2 pm – 5pm, Sunday, May to September. Closed 25 December & 1 January
ADMISSION Garden free until April, then adults £2.30, Senior Citizens and children £1.30
FACILITIES Parking; dogs permitted; loos; facilities for the disabled; shop; museum café
FEATURES Good collection of trees; old roses and climbers; woodland garden; parterre; large monkey puzzle
ENGLISH HERITAGE GRADE II
FRIENDS Friends of Museum & Park, ring 0833 690606 for details

Rather run down and municipal, but the formal gardens are good and fine trees pepper the park, especially conifers.

Houghall
Durham, Co. Durham DH1 3SG
☎ 091 3861351   ☎ 091 3860419

OWNER Durham College of Agriculture & Horticulture
LOCATION Follow A177 from A1 to Durham
OPEN 2 pm – 4 pm; daily
ADMISSION Free
FACILITIES Parking; loos; facilities for the disabled; plants for sale; shop
FEATURES Good collection of trees; rock garden; modern roses; water features; woodland garden; heathers; hardy fuchsias; daffodils; seasonal bedding
NCCPG NATIONAL COLLECTIONS Sorbus, Meconopsis

A well-run teaching garden attached to the County horticultural college. Many trials are conducted here, for example on the hardiness of fuchsias: 'if it grows at Houghall it will grow anywhere'. The arboretum has more than 500 different trees.

University of Durham Botanic Garden
Hollingside Lane, Durham, Co. Durham DH1 3TN
☎ 091 374 2671   ☎ 091 374 7478

OWNER University of Durham

LOCATION In the south of the City of Durham
OPEN 10 am – 5 pm; 1 April to 31 October
ADMISSION Free
FACILITIES Parking; loos; facilities for the disabled; plants for sale; tea, coffee, cold drinks & snacks
FEATURES Good collection of trees; old roses and climbers; primulas; meconopsis; autumn colour
FRIENDS 300 members and a full programme – details from the curator

Moved to its present site in 1970, this garden impresses by its youthful energy. The new 'American arboretum' was planted to copy natural associations 12 years ago. A woodland garden dates from 1988, a wetland one from 1989, and 1992 saw the opening of the 'Prince Bishop's Garden' with statues transferred from the Gateshead garden festival.

Westholme Hall

Winston, Darlington, Co. Durham DL2 3QL
☎ 0325 730442

OWNER Mrs J H McBain
LOCATION On B6274 north towards Staindrop
OPEN 2 pm – 6 pm; 29 May, 3 July, 28 August
ADMISSION Adults £1.50; Children 50p
FACILITIES Parking; dogs permitted; loos; access for the disabled; plants for sale; tea rooms
FEATURES Old roses and climbers; water features; rhododendrons

Five acres of late Victorian gardens, recently restored and revived, around a smashing Jacobean house. Designed and planted for all seasons: there are parts for spring (bulbs and azaleas), summer (roses and lilacs) and autumn (herbaceous borders). All is maintained by the owners' own hard work and enthusiasm. Worth a long detour to see.

ESSEX

Audley End

Saffron Walden, Essex
☎ 0799 522399

OWNER English Heritage
LOCATION On B1383, 1 mile west of Saffron Walden
OPEN Garden: 12 noon – 6 pm; daily except Monday & Tuesday (open Bank Holiday Mondays); 1 April to 30 September
ADMISSION Gardens: Adults £2.70; Senior Citizens £2; Children £1.30
FACILITIES Parking; dogs permitted; loos; shop; restaurant & picnic site
FEATURES Landscape designed by Capability Brown; follies and garden buildings; bedding out; parterre
ENGLISH HERITAGE GRADE I

Capability Brown landscaped the park but the recent excitement at Audley End has been the re-inauguration of the gardenesque formal garden after ten years of restoration. This dates from the 1830s and has 170 geometric flower beds cut out of the turf and planted with simple perennials.

Beth Chatto Gardens

Elmstead Market, Colchester, Essex CO7 7DB
☎ 0206 822007   FAX 0206 825933

OWNER Beth Chatto
LOCATION 7 miles east of Colchester
OPEN 9 am – 5 pm; Monday – Saturday; March to October; 9 am – 4 pm; Monday – Friday; November to February; Closed Sundays & Bank Holidays
ADMISSION £1.50
FACILITIES Parking; loos; big nursery adjacent to the garden
FEATURES Herbaceous borders; gravel or scree garden; water features; colour contrasts

Superb modern planting, particularly good for herbaceous plants, chosen for foliage as much as flower: all made by Beth Chatto since 1960. There are two types of planting here and it is the contrast between them which makes the garden. First there are the parts on dry gravelly soil, where Mediterranean plants flourish; second, there are the water- and bog-gardens made on clay. But gardens are only one of Beth Chatto's gifts: her writings and nearby nursery have made her famous.

RHS Garden, Hyde Hall

Royal Horticultural Society Gardens, Rettendon, Chelmsford, Essex CM3 8ET
☎ 0245 400256   FAX 0245 401363

OWNER Royal Horticultural Society
LOCATION Signposted from A130
OPEN 11 am – 6 pm; Wednesday, Thursday, Saturday, Sunday and Bank Holidays; 27 March to 23 October
ADMISSION RHS members free, Adults £2.50, Children (6 – 16) 50p, Parties (20+) £2.00
FACILITIES Parking; loos; facilities for the disabled; plants for sale; book shop; hot and cold lunches, afternoon teas, tea/coffee
FEATURES Herbaceous borders; fine conifers; fruit and vegetables of special interest; glasshouses to visit; modern roses; old roses and climbers; water features; woodland garden; particularly interesting in winter; extensive roses; bearded irises; magnolias; South African bulbs; paeonies
NCCPG NATIONAL COLLECTIONS Malus, Viburnum
FRIENDS Hyde Hall Garden Society (0245 400256) meets each second Sunday afternoon of month at Hall.

Recently acquired by the RHS, this outstanding modern garden (less than 40 years old) should be seen before its character changes. Even now the scale of the planting is outstanding for a private garden and the roses are particularly comprehensive.

Olivers

Olivers Lane, Colchester, Essex CO2 0HJ
☎ 0206 330575 ☎ 0206 330336

OWNER Mr & Mrs David Edwards
LOCATION 3 miles south west of Colchester between B1022 & B1026
OPEN 2 pm – 6 pm; May 7 & 8. 2 pm – 5 pm; Wednesdays; 20 April to 30 June. Or by appointment
ADMISSION Adults £1.50, Children free
FACILITIES Parking; loos; facilities for the disabled; plants for sale; tea/coffee & biscuits (except Wednesdays)
FEATURES Herbaceous borders; fruit and vegetables of special interest; modern roses; old roses and climbers; water features; bluebells; rhododendrons

Quite a modern garden, started in 1960 around two small lakes, with an eye-catching walk to one side leading down to a statue of Bacchus. Good plants and planting everywhere, from the parterres by the house to the woodland where roses and rhododendrons flourish. This is the garden of enthusiastic and energetic owners: an inspiration.

Park Farm

Chatham Hall Lane, Great Waltham, Chelmsford, Essex CM3 1BZ
☎ 0245 360871

OWNER J Cowley & D Bracey
LOCATION On B1008 north from Chelmsford
OPEN 17 & 18 April; 1 & 2, 8 & 9, 22 & 23, 29 & 30 May; 5 & 6, 12 & 13, 19 & 20, 26 & 27 June; 3 & 4, 17 & 18 July
ADMISSION Adults £1.00; Children 50p
FACILITIES Loos; access for the disabled; plants for sale; teas & home-made cakes
FEATURES Herbaceous borders; plantsman's garden; old roses and climbers

A young garden, still developing, with good colour combinations and a willingness to experiment. Rooms are enclosed by hedges of box and yew for solidity in winter and there is also a winter garden of hellebores, snowdrops and aconites. Add in a Chinese garden, a garden of the Giants (outsize plants), a hot garden, an arid garden and a Russian garden, and Park Farm is clearly a bundle of fun.

Saling Hall

Great Saling, Braintree, Essex CM7 5DT
☎ 0371 850243 ☎ 0371 850274

OWNER Mr & Mrs Hugh Johnson
LOCATION 2 miles north of the Saling Oak on A120
OPEN 2 pm – 5 pm; Wednesdays; May, June & July. Groups by appointment
ADMISSION £1.50, for National Gardens Scheme.
FACILITIES Parking; loos; facilities for the disabled
FEATURES Good collection of trees; herbaceous borders; fine conifers; oriental features; plantsman's garden; old roses and climbers; water features
ENGLISH HERITAGE GRADE II

A thinking man's garden, Saling also provokes thought in its visitors. The plantsmanship is impressive, particularly the choice and placing of trees. Some find the changes of mood (Japanese, Mediterranean etc) confusing; others are stimulated.

Volpaia

54 Woodlands Road, Hockley, Essex SS5 4PY
☎ 0702 203761

OWNER Mr & Mrs Derek B. Fox
LOCATION 3 miles north east of Rayleigh
OPEN 2.30 pm – 6 pm; Thursdays & Sundays; 3 April to 26 June or by appointment
ADMISSION Adult £1; Children 30p; to NGS & NCCPG Essex
FACILITIES Parking; plants for sale; Bullwood Nursery attached; tea & biscuits
FEATURES Herbaceous borders; plantsman's garden; woodland garden; rhododendron species; liliaceous plants; woodlanders

This is the woodland garden of a keen plantsman who has now turned his hobby into a nursery. Rhododendrons, camellias and magnolias are the main shrubs, underplanted with erythroniums and woodland herbaceous plants, plus candelabra primulas in the boggy bits.

GLOUCESTERSHIRE

Abbotswood

Stow-on-the-Wold, Cheltenham, Gloucestershire GL54 1LE
☎ 0451 830173

OWNER Robin Scully
LOCATION 1 mile west of Stow-on-the-Wold
OPEN 2 pm – 6 pm; 3 April, 17 April, 8 May, 22 May, 5 June
ADMISSION Adults £1.50; Children free
FACILITIES Parking; loos; teas
FEATURES Good collection of trees; herbaceous borders; fine conifers; designed by Lutyens; plantsman's

garden; rock garden; modern roses; old roses and climbers; good topiary; water features; woodland garden; magnolias; heather garden
ENGLISH HERITAGE GRADE II*

One of the most interesting gardens in the Cotswolds. Handsome formal gardens in front of the house: very Lutyens, very photogenic. A magnificent rock garden with a stream (artificially pumped, but you would never know) which meanders through alpine meadows, bogs and moraines, past dwarf azaleas, primulas, lysichitons, heaths and heathers until it disappears again. There is also a small arboretum, rather overgrown, but with some unusual forms: fascinating to browse around.

Barnsley House

Barnsley, Cirencester, Gloucestershire GL7 5EE
☎ 0285 740281

OWNER Mrs David Verey
LOCATION On A433/B4425 in village
OPEN 10 am – 6 pm; Monday, Wednesday, Thursday & Saturday; all year
ADMISSION Adults £2; Senior Citizens £1; Children free. Season ticket £4. December to February free. Parties by appointment
FACILITIES Parking; loos; plants for sale
FEATURES Herbaceous borders; follies and garden buildings; fruit and vegetables of special interest; herbs; plantsman's garden; old roses and climbers; garden sculpture; ornamental *potager*; Simon Verity's sculpture

A compact, modern garden, much copying and much copied. Barnsley is interesting at all seasons, but best when the little laburnum walk and the purple alliums underneath are in flower together.

Batsford Arboretum

The Estate Office, Moreton-in-Marsh, Gloucestershire GL56 9QF
☎ 0608 650722   ⊞ 0608 650290

OWNER The Batsford Foundation (a Registered Charity)
LOCATION Off A44, along Broadway Road
OPEN 10 am – 5 pm; daily; 1 March to mid November
ADMISSION Adults £2; Senior Citizens & Children under 16, £1.50
FACILITIES Parking; dogs permitted; loos; plants for sale; shop; light meals & refreshments
FEATURES Good collection of trees; fine conifers; oriental features; woodland garden; bluebells; maple glade; tallest *Betula platyphylla* (and six other tree records) in the British Isles
ENGLISH HERITAGE GRADE I

Batsford has an openness which makes its hillside a joy to wander through, passing from one dendrological

marvel to the next. Begun in the 1880s, the Arboretum also has several oriental curiosities brought from Japan by Lord Redesdale – a large bronze Buddha and an oriental rest-house for instance. Lord Dulverton has renewed the plantings over the last 30 years: both the collection and the amenities are improving all the time.

Berkeley Castle

Berkeley, Gloucestershire GL13 9BQ
☎ 0453 810332

OWNER John Berkeley
LOCATION Off A38
OPEN 2 pm – 5 pm, Tuesday – Sunday; April. 11 am – 5 pm, Tuesday – Saturday; also 2 pm – 4.30 pm, Sundays; May to September. 11 am – 5 pm; Bank Holiday Mondays
ADMISSION Garden only £1; Children 50p
FACILITIES Parking; loos; shop at Castle Farm; light lunches & afternoon tea
FEATURES Herbaceous borders; fine conifers; plantsman's garden; old roses and climbers
ENGLISH HERITAGE GRADE II*

The grim battlements of Berkeley Castle are host to an extensive collection of tender plants. On three terraces are *Cestrum*, *Cistus* and *Rosa banksiae* among hundreds of plant varieties introduced by the owner's grandfather, a nephew of Ellen Willmott. An Elizabethan-style bowling green and a water-lily pond fit well into the overall scheme.

Bourton House

Bourton-on-the-Hill, Moreton-in-Marsh, Gloucestershire GL56 9AE
☎ 0386 700121   ⊞ 0386 701081

OWNER Mr & Mrs Richard Paice
LOCATION On A44 west of Moreton in Marsh
OPEN 12 noon – 5 pm; Thursday & Friday; 28 May to 30 September
ADMISSION £2.00
FACILITIES Parking; loos; plants for sale; self-service tea & coffee
FEATURES Herbaceous borders; follies and garden buildings; gravel or scree garden; modern roses; old roses and climbers; good topiary
ENGLISH HERITAGE GRADE II

First laid out by Lanning Roper in the 1960s, but consistently improved by the present owners, the garden at Bourton House is both fashionable and a delight. A knot garden, a small *potager*, a raised pond, the topiary walk, white-painted trellis work, a croquet lawn, exuberant climbing roses and borders bulging with good colour schemes – purple-leaved prunus with yellow roses, for instance.

Cecily Hill House

Cirencester, Gloucestershire GL7 2EF

☎ 02865 653766

OWNER   Mr & Mrs Rupert de Zoete
LOCATION   West of Cirencester near gates into Park
OPEN   Sunday 17 July
ADMISSION   £2.00
FACILITIES   Parking; dogs permitted; teas on open day at 42 Cecily Hill
FEATURES   Herbaceous borders; fruit and vegetables of special interest; modern roses; old roses and climbers; pots; lilies; ferns; flowering cherries

One of a group of small gardens in Cirencester which open once a year for charity: the others are Nos. 38 & 42 Cecily Hill. Cecily Hill House has a particularly attractive kitchen garden.

The Ernest Wilson Memorial Garden

High Street, Chipping Campden, Gloucestershire GL55 6AF

☎ 0386 840764

OWNER   Chipping Campden Town Council
LOCATION   North end of Main Street
OPEN   Dawn to dusk daily
ADMISSION   Donation
FACILITIES   Dogs permitted; access for the disabled
FEATURES   Herbaceous borders; good collection of trees

A collection of plants introduced by Ernest H. Wilson, the greatest of European plant hunters in China: Chipping Campden was his birthplace. *Acer griseum*, *Clematis montana* var. *rubens* and the pocket-handkerchief tree *Davidia involucrata* are among his best-known introductions: all are represented here.

Frampton Court

Frampton-on-Severn, Gloucestershire GL2 7EU

☎ 0452 740698

OWNER   Mrs Peter Clifford
LOCATION   Two miles from J13 of M5
OPEN   By appointment
ADMISSION   House & Garden: £3.50; Children 9 and under £1.50. Garden: £1.00
FACILITIES   Parking; dogs permitted; loos
FEATURES   Follies and garden buildings; water features
ENGLISH HERITAGE GRADE   I

Beautiful and mysterious garden, little changed since 1750. The Dutch water garden – a long rectangular pool – reflects the orangery of Strawberry Hill Gothic design. But do also ask to see the collection of botanical water colours known as the Frampton Flora.

Hidcote Manor

Hidcote Bartrim, Chipping Campden, Gloucestershire GL55 6LR

☎ 0386 438333

OWNER   The National Trust
LOCATION   Signposted from B4632, Stratford/Broadway Road
OPEN   11 am – 7 pm; daily except Tuesday & Friday; 1 April to 31 October
ADMISSION   Adults £4.80; Children £2.40; Family £13.20 (2 adults & up to 4 children)
FACILITIES   Parking; loos; access for the disabled; plants for sale; National Trust shop; licensed restaurant, coffee & lunches 11 am – 2 pm; teas 2.15 pm – 5 pm
FEATURES   Herbaceous borders; fine conifers; follies and garden buildings; gravel or scree garden; herbs; plantsman's garden; rock garden; modern roses; old roses and climbers; good topiary; water features; woodland garden; plantings by Graham Thomas; tallest pink acacia *Robinia* × *ambigua* 'Decaisneana' in the British Isles
ENGLISH HERITAGE GRADE   I
NCCPG NATIONAL COLLECTIONS *Paeonia*

Probably the most influential 20th century garden in the world – certainly the most important and most copied. Essential visiting for all garden owners.

Hodges Barn

Shipton Moyne, Tetbury, Gloucestershire GL8 8PR

☎ 0666 880202   ☎ 0367 718096

OWNER   Charles Hornby
LOCATION   3 miles south of Tetbury on Malmesbury Road from Shipton Moyne
OPEN   2 pm – 5 pm; Monday, Tuesday and Friday; 1 April to 15 August
ADMISSION   £2.00
FACILITIES   Parking; dogs permitted; loos; lime tolerant herbaceous plants for sale; teas by arrangement
FEATURES   Herbaceous borders; gravel or scree garden; plantsman's garden; modern roses; old roses and climbers; good topiary; woodland garden; daffodils; bluebells; cyclamen

A big garden – six acres – and all intensively planted. Terraces, courtyards and gardens enclosed by stone walks or yew hedges are planted to give year-round colour. One has *rugosa* roses underplanted with hellebores, forget-me-nots and early bulbs for winter. The woodland garden is almost an arboretum of ornamental trees – birches, maples, whitebeams and magnolias – underplanted with daffodils and primroses. Hodges Barn is a garden of great energy and loveliness.

Kiftsgate Court

Chipping Campden, Gloucestershire GL55 6LW
☎ 0386 438777

OWNER Mr & Mrs J Chambers
LOCATION 3 miles from Chipping Campden opposite Hidcote Manor
OPEN 2 pm – 6 pm, Wednesday, Thursday, Sunday & Bank Holiday Mondays, 1 April to 30 September; 2 pm – 6 pm, Saturdays during June & September
ADMISSION Adults £2.50 (£3.00 in June & July); Children £1.00
FACILITIES Parking; loos; plants for sale; tea room in the house
FEATURES Herbaceous borders; plantsman's garden; modern roses; old roses and climbers; woodland garden; rose hedges; colour plantings; rare plants
ENGLISH HERITAGE GRADE II*

Famous for its roses, especially the eponymous *Rosa filipes*, Kiftsgate is all about plants and the use of colour. The best example is the yellow border, where gold and orange are set off by occasional blues and purples. After some dull years, everything about Kiftsgate has revived again: new thinking, new plantings and new enthusiasm have restored its excellence.

Lydney Park Gardens

Lydney Park, Gloucestershire GL15 6BU
☎ 0594 842844

OWNER Viscount Bledisloe
LOCATION Off A48 between Lydney & Aylburton
OPEN 11 am – 6 pm; Mondays, Bank Holidays & Wednesdays; 3 April to 5 June; daily, 29 May to 5 June
ADMISSION £2.00 Sunday & Bank Holidays; £1.00 Wednesdays and other open days
FACILITIES Parking; dogs permitted; loos; plants for sale; some souvenirs for sale; light teas
FEATURES Fine conifers; water features; woodland garden; deer park; rhododendrons, azaleas & camellias

A remarkable collection of rhododendrons planted over the last 45 years is the backbone to this extensive woodland garden. And not just rhododendrons, but azaleas and camellias too, all carefully planted to create distinct effects from March to June. The numbers are still growing, and include plants grown from collected seed and hybrids from distinguished breeders, many as yet unnamed, while others have yet to flower. Lydney is now recognised as one of the best rhododendron gardens in England.

Miserden Park

Miserden, Stroud, Gloucestershire GL6 7JA
☎ 0285 821303   📠 0285 821530

OWNER Major M T N H Wills
LOCATION On Miserden Road off B4070

OPEN 9.30 am – 4.30 pm; Tuesday, Wednesday & Thursday; 1 April to 30 September
ADMISSION Adults £2.00
FACILITIES Parking; loos; access for the disabled; plants for sale
FEATURES Good collection of trees; herbaceous borders; fine conifers; designed by Lutyens; modern roses; old roses and climbers; good topiary; fritillaries; martagon lilies; domed yew hedges
ENGLISH HERITAGE GRADE II*

The Jacobean Cotswold house has wide views across the Golden Valley, while the open spacious gardens lie to the side. Most were laid out in the 1920s – a charming rose garden, the long yew walk and expansive herbaceous borders, but there is also an older arboretum and Edwardian shrubbery.

Owlpen Manor

Uley, Dursley, Gloucestershire GL11 5BZ
☎ 0453 860261   📠 0453 860819

OWNER Nicholas Mander
LOCATION Off B4066 near Ule.
OPEN 2 pm – 5 pm; Tuesday, Thursday, Sunday & Bank Holiday Mondays; 1 April to 30 September. Also Wednesdays in July and August
ADMISSION Adults £3.00; Children £1.50
FACILITIES Parking; loos; guidebooks & postcards for sale; licensed restaurant in 15th century barn
FEATURES Old roses and climbers; good topiary; water features
ENGLISH HERITAGE GRADE II

Dreamy Cotswold manor house whose loveliness depends as much upon its site as its garden, but there are terraced gardens with box parterres and topiary yews and plantings of roses and herbs.

Painswick Rococo Garden

Painswick, Stroud, Gloucestershire GL6 6TH
☎ 0452 813204

OWNER Painswick Rococo Garden Trust
LOCATION Outside Painswick on B4073
OPEN 11 am – 5 pm; Wednesday – Sundays; February to mid December
ADMISSION Adults £2.50; Senior Citizens £2.10; Children £1.25
FACILITIES Parking; dogs permitted; loos; plants for sale; gift shop; licensed restaurant, coffee, teas and light snacks
FEATURES Follies and garden buildings; garden sculpture; woodland garden; snowdrop wood
ENGLISH HERITAGE GRADE II*
FRIENDS The Painswick Rococo Gardens Trust was established in 1988 to preserve the gardens in perpetuity. Details from Lord Dickinson

Only ten years of restoration work lie behind the unique rococo garden at Painswick which is re-emerging from back-to-nature woodland. A white Venetian gothic exedra, a Doric seat, the plunge pool, an octagonal pigeon house, a gothic gazebo called the Eagle House, a bowling green, the fish pond and a gothic alcove have all been reconstructed in their original positions thanks to the efforts of Lord Dickinson and the Painswick Rococo Gardens Trust. A remarkable garden and a brilliant achievement.

The Priory

Kemerton, Gloucestershire GL20 7JN
☎ 0386 725258

OWNER   The Hon. Mrs Healing
LOCATION   In Kemerton village
OPEN   2 pm – 7 pm; Thursdays; 26 May to 29 September; also Sunday 22 May, 12 June, 10 July, 7 & 28 August, 11 September
ADMISSION   £1.50
FACILITIES   Parking; dogs permitted; loos; access for the disabled; plants for sale; refreshments on open Sundays
FEATURES   Herbaceous borders; gravel or scree garden; plantsman's garden; old roses and climbers; particularly good in July-August

The Priory is a late-summer comet, brilliant in August & September when the annuals & tender plants supplement the perennial colour planting. The late Peter Healing spent 50 years perfecting his colour gradings. The results are worth a long journey to see: the crimson border is the best there has ever been.

Rodmarton Manor

Rodmarton, Cirencester, Gloucestershire GL7 6PF
☎ 0285 841253

OWNER   Simon Biddulph
LOCATION   Off A433 between Cirencester & Tetbury
OPEN   Saturdays; 14 May to 27 August, or by appointment
ADMISSION   Saturdays: £1.50; £2 any other time
FACILITIES   Parking; loos; access for the disabled; plants for sale
FEATURES   Herbaceous borders; fine conifers; plantsman's garden; rock garden; modern roses; old roses and climbers; good topiary; woodland garden
ENGLISH HERITAGE GRADE   II*

A splendid arts & crafts garden, with a strong design and exuberant planting. Simon Biddulph says there are 18 different areas within the garden, from the trough garden for alpine plants to the famous double herbaceous borders which lead to a Cotswold summerhouse.

Highly original – contemporary, but made without any contact, with Hidcote. Very photogenic.

Sezincote

Moreton-in-Marsh, Gloucestershire GL56 9AW

OWNER   Mr & Mrs D Peake
LOCATION   On A44 to Evesham, 1½ miles out of Moreton-in-Marsh
OPEN   2 pm – 6 pm; Thursdays, Fridays & Bank Holiday Mondays; all year except December
ADMISSION   Adults £2.50; Children £1.00
FACILITIES   Parking; loos
FEATURES   Good collection of trees; herbaceous borders; landscape designed by Humphry Repton; fine conifers; follies and garden buildings; glasshouses to visit; oriental features; garden sculpture; sub-tropical plants; water features; woodland garden; plantings by Graham Thomas; tallest *Fagus sylvatica* 'Zlatia' and maidenhair tree *Ginkgo biloba* in England
ENGLISH HERITAGE GRADE   I

The house was the model for Brighton Pavilion, and seems inseparable from the cruciform Moghul garden that sets off its Indian facade so well: yet this brilliant formal garden was designed as recently as 1965. On the other side are sumptuous borders planted by Graham Thomas and a luscious water garden of candelabra primulas and astilbes around the Temple to Surya, the Snake Bridge and Brahmin bulls. Humphry Repton had a hand in the original landscape, but the modern gardens are far more satisfying.

Snowshill Manor

Broadway, Gloucestershire WR12 7JU
☎ 0386 852410

OWNER   The National Trust
LOCATION   South west of Broadway, in village
OPEN   1 pm – 6 pm; Saturdays, Sundays & Easter Monday; 1 April to 31 October. 1 pm – 6 pm; daily, May to September
ADMISSION   Adults £4.20; Children £2.10; Family ticket £11.60
FACILITIES   Parking; loos; National Trust shop
FEATURES   Herbaceous borders; follies and garden buildings; old roses and climbers
ENGLISH HERITAGE GRADE   II

Praised for its changes of levels and collection of curious artefacts – an armillary sphere and a gilt figure of St. George and the Dragon, for instance. Snowshill is as curious as its maker, Charles Wade, and the spooky bric-a-brac which fills his house, but many visitors find it 'charming' or 'interesting'. Perhaps its finest ornament is the head gardener, a splendid fellow who persuaded his employers to let him run Snowshill as a completely organic garden, the National Trust's only one.

Stancombe Park

Stinchcombe, Gloucestershire GL11 6AU
☎ 0453 542815

OWNER Mrs Basil Barlow
LOCATION Off the B4060 between Dursley & Wotton-under-Edge
OPEN 2 pm – 6 pm; 30 May. Groups by appointment
ADMISSION Adults £2.00; Children under 10 free
FACILITIES Parking; dogs permitted; loos; access for the disabled
FEATURES Good collection of trees; herbaceous borders; fine conifers; follies and garden buildings; herbs; plantsman's garden; modern roses; old roses and climbers; garden sculpture; good topiary; water features; woodland garden
ENGLISH HERITAGE GRADE I

Stancombe has everything: a handsome house above a wooded valley, a flower garden of wondrous prettiness, and a gothic horror of an historic Folly Garden at the valley bottom. Start at the top. Peter Coates, Lanning Roper and Nada Jennett all worked on the rose gardens and mixed borders by the house: there is more to learn about good modern design and planting here than any other garden in Gloucestershire. Then wander down the valley where the path narrows and the incline steepens to a ferny tunnel, and start the circuit of the follies, best described as an open-air ghost train journey without the ghosts.

Stanway House

Stanway, Cheltenham, Gloucestershire GL54 5PQ
☎ 0386 73469   ⊠ 0386 73688

OWNER Lord Neidpath
LOCATION On B4077
OPEN 2 pm – 5 pm; Tuesdays and Thursdays; June to September
ADMISSION Adults £3.00; Senior Citizens £2.50; Children £1.00
FACILITIES Parking; dogs permitted; loos
FEATURES Good collection of trees; herbaceous borders; fine conifers; follies and garden buildings; woodland garden
ENGLISH HERITAGE GRADE I

Huge terraces behind the house lead up to a pyramid folly. This was the apex of a vast cascade which ran down to a long still tank, now a grassy plateau halfway up the hillside. Little remains, though there are plans for restoration. Rather poignant.

Sudeley Castle

Winchcombe, Gloucestershire GL54 5JD
☎ 0242 602308   ⊠ 0242 602959

OWNER Lady Ashcombe
LOCATION 8 miles north east of Cheltenham B4632
OPEN 11 am – 5.30 pm; daily
ADMISSION Adults £3.10; Senior Citizens £2.75; Children £1.40
FACILITIES Parking; loos; facilities for the disabled; plants for sale; good shop, rather upmarket; restaurant & tea rooms
FEATURES Herbaceous borders; fine conifers; follies and garden buildings; herbs; modern roses; old roses and climbers; good topiary; water features; interesting for children; ruins of banqueting hall, now a pretty garden; adventure playground
ENGLISH HERITAGE GRADE II*

Sudeley tries hard and ought to be a good garden: Jane Fearnley-Whittingstall did the roses and Rosemary Verey planted some borders. There are fine old trees, magnificent Victorian topiary (mounds of green and gold yew) and a raised walk around the pleasure gardens that may be Elizabethan in origin. But it lacks intimacy and some find it too obviously commercial.

Westbury Court

Westbury-on-Severn, Gloucestershire GL14 1PD
☎ 0452 760461

OWNER The National Trust
LOCATION 9 miles south west of Gloucester on A48
OPEN 11 am – 6 pm, Wednesday – Sunday & Bank Holiday Mondays; 1 April to 31 October except Good Friday
ADMISSION Adults £2.20; Children £1.10
FACILITIES Parking; loos; facilities for the disabled; picnic area
FEATURES Herbaceous borders; fruit and vegetables of special interest; herbs; old roses and climbers; garden sculpture; good topiary; water features; biggest holm oak *Quercus ilex* in the British Isles
ENGLISH HERITAGE GRADE II*

Restored over the last 20 years to become the best example of a 17th century Dutch garden in England. A pretty pavilion, tall and slender, looks down along a long tank of water. On the walls are old apple and pear varieties. Parterres, fine modern topiary and a T-shaped tank with a statue of Neptune in the middle make up the rest of the garden, with an opulent rose garden (old varieties only) underplanted with pinks, tulips and herbs. Immaculately maintained.

Westonbirt Arboretum

Westonbirt, Tetbury, Gloucestershire GL8 8QS
☎ 0666 880220   FAX 0666 880559

OWNER Forestry Commission
LOCATION 3 miles south of Tetbury on A433
OPEN 10 am – 8 pm (or dusk if earlier); all year round.
Visitor centre open 10 am – 5 pm; March to December
ADMISSION Adults £2.50; Senior Citizens £1.50;
Children £1.00
FACILITIES Parking; dogs permitted; loos; facilities for
the disabled; plants for sale; gift shop; cafeteria
FEATURES Particularly interesting in winter; sixty one
species of record breaking trees, including twenty one
maples (Acer spp.)
ENGLISH HERITAGE GRADE I
NCCPG NATIONAL COLLECTIONS Salix, Acer

The finest and largest arboretum in the British Isles: 500
acres, 17 miles of paths, 4,000 species, 18,000 trees. The
maple glade is famous, and so are the bluebells in the
part known as Silk Wood. Brilliantly managed by the
Forestry Commission, whose Visitor Centre is a model
of helpfulness. Brightest perhaps in spring and autumn,
but the best place we know for a long winter walk.

GREATER MANCHESTER

Dunham Massey

Altrincham, Greater Manchester WA14 4SJ
☎ 061 941 1025/061 926 9291

OWNER The National Trust
LOCATION 3 miles south west of Altrincham off A56
OPEN 12 noon – 5 pm; daily; 1 April to 30 October
ADMISSION Adults £2.00, Children £1.00
FACILITIES Parking; loos; facilities for the disabled;
garden shop; large restaurant
FEATURES Herbaceous borders; follies and garden
buildings; glasshouses to visit; good topiary; water
features; interesting for children; azaleas; hydrangeas;
Edwardian parterre
ENGLISH HERITAGE GRADE II*

Dunham Massey's 250 acres include an ancient deer
park, a mediaeval moat made into a lake in the 18th
century, an Elizabethan mount, an 18th century
orangery and some early landscape avenues. All remain
as features of the grounds, but the National Trust has
decided to major on its even more interesting Victorian
relics – evergreen shrubberies, ferns and colourful bedding out schemes. Even that does not preclude the Trust
from planting the most modern forms, such as the
hybrids of Rhododendron yakushimanum and latest

occidentale hybrid azaleas. The result is a potent cross-
section of historical and modern styles with a solid core
of Victorian excellence.

Fletcher Moss Botanical Gardens

Mill Gate Lane, Didsbury, Greater Manchester
M20 8SD
☎ 061 434 1877

OWNER Manchester City Council
OPEN 8 am – dusk, Monday – Friday; 9 am – dusk,
Weekend & Bank Holidays
ADMISSION Free
FACILITIES Parking; loos; facilities for the disabled;
cafeteria
FEATURES Fine conifers; glasshouses to visit; gravel
or scree garden; rock garden; old roses and climbers;
water features; bulbs; heathers; rhododendrons; orchid
house

A model municipal botanic garden, beautifully maintained but free to the public. There are good collections
of small conifers, maples and aquatics. Excellent autumn
colour: almost as good in spring.

HAMPSHIRE

Bramdean House

Bramdean, Alresford, Hampshire SO24 0JU
☎ 0962 771214   FAX 0962 771095

OWNER Mr & Mrs H Wakefield
LOCATION On A272 between Winchester & Peters-
field
OPEN 2 pm – 5 pm; 20 March, 3, 4, 17 April, 15 May,
19 June, 17 July, 21 August
ADMISSION Adults £1.50
FACILITIES Parking; loos; refreshments
FEATURES Herbaceous borders; fine conifers; fruit
and vegetables of special interest; plantsman's garden;
rock garden; modern roses; good topiary
ENGLISH HERITAGE GRADE II

Beautifully designed by the late Mrs Feilden and well
maintained by the present owners, the gardens at Bramdean are much admired, and rightly so. Two wide
herbaceous borders lead up from the terrace behind the
house, against the backdrop of mature beeches and
cedars. At the end of the central axis, steps lead to a
walled kitchen garden whose central bed is planted
with roses and annuals. The vista runs yet further still,
through an orchard to a gazebo some 300 yards from
the house. The views in both directions are stunning.

Brandy Mount House

East Street, Alresford, Hampshire SO24 9EG
☎ 0962 732189

OWNER Mr & Mrs Michael Baron
LOCATION Left into East Street from Broad Street, 50 yds first right
OPEN 2 pm – 5 pm; Sundays 13 February, 20 March, 24 April, 8 May, 19 June, (plus 24 July provisionally)
ADMISSION £1
FACILITIES Dogs permitted; access for the disabled; plants for sale; extensive plant sales area; refreshments for groups by arrangement
FEATURES Herbaceous borders; gravel or scree garden; plantsman's garden; rock garden; woodland garden; young garden; paeony species; cardamines; collected plants
NCCPG NATIONAL COLLECTIONS *Daphne, Galanthus*

Essentially a plantsman's garden, but a plantsman who is also a distinguished plant collector and exhibitor of alpine plants. Linked to a thriving small nursery which is always worth a visit.

Broadlands

Romsey, Hampshire
☎ 0794 516878

OWNER Lord & Lady Romsey
LOCATION On Romsey by-pass by town centre roundabout
OPEN 12 noon – 4 pm; daily except Friday; Easter to 30 September. Fridays in August only
ADMISSION Adults £5; Senior Citizens £4.25; Children (12 – 16) £4
FACILITIES Parking; loos; facilities for the disabled; plants for sale; gift shop; tea rooms & picnic area by river
FEATURES Herbaceous borders; landscape designed by Capability Brown; water features; woodland garden
ENGLISH HERITAGE GRADE II

Classic Capability Brown landscape, handsome old trees and an open park which runs slowly down to a lake and the River Test.

Exbury Gardens

Exbury, Southampton, Hampshire SO4 1AZ
☎ 0703 891203

OWNER Edmund de Rothschild
LOCATION Well signposted locally
OPEN 10 am – 5.30 pm (or dusk if earlier); 12 February to 23 October
ADMISSION Adults £2 – £4, Senior Citizens £1.50 – £3.50, Children £1 – £3, Parties (15+) £2 – 3.50

FACILITIES Parking; dogs permitted; loos; facilities for the disabled; plants for sale; hot and cold lunches, cream teas
FEATURES Herbaceous borders; rock garden; old roses and climbers; water features; woodland garden; rhododendrons; azaleas; candelabra primulas; rare trees; tallest shagbark hickory *Carya ovata* in England (and two other tree records)
ENGLISH HERITAGE GRADE II*

Rhododendrons, rhododendrons, rhododendrons: over one million of them in 200 acres of natural woodland. More than 40 have won awards from the Royal Horticultural Society. But there are magnolias, camellias and rare trees too, many grown from the original seed introduced by famous plant collectors. A place of wonder in May.

Fairfield House

Hambledon, Waterlooville, Hampshire PO7 4RY
☎ 0705 632431

OWNER Mrs Peter Wake
LOCATION In Vineyard Lane, Hambledon
OPEN 20 June for NGS, and by appointment
ADMISSION Adults £1.50
FACILITIES Access for the disabled; plants for sale; teas on open day
FEATURES Herbaceous borders; fine conifers; plantsman's garden; modern roses; old roses and climbers; beautifully grown roses

Fairfield is one of the best private rose gardens in England. Old roses and climbers were the late Peter Wake's main interest and he grew them unusually well. The shrubs are trained up a cat's cradle of string drawn between five wooden posts. The results make you gasp – 'Charles de Mills' ten feet high.

Furzey Gardens Trust

Minstead, Lyndhurst, Hampshire SO4 7GL
☎ 0703 812464

OWNER Furzey Gardens Charitable Trust
LOCATION Off A31 or A337 to Minstead
OPEN 10 am – 5 pm (dusk in winter); daily except 25 & 26 December. Closes early in winter
ADMISSION Adults £2.50; Senior Citizens £2.00; Children £1.50
FACILITIES Parking; loos; plants for sale
FEATURES Fine conifers; plantsman's garden; water features; woodland garden; naturalised dieramas; azaleas; heathers; spring bulbs
FRIENDS No friends organisation but the gardens are owned by a charitable trust

This garden belonged to the Dalrymple brothers who owned Bartley nursery, home of many good plants in the 1920s and 1930s. The massed display of azaleas in

April-May is unforgettable, but the late summer flowering of eucryphias runs it close and the autumn colour of nyssas, parrotias and enkianthus are worth a visit in October.

Highclere Castle

Highclere, Newbury, Hampshire RG15 9RN
☎ 0635 255317   ℻ 0635 254051

OWNER The Earl of Carnarvon
LOCATION South of Newbury off A34
OPEN 2 pm – 6 pm; Wednesday – Sunday, Sunday & Bank Holiday Mondays; July to September
ADMISSION Adults £4.00; Senior Citizens £3.50; Children & disabled £2.50. Gardens only £2.00
FACILITIES Parking; loos; facilities for the disabled; plants for sale; shop; good restaurant
FEATURES Herbaceous borders; landscape designed by Capability Brown; fine conifers; follies and garden buildings; fruit and vegetables of special interest; glasshouses to visit; good topiary; good collection of cedars; long avenues
ENGLISH HERITAGE GRADE I

A major historic garden – when Capability Brown landscaped it in the 1770s he left intact the avenues and follies of the early 18th century. Jim Russell advised on the planting in the walled garden, where a range of glasshouses includes one for tea roses. There is also a proper tropical conservatory planted with exotic fruit – grapefruit, bananas and even the coffee plant. Fun for the whole family.

Hinton Ampner House

Bramdean, Alresford, Hampshire SO24 0LA
☎ 0962 771305

OWNER The National Trust
LOCATION On A272 1 mile west of Bramdean
OPEN 1.30 pm – 5 pm; Mondays – Wednesdays, Saturdays, Sundays, Bank Holidays; 1 April to 30 September
ADMISSION Adults £2.30; Children £1.15
FACILITIES Parking; loos; facilities for the disabled; teas & home-made cakes
FEATURES Garden sculpture; good topiary; daffodils; yew trees
ENGLISH HERITAGE GRADE II

The gardens at Hinton Ampner were laid out by the scholarly Ralph Dutton in the middle of this century with great regard to line, landscape and historical propriety. Statues, buildings, axes and views are placed with exquisite judgement to lead you subtly along the exact route that Dutton intended. Good plantings, too.

Houghton Lodge

Houghton, Stockbridge, Hampshire SO20 6LQ
☎ 0264 810502 810177

OWNER Martin Busk
LOCATION Off A30 at Stockbridge
OPEN 2pm – 5pm; Monday, Tuesday & Friday. 10 am – 5 pm; Saturday & Sunday; 1 March to 30 September
ADMISSION £2.50. Parties at special rates
FACILITIES Parking; dogs permitted; loos; facilities for the disabled; plants for sale
FEATURES Follies and garden buildings; glasshouses to visit; good topiary; water features; daffodils; cyclamen
ENGLISH HERITAGE GRADE II*

A lovely gothic *cottage ornée* beside the River Test, restored with advice from David Jacques. Houghton also boasts the first hydroponic greenhouse open to the public, where plants are grown in nutrient-rich solutions instead of soil.

Jenkyn Place

Bentley, Farnham, Hampshire GU10 5LU
☎ 0420 23118

OWNER Mrs Gerald Coke
LOCATION Signposted from Farnham by-pass
OPEN 2 pm – 6 pm; Thursday – Sunday; 7 April to 11 September
ADMISSION Adults £2; Children 75p
FACILITIES Parking; loos; plants for sale
FEATURES Good collection of trees; herbaceous borders; fine conifers; herbs; plantsman's garden; rock garden; modern roses; old roses and climbers; garden sculpture; woodland garden; tallest red horse chestnut *Aesculus × carnea* 'Briotii' in Britain.

The best post-war garden in the Hidcote style, a series of rooms and corridors planted with discrimination and art. Good old roses, heroic herbaceous borders, and something for everyone whatever the weather or season.

Longstock Water Gardens

Longstock, Stockbridge, Hampshire SO20 6EH
☎ 0264 810894   ℻ 0264 810430

OWNER John Lewis Partnership
LOCATION 1½ miles north east of Longstock Village
OPEN 2 pm – 5 pm; 3rd Sunday in the month; 1 April to September
ADMISSION £1.50, (1993) in aid of charity
FACILITIES Parking; loos; facilities for the disabled; plants for sale
FEATURES Herbaceous borders; ecological interest; plantsman's garden; water features; woodland garden; interesting for children

Quite the most extraordinary and beautiful water garden in England, a little Venice where dozens of islands and all-but-islands are linked by small bridges and intensely planted with water-loving plants. Drifts of astilbes, primulas, kingcups, hemerocallis, musks, water irises and lilies. The ground is so soft that the islands seem to float, and a remarkable accumulation of peat has allowed such calcifuge plants as *Meconopsis betonicifolia* and *Cardiocrinum giganteum* to flourish in this chalky valley. Would that it were open more often.

The Manor House, Upton Grey

Upton Grey, Basingstoke, Hampshire RG25 2RD
☎ 0256 862827

OWNER Mrs John Wallinger
LOCATION In Upton Grey village
OPEN 2 pm – 5 pm; Wednesday; May to July. Parties of 20 or more, by appointment
ADMISSION £2.00.
FACILITIES Parking; loos; plants for sale
FEATURES Herbaceous borders; planted by Gertrude Jekyll; old roses and climbers; water features
ENGLISH HERITAGE GRADE II

Ros Wallinger has restored this Jekyll garden over the last ten years using the original planting plans. She has gone to great pains to recreate it exactly in all its Edwardian loveliness. Some of the roses were extinct here until re-introduced from private gardens in France and Italy after years of searching. There is no better place to study Gertrude Jekyll's plantings, but what makes it so special is that it is a 'young' garden again.

Mottisfont Abbey

Romsey, Hampshire SO51 0LJ
☎ 0794 41220

OWNER The National Trust
LOCATION 4 miles north west of Romsey
OPEN 12 noon – 6 pm (8.30 pm in June); Saturday – Wednesday; 1 April to 31 October
ADMISSION £2.50 (£3 in rose season)
FACILITIES Parking; loos; facilities for the disabled; plants for sale; National Trust shop; light refreshments
FEATURES Herbaceous borders; herbs; plantsman's garden; old roses and climbers; water features; plantings by Graham Thomas; biggest London plane tree *Platanus × acerifolia* in the British Isles
ENGLISH HERITAGE GRADE II
NCCPG NATIONAL COLLECTIONS *Platanus, Rosa*

The park and gardens near the house are stately: Russell Page, Geoffrey Jellicoe and Norah Lindsay all worked here. But it is the old rose collection in the walled garden which has made Mottisfont's name. It is Graham Thomas' best known work, a collection of all the roses he has discovered, assembled, preserved and made popular through his writings. They are surrounded by brilliant herbaceous plantings: purple 'Zigeunerknabe' with yellow *Digitalis grandiflora*, for instance. Surely the best rose garden in Britain.

Sir Harold Hillier Gardens & Arboretum

Jermyns Lane, Ampfield, Romsey, Hampshire SO51 0QA
☎ 0794 68787   FAX 0794 68027

OWNER Hampshire County Council
LOCATION Signposted from A31 & A3057
OPEN 10.30 am – 5 pm; Monday – Friday; all year except public holidays at Christmas and New Year. 10.30 am – 6 pm; Saturdays & Sundays; March to November
ADMISSION Adults, £3.00; Senior Citizens, £2.50; child £1.00; season ticket £15
FACILITIES Parking; loos; facilities for the disabled; plants for sale; light refreshments from Easter to end of October, & most week-ends
FEATURES Good collection of trees; herbaceous borders; fine conifers; plantsman's garden; old roses and climbers; interesting for children; particularly good in July-August; particularly interesting in winter; 1993 winner of Sandford Award; six record tree species
NCCPG NATIONAL COLLECTIONS *Quercus, Carpinus, Cornus, Cotoneaster, Ligustrum, Lithocarpus, Corylus, Photinia, Pinus*
FRIENDS Details of the Friends scheme are available from the Curator: benefits include trips to other gardens, coffee mornings and a quarterly newsletter

Quite the most important modern arboretum in UK, for the number of its taxa – over 11,000 in 160 acres and totalling 40,000 plants. Every part of the garden is an education and a pleasure whatever the season or weather. Exemplary labelling and helpful guidebooks available. Hilliers' nursery shares a car park with the arboretum. Guided walks are given on the first Sunday in each month, and on Wednesdays from May to October.

Spinners

Boldre, Lymington, Hampshire SO4 5QE
☎ 0590 673347

OWNER Diana & Peter Chappell
LOCATION Signed off A337
OPEN 10 am – 5 pm; daily; 20 April to 1 September, but closed on Mondays and Tuesdays after 1 July
ADMISSION £1.50
FACILITIES Parking; loos; plants for sale
FEATURES Good collection of trees; herbaceous borders; fine conifers; gravel or scree garden; plantsman's garden; water features; woodland garden; rhododen-

drons; woodland plants; rarities and novelties; biggest *Eucalyptus perriniana* in the British Isles

Only two acres, but what a garden! Spinners is a plantsman's paradise, where the enthusiast can spend many happy hours browsing at any time of the year. Everything is well labelled and Peter Chappell's nursery sells an extraordinary range of good plants: you always come away with a bootful of novelties.

Stratfield Saye House

Stratfield Saye, Reading, Hampshire RG7 2BT
☎ 0250 882882   📠 0250 882345

OWNER   The Duke of Wellington
LOCATION   West of A33 between Reading and Basingstoke
OPEN   11.30 am – 6 pm; daily except Friday; 1 May to 25 September
ADMISSION   House and garden: £4.00
FACILITIES   Parking; dogs permitted; loos; facilities for the disabled; gift shop; light refreshments
FEATURES   Herbaceous borders; fine conifers; modern roses; old roses and climbers; water features; camellia house in walled garden; American garden; tallest Hungarian oak *Quercus frainetto* in the British Isles
ENGLISH HERITAGE GRADE   II

Not a great garden, but there are some fine incidents: a huge kitchen garden, a large and cheerful rose garden, rhododendrons in the park, and magnificent trees, including wellingtonias, named after the Iron Duke.

Tudor House Garden

Tudor House, Bugle Street, Southampton, Hampshire SO1 0A8
☎ 0703 635904   📠 0703 339601

OWNER   Southampton City Council
LOCATION   Bugle Street is just off the High Street in the old city
OPEN   10 am – 5 pm, Tuesday – Friday; 10 am – 4 pm, Saturday; 2 pm – 5 pm, Sunday; closed Mondays
ADMISSION   Adults £1.50, Children 75p
FACILITIES   Loos; facilities for the disabled
FEATURES   Herbaceous borders; herbs; good topiary; interesting for children

Sylvia Landsberg's unique reconstruction of a Tudor garden with knot garden, fountain, secret garden and contemporary plantings of herbs and flowering plants all crammed into a tiny area. Some call it a pastiche, others a living dictionary of Tudor garden language.

White Windows

Longparish, Andover, Hampshire SP11 6PB
☎ 0264 720222

OWNER   Mr & Mrs B Sterndale-Bennett
LOCATION   In village centre

OPEN   2 pm – 6 pm; by appointment from March to September on Wednesday, and on 14 August for NGS
ADMISSION   £1.00
FACILITIES   Plants for sale
FEATURES   Herbaceous borders; plantsman's garden; young garden; euphorbias; hellebores

One of the best small modern plantsman's gardens on chalk, remarkable for the way Jane Sterndale-Bennett uses her material. Leaves and stems are as important as flowers, especially in the combinations and contrasts of colour – gold and yellow, blue and silver, and crimsons, pinks and purples. Much use is made of evergreens and variegated plants. Perhaps the most luxuriant chalk garden in Hampshire.

HEREFORD & WORCESTER

Abbey Dore Court Garden

Abbey Dore, Hereford, Hereford & Worcester HR2 0AD
☎ 0981 240419   📠 0981 240279

OWNER   Mrs Charis Ward
LOCATION   On A465 midway between Hereford – Abergavenny
OPEN   11 am – 6 pm; daily except Wednesdays; March to 3 October. Other times by appointment to see hellebores
ADMISSION   Adults £1.50; Children 50p
FACILITIES   Parking; loos; facilities for the disabled; plants for sale; county gift gallery, teddy bears loft; licensed restaurant, coffee, lunch & tea; all food homemade
FEATURES   Herbaceous borders; fine conifers; plantsman's garden; rock garden; handsome wellingtonias; ferns; hellebores
NCCPG NATIONAL COLLECTIONS *Euphorbia, Sedum*

Plantsman's garden on a damp cold site, with fine borders leading down to the ferny river walk. Growing up, changing and improving every year: very exciting.

Burford House Gardens

Treasures of Tenbury, Tenbury Wells, Hereford & Worcester WR15 8HQ
☎ 0584 810777   📠 0584 810673

OWNER   Treasures of Tenbury Ltd
LOCATION   A456 between Tenbury Wells and Ludlow
OPEN   10 am – 5 pm (dusk in winter); all year

ADMISSION Adults £1.95; Children 80p; Groups (25+) £1.60 (by prior arrangement); Season ticket £7.50 or family £15 (2+2)

FACILITIES Parking; loos; facilities for the disabled; plants for sale; tea rooms (light lunches, afternoon teas), beverages

FEATURES Water features; *Rosa* 'Treasure Trove'

NCCPG NATIONAL COLLECTIONS *Clematis*

Neat 4 acre modern garden to complement a stylish Georgian house. Good roses and herbaceous borders, and a clever series of water gardens, but Burford means *Clematis* – 200 varieties – imaginatively grown and displayed.

Eastgrove Cottage Garden

Sankyns Green, Little Witley, Worcester, Hereford & Worcester WR6 6LQ

OWNER Malcolm & Carol Skinner

LOCATION West of Shawley, turn left at Sankyns Green

OPEN 2 pm – 5 pm; Thursday – Monday; 1 April to 31 July. Also Thursday – Saturday; 2 September to 16 October

ADMISSION £1 for NGS

FACILITIES Parking; loos; shop attached to good small nursery

FEATURES Good collection of trees; herbaceous borders; herbs; plantsman's garden; old roses and climbers

A tiny cottage garden attached to a cottage garden nursery. The scale itself is small, but crammed in are herbs, dwarf conifers, a bog garden, a 'secret garden' and all the elements of modern plantsmanship.

Eastnor Castle

Eastnor, Ledbury, Hereford & Worcester

OWNER Mr James & The Hon. Mrs Hervey-Bathurst

LOCATION 4 miles east of Ledbury

OPEN 12 noon – 6 pm; Sundays; 3 April to 30 September; daily except Saturdays in August; some Bank Holiday Mondays

ADMISSION £1.75 adults; £1 children

FACILITIES Parking; dogs permitted; loos; access for the disabled; souvenirs and gift shop

FEATURES Good collection of trees; fine conifers; water features; woodland garden; spring bulbs; tallest deodar *Cedrus deodara* (38 metres high) in the British Isles, plus twelve more record trees

ENGLISH HERITAGE GRADE II*

Eastnor is all about trees. The arboretum planted by Lord Somers 150 years ago is now mature, and full of champion specimens. Many are rare. The conifers are particularly fine in early spring and complement the shaggy neo-Norman castle.

Hergest Croft

Kington, Hereford & Worcester HR5 3EG

☎ 0544 230160   [FAX] 0544 230160

OWNER W L Banks

LOCATION A44 on west side

OPEN 1.30 pm – 6.30 pm; 1 April to 31 October

ADMISSION Adults £2.30; Children under 15 free

FACILITIES Parking; dogs permitted; loos; plants for sale; home-made teas

FEATURES Good collection of trees; herbaceous borders; fruit and vegetables of special interest; old roses and climbers; rhododendrons; tallest *Cercidiphyllum japonicum* and *Davidia vilmoriniana* in the British Isles, among twentytwo record trees

ENGLISH HERITAGE GRADE II*

NCCPG NATIONAL COLLECTIONS *Acer, Betula, Zelkova*

Wonderful woodland garden and arboretum around a whopping Edwardian house. There is no end to the garden's marvels: huge conifers, magnificent birches, scores of interesting oaks, many acres of billowing rhododendrons. Plus good herbaceous borders, alpine collections, autumn gentians and kitchen garden, all on a scale that most of us have forgotten.

How Caple Court

How Caple, Hereford, Hereford & Worcester HR1 4SX

☎ 0989 86626   [FAX] 0989 86611

OWNER Mr & Mrs Peter Lee

LOCATION Signposted on B4224 & A449 junction

OPEN 9.30 am – 5.00 pm, Monday – Saturday; May to October; Sunday; 10am – 5pm; all year

ADMISSION Adults £2.50; Children £1.25

FACILITIES Parking; dogs permitted; loos; plants for sale; clothes shop; ice cream and soft drinks

FEATURES Old roses and climbers; garden sculpture; good topiary; woodland garden; Italian terraces

Spectacular Italian gardens laid out at the turn of the century and undergoing restoration year by year. Pergolas, loggias, terraces and *giardini segreti* with stunning views across the Wye valley.

Lakeside

Gaines Road, Whitbourne, Worcester, Hereford & Worcester WR6 5RD

OWNER Chris Philip & Denys Gueroult

LOCATION 9 miles west of Worcester off A44

OPEN 2 pm – 6 pm; 11 April, 16 May, 6 June, 11 July

ADMISSION Adults £1.50

FACILITIES Parking; loos; plants for sale; teas

FEATURES Herbaceous borders; plantsman's garden; water features; woodland garden; young garden; ferns; hollies; heathers

Six acres of dramatic planting by the editor of *The Plant Finder*. Good plants, used well: a garden from which to learn.

Overbury Court

Overbury, Tewkesbury, Hereford & Worcester
☎ 0386 725312   📠 0386 725528

OWNER   Mr & Mrs Bruce Bossom
LOCATION   5 miles north east of Tewkesbury
OPEN   2 pm – 6 pm; 27 March
ADMISSION   Adults £1.50
FACILITIES   Parking; dogs permitted; access for the disabled; plants for sale; home-made teas in village hall
FEATURES   Good topiary; landscaped park; daffodils
ENGLISH HERITAGE GRADE   II*

A peaceful and expansive garden laid out around the large, handsome, Georgian house, with a view of the Parish church worked in. Geoffrey Jellicoe, Aubrey Waterfield and Russell Page all worked on the design and planting and the result is a garden of exceptional harmony.

Whitfield

Allensmore, Hereford & Worcester HR2 9BA
☎ 098 121202

OWNER   G M Clive
LOCATION   8 miles south west of Hereford on A465
OPEN   2 pm – 6 pm; 5 June or parties by appointment
ADMISSION   Adults £1.50; Children 50p
FACILITIES   Parking; dogs permitted; loos; access for the disabled; teas on 5 June
FEATURES   Good collection of trees; fine conifers; good topiary; huge grove of redwoods; tallest dwarf alder *Alnus nitida* and durmast oak *Quercus petraea* in the British Isles
ENGLISH HERITAGE GRADE   II

Whitfield has magnificent trees, planted by the Clives over the last 200 years. *Zelkova serrata*, a weeping oak, and a ginkgo planted in 1778 are some of the highlights, but there is nothing to beat the grove of twenty or so *Sequoia sempervirens* now pushing 150ft in height.

HERTFORDSHIRE

The Beale Arboretum

West Lodge Park, Cockfosters Road, Hadley Wood, Barnet, Hertfordshire EN4 0PY
☎ 081 440 8311   📠 081 449 3698

OWNER   Edward Beale CBE
LOCATION   A111 halfway between M25 J24 and Cockfosters station
OPEN   2 pm – 5 pm; Wednesdays; 1 April to 31 October
ADMISSION   £1.50
FACILITIES   Parking; dogs permitted; loos; facilities for the disabled; refreshments
FEATURES   Good collection of trees; fine conifers; water features; woodland garden; trees, trees, trees; 300 year old specimen of *Arbutus unedo*
NCCPG NATIONAL COLLECTIONS   *Carpinus betulus* cvs

10 acres of young arboretum, begun 25 years ago and shortly to double in size. Among some older specimens – Victorian cedars and redwoods – is a fine collection of trees planted with a view to the overall effect and underplanted with rhododendrons. Little known as yet, but undoubtedly to be reckoned among the great late 20th century gardens.

Benington Lordship

Benington, Stevenage, Hertfordshire SG2 7BS
☎ 0438 869228

OWNER   C H A Bott
LOCATION   Off A662 between Stevenage to Hertford
OPEN   12 noon – 5 pm, Wednesdays; 2 pm – 5 pm Sundays; April to August
ADMISSION   Adults £2.20; Season tickets £5.50
FACILITIES   Parking; loos; plants for sale; teas
FEATURES   Herbaceous borders; rock garden; modern roses; old roses and climbers; heather garden; cowslip bank
ENGLISH HERITAGE GRADE   II

A Georgian house with the ruins of a Norman castle in the grounds. All has been charmingly replanted in recent years without destroying the older features: a Pulhamite folly, an Edwardian rock garden, and a sense of spacious parkland.

The Gardens of the Rose

Chiswell Green, St Albans, Hertfordshire AL2 3NR
☎ 0727 850461   📠 0727 850360

OWNER   The Royal National Rose Society
LOCATION   1 mile from junction of M1 and M25
OPEN   9 am – 5 pm; Monday – Saturday. 10 am – 6 pm; Sundays & Bank Holidays. 11 June to 16 October
ADMISSION   Adults £4; groups £3.50; disabled £3; members and children free
FACILITIES   Parking; dogs admitted; loos; facilities for the disabled; plants for sale; shop with rose books and souvenirs; licensed cafeteria
FEATURES   Modern roses; old roses

The most comprehensive rose garden in Britain, with a 1960s design which emphasises modern roses, but also has excellent collections of old roses, shrub roses, ramblers, miniatures, ground cover and wild species of rose. 30,000 rose bushes and 1,750 varieties, plus a further

600 unnamed novelties in the trial grounds. There are plans to expand into the fields around the garden in the next few years, if funds are available.

Hatfield House

Hatfield, Hertfordshire AL9 5NQ
☎ 0707 262823   ⬛ 0707 275719

OWNER The Marquess of Salisbury
LOCATION Off A1(M), J4
OPEN West gardens: 11 am – 6 pm; daily; except Good Friday & Sundays, 1 March to 31 July; east gardens: 2 pm – 5 pm, Mondays only
ADMISSION Adults £2.60; Senior Citizens £2.40; Children £2.00, Park, Gardens & Exhibitions
FACILITIES Parking; loos; facilities for the disabled; plants for sale; souvenirs and gift shop; licensed restaurant, coffee shop, snacks & hot lunches
FEATURES Herbaceous borders; herbs; good topiary; knot gardens; physic garden
ENGLISH HERITAGE GRADE I

Interesting old/new gardens to suit a historic stately home. An 1890s parterre, very pretty, is the main feature. The new knot garden has plants dating from the 17th century (Lady Salisbury is a stalwart of the Tradescant Trust), but there are *allées*, *rondpoints*, more knots and parterres: the complete design vocabulary for how-to-Tudorise your garden.

Hill House

Stanstead Abbots, Ware, Hertfordshire SG12 8BX
☎ 0920 870013

OWNER Mr & Mrs Ronald Pilkington
LOCATION Between Harlow & Ware
OPEN 2 pm – 5 pm; 1 May, 5 & 15 June
ADMISSION Adults £2.00; Senior Citizens £1.50; Children 50p
FACILITIES Parking; dogs permitted; loos; plants for sale; home-made teas
FEATURES Herbaceous borders; glasshouses to visit; water features; woodland garden

Outstanding plantings in the old kitchen garden include colour borders of purple and gold, weeping pears, and vegetables all as neat as imaginable. Pretty woodland garden and lush growth around the small lake.

Knebworth House

Knebworth, Stevenage, Hertfordshire SG3 6PY
☎ 0438 812661   ⬛ 0438 811908

OWNER Lord Cobbold
LOCATION Off A1(M), J7
OPEN 12 noon – 5 pm; daily; weekends, Bank Holidays & School Holidays, 3 April to 23 May; 29 May to 5 September plus weekends only to 3 October

ADMISSION Adults £4.50; Children & Senior Citizens £4
FACILITIES Parking; loos; licensed cafeteria
FEATURES Herbaceous borders; herbs; designed by Lutyens and planted by Gertrude Jekyll; modern roses; dogs cemetery; sunken lawn; gold garden; maze; wilderness
ENGLISH HERITAGE GRADE II*
FRIENDS Knebworth House Education and Preservation Trust – details from the Secretary c/o Knebworth House

Most of the garden was laid out by Lutyens, who married a daughter of the house. It has been well restored over the last 15 years with Jekyll plantings where appropriate. Inventive and harmonious, few gardens make such good use of space and perspective.

St Paul's Walden Bury

Whitwell, Hitchin, Hertfordshire SG4 8BP
☎ 0438 871218   ⬛ 0438 871229

OWNER St Paul's Walden Bury Estate Co
LOCATION B651 5 miles south of Hitchin
OPEN 2 pm – 7 pm; 17 April, 22 May, 12 June, 3 July
ADMISSION £2.00
FACILITIES Parking; dogs permitted; loos; facilities for the disabled; plants for sale; teas & home-made cakes
FEATURES Follies and garden buildings; garden sculpture; woodland garden; formal French landscape
ENGLISH HERITAGE GRADE I

Highly important as a unique example of the French 18th century style – three hedged *allées* lead off into the woodland towards temples, statues and pools. The present owner's father (the Queen Mother's brother) was a past President of the RHS, and was able to blend rhododendrons, azaleas, maples and magnolias (plus much more besides) into parts of the woodland. A garden that appeals to historian, plantsman and artist equally.

HUMBERSIDE

Burnby Hall Gardens

Pocklington, Humberside YO4 2QF
☎ 0759 302068

OWNER Stewarts Trust
LOCATION On B1247 to Hull
OPEN 10 am – 6 pm; daily; first Saturday in April to mid October
ADMISSION Adults £2.00; Senior Citizens £1.50; Children 50p
FACILITIES Parking; loos; facilities for the disabled; plants for sale; snacks & salads, home-made cakes

FEATURES Herbaceous borders; fine conifers; rock garden; water features; museum; winner of *Age Concern* award
NCCPG NATIONAL COLLECTIONS *Nymphaea*

Famed for its water lilies, planted by Frances Perry in the 1930s, but there is much more to Burnby Hall. A rock garden, cheerful modern rose garden and good collection of conifers all contribute to its visitor-friendly style.

Burton Constable Foundation
Burton Constable Hall, Hull, Humberside HU11 4LN
☎ 0964 562400   📠 0964 563229

OWNER   Burton Constable Foundation
LOCATION   Via Hull B1238 to Sproatley follow HH signs
OPEN   12 noon – 5 pm; Sunday – Thursday; Easter Sunday to 30 September
ADMISSION   Adults £3.00, Hall & Garden
FACILITIES   Parking; dogs permitted; loos; facilities for the disabled; shop; light snacks
FEATURES   Herbaceous borders; landscape designed by Capability Brown; water features; woodland garden; interesting for children; fine 18th century orangery
ENGLISH HERITAGE GRADE   II

Essentially a Capability Brown landscape (his original plans are still shown), but the 19th century pleasure gardens are being restored and the whole estate will undoubtedly develop excitingly in future.

Sledmere House
Sledmere, Driffield, Humberside YO25 0XG
☎ 0377 236637   📠 0377 236560

OWNER   Sir Tatton Sykes Bt.
LOCATION   Off A166 between York & Bridlington
OPEN   12 pm – 5 pm; daily except Monday & Friday; Easter to 30 September
ADMISSION   Adults £1.50; Senior Citizens & Children £1
FACILITIES   Parking; dogs permitted; loos; facilities for the disabled; craft & gift shop; tea terrace and cafeteria
FEATURES   Landscape designed by Capability Brown; fine conifers; modern roses; old roses and climbers; deer park
ENGLISH HERITAGE GRADE   I

Sledmere has a classical Capability Brown landscape: his originals plans can be seen in the Library. An Italianate formal garden was added in 1911, with Greek and Roman busts swathed in climbing roses. A new knot garden has been added recently and is growing up quickly. Definitely a garden on the up.

ISLE OF WIGHT

Barton Manor
Whippingham, East Cowes, Isle of Wight PO32 6LB
☎ 0983 292835   📠 0983 293923

OWNER   R Stigwood
LOCATION   Next to Osborne House on East Cowes Road (A3021)
OPEN   10.30 am – 5.30 pm; daily; 1 April to 9 October
ADMISSION   Adults £3.50; Senior Citizens & parties £3; Children free (1 per adult)
FACILITIES   Parking; loos; facilities for the disabled; gift shop with Barton Manor wines; cafeteria
FEATURES   Herbaceous borders; modern roses; water features; woodland garden; rhododendrons; royal connections; new rose maze
NCCPG NATIONAL COLLECTIONS *Kniphofia*, *Watsonia*

Laid out by Prince Albert, Barton was for many years part of the Osborne estate. He planted some of the best trees, including the cork plantation near the house. Now Barton is run as a commercial vineyard and the gardens are being expanded both for private enjoyment and as a commercial resource.

Mottistone Manor
Newport, Isle of Wight

OWNER   The National Trust
LOCATION   On B3399 west of Brighstone
OPEN   2 pm – 5 pm; Wednesdays and Bank Holiday Mondays; 2 March to 28 September
ADMISSION   £1.80
FACILITIES   Parking; dogs permitted; plants for sale
FEATURES   Herbaceous borders; fine conifers; fruit and vegetables of special interest; modern roses; bluebells; irises

A cleverly designed modern garden on a difficult site – steep and narrow. Much has been terraced and enclosed to allow a rose garden and good herbaceous borders. Most of the rest is given to a wide variety of fruit trees, trained to make avenues and underplanted with vegetables or spring bulbs. A model for this type of planting, and made long before the current fashion for ornamental *potagers*.

North Court
Shorwell, Isle of Wight PO30 3JG
☎ 0983 740415   📠 0983 740415

OWNER   Mr & Mrs John Harrison
LOCATION   4 miles south west of Newport, off B3323
OPEN   2.30 pm – 5 pm; certain Sundays (to be announced); May and June for charity, or by appointment
ADMISSION   £1.25

FACILITIES Parking; dogs permitted; access for the disabled; plants for sale

FEATURES Herbaceous borders; fruit and vegetables of special interest; designed by Lutyens; plantsman's garden; modern roses; old roses and climbers; sub-tropical plants; water features; woodland garden; large plane trees

The Harrison family which owns North Court inherited fine grounds with some magnificent trees and a clear stream at the bottom. John Harrison has extensively replanted it with a plantsman's enthusiasm and a special interest in tender exotica. Definitely a garden to watch in future.

Nunwell House

Brading, Ryde, Isle of Wight PO36 OJQ
☎ 0983 407240

OWNER Colonel & Mrs J A Aylmer
LOCATION Off A3055, 1 mile to the west
OPEN 10 am – 5 pm; Sunday – Thursday; 3 July to 29 September
ADMISSION House and Garden: Adults £2.30; Senior Citizens £1.80; Children under 12, 60p
FACILITIES Parking; loos; tea, coffee & biscuits
FEATURES Good collection of trees; ecological interest; herbs; plantsman's garden; modern roses; garden sculpture; obelisks
ENGLISH HERITAGE GRADE II

A pretty garden, largely replanted by Vernon Russell-Smith about 30 years ago: he also planted a small arboretum. The present owners have added some highly attractive garden ornaments and are restoring the fabric and the plantings after some years of neglect.

Owl Cottage

Hoxall Lane, Mottistone, Newport, Isle of Wight PO30 4EE
☎ 0983 740433

OWNER Mrs A L Hutchinson
LOCATION Down Hoxall Lane, opposite Mottistone Manor
OPEN 2.30 pm – 5.30 pm, by appointment, groups only
ADMISSION £1.50
FACILITIES Dogs permitted; access for the disabled
FEATURES Herbaceous borders; plantsman's garden; modern roses; old roses and climbers

A cottage garden, made entirely by the present owner, and remarkable for the range of colour and variety at all seasons, though it is open only in summer. The best plantsman's garden on the Isle of Wight.

Ventnor Botanic Garden

Undercliff Drive, Ventnor, Isle of Wight PO38 1UL
☎ 0983 855397

OWNER South Wight Borough Council
LOCATION 1½ miles to west of Ventnor on A3055
OPEN All day; every day
ADMISSION Garden: free, Show House: 50p. Parking charge
FACILITIES Parking; dogs permitted; loos; facilities for the disabled; cafeteria & bar with snacks, tea/coffee, lunches
FEATURES Herbaceous borders; fine conifers; glasshouses to visit; herbs; plantsman's garden; sub-tropical plants; particularly interesting in winter; palms; olives; bananas; medicinal herbs from all over the world
FRIENDS Friends of Garden (tel: 0983 855397), seed list distributions

Originally an offshoot of Hillier Nurseries, the Ventnor Botanic Garden is devoted to exotic plants. Many – perhaps most – are from the southern hemisphere but flourish in the unique microclimate of the 'Undercliff': widdringtonias from Zimbabwe and Tasmanian olearias, for instance. Almost destroyed by the gales of 1987 and 1990, the collection is rapidly forming again.

KENT

Bedgebury National Pinetum

Goudhurst, Cranbrook, Kent TN17 2SL
☎ 0580 211044   FAX 0580 212423

OWNER Forestry Commission
LOCATION 1 mile east of A21 at Flimwell on B2079
OPEN 10 am to dusk
ADMISSION Adults £1.50; Senior Citizens £1.00; Children 75p
FACILITIES Parking; dogs permitted; loos; plants for sale; drinks & snacks
FEATURES Fine conifers; water features; woodland garden; particularly interesting in winter; rhododendrons; fungi; tallest *Quercus libani* in UK, plus five record conifer species
ENGLISH HERITAGE GRADE II*
NCCPG NATIONAL COLLECTIONS *Taxus, Juniperus, Chamaecyparis lawsoniana*
FRIENDS Details from the Curator

Take any of the trails through this magnificent woodland garden, or go to the excellent Visitors' Centre to see the cone collection, and the new exhibit which tells the story of the Great Storm of 1987. It is difficult to realise that all the plantings are less than 70 years old.

Belmont Park

Belmont, Throwley, Faversham, Kent ME13 OHH
☎ 0795 890202

OWNER The Harris (Belmont) Charity
LOCATION Signposted from Badlesmere
OPEN 2 pm – 5 pm; Saturday, Sunday & Bank Holiday
Mondays; Easter Sunday to September
ADMISSION Adults £1.75; Children 50p
FACILITIES Parking; dogs permitted; loos; facilities for
the disabled; plants for sale; teas
FEATURES Good collection of trees; fine conifers; fol-
lies and garden buildings; rock garden; shell grotto;
rhododendrons; pets' cemetery; pinetum
ENGLISH HERITAGE GRADE II

Quiet parkland surrounds this handsome Samuel
Wyatt house, while the pleasure gardens are so obviously for the pleasure of the owners, not for display,
that they add considerably to the sense of domesticity.
There is nothing spectacular or vulgar about Belmont.

Chartwell

Westerham, Kent TN16 1PS
☎ 0732 866368

OWNER The National Trust
LOCATION A25 to Westerham then signposted from
B2026
OPEN 12 pm – 5.30 pm, Tuesday – Thursday; 11 am
– 5.30 pm, Saturday, Sunday and Bank Holiday Mon-
days; April to October
ADMISSION Adults £2.00; Children £1.00; (1993)
FACILITIES Parking; dogs permitted; loos; facilities for
the disabled; National Trust shop; restaurant
FEATURES Rock garden; old roses and climbers; water
features
ENGLISH HERITAGE GRADE II*

Chartwell trades on its association with Sir Winston
Churchill and offers little to the keen plantsman. However, there is a rose garden planted with the variety
'Winston Churchill' and a deep sense of history
throughout.

Chilham Castle Gardens

Chilham, Canterbury, Kent CT4 8DB
☎ 0227 730319

OWNER Annabelle, Viscountess Massereene & Fer-
rard
LOCATION Off A252 Canterbury – Maidstone
OPEN 11 am – 5 pm; daily; 27 March to 16 October
ADMISSION Adults £3; Children £1.50
FACILITIES Parking; dogs permitted; loos; teas & light
lunches
FEATURES Landscape designed by Capability Brown;
rock garden; modern roses; old roses and climbers; good
topiary; water features; woodland garden; deer park

ENGLISH HERITAGE GRADE II*

One of the Tradescants designed the formal gardens,
restored 100 years ago, and Capability Brown laid out
the park. Modern restoration and replanting make Chilham a garden of increasing interest – a new rose garden,
for instance, and some replanting in the rock garden.
And the views are superb.

Crittenden House

Crittenden Road, Matfield, Tonbridge, Kent
TN12 7EN
☎ 0892 832554

OWNER Crittenden Farm Ltd
LOCATION 2 miles north of Pembury
OPEN 2 pm – 6 pm; 27 March, 3, 4 & 17 April, 1, 2,
15, 29 May, 12 June
ADMISSION Adults £1.50; Children 25p
FACILITIES Parking; loos
FEATURES Herbaceous borders; plantsman's garden;
modern roses; old roses and climbers; water features;
Malus 'Crittenden'

Plantsman's garden built up by the owner over the last
40 years and still intensifying. Island beds surrounded
by grass give an informal structure and there are three
ponds, each planted differently. Fascinating plants
everywhere – many given by famous gardeners and
collectors, some collected by Ben Tompsett himself.

Emmetts Garden

Ide Hill, Sevenoaks, Kent TN14 6AY
☎ 0732 750367 or 750429

OWNER The National Trust
LOCATION Between Sundridge and Ide Hill off B2042
OPEN 1 pm – 6 pm (last ticket 5 pm); reserved for
(pre-booked parties). 11 am – 1 pm; Wednesday, Sunday and Bank Holiday Mondays, Thursday; 1 April to
31 October
ADMISSION Adults £2.50; Children £1.30; Pre-
booked parties £2.00
FACILITIES Parking; dogs permitted; loos; tea room
2 pm – 5 pm (may close in bad weather)
FEATURES Rock garden; modern roses; old roses and
climbers; Italianate rose garden; rare trees and shrubs
ENGLISH HERITAGE GRADE II

Five acres of Edwardian opulence, whose formal Italianate rose garden is surrounded by an informal woodland garden laid out with trees and shrubs in the
William Robinson style. Fabulous views across the
Weald of Kent. Picnic area.

Godington Park

Ashford, Kent TN23 3BW
☎ 0233 620773

OWNER The Godington House Preservation Trust

LOCATION Godington Lane, Potters Corner (A20)
OPEN 2 pm – 5 pm or by appointment; Easter Saturday/Sunday/Monday, Sundays and Bank Holidays; 1 June to 30 September
ADMISSION 70p
FACILITIES Parking; loos
FEATURES Modern roses; garden sculpture; good topiary; water features; formal Italianate garden; waterlilies
ENGLISH HERITAGE GRADE I

Godington is perhaps the prettiest house in Kent, a Jacobean mansion reworked in the early 1900s by Sir Reginald Blomfield, who made the charming Italian garden (statues, loggia, summerhouse). Add in the 18th century park and late 19th century plantings, and you have a garden of great charm and authenticity.

Goodnestone Park

Wingham, Canterbury, Kent CT3 1PL
☎ 0304 840107

OWNER Lord & Lady Fitzwalter
LOCATION Follow brown tourist signs from B2046
OPEN 11 am – 5 pm; weekdays; 28 March to 28 October. 12 noon – 6 pm; Sundays; 3 April to 2 October
ADMISSION Adults £2.00; Senior Citizens £1.60; Children under 12 free; Disabled in wheelchairs £1.00; Group (min 20) £1.80; Guided Group £2.20
FACILITIES Parking; loos; facilities for the disabled; plants for sale; teas 23 May- 29 August, Wednesdays and Sundays only
FEATURES Herbaceous borders; rock garden; old roses and climbers; woodland garden; cedar walk; rhododendrons
ENGLISH HERITAGE GRADE II*

A handsome Palladian house associated with Jane Austen (her brother married a daughter of the house). Fine parkland, a formal garden in front of the house, a 1930s woodland garden (maples, camellias, azaleas), and good mixed plantings in the old kitchen garden.

Great Comp

St Mary's Platt, Borough Green, Sevenoaks, Kent TN15 8QS
☎ 0732 886154

OWNER Great Comp Charitable Trust
LOCATION 2 miles east of Borough Green B2016 off A20
OPEN 11 am – 6 pm; daily; 1 March to 31 October
ADMISSION Adults £2.50; Children £1.00
FACILITIES Parking; loos; facilities for the disabled; plants for sale; gifts, plants and souvenirs; tea room
FEATURES Herbaceous borders; follies and garden buildings; plantsman's garden; garden sculpture; woodland garden; ground cover; dwarf conifers

FRIENDS Great Comp Society, mainly to support the annual music festival in July and September

Great Comp is a controversial garden. Everyone admires the energy of its founder Roderick Cameron, and Clay Jones called it the best garden he had ever seen. Others consider the reliance on heathers, dwarf conifers and ground cover to be tedious, the modern follies hideous, and the meandering design plain boring. But go with an open mind and you will find much to admire.

Hever Castle

Edenbridge, Kent TN8 7NG
☎ 0732 865224   FAX 0732 866796

OWNER Broadland Properties Ltd
LOCATION Near Edenbridge, difficult to find – use a good road map
OPEN 11 am – 5 pm; 15 March to 6 November
ADMISSION Adult £3.60; Senior Citizens £3.00; Children (5-16) £2.10; Family £9.30
FACILITIES Parking; dogs permitted; loos; facilities for the disabled; plants for sale; plant centre; shop; two restaurants
FEATURES Herbaceous borders; fine conifers; follies and garden buildings; modern roses; old roses and climbers; garden sculpture; water features; woodland garden; particularly good in July-August
ENGLISH HERITAGE GRADE I

One of the most important Edwardian gardens in England. The pretty moated castle sits in a park of oaks and firs (underplanted with rhododendrons) with a maze and formal neo-Tudor garden to one side. The best part is a spectacular Italian garden where a long pergola (cool dripping fountains all along) leads past a series of exquisite Italian gardens, stuffed with sculptures, urns, sarcophagi and other loot brought by William Waldorf Astor from Rome; it finally bursts onto a theatrical terrace and a 35-acre lake, hand dug by 800 workmen.

Ladham House

Goudhurst, Kent TM17 1DB
☎ 0580 211203

OWNER Betty, Lady Jessel
LOCATION Past Curtisdem Green turn right, house on left
OPEN 11 am – 6 pm; 1 & 29 May, 10 July or by appointment
ADMISSION Adults £2; Children under 12 yrs 50p; £2.50 private visits
FACILITIES Parking; dogs permitted; loos; teas
FEATURES Good collection of trees; herbaceous borders; water features; woodland garden; magnolias

Laid out by a botanist Master of the Rolls in the mid 19th century, and enthusiastically restored and updated by the present owner. Many new plantings and some fine specimens, especially a deep red form of *Magnolia campbellii* which has been named 'Betty Jessell'.

Leeds Castle
Maidstone, Kent ME17 1PL
☎ 0622 765400   📠 0622 735616

OWNER   Leeds Castle Foundation
LOCATION   Junction 8 off the M20
OPEN   10 am – 5 pm, 1 March to 31 October; 10 am – 3 pm, 1 November to 28 February
ADMISSION   Park & Gardens, Adults £5.50; Students £4.50; Children £3.30; Disabled Adults £3.00; Disabled Children £2.50
FACILITIES   Parking; loos; facilities for the disabled; plants for sale; shop in Castle Greenhouse; refreshments in the 17th century tithe barn
FEATURES   Herbaceous borders; herbs; old roses and climbers; water features; woodland garden; interesting for children; new maze disappears into an underground grotto!
ENGLISH HERITAGE GRADE   II*

More a romantic castle than a garden, best seen across the lake, Leeds is run by a high profile charitable trust with a big advertising budget. The results are admirable, though the 'Culpeper Garden' is not one of Russell Page's best plantings.

Long Barn
Long Barn Road, Weald, Sevenoaks, Kent TN14 6NH
☎ 0732 463714

OWNER   Mr & Mrs Brandon Gough
LOCATION   3 miles south of Sevenoaks; end of village
OPEN   2 pm – 5 pm; 22 May, 19 June, 17 July
ADMISSION   Adults £2; Senior Citizens £1; Children 50p
FACILITIES   Parking; loos
FEATURES   Fruit and vegetables of special interest; herbs; modern roses; old roses and climbers; rhododendron glade; pergola; parterres; secret garden; white garden
ENGLISH HERITAGE GRADE   II*

Chiefly of interest for its association with Harold Nicolson and Vita Sackville-West, and well restored to their period by the present owners. The strong designs and exuberant plantings of Sissinghurst are all here in their infancy.

Northbourne Court
Northbourne, Deal, Kent CT14 0LW
☎ 0304 611281   📠 0304 614512

OWNER   The Hon. Charles James
LOCATION   Just beyond the village centre

OPEN   2 pm – 6 pm; 1 & 29 May; 12 & 26 June; 10 & 24 July; 14 & 28 August; 11 & 25 September
ADMISSION   Adult £2.50; Children & Senior Citizens £1.50.
FACILITIES   Parking; loos; plants for sale; occasional teas
FEATURES   Herbaceous borders; glasshouses to visit; good topiary
ENGLISH HERITAGE GRADE   II*

A series of smallish flower gardens, each intensely planted with cottagey perennials and, for the most part, arranged by the artist Aubrey Waterfield. Wonderful combinations of colours and shades.

Penshurst Place
Penshurst, Tonbridge, Kent TN11 8DG
☎ 0892 870307   📠 0892 870866

OWNER   Viscount De L'Isle
LOCATION   Follow brown tourist signs from Tonbridge
OPEN   11 am – 6 pm, Saturday & Sunday, March & October; All week, 1 April to 30 September
ADMISSION   Gardens only: Adult £3.50; Senior Citizens £3.00; Children £2.25
FACILITIES   Parking; loos; access for the disabled; dried flowers for sale; self-service restaurant
FEATURES   Herbaceous borders; modern roses; formal Italian garden; spring bulbs
ENGLISH HERITAGE GRADE   I

A garden with substantial genuine Tudor remains, but well restored and developed in recent years. A vast Italianate parterre dominates the immediate pleasure garden: it is planted with scarlet polyantha roses – another is planted as a Union Jack. There are borders by Lanning Roper and John Codrington, a 100 yard bed of paeonies, a new lake, and a brand new garden for the blind, straight off the peg from last year's Chelsea Flower Show.

Port Lympne Gardens
Lympne, Hythe, Kent CT21 4PD
☎ 0303 64647   📠 0303 264944

OWNER   John Aspinall
LOCATION   Junction 11 off M20 follow sign to Lympne
OPEN   10 am – 5pm
ADMISSION   Adults £6.50; Senior Citizen & Children £4.50
FACILITIES   Parking; loos; facilities for the disabled; plants for sale; souvenirs and some garden sundries; bar, restaurant, café
FEATURES   Herbaceous borders; follies and garden buildings; garden sculpture; good topiary; interesting

for children; particularly interesting in winter; dahlias; bedding out; clock garden; best known for its zoo
ENGLISH HERITAGE GRADE II*

More than a zoo, Port Lympne is a stylish and luxurious house and its garden, on the steepest of slopes high above Romney Marshes, is both dramatic and well designed. The long, long marble staircase, chessboard garden and dahlia terraces are unique.

Scotney Castle

Lamberhurst, Tunbridge Wells, Kent TN3 8JN
☎ 0892 890651   FAX 0892 890110

OWNER   The National Trust
LOCATION   On A21
OPEN   11 am – 6 pm; Wednesday – Friday; 2 April to 31 October; 2 pm – 6 pm, Saturday & Sunday; 12 noon – 6 pm, Bank Holiday Sunday & Monday
ADMISSION   Adults £3.20; Children £1.60
FACILITIES   Parking; loos; facilities for the disabled; shop
FEATURES   Herbs; plantsman's garden; water features; woodland garden; rhododendrons; azaleas; water lilies; wisteria; ruins of 14th Century Castle
ENGLISH HERITAGE GRADE   I

Moated and abandoned castle surrounded by rhododendrons and azaleas: very romantic and very photogenic. Among the ruins are a herb garden and cottage garden, surprisingly appropriate and effective. Lanning Roper had a hand in it.

Sissinghurst Castle

Sissinghursy, Cranbrook, Kent TN17 2AB
☎ 0580 715330   FAX 0580 713911

OWNER   The National Trust
LOCATION   1½ miles east of Sissinghurst village, ½ mile off A262.
OPEN   1 pm – 6 pm, Tuesday – Friday, 1 April to 15 October; 10 pm – 5.30 pm, Saturday, Sunday and Good Friday; Last admission ½ hour before close
ADMISSION   Adults £5.00, Children £2.50, no party reductions
FACILITIES   Parking; loos; facilities for the disabled; plants for sale; National Trust Gift shop; self-service restaurant
FEATURES   Herbaceous borders; plantsman's garden; old roses and climbers; too many visitors have eroded the fabric of this famous and wonderful garden
ENGLISH HERITAGE GRADE   I

Too well known to need description, Sissinghurst is part of every English gardener's education and a source of wonder and inspiration to which to return time and again. There is a 'timed ticket' system to restrict visitors to 400 at a time, which may mean waiting.

Upper Mill Cottage

Salts Lane, Loose, Maidstone, Kent ME15 0BD

OWNER   Mr & Mrs D Seeney
LOCATION   Park in Loose village, walk 300 yards up Salts Lane
OPEN   For NGS
ADMISSION   For NGS charities
FACILITIES   Refreshments by arrangement
FEATURES   Good collection of trees; herbaceous borders; fine conifers; plantsman's garden; old roses and climbers; water features; woodland garden

A plantsman's garden, thickly planted to give a succession of interest – 'jungle planting', the owners call it – and contrasts of foliage, colour and texture. The garden is divided into rooms. Old-fashioned roses are a particular feature, and the overall effect is cottagey, but everything from the clumps of *Tricyrtis* to the fast-growing *Metasequoia* was planted by the owners.

LANCASHIRE

Bank House

Borwick, Carnforth, Lancashire LA6 1JR
☎ 0524 732768

OWNER   Mr & Mrs R G McBurnie
LOCATION   2 miles north east of Carnforth off A6
OPEN   2 pm – 6 pm; 1 May, 5 June, 3 July, 7 August, 4 September, 2 October
ADMISSION   Adults £1.00; Children 25p
FACILITIES   Loos; access for the disabled; tea & coffee
FEATURES   Good collection of trees; fruit and vegetables of special interest; gravel or scree garden; plantsman's garden; old roses and climbers; woodland garden; collection of carnivorous plants

A successful private garden made over the last 30 years by the present owners. It manages to shoe-horn such features as a woodland garden, gravel garden, old-fashioned rose collection and a mini-arboretum into two acres. But it works.

Leighton Hall

Carnforth, Lancashire LA5 9ST
☎ 0524 734474   FAX 0524 702357

OWNER   R G Reynolds
LOCATION   Signed from A6 junction with M6
OPEN   2 pm – 5 pm; daily except Saturday & Monday; 1 May to 30 September
ADMISSION   Adults £3.20; Children £2.00; Senior Citizens & Parties £2.70
FACILITIES   Parking; loos; access for the disabled; plants for sale; gift shop; tea rooms
FEATURES   Herbaceous borders; fruit and vegetables of special interest; herbs; old roses and climbers; 'cater-

'pillar' path maze; first prize, Britain in Bloom 1993 (north west region)

The handsome semi-castellated house is set in lush parkland with the moors as a backdrop, but the garden is in the old walled garden, where rose borders, herbs and the gravel maze bring a touch of fancy to the whole.

LEICESTERSHIRE

Belvoir Castle

Belvoir, Grantham, Leicestershire
☎ 0476 870262

OWNER The Duke of Rutland
LOCATION 6 miles west of Grantham
OPEN 11 am – 5 pm; Tuesday – Thursday, Saturday & Sunday; 1 April to 30 September. Open Bank Holiday Mondays; also Sundays in October
ADMISSION Castle and gardens: Adults £4; Senior Citizens £2.75; Children £2.50
FACILITIES Parking; loos; refreshments: lunches and teas; picnic site
FEATURES Herbaceous borders; modern roses; old roses and climbers; woodland garden
ENGLISH HERITAGE GRADE II

Formal gardens on the Victorian terraces beneath the castle. A pretty woodland garden.

Burrough House

Burrough on the Hill, Melton Mowbray, Leicestershire LE14 2JQ
☎ 066 477226

OWNER Mrs Barbara Keene
LOCATION 6 miles west of Oakham
OPEN 2.30 pm – 6 pm; Thursday and Bank Holiday Weekends; Easter to 1 October
ADMISSION Weekdays £1.50; Weekends £2.00
FACILITIES Parking; loos; access for the disabled; plants for sale; light refreshments
FEATURES Modern roses; water features; woodland garden; rhododendrons

A 1920s garden revived and improved by the present owner. A parterre, moon gate, Italian garden, rose garden, paeony border, croquet lawn, woodland walk and secret garden are a measure of what pleasure the garden is designed to offer.

Langham Lodge

Langham, Oakham, Leicestershire LE15 7HZ

OWNER Mr & Mrs H M Hemsley
LOCATION On Burley road out of Langham
OPEN 2 pm – 6 pm; 19 June. Other times in June & July by appointment
ADMISSION £1

FACILITIES Parking; access for the disabled; plants for sale; teas
FEATURES Herbaceous borders; fruit and vegetables of special interest; plantsman's garden; old roses and climbers; colour borders

A modern plantsman's garden, full of interesting plants, often chosen for their foliage effects. Good shrub roses, which show up well against the stone walls.

Long Close

60 Main Street, Woodhouse Eaves, Loughborough, Leicestershire LE12 8RZ
☎ 0509 890 376

OWNER Mrs George Johnson
LOCATION 3 miles south of Loughborough
OPEN 2 pm – 6 pm; 27 March, 15 May, 29 May
ADMISSION Adults £1.50
FACILITIES Parking; dogs permitted; plants for sale; teas
FEATURES Fine conifers; old roses and climbers; woodland garden; rhododendrons; azaleas; heathers

A plantsman's garden, begun by the present owner 45 years ago, and now magnificently mature. Five acres, crammed into a long narrow site that spreads out at the end into woodland, underplanted with massed rhododendrons and azaleas.

The University of Leicester Botanic Garden

Beaumont Hall, Stoughton Drive, Oadby, Leicestershire LE2 2NA
☎ 0533 717725

OWNER The University of Leicester
LOCATION 3 miles south of Leicester on A6 London Road opposite Racecourse
OPEN 10 am – 4.30 pm (3.30 pm Friday); Monday – Friday; all year
ADMISSION Free
FACILITIES Parking; loos; plants for sale
FEATURES Fine conifers; ecological interest; glasshouses to visit; herbs; rock garden; modern roses; old roses and climbers; sub-tropical plants; water features; woodland garden; cacti; succulents; heathers; tallest *Quercus petraea* 'Mespilifolia' and *Pinus aristata* in the British Isles
NCCPG NATIONAL COLLECTIONS *Aubrieta, Fuchsia* (hardy vars), *Skimmia, Hesperis, Chamaecyparis lawsoniana*
FRIENDS Send for membership form: The Curator, Botany Dept, Leicester University, Leicester LE1 7RH, Benefits include: newsletters, special access, plant exchanges, meetings once a month and guide

16 acres – one of the best modern (early 20th century) botanic gardens, with a wide variety of plants from historic trees to a 1980s ecological meadow.

Wartnaby Gardens

Wartnaby, Melton Mowbray, Leicestershire LE14 3HY
☎ 0664 822549

OWNER Lady King
LOCATION 3 miles north of Melton Mowbray on A606. Left at A6 Kettleby then 1 mile
OPEN Groups only, by appointment
ADMISSION £2
FACILITIES Parking; dogs admitted; loos; access for the disabled; plants for sale; refreshments
FEATURES Arboretum; borders; interesting fruit and vegetables; glasshouses to visit; old roses; water features; colour borders

A model modern garden, where rare plants are displayed in an endless variety of situations and habitats. Roses feature significantly, with good herbaceous underplanting and satisfying colour schemes.

Whatton House

Long Whatton, Loughborough, Leicestershire LE12 SBG
☎ 0509 842302   ☏ 0509 842268

OWNER Lord Crawshaw
LOCATION A6, J24 towards Hathern
OPEN 2 pm – 6 pm; Wednesdays, Sundays & Bank Holiday Mondays; Easter to 30 August. 5 April & 31st May for NGS
ADMISSION Adults £1.50; Senior Citizens & Children 75p
FACILITIES Parking; dogs permitted; loos; facilities for the disabled; plants for sale; refreshments
FEATURES Good collection of trees; herbaceous borders; follies and garden buildings; fruit and vegetables of special interest; oriental features; rock garden; modern roses; old roses and climbers; climbing plants; bark temple; canyon garden; Chinese garden
ENGLISH HERITAGE GRADE II

15 acres attached to a garden centre. Most of the features date from c.1900 but there has been much replanting in recent years. The Chinese garden sports some extraordinary mythological figures. There is also a mysterious 'bogey hole'. Great fun to visit.

LINCOLNSHIRE

Belton House

Grantham, Lincolnshire NG32 2LS
☎ 0476 61541

OWNER The National Trust

LOCATION 3 miles north east of Grantham on the A607
OPEN 11 am – 5.30 pm; Wednesday – Sunday; 1 April to 31 October
ADMISSION Adults £4; Children £2
FACILITIES Parking; loos; facilities for the disabled; gift shop; lunches, teas, licensed restaurant
FEATURES Herbaceous borders; follies and garden buildings; glasshouses to visit; modern roses; garden sculpture; good topiary; water features; woodland garden; interesting for children; daffodils; adventure playground
ENGLISH HERITAGE GRADE I

Grandeur and amenity go hand in hand at Belton. There are 1,000 acres of wooded deer park, a Wyatville orangery, a Dutch garden and an Italian garden with statues and parterres. But the adventure playground and other facilities make it popular with all ages.

Caythorpe Court

Caythorpe, Grantham, Lincolnshire NG32 3EP
☎ 0400 72521   ☏ 0400 72722

OWNER Lincolnshire College of Agriculture & Horticulture
LOCATION East of Caythorpe village
OPEN 1.30 pm – 5 pm; 11 June. Groups by prior arrangement
ADMISSION £20 per group
FACILITIES Parking; dogs permitted; loos; plants for sale; refreshments by arrangement
FEATURES Herbaceous borders; fine conifers; glasshouses to visit; plantsman's garden; modern roses; old roses and climbers; woodland garden; formal terraces
ENGLISH HERITAGE GRADE II

A teaching garden, and well worth a special visit. The Victorian monkey puzzle and Edwardian terraces predate the modern gardens. These are laid out with demonstration borders and plant collections for roses, irises, annuals, vegetables, herbaceous plants, alpines and a lot more too.

Doddington Hall

Doddington, Lincoln, Lincolnshire LN6 4RU
☎ 0522 694308   ☏ 0522 682584

OWNER A Jarvis
LOCATION Signposted off the A46 Lincoln bypass
OPEN 2 pm – 6 pm; Wednesday, Sunday, Bank Holiday Mondays; Easter Monday; 1 May to 30 September; also daily except Saturday in August
ADMISSION £1.75
FACILITIES Parking; loos; facilities for the disabled; licensed restaurant
FEATURES Herbaceous borders; old roses and climbers; water features; new turf maze

ENGLISH HERITAGE GRADE II*

A ravishing Elizabethan house around which successive generations have made a successful Tudor-style garden. Simple and open at the front, Edwardian knots and parterres in the walled garden (thickly and richly planted), and then a modern herb garden and pleached hornbeams. Wonderfully harmonious.

Grimsthorpe Castle Trust Ltd

Grimsthorpe Castle, Bourne, Lincolnshire PE10 0NB
☎ 0778 32205   📠 0778 32259

OWNER   Grimsthorpe & Drummond Castle Trust Ltd
LOCATION   On A151 Bourne from Colsterworth road
OPEN   2 pm – 6 pm, Easter Sunday, 3 & 4 April; 2 pm – 6 pm; Sunday, Bank Holiday & Thursday, 1 May to 11 September
ADMISSION   Adults £1.00; Senior Citizens & Children 50p
FACILITIES   Parking; dogs permitted; loos; access for the disabled; tea rooms
FEATURES   Good collection of trees; landscape designed by Capability Brown; modern roses; good topiary; water features
ENGLISH HERITAGE GRADE   I

First Capability Brown, then a late Victorian Italian garden, still maintained with summer bedding. The most interesting feature is a formal vegetable garden, made in the 1960s before the craze for *potagers*, right below the Italian garden. Well designed and well maintained, but is it not too close to the house?

Gunby Hall

Gunby, Spilsby, Lincolnshire PE23 5SS

OWNER   The National Trust
LOCATION   2½ miles north west of Burgh-le-Marsh
OPEN   2 pm – 6 pm; Wednesday; 1 April to 30 September
ADMISSION   £1.50 (1993)
FACILITIES   Parking; dogs permitted; loos; access for the disabled; plants for sale
FEATURES   Herbaceous borders; fruit and vegetables of special interest; herbs; old roses and climbers
ENGLISH HERITAGE GRADE   II

Ignore the parkland and make for the two walled gardens. Here is all the action: rich herbaceous borders, an arched apple walk, shrub roses, herbs and vegetables.

Riseholme Hall

Lincolnshire College of Agriculture & Horticulture, Riseholme, Lincolnshire LN2 2LG
☎ 0522 522252   📠 0522 545436

OWNER   Lincolnshire College of Agriculture & Horticulture
LOCATION   2 miles north of Lincoln on A15

OPEN   10.30 am – 4 pm; 15 May; groups by prior arrangement
ADMISSION   £20 (per group) for guided tours during summer
FACILITIES   Parking; dogs permitted; loos; access for the disabled; refreshments by arrangement
FEATURES   Good collection of trees; herbaceous borders; ecological interest; fruit and vegetables of special interest; glasshouses to visit; rock garden; modern roses; old roses and climbers; water features; woodland garden; heather garden; tender plants
ENGLISH HERITAGE GRADE   II

The old house has an 18th century landscape – park, lake and broad trees. The Bishop's Walk is Edwardian: tender plants flourish between the yew hedge and brick wall. However the main garden is strictly educational, with demonstrations of roses, herbaceous plants, fruit and vegetables, alpine plants and annuals, all beautifully maintained and meticulously labelled.

Springfields Show Gardens

Spalding, Lincolnshire PE12 6ET
☎ 0775 724843   📠 0775 711209

OWNER   Springfields Horticultural Society Ltd
LOCATION   1½ miles from Spalding on A151
OPEN   10 am – 6 pm; 19 March to 2 October
ADMISSION   Adults £2.50; Senior Citizens £2.30
FACILITIES   Parking; loos; facilities for the disabled; plants for sale; gift shop; restaurant and café
FEATURES   Modern roses; water features; woodland garden; millions of bulbs

Originally a cor blimey display garden for the Lincolnshire bulb trade, Springfields now offers fun and colour all through the season, with roses providing the midsummer display and bold bedding taking over until the autumn frosts. An eyeful of a garden, splendidly maintained.

LONDON

17 Fulham Park Gardens

London SW6 4JX
☎ 071 736 4890

OWNER   Anthony Noel
LOCATION   Near Putney Bridge underground station
OPEN   2.30 pm – 6 pm; Sunday; 8 May, 19 June, 10 July, 18 September
ADMISSION   Adults £2.00; Senior Citizens £1.00
FEATURES   Good topiary; young garden; urns, pots, troughs; striking plantings; seven years old

A town garden where meticulous attention to detail pays off: neatly clipped cubes and box bobbles are one speciality. The planting is profuse but plants are rigorously controlled – just greens and whites, with occasional silvers and golds. The contrasts, juxtapositions and harmonies, though on a small scale, are ingenious. Alas, it feels like a garden for one person only at a time, two at the most – impossible on Open Days.

Cannizaro Park

West Side Common, Wimbledon, London SW19
☎ 081 946 7349

OWNER   London Borough of Merton
LOCATION   West side of Wimbledon Common
OPEN   8 am – sunset, Monday – Friday; 9 am – sunset, Saturday, Sunday & Bank Holidays; all year
ADMISSION   Free
FACILITIES   Parking; loos; some refreshments at summer week-ends
FEATURES   Herbaceous borders; fine conifers; modern roses; woodland garden; azaleas; magnolias; summer bedding
ENGLISH HERITAGE GRADE   II*

Famous for its azaleas, planted about 40 years ago and almost too much of a good thing when in full flower. Little known, even to Londoners, Cannizaro deserves recognition as one of the leading Surrey-type of woodland gardens in the country.

Capel Manor

Bullsmoor Lane, Enfield, London EN1 4RQ
☎ 0992 763849

OWNER   London Borough of Enfield
LOCATION   By A10 (M25 J25)
OPEN   10 am – 5.30 pm; daily; 1 April to 31 October. 10 am – 4.30 pm; daily except Sunday; 1 November to 31 March
ADMISSION   Adults £2; Senior Citizens £1.50; Children £1
FACILITIES   Parking; dogs permitted; loos; facilities for the disabled; plants for sale; small shop; refreshments
FEATURES   Good collection of trees; fine conifers; ecological interest; follies and garden buildings; fruit and vegetables of special interest; glasshouses to visit; gravel or scree garden; herbs; oriental features; plantsman's garden; rock garden; modern roses; old roses and climbers; sub-tropical plants; good topiary; water features; woodland garden; interesting for children
NCCPG NATIONAL COLLECTIONS *Achillea, Dahlia, Sarcococca*

High profile demonstration garden attached to a horticultural college. Brilliant for new ideas, especially for small gardens: there are a walled garden, herb garden, knot garden, disabled garden, shade garden, pergola, alpine beds and some historical recreations. Perhaps the best garden attached to a local authority college.

Chelsea Physic Garden

66 Royal Hospital Road, London SW3 4HS
☎ 071 352 5646

OWNER   Chelsea Physic Garden Company
LOCATION   Please look at your London A to Z
OPEN   2 pm – 5 pm; Wednesday; 2 pm – 6 pm, Sunday; 3 April to 30 October. 12 noon – 5 pm, 23 – 27 May & 6 – 10 June
ADMISSION   Adults £2.50; Students £1.30
FACILITIES   Loos; facilities for the disabled; plants for sale; teas & lunches 23 – 27 May
FEATURES   Herbaceous borders; glasshouses to visit; rock garden; 18th century rock garden; tallest *Koelreuteria paniculata* in England
ENGLISH HERITAGE GRADE   I
NCCPG NATIONAL COLLECTIONS *Cistus*
FRIENDS   Friends have unrestricted rights of entry: worth considering if you live nearby

This oasis of peace between Royal Hospital Road and the Chelsea Embankment started life in 1673 as a pharmacological collection, and has kept its original design, but it also has the oldest rock garden in Europe, the largest olive tree in Britain, a vast number of rare and interesting plants, and probably the last known specimen of the 1920s white Hybrid Tea rose 'Marcia Stanhope'.

Chiswick House

Burlington Lane, Chiswick, London W4 2RP
☎ 081 742 1225

OWNER   English Heritage
LOCATION   South west London on A4 and A316
OPEN   10 am – dusk; daily
ADMISSION   Garden fre.
FACILITIES   Parking; loos; refreshments
FEATURES   Follies and garden buildings; glasshouses to visit; water features; parterres; summer bedding
ENGLISH HERITAGE GRADE   I

Laid out by Bridgeman and Kent for Lord Burlington, Chiswick is more renaissance than romantic – the Italian garden, Ionic garden, Conservatory (originally a Camellia House), canals, cedars and a strange sense of gloom. It is difficult now to understand how this landscape inspired Pope to write in his *Epistle to Burlington*, 'Consult the Genius of the Place in all'.

Fenton House

Hampstead Grove, London NW3 6RT
☎ 071 435 3471

OWNER   The National Trust
LOCATION   Entrances in Hampstead Grove near Hampstead Underground station
OPEN   2 pm – 6 pm; Saturday & Sunday; March; 11 am – 6 pm, Saturday, Sunday & Bank Holiday Monday;

1 pm – 7 pm, Monday – Wednesday; April to 31 October
ADMISSION Adults £3.00 (1993)
FEATURES Herbaceous borders; herbs; old roses and climbers; restored Edwardian garden

A country garden in Hampstead. Neat, terraced gardens near the house, rather more formal at the bottom. Not outstandingly flowerful, but the hedges are good and plants are firmly trained: definitely worth knowing.

Hampton Court Palace
East Molesey, London KT8 9AU
☎ 081 781 9500

OWNER Historic Royal Palaces Agency
LOCATION North side of Kingston bridge over the Thames on A308 junction with A309
OPEN Dawn – dusk; daily
ADMISSION Free
FACILITIES Parking; dogs permitted; loos; access for the disabled; shop
FEATURES Herbaceous borders; fruit and vegetables of special interest; herbs; modern roses; old roses and climbers; good topiary; water features; interesting for children; particularly good in July-August; famous maze; laburnum walk; knot gardens
ENGLISH HERITAGE GRADE I

66 acres of famous garden and 600 acres of deer park. Here are some highlights: Charles II's Long Canal with radiating lime avenues to imitate the *pattes d'oie* at Versailles, the broad walk, now a herbaceous border 100 yards long, bowling alleys, tilt yards, the great maze and the Great Vine (actually 'Black Hamburgh'), the 16th century Privy Garden, William and Mary's Great Fountain Garden, the priory garden, knot garden and all those bulbs in spring.

Isabella Plantation
Richmond Park, Richmond, London
☎ 081 948 3209

OWNER The Royal Parks
LOCATION Richmond Park
OPEN Dawn – dusk; daily
ADMISSION Free
FACILITIES Parking; dogs permitted; access for the disabled; refreshments
FEATURES Good collection of trees; fine conifers; water features; woodland garden; azaleas; rhododendrons; primulas
NCCPG NATIONAL COLLECTIONS *Rhododendron*

42 acres of rhododendrons and azaleas under a deciduous canopy in Richmond Park. Best in May when the candelabra primulas flower and the hostas are in new leaf. Little known.

Kenwood Park
Hampstead Lane, London NW3

OWNER English Heritage
LOCATION North side of Hampstead Heath
OPEN Dawn to dusk; daily; all year
ADMISSION Free to park
FACILITIES Dogs permitted; loos; access for the disabled; refreshments during the daytime
FEATURES Good collection of trees; herbaceous borders; garden sculpture; water features; woodland garden
ENGLISH HERITAGE GRADE II*

Superb parkland around glittering lakes: a haven of calm from London's busyness.

The Museum of Garden History
Lambeth Palace Road, London SE1 7JU
☎ 071 261 1891   📠 071 401 8869

OWNER The Tradescant Trust
LOCATION Between Lambeth Bridge and Lambeth Palace
OPEN 11 am – 3 pm; Monday – Friday; 6 March to 11 December. Also 10.30 am – 5 pm Sundays
ADMISSION Donations please
FACILITIES Dogs permitted; loos; access for the disabled; plants for sale; books, cards and gifts; light refreshments
FEATURES Herbs
FRIENDS Friends of the Tradescant Trust: ask for details

The garden is small, and secondary to the Museum's collections, but designed as a 17th century knot garden and planted with plants associated with the Tradescants. A garden for contemplation.

Myddelton House
Bulls Cross, Enfield, London
☎ 0992 717711

OWNER Lea Valley Regional Park Authority
LOCATION Off A10 to Bulls Cross
OPEN 10 am – 3.30 pm; weekdays; 1 February to 31 October
ADMISSION Adults £1; Senior Citizens 50p
FACILITIES Parking; loos; access for the disabled; plants for sale
FEATURES Good collection of trees; herbaceous borders; fine conifers; plantsman's garden; old roses and climbers; water features; woodland garden
ENGLISH HERITAGE GRADE II
NCCPG NATIONAL COLLECTIONS *Iris*

Holy ground for plantsmen with a sense of history, E A Bowles' garden has been abandoned for 30 years. Contrary to reports, it has been neither restored nor half-restored, though some effort has been made to stop the decay and there are still good irises and spring bulbs. Myddelton may yet face extinction, though perhaps later rather than sooner.

Osterley Park

Isleworth, London TW7 4RB

☎ 081 560 3918

OWNER The National Trust
LOCATION 5 miles west of central London on A4
OPEN 9 am – 7.30 pm; daily
FACILITIES Parking; loos; facilities for the disabled; tea room
FEATURES Fruit and vegetables of special interest; herbs; water features; woodland garden; fine rare oaks; autumn colour
ENGLISH HERITAGE GRADE II*

Classical 18th century landscape. Fine temple and semi-circular conservatory by Robert Adam. Good trees – cedars and oaks.

Syon Park

Brentford, London TW8 8JF

☎ 081 560 0881

OWNER The Duke of Northumberland
LOCATION Between Brentford and Isleworth, north bank of Thames
OPEN 10 am – 6 pm, daily, March to October; 10 am – sunset, daily, November to February.
ADMISSION Adults £1.75; Children £1.25
FACILITIES Parking; loos; plants for sale; garden centre; shops, restaurants, all the fun of the fair
FEATURES Good collection of trees; herbaceous borders; landscape designed by Capability Brown; fine conifers; follies and garden buildings; glasshouses to visit; modern roses; old roses and climbers; woodland garden; interesting for children; cacti; ferns; exhibition of gardening for the disabled
ENGLISH HERITAGE GRADE I

Syon is a mixture of 18th century landscape, 19th century horticultural seriousness, 20th century plantsmanship and 21st century theme park. Splendid conservatories with good collections, worth visiting in winter.

Walpole House

Chiswick Mall, London W4 2PS

OWNER Mr & Mrs Jeremy Benson
LOCATION Parallel to A4 between Hammersmith flyover & Hogarth roundabout
OPEN 2 pm – 6 pm; 2 days as advertised in Yellow Book
ADMISSION Adults £1.00; Senior Citizens & Children 20p
FACILITIES Parking; plants for sale

FEATURES Herbaceous borders; plantsman's garden; woodland garden
ENGLISH HERITAGE GRADE II

A large town garden, designed and planted in the Hidcote style and made to seem much larger than its ⅔ rd acre. Big trees, a large lily-pond and densely planted herbaceous borders all contribute to the sense of *rus in urbe*.

MERSEYSIDE

Croxteth Hall & Country Park

Croxteth Hall Lane, Liverpool, Merseyside L12 0HB

☎ 051 228 5311

OWNER City of Liverpool
LOCATION Muirhead Avenue East
OPEN 11 am – 5 pm; daily; Easter to 30 September
ADMISSION 60p; walled garden 30p
FACILITIES Parking; loos; facilities for the disabled; plants for sale; cafeteria
FEATURES Herbaceous borders; fruit and vegetables of special interest; glasshouses to visit; herbs; interesting for children
FRIENDS Friends of Croxteth Hall & Country Park: details from Mr E E Jackson

Very much a public amenity, Croxteth Hall majors on fruit, vegetables and herbs – showing in its walled garden what visitors can try at home. Good greenhouses. Heart-warming.

NORFOLK

Blickling Hall

Blickling, Norwich, Norfolk NR11 6NF

☎ 0263 733084   📠 0263 734924

OWNER The National Trust
LOCATION 1 mile west of Aysham on B1354
OPEN 12 noon – 5 pm; daily except Monday & Thursday; March to October
ADMISSION Adults £2.50; Children £1.25 (1993)
FACILITIES Parking; loos; facilities for the disabled; plants for sale; National Trust shop; light snacks, lunches & teas
FEATURES Herbaceous borders; landscape designed by Humphry Repton; old roses and climbers; water features; woodland garden; particularly good in July-August; herbaceous borders at peak July/August;

The garden with everything. Jacobean mansion, handsomely symmetrical; early landscape (Doric Temple, c.1735); smashing conservatory by Samuel Wyatt; then mid 19th century parterre by Nesfield (topiary pillars);

and 1930s herbaceous colour plantings by Norah Lindsay (her masterpiece). Fabulous bluebells in the woods.

Bressingham Gardens

Bressingham, Diss, Norfolk IP22 2AB
☎ 037988 386

OWNER Alan Bloom
LOCATION On main road, 3 miles west of Diss
OPEN 10 am – 5.30 pm; daily; 1 April to 31 October
ADMISSION Adults £3.50
FACILITIES Parking; loos; access for the disabled; plants for sale; refreshments in adjacent plant centre
FEATURES Herbaceous borders; fine conifers; plantsman's garden; water features; particularly good in July-August

There is no better place to learn about herbaceous plants – what they look like, how they grow and how to place them. The garden's design exemplifies Bloom's commitment to island beds, which he popularised 25 years ago. The curves seem to suit the site, a small valley with some lightly wooded parts and a stream at the bottom. Totally absorbing.

Elsing Hall

Elsing Dereham, Norfolk NR20 3DX

OWNER Mr & Mrs D H Cargill
LOCATION Ask in village
OPEN 2 pm – 6 pm; Sundays; 5 June to 10 July
ADMISSION £1.50
FACILITIES Parking; dogs permitted; loos; access for the disabled
FEATURES Good collection of trees; fruit and vegetables of special interest; old roses and climbers; water features; kitchen garden

A garden of great charm, whose owners have planted many good trees, roses and a formal garden to enhance the mediaeval house and its romantic moat. An avenue of ginkgos, a collection of willows and a small arboretum of trees chosen for their coloured bark are some of the most recent additions.

Fairhaven Gardens Trust

South Walsham, Norwich, Norfolk NR13 6EA
☎ 0603 270449

OWNER Fairhaven Garden Trust
LOCATION 9 miles north east of Norwich on the B1140
OPEN 11 am – 6 pm, Saturdays 2 pm – 6 pm; 1 – 10, 17, 24 April; 1, 2, 21, 22 May; 23 – 30 October; plus Wednesday – Sunday and Bank Holiday Mondays 4 May to 25 September. Parties by appointment.
ADMISSION Adult £2.00; Senior Citizens £1.50; Children £1.00

FACILITIES Parking; dogs permitted; loos; access for the disabled; plants for sale; small shop; tea room
FEATURES Water features; woodland garden; rhododendrons; lilies; candelabra primulas

Basically an enormous plantsman's garden (200 acres) round one of the Norfolk broads. Rhododendrons and azaleas under a canopy of oak and alder, plus extensive plantings of primulas, lysichitons, astilbes, and other bog plants in and around the water. Bluebells.

Felbrigg Hall

Roughton, Norwich, Norfolk NR11 8PR
☎ 0263 837444   FAX 0263 838297

OWNER The National Trust
LOCATION Entrance off B1436, signed from A148 & A140
OPEN 11 am – 5.30 pm; Saturday – Monday, Wednesday – Thursday; 26 March to 30 October
ADMISSION £1.80
FACILITIES Parking; loos; facilities for the disabled; National Trust shop; restaurant & tea room
FEATURES Herbaceous borders; fruit and vegetables of special interest; colchicums
ENGLISH HERITAGE GRADE II*
NCCPG NATIONAL COLLECTIONS *Colchicum*

The best bit of Felbrigg is the walled kitchen garden, oriented on a large brick dovecote flanked by Victorian vineries. Fruit trees are trained against the walls (figs, pears, plums) and the garden laid to neatly grown vegetables with herbaceous borders along the box-edged gravel paths.

Holkham Hall

Holkham, Wells-next-the-Sea, Norfolk

OWNER Viscount Coke
LOCATION Off A149, 2 miles west of Wells
OPEN 11.30 am – 5. 30 pm; 3 & 4 April, 2, 29 & 30 May; then 1.30 pm – 5 pm, Sunday – Thursday, 31 May to 29 September
ADMISSION Adults £3
FACILITIES Parking; loos; access for the disabled; plants for sale; gift shop; refreshments
FEATURES Landscape designed by Humphry Repton; garden sculpture; water features
ENGLISH HERITAGE GRADE I

A big landscape garden, worked on by Kent, Brown and Repton. Mighty impressive. In the nearby garden centre (see Nurseries section) is a walled garden with several demonstration gardens – herbs, roses, perennials etc.

Oxburgh Hall

Oxborough, King's Lynn, Norfolk PE33 9PS
☎ 0366 328258

OWNER The National Trust

LOCATION 7 miles south west of Swaffham on Stoke Ferry road
OPEN 12 noon – 5 pm; Saturday – Wednesday; 26 March to 30 October
ADMISSION Adults £2.00; Children £1.00
FACILITIES Parking; loos; facilities for the disabled; gift shop; light lunches & tea
FEATURES Herbaceous borders; fruit and vegetables of special interest; modern roses; French-style parterre; trained fruit trees
ENGLISH HERITAGE GRADE II

The baroque 19th century parterre has been replanted by the National Trust with such herbs as rue and santolina making permanent companions for annuals and bedding plants. Good fruit trees in the walled garden: medlars, quinces, and mulberries. Not a great garden, but a good one.

Rainthorpe Hall Gardens
Tasburgh, Norwich, Norfolk NR15 1RQ
☎ 0508 490191   📠 0508 470618

OWNER George Hastings
LOCATION 8 miles south of Norwich
OPEN 10 am – 5 pm; Wednesdays, Saturdays, Sundays and Bank Holiday Mondays; Easter to 31 October
ADMISSION Adults £1.50; Senior Citizens & Children 75p
FACILITIES Parking; dogs permitted; loos; access for the disabled; plants for sale; tea, coffee, soft drinks
FEATURES Old roses and climbers; water features; knot garden; hazel nuttery
ENGLISH HERITAGE GRADE II

The garden at Rainthorpe is appropriately simple: the long curling knot garden is its best feature. The old kitchen garden is now Willimotts Plant Centre with seven small demonstration gardens within its walls.

Raveningham Hall
Raveningham, Norwich, Norfolk NR14 6NS
☎ 0508 548480   📠 0508 548958

OWNER Sir Nicholas Bacon Bt
LOCATION Signed off A146 at Hales
OPEN 1 pm – 4 pm, Wednesdays and 2 pm – 5 pm, Sundays and Bank Holiday Mondays; mid March to mid September
ADMISSION Adults £2.00; Children free
FACILITIES Parking; dogs permitted; loos; access for the disabled; plants for sale; refreshments on Sundays & Bank Holiday Mondays only
FEATURES Good collection of trees; herbaceous borders; modern roses
ENGLISH HERITAGE GRADE II

Good taste and good plantsmanship characterise Raveningham, both qualities of the owner's mother who collects and plants with enthusiasm. Rather classy.

Sandringham House
Sandringham, King's Lynn, Norfolk PE35 6EN
☎ 0553 772675   📠 0485 541571

OWNER H M The Queen
LOCATION Signed from A148
OPEN 10.30 am (11.30 on Sundays) – 5 pm; daily; 1 April to 2 October (except 23 July to 3 August)
ADMISSION Adults £2.50; Senior Citizens £2.00; Children £1.50
FACILITIES Parking; loos; facilities for the disabled; plants for sale; gift shop; restaurant & tea rooms
FEATURES Herbaceous borders; water features; rhododendrons; azaleas; maples; hydrangeas
ENGLISH HERITAGE GRADE II*

The best of the royal gardens. The woodland and lakes are rich with ornamental plantings, and the splendid herbaceous borders were designed by Geoffrey Jellicoe, but it is the scale of it all that most impresses, and the grandeur too.

Sheringham Park
Gardener's Cottage, Sheringham Park, Sheringham, Norfolk NR26 8TB
☎ 0263 823778

OWNER The National Trust
LOCATION Junction of A148 & B1157
OPEN Dawn – dusk; all year
ADMISSION £2.30
FACILITIES Parking; dogs permitted; loos; facilities for the disabled
FEATURES Landscape designed by Humphry Repton; fine conifers; water features; woodland garden; rhododendrons
ENGLISH HERITAGE GRADE II*

One of the best Repton landscapes outstanding, but fleshed out with a great early 20th century collection of rhododendrons and glorified by a classical temple, designed by Repton but not eventually built until 1975.

NORTHAMPTONSHIRE

Althorp House
Althorp, Northampton, Northamptonshire NN7 4HQ
☎ 0604 770006   📠 0604 770983

OWNER Earl Spencer
LOCATION Signposted from M1
OPEN 1 pm – 5 pm; every Sunday in April & September, plus 1 to 4 April, 24 May, 1 to 31 August

FACILITIES Parking; loos; facilities for the disabled; gift shop; tea room

FEATURES Fine conifers; formal gardens; biggest *Abies bracteata* in the British Isles

ENGLISH HERITAGE GRADE I

Interesting more for its royal associations than as a great garden, which it is not. But the 19th century formal gardens are impressive and the traditional parkland deeply pastoral. New gardens are planned.

Castle Ashby Gardens

Castle Ashby, Northampton, Northamptonshire NN7 1LQ

☎ 0604 696696   📠 0604 696516

OWNER Marquess of Northampton

LOCATION Off A428 between Northampton and Bedford

OPEN 10 am – dusk; all year

ADMISSION Adults £2.00, Senior Citizens and Children £1.00

FACILITIES Parking; dogs permitted; facilities for the disabled; gift shops; refreshments

FEATURES Good collection of trees; glasshouses to visit; good topiary; water features

ENGLISH HERITAGE GRADE I

Much thought and money has been spent on restoring the gardens recently. The Italian formal gardens were among the first to be renewed, and the arboretum has been restocked. There are a stylish orangery and greenhouses by Sir Matthew Digby Wyatt but perhaps the best thing about Castle Ashby is the park – 200 acres of it, designed by Capability Brown.

Coton Manor

Guilsborough, Northampton, Northamptonshire NN6 8RQ

☎ 0604 740219   📠 0604 740838

OWNER Ian Pasley-Tyler

LOCATION Signposted from A50 and A428

OPEN 2 pm – 6 pm; Wednesdays, Sundays & Bank Holiday Mondays; Easter to 30 September; Thursdays in July and August

ADMISSION Adults £2.70; Senior Citizens £2.10; Children £1.00

FACILITIES Parking; dogs permitted; loos; access for the disabled; plants for sale; home produce & gifts; tea room

FEATURES Herbaceous borders; gravel or scree garden; modern roses; water features; woodland garden; bluebells; waterfowl; fifty different hebes; lots of pots

A nicely designed and thoughtfully planted garden – rarities and common plants chosen for effect – made by three generations over 70 years. The standard of maintenance is excellent, but there are rather too many birds for many visitors' tastes.

Cottesbrooke Hall

Northampton, Northamptonshire NN6 8PF

☎ 060 124808   📠 060 124742

OWNER Captain & Mrs John Macdonald-Buchanan

LOCATION 10 miles north of Northampton

OPEN 2 pm – 5.30 pm; Thursdays & Bank Holiday Mondays; Easter to 30 September

ADMISSION Adults £1.50; Children 75p

FACILITIES Parking; loos; plants for sale; tea/coffee & cold drinks

FEATURES Herbaceous borders; old roses and climbers; garden sculpture; water features

ENGLISH HERITAGE GRADE II

The garden with everything: a handsome house, an 18th century park, lakes, waterfalls, bluebell woods, rhododendrons, acres of daffodils, 27 varieties of snowdrop, half-a-dozen formal gardens, Scheemaker's statues from Stowe, an armillary garden, pergolas, *allées*, 300-year old cedars, plants a plenty, and the signatures of Geoffrey Jellicoe and Sylvia Crowe among the designers who have helped to develop it. If only more people knew of it.

Holdenby House Gardens

Holdenby, Northampton, Northamptonshire NN6 8DJ

☎ 0604 770074   📠 0604 770962

OWNER Mr & Mrs James Lowther

LOCATION Off A50 or A428

OPEN 1 pm – 6 pm weekdays; 2 pm – 6 pm, Sundays; 1 pm – 6 pm, Bank Holiday Sunday & Monday; 1 April to 30 September (except May Day)

ADMISSION Adults £2.50; Senior Citizens £2.00; Children £1.50

FACILITIES Parking; dogs permitted; loos; facilities for the disabled; plants for sale; souvenirs and crafts for sale; tea room in original Victorian kitchen

FEATURES Herbaceous borders; follies and garden buildings; herbs; old roses and climbers; interesting for children; Elizabethan garden; fragrant and silver borders; yew knot; current holder of Sandford Award

ENGLISH HERITAGE GRADE II*

Pretty modern gardens designed and planted by the present owners with help from Rosemary Verey. The Elizabethan garden uses only plants available in 1580.

The Old Rectory, Sudborough

Sudborough, Northamptonshire NN14 3BX

☎ 0832 73324   📠 0832 733832

OWNER Mr & Mrs A P Huntington

LOCATION By church off the A6116

OPEN By appointment
ADMISSION Adults £2.50; Senior Citizens £1.25; Children free
FACILITIES Parking; loos; plants for sale
FEATURES Herbaceous borders; fruit and vegetables of special interest; herbs; modern roses; old roses and climbers; water features; handsome new *potager*;

Neat new garden, three acres in size, around a handsome Georgian rectory. Good snowdrops and hellebores; unusual vegetables. The garden is thickly and thoughtfully planted so that every season is rich in interest.

Rockingham Castle

Market Harborough, Northamptonshire LE16 8TH
☎ 0586 770240   FAX 0586 771692

OWNER Cdr L R R Saunders Watson
LOCATION 2 miles north of Corby on A6003
OPEN 1.30 pm – 5.30 pm; Sunday, Thursday, Bank Holiday Monday & following Tuesday; Easter Sunday to 30 September
ADMISSION Adults £2.20
FACILITIES Parking; dogs permitted; loos; access for the disabled; tea room
FEATURES Good collection of trees; herbaceous borders; old roses and climbers; current holder of Sandford Award
ENGLISH HERITAGE GRADE II*

12 acres around the historic castle. The formal circular rose garden on the site of the old keep is surrounded by a billowing 400 year old yew hedge. The wild garden in a ravine was replanted 20 years ago as a mini-arboretum: very effective.

Sulgrave Manor

Sulgrave, Banbury, Northamptonshire OX17 2SD
☎ 0295 760205

OWNER Sulgrave Manor Board
LOCATION 7 miles from Banbury
OPEN 10.30 am – 1 pm & 2 pm – 4 pm; Thursday – Tuesday; 1 April to 31 October (closes 4 pm in October). 10.30 am – 1 pm & 2 pm – 4 pm; Saturdays and Sundays; March, November, December. And by appointment.
ADMISSION Adults £3.00; Children £1.50
FACILITIES Parking; dogs permitted; loos; plants for sale; tea room
FEATURES Herbaceous borders; fruit and vegetables of special interest; herbs; modern roses; good topiary
ENGLISH HERITAGE GRADE II

Famous (and highly visitable) for two reasons: first, its association with George Washington; second, its formal design, unchanged since it was laid out by Sir Reginald Blomfield in 1921.

NORTHUMBERLAND

Belsay Hall

Belsay, Newcastle-upon-Tyne, Northumberland
NE20 0DX
☎ 0661 881636   FAX 0661 881043

OWNER English Heritage
LOCATION 15 miles north west of Newcastle-upon-Tyne
OPEN 10 am – 6 pm; daily; Good Friday to 30 September. 10 am – 4 pm; Tuesday – Sunday; 1 October to 31 March
ADMISSION Adults £2.20; Concessions £1.60; Children £1.10 (1993)
FACILITIES Parking; dogs permitted; loos; facilities for the disabled; plants for sale; gift shop; refreshments in summer and at week-ends
FEATURES Fine conifers; rock garden; woodland garden; particularly interesting in winter; rhododendrons; tallest surviving *Ulmus procera* in the British Isles
ENGLISH HERITAGE GRADE I
NCCPG NATIONAL COLLECTIONS *Iris spuria*

Wildly romantic Victorian gardens, including several acres of disused quarry with *Trachycarpus* palms, splendid woodfuls of hardy hybrid rhododendrons, intensive modern herbaceous plantings, brooding conifers and the ruins of Belsay Castle.

Bide-a-Wee Cottage

Stanton, Netherwitton, Morpeth, Northumberland
NE65 8PR
☎ 067072 262

OWNER N M Robson
LOCATION 7 miles north west of Morpeth
OPEN 1.30 pm – 4.30 pm; Saturdays; 2 April – 27 August
ADMISSION £1.50
FACILITIES Parking; plants for sale
FEATURES Gravel or scree garden; plantsman's garden; rock garden; water features

Mark Robson's youth has turned this ten year old garden, entirely hidden in a small disused quarry, into something of a cult. But deservedly so, for both design and plantings are brilliant.

Chillingham Castle

Chillingham, Northumberland NE66 5NJ
☎ 0668 5359   FAX 0668 5463

OWNER Sir Humphry Wakefield Bt
LOCATION Off A1 between Alnwick and Berwick
OPEN 1.30 pm – 5.30 pm; daily except Tuesday;
1 May to 1 October; Open Easter and Bank Holidays

ADMISSION Adults £3.30; Senior Citizens and Children £2.75
FACILITIES Parking; loos; museum, antique and curio shop; tea room
FEATURES Herbaceous borders; rock garden; modern roses; old roses and climbers; good topiary; water features; woodland garden; Italian ornamental garden; daffodils; bluebells
ENGLISH HERITAGE GRADE II

Chillingham has made great efforts to smarten up for visitors. The results are very encouraging: a 19th century Italian garden, a modern herbaceous border in the old walled garden and splendid hardy hybrid rhododendrons in the woodland walks which surround the lake. Chillingham itself is a formidable mediaeval castle with amazing views.

Cragside
Rothbury, Morpeth, Northumberland NE65 7PX

OWNER The National Trust
LOCATION 15 miles north west of Morpeth off A697 & B6341
OPEN 10.30 am – 5.30 pm; Tuesday – Sunday; 1 April to 30 October;
ADMISSION Adults £3.40; Children £1.70;
FACILITIES Parking; loos; National Trust shop; refreshments
FEATURES Fine conifers; rock garden; old roses and climbers; water features; interesting for children; massive rock garden, rather dimly planted with heathers; Armstrong's hydroelectric system fascinates adults and children alike; tallest *Abies nordmanniana* in the British Isles
ENGLISH HERITAGE GRADE II*

Two gardens. The newly-acquired Italianate formal garden has splendid carpet bedding, ferneries and a fruit house with rotating pots. Even more impressive are the rhododendron woods – hundreds and hundreds of acres of 19th century hybrids, plus trusty *RR. ponticum* and *luteum*, breathtaking in late May.

Herterton House Gardens & Nursery
Hartington, Cambo, Northumberland NE61 6BN
☎ 067 074 278

OWNER Mr & Mrs Frank Lawley
LOCATION 2 miles north of Cambo
OPEN 1.30 pm – 5.30 pm; daily except Tuesdays and Thursdays; 1 April to 30 September
ADMISSION £1.10 (1993)
FACILITIES Parking; loos; plants for sale; attached to nursery
FEATURES Herbaceous borders; herbs; plantsman's garden; good topiary; knot garden

A plantsman's garden attached to a small nursery. The knot garden is famous, and much photographed, full of herbs and pharmacological plants. More impressive still are the herbaceous plantings, all weaving through each other in beautiful colour schemes.

Hexham Herbs
Chesters Walled Garden, Humshaugh, Hexham, Northumberland NE46 4BQ
☎ 0434 681483

OWNER Mrs S White
LOCATION 6 miles north of Hexham, off B6318 near Chollerford
OPEN 10 am – 5 pm; daily; March to October or by appointment
ADMISSION Adults £1.00; Children free
FACILITIES Parking; loos; access for the disabled; plants for sale; nursery attached
FEATURES Herbs; old roses and climbers; woodland garden; 'Roman' garden
NCCPG NATIONAL COLLECTIONS *Thymus*, *Origanum*

An energetic and successful small modern nursery garden, strategically placed near the fort at Chesters. The herb collection is remarkable – over 900 varieties – and the design within a brick walled garden is charming.

Howick Hall
Alnwick, Northumberland NE66 3LB
☎ 0665 577285   FAX 0665 577285

OWNER Howick Trustees Ltd
LOCATION Off B1399 between Longhoughton and Howick
OPEN 1 pm – 6 pm; daily; 1 April to 31 October
ADMISSION Adults £1.50; Senior Citizens & Children 75p
FACILITIES Parking; loos
FEATURES Fine conifers; plantsman's garden; old roses and climbers; water features; woodland garden; rhododendrons; spring bulbs; eucryphias
ENGLISH HERITAGE GRADE II

Rather an un-Northumbrian garden, because its closeness to the sea makes possible the cultivation of such tender plants as *Carpenteria* and *Ceanothus*. Formal terraces below the house, well planted, but the great joy of the garden at Howick is a small woodland which has acid soil. This was planted in the 1930s with a fine collection of rhododendrons and camellias. The result looks more west coast than east.

Wallington Hall
Cambo, Morpeth, Northumberland NE61 4AR
☎ 067 074283

OWNER The National Trust

LOCATION 6 miles north west of Belsay (A696)
OPEN 10.30 am – 7 pm, 1 April to 30 September;
10.30 am – 6 pm, October; 10.30 am – 4 pm or dusk, if
earlier; 1 November to 31 March
ADMISSION Adults £2.20; Children £1.10
FACILITIES Parking; dogs permitted; loos; access for
the disabled; restaurant
FEATURES Herbaceous borders; glasshouses to visit;
water features; woodland garden; plantings by Graham
Thomas
ENGLISH HERITAGE GRADE II*
NCCPG NATIONAL COLLECTIONS *Sambucus*

There are three reasons to visit Wallington. First,
because Capability Brown was born in nearby Kirk-
harle. Second, to gawp at the ancient tree-like specimens of *Fuchsia* 'Rose of Castille' in the conservatories.
Third, to admire the modern mixed borders (*very* Graham Thomas). Worth a long journey for any of them.

NOTTINGHAMSHIRE

Clumber Park

The Estate Office, Worksop, Nottinghamshire
S80 3AZ
☎ 0909 476592 📠 0909 500721

OWNER The National Trust
LOCATION Off A614 Nottingham Road, 4 miles
south of Worksop
OPEN 10.30 am – 5 pm (6 pm in summer); every day;
all year
ADMISSION Walled garden, vineries and tool collection: Adults 60p, Children 30p; car parking £2.50
FACILITIES Parking; dogs permitted; loos; facilities for
the disabled; National Trust shop; restaurant
FEATURES Herbaceous borders; landscape designed
by Capability Brown and Humphry Repton; follies and
garden buildings; fruit and vegetables of special interest;
glasshouses to visit; herbs; water features; woodland
garden; autumn colour; vineries; old rhubarb cultivars;
superb trees; tallest *Ilex aquifolium* 'Laurifolia' in the
British Isles
ENGLISH HERITAGE GRADE I

3,800 acres of parkland with a Gothic chapel, classical
bridge, temples, an avenue of cedars, a double avenue
of limes and masses of rhododendrons. 19th century
formal terraces by the house, and a garden tools exhibition in the walled garden. One of the best of the big
country house gardens, and all maintained by a staff of
two.

Felley Priory

Underwood, Jacksdale, Nottinghamshire NG16 5FL
☎ 0773 810230 / 812056

OWNER The Hon. Mrs Chaworth-Musters
LOCATION ½ mile west of M1 on A608
OPEN 9 am – 4.30 pm; 2nd & 4th Wednesday every
month; February to October
ADMISSION £1.00
FACILITIES Parking; dogs permitted; loos; facilities for
the disabled; plants for sale; tea room
FEATURES Herbaceous borders; modern roses; knot
gardens, two pergolas and new rose garden, orchard of
daffodils

Newish plantsman's garden, attached to small but
promising nursery. Handsome yew hedges, only 15
years old, with wavy pattern and bobbles on top.
Definitely a garden to watch.

Hodsock Priory

Blyth, Worksop, Nottinghamshire S81 0TY
☎ 0909 591204 📠 0909 591578

OWNER Sir Andrew & Lady Buchanan
LOCATION Signed off the B6045 Blyth – Worksop
OPEN 2 pm – 5 pm; Sundays; Easter to 10 July, but
not 1 May or 29 May; by appointment in February for
snowdrops
ADMISSION Adults £1.80; Children free
FACILITIES Parking; loos; facilities for the disabled;
plants for sale; tea room
FEATURES Herbaceous borders; old roses and
climbers; water features

Richly planted modern garden on an ancient moated
site. Excellent rose gardens and mixed borders, plus
some fine old trees.

Morton Hall

Ranby, Retford, Nottinghamshire DH22 7HW
☎ 0777 701142

OWNER Lady Mason
LOCATION Between A620 & A1, drive on left
OPEN 2 pm – 6 pm; 24 April, 8, 22, 29 May, 9 October
ADMISSION £2.00 a car or £1.25 per head, whichever
is the least
FACILITIES Parking; dogs permitted; loos; access for
the disabled; teas
FEATURES Fine conifers; rock garden; woodland gar-
den

A Victorian amateur's arboretum is the basis of the
garden at Morton and the splendid nursery which
adjoins it. Best in spring, when daffodils and rhododendrons make a blaze of colour, before the grass grows up
to turn it into a green garden later.

Newstead Abbey

Newstead Abbey Park, Nottinghamshire NG15 8GE
☎ 0623 793557

OWNER Nottingham City Council

LOCATION   4 miles south of Mansfield on A60
OPEN   10 am – 7 pm, summer; 10 am – 5 pm, winter
ADMISSION   Adults £1.50; Children £1
FACILITIES   Parking; dogs permitted; loos; facilities for the disabled; plants for sale; restaurant & refreshments
FEATURES   Herbs; oriental features; rock garden; modern roses; old roses and climbers; water features
ENGLISH HERITAGE GRADE   I

Chiefly of interest for being the debt-ridden estate Lord Byron inherited and had to sell, but Newstead has a good modern garden. Best are the Japanese garden and substantial rockery. The Council has restored and replanted it all extensively as a public amenity: lots of cheerful roses and summer bedding.

OXFORDSHIRE

Blenheim Palace

Woodstock, Oxford, Oxfordshire OX20 1PX
☎ 0993 811091   ⓕ 0993 813527

OWNER   The Duke of Marlborough
LOCATION   8 miles north of Oxford
OPEN   10.30 am – 4.45 pm; daily; 15 March to 31 October
ADMISSION   Adults £3; Children £1.50
FACILITIES   Parking; loos; plants for sale; good shops; light meals & refreshments
FEATURES   landscape designed by Capability Brown; follies and garden buildings; herbs; garden sculpture; water features; interesting for children; formal gardens; new maze; current holder of Sandford Award
ENGLISH HERITAGE GRADE   I

The grandest of grand gardens. Vanburgh, Bridgeman, Hawksmoor and Wise worked here. The huge (2,000 acre) park was laid out by Capability Brown and Achille Duchêne restored the formal baroque gardens in the 1920s; most impressive too are the 8 acres of walled kichen garden.

Brook Cottage

Well Lane, Alkerton, Banbury, Oxfordshire OX15 6NL
☎ 0295 87303

OWNER   Mr & Mrs D M Hodges
LOCATION   6 miles west of Banbury
OPEN   9 am – 6 pm; Monday – Friday ; 1 April to 31 October
ADMISSION   Adults £2.00; Senior Citizens £1.50; Children free
FACILITIES   Parking; dogs permitted; loos; plants for sale; DIY tea and coffee; groups by arrangement

FEATURES   Herbaceous borders; plantsman's garden; rock garden; modern roses; old roses and climbers; water features; 40 different clematis

First-rate modern garden made by present owners over the last 30 years. Good plants and good plantings but, above all, a good sense of colour and form. Four acres: allow lots of time, and follow the suggested route.

Broughton Castle

Banbury, Oxfordshire OX15 5EB
☎ 0295 262624

OWNER   Lord Saye
LOCATION   2½ miles west of Banbury on the B4035
OPEN   2 pm – 5 pm; Wednesdays and Sundays; 18 May to 14 September. Plus Thursdays in July and August, and all Bank Holiday Sundays and Mondays
ADMISSION   Adults £3.20; Senior Citizens & Students £2.70; Children £1.50
FACILITIES   Parking; dogs permitted; loos; facilities for the disabled; plants for sale; tea room
FEATURES   Herbaceous borders; old roses and climbers
ENGLISH HERITAGE GRADE   II*

Mainly designed and planted by Lanning Roper 25 years ago, with a blue-yellow-white border contrasting with a pink-and-silver one. Neat knot garden with roses and lavender.

Buscot Park

Faringdon, Oxfordshire SN7 8BU

OWNER   The National Trust
LOCATION   On A417 west of Faringdon
OPEN   2 pm – 6 pm; Wednesday – Friday, plus 2nd & 4th Saturday/Sunday each month; April to September
ADMISSION   Adults £3
FACILITIES   Parking; loos; plants for sale; light refreshments
FEATURES   Herbaceous borders; follies and garden buildings; fruit and vegetables of special interest; old roses and climbers; garden sculpture; good topiary; water features; woodland garden; tallest *Pinus nigra* var. *cebennensis* in the British Isles
ENGLISH HERITAGE GRADE   II*

One of the most original gardens of this century, planned by Harold Peto as a water garden (long canals & bridges), with a *patte d'oie* groundplan. Peter Coates planted lush herbaceous borders in the 1970s and Tim Rees did a good conversion job in the walled garden ten years later: vegetables as climbing plants and gooseberries grown as standards are among his quirkier features.

Clock House

Coleshill, Faringdon, Oxfordshire
☎ 0793 762476

OWNER   Mr & Mrs Michael Wickham
LOCATION   On B4019 between Highworth & Faringdon
OPEN   2 pm – 6 pm; 19 June, 11 September and by appointment
ADMISSION   £1.00
FACILITIES   Parking; loos; access for the disabled; teas & cakes
FEATURES   Herbaceous borders; herbs; old roses and climbers

A garden of charm and vigour, whose borders burgeon with good growth, unusual juxtapositions and original colour schemes. An inspiration.

Faringdon House

Faringdon, Oxfordshire SN7 8AE
☎ 0367 240240/240145

OWNER   Sofka Zinovieff
LOCATION   Entrance by the church
OPEN   2 pm – 5 pm; 3 April, 4 September, for NGS
ADMISSION   Adults £1.00; Children free
FACILITIES   Parking; dogs permitted; loos; access for the disabled; plants for sale; teas usually available
FEATURES   Herbaceous borders; 18th century Orangery

A handsome house and straightforward landscaped park – at first sight. But the garden is full of dottinesses concocted by the late Lord Berners: a bust of General Havelock sinking below the surface of a lily pond, and a gazebo paved with old pennies. Surreal, but fun.

Greenways

40 Osler Road, Headington, Oxford, Oxfordshire OX3 9BJ
☎ 0865 56767 Ext: 4201   📠 0865 56646

OWNER   Mr & Mrs N H N Coote
LOCATION   Osler Road is off London Road, within ring road
OPEN   2 pm – 6 pm; 8 May, 22 May, 17 July, 14 August
ADMISSION   £1.00 on 8 May, otherwise £1.80 (Senior Citizens £1.50)
FACILITIES   Parking; loos; plants for sale; teas
FEATURES   Herbaceous borders; plantsman's garden; sub-tropical plants

Quite new, and totally different. The Cootes have emphasised the Provençal looks of the house by planting a Mediterranean garden – evergreen hedges, terracotta pots, old oil jars, gravel, parterres – with an exuberance of tender plants including olives, yuccas, oleanders, Acanthus and albizias.

Greystone Cottage

Colmore Lane, Kingwood Common,
Henley-on-Thames, Oxfordshire RG9 5NA
☎ 0491 628559   📠 0491 628839

OWNER   Mr & Mrs William Roxburgh
LOCATION   Between B481 & Stoke Row road
OPEN   2 pm – 6 pm; 6 March, 8 May, 19 June & by appointment
ADMISSION   Adults £1.00; Children free
FACILITIES   Parking; access for the disabled; small nursery; home-made teas
FEATURES   Fine conifers; rock garden; old roses and climbers; woodland garden; snowdrops; hellebores; narcissus; fritillaries

Small but near-perfect plantsman's garden, full of unusual plants in innumerable mini-habitats. An inspiration at its March opening but highly rewarding at all seasons.

The Mill House

Sutton Courtenay, Abingdon, Oxfordshire OX14 4NH
☎ 0235 848219

OWNER   Mrs Jane Stevens
LOCATION   Opposite The Fish in Appleford Road
OPEN   2 pm – 6 pm; 3 April, 26 June, 2 October
ADMISSION   Adults £2.00; Children £1.00
FACILITIES   Parking; access for the disabled; plants for sale; home-made teas
FEATURES   Old roses and climbers; water features; old yews; cherries; wisteria; three islands in the River Thames

A garden of romantic exuberance, long famed for its drapes of climbing roses. Its spirit has been intensified by Mrs Stevens, who combines the highest standards of maintenance with some inspired planting.

Mount Skippet

Ramsden, Witney, Oxfordshire GX7 3AP
☎ 0993 868253

OWNER   Dr M A T Rogers
LOCATION   4 miles north of Witney. At crossroads, turn east to Finstock, after 400 yds, left along no through road
OPEN   By appointment
ADMISSION   £1 for NGS
FACILITIES   Parking; loos; access for the disabled; plants for sale
FEATURES   Herbaceous borders; glasshouses to visit; gravel or scree garden; plantsman's garden; rock garden; alpine troughs

An alpine plantsman's collection, brimful with rarities in pots, troughs, screes, and raised beds. The owner considers that his garden maintenance is not as good as it used to be, but many visitors disagree and find infinite interest in this beautifully sited two-acre treasure house for good plants. And not just alpines, but trees, shrubs, bulbs and herbaceous plants too.

Nuneham Courtenay Arboretum

Nuneham Courtenay, Oxfordshire

OWNER University of Oxford
LOCATION 4 miles south of Oxford on the Henley road
OPEN 9 am – 5 pm; Monday – Saturday; plus 2pm – 5 pm Sundays; 1 May to 31 October
ADMISSION Free
FACILITIES Parking
FEATURES Good collection of trees; fine conifers; woodland garden
NCCPG NATIONAL COLLECTIONS Bamboos

50 acre arboretum developed since 1950 around a nucleus of American conifers planted c.1840. Experimental plantations and conservation areas rub along with cushioned rhododendrons, a bluebell wood and an *Acer* glade to match Westonbirt.

The Old Rectory, Farnborough

Farnborough, Wantage, Oxfordshire OX12 8NX
☎ 0488 638298

OWNER Mr & Mrs Michael Todhunter
LOCATION In village
OPEN 2 pm – 6 pm; 24 April, 15 May, June 26 & by appointment
ADMISSION £1.50; Private parties £3.00 each
FACILITIES Parking
FEATURES Herbaceous borders; old roses and climbers

Excellent modern garden, made by the owners on a high, cold, windy site over the last 25 years. Lots of hedges and thick planting were the keys to survival, but the effect now is of shelter and luxuriance. Splendid double herbaceous border and clever colour plantings.

Oxford Botanic Garden

High Street, Oxford, Oxfordshire OX1 4AX
☎ 0865 276920

OWNER University of Oxford
LOCATION East end of High Street next to river
OPEN 9 am – 5 pm; daily; all year except Good Friday & Christmas Day
ADMISSION £1 July & August; other times free
FACILITIES Facilities for the disabled
FEATURES Fine conifers; glasshouses to visit; herbs; rock garden; modern roses; old roses and climbers; garden sculpture; interesting for children; systematic

beds; huge service tree; tallest *Diospyros virginiana* in UK
ENGLISH HERITAGE GRADE I
NCCPG NATIONAL COLLECTIONS *Euphorbia*
FRIENDS Friends of Oxford Botanic Garden: details from the Secretary, c/o Oxford University Botanic Garden. Seed list, lectures, use of library, plant sales

A beautifully laid out, well-labelled, progressive, yet classical, botanic garden, founded in 1621. Everything you would expect, from ferns to carnivorous plants, but also a grace and calm that is far from the bustle outside.

Rousham House

Steeple Aston, Oxford, Oxfordshire OX5 3QX
☎ 0869 47110/0860 360407

OWNER C Cottrell-Dormer
LOCATION A4260 then off the B4030
OPEN 10 am – 4.30 pm; daily; all year
ADMISSION £2.50; no children under 15
FACILITIES Parking; loos
FEATURES Old roses and climbers; water features; early 18th century landscape
ENGLISH HERITAGE GRADE I

Rousham is the most perfect surviving example of William Kent's landscaping: *Kentissimo*, according to Horace Walpole. The main axis focuses on Scheemakers's statue of a lion and a horse and down to the River Cherwell. Follow the right sequence: the serpentine landscape lies away to the side. Here are Venus' Vale, the Cold Bath and Townsend's Building, from which the lime walk will lead you to the Praeneste. Rousham is an experience.

Stansfield

49 High Street, Stanford-in-the-Vale, Oxfordshire SN7 8NQ
☎ 0367 710340

OWNER Mr & Mrs D Keeble
LOCATION Off A417 opposite Vale garage
OPEN 10 am – 4 pm; Tuesdays; 5 April to 27 September
ADMISSION Adults £1.00; Children free
FACILITIES Parking; access for the disabled
FEATURES Herbaceous borders; gravel or scree garden; plantsman's garden

A modern plantsman's garden, and a model of what enthusiastic collecting can produce in a few years. Over 2,000 different plants in just over one acre, with troughs, screes, open borders and endless micro-habitats. Fascinating.

Waterperry Gardens
Wheatley, Oxford, Oxfordshire OX33 1JZ
☎ 0844 339226   📠 0844 339883

OWNER   School of Economic Science
LOCATION   Near junction 8 on M40, signed locally
OPEN   10.30 am – 5.30 pm (6 pm Saturday and Sunday), March to October; 10 am – 5 pm, November to March
ADMISSION   March to October; Adults £2.20; Senior Citizens £1.70; Children £1.00. November to February; all 75p. Other – 75p
FACILITIES   Parking; dogs permitted; loos; access for the disabled; plants for sale; home produce, stoneware, books; tea shop; wine licence
FEATURES   Herbaceous borders; fine conifers; fruit and vegetables of special interest; glasshouses to visit; herbs; rock garden; modern roses
NCCPG NATIONAL COLLECTIONS *Saxifraga*

Essentially a teaching garden with a commercial nursery grafted on, Waterperry has a slightly unco-ordinated feel to it. But the herbaceous borders and alpine collections are worth the journey.

Westwell Manor
Burford, Oxfordshire OX18 4JT   📠 071 371 2178

OWNER   Mr & Mrs T H Gibson
LOCATION   2 miles from A40, west of Burford roundabout
OPEN   2 pm – 6.30 pm; 1 May & 3 July
ADMISSION   £2.00
FACILITIES   Parking; loos; plants for sale; light teas
FEATURES   Herbaceous borders; fruit and vegetables of special interest; old roses and climbers; good topiary

Busy Cotswold garden with several distinct 'rooms' and well-used converted outbuildings. Roses in profusion, bulbs for spring and climbers draping the walls and hedges.

Wilcote House
Wilcote, Finstock, Oxfordshire OX7 3DY
☎ 0993 868606

OWNER   The Hon. Charles Cecil
LOCATION   ½ mile from Finstock on the Northleigh road
OPEN   2 pm – 5.30 pm; 8 May, 26 June, 29 October and by arrangement
ADMISSION   £1.00
FACILITIES   Parking; dogs permitted; loos; access for the disabled; plants for sale; refreshments on open days or by arrangement
FEATURES   Good collection of trees; old roses and climbers; laburnum walk

Fast developing garden around a stunning Jacobethan house. Courtyards and terraces with Mediterranean goodies and climbers. Borders with clever colours and wonderful roses. The arboretum is young and small, but promising.

Woodperry House
Stanton St John, Oxford, Oxfordshire OX33 1AJ
☎ 0865 351204

OWNER   Mrs R Lush
LOCATION   On Horton-cum-Sindey road ⅓ mile after crossing B4027
OPEN   2 pm – 5 pm; 15 May and 21 August
ADMISSION   Adults £1.50; Children free
FACILITIES   Parking; loos; plants for sale; teas
FEATURES   Herbaceous borders; fruit and vegetables of special interest; garden sculpture; water features; parterres

A large new garden designed with style and planted with enthusiasm, much influenced by pre-landscape ideas. Avenues of cherry and limes. Parterre with chunky statues. New water gardens. Definitely a garden to revisit as it grows.

SHROPSHIRE

Benthall Hall
Broseley, Shropshire TF12 5RX
☎ 0952 884028

OWNER   The National Trust
LOCATION   1 mile north west of Broseley (B4375)
OPEN   1.30 pm – 5.30 pm; Sundays, Wednesdays and Bank Holiday Mondays; April to September
ADMISSION   Adults £2.00
FACILITIES   Parking; loos; facilities for the disabled
FEATURES   Herbaceous borders; fruit and vegetables of special interest; glasshouses to visit; herbs; old roses and climbers; plantings by Graham Thomas

Smallish, but well restored with a Graham Thomas rose garden. Home of the 19th Century botanist George Maw. His Mediterranean collection is still the backbone of the garden – *Crocus* naturalised everywhere.

Erway Farm House
Ellesmere, Shropshire SY12 9ED

OWNER   A A & B N Palmer
LOCATION   Signposted from B5068 & B5069
OPEN   2 pm – 6 pm; last Sunday of month, February to September; plus Easter Saturday – Monday
ADMISSION   Adults £1.00; Children free
FACILITIES   Parking; loos; plants for sale
FEATURES   Oriental features; plantsman's garden

A cottage garden full of rare plants, inspired by Margery Fish. Layers of different plants from tiny bulbs to tall trees. Visit early for the snowdrops and *Helleborus orientalis* forms.

Hodnet Hall

Hodnet, Market Drayton, Shropshire TF9 3NN
☎ 0630 685202   ▣ 0630 84853

OWNER   A E H Heber-Percy
LOCATION   Near junction of A53 & A442
OPEN   2 pm – 5 pm; Monday – Saturday; 12 pm – 5.30 pm Sundays & Bank Holiday Mondays; April to September
ADMISSION   Adults £2.50; Senior Citizens £2.00; Children £1.00; (1993)
FACILITIES   Parking; dogs permitted; loos; access for the disabled; plants for sale; gift shop; 17th century tea rooms
FEATURES   Herbaceous borders; old roses and climbers; water features; woodland garden; camellias; primulas; rhododendrons; HHA/Christie's Garden of the Year in 1985
ENGLISH HERITAGE GRADE   II

A large garden, still expanding, and well maintained. Best known for the lakes and ponds planted with primulas and aquatics, but the rhododendrons alone demand a visit. Good in late summer too, with hydrangeas and astilbes. One of the greatest 20th century gardens.

Lower Hall

Worfield, Bridgnorth, Shropshire WV15 5LH
☎ 07464 607   ▣ 07464 607

OWNER   C F Dumbell
LOCATION   In centre of village of Worfield
OPEN   By appointment
ADMISSION   £2.00
FACILITIES   Loos; access for the disabled; plants for sale; tea & coffee
FEATURES   Herbaceous borders; plantsman's garden; modern roses; old roses and climbers; water features

Lanning Roper helped to get this splendid garden going 30 years ago. It bestrides the River Worfe and every part has a distinct character. Lush streamside plantings, infinite colour schemes, and a woodland area at the bottom. Formal designs, straight brick paths, a pergola and more colour themes in the old walled garden. One of the best modern gardens and neatly kept.

Preen Manor

Church Preen, Church Stretton, Shropshire SY6 7LQ
☎ 0694 771207

OWNER   Philip Trevor-Jones

LOCATION   From B4371 Much Wenlock/Church Stretton
OPEN   For NGS and by appointment
ADMISSION   Adults £1.75; children 50p
FACILITIES   Parking; loos; home-made teas
FEATURES   Fruit and vegetables of special interest; gravel or scree garden; water features; woodland garden; fern garden

A new garden for an old site, with some original ideas. A chess garden, a collection of plants in handsome old pots, a fern garden and that symbol of the 1990s – a gravel garden. And it gets better every year.

Ruthall Manor

Ditton Priors, Bridgnorth, Shropshire WV16 6TN
☎ 074 634 608

OWNER   Mr & Mrs G T Clarke
LOCATION   Take Weston road from church then 2nd left
OPEN   2 pm – 6 pm; Spring Bank Holiday weekend, NGS open day & by appointment
ADMISSION   £1.50
FACILITIES   Parking; dogs permitted; loos; access for the disabled
FEATURES   Plantsman's garden; water features

One acre plantsman's garden made over 20 years. Good trees, rare shrubs and lots of ground cover. Pretty pool with aquatics and marginals. Very satisfying.

Swallow Hayes

Rectory Road, Albrighton, Wolverhampton, Shropshire WV7 3EP
☎ 0902 372624

OWNER   Mrs P Edwards
LOCATION   First lane on right on A41 after garden centre
OPEN   11 am – 4 pm; 9 January. 2 pm – 6 pm; 24 April and 8 May. And by appointment
ADMISSION   £1 (1993)
FACILITIES   Parking; dogs permitted; loos; access for the disabled; plants for sale; teas on open days
FEATURES   Herbaceous borders; fine conifers; fruit and vegetables of special interest; gravel or scree garden; herbs; rock garden
NCCPG NATIONAL COLLECTIONS   *Hamamelis*, *Lupinus* (Russell)

25 years of plantsmanship and 3,000 plants have made Swallow Hayes a model modern garden, where ground cover helps to minimise labour and maximise enjoyment. The owners have crazes which add enormously to the visitor's pleasure: the current one is geraniums – over 70 different varieties 'on trial'.

Weston Park

Weston-under-Lizard, Shifnal, Shropshire TF11 8LE
☎ 095276 207   ⊠ 095276 430

OWNER The Weston Park Foundation
LOCATION Off the A5 to Telford
OPEN Easter – mid September (full dates and times not yet known)
ADMISSION Adults £3.00; Children £2.00 (1993)
FACILITIES Parking; dogs permitted; loos; facilities for the disabled; gift shop; tea rooms
FEATURES Good collection of trees; landscape designed by Capability Brown; old roses and climbers; woodland garden; landscaped park; rhododendrons;
ENGLISH HERITAGE GRADE II*

18th century landscape with 19th century Italianate parterre, a temple of Diana and a handsome orangery by Paine. But best for its trees, some of them record-breakers, and the collection of *Nothofagus* planted by the late Lord Bradford.

SOMERSET

Ammerdown Park

Kilmersdown, Radstock, Bath, Somerset BA3 5SH
☎ 0761 437382

OWNER Lord Hylton
LOCATION West of Terry Hill crossroads
OPEN 11 am – 5 pm; Bank Holiday Mondays; April to August
ADMISSION Adults £2; Children free
FACILITIES Parking; access for the disabled
FEATURES Designed by Lutyens
ENGLISH HERITAGE GRADE II*

Ammerdown's lay-out is Lutyens at his most ingenious. The lie of the land precludes right angles, but long straight views cover up the irregularities. Some nice plants, particularly trees, but the design is everything.

Barrington Court

Barrington, Ilminster, Somerset TA19 0NQ
☎ 0460 41480

OWNER The National Trust
LOCATION In Barrington village
OPEN 11.30 – 5.30 pm; Saturday – Wednesday; 1 April to 30 September
ADMISSION Adults £3
FACILITIES Parking; loos; access for the disabled; plants for sale; tea room & licensed restaurant
FEATURES Good collection of trees; fruit and vegetables of special interest; planted by Gertrude Jekyll; old roses and climbers; water features; particularly good in July-August
ENGLISH HERITAGE GRADE II*

Gertrude Jekyll's work has been updated by the National Trust but there is still an Edwardian opulence about Barrington. Massive plantings of irises, lilies and rich dark dahlias. And good design detail too: the patterns of the brick paving are a study in themselves.

Chapel Knap

Porlock Weir, Somerset TA24 8PA
☎ 0643 862364

OWNER Dr & Mrs Keith Lister
LOCATION Ask at Porlock Weir
OPEN By appointment only
ADMISSION £1.50
FACILITIES Parking; loos
FEATURES Sub-tropical plants; woodland garden
NCCPG NATIONAL COLLECTIONS *Osteospermum, Origanum, Argyranthemum*

An established plantsman's garden, with mature flowering dogwoods and exotic palms *Trachycarpus fortunei* to emphasise the mildness of the climate. A garden for browsing.

Clapton Court Gardens

Clapton, Crewkerne, Somerset TA18 8PT
☎ 0460 73220   ⊠ 0460 73220

OWNER Captain S J Loder
LOCATION 3 miles south of Crewkerne on B3165
OPEN 10.30 am – 5 pm; Monday – Friday; March to October
ADMISSION Adults £3.00; Child (4-14) £1.00; Students £1.50
FACILITIES Parking; loos; access for the disabled; plants for sale; light meals, teas, licence
FEATURES Herbaceous borders; plantsman's garden; modern roses; water features; woodland garden; biggest ash tree in United Kingdom

Slightly too Surrey-style formal garden with strong structure and super-human standards of tidiness. Good stream garden (*Primula florindae*) and young woodland garden.

Dunster Castle

Minehead, Somerset TA24 6SL
☎ 0643 821314

OWNER The National Trust
LOCATION 3 miles south east of Minehead on A39
OPEN 11 am – 4 pm; daily; February, March and October to 12 December; 11 am – 5 pm; April to September
ADMISSION Adults £2.50; Children £1.20; Family £6.50 (1993)
FACILITIES Parking; loos; facilities for the disabled; National Trust shop; tea rooms at Dunster Mill

FEATURES Sub-tropical plants; water features; woodland garden; particularly interesting in winter; *Arbutus* grove
NCCPG NATIONAL COLLECTIONS *Arbutus*

A Victorian woodland on a steep slope, terraced in places and planted with tender exotica – mimosa, *Beschorneria* and a 150 year old lemon tree in an unheated conservatory.

East Lambrook Manor

East Lambrook, South Petherton, Somerset
TA13 5HL
☎ 0460 240328   📠 0460 242344

OWNER Mr & Mrs Andrew Norton
LOCATION Off A303 at South Petherton
OPEN 10 am – 5 pm; Monday – Saturday; 1 March to 31 October
ADMISSION Adults £2; Children & students 50p; parties by arrangement £1.80 each
FACILITIES Parking; loos; book, picture gallery & gift shop; coffee & biscuits
FEATURES Herbaceous borders; plantsman's garden; cottage garden plants; geraniums
ENGLISH HERITAGE GRADE I
NCCPG NATIONAL COLLECTIONS *Geranium*

The archetypal super-cottage garden, made by Margery Fish, the popular and influential writer, and ambitiously restored by the present owners. Ground cover, narrow paths and, above all, plants, plants, plants.

Gaulden Manor

Tolland, Lydeard St Lawrence, Somerset TA4 3PN
☎ 0984 7213

OWNER J H N Lee-Starkie
LOCATION 9 miles north west of Taunton off A358
OPEN 2 pm – 5.30 pm; Sundays & Thursdays; 1st Sunday in May to 1st Sunday in September. Also Easter Sunday, Monday and Bank Holidays
ADMISSION £1.25
FACILITIES Parking; loos; access for the disabled; plants for sale; book & gift shop; tea room
FEATURES Herbaceous borders; herbs; modern roses; old roses and climbers; water features; woodland garden; scent gardens; secret garden

A modern garden, and well planted. Small garden rooms, each devoted to a different theme (roses, herbs etc.), and a good stream garden made beneath the monks' pond, its sides planted with candelabra primulas, ferns and *Gunnera*.

Greencombe Garden Trust

Porlock, Somerset TA24 8NU
☎ 0643 862363

OWNER Greencombe Garden Trust

LOCATION ½ mile west of Porlock on left of road to Porlock Weir
OPEN 2 pm – 6 pm; Saturday – Tuesday; April to July
ADMISSION Adults £2.50; Children (under 16) 50p
FACILITIES Parking; loos; access for the disabled; plants for sale; teas for large groups
FEATURES Herbaceous borders; fine conifers; ecological interest; plantsman's garden; woodland garden
NCCPG NATIONAL COLLECTIONS *Erythronium, Gaultheria, Polystichum, Vaccinium*

Rather a cult garden, an organic showpiece, best for its woodland walks where stately gentleness dominates. Interesting plants galore.

Hadspen House

Castle Cary, Somerset BA7 7NG
☎ 0963 50939

OWNER N A Hobhouse
LOCATION 2 miles east of Castle Cary on A371
OPEN 9 am – 6 pm; Thursday – Sunday & Bank Holiday Mondays; 1 March to 1 October
ADMISSION Adults £2.00; Children 50p
FACILITIES Parking; loos; facilities for the disabled; nursery; light lunches & teas
FEATURES Herbaceous borders; gravel or scree garden; plantsman's garden; old roses and climbers; water features; Eric Smith's *Hosta* collection
NCCPG NATIONAL COLLECTIONS *Rodgersia*

Penelope Hobhouse's own first garden, full of good plants and unusual colour combinations. Restored and improved by two active young Canadians.

Hestercombe House

Somerset County Council, Cheddon Fitzpaine, Taunton, Somerset TA2 8LQ
☎ 0823 337222   📠 0823 413030

OWNER Somerset County Council Fire Brigade
LOCATION 4 miles north of Taunton
OPEN 9 am – 5 pm; Monday – Friday. 2 pm – 5 pm; Saturday – Sunday. 1 May to 30 September
ADMISSION Adults £2.00; Senior Citizens £1.50; Children free
FACILITIES Parking; dogs permitted; loos
FEATURES Herbaceous borders; designed by Lutyens and planted by Gertrude Jekyll
ENGLISH HERITAGE GRADE I

Famously restored garden with lots of Lutyens' hallmarks: iris-choked rills, pergolas, relieved staircases and pools where reflections twinkle on recessed apses. Gertrude Jekyll's planting is bold and simple, which adds to the vigour. Very photogenic.

Lyte's Cary Manor

Charlton Mackrell, Somerton, Somerset TA11 7HU
☎ 0458 223297

OWNER The National Trust
LOCATION Off A372 near Somerton
OPEN 2 pm – 6 pm; Monday, Wednesday & Saturday; April to October
ADMISSION Adults £3.50
FACILITIES Parking; loos; access for the disabled; plants for sale
FEATURES Herbaceous borders; garden sculpture; good topiary; plantings by Graham Thomas
ENGLISH HERITAGE GRADE II

Neo-Elizabethan garden to go with the prettiest of manor houses. Yew hedges, hornbeam walks, alleys and lawns. Medlars, quinces and a simple Elizabethan flower border.

Milton Lodge

Old Bristol Road, Wells, Somerset BA5 3AQ
☎ 0749 672168

OWNER D C Tudway Quilter
LOCATION Old Bristol road off of A39
OPEN 2 pm – 6 pm; Sunday – Friday; Easter to end of October
ADMISSION Adults £2.00; Children (under 14) free
FACILITIES Parking; loos; plants for sale; teas on Sundays (May to August)
FEATURES Good collection of trees; herbaceous borders; modern roses; woodland garden; tallest *Populus alba* in British Isles

Terraced Edwardian garden with stone paving and walling against a backdrop of Wells Cathedral. Yew hedges, good modern plantings, an 8 acre arboretum in a combe, replanted in recent years.

Montacute House

Montacute, Yeovil, Somerset TA15 6XP
☎ 0935 823289

OWNER The National Trust
LOCATION In Montacute village
OPEN 11.30 am – 5.30 pm; daily except Tuesday
ADMISSION Adults £2.50; Children £1.20 (1993)
FACILITIES Parking; loos; facilities for the disabled; plants for sale; light lunches & teas; licensed restaurant
FEATURES Herbaceous borders; old roses and climbers; water features; exquisite gazebos
ENGLISH HERITAGE GRADE I

The garden is subsidiary to the amazing Elizabethan mansion, apart from a border started by Vita Sackville-West, worked over by Phyllis Reiss and finished by Graham Thomas. But it cannot be beaten for its sense of English renaissance grandeur.

Ston Easton Park

Ston Easton, Bath, Somerset BA3 4DF
☎ 0761 241631

OWNER Peter L Smedley
LOCATION Intersection of A37 and A39
OPEN By appointment unless visiting restaurant
ADMISSION Free
FACILITIES Parking; dogs permitted; loos; plants for sale; Ston Easton Park is a hotel: all meals available to non-residents
FEATURES Landscape designed by Humphry Repton; fine conifers; follies and garden buildings; fruit and vegetables of special interest; water features; ice-house
ENGLISH HERITAGE GRADE II

A country house hotel, voted Hotel of the Year in 1992, with a Humphry Repton landscape. His 'red book' still exists. A sham castle and ruined grotto are two of the features he built, but there are fine trees, spacious lawns and the highest standard of maintenance to enjoy, too.

Tintinhull House

Tintinhull, Yeovil, Somerset BA22 8PZ
☎ 0985 847777

OWNER The National Trust
LOCATION In Tintinhull village
OPEN 2 pm – 6 pm; Wednesdays, Thursdays, Saturdays & Bank Holiday Mondays; April to September
ADMISSION Adults £3.20 (1993)
FACILITIES Parking; loos; access for the disabled; refreshments
FEATURES Herbaceous borders; old roses and climbers; good topiary; water features; particularly good in July-August; colour borders
ENGLISH HERITAGE GRADE II

A series of formal garden rooms, beautifully designed to maximise a small site (only 1½ acres) and planted with rarities in exquisite colour combinations. No labels: they would spoil the dream.

Wayford Manor

Crewkerne, Somerset TA18 8QG
☎ 0460 73253

OWNER Mr & Mrs R L Goffe
LOCATION 3 miles south west of Crewkerne off A30 or B3165
OPEN 2 pm – 6 pm; 10 April, 1, 15 & 29 May for NGS or parties by appointment
ADMISSION Adults £1.50; Children 50p
FACILITIES Parking; dogs permitted; loos; plants for sale; teas
FEATURES Herbaceous borders; follies and garden buildings; garden sculpture; water features; rhododendrons; spring bulbs; maples
ENGLISH HERITAGE GRADE II

One of the best gardens designed by Harold Peto: terraces and courtyards, pools and arbours, balustrades and staircases, Tuscan and Byzantine. Parts are now rather dominated by overgrown shrubs, but the whole garden is presently being restored by the enthusiastic and knowledgeable owners.

STAFFORDSHIRE

Alton Towers
Alton, Stoke-on-Trent, Staffordshire ST10 4DB
☎ 0538 702200   [FAX] 0538 702724

OWNER Tussauds Group
LOCATION Signposted for miles around
OPEN 9 am – 6/7/8 pm depending on season; daily; all year
ADMISSION Adults £13; Children £9.99; Senior Citizens £5.50
FACILITIES Parking; loos; many restaurants
FEATURES Good collection of trees; herbaceous borders; fine conifers; follies and garden buildings; oriental features; rock garden; modern roses; water features; woodland garden; interesting for children
ENGLISH HERITAGE GRADE I

300 acres of dotty and exuberant display, best seen from the cable-car. Ignore the theme park: the gardens are by and large detached from the razzmatazz. Splendid Victorian conifers and gaudy bedding, magnificently done. A Swiss Cottage, Roman bridge, Chinese pagoda, flag tower, and corkscrew fountain. Excellent entertainment but not for contemplative souls. Best in term time.

Biddulph Grange
Biddulph, Stoke-on-Trent, Staffordshire ST8 7SD
☎ 0782 517999

OWNER The National Trust
LOCATION ½ mile north of Biddulph
OPEN 12 pm – 6 pm; Wednesday – Friday; 11 am – 6 pm, Good Friday; Saturday, Sunday and Bank Holiday Mondays; 30 March to 30 October
ADMISSION Adults £3.90; Children £1.95; Family £9.75
FACILITIES Parking; loos; facilities for the disabled; gift shop; tea room
FEATURES Follies and garden buildings; oriental features; water features; interesting for children
ENGLISH HERITAGE GRADE I

An oddity among gardens: yews cut as an Egyptian temple; a statue of a sacred cow; a four acre Chinese garden complete with Great Wall of China and lookout tower; a bowling green, quoits ground and 'stumpery'. All energetically and successfully restored by the National Trust.

The Dorothy Clive Garden
Willoughbridge, Market Drayton, Staffordshire
TF9 4EU
☎ 0630 647237

OWNER Willoughbridge Garden Trust
LOCATION A51, midway between Nantwich and Stone
OPEN 10 am – 5.30 pm; daily; 1 April to 31 October
ADMISSION Adults £2.00, Children 50p
FACILITIES Parking; dogs permitted; loos; facilities for the disabled; tea room with beverages & home-baked food
FEATURES Herbaceous borders; fine conifers; gravel or scree garden; rock garden; modern roses; old roses and climbers; woodland garden; rhododendrons; azaleas; heather; cyclamen

Meticulously maintained and still expanding, this 40 year old garden seems ageless. Made on an unpromising site, a cold windy hilltop, it is best perhaps in May, when the woodland quarry is brilliant with rhododendrons. But the scree and rock garden (reflected in the lake) are hard to beat at any season. Highly recommended.

Moseley Old Hall
Moseley Old Hall Lane, Fordhouses, Staffordshire
WV10 7HY
☎ 0902 782808

OWNER The National Trust
LOCATION South of M54 between A449 & A460
OPEN 2 pm – 5.30 pm; Wednesdays, Saturdays & Sundays; (and Tuesdays in July & August); 11 am – 5 pm, Bank Holiday Mondays; 26 March to 31 October
ADMISSION Adults £3.20; Children £1.60; Family £8.00
FACILITIES Parking; loos; access for the disabled; plants for sale; National Trust gift shop; National Trust tea room
FEATURES Herbs; good topiary; current holder of Sandford Award

Modern reconstruction of a 17th century town garden. Neat box parterres, a nut walk and an arched pergola hung with clematis. Plantings all of a period. Quietly inspirational.

Oulton House
Oulton, Stone, Staffordshire ST15 8UR
☎ 0785 813556

OWNER Mr & Mrs John Bridger
LOCATION From Stone take Oulton Road and turn left after Oulton sign: 3rd driveway on right
OPEN 12 – 19 June, by appointment
ADMISSION Adults £1.50; Children 50p
FACILITIES Parking; loos; plants for sale; tea & coffee

FEATURES Herbaceous borders; glasshouses to visit; rock garden; old roses and climbers

Newish three-acre garden, made for private enjoyment and full of good plants – roses, rhododendrons, geraniums and clematis – arranged in colour groupings.

Shugborough Hall

Great Haywood, Milford, Staffordshire ST17 0XB
☎ 0889 881388   ☒ 0889 881323

OWNER The National Trust
LOCATION Signed from Junction 13, M6
OPEN 11 am – 5 pm; 26 March to 28 October, parties at other times by appointment
ADMISSION Vehicle £1.50; Coaches free
FACILITIES Parking; dogs permitted; loos; facilities for the disabled; plants for sale; garden centre; lunches, snacks, tea & evening dinners
FEATURES Herbaceous borders; follies and garden buildings; oriental features; old roses and climbers; water features; woodland garden; plantings by Graham Thomas; interesting for children
ENGLISH HERITAGE GRADE I

Classical and neo-classical landscape with Chinese additions and a handsome Nesfield terrace dominated by dumplings of clipped golden yew. 50 oaks in the new arboretum. Rose garden restored by Graham Thomas. All very popular with the locals.

Trentham Park Gardens

Trentham, Stoke-on-Trent, Staffordshire

OWNER Trentham Leisure Ltd
LOCATION Signposted from M6
OPEN 10 am – 6 pm; daily; 4 April to 3 October
ADMISSION Adults £1.50
FACILITIES Parking; dogs permitted; loos; access for the disabled; plants for sale; shop; refreshments
FEATURES Good collection of trees; modern roses; water features; interesting for children; Capability Brown landscape; good bedding; play area; boats on the lake
ENGLISH HERITAGE GRADE II*

It is the grand Italian garden designed by Charles Barry that most impresses the visitor, as well as the sheer size of the whole park and its lake. Now it is a popular place for family outings, and caters for many tastes: not for quiet contemplative plantsmen.

Wolseley Garden Park

Wolseley Bridge, Stafford, Staffordshire ST17 0YT
☎ 0889 574888

OWNER Sir Charles Wolseley Bt
LOCATION At junction of A51 & A513

OPEN 10 am – 6 pm; daily; April to October. 10 am – 4pm; daily except Christmas Day and New Year's Day; November to March
ADMISSION Adults £2.00; Senior Citizens £1.50; Children £1.00
FACILITIES Parking; loos; access for the disabled; plants for sale; cafeteria
FEATURES Fine conifers; herbs; rock garden; old roses and climbers; water features; young garden; started in 1988
NCCPG NATIONAL COLLECTIONS *Salix*

A brand-new garden developed as part of a leisure investment, complete with garden centre at the gate. Lakes, bulbs, roses and planting on a big scale. Some banalities and vulgarities, but the scale is impressive: judge for yourself.

SUFFOLK

Bucklesham Hall

Bucklesham, Ipswich, Suffolk IP10 0AY
☎ 0473 659263

OWNER Mr & Mrs P A Ravenshear
LOCATION 1 mile east of Bucklesham village
OPEN By appointment
ADMISSION £2.00
FACILITIES Parking; plants for sale; refreshments by arrangement
FEATURES Old roses and climbers; water features; woodland garden; young garden; made since 1973

Youngish garden, mainly trees and shrubs thickly planted and underplanted with ground cover. Plants in pots around the house, richly arranged streamside plantings and very explorable woodland garden.

Euston Hall

Euston, Thetford, Suffolk IP24 2QP
☎ 0842 766366   ☒ 0842 766764

OWNER The Duke of Grafton
LOCATION On A1088 3 miles south of Thetford
OPEN 2.30 pm – 5 pm; Thursdays; 2 June to 29 September, plus 26 June and 4 September
ADMISSION Adults £2.50; OAPs £2.00; Parties (over 12) £2; Children 50p
FACILITIES Parking; loos; access for the disabled; craft shop; home-made teas
FEATURES Landscape designed by Capability Brown; old roses and climbers; water features; William Kent temple and summerhouse
ENGLISH HERITAGE GRADE II*

Classic 18th century parkland on a sweeping site, formal terraces by the house and a pretty modern garden with shrub roses. Not spectacular, but satisfying.

Haughley Park

Stowmarket, Suffolk IP14 3JY

☎ 0359 240205   📠 0359 240546

OWNER A J Williams

LOCATION Signed from A45

OPEN 3 pm – 5.30 pm; Tuesdays; May to September plus first two Sunday afternoons in May

ADMISSION Adults £2.00; Children £1.00

FACILITIES Parking; dogs permitted; loos; facilities for the disabled

FEATURES Herbaceous borders; woodland garden; rhododendrons; bluebells; lily-of-the-valley; 1,000 year old oak

Parkland round a Jacobean mansion with competent modern flower gardens and fine trees (*Davidia involucrata*). But the acres of lily-of-the-valley in the woodland garden are worth the journey no matter how far.

Helmingham Hall

Stowmarket, Suffolk IP14 6EF

☎ 0473 890363   📠 0473 890776

OWNER Lord Tollemache

LOCATION 9 miles north of Ipswich on B1077

OPEN 2 pm – 6 pm; Sundays; 1 May – 11 September; groups on Wednesdays by prior arrangement

ADMISSION Adults £2.50; Senior Citizens £2.30; Children £1.50

FACILITIES Parking; dogs permitted; loos; access for the disabled; plants for sale; shop; tea rooms

FEATURES Herbaceous borders; old roses and climbers; deer park; fine walled garden

ENGLISH HERITAGE GRADE I

Most of the garden is modern, but well done with parterres in the Tudor style to suit the Elizabethan house and planted with old flower varieties. Wonderful modern planting in the walled garden.

Shrubland Hall

Coddenham, Ipswich, Suffolk IP6 9QP

☎ 0473 830221   📠 0473 832202

OWNER Lord de Saumarez

LOCATION In village: come by A45 or A140

OPEN 2 pm – 6 pm; 17 July.

ADMISSION Adults £2; Senior Citizens & Children £1

FACILITIES Parking; loos; plants for sale; tea tent

FEATURES Herbaceous borders; follies and garden buildings; modern roses; water features; woodland garden; box maze; Swiss Chalet

ENGLISH HERITAGE GRADE I

A grand Victorian garden designed by Charles Barry and famous for its spectacular Italianate staircase which connects the terrace around the house with the formal gardens below. William Robinson later helped with the planting, both around the formal garden and in the park and woodland gardens beyond. Much restoration and recovery has been completed in recent years: Shrubland is getting better and better.

Somerleyton Hall

Lowestoft, Suffolk NR32 5QQ

☎ 0502 730224   📠 0502 732143

OWNER Lord & Lady Somerleyton

LOCATION 4 miles north west of Lowestoft off B1074

OPEN 12.30 pm – 5.30 pm; Sundays and Thursdays, plus Wednesday – Thursday in July and August; Easter Sunday to 30 September

ADMISSION Adults £3.50; Senior Citizens £2.70; Children £1.60 (1993)

FACILITIES Parking; loos; facilities for the disabled; souvenir gift shop; tea room

FEATURES Glasshouses to visit; modern roses; maze, miniature railway; some evening openings (ask for details)

ENGLISH HERITAGE GRADE II*

A grand formal garden around the monstrous Victorian house. Nesfield laid out the terraces, and Paxton built the curving greenhouses. Good 19th century maze (not too difficult) and masses of cheerful bedding and roses.

Wyken Hall

Stanton, Bury St Edmunds, Suffolk IP31 2DW

☎ 0359 50287   📠 0359 50240

OWNER Kenneth Carlisle

LOCATION Stanton, 9 miles north east from Bury St Edmunds along A143

OPEN 10 am – 6 pm; Thursdays, Sundays and Bank Holiday Mondays; 1 May to 1 October

ADMISSION Adults £2.00, Senior Citizens £1.50, Children free

FACILITIES Parking; dogs permitted; loos; facilities for the disabled; plants for sale; country store shop; lunches & teas

FEATURES Herbaceous borders; fine conifers; fruit and vegetables of special interest; herbs; plantsman's garden; modern roses; old roses and climbers; woodland garden; award-winning seven-acre vineyard

Well run estate with modern gardens to complement the Elizabethan house. Knot garden, herb garden, traditional English kitchen garden, wildflower meadows, nuttery and new copper beech maze. Ancient woodland walk (SSSI).

SURREY

Brook Lodge Farm Cottage

Blackbrook, Dorking, Surrey RH5 4DT
☎ 0306 888368

OWNER Mrs Basil Kingham
LOCATION 3 miles south of Dorking
OPEN 11 am – 3 pm; 18 May, 10 August, 19 October;
2 pm – 6 pm; 15 May, 19 June, 24 July, 21 August
ADMISSION Adults £1.50, Children free
FACILITIES Parking; loos; access for the disabled;
plants for sale; home-made lunches & afternoon cakes
FEATURES Herbaceous borders; fine conifers; glasshouses to visit; herbs; plantsman's garden; rock garden;
old roses and climbers; water features; woodland
garden

Planted by the present owner 45 years ago, this garden
has matured into a fine plantsman's garden with much
variety: shrub roses, a rockery, a woodland walk, herbaceous borders and two cottage gardens.

Chilworth Manor

Chilworth, Guildford, Surrey
☎ 0483 61414

OWNER Lady Heald
LOCATION In middle of village, up Blacksmiths Lane
OPEN 2 pm – 6 pm; 9 & 10 April, 7 & 8 May, 11 &
12 June, 16 & 17 July, 6 & 7 August, or by appointment
ADMISSION £1.50
FACILITIES Parking; dogs permitted; loos; facilities for
the disabled; teas & cakes
FEATURES Herbaceous borders; water features;
woodland garden; rhododendrons

A remarkable garden, tiered up seven distinct levels, the
top three being c.1700 and walled around (beautiful
brickwork). Good climbers and shrubs against the
walls, and a bog garden in the woods at the bottom.

Clandon Park

West Clandon, Guildford, Surrey GU4 7RQ
☎ 0483 222482

OWNER The National Trust
LOCATION Off the A247 at West Clandon
OPEN 1.30 pm – 5.30 pm; Saturday – Wednesday and
Good Friday; 3 April to 31 October
ADMISSION Adults £3.60; Children (under 17) £1.80
FACILITIES Parking; loos; access for the disabled; gar-
den centre; restaurant
FEATURES Parterres; grotto; Dutch garden; Maori
house
ENGLISH HERITAGE GRADE II

A modern garden around a handsome early 18th century park, originally laid out by Capability Brown. Best
in spring when the daffodils and cowslips are out, but
the Dutch garden comes into its own when the lavender
flowers in high summer.

Claremont Gardens

Portsmouth Road, Esher, Surrey KT10 9JG
☎ 0372 469421

OWNER The National Trust
LOCATION On southern edge of town
OPEN 10 am – 6 pm, but 5 pm from November to
March and 7 pm on Saturdays, Sundays & Bank Holi-
day Mondays from April to October; all year
ADMISSION Adults £2.50
FACILITIES Parking; dogs permitted; loos; access for
the disabled; shop; restaurant
FEATURES Follies and garden buildings; water fea-
tures; tallest false acacia Robinia pseudoacacia in the
British Isles
ENGLISH HERITAGE GRADE I

A vast historic landscape worked over by Vanburgh,
Bridgeman, Kent and Capability Brown. The stunning
turf amphitheatre is best seen flanked by spreading
cedars from across the dark lake. Very popular locally,
and apt to get crowded at summer week-ends.

Hascombe Court

Hascombe, Surrey GU8 4AF

OWNER Mr & Mrs O Poulsen
LOCATION 2½ miles from Godalming on B2130,
straight on at sharp left bend, into no through road
OPEN 2 pm – 5 pm; Sundays; 17 April, 15 May, 19
June
ADMISSION £1.50
FACILITIES Parking; loos; teas
FEATURES Herbaceous borders; rock garden; modern
roses; old roses and climbers; rhododendrons; 1930s
Percy Cane rock garden; daffodils; specimen notable
trees

Gertrude Jekyll and Percy Cane both had a hand in this
important garden, whose plantings have been well-re-
stored by the present owners.

Hatchlands

East Clandon, Guildford, Surrey GU4 7RT
☎ 0483 222482

OWNER The National Trust
LOCATION Off A246 Guildford to Leatherhead
OPEN 2 pm – 5.30 pm; Tuesday – Thursday, Sunday
& Bank Holiday Mondays; 1 April to 31 October
ADMISSION Adults £3.50; Children (under 17) £1.75
FACILITIES Parking; loos; access for the disabled; Na-
tional Trust shop; restaurant

FEATURES Landscape designed by Humphry Repton; designed by Lutyens and planted by Gertrude Jekyll; woodland garden

Apart from the Jekyll garden (roses, lupins, box and columbines) Clandon is an 18th century landscape with parkland. But the garden buildings are charming and the National Trust has started to restore and replant it.

Munstead Wood
Heath Lane, Busbridge, Godalming, Surrey GU7 1UN
☎ 0483 417867   [FAX] 0483 425041

OWNER Sir Robert & Lady Clark
LOCATION Take Heath Lane from B2130, turn left after 400 yards, entrance on right
OPEN 2 pm – 6 pm; 22 & 29 May
ADMISSION Adults £2.00; Children 50p
FACILITIES Parking; loos; access for the disabled; plants for sale; cream teas
FEATURES Herbaceous borders; planted by Gertrude Jekyll; rock garden; old roses and climbers; woodland garden
ENGLISH HERITAGE GRADE I

Gertrude Jekyll's own garden was nearly lost before the Clarks bought it. They have acknowledged that parts are beyond restoration while others have been put back to their original state. But the lawns still end where the birches begin, to make Munstead 'a garden in a wood'.

Painshill Park
Portsmouth Road, Cobham, Surrey KT11 1JE
☎ 0932 868113/864674   [FAX] 0932 868001

OWNER Painshill Park Trust
LOCATION West of Cobham on A245
OPEN 11 am – 5 pm; Sundays & pre-booked groups any other day; 10 April to 16 October
ADMISSION Adults £3.00; Senior Citizens and Students £2.50; Children (under 14) free
FACILITIES Parking; loos; facilities for the disabled; souvenirs, books, cards, etc.; light refreshments
FEATURES Follies and garden buildings; water features; 'American' garden; grotto; Turkish tent; tallest *Juniperus virginiana* in the British Isles
ENGLISH HERITAGE GRADE I

Charles Hamilton went bust making this extravagant gothic landscape in the 1770s. It has been industriously restored over the last ten years and now looks as new and stagey as ever.

Pinewood House
Heath House Road, Worplesdon Hill, Woking, Surrey GU22 0QU
☎ 0483 473241

OWNER Mr & Mrs J Van Zwanenberg

LOCATION Turning off A322, opposite Brookwood cemetery wall
OPEN Parties by appointment, 1 April to 31 October
ADMISSION Adults £1.50
FACILITIES Parking; loos; access for the disabled; home-made teas if pre-booked
FEATURES Good collection of trees; fine conifers; glasshouses to visit; water features; young garden; wild garden; walled garden; rhododendrons

5 acres of old garden, to go with a new house. Lovely woodland, lakes and underplantings with rhododendrons.

Polesden Lacey
Great Bookham, Dorking, Surrey RH5 6BD
☎ 0372 458203

OWNER The National Trust
LOCATION On southern edge of Dorking – signposted
OPEN 11 am – 6 pm; daily; all year
ADMISSION Adults £2.50
FACILITIES Parking; dogs permitted; loos; access for the disabled; shop; tea rooms
FEATURES Herbaceous borders; herbs; old roses and climbers; garden sculpture; plantings by Graham Thomas
ENGLISH HERITAGE GRADE II*

Best for the long terraced walk, laid out by Sheridan, and the return through an Edwardian-style rose garden whose pergolas drip with ramblers.

Ramster
Chiddingfold, Surrey GU8 4SN
☎ 0428 644422

OWNER Mr & Mrs Paul Gunn
LOCATION 1½ miles south of Chiddingfold on A283
OPEN 2 pm – 6 pm; daily; 30 April to 5 June. Also Saturdays & Sundays in June. 14 & 15 May early morning (photographic special). Also by appointment
ADMISSION £1.50, 30 April to 5 June; other times £1; Children free
FACILITIES Parking; dogs permitted; loos; facilities for the disabled; plants for sale; home-made teas at weekends or by arrangement
FEATURES Good collection of trees; fine conifers; water features; rhododendrons; camellias; azaleas; bluebells

20 acres of Surrey woodland underplanted with camellias, rhododendrons and all manner of rare shrubs by Mrs Gunn's grandmother 70 years ago. She was the second Lord Aberconway's sister and many of her plants came from Bodnant: some of the rhododendrons and azaleas are her hybrids.

RHS Garden, Wisley

Woking, Surrey GU23 6QB
☎ 0483 224234

OWNER The Royal Horticultural Society
LOCATION Near junction of M25 & A3
OPEN 10 am – 7 pm or dusk if earlier (4.30 pm
November to January); daily through year. Sundays
reserved for RHS members only
ADMISSION £4.20 adults; £1.75 children
FACILITIES Parking; loos; facilities for the disabled;
plants for sale; marvellous bookshop and souvenir shop;
two restaurants
FEATURES Good collection of trees; herbaceous borders; fine conifers; ecological interest; fruit and vegetables of special interest; glasshouses to visit; gravel or
scree garden; herbs; plantsman's garden; rock garden;
modern roses; old roses and climbers; sub-tropical
plants; water features; woodland garden; particularly
good in July-August; particularly interesting in winter
ENGLISH HERITAGE GRADE II*
NCCPG NATIONAL COLLECTIONS Calluna vulgaris,
Galanthus, Hosta, Rheum, Colchicum, Crocus, Daboe-
cia, Daphne, Erica, Epimedium, Pulmonaria

Too well known to need description, Wisley is a garden
to visit and revisit in search of new knowledge and
inspiration. You can spend a week there and still find
corners you never knew existed.

Royal Botanic Gardens, Kew

Kew, Richmond, Surrey TW9 3AB
☎ 081 940 1171

OWNER Trustees of the Royal Botanic Gardens
LOCATION Kew Green, south of Kew bridge, or
Underground Station
OPEN 10 am – 4 pm; daily; November to January. 10
am – 5 pm; daily; February. 10 am – 6 pm; March to
October. 10 am – 7 pm; April to September
ADMISSION Adults £3.50 (last hour £1.20); Senior
Citizens & students £1.80; Children (5-16) £1.30,
under 5 free; wheelchair occupants free; family day
ticket £9 (2+4); season ticket £17, family season ticket
£33
FACILITIES Parking; loos; facilities for the disabled;
gift & book shop; orangery & pavilion restaurants &
bakery
FEATURES Good collection of trees; herbaceous borders; fine conifers; ecological interest; follies and garden
buildings; fruit and vegetables of special interest; glasshouses to visit; gravel or scree garden; herbs; oriental
features; plantsman's garden; rock garden; modern
roses; old roses and climbers; garden sculpture; sub-
tropical plants; water features; woodland garden; particularly interesting in winter; heather gardens
ENGLISH HERITAGE GRADE I

FRIENDS Friends of Kew: very active and good value,
see Societies section

Kew has such superstar status that it needs no description. Go in lilac time, if you wish, but go too in winter
when there is much to see both in and out of the
glasshouses. Visit the newly restored Palm House, as
well as the new Princess of Wales Conservatory
(worth a whole afternoon) and do not miss the alpine
house. In summer there are very good bedding out
schemes, but the garden is plagued by Canada geese,
which foul the grass and aircraft noise.

The Savill Garden

Wick Lane, Windsor, Surrey SL4 2HT
☎ 0753 860222

OWNER Crown Property
LOCATION 3 miles west of Egham off the A30, 5 miles
from Windsor
OPEN 10 am – 6 pm; daily; closed 25 & 26 December
ADMISSION Adults £3.20, Senior Citizens £2.70,
Children under 16 free. Groups (20+) £2.70, Guided
tours apply to Keeper of the Gardens
FACILITIES Parking; loos; plants for sale; gift and book
shop; licensed restaurant & picnic area
FEATURES Good collection of trees; herbaceous bor-
ders; gravel or scree garden; plantsman's garden; rock
garden; modern roses; water features; woodland garden; particularly good in July-August; particularly inter-
esting in winter; Kurume azaleas; camellias; mahonias;
magnolias; magnificent late summer borders; tallest Betula populifolia and Sorbus 'Joseph Rock' in the British
Isles
ENGLISH HERITAGE GRADE I
NCCPG NATIONAL COLLECTIONS Mahonia, Rhododendron
FRIENDS Active Friends Organisation: details from
John Bond, Keeper of the Gardens

Quite simply the finest woodland garden in England,
crammed with rhododendrons, magnolias, azaleas,
maples, mahonias and hydrangeas and underplanted
with drifts of meconopsis, primulas and wild narcissus.
But the herbaceous borders are also an inspiration and
the gravel garden is one of the oldest and largest.

The Valley Gardens, Windsor

Windsor Great Park, Wick Road, Englefield Green,
Surrey
☎ 0753 860222

OWNER Crown Estate Commission
LOCATION 5 miles from Windsor, off A30 following
signs for Savill Garden
OPEN 8 am – 7 pm or sunset if earlier; all year
ADMISSION Car and occupants £2 (use 10p, 50p & £1
coins only)

FACILITIES Parking; dogs permitted; refreshments at the Savill Garden
FEATURES Good collection of trees; fine conifers; plantsman's garden; water features; woodland garden; deciduous azaleas; hollies; magnolias; heathers; rhododendrons; hydrangeas
NCCPG NATIONAL COLLECTIONS *Ilex, Magnolia, Pernettya, Pieris, Rhododendron*

A bigger and better Savill Gardens: all is planted on a royal scale in a wilder woodland setting. Best known is the Punch Bowl, where massed ranks of Kurume azaleas fill a natural combe with amazingly garish mixtures. Other parts are underplanted with hostas, ferns, bergenias and candelabra primulas. There is also a fine pinetum and a good collection of hydrangeas. But the gardens extend to 300 acres: not to be undertaken by the frail or faint-hearted.

Vann

Hambledon, nr Godalming, Surrey GU8 4EF
☎ 0428 68 3413   📠 07267 9344

OWNER Mr & Mrs Martin Caroe
LOCATION NGS signs from A283
OPEN 10 am – 6 pm; daily; 5 to 10 April, 3 to 8 May; 31 May to 5 June
ADMISSION Adults £2; Children 50p
FACILITIES Parking; loos; plants for sale; teas by arrangement
FEATURES Fruit and vegetables of special interest; planted by Gertrude Jekyll; water features
ENGLISH HERITAGE GRADE II

High-profile garden, planted by Gertrude Jekyll and well restored by the present Caroes, the third generation to live here. Five or six distinct gardens lead from one to the next and melt into the Surrey woods: a yew walk, a water garden, a stone pergola, a pond. The plantings are dense and thoughtful.

Winkworth Arboretum

Hascombe Road, Godalming, Surrey GU8 4AD
☎ 048 632477

OWNER The National Trust
LOCATION 2 miles south east of Godalming, off B2130
OPEN All year; dawn – dusk
ADMISSION Adults £2.00; Children £1.00;
FACILITIES Parking; dogs permitted; loos; shop; tea room
FEATURES Good collection of trees; water features; woodland garden; plantings by Graham Thomas; bluebells; wood anemones; autumn colour; tallest *Acer davidii* in the British Isles
NCCPG NATIONAL COLLECTIONS *Sorbus*

Beautiful arboretum, planted with particularly decorative species (maples, *Sorbus*, magnolias and *Hama-*

melis) in large groups for maximum effect. Good in May when the azaleas are underscored by bluebells: better still for autumn colour in October.

EAST SUSSEX

Bateman's

Burwash, Etchingham, East Sussex TN19 7DS
☎ 0435 882302

OWNER The National Trust
LOCATION Signposted at west end of village
OPEN 11 am – 5 pm; Saturday – Wednesday; 1 April to 31 October
ADMISSION Adults £3.50; Children £1.80; Bank Holidays & Sundays – Adults £4; Children £2 (1993)
FACILITIES Parking; loos; National Trust shop; restaurant & café
FEATURES Herbaceous borders; fruit and vegetables of special interest; herbs; old roses and climbers; interesting for children; arcade planted with pears and clematis; water mill
ENGLISH HERITAGE GRADE II

10 acres on the banks of the River Dudwell, where Rudyard Kipling lived from 1902 until his death in 1936. Fun for children, because there is a working flour mill, but not spectacular for the knowledgeable gardener, except for the *Campsis grandiflora* on the house.

Bates Green Farm

Arlington, Polegate, East Sussex BN26 6SH
☎ 0323 482039

OWNER Mr & Mrs J R McCutchan
LOCATION 3 miles south west of Hailsham
OPEN For NGS and by appointment
ADMISSION £1.50
FACILITIES Parking; loos; access for the disabled; plants for sale; refreshments by arrangement
FEATURES Herbaceous borders; rock garden; water features; woodland garden; colour borders; bluebells

Made by the present owners over the last 20 years. Several different areas: a large rock garden, a shady garden, and wonderful mixed borders planted for year-round colour associations.

Brickwall House

Frewen College, Northiam, East Sussex TN31 6NL
☎ 0797 223329   📠 079 742567

OWNER Frewen Educational Trust
LOCATION Off B2088
OPEN 2 pm – 5 pm; Saturdays & Bank Holiday Mondays; 1 April to 30 September
ADMISSION £2.00

FACILITIES Parking; dogs permitted; loos; access for the disabled; postcards and guide books
FEATURES Good collection of trees; herbaceous borders; good topiary; young garden; extensively redesigned since 1980
ENGLISH HERITAGE GRADE II*

Designed as a Stuart garden, to match the house, Brickwall has borders planted exclusively with old-fashioned plants and a chess garden where green and yellow yew shapes are grown in squares of black or white chips. Very neatly maintained.

Charleston Farmhouse

Firle, Lewes, East Sussex BN8 6LL
☎ 0323 811265   📠 0323 811628

OWNER The Charleston Trust
LOCATION Off the A27 Lewes to Eastbourne road
OPEN 2 pm – 6 pm; Wednesday, Thursday, Saturday, Sunday and Bank Holiday Mondays; April to October; 2 pm – 5 pm; Saturday & Sunday; November to December
ADMISSION Adults £1.50; Children (5-16) 50p
FACILITIES Parking; loos; facilities for the disabled; plants for sale; small shop
FEATURES Herbaceous borders; follies and garden buildings
FRIENDS Details from the Secretary

This witness to the Bloomsbury group is not a gardener's garden, but full of vivacious quirks and follies. The bric-a-brac which decorates every corner is sometimes amusing, always provocative.

Clinton Lodge

Fletching, Uckfield, East Sussex TN22 3ST
☎ 0825 722952

OWNER Mr & Mrs M R Collum
LOCATION In main village street
OPEN 2 pm – 6 pm; 12, 13, 20, 27 June
ADMISSION £2.00
FACILITIES Dogs permitted; loos; access for the disabled; plants for sale; home-made teas
FEATURES Herbaceous borders; herbs; old roses and climbers; yew hedges; lime walks; *potager*; knot gardens

A rising star among new gardens, designed round a handsome 17th century house. 6 acres of formal gardens of different periods, starting with a mediaeval *potager* and an Elizabethan herb garden. The most successful parts are the pre-Raphaelite walk of lilies and pale roses, and the Victorian herbaceous borders in soft pastel shades.

Cobblers

Mount Pleasant, Jarvis Brook, Crowborough, East Sussex TN6 2ND
☎ 0892 655969

OWNER Mr & Mrs Martin Furniss
LOCATION Turn off B2100 into Tollwood Road: ¼ mile on right
OPEN For NGS
ADMISSION Adults £3.50; Children £1; prices include teas
FACILITIES Parking; loos; access for the disabled; plants for sale; home-made teas
FEATURES Herbaceous borders; gravel or scree garden; herbs; plantsman's garden; modern roses; water features

Tightly planned and beautifully planted garden made by an architect who is also a plantsman. There is a great variety of habitats and plants (bog, alpine, hot-coloured, shade-loving etc) within a design which opens out its perspectives slowly. Colour all season.

Great Dixter

Dixter Road, Northiam, East Sussex TN31 6PH
☎ 0797 253160

OWNER Christopher Lloyd
LOCATION Off A28 at Northiam Post Office
OPEN 2 pm – 5 pm; daily except Monday; 1 April to 9 October, open Bank Holiday Mondays
ADMISSION Adults £2.50; Children 25p
FACILITIES Parking; loos; plants for sale; gift shop
FEATURES Herbaceous borders; fruit and vegetables of special interest; herbs; designed by Lutyens; plantsman's garden; modern roses; old roses and climbers; sub-tropical plants; good topiary; particularly good in July-August; meadow garden; colour schemes; long border
ENGLISH HERITAGE GRADE I

Several well-defined enclosures surround the Lutyens house but they change constantly as Christopher Lloyd rethinks, reworks and replants. Dixter is a living lesson in the choice and use of plants, a garden to revisit frequently.

Michelham Priory

Upper Dicker, Hailsham, East Sussex BN27 3QS
☎ 0323 844224   📠 0323 844030

OWNER The Sussex Archeological Society
LOCATION Signposted from A22 and A27
OPEN 11 am – 5.30 pm; 25 March to 31 October
ADMISSION Adults £3.50; Senior Citizens £2.90; Children £1.90; Family £9.20 (2+2)
FACILITIES Parking; loos; facilities for the disabled; plants for sale; restaurant & tea room

FEATURES Herbaceous borders; fine conifers; herbs; modern roses; old roses and climbers; water features

Previous Augustinian priory with Elizabethan barn, blacksmith shop, rope museum, moat. Physic Garden with medieval herb examples. Working watermill with bakery.

Offham House
Offham, Lewes, East Sussex BN7 3QE
☎ 0273 474824

OWNER Mr & Mrs H N A Goodman
LOCATION 2½ miles north of Lewes on A275
OPEN 2 pm – 6 pm for NGS
ADMISSION Adults £1.00; Children 50p
FACILITIES Parking; dogs permitted; loos; access for the disabled; plants for sale; home-made cakes & tea
FEATURES Good collection of trees; herbaceous borders; fruit and vegetables of special interest; glasshouses to visit; herbs; plantsman's garden; old roses and climbers; cherry orchard; lilacs

Good modern garden, burgeoning with energy and interest. The plantings are thick and show an eye for good new plants. Lilacs, fritillaries and early purple orchids in spring; shrub roses, paeonies and columbines in June. There is much more for high summer and autumn interest if only the owners could be persuaded to open a little more often!

Pashley Manor
Ticehurst, Wadhurst, East Sussex TN5 7NE
☎ 0580 200692

OWNER James Sellick
LOCATION On B2099 between A21 and Ticehurst
OPEN Tuesday – Thursday, Saturday & Bank Holiday Mondays; 4 April to 15 October
ADMISSION Adults £3.00; Senior Citizens £2.50
FACILITIES Parking; loos; plants for sale; fresh produce for sale; home-made refreshments on fine days
FEATURES Fine conifers; follies and garden buildings; glasshouses to visit; water features; Victorian shrubberies; hydrangeas; irises
FRIENDS No friends organisation yet, but Pashley Manor is sponsoring a new annual competition for garden paintings. Details from James Sellick

A new/old garden, made or remade in the Victorian style over the last ten years with advice from Tony Pasley. The results are gentle shapes, spacious expanses, harmonious colours and solid plantings. It gets better every year.

Sheffield Park
Uckfield, East Sussex TN22 3QX
☎ 0825 790655

OWNER The National Trust

LOCATION Between East Grinstead & Lewes on A275
OPEN 11 am – 6 pm, Tuesday – Saturday, Sunday & Bank Holiday Mondays, 1 April to 6 November; 11am – 4pm, Wednesday – Saturday; 9 November to 17 December
ADMISSION May, October, November – Adults £4.00; Children £2.00 Other – Adults £3.50; Children £1.80 (1993)
FACILITIES Parking; loos; facilities for the disabled; National Trust shop; refreshments nearby
FEATURES Good collection of trees; landscape designed by Capability Brown and Humphry Repton; fine conifers; plantsman's garden; water features; woodland garden; plantings by Graham Thomas; daffodils; bluebells; kalmias; autumn crocuses; rhododendrons; tallest *Acer maximowiczianum* (syn. *nikoense*) in the British Isles
ENGLISH HERITAGE GRADE I
NCCPG NATIONAL COLLECTIONS *Rhododendron*

Little remains of Capability Brown and Repton except the lakes which now reflect the plantings of exotic trees – landscaping on the grandest of scales. Wonderful leaf colours whatever the season, plus gentians in autumn.

Standen
East Grinstead, East Sussex RH19 4NE
☎ 0342 323029

OWNER The National Trust
LOCATION 2 miles south of East Grinstead, signposted from B2110
OPEN 12.30 pm – 5.30 pm; Wednesday – Sunday and Bank Holiday Mondays; 1 April to 31 October
ADMISSION Weekdays £2.50; Other £3.00
FACILITIES Parking; dogs permitted; loos; National Trust shop; light lunches & afternoon teas
FEATURES Herbaceous borders; fine conifers; rock garden; old roses and climbers; rhododendrons; azaleas; woodland shrubs

Small Edwardian garden with magnificent views across the valley. A series of enclosed gardens around the house give way to woodland slopes and an old quarry furnished with ferns.

WEST SUSSEX

Berri Court
Yapton, Arundel, West Sussex BN18 0ED
☎ 0243 551663

OWNER Mr & Mrs John Turner
LOCATION Yapton, 5 miles south west of Arundel, centre of village next to Black Dog pub

OPEN 2 pm – 5 pm, Sundays & Mondays, 3 & 4 April, 8 & 9 May, 26 & 27 June; 12 noon – 4 pm, 23 & 24 October

ADMISSION Adults £1; Children 30p

FACILITIES Parking; dogs permitted; loos; facilities for the disabled; plants for sale

FEATURES Herbaceous borders; modern roses; old roses and climbers; rhododendrons; eucalyptus; hydrangeas; lily ponds

A plantsman's garden with a compact design, some 3 acres in extent.

Borde Hill Garden

Haywards Heath, West Sussex RH16 1XP

☎ 0444 450326   ☏ 0444 440427

OWNER Borde Hill Garden Ltd

LOCATION 1½ miles north of Haywards Heath

OPEN 10 am – 6 pm; daily; 1 April to 16 October

ADMISSION Adults £3; Senior Citizens £2.50; Children £1

FACILITIES Parking; dogs permitted; loos; facilities for the disabled; plants for sale; small gift shop; tea rooms, restaurant & pub

FEATURES Good collection of trees; plantsman's garden; water features; woodland garden; rhododendrons; azaleas; magnolias; plants from original seed; tallest *Magnolia delavayi, Juniperus virginiana* in the British Isles, and 19 other record trees

ENGLISH HERITAGE GRADE II*

FRIENDS The Friends of Borde Hill Garden run events throughout the year: details from the administrator

This important woodland garden has a significant collection of rhododendron species grown from such introducers as Forrest and Kingdon Ward. It has recently been revamped for the recreation market and is all the better for the new capital. There are good new borders, a lake, and all sorts of facilities like a smart restaurant: very cockle-warming to see Borde Hill on the up again.

Coates Manor

Fittleworth, Pulborough, West Sussex RH20 1ES

☎ 079 882356

OWNER Mrs S M Thorp

LOCATION ½ miles off B2138, signposted Coates

OPEN 11 am – 6 pm; Sunday – Tuesday; 12 to 14 June and by appointment

ADMISSION Adults £1.50; Children free

FACILITIES Parking; loos; plants for sale; refreshments on open days

FEATURES Herbaceous borders; colour planting; foliage plants

A small, neatly designed and intensely planted garden which crams a lifetime's learning into its plantings. Long-term colour effects are its outstanding quality:

leaves, berries, trunks, stems, form, shadow and texture are all individually exploited to the maximum. A model of its kind and beautifully maintained.

Cooke's House

West Burton, Pulborough, West Sussex RH20 1HD

☎ 079 881353

OWNER Miss J B Courtauld

LOCATION Off A29 at White Horse in Bury Hill

OPEN 2 pm – 6 pm; 17 – 19 and 24 – 26 April; and by appointment

ADMISSION £1.00

FACILITIES Parking; loos; access for the disabled

FEATURES Herbaceous borders; old roses and climbers; good topiary

ENGLISH HERITAGE GRADE II

A neat and well maintained garden, pretty in spring when the primulas and bulbs are out. Even better at midsummer when the roses and herbaceous plants crammed into small enclosures create a sense of great richness and harmony.

Cowdray Park

Midhurst, West Sussex GU29 0AY

☎ 0730 812423   ☏ 0730 815608

OWNER The Viscount Cowdray

LOCATION South of A272, 1 mile east of Midhurst

OPEN 2 pm – 7 pm; Sunday; 15 May

ADMISSION £1.00

FACILITIES Parking

FEATURES 300 year old Lebanon cedar; wellingtonia avenue; rhododendrons; tallest *Chamaecyparis pisifera* (and two other conifers) in the British Isles.

ENGLISH HERITAGE GRADE II*

Seldom open, but worth a long journey to see the extraordinarily overwrought house and its contemporary (100 years old) collection of trees, particularly conifers. Some are now record-breakers, and the sweeps of rhododendrons and azaleas are on the grand scale too. Pretty awesome.

Denmans

Fontwell, Arundel, West Sussex BN18 0SU

☎ 0243 542808   ☏ 0243 544064

LOCATION Off A29 or A27, near Fontwell racecourse

OPEN 9 am – 5 pm; daily; 1 March to 24 December; or by appointment

ADMISSION Adults £2.25; Senior Citizens £1.85; Children (over 5) £1.25; groups (15+) £1.65

FACILITIES Shop; garden centre; full lunches & teas

FEATURES Herbaceous borders; gravel or scree garden; herbs; old roses and climbers; water features; spring bulbs

This small modern garden is a showpiece for John Brookes' ideas: easy care, using foliage, gravel mulches, contrasts of form, coloured stems, winter bark, plants as elements of design. Garden decoration *in excelsis*.

Gravetye Manor

East Grinstead, West Sussex RH19 4LJ
☎ 0342 810567

OWNER Peter Herbert
LOCATION 4 miles south west of East Grinstead
OPEN To hotel guests only
FACILITIES Parking
FEATURES Good collection of trees; herbaceous borders; fine conifers; plantsman's garden; old roses and climbers; good topiary; water features; woodland garden; alpine meadow
ENGLISH HERITAGE GRADE II*

William Robinson's own garden, very influential 80 years ago, and scrupulously maintained by Peter Herbert as it was in its prime. Gravetye is still a garden to learn from: there is much to admire and copy.

The High Beeches

Handcross, West Sussex RH17 6HQ
☎ 0444 400589

OWNER High Beeches Gardens Conservation Trust
LOCATION South of B2110, 1 mile east of M23 at Handcross
OPEN 1 pm – 5 pm; daily; 4 April to 26 June; 3 September to 30 October
ADMISSION Adults £2.50
FACILITIES Parking; loos
FEATURES Good collection of trees; fine conifers; ecological interest; plantsman's garden; woodland garden; rhododendrons
ENGLISH HERITAGE GRADE II
NCCPG NATIONAL COLLECTIONS *Stewartia*
FRIENDS High Beeches Gardens Conservation Trust is an active organisation with many events of interest to gardeners: details from the Curator

One of the best of the famous Sussex gardens, with splendid rhododendrons, azaleas, magnolias and camellias, but also an emphasis on colour planting, wonderful autumn colour and a policy of letting good plants naturalise. A great credit to the Boscawen family who have devoted 25 years to its maintenance and improvement.

Highdown

Littlehampton Road, Goring-by-Sea, West Sussex BN12 6NY
☎ 0903 248067

OWNER Worthing Borough Council
LOCATION Off the Littlehampton road, poorly signposted

OPEN 10 am – 4.30 pm; daily; all year. Closes at 8 pm at weekends and on Bank Holiday Mondays from April to September
ADMISSION Free – donations welcome
FACILITIES Parking; loos; facilities for the disabled; refreshments in high season
FEATURES Good collection of trees; herbaceous borders; fine conifers; plantsman's garden; rock garden; old roses and climbers; woodland garden; tallest specimen of *Carpinus turczaninowii* in the British Isles, a handsome tree
ENGLISH HERITAGE GRADE II*

A very important garden. Its maker, Sir Frederic Stern, was determined to try anything that might grow on chalk. 80 years on, the results are some handsome trees, vigorous roses, and long-forgotten paeony hybrids. Best of all are the naturalised hellebores, tulips and anemones. Alas, Stern made a mistake in leaving it to Worthing Borough Council.

Leonardslee Gardens

Lower Beeding, Horsham, West Sussex RH13 6PP
☎ 0403 891212   FAX 0403 891336

OWNER R R Loder
LOCATION 3 miles south west of Handcross
OPEN 10 am – 6 pm; daily 1 April to 31 October
ADMISSION May – £4.00; April & June to October £3; children £2
FACILITIES Parking; loos; plants for sale; gift shop; licensed restaurant & café
FEATURES Fine conifers; glasshouses to visit; oriental features; plantsman's garden; rock garden; water features; woodland garden; new alpine house; wallabies; rhododendrons; azaleas; bluebells; tallest fossil tree *Metasequoia glyptostroboides* and *Magnolia campbellii* in the British Isles
ENGLISH HERITAGE GRADE I

A spectacular collection of rhododendrons and azaleas is the essence of Leonardslee, and the way they are planted in drifts of one colour. But there are magnolias, camellias and innumerable rare plants, as well as a formidable bonsai collection. The 80 acres of woodland garden are laced with lakes, dells and groves. Ravishing in May.

Nymans

Handcross, Haywards Heath, West Sussex RH17 6EB
☎ 0444 400321

OWNER The National Trust
LOCATION Handcross, off the main road
OPEN 11 am – 7 pm; daily; 1 April to 31 October
ADMISSION Adults £3.50

FACILITIES Parking; loos; facilities for the disabled; plants for sale; shop; teas
FEATURES Good collection of trees; herbaceous borders; fine conifers; plantsman's garden; rock garden; modern roses; old roses and climbers; good topiary; woodland garden; tallest *Magnolia campbellii alba* in the British Isles
ENGLISH HERITAGE GRADE II*

The sumptuous mansion in the West Country style has been gutted by fire, but the garden is intact, with opulent herbaceous borders in the walled garden, a pioneering collection of old roses, a stupendous wisteria pergola and vast collections of magnolias and camellias. Yet some say Nymans is overrated.

Parham

Parham House, Pulborough, West Sussex RH20 4HS
☎ 0903 744888

OWNER Trustees of Parham Estate
LOCATION On A238 midway between Pulborough and Storrington
OPEN 1 pm – 6 pm; Wednesdays, Thursdays, Sundays & Bank Holiday Mondays; 3 April to 2 October
ADMISSION Adults £2.50; Children £1
FACILITIES Parking; dogs permitted; loos; facilities for the disabled; plants for sale; shop; self-service teas
FEATURES Herbaceous borders; fruit and vegetables of special interest; plantsman's garden; old roses and climbers; water features; new maze; HHA/Christie's Garden of the Year in 1990
ENGLISH HERITAGE GRADE I

An ethereal English garden for the loveliest of Elizabethan manor houses. In the park are a landscaped lake and a cricket ground. The fun for garden-lovers is in the old walled garden: lush borders, colour plantings, old and new fruit trees, and all maintained to the highest standard.

Petworth House

Petworth, West Sussex GU28 0AE
☎ 0798 42207

OWNER The National Trust
LOCATION At Petworth, well signed
OPEN 8 am – dusk, daily except Monday & Friday (open Bank Holidays), 1 April to 31 October
ADMISSION Adults £4.00; Children £2.00 (1993)
FACILITIES Parking; loos; facilities for the disabled; shop; restaurant; tea rooms
FEATURES Herbaceous borders; landscape designed by Capability Brown; water features; woodland garden; deer park; daffodils; nine record-holding trees all felled by the Great Gale of 1987
ENGLISH HERITAGE GRADE I

One of the best Capability Brown landscapes in England sweeps up to the windows of the house itself. The National Trust has decided to add modern attractions: herbaceous borders and acres of azaleas in a new woodland garden.

Stonehurst

Ardingly, West Sussex RH17 6TN
☎ 0444 892052

OWNER D R Strauss
LOCATION 1 mile north of Ardingly on B2028
OPEN 11 am – 5 pm; 4 April, 2 May, 15 May
ADMISSION Adults £2.50; Children £1.00
FACILITIES Parking; dogs permitted; loos; plants for sale; orchids, rhododendrons & camellias for sale; teas
FEATURES Herbaceous borders; follies and garden buildings; rock garden; water features; camellias; magnolias; azaleas; SSSI
ENGLISH HERITAGE GRADE II

Stonehurst is in a rock-lined secret valley, where springs issue to form a series of small lakes, and rare liverworts have special scientific interest. The Strausses have made it known as a garden for rhododendrons, camellias and rare trees and shrubs which regularly win prizes at RHS shows in London. Well maintained.

Telegraph House

North Marden, nr Chichester, West Sussex
P018 9JX
☎ 0730 825206

OWNER Mr & Mrs Gault
LOCATION Entrance on B2141, 2 miles south of Harting
OPEN 2 pm – 6 pm, 11 & 12 June, 16 & 17 July, or 1 May to 30 August by appointment
ADMISSION Adults £1.50; Children 75p
FACILITIES Parking; dogs permitted; loos; refreshments on open week-ends
FEATURES Herbaceous borders; old roses and climbers; woodland garden; 1 mile avenue of copper beeches

The house is c.1900 and French in style, but the garden has been made by the present owners over the last 20 years. Yew hedges enclose a series of terraces and intimate gardens: roses, shrubs and herbaceous plantings. Nearby are 150 acres of natural woodland, much of it ancient yew.

Wakehurst Place

Ardingly, Haywards Heath, West Sussex RH17 6TN

OWNER R B G, Kew
LOCATION On B2028 between Turner's Hill & Ardingly

OPEN Daily except Christmas Day & New Year's Day; opens at 10 am all year; closes at 4 pm from November to January; 5 pm in February; 6 pm in March & October; 7 pm from April to September.

ADMISSION £3.50 adults (1993); free to NT members

FACILITIES Parking; loos; facilities for the disabled; bookshop & giftshop; light refreshments, plus new restaurant in April

FEATURES Good collection of trees; herbaceous borders; fine conifers; ecological interest; gravel or scree garden; plantsman's garden; old roses and climbers; water features; woodland garden; particularly interesting in winter; Asian heath garden; pinetum; cardiocrinums; bluebells; tallest scarlet oak *Quercus coccinea* in the British Isles, plus 16 further tree records

ENGLISH HERITAGE GRADE II*

NCCPG NATIONAL COLLECTIONS *Betula*, *Hypericum*, *Nothofagus*, *Skimmia*

FRIENDS Part of the Friends of Kew organisation

Allow plenty of time for Wakehurst: it is very big, and there is much to see. Near the house are the winter garden, two ponds, the new Asian heath garden and the southern hemisphere garden. No garden combines so perfectly the function of a major botanic institute with the sense of being a private garden still.

West Dean Gardens

West Dean, Chichester, West Sussex PO18 0QZ
☎ 0243 811303   ☎ 0243 811342

OWNER The Edward James Foundation

LOCATION 6 miles north of Chichester on A286

OPEN 11 am – 6 pm; daily; 1 March to 31 October

ADMISSION Adults £2.50; Senior Citizens £2.25; Children £1.00; Parties (over 20) £2.00 each

FACILITIES Parking; dogs permitted; loos; facilities for the disabled; plants for sale; tea, coffee, sandwiches, etc

FEATURES Good collection of trees; fine conifers; fruit and vegetables of special interest; glasshouses to visit; old roses and climbers; museum of old lawn mowers; tallest *Cupressus goveniana* in U.K.

ENGLISH HERITAGE GRADE II*

NCCPG NATIONAL COLLECTIONS *Liriodendron*, *Aesculus*

Laid out in the 1890s and 1900s, West Dean has now been extensively restored: Harold Peto's 100 metre pergola has been replanted with roses; much of the damage to the arboretum caused by the 1987 storm has been made good; and the great range of glasshouses in the walled garden has been repaired – the garden itself planted as a working kitchen garden. Everything about West Dean gets better and better.

Yew Tree Cottage

Crawley Down, Turners Hill, West Sussex
RH10 4EY
☎ 0342 714633

OWNER Mrs K Hudson

LOCATION Opposite Grange Farm on B20

OPEN 2 pm – 6 pm; 25 – 26 June or by appointment

ADMISSION £1.00

FACILITIES Parking; plants for sale; refreshments

FEATURES Herbaceous borders; fruit and vegetables of special interest; old roses and climbers; cottage garden style; colour borders

This miraculous small garden (⅓rd acre) has been designed, planted and maintained by the 88 year old owner over many years and won infinite plaudits for its display of plants in the Jekyll manner. There is no better example of the cottage garden style.

WARWICKSHIRE

Arbury Hall

Nuneaton, Warwickshire CV10 7PT
☎ 0203 382804   ☎ 0203 641147

OWNER Viscount Daventry

LOCATION 3 miles south east of Nuneaton off the B4102

OPEN 2 pm – 5.30 pm; Easter Sunday to 30 September; Sundays & Bank Holidays

ADMISSION Adults £1.60; Children 80p

FACILITIES Parking; dogs permitted; loos; access for the disabled; gift & crafts shop; tea rooms

FEATURES Follies and garden buildings; modern roses; old roses and climbers; water features; woodland garden; daffodils; rhododendrons; azaleas; bluebells; wisteria

ENGLISH HERITAGE GRADE II*

Good trees (especially purple beeches), handsome parkland, lakes and ponds – Arbury has good bones for a garden. Then there are bluebell woods, pollarded limes, a large rose garden, a walled garden and a huge wisteria. Nothing is outstanding in itself, but the ensemble is an oasis of peace on the edge of industrial Daventry and worth the journey from far away.

Charlecote Park

Wellesbourne, Warwick, Warwickshire CV35 9ER
☎ 0789 470277

OWNER The National Trust

LOCATION Signed from A429

OPEN 11 am – 6 pm; Friday – Tuesday (closed Good Friday); 1 April to 31 October

ADMISSION £4.00; Children (5-16) £2.00

FACILITIES Parking; loos; facilities for the disabled; National Trust shop; restaurant

FEATURES Landscape designed by Capability Brown; fine conifers; glasshouses to visit; good topiary; water features; deer park; orangery

ENGLISH HERITAGE GRADE II*

Fine cedars and a Capability Brown park are the main claims to Charlecote's fame, but the young William Shakespeare is reputed to have poached deer from the park, so the National Trust has planted a border with plants mentioned in his works.

Farnborough Hall

Banbury, Warwickshire OX17 1DU
☎ 0295 89202

OWNER The National Trust

LOCATION A423, 6 miles north of Banbury

OPEN 2 pm – 6 pm; Wednesdays – Saturdays; 1 April to 30 September

ADMISSION Grounds £1.50; Terrace Walk £1.00

FACILITIES Parking; dogs permitted; loos; access for the disabled

FEATURES Follies and garden buildings; old roses and climbers; good topiary; water features; woodland garden

Sanderson Millar's masterpiece – grand vistas, classical temples and a dominating obelisk. Plus a long curving terraced walk to the adjoining estate of Mollington. No flowers, but space and peace.

Ryton Organic Gardens

Henry Doubleday Research Association, Ryton-on-Dunsmore, Coventry, Warwickshire CV8 3LG

OWNER The Henry Doubleday Research Association (HDRA)

LOCATION 5 miles south east of Coventry off A45

OPEN 10 am – 5.30 pm; daily

ADMISSION Adults £2.50; Senior Citizens £1.75; Children £1.25; group rates

FACILITIES Parking; loos; facilities for the disabled; shop with gardening products, books, food, wine & gifts; organic wholefood restaurant

FEATURES Herbaceous borders; ecological interest; fruit and vegetables of special interest; glasshouses to visit; herbs; plantsman's garden; rock garden; modern roses; old roses and climbers; woodland garden; interesting for children

FRIENDS Join the HDRA – see Societies section

Ryton is the UK centre for organic gardening where experiments are made in using only natural fertilisers and trying to operate without pesticides. It is very well laid out, with dozens of different small gardens, all highly instructive. The staff's commitment is also im-

pressive. You may not be convinced by what you see, but it will make you think. The excellent restaurant and substantial shop will add considerably to your enjoyment.

Sherbourne Park

Sherbourne, Warwick, Warwickshire CV35 8AP
☎ 0926 624255

OWNER The Hon. Lady Smith-Ryland

LOCATION A429 between M40 and Barford

OPEN By appointment

ADMISSION £2.50; Senior Citizens £2.00; Children (under 13) free

FACILITIES Parking; dogs permitted; loos; access for the disabled; refreshments by arrangement

FEATURES Herbaceous borders; plantsman's garden; old roses and climbers; water features; lilies

35 years of good planning and planting by the present owner has produced a series of smallish enclosed gardens around the house, each distinct and beautifully planted. The shelter of walls and hedges allows such tender plants as *Olearia* and *Carpenteria* to survive, and sometimes to flourish.

Upton House

Banbury, Warwickshire OX15 6HT
☎ 0295 87266

OWNER The National Trust

LOCATION A422, 7 miles north west of Banbury

OPEN 2 pm – 6 pm; Saturday – Wednesday; 1 May to 31 October; plus Saturday, Sunday & Bank Holiday Monday in April

ADMISSION Adults £2.15; Children £1.10

FACILITIES Parking; loos; facilities for the disabled; plants for sale; National Trust shop; tea room

FEATURES Herbaceous borders; fruit and vegetables of special interest; water features

ENGLISH HERITAGE GRADE II*

NCCPG NATIONAL COLLECTIONS *Aster amellus*

High on a ridge near the site of the battle of Edgehill, Upton is terraced right down to the pool at the bottom. The centrepiece is a kitchen garden, reached by flights of Italianate stairs. There are also modern formal gardens, one with standard *Hibiscus* 'Bluebird' underplanted with eryngiums, another a rose garden. Further down are a bog garden, a cherry garden and grand herbaceous borders to lead you back to the house. Fascinating, and not at all what you expect when you first see the house.

Warwick Castle

Warwick, Warwickshire CV34 4QU
☎ 0926 495421

OWNER Tussauds Group

LOCATION   In town centre
OPEN   10 am – 5.30 pm (4.30 pm in winter); daily except 25 December
ADMISSION   Adults £6.75 (1993)
FACILITIES   Parking; loos; shop; refreshments nearby
FEATURES   Fine conifers; old roses and climbers; good topiary; Capability Brown landscape
ENGLISH HERITAGE GRADE   I

A classic 18th century landscape, looking good after recent restoration, to which have been added a late 19th century formal garden and a 1980s Victorian rose garden, pretty but not very profound.

WEST MIDLANDS

Birmingham Botanical Gardens

Westbourne Road, Edgbaston, Birmingham, West Midlands B15 3TR
☎ 021 454 1860

OWNER   Birmingham Botanical & Horticultural Society
LOCATION   2 miles west of city centre
OPEN   9 am (Sunday 10 am) – dusk; daily; all year
ADMISSION   Adults £2.90; Concessions £1.60; (Summer Sunday & Bank Holiday £3.20
FACILITIES   Parking; loos; facilities for the disabled; plants for sale; gift shop; restaurant & light refreshments
FEATURES   Herbaceous borders; fine conifers; fruit and vegetables of special interest; glasshouses to visit; plantsman's garden; rock garden; modern roses; old roses and climbers; water features; interesting for children; children's gardens; adventure playground
ENGLISH HERITAGE GRADE   II*
NCCPG NATIONAL COLLECTIONS Bonsai, *Verbascum*
FRIENDS   Membership details available from the gate

Part botanic garden, part public park, wholly delightful, the Birmingham Botanical Gardens can boast a historic lay-out (John Loudon), rare trees and shrubs, gardens for rhododendrons, roses, herbs and alpines, and four glasshouses (tropical, palm house, orangery and cacti house) as well as a good restaurant, brilliant standards of maintenance and a brass band playing on Sunday afternoons in summer. A garden to enjoy.

Castle Bromwich Hall

Chester Road, Castle Bromwich, West Midlands B36 9BT
☎ 021 749 4100

OWNER   Castle Bromwich Hall Gardens Trust
LOCATION   5 miles from city centre just off A47

OPEN   1.30 pm – 4 30 pm; Monday – Thursday; 2 pm – 6 pm; Weekend & Bank Holiday Monday
ADMISSION   Adults £3.00; Concessions £1.50
FACILITIES   Parking; dogs permitted; loos; access for the disabled; plants for sale; gift shop; refreshments
FEATURES   Interesting for children; green walks; fruit garden; maze; wilderness; historic garden undergoing restoration
ENGLISH HERITAGE GRADE   II*
FRIENDS   Friends of the Gardens organisation

Garden archaeology at work. Castle Bromwich is being restored as it was in 1700 by a privately funded trust. Quietly awe-inspiring, and the tiny orangery, little more than a summerhouse, is very covetable.

Wightwick Manor

Wightwick, Wolverhampton, West Midlands WV6 8EE
☎ 0902 761108   📠 0902 764663

OWNER   The National Trust
LOCATION   3 miles west of Wolverhampton on A454
OPEN   Thursday & Saturday; 2 pm – 6 pm; 30 April to 30 September
ADMISSION   Adults £2.00; Children £1.00
FACILITIES   Parking; dogs permitted; loos; coffee & soft drinks
FEATURES   Herbaceous borders; rock garden; old roses and climbers; good topiary

High Victorian camp, designed by Thomas Mawson and planted by Alfred Parsons. Topiary, a rose arbour, avenues of Irish yews and a Poets' Corner where all the plants were taken as cuttings from the gardens of literary men – Keats, Tennyson and Dickens among them.

WILTSHIRE

Ashtree Cottage

Kilmington Common, Warminster, Wiltshire BA12 6QY
☎ 0985 844740

OWNER   Mr & Mrs L J Lauderdale
LOCATION   B3092 ½ mile north of Stourhead garden; 1 mile west towards Alfred's Tower
OPEN   For NGS and by appointment
ADMISSION   Adults £1.50; Children 50p
FACILITIES   Parking; plants for sale; small garden nursery
FEATURES   Plantsman's garden; old roses and climbers; young garden

Small high-profile new garden, prettily planted for year-round interest but best at high summer with shrub roses, ramblers and perennials. See *The Garden at*

Ashtree Cottage by Wendy Lauderdale (Weidenfeld & Nicolson, 1993, £14.99)

Avebury Manor

Avebury, Marlborough, Wiltshire
☎ 0985 847777

OWNER The National Trust
LOCATION In the village, well signposted
OPEN 11 am – 5.30 pm; daily except Mondays & Thursdays; 26 March to 31 October
ADMISSION Adults £2 (1993)
FACILITIES Parking; access for the disabled; shop just outside the garden; refreshments in village
FEATURES Herbaceous borders; old roses and climbers; good topiary; double lavender walk

A recent owner did much to revive and restore this great Edwardian garden. It is to be hoped that the National Trust will continue the work.

Bolehyde Manor

Allington, Chippenham, Wiltshire
☎ 0249 652105   FAX 0249 659296

OWNER Earl & Countess Cairns
LOCATION 2 miles west of Chippenham
OPEN 2.30 pm – 6 pm; Sunday 19 June; and by appointment
ADMISSION £1.50
FACILITIES Parking
FEATURES Herbaceous borders; fruit and vegetables of special interest; plantsman's garden; old roses and climbers; climbing roses; half-hardy plants

Charming series of enclosed gardens around old stone-built house. Brilliantly developed by the owners with help from Melanie Chambers.

Bowood House

Calne, Wiltshire SN11 0LZ
☎ 0249 812102   FAX 0249 821757

OWNER The Earl of Shelburne
LOCATION Off A4 in Derry Hill village between Calne and Chippenham
OPEN 11 am – 6 pm; daily; 26 March to 30 October
ADMISSION Adults £4.50; Senior Citizens £4; Children £2.30
FACILITIES Parking; loos; facilities for the disabled; plants for sale; gift shop & garden centre; buffet lunches & afternoon teas in licensed restaurant
FEATURES Good collection of trees; landscape designed by Capability Brown and Humphry Repton; fine conifers; follies and garden buildings; modern roses; garden sculpture; good topiary; water features; woodland garden; interesting for children; bluebells; immodest sculpture; adventure playground; tallest *Populus* × *canadensis* 'Serotina' in UK (and two other tree records)

ENGLISH HERITAGE GRADE I

Beautifully maintained and welcoming, Bowood has something from every period of English garden history. Capability Brown made the lake and Charles Hamilton the famous cascade. There are an important 19th century pinetum laid out on pre-Linnean principles, handsome Italianate formal gardens, and modern rhododendron drives in a bluebell wood. Be sure to miss the reclining nude above the formal gardens.

Broadleas

Devizes, Wiltshire
☎ 0380 722035

OWNER Broadleas Gardens Trust
LOCATION 1 mile south of Devizes
OPEN 2 pm – 6 pm; Wednesday, Thursday & Sunday; 1 April to 31 October
ADMISSION £1.50 (1993)
FACILITIES Parking; loos; access for the disabled; plants for sale; teas on summer Sundays
FEATURES Good collection of trees; herbaceous borders; fine conifers; plantsman's garden; modern roses; old roses and climbers; woodland garden
ENGLISH HERITAGE GRADE II

Broadleas has a rose garden, grey border, a rock garden and a 'secret' garden hidden behind a hedge of *Prunus* × *blireana*, all near the Regency house. But the main attraction is the Dell, a greensand combe that stretches down to the valley below, its sides just stuffed with good things – rare trees, vast magnolias, sheets of *Primula whitei* and cyclamen.

Conock Manor

Devizes, Wiltshire SN10 3QP
☎ 0380 840227

OWNER Mr & Mrs Bonar Sykes
LOCATION 5 miles south east of Devizes off A342
OPEN 2 pm – 6 pm; for NGS
ADMISSION Adults £1.00
FACILITIES Parking; access for the disabled; some shrubs & herbaceous plants for sale; tea & home-made biscuits
FEATURES Good collection of trees; herbaceous borders; old roses and climbers
ENGLISH HERITAGE GRADE II

Beautiful parkland surrounds this covetable Georgian house. Behind the copper-domed stables an elegant shrub walk meanders past *Sorbus*, maples and magnolias.

Corsham Court

Corsham, Wiltshire SN13 0BZ
☎ 0249 712214

OWNER Lord Methuen

LOCATION Signposted from A4 Bath to Chippenham
OPEN 2 pm – 6 pm; 1 August to 30 September
ADMISSION £1.50
FACILITIES Parking; dogs permitted; loos; access for the disabled
FEATURES Good collection of trees; oriental features; designed by Capability Brown and Humphry Repton; amazing oriental plane *Platanus orientalis* whose sweeping limbs have rooted over a huge area
ENGLISH HERITAGE GRADE II*

Major 18th century landscape garden, with pretty 1820s flower garden and ambitious modern arboretum: strongly recommended.

The Courts
Holt, Trowbridge, Wiltshire BA14 6RR
☎ 0225 782340

OWNER The National Trust
LOCATION In the middle of Holt village
OPEN 2 pm – 5 pm; Sunday – Friday; 1 April to 1 November
ADMISSION Adults £2.50; Children £1.50
FACILITIES Parking; loos; access for the disabled
FEATURES Herbaceous borders; plantsman's garden; good topiary; water features
ENGLISH HERITAGE GRADE II

1920s masterpiece in the Hidcote style. Rich colour plantings in a series of garden rooms. Excellent plants, beautifully used: well maintained.

Heale House
Middle Woodford, Salisbury, Wiltshire SP4 6NT
☎ 0722 72504

OWNER Guy Rasch
LOCATION Signposted off the western Woodford valley road
OPEN 10 am – 5 pm; all year
ADMISSION £2.00 each. Parties over 20, £1.75 each (1993)
FACILITIES Parking; dogs permitted; loos; access for the disabled; large plant centre; garden & gift shop
FEATURES Herbaceous borders; fruit and vegetables of special interest; oriental features; old roses and climbers; water features; Christie's/HHA Garden of the Year in 1984
ENGLISH HERITAGE GRADE II*

A Peto garden round the prettiest house in Wiltshire. Formal walks, ponds, lawns and balustrading. Rich colours and clever planting. Japanese garden around genuine tea-house. Pure enchantment.

Hillbarn House
Great Bedwyn, Marlborough, Wiltshire SN8 3NU
☎ 0672 870207   FAX 0672 871015

OWNER Alastair J Buchanan
LOCATION In High Street, opposite garage
OPEN 2 pm – 6 pm; 19 June & 18 September
FACILITIES Loos; tea & biscuits
FEATURES Herbaceous borders; plantman's garden

Lanning Roper's masterpiece makes brilliant use of a small steep site by dividing space to create an illusion of size. Well maintained.

Home Covert
Roundway, Devizes, Wiltshire SN10 2JA
☎ 0380 723407

OWNER Mr & Mrs John Phillips
LOCATION 1 mile north of Devizes in Roundway Village
OPEN Any time for parties by appointment; NGS open days
ADMISSION £2.00 by appointment; £1.50 NGS open days
FACILITIES Parking; dogs permitted; teas on NGS days
FEATURES Plantsman's garden; water features; woodland garden

One of the finest plantsman's gardens in southern England; 'a botanical madhouse' say the owners. Rare trees (*Cercis racemosa*) and shrubs (*Heptacodium jasminoides*): *Lathraea clandestina* and swathes of candelabra primulas in the bog garden.

Iford Manor
Iford, Bradford-on-Avon, Wiltshire BA15 2BA
☎ 0225 863146

OWNER Mrs E Cartwright-Hignett
LOCATION Signed off A36, 7 miles south east of Bath
OPEN 2 pm – 5 pm; Sundays; April to October. Plus Tuesday – Thursday, Saturdays and Bank Holiday Mondays from May to September
ADMISSION Adults £2.00; Senior Citizens & Children (over 10) £1.50
FACILITIES Parking; dogs permitted; loos; teas on Sundays (May to August)
FEATURES Follies and garden buildings; fruit and vegetables of special interest; garden sculpture; woodland garden; Italian cypresses and handsome *Phillyrea*; martagon lilies; cyclamen
ENGLISH HERITAGE GRADE I
NCCPG NATIONAL COLLECTIONS *Acanthus*

Harold Peto's own Italianate garden on a steep wooded hillside, meticulously restored and maintained. Romanesque cloister, octagonal summer house and much architectural bric-a-brac. Wonderfully photogenic.

Longleat House

Warminster, Wiltshire BA12 7NW
☎ 0985 844400   FAX 0985 844885

OWNER The Marquess of Bath
LOCATION Off A362 Warminster to Frome road
OPEN All year
ADMISSION Adults £2.00; Senior Citizens £1.50;
Children 50p (1993)
FACILITIES Parking; dogs permitted; loos; access for
the disabled; shops; cafeterias & restaurants
FEATURES Good collection of trees; herbaceous bor-
ders; landscape designed by Capability Brown and
Humphry Repton; fine conifers; glasshouses to visit;
modern roses; old roses and climbers; good topiary;
water features; woodland garden; interesting for child-
ren; particularly good in July-August; Safari Park;
world's largest maze
ENGLISH HERITAGE GRADE I

Forget the lions and the loins, Longleat has a classic
18th century landscape by Capability Brown, a home
park of 600 acres best seen from Heaven's Gate; a grand
Victorian garden reworked by Russell Page in the
1930s and a new rose maze. Very visitable.

Oare House

Oare, Marlborough, Wiltshire SN8 4JQ
☎ 0672 62428

OWNER Henry Keswick
LOCATION In village, west side of A345
OPEN 2 pm – 6 pm; 24 April & 31 July
ADMISSION Adults £1; Children 20p
FACILITIES Parking; dogs permitted; loos; light re-
freshments
FEATURES Good collection of trees; herbaceous bor-
ders; fruit and vegetables of special interest; modern
roses; tall hedges of field maple
ENGLISH HERITAGE GRADE II

Oare has an approach along lime avenues and tall hedges
whose grandeur is echoed by the main garden behind:
a huge apron of walled lawn, with majestic mixed
borders at the sides, leads the eye over a half-hidden
swimming pool to a grand ride and on to the Marlborough Downs beyond. Intimacy exists only in some
small enclosed gardens to the side and in the kitchen
garden. Here are a magnificent herbaceous border in
reds and yellows, a tunnel of fruit trees and vegetables
in neat rows. A delight.

The Old Vicarage

Edington, Westbury, Wiltshire BA13 4QF
☎ 0380 830512

OWNER John d'Arcy
LOCATION On B3098 in Edington village
OPEN NGS open days or by appointment

ADMISSION £2
FACILITIES Plants for sale
FEATURES Gravel or scree garden; plantsman's gar-
den; young garden; particularly good in July-August
NCCPG NATIONAL COLLECTIONS Oenothera

2 acres of intensively cultivated plantsmanship. The
owner is a distinguished plant collector: his garden is
immaculately maintained and bristles with new species
(Salvia darcyi) and living holotypes.

Roche Court

East Winterslow, Salisbury, Wiltshire SP5 1BG
☎ 0980 862204   FAX 0980 862447

OWNER Mrs Arthur Ponsonby
LOCATION Just south of A30 at Lopcombe corner
OPEN 11 am – 5 pm; Saturday & Sunday; 1 May to
30 October
ADMISSION Free
FACILITIES Parking; access for the disabled
FEATURES Herbaceous borders; garden sculpture;
woodland garden

As a garden, nothing special, but a show place for Mrs
Ponsonby's contemporary sculpture shop. Everything
is for sale, so the garden is ever changing.

Sheldon Manor

Chippenham, Wiltshire SN14 0RG
☎ 0259 853120

OWNER Major Martin Gibbs
LOCATION Signposted from A420 west of Chippen-
ham
OPEN 12.30 pm – 6 pm; Thursdays, Sundays & Bank
Holidays; Easter to the first Sunday in October
ADMISSION £1.75
FACILITIES Parking; dogs permitted; loos; access for
the disabled; plants for sale; shop in house; lunch & tea
on open days; parties by arrangement
FEATURES Plantsman's garden; old roses and climbers;
water features; flowering cherries and ornamental
apples
ENGLISH HERITAGE GRADE II

The best things about these romantic gardens and their
Cotswold manor house are the informal roses (climbers
and shrubs), the welcome from the owners and the
delicious food in the old stables. Highly recommended.

Stourhead

Stourton, Wiltshire BA12 6QH
☎ 0747 840348

OWNER The National Trust
LOCATION Signposted off the A303
OPEN 8 am – 7 pm; daily ; all year
ADMISSION Adults £4 (1993)

FACILITIES Parking; dogs permitted; loos; facilities for the disabled; National Trust shop near entrance; famous hotel/pub opposite gate

FEATURES Good collection of trees; fine conifers; follies and garden buildings; garden sculpture; water features; woodland garden; interesting for children; tallest tulip tree *Liriodendron tulipifera* in the British Isles, and seven other record tree species

ENGLISH HERITAGE GRADE I

Whatever the weather or season, Stourhead conveys a sense of majesty and harmony. Try it early on a May morning, before it opens officially, when the air is sweet with azaleas. Or scuff the fallen leaves in late November. Think of it 200 years ago, without the rhododendrons, when all the beech trees were interplanted with spruces. Ponder the 18th century aesthetic, which esteemed tones and shades more highly than colours. Spot the change from classical to gothic, from Pope to Walpole. And wonder at the National Trust's ability to maintain it so well with only 6 gardeners.

Stourton House

Stourton, Warminster, Wiltshire BA12 6QF
☎ 0747 840417

OWNER Mrs Anthony Bullivant
LOCATION Next to Stourhead
OPEN 11 am – 6 pm; April to November
ADMISSION Adults £2.00; Children 50p; Parties (over 12) £1.50
FACILITIES Parking; loos; facilities for the disabled; plants for sale; teas; light lunches; sticky cakes
FEATURES Herbaceous borders; good topiary; woodland garden; particularly good in July-August; Victorian conservatory; elegantly curving hedges; hosts of daffodils, in innumerable shapes, sizes and colours

This five acre Old Vicarage garden, next to Stourhead, is famous for its dried flowers, thanks to the energy and personality of Elizabeth Bullivant. Strongly recommended at any season: over 200 hydrangea varieties in late summer.

Thompson's Hill

Sherston, Malmesbury, Wiltshire SN16 0PZ
☎ 0666 840766

OWNER Mr & Mrs Sean Cooper
LOCATION At Sherston village church turn left down hill, then right up hill
OPEN 2 pm – 6.30 pm; for NGS
ADMISSION £1.50
FACILITIES Parking; plants for sale
FEATURES Herbaceous borders; old roses and climbers; young garden

Half-acre modern garden, growing up quickly and changing all the time. Well planted and maintained by owners' own efforts: almost too tidy. Much featured in the glossies.

Wilton House

Wilton, Salisbury, Wiltshire SP2 0BJ
☎ 0722 743115   FAX 0722 744447

OWNER Earl of Pembroke/Wilton House Trust
LOCATION In village, 2 miles west of Salisbury on A30
OPEN 11 am – 6 pm; daily; 29 March to 30 October
ADMISSION Adults £5.50; OAPs £4.50; Children £3.50
FACILITIES Parking; loos; access for the disabled; plants for sale in adjoining Wilton House garden centre; self-service restaurant
FEATURES Fine conifers; oriental features; old roses and climbers; interesting for children; handsome cedars; famous Palladian bridge; magnificent golden-leaved oak; adventure playground

ENGLISH HERITAGE GRADE I

Sublime 18th century park around classical Inigo Jones pile famous for its paintings. Recently courting popularity: pretty new rose garden and Japanese gardens.

Wincombe Park

Donhead St Mary, Shaftesbury, Wiltshire SP7 9AB
☎ 0747 52161

OWNER The Hon. Martin Fortescue
LOCATION Off A350, follow signs for Wincombe
OPEN 2 pm – 5.30 pm; 18 May and 19 October
ADMISSION Adults £1.50; Children free
FACILITIES Parking; dogs permitted; loos; plants for sale; tea available in house
FEATURES Herbaceous borders; plantsman's garden

Wonderful borders in the walled garden, planted by the owner's late wife, but nothing can beat the spacious view across the lawns, and a lake, to the wooded combe beyond.

NORTH YORKSHIRE

Beningbrough Hall

Shipton-by-Beningbrough, York, North Yorkshire YO6 1DD
☎ 0904 470666

OWNER The National Trust
LOCATION 8 miles north west of York off the A19
OPEN 11 am – 5.30 pm; Saturday – Wednesday; 30 March to 30 October
ADMISSION Adults £3.00; Children £1.50
FACILITIES Parking; loos; facilities for the disabled; plants for sale; National Trust gift shop; morning coffee; hot & cold lunches; afternoon teas

FEATURES Herbaceous borders; fruit and vegetables of special interest; oriental features; water features; woodland garden; plantings by Graham Thomas; American garden; good conservatory on house; vast Portuguese laurel *Prunus lusitanica*
ENGLISH HERITAGE GRADE II

Pretty modern National Trust plantings: two small formal gardens, one with reds and oranges and the other with pastel shades, on either side of the early Georgian house and a sumptuous mixed border which grades from hot colours to cool.

Castle Howard

York, North Yorkshire YO6 7DA
☎ 0653 648333   FAX 0653 648462

OWNER Castle Howard Estates Ltd
LOCATION 5 miles south west of Malton
OPEN 10 am – 4.30 pm (last entry); daily; 18 March to 31 October
ADMISSION House & grounds: Adults £6, Children £3, Senior Citizens £5; grounds only: Adults £4, Children £2
FACILITIES Parking; dogs admitted; loos; access for the disabled; shop and plant centre; cafeteria
FEATURES Borders; garden architecture; old roses; sculpture; woodland garden; biggest *Populus alba* in British Isles
ENGLISH HERITAGE GRADE I

Heroic megapark (1200 ha) laid out with fives axes by the 3rd Earl of Carlisle, Vanburgh and Hawksmoor with important buildings (Temple of the Four Winds, Mausoleum). Grand 1980s rose gardens (slightly Surrey) designed by Jim Russell, with every type of rose from ancient to modern. In Ray Wood, a fine and historic collection of rhododendrons and other erica-ceous plants, meticulously labelled. A must for botanist and gardener alike – be prepared to spend all day there – and essential visiting for anyone with a sense of history.

Duncombe Park

Helmsley, North Yorkshire YO6 5EB
☎ 0439 70213   FAX 0439 71114

OWNER Lord Feversham
LOCATION Off A170; signed from Helmsley
OPEN 11 am – 6 pm; Sunday – Thursday; May to October
ADMISSION Adults £2.75; Children £1.50
FACILITIES Parking; loos; gift shop; restaurant
FEATURES Follies and garden buildings; garden sculpture; Rysbrack statue of Old Father Time
ENGLISH HERITAGE GRADE I

Major early 18th century landscape, a grass terrace which sweeps between Vanburgh's Ionic rotunda and a Tuscan temple with views across the valley to Helm-sley and the moors, matched only by views from its sister terrace at Rievaulx, in the care of the National Trust.

Harlow Carr Botanical Gardens

Beckwithshaw, Harrogate, North Yorkshire HG3 1QB
☎ 0423 565418

OWNER Northern Horticultural Society
LOCATION Crag Lane off Otley Road (B6162), 1½ miles from Harrogate centre
OPEN 9.30 am – 6.00 pm or dusk if earlier; daily
ADMISSION Adults £3.20; Senior Citizens £2.50; Children free; Parties (20+) £2.50. Special winter rate (Nov – Feb)
FACILITIES Parking; loos; facilities for the disabled; plants for sale; gift shop; licensed restaurant
FEATURES Fruit and vegetables of special interest; rock garden; modern roses; old roses and climbers; woodland garden; heathers and alpines; good autumn colour
NCCPG NATIONAL COLLECTIONS *Dryopteris, Poly-podium, Rheum, Calluna, Hypericum*

The headquarters of the Northern Horticultural Society with innumerable demonstration gardens in a land-scaped sequence. The best, including the rock gardens and stream garden, are brilliant.

Newby Hall

Ripon, North Yorkshire HG4 5AE
☎ 0423 322583   FAX 0423 324452

OWNER Robin Compton
LOCATION Off B6265, 2 miles from A1
OPEN 11 am – 5.30 pm; Tuesday – Sunday & Bank Holiday Mondays; April to September
ADMISSION Adults £3.00; Children & Disabled £2.00 (1993)
FACILITIES Parking; loos; facilities for the disabled; shop and plant stall; licensed restaurant
FEATURES Herbaceous borders; rock garden; old roses and climbers; garden sculpture; water features; woodland garden; HHA/Christie's Garden of the Year in 1986; biggest *Acer griseum* and *Sorbus intermedia* in UK; adventure playground
ENGLISH HERITAGE GRADE II*
NCCPG NATIONAL COLLECTIONS *Cornus*

The garden with everything: firm design, an endless variety of features, great plantsmanship, immaculate maintenance. Its axis is a bold wide double border stretching endlessly down to the River Ure. Second only to Hidcote as an example of 20th century garde-ning. Visit Newby at any season and expect to spend all day there.

Parcevall Hall Gardens

Skyreholme, Skipton, North Yorkshire BD23 6DE
☎ 0756 720311

OWNER Walsingham College (Yorkshire Properties) Ltd
LOCATION Off B6160 from Burnsall
OPEN 10 am – 6 pm; daily; Good Friday to 31 October; winter visits by appointment
ADMISSION Adults £2.00; Children (5-12) 50p
FACILITIES Parking; dogs permitted; loos; plants for sale; tea shop (summer weekends)
FEATURES Rock garden; water features; rhododendrons; primulas
FRIENDS Ask for details

Breathtaking architectural layout, and views. Planted by Sir William Milner 70 years ago and best now for its wonderful rhododendrons growing alongside limestone outcrops, daffodils (including 'W F Milner') and *Primula florindae* given by Kingdon Ward now naturalised round the lily pond.

Ripley Castle

Ripley, Harrogate, North Yorkshire HG3 3AY
☎ 0423 770152   FAX 0423 771745

OWNER Sir Thomas Ingilby Bt
LOCATION 3½ miles north of Harrogate, off A61
OPEN 11 am – 5 pm (4 pm in March, 3.30 pm November – December); daily (Thursday – Sunday in March); 1 March to 23 December
ADMISSION Adults £2.25; Senior Citizens £1.75; Children £1.00
FACILITIES Parking; loos; facilities for the disabled; gift shop with plants, fruit and vegetables; castle tearoom
FEATURES Herbaceous borders; landscape designed by Capability Brown; fruit and vegetables of special interest; glasshouses to visit; herbs; sub-tropical plants; interesting for children; particularly interesting in winter; birds of prey sanctuary
ENGLISH HERITAGE GRADE II
NCCPG NATIONAL COLLECTIONS Tropical plants, *Hyacinthus*

14th Century castle (restored); Capability Brown landscape; temples; smashing Regency conservatory; Victorian formal garden; evergreen shrubberies (handsome yews); hundreds of thousands of bulbs (daffodils in hosts). A garden with something for everyone.

Sleightholmedale Lodge

Fadmoor, Kirkbymoorside, North Yorkshire YO6 6JG
☎ 0751 31942

OWNER Mrs R James
LOCATION Signed from Fadmoor

OPEN 11.30 am – 5 pm; 5 June & 3 July. 2 pm – 7 pm; 17 July. And by appointment.
ADMISSION £1.25
FACILITIES Parking; dogs permitted; loos; plants for sale; teas on July open days
FEATURES Herbaceous borders; herbs; plantsman's garden; modern roses; old roses and climbers; woodland garden

Plantsman's paradise on the edge of the moors: not just azaleas and *Meconopsis* but Mexican and Mediterranean plants too – a triumph for good cultivation and manipulation of the microclimate. Roses of every sort – hundreds of them, perhaps thousands.

Studley Royal

Fountains, Ripon, North Yorkshire HG4 3DZ
☎ 0765 608888   FAX 0765 608889

OWNER The National Trust
LOCATION 4 miles west of Ripon off B6265
OPEN 10 am – 5 pm (7 pm in summer); daily except Fridays November to January & 24 & 25 December
ADMISSION Adults £4.00; Children £2.00; Family £10.00 Parties (over 15) Adults £3.50; Children £1.70
FACILITIES Parking; dogs permitted; loos; facilities for the disabled; National Trust shop; tea room
FEATURES Water features; World Heritage site; 400 acre deer park; biggest *Prunus avium* (bird cherry) in British Isles
ENGLISH HERITAGE GRADE I

Inextricably linked to Fountains Abbey, which forms the focus of an unsurpassed surprise view from Anne Boleyn's Seat, Studley is a classical, geometrical landscape of major importance. Best seen high up from the banqueting house lawn and the Octagon tower – the formal canal, Moon pools, Grotto Springs, rustic bridge and Temple of Filial Piety.

Sutton Park

Sutton-in-the-Forest, York, North Yorkshire YO6 1DP
☎ 0347 810249

OWNER Mrs N M D Sheffield
LOCATION 8 miles north of York on B1363
OPEN 11 am – 5 pm; daily; Easter to October
ADMISSION £1.00 (1993)
FACILITIES Parking; loos; plants for sale occasionally; tea room; private parties by arrangement only
FEATURES Herbaceous borders; plantsman's garden; woodland garden

Capability Brown was here 200 years ago, but the joy of Sutton is the formal garden laid out on terraces below the house by Percy Cane in the 1960s and planted by Mrs Sheffield with exquisite taste. Quite the prettiest garden in Yorkshire.

Thorp Perrow Arboretum

Bedale, North Yorkshire DL8 2PR
☎ 0677 425323   ✆ 0677 422710

OWNER   Sir John Ropner Bt
LOCATION   On the Well to Ripon road, just south of Bedale
OPEN   Dawn to dusk; all year
ADMISSION   Adults £2.20; Children, Senior Citizens & Students £1.10
FACILITIES   Parking; dogs permitted; loos; facilities for the disabled; plants for sale; tea room
FEATURES   Good collection of trees; fine conifers; woodland garden; biggest golden beech *Fagus sylvatica* 'Aurea' in UK
ENGLISH HERITAGE GRADE   II
NCCPG NATIONAL COLLECTIONS   *Fraxinus, Juglans, Quercus, Tilia*
FRIENDS   Friends of Thorp Perrow

Important modern arboretum undergoing restoration after some years of neglect. Wonderful avenues of laburnum, glades of cherries and coniferous groves.

The Valley Gardens, Harrogate

Harrogate Borough Council, Harrogate, North Yorkshire
☎ 0423 500600 Ext: 3211

OWNER   Harrogate Borough Council
LOCATION   Harrogate
OPEN   At all times
ADMISSION   Free
FACILITIES   Parking; dogs permitted; loos; access for the disabled; small cafeteria
FEATURES   Herbaceous borders; rock garden; subtropical plants; interesting for children; wonderful meconopsis & primulas alongside the stream; children's play area
ENGLISH HERITAGE GRADE   II

The best example of plantsmanship in a public garden in England, laid out 1880-1910: the Sun Colonnade, which incorporates an elegant pergola, has just been restored. Alpine rarities in spring, a romantic dell, magnificent dahlia display in late summer and the best colour bedding in Yorkshire.

Yorkshire Museum Gardens

Yorkshire Museum, Museum Gardens, York, North Yorkshire YO1 2DR
☎ 0904 629745   ✆ 0904 651221

OWNER   North Yorkshire County Council
LOCATION   Follow signs for Yorkshire Museum
OPEN   7.30 am – 8 pm; daily
ADMISSION   Free
FACILITIES   Dogs permitted; loos; access for the disabled

FEATURES   Rock garden
ENGLISH HERITAGE GRADE   II

Nice example of an upmarket amenity garden round a public heritage site. Laid out by Sir John Naysmith 150 years ago and still basically intact. Good trees, including *Alnus glutinosa* 'Laciniata' and *Fraxinus excelsior* f. *diversifolia*.

SOUTH YORKSHIRE

Sheffield Botanical Gardens

Clarkehouse Road, Sheffield, South Yorkshire S10 2LN
☎ 0742 671115

OWNER   Sheffield Town Trust (administered by City Council)
LOCATION   Jct 33 of M1, follow A57 signs to Glossop, left at Royal Hallamshire Hospital, 500 m on left
OPEN   8 am – 8 pm, summer; 8 am – 4 pm, winter
ADMISSION   Free
FACILITIES   Dogs permitted; loos; facilities for the disabled
FEATURES   Herbaceous borders; fine conifers; glasshouses to visit; rock garden; modern roses; old roses and climbers; woodland garden; conservatories by Paxton; peat garden; heath garden
FRIENDS   (0742 670544, Don Williams)

Founded in 1833 by public subscription and still burgeoning with civic pride. Good camellias and magnolias, ericas and sorbuses. Splendid summer bedding too, and lots of seats and waste bins: an exemplary combination of botany and amenity.

Wentworth Castle Gardens

Northern College, Wentworth Castle, Stainborough, Barnsley, South Yorkshire S75 3ET
☎ 0226 285426   ✆ 0226 284308

OWNER   Barnsley Metropolitan District Council
LOCATION   3 miles south of Barnsley; 2 miles from M1
OPEN   10 am – 5 pm; Spring Bank Holiday (Sunday and Monday); By arrangement in May and June
ADMISSION   Adults £2.00; Students & Children £1.00
FACILITIES   Parking; dogs permitted; loos
FEATURES   Woodland garden; interesting for children; educational collection of rhododendrons
ENGLISH HERITAGE GRADE   I
NCCPG NATIONAL COLLECTIONS   *Rhododendron*
FRIENDS   Friends of the Gardens Society

Major landscape garden currently undergoing development as an educational and cultural resource. Twinned with the Kun-ming Academy of Sciences. A garden to watch.

WEST YORKSHIRE

Canal Gardens

Roundhay Park, Street Lane, Leeds, West Yorkshire
☎ 0532 661850

OWNER   Leeds City Council
LOCATION   3 miles north west of city centre, off
A6120 ring road
OPEN   All year, but Tropical World closes at dusk
ADMISSION   Free
FACILITIES   Parking; dogs permitted; loos; access for
the disabled; souvenirs; cafeteria by lakeside
FEATURES   Glasshouses to visit; modern roses; sub-
tropical plants; water features; particularly interesting
in winter; good carpet bedding
ENGLISH HERITAGE GRADE   II

Tropical World glasshouses containing South American rain forest plants, bromeliads, hoyas, cacti and
Butterfly House. A wonderful retreat from a Yorkshire
winter and a triumph of municipal horticultural excellence.

Golden Acre Park

Otley Road, Bramhope, Leeds, West Yorkshire
LS16 5NZ
☎ 0532 782030

OWNER   Leeds City Council
LOCATION   4 miles north on A660 Otley Road
OPEN   All year
ADMISSION   Free
FACILITIES   Parking; dogs permitted; loos; access for
the disabled; gifts/souvenirs; restaurant
FEATURES   Rock garden; water features; large heather
garden

Part park, part botanic collection, part demonstration
garden, part test ground for Fleuroselect; perhaps the
best of Leeds' five impressive public gardens.

Harewood House

Harewood House Estate, Leeds, West Yorkshire
LS17 9LQ
☎ 0532 886331   📠 0532 886467

OWNER   The Earl of Harewood
LOCATION   Between Leeds and Harrogate on A61
OPEN   10 am – 5 pm; daily; 13 March to 31 October
ADMISSION   House and Gardens: Adults £5.75, Child-
ren £3.00
FACILITIES   Parking; loos; plants for sale; refreshments
FEATURES   Landscape designed by Capability Brown;
oriental features; woodland garden; interesting for
children; adventure playground; Japanese garden; rho-
dodendrons; current holder of Sandford Award
ENGLISH HERITAGE GRADE   I

Capability Brown landscaped Harewood, and Charles
Barry added the grand Italianate terrace, but Repton
and Loudon also had a hand in this most grand of
Yorkshire gardens. Well maintained and welcomingly
run.

The Hollies Park

Weetwood Lane, Leeds, West Yorkshire LS16 5NZ
☎ 0532 782030

OWNER   Leeds City Council
LOCATION   3 miles north of city off A660
OPEN   All year
ADMISSION   Free
FACILITIES   Parking; dogs permitted; loos
FEATURES   Woodland garden; rhododendrons; eucry-
phias

Slightly dilapidated plantsman's garden, underre-
sourced but well run by a hard-pressed and enthusiastic
team.

Lotherton Hall

Aberford, Leeds, West Yorkshire
☎ 0532 813259

OWNER   Leeds City Council
LOCATION   Off A1, ¾ mile east on B1217
OPEN   Dawn to dusk; daily
ADMISSION   Free
FACILITIES   Parking; loos; facilities for the disabled;
shop; cafeteria
FEATURES   Oriental features; modern roses
ENGLISH HERITAGE GRADE   II

Edwardian showpiece garden, now recovering from
neglect and on the move again. Formal rose gardens and
lily pond, recently replanted with period varieties.

Temple Newsam Park

Manager's Office, Temple Newsam Park, Leeds 15,
West Yorkshire
☎ 0532 645535

OWNER   Leeds City Council
LOCATION   3 miles south east of city, off A63 Selby
Road
OPEN   All year
ADMISSION   Free. Small admission charge to house
FACILITIES   Parking; dogs permitted; loos; access for
the disabled; souvenirs; restaurant
FEATURES   Herbaceous borders; landscape designed
by Capability Brown; glasshouses to visit; modern
roses; old roses and climbers; rhododendrons
ENGLISH HERITAGE GRADE   II
NCCPG NATIONAL COLLECTIONS   Aster novi-belgii,
Delphinium, Phlox

1,200 acres of parkland, now a 'green lung' for Leeds.
Cheerful borders in the old walled garden. Somewhat

neglected in the past, now undergoing extensive restoration and improvement.

York Gate

Back Church Lane, Adel, Leeds, West Yorkshire
LS16 8DW
☎ 0532 648240

OWNER   Mrs S B Spencer
OPEN   By appointment only
ADMISSION   £3.00
FACILITIES   Parking; loos
FEATURES   Herbaceous borders; plantsman's garden; good topiary; colour borders; mini-pinetum; nut walk; an espaliered *Cedrus atlantica* 'Glauca'

Quite the busiest small garden in England, a much photographed masterpiece of tight design, invention, opportunism and colour sense. No modern garden has so much to teach us.

WALES

CLWYD

Bodnant Gardens

Tal-y-Cafn, Colwyn Bay, Clwyd LL28 5RE
☎ 0492 650460   ☎ 0492 650448

OWNER   The National Trust
LOCATION   8 miles south of Llandudno and Colwyn Bay on A470. Entrance ½ mile along Eglwysbach Road
OPEN   10 am – 5 pm; daily; Mid March to 31 October
ADMISSION   £3.60
FACILITIES   Parking; loos; plants for sale; light lunches, teas, refreshments
FEATURES   Good collection of trees; herbaceous borders; fine conifers; follies and garden buildings; glasshouses to visit; plantsman's garden; water features; woodland garden; rhododendrons; azaleas; magnolias; camellias; tallest Californian redwood *Sequoia sempervirens* (47 metres) in the British Isles and 19 further record-breaking tree species
NCCPG NATIONAL COLLECTIONS   *Embothrium, Eucryphia, Magnolia, Rhododendron*

The greatest garden in Wales, some would say in all Britain. The grand Italianate terraces above a woodland 'dell' are only part of its renown: Bodnant is famous for its laburnum tunnel, white wisterias, vast *Arbutus* × *andrachnoides*, the 1730s gazebo called the Pin Mill, the green theatre, *Viburnum* × *bodnantense*, hybrid camellias, huge rhododendrons, flaming embothriums, the two Lords Aberconway, father and son, both past-Presidents of the Royal Horticultural Society, and the three generations of the Puddle family who have been Head Gardeners.

Chirk Castle

Chirk, Clwyd LL4 5AF
☎ 0691 777701   ☎ 0691 774706

OWNER   The National Trust
LOCATION   ½ mile west of Chirk off A5
OPEN   12 noon – 5 pm; daily except Monday & Saturday; 1 April to 30 September. 12 noon – 5 pm; Saturday, Sunday and Bank Holiday Mondays; 1 October to 30 October
ADMISSION   Adults £2.20; Children £1.10
FACILITIES   Parking; dogs permitted; loos; facilities for the disabled; shop; restaurant & tea room
FEATURES   Herbaceous borders; follies and garden buildings; rock garden; modern roses; old roses and climbers; garden sculpture; good topiary; woodland garden; rhododendrons; azaleas; eucryphias; hydrangeas; lime avenue

Chirk has handsome 19th century formal gardens, one planted with roses and another with billowing yew topiary. There is also a good 1930s collection of trees and shrubs, the relics of a garden by Norah Lindsay. But some say the whole garden is 'a little too National Trust' now.

Erddig

Wrexham, Clwyd LL130YT
☎ 0978 355314

OWNER   The National Trust
LOCATION   Signposted from A483 and A525
OPEN   11 am to 6 pm, (House 12 noon – 5 pm) last entry 4 pm, daily except Thursday and Friday (open Good Friday), 1 April to 31 August
ADMISSION   House and garden: Adults £5.00, Children £2.50, Groups pre booked (20+) £4.00
FACILITIES   Parking; loos; plants for sale; restaurant, tea room
FEATURES   Fruit and vegetables of special interest; old roses and climbers; water features; woodland garden; spring bulbs; current holder of Sandford Award
ENGLISH HERITAGE GRADE   I

More of a re-creation than a restoration, Erddig today majors on domestic life in the early 18th century. There are old-fashioned fruit trees, an avenue of pleached limes, and a long canal to frame the house, but all are slightly awed by the Victorian overlay – avenues of monkey puzzles and wellingtonias.

DYFED

Cae Hir

Cribyn, Lampeter, Dyfed SA48 7NG
☎ 0570 470839

OWNER W Akkermans
OPEN 1 pm – 6 pm; daily except Mondays & Bank Holiday Mondays
ADMISSION Adults £1.50; Senior Citizens £1.25; Children 50p
FACILITIES Parking; dogs permitted; loos; plants for sale; small gift shop; light refreshments
FEATURES Herbaceous borders; water features; colour gardens; bonsai

Young and expanding garden, only eight years old. Six acres have been taken from meadows and made into a series of beautiful colour-conscious gardens by the present owner. Trees, shrubs and herbaceous plants, often used in original ways. Immaculately tidy: Mr Akkermans's energy and achievement are an inspiration.

Carrog

Llanddeiniol, Llanfhystud, Dyfed SY23 5DS
☎ 0974 202369

OWNER Mr & Mrs Geoffrey Williams
LOCATION 6 miles south of Aberystwyth on A487
OPEN 2 pm – 6 pm; 19 June
ADMISSION Adults £1; Children 30p
FACILITIES Parking; dogs permitted; loos; plants for sale; refreshments
FEATURES Good collection of trees; herbaceous borders; glasshouses to visit; plantsman's garden; old roses and climbers

A plantsman's garden with everything from rare rhododendrons to good autumn colour. Featured in 'Gardener's World' TV programme.

The Dingle (Crundale)

Crundale, Haverfordwest, Dyfed SA62 4DJ
☎ 0437 764 370

OWNER Mrs A J Jones
LOCATION On the A40 to Haverfordwest turn right on first two roundabouts, fork right then 1st right
OPEN 10 am – 6 pm, Wednesday – Monday; March to October
ADMISSION Adults £1.00; Children 50p
FACILITIES Parking; loos; access for the disabled; nursery; tea room
FEATURES Herbaceous borders; gravel or scree garden; rock garden; old roses and climbers; water features; woodland garden; young garden; bluebells; primroses

This excellent young garden was started in 1982 to display the plants which Mrs Jones grows in the adjoining nursery – roses, clematis, herbaceous plants and alpines – but it has the feel of a private garden. Plants are arranged to show off their form as well as their flowers and leaf-colours. A good garden – it works well.

Picton Castle

The Rhos, Haverfordwest, Pembrokeshire, Dyfed SA62 4AS
☎ 0437 751326

OWNER Picton Castle Trust
LOCATION 4 miles east of Haverfordwest off A40
OPEN 10.30 am – 5.30 pm; Tuesday – Sunday & Bank Holidays; 1 April to 30 September
ADMISSION Adults £1.00; Children & Senior Citizens 50p
FACILITIES Parking; dogs permitted; loos; facilities for the disabled; plants for sale; garden shop selling surplus garden produce; restaurant
FEATURES Herbs; woodland garden; rhododendrons; azaleas; camellias

Essentially a 50-acre woodland garden with rhododendrons and similar shrubs planted over the last fifty years, but the Trust is replanting the kitchen garden as a flower garden and visitors can expect further improvements.

Post House Gardens

Cwmbach, Whitland, Dyfed SA34 0DR
☎ 0994 484213

OWNER Mrs Jo Kenaghan
LOCATION Four miles north west of Meidrim
OPEN 9 am – sunset; daily ; all year
ADMISSION Adults £1.50; Senior Citizens £1.00; Children 50p
FACILITIES Parking; dogs permitted; loos; plants for sale; tea & coffee
FEATURES Good collection of trees; herbaceous borders; glasshouses to visit; plantsman's garden; rock garden; old roses and climbers; water features; woodland garden; rhododendrons; wood anemones; bluebells

Four acres of plantsmanship on a long, narrow site above the River Sien, so steep that it appears much larger. Hardy trees and shrubs are the main feature, especially rhododendrons which are also available for purchase, but there are also alpines, gunneras, *Meconopsis* and wonderful wild woodland flowers.

SOUTH GLAMORGAN

Dyffryn Botanic Garden

St Nicholas, Cardiff, South Glamorgan CF5 6SU

☎ 0222 593328   📠 0222 591966

OWNER   Mid & South Glamorgan County Councils

LOCATION   Exit 33 M4 on A48 then follow signs

OPEN   10 am – 5.30 pm; daily; all year

ADMISSION   Adults £2.00; Senior Citizens & Children £1.50; Family £6.00

FACILITIES   Parking; dogs permitted; loos; access for the disabled; plants for sale on Bank Holidays; refreshments

FEATURES   Good collection of trees; herbaceous borders; fruit and vegetables of special interest; modern roses; spring bulbs; summer bedding; tallest *Kalopanax semptemlobus* (syn. *K. pictus* in the British Isles (and six other record trees)

NCCPG NATIONAL COLLECTIONS *Salvia, Dahlia*

55 acres of sumptuous gardens designed by Thomas Mawson around an Edwardian prodigy house. Intended partly for display – there is a Roman garden with a temple and fountain – and partly for the owners' own pleasure, Dyffryn has a huge collection of good plants built up by Reginald Cory in the early years of this century. The garden as a status symbol.

WEST GLAMORGAN

Clyne Gardens

Mumbles Road, Blackpill, Swansea, West Glamorgan

☎ 0792 302420   📠 0792 302408

OWNER   Swansea City Council

LOCATION   3 miles west of Swansea on coast road

OPEN   Dawn to dusk; daily; all year

ADMISSION   Free

FACILITIES   Parking; dogs permitted; loos; access for the disabled; occasional light refreshments

FEATURES   Herbaceous borders; oriental features; water features; woodland garden

NCCPG NATIONAL COLLECTIONS *Pieris, Enkianthus, Rhododendron*

FRIENDS   Details from Ivor Stokes

A well kept woodland garden in the care of an enthusiastic and knowledgeable staff. Several National Collections and a good range of tender plants, including *maddenii* rhododendrons.

Margam Park

Port Talbot, West Glamorgan SA13 2TJ

☎ 0639 881635   📠 0639 895897

OWNER   West Glamorgan County Council

LOCATION   Follow directions from Junction 38, M4

OPEN   10 am – 7 pm; daily; summer. 9.30 am – 5 pm; daily; winter

ADMISSION   Adults £3.00; Children £2.00; Family £9.00

FACILITIES   Parking; dogs permitted; loos; facilities for the disabled; restaurant & light refreshments

FEATURES   Good collection of trees; follies and garden buildings; fruit and vegetables of special interest; oriental features; modern roses; old roses and climbers; garden sculpture; interesting for children; bedding out; daffodils; rhododendrons; maze; orangery; tallest bay tree *Laurus nobilis* in the British Isles

A popular country park with lots to interest the garden historian and plantsman. A wonderful range of conservatories and glasshouses, including the orangery for which Margam is famous, big trees and rhododendrons (some grown from Kingdon Ward's seed), and cheerful bedding out. The council has added a collection of dwarf conifers, a permanent exhibition of modern sculptures, a maze (one of the largest in Europe) and a new pergola 450 yards long: further work is promised.

Plantasia

Parc Tawe, Swansea, West Glamorgan SA1 2AL

☎ 0792 474555/302420   📠 0792 652588

OWNER   Swansea City Council

LOCATION   Off main Eastern approach to Swansea

OPEN   10.30 am – 5.30 pm; Tuesdays – Sundays & Bank Holidays; all year

ADMISSION   Adults £1.00; Concessions 75p

FACILITIES   Parking; loos; access for the disabled; souvenirs & plant-related materials; soft drinks

FEATURES   Glasshouses to visit; sub-tropical plants; interesting for children; particularly interesting in winter; aviary and tropical fish

A major modern amenity commitment by the go-ahead City Council. Plantasia is a large glasshouse (1600 sq m) with three climatic zones (arid, tropical, and rain forest) and each is stuffed with the exotic plants – palms, strelitzias, tree ferns, *Nepenthes*, cacti and such economic plants as coconuts and pineapple. The perfect goal for a winter expedition.

GWENT

Lower House Farm

Nantyderry, Abergavenny, Gwent NP7 9DP

☎ 0873 880257   📠 0873 880108

OWNER   Mr & Mrs Glynne Clay

LOCATION   500 yards from Chain Bridge

OPEN   For NGS and by appointment

ADMISSION   Adults £1.50; Children 50p

FACILITIES Parking; loos; plants for sale; plants on NGS days; teas on NGS days

FEATURES Good collection of trees; herbaceous borders; fine conifers; herbs; plantsman's garden; old roses and climbers; *Lathraea clandestina*; good autumn colour

A modern garden, substantially made by the present owners. Many good features, notably the bog garden and fern island, and unusual young trees.

GWYNEDD

Bodysgallen Hall

Llandudno, Gwynedd LL30 1RS
☎ 0492 584466 📠 0492 582519

OWNER Historic House Hotels Ltd
LOCATION On right of A470 to Llandudno
OPEN All year
ADMISSION Open only to hotel customers
FACILITIES Parking; refreshments at hotel
FEATURES Follies and garden buildings; fruit and vegetables of special interest; herbs; rock garden; old roses and climbers; water features; woodland garden; knot garden; parterres

Good gardens and good grounds for a good hotel. Partly 1920s and partly modern, the gardens include a knot garden divided into eight segments, an extremely busy kitchen garden, a little sunken garden with a lily pond and a modern parterre with white floribundas in the old walled garden. Handy for Bodnant.

Cefn Bere

Cae Deintur, Dolgellau, Gwynedd LL40 2YS
☎ 0341 422768

OWNER Mr & Mrs M Thomas
LOCATION At Cae Deintur up short steep hill, left at top, 4th house
OPEN Spring to Early Autumn by appointment
ADMISSION Contribution to NGS
FACILITIES Parking; plants for sale
FEATURES Glasshouses to visit; plantsman's garden; old roses and climbers; troughs

A plantsman's garden within a disciplined design: the owners say that it encapsulates their own development as gardeners over the last forty years. A great variety of rare plants within a small compass, especially alpines, dwarf conifers, ferns and evergreens. Wonderful views.

Penrhyn Castle

Bangor, Gwynedd LL57 4HN
☎ 0248 353084 📠 0248 371281

OWNER The National Trust

LOCATION 3 miles east of Bangor on A5122, signposted from A55 – A5 junction
OPEN 12 noon – 5 pm, daily except Tuesday, 1 April to 31 October; 11 am – 5 pm, July and August
ADMISSION Adults £4.40; Children £2.20; Family (2A + 2C) £11.00
FACILITIES Parking; dogs permitted; facilities for the disabled; plants for sale; light lunches in licensed tea room
FEATURES Good collection of trees; fine conifers; fruit and vegetables of special interest; sub-tropical plants; water features; woodland garden; Victorian walled garden; rhododendrons; trees planted by royals

A Norman castle (actually a Victorian fake) with a distant walled garden of parterres and terraces merging into the slopes of rhododendrons and camellias. There is much of dendrological interest: ancient conifers, holm oaks and naturalised arbutus trees.

Plas Brondanw Gardens

Llanfrothen, Panrhyndeudraeth, Gwynedd LL48 6SW
☎ 0766 770484

OWNER Trustees of the Second Portmeirion Foundation
LOCATION On Croesor road off A4085
OPEN 9 am – 5 pm; daily; all year
ADMISSION Adults £1.50; Children 25p
FEATURES Follies and garden buildings; glasshouses to visit; good topiary

Highly original and architectural Edwardian garden laid out by Clough Williams-Ellis seventeen years before he began Portmeirion, and now assiduously restored by his granddaughter Menna. One of the best-kept secrets in North Wales, full of such original design ideas as the arbour of four red-twigged limes.

Plas Newydd

Llanfairpwll, Anglesey, Gwynedd LL61 6EQ
☎ 0248 714795

OWNER The National Trust
LOCATION 2 miles south west of Llanfairpwll on A4080
OPEN 12 noon – 5pm; Sunday – Friday; 30 March to 30 September; Fridays & Sundays only; 1 to 30 October
ADMISSION Adult £3.80; Children £1.90; Group £3.00; Family £9.50
FACILITIES Parking; loos; access for the disabled; National Trust shop; tea room
FEATURES Landscape designed by Humphry Repton; fine conifers; follies and garden buildings; modern roses; water features; woodland garden; azaleas; magnolias; rhododendrons; maples

A grand collection of rhododendrons (plus azaleas, magnolias and acers) within a Repton landscape on a spectacular site above the Menai Straits. The fine Italianate garden below the house is 1930s, most surprising.

Plas Penhelig

Aberdovey, Gwynedd LL35 0NA
☎ 0654 767676　　🖷 0654 767783

OWNER　Mr & Mrs A C Richardson
LOCATION　On the hillside above Aberdovey Bay
OPEN　15 March to 31 October
ADMISSION　Adults £1; Children 50p
FACILITIES　Parking; dogs permitted; loos; Country House Hotel; light meals to full restaurant fare
FEATURES　Herbaceous borders; fruit and vegetables of special interest; glasshouses to visit; rock garden; old roses and climbers; sub-tropical plants; woodland garden; rhododendrons; azaleas; bluebells

14 acres of woodland garden around a hotel on the west coast of Wales. The Richardsons have been reclaiming and replanting it after years of neglect: the results are admirable.

Plas-yn-Rhiw

Rhiw, Pwllheli, Gwynedd LL53 8AB
☎ 075 888 219

OWNER　The National Trust
LOCATION　12 miles from Pwllheli on south coast road to Aberdarow
OPEN　12 noon – 5 pm; daily except Saturday; 1 April
ADMISSION　Adults £2.30; Children £1.15; Family £6.00
FACILITIES　Parking; loos
FEATURES　Herbaceous borders; formal gardens

Pretty garden, small and formal, with box-edged parterres filled with billowing cottage garden flowers. A few rhododendrons and camellias beyond.

POWYS

The Dingle (Welshpool)

Welshpool, Powys
☎ 0938 555145

OWNER　Mr & Mrs Roy Joseph
LOCATION　Left turn to Nurseries off of A490 to Llantyllin
OPEN　9 am – 5 pm; daily except Tuesdays; all year
ADMISSION　£1.00
FACILITIES　Parking; loos; access for the disabled; good nursery attached

FEATURES　Herbaceous borders; fine conifers; rock garden; water features; woodland garden; colour borders

Steep and stony garden attached to a nursery, but essentially a private garden still. Mainly trees and shrubs, mulched with bark, but some herbaceous plants too, and a stream with bridges leading to a pool.

Dolwen

Cefn Coch, Llanrhaedr-ym-Mochnant, Powys SY10 0BLL
☎ 0691 780411

OWNER　Mrs Frances Denby
LOCATION　Right at Three Tuns Inn, 1 mile up lane
OPEN　2 pm – 4.30 pm; Fridays, 1 May to 14 September; plus last Sunday in month from May to August
ADMISSION　£1
FACILITIES　Parking; loos; plants for sale; tea room
FEATURES　Herbaceous borders; gravel or scree garden; plantsman's garden; old roses and climbers; garden sculpture; water features; woodland garden; garden school

A plantsman's garden on a steep 4 acre site, energetically made by Mrs Denby over the last 20 years. Beautiful plantings around three large ponds, fed by natural springs and connected by waterfalls. One of the best young gardens in Wales.

Maenllwyd Isaf

Abermule, Montgomery, Powys SY15 6NW
☎ 0686 630204

OWNER　Mrs Denise Hatchard
LOCATION　B4368 1 mile from Abermule village
OPEN　All year by appointment
ADMISSION　Adults £1.00; Children free
FACILITIES　Parking; loos
FEATURES　Water features; woodland garden; rhododendrons; bulbs; trilliums; arisaemas

Entirely the creation of the present owner, Maenllwyd Isaf has a wide variety of plants: trees underplanted by shrubs and herbaceous plants, many of them rare and all well cared for.

Powis Castle

Welshpool, Powys SY21 8RF
☎ 0938 554338　　🖷 0938 554336

OWNER　The National Trust
LOCATION　1 mile south of Welshpool off the A483
OPEN　Tuesday – Sunday, 1 July to 31 August; Wednesday – Sunday, 1 September to 31 October
ADMISSION　Adults £3.60; Children (under 17) £1.80; Family £9.00

FACILITIES Parking; loos; facilities for the disabled; plants for sale; gift shop; restaurant for light lunches & teas

FEATURES Herbaceous borders; glasshouses to visit; old roses and climbers; good topiary; woodland garden; plantings by Graham Thomas; particularly good in July-August; tender climbers; colour plantings; largest (i.e. thickest trunk) sessile oak *Quercus petraea* in the British Isles

Famous hanging terraces swamped by bulky overgrown yews and wonderfully rich colour planting by Graham Thomas. Smashing in later summer.

SCOTLAND

BORDERS

Dawyck Botanic Garden

Stobo, Borders EH45 9JV
☎ 0721 760254   📠 0721 760214

OWNER Royal Botanic Garden, Edinburgh
LOCATION 8 miles south west of Peebles on B71
OPEN 10 am – 6 pm; daily; 15 March to 22 October
ADMISSION Adults £1; senior citizens 50p; season tickets available
FACILITIES Parking; loos; facilities for the disabled; plants for sale; gift shop; light refreshments
FEATURES Good collection of trees; herbaceous borders; fine conifers; glasshouses to visit; water features; woodland garden; particularly interesting in winter; meconopsis; Chinese conifers; Dawyck beech; Douglas fir from original seed; tallest *Fagus crenata* in the British Isles, and eight further record trees

A woodland garden, run as an annexe of the Royal Botanic Garden in Edinburgh and long famous for its trees. The Dawyck beech is the upright, fastigiate form, first found in the policies in the mid 19th century. Edinburgh have underplanted with interesting shrubs, and some herbaceous plants. Dawyck is a getting-better garden.

Manderston

Duns, Borders TD11 3PP
☎ 0361 83450   📠 0361 82010

OWNER Lord Palmer
LOCATION On A6105 east of Duns
OPEN 2 pm – 5.30 pm; Sunday & Thursdays; 5 May to 29 September, plus 30 May & 29 August. Parties welcome by appointment
ADMISSION House & Garden: Adults £3.90; Children £1. Gardens: Adults £2; Children 50p.

FACILITIES Parking; dogs permitted; loos; facilities for the disabled; plants for sale; cream teas & ice cream
FEATURES Herbaceous borders; fine conifers; good topiary; water features; woodland garden; good bedding out; rhododendrons & azaleas

The house is sort-of-Georgian. Below it are four expansive terraces, richly planted with traditional bedding out plants or bright modern substitutes. They lead to a small lake, a Chinese-style bridge (18th century) and over to a woodland garden with modern rhododendrons and azaleas. All is planted and maintained in the grand manner.

Mellerstain

Gordon, Borders TD3 6LG
☎ 0573 410225   📠 0573 410388

OWNER Mellerstain Trust
LOCATION 1 mile west of A6089
OPEN 12.30 pm – 5 pm; daily except Saturdays; 1 May to 30 September or by appointment
ADMISSION £1.50
FACILITIES Parking; dogs permitted; loos; access for the disabled; tweed and gift shop; tea room
FEATURES Modern roses; good topiary; water features; Italian terraced garden by Sir Reginald Blomfield (1909)

The house has extensive views south to the Cheviots. Below it lies Blomfield's formal garden planted with floribundas and lavender. Beneath it runs the landscape laid out by William and Robert Adam, sauntering down to a lake. Uncompromisingly grand.

CENTRAL

Blairhoyle

Port of Menteith, by Stirling, Central FK8 3LF
☎ 0877 385210

OWNER Lt Col & Mrs J D Pattullo
LOCATION On A873 west of Thornhill
OPEN 1 pm – 5 pm; Wednesdays; April to October: or by appointment
ADMISSION £1.00 per head unaccompanied; £1.50 each for conducted tour
FACILITIES Parking; dogs permitted; loos; some plants for sale, when available
FEATURES Good collection of trees; herbaceous borders; fruit and vegetables of special interest; plantsman's garden; old roses and climbers; water features; woodland garden

A plantsman's garden, originally designed as a small arboretum, actively restored and improved by the present owners over the last 25 years.

DUMFRIES & GALLOWAY

Arbigland

Kirkbean, Dumfries & Galloway DG2 8BG

☎ 038788 288

OWNER Arbigland Estate Trust
LOCATION South of Kirkbean on A710
OPEN 2 pm – 6 pm; Tuesday – Sunday, and Bank
Holiday Mondays; 1 May to 30 September
ADMISSION Adults £2; Senior Citizens £1.50; Children 50p
FACILITIES Parking; loos; home-made teas
FEATURES Old roses and climbers; water features; woodland garden; interesting for children; rhododendrons; maples

A woodland garden, with many different features. Best is the area called Japan, where ancient Japanese maples surround a water garden. But there are also a hidden rose garden, splendid large-leaved rhododendrons, and paths down to the sandy shore.

Castle Kennedy

Rephad, Stranraer, Dumfries & Galloway DG9 8BX

☎ 0776 702024   ⊠ 0776 706248

OWNER Lochinch Heritage Estate
LOCATION East of Stranraer on A75
OPEN 10 am – 5 pm; Easter until 30 September
ADMISSION Adults £2.00; Senior Citizens & Children £1.00
FACILITIES Parking; dogs permitted; loos; access for the disabled; plant centre; tea rooms
FEATURES Herbaceous borders; fine conifers; water features; woodland garden; rhododendrons; embothriums; eucryphias; monkey puzzle avenue; tallest *Pittosporum tenuifolium* (16 metres) in the British Isles

A huge garden, with early 18th century rides, avenues and *allées*, a complete 19th century pinetum, rhododendrons from Hooker's Himalayan expedition, a vast collection of trees and shrubs, and handsome herbaceous plantings in the walled garden. Important and impressive.

Glenwhan Garden

Dunragit, by Stranraer, Dumfries & Galloway DG9 8PH

☎ 0581 400222

OWNER Mr & Mrs William Knott
LOCATION Off A75 at Dunragit
OPEN 10 am – 5 pm; Tuesday – Sunday, plus Bank Holidays; 1 April to 30 September
ADMISSION Adults £1.50; Senior Citizens £1.50; Children over 12 £1.00
FACILITIES Parking; dogs permitted; loos; facilities for the disabled; plants for sale; shop; garden restaurant
FEATURES Plantsman's garden; old roses and climbers; water features; woodland garden; bluebells; trees and shrubs

A new garden on a large scale, started by the owners in 1979 and worked by them and one gardener. Very much a plantsman's garden, but it uses plants to create effects, and capitalises upon the lie of the land to produce different habitats. The achievement to date is commendable: definitely a garden to watch.

Logan Botanic Gardens

Port Logan, Stranraer, Dumfries & Galloway DG9 9ND

☎ 0776 860231   ⊠ 0776 860333

OWNER Royal Botanic Garden, Edinburgh
LOCATION 14 miles south of Stranraer on B7065
OPEN 10 am – 6pm; daily; 15 March to 31 October
ADMISSION Adults £1.50; Concession £1.00; Children 50p
FACILITIES Parking; loos; facilities for the disabled; plants for sale; shop selling books, gifts and local crafts; light meals & refreshments
FEATURES Good collection of trees; herbaceous borders; fine conifers; fruit and vegetables of special interest; plantsman's garden; sub-tropical plants; water features; woodland garden; particularly good in July-August; tree ferns; cardiocrinums; gunnera; cordylines; trachycarpus palms
FRIENDS Part of the Friends of the Royal Botanic Garden at Edinburgh

The extraordinary effects of Logan are created by palms, cordylines and tree ferns within the semi-formal setting of a walled garden. Huge gunneras and cardiocrinums pile on the message, but the richness extends also to diversity, for here is one of the great botanic collections of tender exotica, worth a long journey on a sunny day in summer.

Threave School of Gardening

Stewartry, Castle Douglas, Dumfries & Galloway DG7 1RX

☎ 0556 502575

OWNER The National Trust for Scotland
LOCATION 1 mile west of Castle Douglas
OPEN Gardens: 9 am – sunset. Visitor Centre: 9 am – 5.30 pm
ADMISSION Adults £3.00; Senior Citizens & Children £1.50; Party rates £2.30 & £1.20 respectively
FACILITIES Parking; loos; facilities for the disabled; plants for sale; shop; restaurant & snacks

FEATURES   Good collection of trees; herbaceous borders; fine conifers; fruit and vegetables of special interest; glasshouses to visit; plantsman's garden; rock garden; modern roses; old roses and climbers; water features; woodland garden; peat garden; heath garden

NCCPG NATIONAL COLLECTIONS *Penstemon*

A teaching garden with a very wide range of attractions – something to interest every gardener, in fact. Developed over the last 30 years with the needs of students at the School of Horticulture, garden-owners and tourists all in mind, Threave has quickly acquired the reputation of a Scottish Wisley. You can spend all day here.

FIFE

Balcaskie

Pittenweem, Fife KY10 2RD

OWNER   Major Sir Ralph Anstruther of that Ilk
LOCATION   Off B9171 to Pittenweem
OPEN   2 pm – 6 pm; Saturday – Wednesday; 1 June to 31 August
ADMISSION   £1.50
FACILITIES   Parking; loos; informal tea & biscuits
FEATURES   Long avenues; parterres; old trees; tender plants

The garden was grandly laid out in the 17th century with parterres below the house and a long straight drive to the sea. Nesfield made terraces where tender climbers shelter in the bays of the retaining walls.

Falkland Palace

Falkland, Fife KY7 7BU
☎ 0337 857397

OWNER   The National Trust for Scotland
LOCATION   On A912, 11 miles north of Kirkaldy
OPEN   11am – 5.30pm, Monday – Saturday; 1.30pm – 5.30pm, Sunday; 1 April to 24 October
ADMISSION   Adults £2.00; Children £1.0.
FACILITIES   Parking; loos; facilities for the disabled; gift shop
FEATURES   Herbaceous borders; fruit and vegetables of special interest; glasshouses to visit; modern roses; autumn colour; spectacular delphinium border

Percy Cane's reconstruction of a Scottish renaissance garden, with a herb garden, an astrolabe walk and formal parterres prettily planted in pastel colours.

Kellie Castle

Pittenween, Fife KY10 2RF
☎ 03338 337

OWNER   The National Trust for Scotland
LOCATION   Signposted from main roads

OPEN   10 am – dusk; daily; 1 May to 23 October, plus 1 to 4 April and weekends in April
ADMISSION   Adults £1.00; Concessions 50p
FACILITIES   Parking; loos; access for the disabled; gift shop; tea room
FEATURES   Herbaceous borders; fruit and vegetables of special interest; old roses and climbers; particularly good in July-August; strong design

Robert Lorimer's family house: it was he who remade the garden in its present form, though much of the planting is modern. Only one acre, but strong lines and thick planting create a sense of both space and enclosure. Kellie has much to teach modern gardeners.

The Murrel Gardens

The Murrel, Aberdour, Fife KY3 0RN

OWNER   J E Milne
LOCATION   On south side of B9157
OPEN   10 am – 5 pm; Monday – Friday; 1 April to 30 September
FACILITIES   Parking; loos; tea/coffee and biscuits
FEATURES   Herbaceous borders; plantsman's garden; modern roses; old roses and climbers; water features

The house is Arts & Crafts, and the garden was laid out in 1910, but thickly replanted by the present owner in 1980. Its protected position allows many tender plants to grow in this normally cool and difficult part of Scotland.

St Andrews Botanic Garden

The Canongate, St Andrews, Fife KY16 8RT
☎ 0334 76452

OWNER   North-East Fife District Council
LOCATION   A915, Largo Road, then entrance in The Canongate
OPEN   10 am – 7 pm; daily; 1 May to 30 September. 10 am – 4 pm; daily in April and October, otherwise Monday – Friday only; 1 November to 31 April
ADMISSION   Adults £1.00, Senior Citizens & Children 50p
FACILITIES   Parking; loos; plants for sale
FEATURES   Good collection of trees; herbaceous borders; fine conifers; glasshouses to visit; gravel or scree garden; rock garden; sub-tropical plants; water features; woodland garden; peat beds; orchids; ferns; heath garden; order beds
FRIENDS   Friends have lectures, workshops, garden visits, a newsletter and seed scheme: details from Honorary Curator

Financial constraints obliged the University to abandon control of its botanic garden in 1987, and lease it to the Council. It will be interesting to see what effect this change has upon its educational facilities. So far, so good: the garden's main asset, the peat, rock and water complex (crag, scree, moraine, alpine meadow and bog) is looking pretty good.

GRAMPIAN

Crathes Castle
near Banchory, Grampian AB31 3QJ
☎ 033 044 525　　📠 033 044 797

OWNER The National Trust for Scotland
LOCATION 15 miles west of Aberdeen
OPEN 9.30 to sunset; daily; all year
ADMISSION Adults £4.00, Senior Citizens, Children £2.00
FACILITIES Parking; dogs permitted; loos; facilities for the disabled; plants for sale; NTS shop; restaurant/cafeteria open April to October
FEATURES Herbaceous borders; fine conifers; glasshouses to visit; plantsman's garden; modern roses; old roses and climbers; woodland garden; specimen trees; colour borders; current holder of Sandford Award; tallest *Zelkova × verschaffeltii* in the British Isles
NCCPG NATIONAL COLLECTIONS *Viburnum, Dianthus* (Malmaison)

Famous for its walled garden, with dreamy high summer borders – pastel shades for long Highland evenings. Only four acres but intensively planted.

Cruickshank Botanic Garden
University of Aberdeen, Dept of Plant and Soil Science, St Machar Drive, Aberdeen, Grampian AB9 2UD
☎ 0224 272704

OWNER Aberdeen University
LOCATION Follow signs for Aberdeen University or Old Aberdeen
OPEN 9 am – 4.30 pm; Monday – Friday, 1 October to 30 April. 2 pm – 5 pm; Saturday and Sunday; 1 May to 30 September
ADMISSION Free
FACILITIES Dogs permitted; access for the disabled
FEATURES Good collection of trees; herbaceous borders; fine conifers; rock garden; old roses and climbers; water features; woodland garden; stone troughs; peat beds
FRIENDS Active Friends group, with plant sales, lectures, excursions and a seed list. Contact 0224 272704

12 acres of classic botanic garden, with every educational element: rock gardens, an arboretum, collections of native plants, beds which illustrate the history of the rose, water plants and systematic beds. Well worth exploration.

Kildrummy Castle
Kildrummy, Alford, Grampian AB33 8RA
☎ 09755 71264 or 71277

OWNER Kildrummy Castle Garden Trust
LOCATION On A97, off A944
OPEN 10 am – 5 pm; daily; 1 April to 31 October
ADMISSION Adults £1.70; Children 50p over 5 years
FACILITIES Parking; dogs permitted; loos; access for the disabled; plants for sale; tea & coffee
FEATURES Good collection of trees; plantsman's garden; old roses and climbers; water features; woodland garden; interesting for children; autumn colour; heathers; play area & nature trails

A romantic glen-garden, laid out nearly 100 years ago. Richly planted pools and ponds, a plantsman's collection on the hillside, and a large mature rock garden made from the natural sandstone. One of the most romantic gardens in Scotland.

Leith Hall
Kennethmont, by Huntly, Aberdeen, Grampian AB54 4QQ
☎ 04643 269

OWNER The National Trust for Scotland
LOCATION On B9002 west of Kennethmont
OPEN 9.30am – sunset; daily; all year
ADMISSION Free
FACILITIES Parking; loos; facilities for the disabled; refreshments in May to September, 2 pm – 6 pm
FEATURES Herbaceous borders; rock garden; modern roses; particularly good in July-August; bluebells

Richly planted borders are the pride of Leith Hall: they are full of colour all through the summer. Also impressive is the rock garden, restored and replanted by that most successful of societies, the Scottish Rock Garden Club. Leith gets better and better.

Pitmedden
Ellon, Grampian AB4 0PD
☎ 0651 842352

OWNER The National Trust for Scotland
LOCATION 1 mile west of Pitmedden on A920
OPEN 10 am – 5.30 pm; daily; 1 May to 30 September
ADMISSION Adults £3
FACILITIES Parking; loos; facilities for the disabled; tea room
FEATURES Herbs; good topiary; gazebos; parterres

A 17th century formal garden meticulously created by the National Trust for Scotland 40 years ago. It has 3 miles of box hedging and uses 40,000 bedding plants every summer. The result is impressive, satisfying and peaceful, but lacks authenticity.

HIGHLAND

Allangrange

Munlochy, Black Isle, Highland IV8 8NZ
☎ 046 381 249   📠 046 381 407

OWNER   Major Allan Cameron
LOCATION   Off A9, 5 miles north of Inverness
OPEN   2 pm – 5.30 pm; 8 May, 13 June & 4 July; or by appointment
ADMISSION   £1
FACILITIES   Parking; dogs permitted; loos; facilities for the disabled; plants for sale; teas in house at £1 per head
FEATURES   Old roses and climbers; water features; woodland garden; primulas; rhododendrons; colour borders

Colour gardening by the owner's wife, a botanical artist, has made this one of the loveliest summer gardens in the British Isles. Good spring flowers, too.

Cawdor Castle

Cawdor Castle, Nairn, Highland IV12 5RD
☎ 0667 404615   📠 0667 404674

OWNER   Countess Cawdor
LOCATION   Between Inverness and Nairn on B9090.
OPEN   10 am – 5.30 pm; daily; 1 May to 2 October
ADMISSION   Adults, £2.00
FACILITIES   Parking; loos; facilities for the disabled; gift shop; licensed restaurant in castle
FEATURES   Herbaceous borders; fruit and vegetables of special interest; old roses and climbers; woodland garden; maze; paradise garden

A Victorian garden which has been replanted and, in part, redesigned in recent years by the addition of the holly maze and colour plantings. Elsewhere the combination of old shapes and new plants makes for a garden of exceptional accessibility. Not grand, just charming, while the house is as Scottish a castle as ever was seen.

Dochfour Gardens

Inverness, Highland IV3 6JY
☎ 0463 86218   📠 0463 86336

OWNER   Lord & Lady Burton
LOCATION   5 miles south west of Inverness on the A82
OPEN   10 am – 5 pm, Monday – Friday; 2 pm – 5 pm, Saturday & Sunday; 1 April to 31 October
ADMISSION   £1.50, reductions for Senior Citizens and children
FACILITIES   Parking; plants for sale; pick your own fruit in season
FEATURES   naturalised daffodils; tallest *Thuja occidentalis* 'Lutea' in the British Isles, plus three further tree records

Dunrobin Castle Gardens

Golspie, Sutherland, Highland KW10 6RR
☎ 0408 633177   📠 0408 633800

OWNER   The Sutherland Trust
LOCATION   55 miles north of Inverness on A9
OPEN   Dawn to dusk; daily; all year round. Castle: 10.30 am – 5.30 pm, Monday – Saturday; 1 pm – 5.30 pm, Sunday; 1 May to 15 October
ADMISSION   Castle: Adults £3.30; Children £1.60. Gardens free when castle closed
FACILITIES   Parking; loos; tea room in castle
FEATURES   Herbaceous borders; modern roses; good topiary; water features; woodland garden; formal gardens

Grand terrace gardens, designed by Nesfield, striding down to the Dornoch Forth. Recently replanted and partially restored. New features have been added, like rhododendrons: there will be further improvements.

Inverewe

Poolewe, Ross and Cromarty, Highland IV22 2LQ
☎ 044 586 441   📠 044 586 497

OWNER   The National Trust for Scotland
LOCATION   On A832, 6 miles north of Gairloch
OPEN   9.30 am – dusk; all year. Visitors centre open 1 April to 23 October
ADMISSION   Adults £3.00; Senior Citizens & Children £1.50; Group rate £2.40 – £1.20
FACILITIES   Parking; loos; facilities for the disabled; plants for sale; large shop; self-service restaurant
FEATURES   Good collection of trees; herbaceous borders; fine conifers; fruit and vegetables of special interest; plantsman's garden; rock garden; sub-tropical plants; water features; woodland garden; particularly good in July-August; autumn colour; meconopsis; candelabra primulas; tallest *Eucalyptus cordata* and *E. gunnii* in the British Isles
NCCPG NATIONAL COLLECTIONS *Olearia*, *Brachyglottis*, *Ourisia*, *Rhododendron*

One of the wonders of the horticultural world, a sub-tropical garden in the north west Highlands. Fabulous large-leaved Himalayan rhododendrons, magnolias, eucalyptus, tree ferns, palms and tender rarities underplanted with drifts of blue poppies and candelabra primulas. Best on a sunny dry day in May, before the midges breed.

Lochalsh Woodland Garden

Balmacara, By Kyle of Lochalsh, Ross, Highland IV40 8DN
☎ 059 986 231

OWNER   The National Trust for Scotland
LOCATION   On A87 near Kyle
OPEN   9 am – dusk

ADMISSION Adults £1.00; Children 50p
FACILITIES Parking; dogs permitted; loos; facilities for
the disabled
FEATURES Fine conifers; plantsman's garden; sub-
tropical plants; woodland garden; ferns; primulas; rhododendrons
NCCPG NATIONAL COLLECTIONS *Arundinaria*

A woodland garden and still developing. The structure
is about 100 years old – tall trees, both native and
exotic, planted as shelter. Ornamental plantings started
about 30 years ago, with rhododendrons from Euan
Cox at Glendoick. These are now filled out with other
shrubs, especially tender species from Tasmania and
New Zealand, and herbaceous underplantings.

LOTHIAN

Dalmeny House
Rosebery Estates, South Queensferry, Lothian
EH30 9TQ

OWNER The Earl of Rosebery
LOCATION B924 off A90
OPEN 12 noon – 5.30 pm, Monday & Tuesday; 1 pm
– 5.30 pm, Sunday; 1 May to 30 September
ADMISSION Free
FACILITIES Parking; access for the disabled; refresh-
ments
FEATURES Fine conifers; water features; woodland
garden; rhododendrons & azaleas; wellingtonias

The grounds at Dalmeny are extensive, and visitors are
encouraged to see the valley walk with rhododendrons,
wellingtonias and other conifers.

Inveresk Lodge Garden
24 Inveresk Village, Musselburgh, Lothian EH21 7TE

OWNER The National Trust for Scotland
LOCATION A6124 south of Musselburgh, 6 miles east
of Edinburgh
OPEN 10 am – 4.30 pm, Monday – Friday; 2 pm – 5
pm, Sunday; all year
ADMISSION Donation, please
FACILITIES Loos
FEATURES Herbaceous borders; old roses and
climbers; plantings by Graham Thomas; raised beds;
peat beds

A modern garden, tailor-made for a modest NTS estate
and maintained to a high standard. Graham Thomas
designed the rose borders. Good climbing plants.

Malleny House
Balerno, Lothian EH14 7AF
☎ 031 449 2283

OWNER The National Trust for Scotland

LOCATION South west of Edinburgh, off A70 Lanark
Road West
OPEN 10 am – dusk; daily; all year
ADMISSION Adults £1; Senior Citizens & Children
50p
FACILITIES Parking; loos; access for the disabled
FEATURES Herbaceous borders; fruit and vegetables
of special interest; glasshouses to visit; herbs; modern
roses; old roses and climbers; good topiary; particularly
good in July-August; bonsai collection
NCCPG NATIONAL COLLECTIONS *Rosa*
FRIENDS The Friends of Malleny enjoy garden visits,
lectures and other benefits

One of the NTS's best gardens, much praised for its
'personal' quality. The 19th century shrub roses are
underplanted with herbaceous plants which take the
display into the autumn. The bonsai collection creates
quite another dimension, as do the huge cones of yew
topiary. Very peaceful.

Royal Botanic Garden, Edinburgh
Inverleith Row, Edinburgh, Lothian EH3 5LR
☎ 031 552 7171   [FAX] 031 552 0382

OWNER Board of Trustees & Scottish Office
LOCATION 1 mile north of Princes Street
OPEN 10 am – 6 pm, 1 March to 30 April; 10 am – 8
pm 1 May to 31 August; 10 am – 6 pm, 1 September to
31 October; 10 am – 4 pm, 1 November to 28 February
ADMISSION Free, donations welcome
FACILITIES Parking; loos; facilities for the disabled;
plants for sale; shop; licensed terrace café
FEATURES Good collection of trees; herbaceous borders; fine conifers; ecological interest; glasshouses to
visit; gravel or scree garden; herbs; oriental features;
rock garden; modern roses; old roses and climbers;
garden sculpture; sub-tropical plants; water features;
woodland garden; interesting for children; particularly
interesting in winter; tallest *Pinus coulteri* in the British
Isles, and twelve further tree records
FRIENDS See Societies section

Edinburgh outclasses Kew in some ways – better rock
gardens, peat beds, rhododendrons and woodland gardens. And entry is free. Wonderful cantilevered glasshouses and good facilities for people with special needs
– children, disabled persons and the blind. No visitor
can fail to respond, above all, to the friendly welcome
and helpfulness of all the staff.

STRATHCLYDE

Achamore Gardens

Isle of Gigha, Strathclyde PA41 7AD
☎ 05835 268   📠 05835 267

OWNER   Holt Leisure Parks Ltd
LOCATION   Take Gigha ferry from Tainloan (20 mins)
OPEN   Dawn – dusk; daily; all year
ADMISSION   Adults £2; Children £1
FACILITIES   Parking; dogs permitted; loos; access for
the disabled; lunches & teas at Gigha Hotel
FEATURES   Good collection of trees; fine conifers;
plantsman's garden; old roses and climbers; sub-tropical
plants; woodland garden; rhododendrons; azaleas; big-
gest *Larix gmelinii* in the British Isles

One of the best rhododendron gardens in the British
Isles, and only 50 years old. Mainly planted by Sir James
Horlick with advice from Jim Russell. The collection of
large-leaved Himalayan rhododendrons is breathtaking.

Ardtornish Garden

Lochaline, Morvern by Oban, Strathclyde PA34 5XA
☎ 0967 421288

OWNER   Mrs John Raven
LOCATION   2 miles north of Lochaline
OPEN   10 am – 5 pm; daily; 1 April to 31 October
ADMISSION   £1.00
FACILITIES   Parking; dogs permitted; loos; plants for
sale
FEATURES   Good collection of trees; fine conifers; fruit
and vegetables of special interest; plantsman's garden;
water features; woodland garden; kitchen garden; blue-
bells; gunnera; rhododendrons

This is Faith Raven's other garden – see Docwra's
Manor in Cambridgeshire – and a complete contrast:
28 acres of rocky hillside full of Edwardian hybrid
rhododendrons like 'Pink Pearl' and 'Cynthia'. Mrs
Raven has actively improved it with a great range of
interesting plants. Remote, but worth every inch of the
journey.

Arduaine Gardens

Loch Melfort Hotel, by Oban, Strathclyde
PA34 4XQ
☎ 08522 366

OWNER   The National Trust for Scotland
LOCATION   Between Oban & Lochgilphead
OPEN   9.30 am – sunset; daily; all year
ADMISSION   Adults £2; Senior Citizens £1
FACILITIES   Parking; loos; access for the disabled; no
refreshments, but Loch Melfort Hotel is next door
FEATURES   Herbaceous borders; fine conifers; rock
garden; sub-tropical plants; water features; rhododen-

drons; tallest *Nothofagus antarctica* (26 metres) in the
British Isles
NCCPG NATIONAL COLLECTIONS *Ampelopsis, Par-
thenocissus*

A wonderful rhododendron garden, with a flowing
design and a profusion of flower in spring. It was
replanted in the 1970s by two nurserymen and now has
interest at all seasons. Arduaine is in excellent condition, too.

Biggar Park

Biggar, Strathclyde ML12 6JS
☎ 0899 21085

OWNER   Captain & Mrs David Barnes
LOCATION   South end of Biggar on A702
OPEN   10 July or by appointment
ADMISSION   £1.50
FACILITIES   Parking; dogs permitted; loos; plants for
sale; home-made teas on open day
FEATURES   Good collection of trees; herbaceous bor-
ders; oriental features; plantsman's garden; rock garden;
old roses and climbers; water features; woodland gar-
den; daffodils; fritillaries; meconopsis

Ten acres of plantsmanship, with drifts of naturalised
fritillaries in spring, and deep traditional herbaceous
borders in summer when the garden has its open day.

Brodick Castle

Isle of Arran, Strathclyde KA27 8HY
☎ 0770 302202

OWNER   The National Trust for Scotland
LOCATION   Ferry from Ardrossan to Brodick, follows
signs
OPEN   9.30 am – dusk; daily; all year
ADMISSION   £2 adults (1993)
FACILITIES   Parking; dogs permitted; loos; facilities for
the disabled; plants for sale; NTS shop; tea rooms open
Easter to October
FEATURES   Good collection of trees; herbaceous borders; fine conifers; old roses and climbers; sub-tropical
plants; water features; woodland garden; candelabra
primulas; meconopsis; tallest *Embothrium coccineum*
(20m) and *Leptospermum scoparium* (10m) in the British Isles (2 further records)
NCCPG NATIONAL COLLECTIONS *Rhododendron*

Ravishing 60 acre rhododendron garden on sloping
woodland in a mild wet climate. Good magnolias, camellias, crinodendrons and olearias too, but they are never
a match for the rhododendrons, many from collectors'
seed (Forrest, Kingdon Ward etc.).

Crarae Gardens

Crarae, by Inverary, Strathclyde PA32 8YA
☎ 0546 86614

OWNER The Crarae Garden Charitable Trust
LOCATION South of Inveraray on A83
OPEN 9 am – 6 pm; daily; Easter to 31 October.
Daylight hours; 1 November to Easter
ADMISSION Adults £2.50; Children £1.50; Family
£7.00
FACILITIES Parking; dogs permitted; loos; facilities for
the disabled; plants for sale; shop selling books, china
& local crafts; light refreshments
FEATURES Good collection of trees; water features;
woodland garden; camellias; rhododendrons; euca-
lyptus; autumn colour; tallest *Eucalyptus coccifera* in
the British Isles (and ten further tree records)
NCCPG NATIONAL COLLECTIONS *Nothofagus*
FRIENDS Friends of Crarae

Fifty acres of exotic woodland, centred on a steep glen
spanned by wooden bridges. The long but gentle climb
up the glen is a pilgrim's progress for plantsmen, past all
manner of exotic plants displayed for effect. At the top,
you pass out of the enchanted garden into wild moorland: no other garden offers such catharsis.

Culzean Country Park

Maybole, Ayrshire, Strathclyde KA19 8LE
☎ 06556 269   FAX 06556 615

OWNER The National Trust for Scotland
LOCATION Off A719, west of Maybole & South of
Ayr
OPEN 9.30 am – dusk; daily; all year
ADMISSION Adults, £3.30; children £1.70 (1993)
FACILITIES Parking; dogs permitted; loos; facilities for
the disabled; plants for sale; good shop; self-service
restaurant; light refreshments in car park
FEATURES Herbaceous borders; follies and garden
buildings; glasshouses to visit; herbs; water features;
woodland garden; interesting for children; deer park;
formal garden; adventure playground; tallest Irish yew
Taxus baccata 'Fastigiata' (19 metres) in the British Isles
(plus two further tree records)

An important historic landscape, recently restored and
seriously open to the public (400,000 visitors a year).
Good trees as well as a gothic camellia house, gazebos
and a pagoda.

Glasgow Botanic Garden

Great Western Road, Glasgow, Strathclyde
G12 OUE
☎ 041 334 2422

OWNER Glasgow City Council
LOCATION On A82, 2 miles from city centre

OPEN Grounds: 7 am – dusk; daily; all year. Glasshouses & Kibble Palace: 10 am – 4.45 pm; Main Range:
1 pm – 4.45 pm
ADMISSION Free
FACILITIES Dogs permitted; loos; facilities for the disabled
FEATURES Good collection of trees; herbaceous borders; fine conifers; glasshouses to visit; herbs; rock
garden; modern roses; old roses and climbers; good
topiary; water features; particularly interesting in
winter; beautiful glasshouse (the 'Kibble Palace'); systematic beds
NCCPG NATIONAL COLLECTIONS *Begonia, Dendro-
bium*, Dicksoniaceae

Most of the elements of the botanic garden are here,
including systematic beds and chronological beds, but
the glory of Glasgow is the two glasshouses – the Kibble
Palace and the Main Range. From tree ferns to palms
and from cacti to orchids, the Main Range is an essay
in plant types. The Kibble Palace, however, is divided
between geographical areas –South Africa, Australia,
China, South America, the Canaries and so on. There
is no better place to enjoy a winter's day in Glasgow.

Glenarn

Rhu, Helensburgh, Dunbartonshire, Strathclyde
G84 8LL
☎ 0436 820493

OWNER Mr & Mrs Michael Thornley
LOCATION Turn up Pier Road at Rhu Marina, first
right is Glenarn Road
OPEN Dawn to dusk; daily; 21 March to 21 June
ADMISSION Adults £1.00; Senior Citizens & Children 50p
FACILITIES Dogs permitted; access for the disabled;
plants for sale; refreshments may be booked in advance
FEATURES Fine conifers; plantsman's garden; rock garden; water features; woodland garden; rhododendrons;
embothriums

Ten acres of woodland garden, with some rhododendrons dating from Sir Joseph Hooker's Himalayan expedition and others from the 1930s trips of Kingdon
Ward and Ludlow and Sheriff. Good hybrids too – the
original Gibson plants. But plenty of magnolias, camellias, pieris, and other good plants.

Greenbank Garden

Flenders Road, Clarkston, Glasgow, Strathclyde
G76 8RB
☎ 041 6393281

OWNER The National Trust for Scotland
LOCATION One mile along Mearns Road from Clark-
ston Toll, take 1st left
OPEN 9.30 am to sunset; daily; all year

ADMISSION Adults £2.00; Concessions £1.00
FACILITIES Parking; loos; facilities for the disabled; plants for sale; NTS gift shop; light refreshments & drinks
FEATURES Herbaceous borders; fruit and vegetables of special interest; rock garden; modern roses; old roses and climbers; garden sculpture; woodland garden; garden for the disabled
NCCPG NATIONAL COLLECTIONS *Verbena*
FRIENDS Friends of Greenbank organise events throughout the year. Details from head gardener

Greenbank is a demonstration garden: it was left to the Trust in 1976 on condition that it was developed as a teaching resource for people with small gardens. The walled garden has therefore been divided into a great number of sections which represent different interests and skills: a rock garden, fruit garden, dried flower plot, raised beds, winter garden, and so on. Does it *work*? Yes, definitely.

The Younger Botanic Garden

Benmore, Dunoon, Strathclyde PA23 8QU
☎ 0369 6261   ⓕ 0369 6369

OWNER Board of Trustees/Royal Botanic Garden, Edinburgh
LOCATION 7 miles north of Dunoon on A815
OPEN 10 am – 6 pm; daily; 15 March to 31 October
ADMISSION Adults £1.50; Senior Citizens £1; Children 50p
FACILITIES Parking; dogs permitted; loos; facilities for the disabled; plants for sale; gift shop; tea room
FEATURES Good collection of trees; fine conifers; plantsman's garden; water features; woodland garden; interesting for children; giant redwood avenue planted in 1863; rhododendrons; ferns

Benmore has been an annexe of the Royal Botanic Garden at Edinburgh since 1929. The mild, wet climate makes possible the cultivation of tender plants from lower altitudes of the Sino-Himalaya, Bhutan, Japan and the New World. Benmore is a living textbook of the genus *Rhododendron*. Their background is of conifers planted early in the 19th century, perhaps the best collection in Scotland.

TAYSIDE

Branklyn Garden

Dundee Road, Perth, Tayside PH2 7BB
☎ 0738 33199

OWNER The National Trust for Scotland
LOCATION On Dundee Road, east of Perth on edge of city
OPEN 9.30 am – sunset; daily; 1 March to 31 October

ADMISSION Adults £2, Senior Citizens £1
FACILITIES Parking; loos; access for the disabled; plants for sale; small NTS gift shop
FEATURES Gravel or scree garden; plantsman's garden; rock garden; rhododendrons; alpines; *Meconopsis grandis* 'Branklyn'
NCCPG NATIONAL COLLECTIONS *Cassiope, Paeonia*

The apotheosis of Scottish rock gardening, a small suburban garden absolutely stuffed with rare plants in an ideal microclimate.

Cluny House

by Aberfeldy, Perthshire, Tayside PH15 2JT
☎ 0887 820795

OWNER Mr & Mrs John Mattingley
LOCATION 3½ miles from Aberfeldy, on the Weem to Strathtay Road
OPEN 10 am – 6 pm; daily; March to October
ADMISSION Adults £1.50; Children under 16 free
FACILITIES Parking; plants for sale
FEATURES Good collection of trees; fine conifers; plantsman's garden; woodland garden; meconopsis; primulas; cardiocrinums; tallest *Prunus maackii* in the British Isles
NCCPG NATIONAL COLLECTIONS *Primula*

A plantsman's garden, largely made in the 1950s by Mrs Mattingley's father, who subscribed to the Ludlow and Sherriff expeditions. Superb rhododendrons and, above all, candelabra primulas – sheets of them from April to July.

Drummond Castle Gardens

Muthill, Crieff, Tayside PH7 4HZ
☎ 0764 681257   ⓕ 0764 681550

OWNER Grimsthorpe & Drummond Castle Trust Ltd
LOCATION South of Crieff on A822
OPEN 2 pm – 6 pm; daily; 1 May to 30 September
ADMISSION Adults £2.00; Senior Citizens & Children £1.00
FACILITIES Parking; loos; access for the disabled; teas on first Sunday in August (charity day)
FEATURES Fruit and vegetables of special interest; glasshouses to visit; important formal garden

Drummond has probably the most important formal garden in Scotland, laid out c.1830 as a St Andrew's cross, with complex parterres filled with roses, statues, clipped cones, herbaceous plants, gravel and lots more beside. The result is order, shape, structure, mass, profusion and colour.

Dundee University Botanic Garden

Riverside Drive, Dundee, Tayside DD2 1QH

☎ 0382 566939

OWNER University of Dundee

LOCATION Signposted from Riverside Drive (A85), near its junction with Perth Road

OPEN 10 am – 4.30 pm, Monday – Saturday; also 11 am – 4 pm Sunday. 10 am – 3.30 pm, Monday – Saturday; also 11 am – 3 pm, Sundays; 1 November to 28 February

ADMISSION Adults £1, Senior Citizens and Children 50p

FACILITIES Parking; loos; facilities for the disabled; plants for sale; some small souvenirs for sale; DIY soft drinks

FEATURES Fine conifers; ecological interest; glasshouses to visit; herbs; sub-tropical plants; water features; drought-resistant plants; carnivorous plants

FRIENDS Friends: Individual £5.00, Family £8.00 minimum. Newsletters, botanical excursions and illustrated lectures

A fine botanic garden which caters well for visitors. As well as historic plant collections, systematic and chronological borders, there are areas which illustrate native plant communities, including both montane and coastal habitats.

Edzell Castle

Edzell, Angus, Tayside DD9 7TG

☎ 0365 648631

OWNER Historic Scotland

LOCATION On B966 to Edzell Village

OPEN 9.30 am – 6 pm; Monday – Saturday: 2pm – 6pm, Sunday; 1 April to 30 September. 9.30 am – 4 pm; Monday – Saturday: 2 pm – 4 pm, Sunday; 1 October to 31 March

ADMISSION Adults £1.70; Senior Citizens and Children 90p; Family £4.50

FACILITIES Parking; dogs permitted; loos; facilities for the disabled; plants for sale; shop

FEATURES Formal garden

FRIENDS Historic Scotland

A 1930s formal garden in the 17th century style, designed to be seen from the ruined keep. A quincunx, of sorts, with yew bobbles, box edging and roses in the beds. The four main segments have the motto of the Lindsey family *DUM SPIRO SPERO* cut round their edges in box. Fun, though not a garden to linger in.

Glendoick Gardens

Glendoick, Perth, Tayside PH2 7NS

☎ 073 886205   📠 073 886735

OWNER Mr & Mrs Peter A Cox

LOCATION A85 between Perth & Dundee

OPEN 2 pm – 5 pm; 1, 8, 15 and 22 May only

ADMISSION £1.50

FACILITIES Parking; loos; famous garden centre attached

FEATURES Plantsman's garden; woodland garden; rhododendrons

NCCPG NATIONAL COLLECTIONS *Enkianthus, Kalmia, Phyllodoce*

Everyone knows of the Glendoick nursery, but the garden is even more important. Started by Farrer's friend Euan Cox in the 1920s, it has one of the best collections of plants, especially rhododendron species, forms and hybrids, in the British Isles. More's the pity that it is so seldom open.

Gowranes

Kinnaird, by Inchture, Tayside PH14 9QY

☎ 0828 86752

OWNER Professor & Mrs W W Park

LOCATION Midway between Perth & Dundee, 1½ miles North of A85

OPEN Any time, by appointment

ADMISSION £2.00

FACILITIES Parking; loos; access for the disabled; plants for sale; refreshments by arrangement

FEATURES Fine conifers; plantsman's garden; rock garden; water features; woodland garden

A newish plantsman's garden on a steeply sloping site above a burn which has been dammed to create pools and waterfalls. Rhododendrons, camellias, pieris and similar shrubs in the woodland parts: gunneras and candelabra primulas down among the boggy bits.

House of Pitmuies

House of Pitmies, by Forfar, Angus, Tayside DD8 2SN

☎ 0241 828245

OWNER Mrs Farquhar Ogilvie

LOCATION Off A932 Forfar to Arbroath Road

OPEN 10 am – 5 pm; daily; 1 April to 31 October

ADMISSION £1.50 (1993)

FACILITIES Parking; dogs permitted; loos; access for the disabled; plants for sale; home-raised plants & produce in season

FEATURES Herbaceous borders; fruit and vegetables of special interest; glasshouses to visit; modern roses; old roses and climbers; water features; alpine meadow; ferns; colour schemes; tallest *Ilex aquifolium* 'Argenteomarginata' in the British Isles

One of the most beautiful modern gardens in Scotland. Laid out and planted in the Hidcote style, Pitmuies has wonderful shrub roses in mixed plantings, clever colour schemes, and innumerable different gardens within the garden: a delphinium border, cherry walk, an alpine meadow for wild flowers, rhododendrons glades, vast hollies and splendid monkey puzzles inherited from Victorian times. Enchanted and enchanting.

NORTHERN IRELAND

CO. DOWN

Castlewellan National Arboretum

Castlewellan Forest Park, Castlewellan, Co. Down BT25 9KG
☎ 03967 78664

OWNER   Department of Agriculture, Forest Services
LOCATION   30 miles south of Belfast, 4 miles west of Newcastle
OPEN   10 am – sunset all year
ADMISSION   £2.20 per car
FACILITIES   Parking; dogs permitted; access for the disabled; light refreshments at peak times
FEATURES   Good collection of trees; herbaceous borders; fine conifers; plantsman's garden; woodland garden; particularly interesting in winter; autumn colours; embothriums; eucryphias; tallest *Chamaecyparis nootkatensis* 'Lutea' in the British Isles, plus 5 other tree records

Castlewellan means trees: several record breakers and many rarities. The heart of the collection is in a huge walled garden, interplanted with rhododendrons and other shrubs. The central path has mixed borders at the top: dwarf rhododendrons are prominent even here. Labelling is good, and the standard of maintenance high.

Mount Stewart

The National Trust, Mount Stewart Estate, Grey Abbey, Newtownards, Co. Down BT22 2AD
☎ 02477 88387

OWNER   The National Trust
LOCATION   East of Belfast on A20
OPEN   10.30 am – 6.00 pm; daily; 1 April to 30 September; weekends only in October
ADMISSION   Adults £2.70; Children half price
FACILITIES   Parking; dogs permitted; loos; facilities for the disabled; souvenir shop; refreshments from 1.30 pm
FEATURES   Good collection of trees; herbaceous borders; fine conifers; follies and garden buildings; plantsman's garden; old roses and climbers; good topiary; water features; woodland garden; plantings by Graham Thomas; rare and tender shrubs galore
NCCPG NATIONAL COLLECTIONS   *Phormium*

One of the best gardens in the British Isles and very little known outside Ireland. The formal gardens by the house are utterly original: a Spanish garden, statues of mythical beasts, and the red hand of Ulster set in a shamrock surround. Good plants too: *Rosa gigantea* grows on the house walls, and the herbaceous and woodland plantings are brilliant with colour and variety. Better still is the walk around the lake, where rhododendrons flood the woodlands. They are underplanted in places with *Meconopsis* and candelabra primulas and, at one point, you catch a glimpse of a white stag in a glade. For design, variety, plants and plantings, Mount Stewart is a place of miracles. Allow lots of time for your visit.

Rowallane Garden

Saintfield, Ballynahinch, Co. Down BT24 7LH
☎ 0238 510131

OWNER   The National Trust
LOCATION   One mile south of Saintfield on A7
OPEN   10.30 pm – 6 pm, Monday – Friday; 2 pm – 6 pm, Saturday & Sunday; 1 April to 31 October. 10.30 am – 5 pm; Monday – Friday; 1 November to 31 March
ADMISSION   Adults, April to October, £2.50; Children £1.15; Groups £1.60. Adults, November to March, £1.90
FACILITIES   Parking; facilities for the disabled; National Trust shop; light refreshments 2 pm – 6 pm May to August & weekends in April & September
FEATURES   Good collection of trees; herbaceous borders; fine conifers; plantsman's garden; rock garden; woodland garden; rhododendrons & azaleas
NCCPG NATIONAL COLLECTIONS   *Penstemon*

52 acres of rhododendrons and azaleas, which started near the house and expanded into the fields beyond as the seedlings came and needed to be planted. No garden can match it on a sunny day in April or May, as you amble from a glade of *Rh. augustinii* forms to a line of *Rh. macabeanum* or back through *Rh. yakushimanum* hybrids.

CO. FERMANAGH

Florence Court

The National Trust, Florence Court, Enniskillen, Co. Fermanagh BT92 1DB
☎ 0365 348249

OWNER   The National Trust
LOCATION   4 miles from Marble Arch Caves on A32
OPEN   1 pm – 6 pm; daily except Tuesday; 1 June to 31 August; plus Saturday, Sunday and Bank Holidays in April, May & September
ADMISSION   Adults £2.30; Children £1.15; Groups £1.80 (12 or more people); Garden/Estate £1.50 per car (1993)

FACILITIES Parking; dogs permitted; loos; facilities for the disabled; National Trust shop; light lunches & teas; picnics welcome
FEATURES Good collection of trees; woodland garden; interesting for children; ice-house; water-powered sawmill

Classic 18th century parkland, with some fine trees, notably the original 'Irish Yew' *Taxus baccata* 'Fastigiata' and a beautiful form of weeping beech with a broad curving crown. The sawmill is fun for children.

CO. LONDONDERRY

Guy Wilson Daffodil Garden

University of Ulster, Coleraine, Co. Londonderry
BT52 1SA
☎ 0265 44141   ⟪FAX⟫ 0265 40912

OWNER University of Ulster at Coleraine
LOCATION Signposted from sports centre
OPEN All year
ADMISSION Free
FACILITIES Parking; dogs permitted; loos; facilities for the disabled
FEATURES Daffodils; exceptional collection of daffodils best second half April
NCCPG NATIONAL COLLECTIONS *Narcissus*

The name says it all – this is both a celebration of Guy Wilson as a daffodil breeder and a museum of his hybrids. His achievements are revered in Northern Ireland, and rightly so.

EIRE

CO. CORK

Annes Grove Gardens

Castletownroche, near Mallow, Co. Cork, Eire
☎ 010 353 22 26145

OWNER Patrick Annesley
LOCATION 1 mile north of Castletownroche on N72
OPEN 10 am – 5 pm, Monday – Saturday; 1 pm – 6 pm, Sunday; 17 March to 30 September
ADMISSION Adults I£2.50; Senior Citizens & Students I£1.50; Children I£1.00
FACILITIES Parking; dogs permitted; loos; plants for sale; lunches & teas by arrangement for groups
FEATURES Good collection of trees; herbaceous borders; fine conifers; plantsman's garden; water features; woodland garden; rhododendrons from wild seeds; rare trees

Annes Grove has long been famous for its 30-acre garden: 'Robinsonian' is the word most often used to describe it. The walled garden has a 17th century mount with a summer house on top. The river garden is lushly wild with lysichiton, gunnera and candelabra primulas. In the glen garden lies a wonderfully dense collection of rhododendrons and azaleas, many from Kingdon Ward's seed.

Fota

Fota Island, Carrigtwohill, Co. Cork, Eire
☎ 010 353 21 812728   ⟪FAX⟫ 010 353 21 270244

OWNER Fota Trust Company Ltd
LOCATION 10 miles from Cork city, off N25 towards Cobh
OPEN 10 am – 6 pm, weekdays; 11 am – 6 pm, Sundays, 14 March to 31 October
ADMISSION Cars I£1.00; Pedestrians free of charge
FACILITIES Parking; dogs permitted; loos; facilities for the disabled
FEATURES Good collection of trees; fine conifers; ecological interest; water features; woodland garden; interesting for children; wildlife park; tallest Italian cypress *Cupressus sempervirens* (25 metres) in the British Isles, plus 10 other record trees

Fota has a handsome formal garden and walled garden, now undergoing restoration, but is famous above all for its trees. As well as a fine collection of Victorian conifers (huge redwoods and wellingtonias), there are flowering mimosas, a wonderful *Cornus capitata* and such tender trees as the Canary Islands palm *Phoenix canariensis*.

CO. DONEGAL

Ardnamona

Lough Eske, Co. Donegal, Eire
☎ 010 353 73 22650   ⟪FAX⟫ 010 353 73 22819

OWNER Mr & Mrs Kieran Clarke
LOCATION On Lough Eske, 5 miles north east of Donegal
OPEN 2 pm – 5 pm; daily; 1 April to 30 June
ADMISSION I£2
FACILITIES Parking; bed & breakfast offered
FEATURES Fine conifers; water features; woodland garden; ancient rhododendrons

A wilderness of huge rhododendrons, some as much as 60ft high, like a Himalayan forest, now taken in hand, cleared and revitalised.

Glenveagh

Church Hill, Letterkenny, Co. Donegal, Eire
☎ 010 353 74 37090 ☒ 010 353 74 37072

OWNER   The Office of Public Works
LOCATION   14 miles north west of Letterkenny
OPEN   10 am – 6 pm (7 pm on Sundays, June – August); Easter to 31 October
ADMISSION   I£1.50 adults, I£1 senior citizens, 70p students
FACILITIES   Parking; loos; access for the disabled; restaurant at visitor centre; tearoom at castle
FEATURES   Good collection of trees; herbaceous borders; fine conifers; fruit and vegetables of special interest; glasshouses to visit; herbs; plantsman's garden; modern roses; old roses and climbers; garden sculpture; sub-tropical plants; woodland garden

Glenveagh was built for its view down the rocky slopes of Lough Veagh, and part of the gardens is known as the View Garden. Lanning Roper laid out a formal Italianate courtyard garden. Jim Russell advised on planting. There are wonderful borders and conservatories as well as rhododendrons and camellias. The unusual shrubs are magnificent: tree-like griselinias and *Michelia doltsopa*, for instance.

CO. DUBLIN

45 Sandford Road

Ranelagh, Dublin 6, Co. Dublin, Eire
☎ 010 353 1 971308

OWNER   Helen & Val Dillon
LOCATION   Junction of Sandford Road and Marlborough Road
OPEN   2 pm – 6 pm; Sundays; 1 March to mid-October. Groups by appointment
ADMISSION   Adults I£3; Senior ciitizens I£2
FACILITIES   Loos; access for the disabled; plants for sale
FEATURES   Herbaceous borders; glasshouses to visit; plantsman's garden; raised beds

A plantsman's garden with a fantastic range of rarities, from snowdrops and hellebores in spring, to tropaeolums in autumn. Unlike some collectors' gardens, this is immaculately maintained and beautifully designed as a series of garden rooms.

Ardgillan Park

Balbriggan, Co. Dublin, Eire
☎ 010 353 1 849 1200

OWNER   Dublin County Council
LOCATION   Coast road between Skerries and Balbriggan
OPEN   10 am – 5 pm; daily; all year

FACILITIES   Parking; loos; facilities for the disabled; refreshments
FEATURES   Herbaceous borders; follies and garden buildings; fruit and vegetables of special interest; herbs; rock garden; modern roses; old roses and climbers; ice house; 200 year old yew walk

Ardgillan was all but lost in the troubles, but restored ten years ago by the Council as a public amenity. A new rose garden and herbaceous borders have been added. The four-acre walled garden is being developed too – it has a herb garden now and fruit trees grown against the walls.

Fernhill

Sandyford, Co. Dublin, Eire
☎ 010 353 1 295 6000

OWNER   Mrs Sally Walker
LOCATION   7 miles south of the central Dublin on the Enniskerry Road
OPEN   11 am – 5 pm (2 pm – 6 pm on Sundays); Tuesday – Sunday (and Bank Holidays); 1 March to 30 November
ADMISSION   I£2.50; Senior Citizens I£1; Children I£1
FACILITIES   Parking; loos; plants for sale
FEATURES   Good collection of trees; herbaceous borders; fine conifers; rock garden; garden sculpture; water features; woodland garden; sculpture exhibitions; rhododendrons

A popular garden on the outskirts of Dublin, with a good collection of rhododendrons and other woodland plants and some magnificent trees c.150 years old. Steep woodland walks and an excellent nursery add to the pleasure.

National Botanic Gardens, Dublin

Glasnevin, Dublin 9, Co. Dublin, Eire
☎ 010 353 1 374388 ☒ 010 353 1 360080

OWNER   Office of Public Works
LOCATION   1 mile north of Dublin near Glasnevin cemetery
OPEN   9 am – 6 pm (4.30 in winter); daily except 25 December; opens at 11 am on Sundays
ADMISSION   Free
FACILITIES   Loos; facilities for the disabled; refreshments by arrangement
FEATURES   Good collection of trees; herbaceous borders; fine conifers; ecological interest; fruit and vegetables of special interest; glasshouses to visit; plantsman's garden; rock garden; modern roses; old roses and climbers; sub-tropical plants; water features; woodland garden; particularly interesting in winter; carpet-bedding; fern house; tallest hardy rubber tree *Eucommia ulmoides* in the British Isles, plus eight further tree records

NCCPG NATIONAL COLLECTIONS *Garrya, Potentilla fruticosa*

Glasnevin garden greets you with beautiful old-fashioned summer bedding and a bed of *Rosa chinensis* 'Parson's Pink', known here as 'The Last Rose of Summer'. Very much a botanic garden in the old tradition: public education and amenity hand in hand. Handsome old glasshouses, interesting plant collections and some good trees, most notably a weeping Atlantic cedar: allow a full day to do it justice.

Shackleton Garden

Beech Park, Clonsilla, Co. Dublin, Eire
☎ 010 353 1 8212216

OWNER   Shackleton Family
LOCATION   1 mile from Clonsilla on the road to Lucan, 10 miles west of Dublin
OPEN   Sundays and Bank Holidays; 6 March to 25 September
ADMISSION   I£2.50
FACILITIES   Parking; loos; access for the disabled; plants for sale; home-made teas
FEATURES   Herbaceous borders; fruit and vegetables of special interest; old roses and climbers; raised beds

A walled garden, attached to a Regency house. The owners claim to have the largest private collection of herbaceous plants in Ireland: celmisias are a speciality. Gardening day courses throughout the summer.

Talbot Botanic Gardens

Malahide Castle, Malahide, Co. Dublin, Eire
☎ 010 353 1 845 0954

OWNER   Dublin County Council
LOCATION   10 miles north of Dublin on Malahide Road
OPEN   2 pm – 5 pm (or by appointment); daily; 1 May to 30 September
ADMISSION   I£1.00
FACILITIES   Parking; loos; facilities for the disabled; souvenir shop and refreshments in castle
FEATURES   Good collection of trees; fine conifers; plantsman's garden; woodland garden; Tasmanian plants
NCCPG NATIONAL COLLECTIONS *Olearia*

The garden at Malahide was the work of Milo Talbot, a passionate amateur botanist with a particular interest in Tasmanian flowers. He built up a collection of 5,000 different taxa and, since the soil is limey, all are calcicole. Best visited on Wednesday afternoons when guided tours are offered of the walled garden (not otherwise open).

Trinity College Botanic Garden

Palmerston Park, Dartry, Dublin 6, Co. Dublin, Eire
☎ 010 353 1 972070   📠 010 353 1 7021147

OWNER   Trinity College
LOCATION   Near Ranelagh, opposite Municipal Park
OPEN   9 am – 5 pm; weekdays; by prior arrangement only
ADMISSION   Free
FACILITIES   Loos; access for the disabled; occasional plant sales
FEATURES   Good collection of trees; herbaceous borders; ecological interest; glasshouses to visit; gravel or scree garden; rock garden; old roses and climbers; woodland garden

A charming old-fashioned botanic garden, full interesting plants, including a collection of Irish natives.

CO. KERRY

Derreen

Lauragh, Killarney, Co. Kerry, Eire
☎ 010 353 64 83103

OWNER   The Hon. David Bigham
LOCATION   15 miles from Kenmare on the Castletown Road
OPEN   11 am – 5.30 pm; daily; 1 April to 30 September
ADMISSION   Adults I£2.00, Children I£1.00
FACILITIES   Parking; dogs permitted; loos; teas occasionally available
FEATURES   Good collection of trees; fine conifers; plantsman's garden; rock garden; sub-tropical plants; water features; woodland garden; tree ferns; rhododendrons

Derreen is quite extraordinary. The rocky outcrops come right to the front door, but the fast lush growth of its trees and shrubs is boundless. Tree ferns *Dicksonia antarctica* and myrtles *Myrtus communis* have gone native, and seed themselves everywhere. Moss lichen and ferns abound. Large-leaved rhododendrons grow to great heights. Wonderful on a sunny day in late April.

Muckross House & Gardens

Muckross, Killarney, Co. Kerry, Eire
☎ 010 353 64 31440   📠 010 353 64 33926

OWNER   Office of Public Works
LOCATION   Near Killarney town
OPEN   Daylight hours, all year
ADMISSION   Free
FACILITIES   Parking; dogs permitted; loos; facilities for the disabled; lunches, hot and cold snacks daily
FEATURES   Good collection of trees; fine conifers; rock garden; water features; woodland garden; rhododendrons; azaleas

Muckross is in the Killarney National Park, which gives it special interest. There are a young arboretum and some enormous old rhododendrons, but the native woodland is of Scots pines and arbutus trees and, even more exciting for a garden-visitor, the rock garden is a natural one, of carboniferous limestone.

Co. KILDARE

Japanese Gardens, Tully
Tully, Co. Kildare, Eire
☎ 010 353 45 21617 📠 010 353 45 22129

OWNER Irish National Stud
LOCATION Signposted in Kildare
OPEN 10.30 am – 5 pm, Monday – Friday; 10.30 am – 6 pm, Saturdays & Bank Holidays; 2 pm – 6pm, Sundays (opens 11 am June to August); Easter Sunday to 31 October
ADMISSION Adults I£4; Senior Citizens I£3; Children I£2
FACILITIES Parking; loos; access for the disabled; plants for sale; souvenir shop; light refreshments
FEATURES Famous Japanese garden

The garden is a sequence which symbolises the journey through life. It was made by Japanese gardeners in the early years of this century.

Co. MEATH

Butterstream
Kildalkey Road, Trim, Co. Meath, Eire
☎ 010 353 46 36017 📠 010 353 46 31702

OWNER Jim Reynolds
LOCATION Outskirts of Trim on Kildalkey Road
OPEN 2 pm – 6 pm; daily except Monday; 1 May to 30 September
ADMISSION I£3.00
FACILITIES Parking; loos; access for the disabled; plants for sale; teas on Sundays, and daily in July and August
FEATURES Herbaceous borders; fruit and vegetables of special interest; plantsman's garden; modern roses; old roses and climbers; water features; colour borders

A series of formal compartments in the Hidcote style around an old farmhouse. Each is different in style, but connected to the next. Butterstream boasts a green garden, a white garden, a hot-coloured garden, a Roman garden, a pool garden (with Tuscan portico reflected in it), an obelisk garden, and many others. The plants are determined by the soil – heavy, cold, limey clay.

Co. OFFALY

Birr Castle Demesne
Birr, Co. Offaly, Eire
☎ 010 353 509 20056 📠 010 353 509 20056

OWNER Earl of Rosse
LOCATION Rosse Row in Birr, Co. Offaly
OPEN 9 am – 6 pm or dusk; daily; all year
ADMISSION Adults I£3.20; Children I£1.60, April to October; Adults I£2.60; Children I£1.30 January to March & November to December
FACILITIES Parking; dogs permitted; loos; plants for sale; craft shop; good guide books; morning coffee, lunch & tea at gates
FEATURES Good collection of trees; herbaceous borders; fine conifers; herbs; plantsman's garden; old roses and climbers; good topiary; water features; woodland garden; *Paeonia* 'Anne Rosse'; *Magnolia* 'Anne Rosse'; winner of all-Ireland Property of the Year Award in 1992; tallest *Acer monspessulanum* and boxwood *Buxus sempervirens* (12 metres) in the British Isles, plus 14 other record species
FRIENDS Friends of the Birr Castle Demesne organisation formed recently: details from the estate manager

The best garden in the Irish Midlands. Birr has 50ha of grounds, a huge collection of trees and shrubs, and a wonderful walled garden with a tunnel down the middle. Many of the plants are grown from original collector's material: some were collected in the wild by the owner's parents, Michael and Anne Rosse. Birr also has the tallest box hedges in the world. In the grounds is the famous telescope, once the largest in the world, and witness to the polymath abilities of the owner's family over the generations.

Co. WATERFORD

Lismore Castle
Lismore, Co. Waterford, Eire
☎ 010 353 058 54424 📠 010 353 58 54896

OWNER Lismore Estates
LOCATION Centre of Lismore
OPEN 1.45 pm – 4.45 pm; daily; 30 April to 11 September
ADMISSION Adults I£2; children I£1; group rates available
FACILITIES Parking; dogs permitted
FEATURES Herbaceous borders; fruit and vegetables of special interest; old roses and climbers; woodland garden; yew walk; magnolias; camellias; spring bulbs

Best for the castellated house: the gardens are interesting rather than exceptional, but there is a pretty grove of camellias and an ancient double yew walk. Plus some fine traditional kitchen gardening to be seen in the walled garden.

CO. WEXFORD

The John F. Kennedy Arboretum

New Ross, Co. Wexford, Eire
☎ 010 353 51 88171 [FAX] 010 353 51 88172

OWNER The Office of Public Works
LOCATION 7 miles south of New Ross off R733
OPEN 10 am – 8 pm, 1 May to 31 August; 10 am – 6.30 pm, April and September; 10 am – 5 pm, 1 October to 31 March
ADMISSION Adults I£1.00; Senior Citizens 70p; Children & Students 40p; Family I£3.00; Groups 70p
FACILITIES Parking; dogs permitted; loos; facilities for the disabled; plants for sale; souvenirs; cafeteria for teas/refreshments
FEATURES Fine conifers; water features; woodland garden

125 hectares planted over the last 25 years. The statistics are impressive: 4,500 types of trees and shrubs arranged with artistry and all meticulously labelled. There are picnic areas, viewpoints, signposted walks, a vigorous visitors' centre and further hectares of experimental forestry.

Johnstown Castle Gardens

Wexford, Co. Wexford, Eire
☎ 010 353 53 42888 [FAX] 010 353 53 42004

OWNER TEAGASC (Food & Agriculture Development Authority)
LOCATION 4 miles south west of Wexford
OPEN 9.00 am – 5.30 pm; daily; all year
ADMISSION I£2.50 per car
FACILITIES Parking; dogs permitted; loos; access for the disabled; coffee shop, July and August only
FEATURES Fine conifers; glasshouses to visit; water features; woodland garden; walled gardens; agricultural museum; tallest *Cupressus macrocarpa* (40 metres) in the British Isles

50 acres of ornamental grounds with good trees, tall cordylines, three lakes and the Irish Agricultural Museum.

CO. WICKLOW

Mount Usher Gardens

Ashford, Co. Wicklow, Eire
☎ 010 353 404 40205

OWNER Mrs Madelaine Jay

LOCATION Ashford, 30 miles south of Dublin on the main road
OPEN 10.30 am – 6.00 pm; daily; 17 March to 31 October
ADMISSION Adults I£2.80; Senior Citizens & Children I£1.80; Groups (20+) I£2.20
FACILITIES Parking; loos; access for the disabled; courtyard shops with pottery, books, furniture, etc.; tea room with home-baked food
FEATURES Good collection of trees; herbaceous borders; fine conifers; plantsman's garden; sub-tropical plants; water features; woodland garden; spring bulbs; tallest *Eucalyptus dalrympleana* in the British Isles, plus 16 other record tree species

20 acres of garden with the River Vartry through the middle, crowded with rare trees and shrubs – 5,000 different species, some very rare. The self-sown *Pinus montezumae* are justly famous. Good herbaceous plants too, and lilies in July. A truly remarkable plantsman's garden.

Powerscourt Gardens

Powerscourt Estate, Enniskerry, Co. Wicklow, Eire
☎ 010 353 1 2867676 [FAX] 010 353 1 2863561

OWNER Powerscourt Estate
LOCATION 12 miles south of Dublin off N11
OPEN 9.30 am – 5.30pm; daily; 1 March to 31 October
ADMISSION Adults I£2.80; Students & Senior Citizens I£2.30; Children I£1.70
FACILITIES Parking; dogs permitted; loos; plants for sale; garden centre; tea rooms with light lunches
FEATURES Good collection of trees; fine conifers; oriental features; garden sculpture; water features; woodland garden; interesting for children; tallest *Abies spectabilis* in the British Isles, plus 8 other record tree specimens

Powerscourt is a wonderful mixture of awesome grandeur and sheer fun. It is also extremely well organised for visitors. The main Italian garden, a stately staircase down to a lake, has Great Sugarloaf Mountain as an off-centre backdrop. It is lined with bedding plants, statues and urns (look out for the sulky cherubs). To one side is the Japanese garden – not strongly Japanese – but full of twists and hummocks and scarlet paintwork. In the arboretum, Alan Mitchell has designed a tree trail. Powerscourt is busy in summer, but you can escape into solitude along the avenue of monkey puzzles.

17

Garden features

Graham Thomas

Graham Stuart Thomas's contribution to English gardening is seen everywhere - above all, in his books and in his gardens. We have however never found a list of the gardens on which he worked when Gardens Advisor to the National Trust. This list is an attempt to put the record straight. They are gardens in which to study his work, whether as a restorer and maintainer of other men's plantings or as an original garden designer and plantsman himself.

> Beningbrough Hall, North Yorkshire
> Benthall Hall, Shropshire
> Cliveden, Buckinghamshire
> Hidcote Manor, Gloucestershire
> Inveresk Lodge Garden, Lothian
> Knightshayes Court, Devon
> Little Moreton Hall, Cheshire
> Lyte's Cary Manor, Somerset
> Mottisfont Abbey, Hampshire
> Mount Stewart, Co. Down
> Polesden Lacey, Surrey
> Powis Castle, Powys
> Sezincote, Gloucestershire
> Sheffield Park, East Sussex
> Shugborough Hall, Staffordshire
> Wallington Hall, Northumberland
> Winkworth Arboretum, Surrey

Interesting for children

Garden visiting is seldom such a pleasure to children as it is for adults: children are quickly bored if a garden has nothing to interest or occupy them. Finding gardens where children can be relied upon not to spoil the outing for older members of the party is difficult. All the gardens we list here pass the boredom test easily, but for widely differing reasons. Some such as Bowood and Wilton House have adventure playgrounds. Others have special fa-

cilities, often educational, which explain everything to children in such a way that their interest is aroused. Many of the gardens which have won Sandford awards fit in here, as do such brilliant examples of child-management as Trebah. Some have such exciting plants and design features that the gardens themselves can be made to interest the young.

> Alton Towers, Staffordshire
> Arbigland, Dumfries & Galloway
> Bateman's, East Sussex
> Belton House, Lincolnshire
> Bicton Park Gardens, Devon
> Biddulph Grange, Staffordshire
> Birmingham Botanical Gardens, West Midlands
> Blenheim Palace, Oxfordshire
> Bowood House, Wiltshire
> Burton Constable Foundation, Humberside
> Capel Manor, London
> Castle Bromwich Hall, West Midlands
> Castle Drogo, Devon
> Chatsworth, Derbyshire
> Cragside, Northumberland
> Croxteth Hall & Country Park, Merseyside
> Culzean Country Park, Strathclyde
> Dalemain, Cumbria
> Dunham Massey, Greater Manchester
> Florence Court, Co. Fermanagh
> Fota, Co. Cork, Eire
> Goldney Hall, Avon
> Hampton Court Palace, London
> Harewood House, West Yorkshire
> Holdenby House Gardens, Northamptonshire
> Kildrummy Castle, Grampian
> Leeds Castle, Kent
> Longleat House, Wiltshire
> Longstock Water Gardens, Hampshire
> Margam Park, West Glamorgan
> Oxford Botanic Garden, Oxfordshire

Paignton Zoo & Botanical Gardens, Devon
Plantasia, West Glamorgan
Port Lympne Gardens, Kent
Powerscourt Gardens, Co. Wicklow, Eire
Ripley Castle, North Yorkshire
Royal Botanic Garden, Edinburgh, Lothian
Ryton Organic Gardens, Warwickshire
Shugborough Hall, Staffordshire
Sir Harold Hillier Gardens & Arboretum, Hampshire
Stapeley Water Gardens Ltd, Cheshire
Stourhead, Wiltshire
Sudeley Castle, Gloucestershire
The Swiss Garden, Bedfordshire
Syon Park, London
Tapeley Park, Devon
Trebah Garden Trust, Cornwall
Trentham Park Gardens, Staffordshire
Tresco Abbey, Cornwall
Tudor House Garden, Hampshire
The Valley Gardens, Harrogate, North
  Yorkshire
Wentworth Castle Gardens, South Yorkshire
Wilton House, Wiltshire
Wimpole Hall, Cambridgeshire
Woburn Abbey, Bedfordshire
The Younger Botanic Garden, Strathclyde

Late opening hours

Many working people like to visit a garden on summer evenings after they have left their workplace. It is difficult to find good gardens, apart from the best of the public parks: Regent's Park in London is open from dawn to dusk, but is even better at 7 am than 7 pm. Few gardens are more magical than Winkworth Arboretum on a mid May evening, or the great rhododendron collections of Brodick Castle and the Valley Gardens in Windsor Great Park at the same time of the year. Some gardens open late for a few special days each year: it is worth finding out about the evening openings at peak rose time at Mottisfont Abbey, not least because you avoid the afternoon crowds. And if you visit Glenveagh Castle or Inverewe late in the day you may have the gardens entirely to yourself.

Achamore Gardens, Strathclyde
Arduaine Gardens, Strathclyde
Brodick Castle, Strathclyde
Canal Gardens, West Yorkshire
Cannizaro Park, London

Castle Ashby Gardens, Northamptonshire
Castlewellan National Arboretum, Co. Down
Chiswick House, London
Clyne Gardens, West Glamorgan
Crossing House Garden, Cambridgeshire
Culzean Country Park, Strathclyde
Dartington Hall, Devon
Dawyck Botanic Garden, Borders
Dyffryn Botanic Garden, South Glamorgan
Elvaston Castle County Park, Derbyshire
Glasgow Botanic Garden, Strathclyde
Hampton Court Palace, London
Harlow Carr Botanical Gardens, North
  Yorkshire
Heale House, Wiltshire
Highdown, West Sussex
The Hollies Park, West Yorkshire
Isabella Plantation, London
Killerton, Devon
Lochalsh Woodland Garden, Highland
Lotherton Hall, West Yorkshire
Malleny House, Lothian
Marwood Hill Gardens, Devon
Muckross House & Gardens, Co. Kerry, Eire
RHS Garden, Rosemoor, Devon
Royal Botanic Garden, Edinburgh, Lothian
Royal Botanic Gardens, Kew, Surrey
Sheffield Botanical Gardens, South Yorkshire
Somerleyton Hall, Suffolk
Stourhead, Wiltshire
Syon Park, London
Temple Newsam Park, West Yorkshire
The Valley Gardens, Windsor, Surrey
Ventnor Botanic Garden, Isle of Wight
Wakehurst Place, West Sussex
Westonbirt Arboretum, Gloucestershire
Winkworth Arboretum, Surrey

Young gardens

Newly made gardens are a great inspiration to visitors who are starting to make gardens for themselves. The examples we list here are all comparatively young - a few are very new indeed. Some show what plants grow quickly: others reveal the latest ideas on design. The best will motivate you to get going in your own garden.

17 Fulham Park Gardens, London
Ashtree Cottage, Wiltshire
Bosvigo House, Cornwall

Brandy Mount House, Hampshire
Brickwall House, East Sussex
Bridgemere Garden World, Cheshire
Broadlands, Dorset
Bucklesham Hall, Suffolk
The Dingle (Crundale), Dyfed
Hazelby House, Berkshire
Lakeside, Hereford & Worcester
Lamorran House, Cornwall
North End House, Cambridgeshire
The Old Vicarage, Wiltshire
Pinewood House, Surrey
RHS Garden, Rosemoor, Devon
Sticky Wicket, Dorset
Thompson's Hill, Wiltshire
White Windows, Hampshire
Wolseley Garden Park, Staffordshire

Seldom open to the public

We often find that a garden that we wanted to visit has already had its annual visitors day. This is a check list for some of the gardens which open seldom. If you have long nurtured the ambition to visit such gardens as Badminton, Cowdray Park or Munstead Wood, you should look up its open days in the main chapter on gardens, and make a note of the dates when it receives visitors. Then plan your other garden visiting round it.

Abbotswood, Gloucestershire
Badminton, Avon
Bank House, Lancashire
Barningham Park, Durham
The Beale Arboretum, Hertfordshire
Bolehyde Manor, Wiltshire
Brandy Mount House, Hampshire
Brook Lodge Farm Cottage, Surrey
Carrog, Dyfed
Caythorpe Court, Lincolnshire
Cecily Hill House, Gloucestershire
Chyverton, Cornwall
Cowdray Park, West Sussex
Darley House, Derbyshire
Elsing Hall, Norfolk
Fairfield House, Hampshire
Faringdon House, Oxfordshire
Folly Farm, Berkshire
Glendoick Gardens, Tayside
Great Barfield, Buckinghamshire
Greenways, Oxfordshire

Hardwicke House, Cambridgeshire
The Harris Garden, Berkshire
Hascombe Court, Surrey
Hazelby House, Berkshire
Hillbarn House, Wiltshire
Long Barn, Kent
Longstock Water Gardens, Hampshire
The Manor House, Bledlow, Buckinghamshire
Mottistone Manor, Isle of Wight
Munstead Wood, Surrey
North End House, Cambridgeshire
Odell Castle, Bedfordshire
Offham House, East Sussex
Old Rectory Cottage, Berkshire
Overbury Court, Hereford & Worcester
Riseholme Hall, Lincolnshire
Stancombe Park, Gloucestershire
Stonehurst, West Sussex
Tirley Garth Trust, Cheshire
White Windows, Hampshire
Wincombe Park, Wiltshire
Yew Tree Cottage, West Sussex

Good to visit in the summer gap

It is easy for a garden to look good in May or June, but much more difficult for it to hold the visitor's interest in the dog days of August. Many people take their annual holidays then and are mildly disappointed to discover that there are no camellias, magnolias or rhododendrons in flower at Trengwainton or Caerhays. Some gardens, however, make a point of building up to a climax of colour in late summer.

Barrington Court, Somerset
Blickling Hall, Norfolk
Bressingham Gardens, Norfolk
Bridgemere Garden World, Cheshire
Cambridge University Botanic Garden, Cambridgeshire
Great Dixter, East Sussex
Hampton Court Palace, London
Hever Castle, Kent
Inverewe, Highland
Kellie Castle, Fife
Leith Hall, Grampian
Logan Botanic Gardens, Dumfries & Galloway
Longleat House, Wiltshire
Malleny House, Lothian
The Manor House, Walton-in-Gordano, Avon

Old Rectory Cottage, Berkshire
The Old Vicarage, Wiltshire
Powis Castle, Powys
The Priory, Gloucestershire
RHS Garden, Wisley, Surrey
The Savill Garden, Surrey
Sir Harold Hillier Gardens & Arboretum,
  Hampshire
Stourton House, Wiltshire
Tintinhull House, Somerset
Trelissick (Feock), Cornwall
Tresco Abbey, Cornwall

Underrated - a personal choice

We have all visited gardens which were a disappointment. Sometimes, however, we are lucky to stumble on a really smashing garden which no-one seems to know about. Here are some gardens we particularly want to visit again soon, and encourage our readers to do so too. Some are well known, but underrated, while others are little known but undeservedly.

Athelhampton, Dorset
The Beale Arboretum, Hertfordshire
Chenies Manor, Buckinghamshire
Cottesbrooke Hall, Northamptonshire
Crowe Hall, Avon
Fairhaven Gardens Trust, Norfolk
Hinton Ampner House, Hampshire
How Caple Court, Hereford & Worcester
Isabella Plantation, London
Kingston Maurward Gardens, Dorset
Lower Hall, Shropshire
Mount Stewart, Co. Down
Parcevall Hall Gardens, North Yorkshire
Sleightholmedale Lodge, North Yorkshire
St Paul's Walden Bury, Hertfordshire
Stancombe Park, Gloucestershire
Thorp Perrow Arboretum, North Yorkshire
Vine House, Avon
Wrest Park, Bedfordshire

Winter gardens

Sometimes the urge to go visiting gardens in winter is very strong, especially in late winter when the sun is higher in the sky and the first signs of new life appear. There are three types of garden worth visiting in winter. First are those with good glasshouse collections: most botanic gardens are therefore rewarding to explore whatever the season or weather. Second, there are those which have good collections of evergreen trees and shrubs, set off perhaps by the colours of bark and twigs: Bedgebury National Pinetum and Westonbirt Arboretum are both perfect for a brisk winter exploration. Third, there are gardens with a strong floral display in winter, particularly towards the end: such gardens as Great Barfield are thick with hellebores, crocus, *Leucojum* and many other genera, while those in milder regions have camellias, rhododendrons and the first primroses early in the year. Some gardens qualify on all three counts, though they are few. The Royal Horticultural Society's garden at Wisley is perhaps the best example.

Bedgebury National Pinetum, Kent
Belsay Hall, Northumberland
Cambridge University Botanic Garden,
  Cambridgeshire
Canal Gardens, West Yorkshire
Castlewellan National Arboretum, Co. Down
Dawyck Botanic Garden, Borders
Dunster Castle, Somerset
Elvaston Castle County Park, Derbyshire
Glasgow Botanic Garden, Strathclyde
Great Barfield, Buckinghamshire
The Harris Garden, Berkshire
Hill House Garden, Devon
Hyde Hall, Essex
Killerton, Devon
Marwood Hill Gardens, Devon
National Botanic Gardens, Dublin, Co. Dublin,
  Eire
Plantasia, West Glamorgan
Port Lympne Gardens, Kent
RHS Garden, Rosemoor, Devon
RHS Garden, Wisley, Surrey
Ripley Castle, North Yorkshire
Royal Botanic Garden, Edinburgh, Lothian
Royal Botanic Gardens, Kew, Surrey
The Savill Garden, Surrey
Sir Harold Hillier Gardens & Arboretum,
  Hampshire
Stapeley Water Gardens Ltd, Cheshire
Trebah Garden Trust, Cornwall
Tresco Abbey, Cornwall
Ventnor Botanic Garden, Isle of Wight
Wakehurst Place, West Sussex
Westonbirt Arboretum, Gloucestershire

Hotels with good gardens

Some of the houses attached to historic landscapes
have become hotels. In several cases the gardens
themselves have been well maintained or even improved by the new owners. Sometimes the gardens
remain in good condition but in different ownership:
the house is sold separately as a hotel. Many people
find the idea of staying in a hotel with a beautiful
garden particularly attractive. Here is a selection of
hotels with gardens which are good enough to mention in their own right. Their size and services vary
considerably, from simple B & B to 5-Star ratings.

Ardnamona, Co. Donegal
Arduaine (Loch Melfort Hotel), Strathclyde
Bodysgallen Hall, Gwynedd
Gidleigh Park, Devon
Gravetye Manor, East Sussex
Kildrummy Castle, Grampian
Owlpen Manor, Gloucestershire
Plas Penhelig, Gwynedd
Ston Easton Park, Somerset
West Park Lodge, Beale Arboretum, Herts

Awards to Gardens

Two schemes for awarding recognition to gardens
have started up in recent years. Both are private
initiatives and Holker Hall in Cumbria has had the
distinction of winning the *Garden of the Year
Award* in 1991 while also being a current holder of
the *Sandford Award*. The *Garden of the Year
Award* was introduced jointly by the Historic
Houses Association (HHA) and Christie's in 1984.
It is designed to recognise the importance of gardens,
either in their own right or as settings for historic
houses. It reflects public enjoyment of those privately owned gardens which are open regularly to
the public, rather than their horticultural excellence,
although many winners can claim that too. All HHA
members and friends of the HHA may vote for any
garden which is owned by a member of the HHA
and open regularly to the public. Marks are awarded
for features of special interest, such as recent restoration work or unusual selections of plants, trees and
shrubs. The award carries no cash prize but the
resulting publicity is helpful in raising visitor numbers. The award winners have been:

1984 Heale House, Wiltshire

1985 Hodnet Hall, Shropshire
1986 Newby Hall, North Yorkshire
1987 Arley Hall, Cheshire
1988 Barnsley House, Gloucestershire
1989 Brympton d'Evercy, Somerset
1990 Parham Park, West Sussex
1991 Holker Hall, Cumbria
1992 Forde Abbey, Dorset

Details of the 1993 winner will be revealed when
the award is presented in spring 1994.

The *Sandford Awards* are given by the Heritage
Education Trust to historic properties in recognition
of the educational facilities they offer school parties.
The award lasts for five years and is then reviewed.
It is always based on properties meeting five educa-
tional criteria:-

1. Good liaison with potential school visitors.
2. Imagination applied to developing the educational
potential.
3. The design of educational materials and facilities.
4. Encouraging preparation for a visit, managing that
visit effectively and offering good follow-up.
5. The use of interpretive facilites to relate the visit
to a school curriculum and encourage exciting and
imaginative work.

The Trust is principally concerned with historic
buildings. It follows that a property can get an award
even though it does not use its garden for educational purposes. In practice this rarely happens. Two
or three properties with gardens receive a Sandford
Award every year. Current holders include the
following:

Blenheim Palace, Oxfordshire
Boughton House, Northamptonshire
Castle Museum, York
Crathes Castles, Grampian
Drumlarig Castle, Dumfries & Galloway
Erdigg Hall, Clwyd
Harewood House, West Yorkshire
Holdenby House, Northamptonshire
Holker Hall, Cumbria
Kingston Lacy, Dorset
Molseley Old Hall, West Midlands
Rockingham Castle, Northamptonshire
Tatton Park, Cheshire

Further details are available from: The Heritage
Education Trust, The University College of Ripon
and York St John, College Road, Ripon. HG4 2QX.
Tel: 0969 50294. Secretary: Martyn Dyer.

18

English Heritage Garden Grades

During the 1980s, *The Historic Buildings and Monuments Commission* for England compiled a register of gardens and parks of special historic interest. The aim was to draw attention to the nation's heritage, so that designed landscapes were not, for example, overlooked in plans for new development. The register was largely the work of the distinguished garden historian Dr Christopher Thacker. There are three gradings:

Grade I - Parks and gardens which by reason of their historic layout, features and architectural ornaments considered together are of exceptional interest.

Grade II* - Parks and gardens which by reason of their historic layout, features and architectural ornaments considered together are, if not of exceptional interest, nevertheless of great quality.

Grade II - Parks and gardens which by reason of their historic layout, features and architectural ornaments considered together are of special interest.

These gradings reflect the importance of the garden or park concerned in comparison with other gardens or parks in England as a whole. They are not influenced by the presence of a listed building within the limits of a registered garden or park. If there is such a listed building, its grade may not necessarily be the same, since the building and the garden or park are seldom of equal importance. The register introduced no new regulations and had no effect upon existing planning or building controls. Only gardens and parks with historic features dating from 1939 or earlier were included in the register. Additions since that date were of no account, because the register was only concerned with a garden's historic interest. In practice that rule was sometimes broken in the case of an influential modern garden: Great Dixter and East Lambrook Manor might not have merited Grade I status in 1939. It has also been suggested that gradings took into account the park or garden's actual state and condition.

We have chosen to list all the Grade I and II* gardens but to omit the Grade II gardens, at least in the 1994 edition of *The Gardener's Yearbook*. Many are open to the public and appear in the main Gardens section of this book, but many others are in private ownership and remain private. The Commission was at pains to emphasise that including a garden in the register did not mean that there was any public right of access, other than along public rights of way. That remains the position today.

The register is in forty-six parts, one for each English county. Copies are available from English Heritage, Fortress House, 23 Savile Row, London W1X 2HE at a price of £3.50 or £4 each. The information they contain about the individual gardens is very comprehensive. It covers the site; area; dates and designers of key surviving elements; surviving features of the garden or park; and other interesting aspects such as historic associations. There is also a list of published references.

Avon
Grade I
    Badminton
    Prior Park
Grade II*
    Ashton Court
    Blaise Hamlet
    Clevedon Court
    Dodington House
    Dyrham Park
    Goldney House
    St Catherine's Court
    Tyntesfield

Bedfordshire
Grade I
    Woburn Abbey
    Wrest Park
Grade II*
    Luton Hoo
    Swiss Garden
    Southill Park

Berkshire
Grade I
    Windsor Great Park
Grade II*
    Ascot Place
    Bearwood College
    The Deanery, Sonning
    Folly Farm
    Frogmore Gardens
    Inkpen House
    Park Place
    Purley Hall

Buckinghamshire
Grade I
    Cliveden
    Stowe
    West Wycombe Park
Grade II*
    Ascott
    Bulstrode Park
    Chenies Place
    Chicheley Hall
    Fawley Court
    Hall Barn
    Hartwell House
    Shardeloes

    Tyringham
    Waddesdon Manor
    Wotton Underwood

Cambridgeshire
Grade I
    The Backs
    Wimpole Hall
Grade II*
    Anglesey Abbey
    Botanic Gardens, Cambridge
    Burghley House
    Childerley Hall
    Christ's College
    Elton Hall
    Emmanuel College
    King's College
    Longstowe Hall
    Milton Hall
    St John's College
    Thorpe Hall
    Trinity College

Cheshire
Grade II*
    Adlington Hall
    Arley Hall
    Eaton Hall
    Gawsworth Hall
    Lyme Park
    Tatton Park

Cleveland
Grade II*
    Wynyard Park

Cornwall
Grade I
    Mount Edgcumbe
    Port Eliot
    Tresco
Grade II*
    Caerhays Castle
    Lanhydrock
    Tregothnan
    Tregrehan
    Trewithen

Cumbria
Grade I
    Levens Hall
Grade II*
    Appleby Castle
    Belle Isle
    Dalemain
    Holker Hall
    Muncaster Castle
    Sizergh Castle

Derbyshire
Grade I
    Chatsworth
    Haddon Hall
    Hardwick Hall
    Kedleston Hall
    Melbourne Hall
Grade II*
    Bolsover Castle
    Buxton Pavilion Gardens
    Calke Abbey
    Derby Arboretum
    Elvaston Castle
    Heights of Abraham
    Renishaw Hall
    Swarkstone Hall

Devon
Grade I
    Bicton
    Endsleigh
Grade II*
    Castle Drogo
    Castle Hill
    Dartington Hall
    Killerton
    Knighthayes Court
    Lindridge
    Luscombe Castle
    Mamhead
    Saltram House
    Tapeley Park
    Ugbrooke Park
    Wood House

Dorset
Grade I
    Abbotsbury Gardens
    Athelhampton

Grade II*
Chantmarle
Charborough Park
Compton Acres
Cranborne Manor
Creech Grange
Eastbury
Encombe
Forde Abbey
Kingston Maurwood
Mapperton House
Melbury Park
Milton Abbey
Parnham
St Giles' House
Sherborne Castle
Pleasure Gardens,
Bournemouth

Durham
Grade II*
Raby Castle
Rokeby Park

Essex
Grade I
Audley End
Braxted Park
Grade II*
Bridge End Gardens
Copped Hall
Thorndon Park

Gloucestershire
Grade I
Batsford Park
Cirencester Park
Frampton Court
Hidcote Manor
Sezincote
Stancombe Park
Stanway House
Westonbirt Arboretum
Westonbirt House
Grade II*
Abbotswood
Barnsley Park
Berkeley Castle
Cowley Manor
Daylesford House

Highnam Court
Lypiatt Park
Miserden Park
Painswick House
Rodmarton Manor
Sudeley Castle
Westbury Court

Greater London
Bushy Park
Chelsea Physic Garden
Chiswick House
Greenwick Place
Hampton Court
Hyde Park
Kensington Gardens
Kew Gardens
Regent's Park
Richmond Park
St James' Park
Syon Park
Grade II*
Battersea Park
Bedford Square
Belair
Buckingham Palace Gardens
Cannizaro Park
City of London Cemetery
Crystal Palace Park
Dulwich Park
Fulham Palace
Gray's Inn
Grovelands
Hall Place
Ham House
Highgate Cemetery
The Hill
Kensal Green Cemetery
Kenwood
Lambeth Palace
Lincoln's Inn Fields
Marble Hill
Osterley Park
St George's Gardens
Victoria Embankment
 Gardens
Victoria Park
Waterlow Park
Wimbledon Park

Greater Manchester
Grade II*
Dunham Massey

Hampshire
Grade I
Hackwood Park
Highclere Park
Grade II*
Avington Park
Bramshill Park
Compton End
Cranbury Park
Exbury House
Houghton Lodge
Lainston House
Leigh Park
March Court
Moundsmere Manor
Pylewell Park
Tylney Hall
The Wakes
Warbrook House

Hereford & Worcester
Grade I
Croome Court
Hagley Hall
Grade II*
Berrington Hall
Croft Castle
Downton Castle
Eastnor Castle
Garnons
Hergest Croft
Holme Lacey
Kentchurch Court
Madresfield Court
Moccas Court
Overbury Court
Rous Lench Court
Spetchley Park
Sufton Court
Witley Court

Hertfordshire
Grade I
Hatfield House
St Paul's Walden Bury

Grade II*
Ashridge
Bayfordbury
The Garden House, Cottered
Knebworth
Moor Park
Panshanger
Putteridge Bury
Scott's Grotto
Youngsbury

Humberside
Grade I
Sledmere House
Grade II*
Londesborough Park

Isle of Wight
Grade II*
Osborne

Kent
Grade I
Godington Park
Hever Castle
Knole
Penshurst Place
Scotney Castle
Sissinghurst Castle
Grade II*
Chartwell
Chevening
Chilham Castle
Cobham Hall
Combe Bank
Godmersham Park
Goodnestone Park
Groombridge Place
Hall Place
Japanese Garden,
   Bitchet Wood
Leeds Castle
Linton Park
Long Barn
Mereworth Castle
Northbourne Court
Port Lympne

Lancashire
Grade II*
Stanley Park
Stonyhurst College

Leicestershire
Grade II*
Coleorton Hall
Staunton Harold Hall

Lincolnshire
Grade I
Belton House
Brocklesby Park
Grimsthorpe Castle
Grade II*
Doddington Hall
Harlaxton Manor

Merseyside
Grade I
Birkenhead Park
Grade II*
Ince Blundell Hall
Sefton Park, Liverpool

Norfolk
Grade I
Holkham Hall
Houghton Hall
Grade II*
Felbrigg Hall
Gunton Park
Kimberley Hall
Melton Constable Hall
The Pleasaunce, Overstrand
Sandringham House
Sheringham Hall

Northamptonshire
Grade I
Althorp
Boughton House
Castle Ashby
Drayton House
Grade II*
Canons Ashby
Easton Neston
Great Harrowden Hall
Harrington

Holdenby House
Kirby Hall
Lyveden New Bield
Rockingham Castle

Northumberland
Grade I
Alnwick Castle
Belsay Hall
Grade II*
Cragside
Seaton Delaval
Wallington

Nottinghamshire
Grade I
Clumber Park
Newstead Abbey
Thoresby Park
Grade II*
Annesley Hall
Flintham Hall
Papplewick Hall
Shireoaks Hall

Oxfordshire
Grade I
Blenheim Palace
Christ Church
Magdalen College
New College
Nuneham Courtney
Oxford Botanic Garden
Rousham
Shotover
Stonor
Grade II*
Ashdown House
Beckley Park
Broughton Castle
Buckland House
Buscot
Chastleton House
Cornbury
Corpus Christi
Ditchley
Garsington Manor
Greys Court
Heythrop College
Merton College

St Hugh's College
St John's College
Sarsden House
Tackley
Trinity College
Worcester College
Wroxton Abbey

Shropshire
Grade I
Hawkstone
Grade II*
Attingham Park
Davenport House
Ludstone Hall
Millicope Hall

Somerset
Grade I
Dunster Castle
East Lambrook
Hestercombe
Mells Manor
Montacute House
Grade II*
Ammerdown House
Barrington Court
Barwick Park
Brympton d'Evercy
The Chantry
Cricket House
Nynehead Court
Orchardleigh

Staffordshire
Grade I
Alton Towers
Biddulph Grange
Shugborough
Grade II*
Chillington
Enville
Trentham Park
Weston Park

Suffolk
Grade I
Helmingham Hall
Shrubland Park

Grade II*
Campsey Ashe Park
Euston Park
Heveningham Park
Ickworth Park
Kentwell Hall
Melford Hall
Somerleyton Park
Trinity Hospital

Surrey
Grade I
Albury Park
Claremont
Munstead Wood
Painshill
Savill Garden
Virginia Water
Grade II*
Busbridge Lakes
Orchards
Polesden Lacey
St Ann's Hill
Wisley Gardens
Wotton

East Sussex
Grade I
Great Dixter
Sheffield Park
Grade II*
Brickwall
Charleston Manor
Eridge Park
Glynde Place
Herstmonceux Castle
The Hoo
Penns in the Rocks
Rotherfield Hall

West Sussex
Grade I
Goodwood House
Leonardslee
Parham
Petworth House
Stansted Park
Grade II*
Arundel Castle
Borde Hill

Brockhurst
Cowdray House
Gravetye Manor
Highdown
Hollycombe House
Little Thakeham
Nymans
Uppark
Wakehurst Place
West Dean

Tyne & Wear
Grade II*
Gibside

Warwickshire
Grade I
Compton Verney
Farnborough Hall
Packwood House
Warwick Castle
Grade II*
Arbury Hall
Baddesley Clinton Hall
Charlecote Park
Combe Abbey
Honington Hall
Radway Grange
Ragley Hall
Upton House

West Midlands
Grade I
The Leasowes
Grade II*
Birmingham Botanic Gardens
Castle Bromwich Hall

Wiltshire
Grade I
Bowood House
Iford Manor
Longleat House
Stourhead
Wilton House
Grade II*
Amesbury Abbey
Belcombe Court
Corsham Court
Fonthill

Heale House
Larmer Tree Gardens
Longford Castle
The Moot, Downton
Tottenham Park
Wardour Castle

North Yorkshire
Grade I
Castle Howard
Duncombe Park
Forcett Hall
Hackfall
Rievaulx Terrace

Studley Royal
Grade II*
Aske Hall
Ebberston Hall
Mulgrave Castle
Newby Hall
Plumpton Rocks
St Nicholas, Richmond
Scampston Hall

South Yorkshire
Grade I
Wentworth Castle

Grade II*
Sandbeck Park
Wentworth Woodhouse

West Yorkshire
Grade I
Bramham Park
Harewood House
Grade II*
Nostell Priory
Oulton Hall
People's Park, Halifax

19

Garden Supplies

There is no uniform gardener: we all enjoy gardens and gardening in our different ways. As you would expect, this diversity is carried over into suppliers of garden products. The list below is unashamedly eclectic, from trade specialists to floral art supplies, from organic manure to stylish metal chairs. Most of the everyday products are available from garden centres, garden shops and DIY outlets. Others are available by mail order from a specialist supplier or direct from the producer. We have indicated who does what. Armchair shoppers may be particularly interested in some of the more substantial or specialised mail order merchants: try Wells & Winter and Wartnaby Gardens for unobtrusive old-fashioned labels; Two Wests and Elliott for greenhouse and propagating kit; John McLauchlan Horticulture and Garden Direct (from Chempak) for growing media and chemicals; The Traditional Garden Supply Company for good looking accessories; and Chase Organics for organics. The major seed companies (see Seedsmen section) also have useful collections of equipment at the back of their catalogues. See the essays on Organic Gardening, Composts and Bulk Buying for general information on these topics.

A T Lee & Co Ltd

32 New Broadway, Tarring Road, Worthing, West Sussex BN11 4HP
☎ 0903 210225   ☎ 0903 821936

CONTACT   Doreen Teale
PRODUCTS   Plant hanger
NEW PRODUCTS   Hanging growing bag
CATALOGUE   On request
MAIL ORDER   Yes

Suppliers of a plant pot hanger, and growing bag.

Access Garden Products

17 Yelvertoft Road, Crick, Northampton, Northamptonshire NN6 7XS
☎ 0788 822301   ☎ 0788 824256

CONTACT   Sales Department
PRODUCTS   Mini greenhouses; frames; watering systems
CATALOGUE   On request
MAIL ORDER   Yes

Established family firm supplying high quality aluminium frames and mini greenhouses. They also have a complete range of watering and irrigation systems. Access Irrigation Ltd (0788 823811) supplies sprinkler systems to nurseries and garden centres.

Agriframes

Charlwood Road, East Grinstead, West Sussex RH19 2HT
☎ 0342 328644

PRODUCTS   Frames; pergolas; cages
CATALOGUE   On request
MAIL ORDER   Yes

Practical and decorative metal products including fruit cages, frames, arches, pergolas and gazebos. They also sell horticultural fleece for frost protection. Trade customers should contact them on 0342 318181.

Algoflash UK Ltd

Church Farm, Northgate Way, Terrington St Clement, Kings Lynn, Norfolk PE34 4LD
☎ 0553 828882   ☎ 0553 827244

CONTACT   James Sutton
PRODUCTS   Fertilisers
MAIL ORDER   Yes

Suppliers of 'Algoflash' all purpose liquid fertilisers and other fertilisers.

Alitex Ltd
Station Road, Alton, Hampshire GU34 2PZ
☎ 0420 82860   ☎ 0420 82860

CONTACT Chris Sawyer
PRODUCTS Greenhouses
MAIL ORDER No

Top quality aluminium glasshouses and greenhouses in Victorian styles and models for professional and hobbyist users. All are individually designed.

Alton Greenhouses
Station Works, Fenny Compton, Leamington Spa, Warwickshire CV33 0XB
☎ 0295 770795   ☎ 0295 770819

CONTACT Grahame Lester
PRODUCTS Greenhouses
CATALOGUE On request (0800 269850)
MAIL ORDER No

Long-established firm producing traditional greenhouses in red cedarwood. They claim superior strength and heat retention over aluminium products.

Amdega Ltd
Faverdale, Darlington, Co. Durham DL3 0PW
☎ 0325 468522   ☎ 0325 489209

CONTACT Mr T. A. Ruddle (Sales Director)
PRODUCTS Conservatories; summerhouses
CATALOGUE Ring 0800 591523
MAIL ORDER No

Designers, suppliers and installers of conservatories and wooden summerhouses. One of the leading companies: established in 1874. See also Machin Conservatories.

Andrew Crace Designs
90 Bourne Lane, Much Hadham, Hertfordshire SG10 6ER
☎ 0279 842685   ☎ 0279 843646

PRODUCTS Plant labels; garden furniture; terracotta pots; garden statuary
CATALOGUE On request
MAIL ORDER Yes

The eclectic collection includes 'Alitag' aluminium plant labels, stylish wooden garden furniture and gazebos. Also bronze sculptures, terracotta pots and bamboo cloches.

Aqua-Soil Products Ltd
Blue Waters Estate, Bovey Tracey, Devon TQ13 9YF
☎ 0626 835135

CONTACT B. K. Read
PRODUCTS Aquatic products; fertilisers
NEW PRODUCTS 'Aqua-Check' water testing kit; 'Aqua-Liner' basket liner

CATALOGUE No
MAIL ORDER No

Manufacturers of products for water gardening including special soils and slow release fertiliser pellets.

Architectural Heritage Ltd
Taddington Manor, Taddington, Cutsdean, Cheltenham, Gloucestershire GL54 5RY
☎ 038673 414   ☎ 038673 236

CONTACT Nina Ziegler
PRODUCTS Garden statuary
CATALOGUE On request
MAIL ORDER No

Suppliers of antique garden statuary and reproduction statues. They ship worldwide and can also provide insurance valuations (£50 plus VAT). Interior panelling and fire surrounds also stocked.

Ascalon Design
The Coach House, Aylesmore Court, St Briavels, Gloucestershire GL15 6UQ
☎ 0594 530567   ☎ 0594 530579

PRODUCTS Parchment flowers
CATALOGUE Free to Trade
MAIL ORDER Trade only

Importers and distributors of parchment flowers: they deal with the trade only, but can refer retail customers to their stockists.

Atco-Qualcast
Suffolk Works, Stowmarket, Suffolk IP14 1EY
☎ 0449 612183   ☎ 0449 675444

PRODUCTS Lawnmowers; garden machinery
NEW PRODUCTS New lawnmower and hedgetrimmer range
MAIL ORDER No

Long-established manufacturer of lawnmowers, hedgetrimmers and other garden machinery. Sold through garden centres and DIY stores.

B J Crafts
17 Coopers Wood, Crowborough, East Sussex TN6 1SW
☎ 0892 655899

CONTACT B. R. or I. J. Welbury
PRODUCTS Watercolours
CATALOGUE On request
MAIL ORDER Yes

Original watercolours of flowers from miniatures to larger compositions.

Backwoodsman Horticultural Products

Barcaldine, Oban, Strathclyde PA37 1SL
☎ 0631 72539   ▦ 0631 72539

CONTACT Andrew McIntyre
PRODUCTS Greenhouses; frames
NEW PRODUCTS New 2 foot by 4 foot balcony greenhouse
CATALOGUE On request
MAIL ORDER Yes

Manufacturers of an eye-catching pyramidal rotating mini-greenhouse: the 'GrowMate'. It is sold by mail for self assembly. The new balcony model is pre-assembled.

Barralets of Ealing

Pitshanger Lane, Ealing, London W5 1RH
☎ 081 997 0576

CONTACT Derek Barralet
PRODUCTS Garden sundries
CATALOGUE No
MAIL ORDER Yes

Garden centre and garden shop which also does mail order.

BCS Tracmaster Ltd

Teknol House, Victoria Road, Burgess Hill, West Sussex RH15 9QF
☎ 0444 247689   ▦ 0444 871612

CONTACT Chris Trull
PRODUCTS Garden machinery
NEW PRODUCTS Shredders; chippers; scythe units
CATALOGUE On request
MAIL ORDER Yes

Suppliers of heavy duty two-wheeled tractors which handle tasks from grass cutting and cultivating, to trailer towing and snow blowing.

Bel Mondo Garden Features

11 Tatnell Road, Honor Oak Park, London SE23 1JX
☎ 081 291 1920

CONTACT Jamie Ripman
PRODUCTS Fountains; decorative taps
NEW PRODUCTS New wall fountains
CATALOGUE On request
MAIL ORDER Yes

Attractive cast iron fountains, wall basins and decorative taps and spouts.

Blackwall Products

Unit 1 – 4 Riverside Industrial Estate, 150 River Way, London SE10 0BH
☎ 081 305 1431   ▦ 081 305 1418

CONTACT Mrs P. Napier
PRODUCTS Compost bins; cloches; garden sundries
CATALOGUE On request
MAIL ORDER Yes

Manufacturers and suppliers of compost making bins, water butts, propagating aids and other garden supplies.

Bob Andrews Ltd

1 Bilton Industrial Estate, Bracknell Road, Bracknell, Berkshire RG12 8YT
☎ 0344 862111   ▦ 0344 861345

CONTACT Roy or Joan
PRODUCTS Garden machinery; sprayers
NEW PRODUCTS Petrol powered shredder and chipper
CATALOGUE On request
MAIL ORDER Yes

Powered and wheeled garden machinery for domestic gardeners and professionals, including vacuums, leaf sweepers, scarifiers, sprayers, spreaders and trimmers. Mail order if no local dealer.

Bolingbroke

Rectory Lodge, The Fairland, Hingham, Norfolk NR9 4HN
☎ 0953 850197   ▦ 0953 850197

CONTACT Christine Boswell
PRODUCTS Garden furniture; summerhouses
NEW PRODUCTS New pavilion; lounger
CATALOGUE On request
MAIL ORDER Yes

Manufacturers of wooden garden furniture, summerhouses, and pavilions in classic styles.

Boughton Loam Ltd

Telford Way, Telford Way Industrial Estate, Kettering, Northamptonshire NN16 8UN
☎ 0536 510515   ▦ 0536 510691

CONTACT Mike Franklin or Richard Chinn
PRODUCTS Composts; turf-dressings
CATALOGUE On request
MAIL ORDER No

Suppliers of specialist turf-dressings, general horticultural composts and landscaping mixes to the trade and the public.

British Museum Collection

46 Bloomsbury Street, London WC1B 3QQ
☎ 071 323 1234   ▦ 071 436 7315

CONTACT Kate Cooper
PRODUCTS Garden statuary
CATALOGUE On request
MAIL ORDER Yes

Replica classical statues, reliefs and busts from the museum's collection: the reconstituted marble items can be placed outside.

Bulbeck Foundry
Reach Road, Burwell, Cambridgeshire CB5 0AH
☎ 0638 743153　　☎ 0638 743374

CONTACT　H. Smith
PRODUCTS　Garden statuary; fountains
NEW PRODUCTS　A pair of foxes from an eighteenth century mould
CATALOGUE　On request
MAIL ORDER　Yes

A lead foundry which produces statues, urns and planters. Cisterns can be designed to commission, as can leadwork for rainwater systems. They will restore antique leadwork.

Bulldog Tools Ltd
Clarington Forge, Wigan, Lancashire WN1 3DD
☎ 0942 44281　　☎ 0942 824316

CONTACT　Jacqui Foulkes
PRODUCTS　Hand tools
CATALOGUE　On request
MAIL ORDER　Yes

Manufacturer of hand tools and other horticultural tools.

Burton McCall Group
163 Parker Drive, Leicester, Leicestershire LE4 0JP
☎ 0533 340800

CONTACT　Sue Isaacs
PRODUCTS　Tools; gloves
CATALOGUE　On request
MAIL ORDER　Yes

Suppliers of hand tools and clothing, including pruning saws, horticultural knives and the top of the range secateurs 'Felco'.

C H Whitehouse
Buckhurst Works, Bells Yew Green, Frant, Tunbridge Wells, Kent TN3 9BN
☎ 0892 750247
PRODUCTS　Greenhouses; garden buildings; summerhouses; frames
CATALOGUE　On request
MAIL ORDER　No

Attractive traditional red cedar greenhouses, summerhouses and frames made to order. They have specialist models for alpine growers and orchidists including ones on a brick base.

Cambrian Controls
P O Box 35, Woodchurch, Ashford, Kent TN26 3YW
☎ 0233 861218　　☎ 0233 860029

CONTACT　Barbara Mark
PRODUCTS　Greenhouse controllers; propagators
NEW PRODUCTS　Environmental monitoring units
CATALOGUE　On request

Manufacturers of sophisticated controllers for greenhouses and of propagating equipment.

Cambridge Glasshouse Co Ltd
Barton Road, Comberton, Cambridge, Cambridgeshire CB3 7BY
☎ 0223 262395　　☎ 0223 262713

PRODUCTS　Glasshouses
CATALOGUE　On request
MAIL ORDER　Direct supply

Professional quality greenhouses made to order in almost any size. For the amateur and hobbyist as well as nurserymen and botanic gardens.

Chase Organics
Addlestone, Surrey KT15 1HY
☎ 0932 820958

PRODUCTS　Organic supplies; seeds
CATALOGUE　On request
MAIL ORDER　Yes

Produce 'The Organic Gardening Catalogue' in association with the HDRA. A full range of organic supplies and untreated seed is sold: many items are stocked at Ryton Organic Gardens too. Discounts for HDRA members.

Chempak Products
Geddings Road, Hoddesdon, Hertfordshire EN11 0LR
☎ 0992 441888　　☎ 0992 467908

CONTACT　W. Richardson
PRODUCTS　Fertilisers; pesticides; garden sundries
CATALOGUE　On request
MAIL ORDER　Yes; (£10 minimum)

A very wide range of garden chemicals and fertilisers, as well as general garden products. Mail order is available through the Garden Direct catalogue.

Clear Span Ltd
Greenfield, Oldham, Lancashire OL3 7AG
☎ 0457 873244　　☎ 0457 870151

CONTACT　Mr G. Horton
PRODUCTS　Glasshouses
CATALOGUE　On request
MAIL ORDER　No

Manufacturers and designers of aluminium greenhouses from the smaller Hartley and Chelsea ranges up to garden centre and historic garden glasshouses. Structures can be custom built to any design.

Connoisseur Sun Dials

19 Ridgeway Avenue, Coventry, West Midlands
CV3 5BP
☎ 0203 415250

CONTACT Silas Higgon
PRODUCTS Sun dials; armillary spheres
NEW PRODUCTS 24 inch diameter armillary sphere
CATALOGUE On request
MAIL ORDER Yes

A range of brass and bronze sun dials: equatorial, horizontal, vertical, and analemmatic, as well as indoor models. They take commissions and the dials can be inscribed to order.

Consumer Direct Ltd

Lower Street, Quainton, Aylesbury,
Buckinghamshire HP22 4BL
☎ 0296 75217   ☎ 0296 75371

CONTACT Carol Lane
PRODUCTS Cloches; frames; propagating equipment
CATALOGUE On request
MAIL ORDER Yes

Long-established company selling plastic greenhouses, cloches, frames and a potting bench.

Cookson Plantpak Ltd

Burnham Road, Mundon, Maldon, Essex CM9 6NT
☎ 0621 740140   ☎ 0621 742400

CONTACT Chris Breed
PRODUCTS Plastic plant pots; plastic plant containers
NEW PRODUCTS Plug growers kit
MAIL ORDER No

A very wide range of plastic pots, seed trays, hanging baskets and other plastic items. Sold through garden centres.

Cooper Pegler

North Seaton Industrial Estate, Ashington,
Northumberland NE63 0XA
☎ 0670 522225   ☎ 0670 523992

CONTACT Lorraine Surtees
PRODUCTS Sprayers
NEW PRODUCTS Agricultural knapsack sprayer
CATALOGUE On request
MAIL ORDER No

Leading suppliers of spraying equipment for gardeners and professional users. The range includes hand held, knapsack and wheeled sprayers with a full choice of nozzles and appropriate safety equipment.

Cotswold Buildings Ltd

Standlake, Oxfordshire OX8 7QG
☎ 0865 300711   ☎ 0865 300284

CONTACT Gordon Bywater
PRODUCTS Garden buildings; conservatories; greenhouses
NEW PRODUCTS Extended workshop range; white wood summerhouse
CATALOGUE On request
MAIL ORDER Yes

Large range of garden buildings and garages, including greenhouses and summerhouses: most in cedarwood. They can install bases and construct nationwide.

Courtyard Designs

Suckley, Worcester, Hereford & Worcester
WR6 5EH
☎ 0886 884460   ☎ 0886 884444

CONTACT Ursula Mason
PRODUCTS Summerhouses
CATALOGUE On request
MAIL ORDER No

Manufacturers and suppliers of traditional wooden summerhouses and pavilions. Complete service, including installation, offered. They can design to order as well.

Courtyard Pottery

Groundwell Farm, Cricklade Road, Swindon,
Wiltshire SN2 5AU
☎ 0793 727466

CONTACT John Huggins
PRODUCTS Terracotta pots; garden ornaments
NEW PRODUCTS Dragon finial for gateposts
CATALOGUE Sae
MAIL ORDER Yes

Handmade terracotta pots, decorative planters, pot feet, edging tiles and forcing domes. Their pots are frostproof, and they accept commissions.

Crowther of Syon Lodge

Busch Corner, London Road, Isleworth, London
TW7 5BH
☎ 081 560 7978   ☎ 081 568 7572

CONTACT Donald Cameron
PRODUCTS Garden statuary; garden ornaments; architectural stonework
CATALOGUE Photographs available of all stock
MAIL ORDER No

This family owned business is the oldest specialist for architectural antiques in the country. If you have a specific request they can supply a photograph of appropriate items in stock. Armillary spheres are made on site; the display garden is worth a visit.

Croxden Horticultural Products Ltd
Cheadle, Stoke on Trent, Staffordshire ST10 1HR
☎ 0538 723641   📠 0538 723041

CONTACT David Chapman
PRODUCTS Growing media; bark products
NEW PRODUCTS Cambark decorative bark chips

Suppliers of bark products, specialist composts and growing media to the public via garden centres. They also supply nurseries and groundsmen with bulk products.

Dannell
P O Box 44, Hemel Hempstead, Hertfordshire
HP1 1XE
☎ 0442 248723

PRODUCTS Vases
CATALOGUE Leaflets
MAIL ORDER Yes

Hand assembled glass vases for flower arrangers.

Darlac Products
P O Box 996, Slough, Berkshire SL3 9JF
☎ 0753 547790   📠 0753 580524

CONTACT Peter Darban
PRODUCTS Garden tools
CATALOGUE On request
MAIL ORDER Yes

Garden tools including secateurs and a fruit picker: some items feature innovative designs.

David Bell Ltd
Eastfield Drive, Penicuik, Midlothian EH26 8BA
☎ 0968 678480   📠 0968 678878

PRODUCTS Fertilisers; grass seed
CATALOGUE Lawngrass brochure
MAIL ORDER Yes

Scottish seed wholesalers who supply grass mixtures and specialised lawn fertilisers.

David Craig
Units 10-11, Langley Moor Industrial Estate, Langley Moor, Co. Durham DH7 8JE
☎ 091 386 0384   📠 091 386 0384

CONTACT David Kuegler
PRODUCTS Garden furniture; parasols
NEW PRODUCTS Curved window boxes; folding rocking chair

CATALOGUE On request

Designers and manufacturers of top quality garden furniture. They use sustainable wood sources only and reclaimed timber (up to 300 years old).

Defenders Ltd
P O Box 131, Wye, Ashford, Kent TN25 5TQ
☎ 0233 813121   📠 0233 813383

PRODUCTS Biological controls
CATALOGUE On request
MAIL ORDER Yes

Biological controls for professional and amateur gardeners for the following organisms: whitefly, red spider mite and vine weevils. Thursday despatch ensures they arrive by the weekend. A sister company of Biological Crop Protection.

Dennis
Ashbourne Road, Kirk Langley, Derby, Derbyshire
DE6 4NJ
☎ 0332 824777   📠 0332 824525

CONTACT Michael Smout
PRODUCTS Cylinder mowers; grass care equipment
CATALOGUE On request
MAIL ORDER No

Manufacturers of high quality cylinder grass cutting equipment for amenity use and large gardens.

Dickenson's Compost
Eswip Edmonton, Angel Road, Edmonton, London
N18 3AG
☎ 081 803 1322   📠 081 884 0537

CONTACT B. A. Gallyot
PRODUCTS Organic composts and mulches
CATALOGUE On request
MAIL ORDER No

Organic composts and mulches for commercial and domestic customers. Made from recycled materials. Separate ranges include worm worked multi-purpose compost; tree and shrub compost; decorative mulch and traditional garden compost.

Diplex Ltd
P O Box 172, Watford, Hertfordshire WD1 1BX
☎ 0923 231784   📠 0923 243791

CONTACT Ernest Danzig, Barbara Leach, Sheila Rodel
PRODUCTS Thermometers; rain gauges; weather equipment
NEW PRODUCTS Stainless steel thermometers; 12 inch dial thermometers; electronic max/min thermometers
CATALOGUE On request

MAIL ORDER Yes

Manufacturers of an extensive range of thermometers, rain gauges and other meteorological measuring equipment for amateur and professional use. Models include inexpensive, decorative and scientific devices.

DIY Plastics (UK) Ltd

Regal Way, Faringdon, Oxfordshire SN7 7XD
☎ 0367 242932   FAX 0367 242200

CONTACT C. L. Stone
PRODUCTS Plastic sheeting
CATALOGUE 2 first class stamps
MAIL ORDER Yes

Plastic sheeting for house and garden use including netting, shading, pond liners and horticultural acrylic sheets.

Dupre Vermiculite

Tamworth Road, Hertford, Hertfordshire SG13 7DL
☎ 0992 582541   FAX 0992 553436

CONTACT Freya Denton
PRODUCTS Vermiculite
CATALOGUE On request
MAIL ORDER No

Suppliers of horticultural vermiculite, through trade wholesalers. High water retaining and nutrient absorbing characteristics.

Durston Peat Products

Avalon Farm, Sharpham, Street, Somerset BA16 9SE
☎ 0458 42688   FAX 0458 48327

CONTACT Tony Jones
PRODUCTS Peat-based and alternative growing media and mulches
NEW PRODUCTS Budget growing bag; bulb fibre
CATALOGUE On request
MAIL ORDER No

Manufacturer of peat-based composts and growing media, with alternative products including bark, vegetable waste and coir.

E H Thorne (Beehives) Ltd

Louth Road, Wragby, Lincoln, Lincolnshire LN3 5LA
☎ 0673 858555   FAX 0673 857004

CONTACT Sales Dept
PRODUCTS Beekeeping equipment
NEW PRODUCTS Honey labels
CATALOGUE On request
MAIL ORDER Yes

A complete range of beekeeping equipment, including hives and protective clothing.

E J Godwin (Peat Industries) Ltd

Batch Farm, Meare, Glastonbury, Somerset BA6 9SP
☎ 0458 860644   FAX 0458 860587

CONTACT Simon Stock
PRODUCTS Peat; composts; growing media; peat alternatives
CATALOGUE On request
MAIL ORDER No

Suppliers of composts and peat products under the Godwin's and Fruit of the Earth brand names. Organic alternatives as well as peat-based mixes.

Earlfarm

Monk Soham Hall, Monk Soham, Framlingham, Suffolk IP13 7EN
☎ 0728 685428   FAX 0728 685528

CONTACT A. H. Waugh
PRODUCTS Japanese garden supplies
NEW PRODUCTS Garden design service
CATALOGUE On request
MAIL ORDER Yes

Importers and suppliers of decorative items for Japanese gardens including a large range of pottery, and a selection of wind chimes, deer scarers, lanterns and bridges. They have a design service too.

Edwin Tucker & Sons Ltd

Brewery Meadow, Stonepark, Ashburton, Devon TQ13 7DG
☎ 0364 652403

PRODUCTS Plastic pots; ties; netting; clothing; chemicals and fertilisers
CATALOGUE On request
MAIL ORDER Yes

Commercial and retail seed merchants. They sell garden seeds mail order as well as products. See Seeds section for more details.

English Woodlands Biocontrol

Hoyle, Graffham, Petworth, West Sussex GU28 0LR
☎ 07986 574   FAX 07986 574

CONTACT Mrs Sue Cooper
PRODUCTS Biological controls
NEW PRODUCTS Hypoaspis for sciarid fly control
CATALOGUE On request
MAIL ORDER Yes

Biological controls for whitefly, red spider mite, aphids, mealy bugs, caterpillars, vine weevils and leafhoppers. Larger quantities are available at professional prices, and they produce a useful guide on the compatibility of garden chemicals with biological controls.

Ferrum Dried Flowers

Love Hill Farm, Trotton, Petersfield, West Sussex
GU31 5ER

☎ 0730 817277   📠 0730 817277

CONTACT Mrs A. Ferrier
PRODUCTS Dried flowers; silk flowers
NEW PRODUCTS Baskets, leaves, bouquets
MAIL ORDER Yes

Suppliers of dried flower and foliage arrangements, dyed flowers and silk flowers.

Fiskars UK Ltd

Bridgend Business Centre, Bridgend, Mid Glamorgan
CF31 3XJ

☎ 0656 655595   📠 0656 659582

CONTACT Julian Williams
PRODUCTS Hand tools
NEW PRODUCTS New tools in Classic and Power ranges
CATALOGUE On request
MAIL ORDER No

Hand and garden tools carrying the Wilkinson Sword brand name. Design ranges include Garden Devils, Classic, Professional, Power and the Ladies Collection. The UK market leader.

Fisons Horticulture

Paper Mill Lane, Bramford, Ipswich, Suffolk IP8 4BZ

☎ 0473 830492   📠 0473 830386

CONTACT Consumer Relations Dept
PRODUCTS Composts; fertilisers; garden chemicals; growing media
NEW PRODUCTS 'Levington' all purpose plant food
CATALOGUE Trade only
MAIL ORDER No

Household name whose range includes Levington composts, fertilisers and additives for most garden situations, and Murphy products. Available from garden centres. Consumer advice line: 0473 830492.

Flora & Fauna Europe Ltd

Orchard House, Patmore End, Ugley, Bishops Stortford, Hertfordshire CM22 6JA

☎ 0799 88289   📠 0799 88586

CONTACT Lynne Ellis
PRODUCTS Decorative taps; windchimes; weathervanes
NEW PRODUCTS Watering cans and door foot scrapers
CATALOGUE On request
MAIL ORDER Yes

Decorative and amusing sundials, animal shaped tap heads, trellises, weathervanes, path signs, and windchimes for garden and home.

The Flower Arrangers Show Shop

P O Box 38, Stratford upon Avon, Warwickshire
CV37 6WJ

CONTACT Mr and Mrs S. E. Grant
PRODUCTS Floral accessories; containers; figurines
CATALOGUE Sae
MAIL ORDER Yes

Flower arranging accessories, verdigris figurines and dried plant material. Only the figurines and containers are available mail order: look out for the stand at shows.

Forsham Cottage Arks

Goreside Farm, Great Chart, Ashford, Kent
TN26 1JU

☎ 0233 820229   📠 0233 820157

CONTACT Cindy Pellett
PRODUCTS Dovecotes; summerhouses
CATALOGUE On request
MAIL ORDER Yes

Decorative and functional dovecotes and small poultry units for the garden. They also have a summerhouse with a cote on top, based on their Chelsea Flower Show site hut.

Franshams Ltd

Holme Court, Biggleswade, Bedfordshire SG18 9ST

☎ 0767 681900   📠 0767 683481

CONTACT Mrs Rose Clark
PRODUCTS Garden shoes and boots; pruning saw
CATALOGUE On request
MAIL ORDER Yes

Stylish waterproof shoes and boots for gardeners and other outdoor use, and a folding pruning saw.

Frolics of Winchester

82 Canon Street, Winchester, Hampshire SO23 9JQ

☎ 0962 856384   📠 0962 844896

CONTACT Robert Dick-Read
PRODUCTS Garden furniture; ornamental trellis
CATALOGUE On request
MAIL ORDER Yes

Manufacturers of wooden garden furniture in stylish designs and of painted trellis work cut to intricate shapes. Individual pieces made to order as well. Trade and garden designer discounts.

Frost & Co

The Old Forge, Tempsford, Sandy, Bedfordshire
SG19 2AG

☎ 0767 40808   📠 0767 40561

CONTACT Charles Frost
PRODUCTS Hardwood conservatories
CATALOGUE On request

MAIL ORDER No

Manufacturers of high quality hardwood conservatories: their brochure is particularly informative.

Gardena UK Ltd

Dunhams Lane, Letchworth, Hertfordshire SG6 1BD
☎ 0462 686688   📠 0462 686789

CONTACT Sales
PRODUCTS Watering systems; garden tools
NEW PRODUCTS Holiday watering system for indoor plants
CATALOGUE On request
MAIL ORDER No

Manufacturers of watering systems. Also a range of interchangeable tool heads.

Gayways Lawn Mower Centre

215 – 217 Watford Road, Harrow, London HA1 3UA
☎ 081 908 4744   📠 081 904 6520

CONTACT Michael Fry
PRODUCTS Lawnmowers; garden machinery
MAIL ORDER Yes; nationwide distribution

Garden machinery sales and spares. You can order by telephone for nationwide delivery.

GEEBRO Ltd

South Road, Hailsham, East Sussex BN27 3DT
☎ 0323 840771   📠 0323 440109

CONTACT Ray Scott
PRODUCTS Garden furniture; tree ties; thermometers
NEW PRODUCTS Lister luxury lounger; Fairford drinks table; Rainbow wigwam cane clip
CATALOGUE On request
MAIL ORDER No

Founded over 100 years ago, Lister teak garden furniture in a variety of styles is well known. Geebro also sells tree ties, labels and guards for growers, and a range of horticultural sundries under the Rainbow brand name.

Glowcroft Ltd

P O Box 137, Gloucester, Gloucestershire GL4 7YB
☎ 0452 372385   📠 0452 372381

CONTACT Steve Tarrant
PRODUCTS Water storage granules; horticultural sundries
CATALOGUE On request
MAIL ORDER Yes

Their main product is the water retaining gel 'SwellGel' which stores up to 400 times its own weight. Other items include a trough to hide growbags and caps for bamboo canes.

Green Gardener Products

41 Strumpshaw Road, Brundall, Norfolk NR13 5PG
☎ 0603 715096

CONTACT John Manners
PRODUCTS Biological controls
CATALOGUE On request
MAIL ORDER Yes

Suppliers of biological pest controls for whitefly, red spider mite, vine weevil, aphids and mealy bug. There is a daytime helpline (on the number above); they can advise on integrated pest control using a combination of traps, sprays and controls.

Greenacres Horticultural Supplies

P O Box 1228, Iver, Buckinghamshire SL0 0EH
☎ 0895 835235

CONTACT I. Ludford
PRODUCTS Composts; fertilisers; herbicides; lawn products
NEW PRODUCTS 'Liquid Sod' lawn repair system; sulphur chips; sulphur lawn food
CATALOGUE On request
MAIL ORDER Yes

Suppliers of commercial and amenity products to the amateur gardener. Mail order, local delivery and collection from yard.

Greenspan Designs Ltd

8 Mentmore Close, Kenton, Harrow, London HA3 0EA
☎ 081 907 8695   📠 081 904 4101

PRODUCTS Container systems; growing media
CATALOGUE On request
MAIL ORDER Yes

Manufacturers and suppliers of container systems for public floral displays, including specially developed growing media. They supply over 80 local authorities and city councils.

Greenvale Farm Ltd

Clapham Lodge, Leeming, Northallerton, North Yorkshire DL7 9LY
☎ 0677 422953   📠 0677 425358

CONTACT Julie McAfee
PRODUCTS Fertilisers; soil conditioners
NEW PRODUCTS Rooster lawn food
MAIL ORDER No

Pelleted poultry manure and organic composted manure.

GWS Ltd

The Walnuts, Pinfold Lane, Harby, Melton
Mowbray, Leicestershire LE14 4BU
☎ 0949 61379   ☎ 0949 61487

CONTACT   Chris Tetley
PRODUCTS   Conservatories
NEW PRODUCTS   Rotating wooden summerhouse
CATALOGUE   On request
MAIL ORDER   No

Family firm selling UPVC Georgian sun rooms direct
to the public. Designed for easy installation and maintenance.

H₂O

The Stables, Winwick Warren, West Haddon,
Northampton, Northamptonshire NN6 7NS
☎ 0788 510529   ☎ 0788 510728

CONTACT   Richard Allen
PRODUCTS   Irrigation systems
CATALOGUE   On request
MAIL ORDER   No

Suppliers and installers of automatic watering systems.
Individual service; site visits and estimates are free of
charge, and service contracts can be arranged.

Haddonstone Ltd

The Forge House, East Haddon, Northampton,
Northamptonshire NN6 8DB
☎ 0604 770711   ☎ 0604 770027

CONTACT   Sales Department
PRODUCTS   Garden ornaments; architectural stone-
work
NEW PRODUCTS   Additional urns, statuary, sundials,
bird baths and finials
CATALOGUE   Full colour 108 pages £5.00
MAIL ORDER   Delivery

Leading manufacturers and suppliers of garden ornaments, statuary and architectural stonework in the
reconstituted stone material 'Haddonstone'. The range
is exceptionally large, but they can design to order also.
Antique finishes available.

Hanging Garden Pot Holders

Grangewood, High Shincliffe, Durham, Co. Durham
DH1 2PP
☎ 091 384 7726   ☎ 091 386 7726

CONTACT   Mr A. G. Stead
PRODUCTS   Pot holders
MAIL ORDER   Yes

Ingenious but simple device which attaches flowerpots
to drainpipes and walls. Expandable size.

Haws Watering Cans

120 Beakes Road, Smethwick, Warley, West
Midlands B67 5AB
☎ 021 420 2494   ☎ 021 429 1668

CONTACT   John Massey
PRODUCTS   Watering cans; sprayers
NEW PRODUCTS   New long reach cans (indoor & out-
door); compression sprayers and lances; Victorian
waterbarrow
CATALOGUE   On request
MAIL ORDER   Yes

Watering cans that look like watering cans from this
well known company. They also sell other watering
equipment, and supply spares – and cans if necessary –
by mail order.

Hayters plc

Spellbrook, Bishop's Stortford, Hertfordshire
CM23 4BU
☎ 0279 723444   ☎ 0279 600338

CONTACT   Tina Moseley
PRODUCTS   Lawnmowers
NEW PRODUCTS   Engine safety system
CATALOGUE   On request (0279 600919)

Well known lawnmower manufacturers: most of their
products are rotary cutting.

Heritage Woodcraft

Unit 5, Shelley Farm, Ower, Romsey, Hampshire
SO51 6AS
☎ 0703 814145

CONTACT   David Finch
PRODUCTS   Garden furniture; wooden wheelbarrows
NEW PRODUCTS   Gazebo
CATALOGUE   Free leaflets
MAIL ORDER   Yes

Traditionally crafted wooden garden furniture made
from iroko (derived from managed sources) with a new
range in English oak.

The Hop Shop

Castle Farm, Shoreham, Sevenoaks, Kent TN14 7UB
☎ 0959 523219   ☎ 0959 524220

CONTACT   Caroline Alexander
PRODUCTS   Dried flowers and grasses
NEW PRODUCTS   New varieties every year
CATALOGUE   4 first class stamps
MAIL ORDER   Yes

Dried flower producers and suppliers: they won a gold
medal at Chelsea. Trade and retail.

Hotbox Heaters Ltd
7 Gordleton Industrial Park, Sway Road, Lymington, Hampshire SO41 8JD
☎ 0590 683788   ⊞ 0590 683511

CONTACT   R. Spencer
PRODUCTS   Greenhouse heaters; propagators
NEW PRODUCTS   Heaters and range of propagation panels
MAIL ORDER   Yes

Electric and gas heaters for small greenhouses and larger units for professional users and hobbyists. There is also a range of propagating benches.

Hotterotter Group
The Old Rectory, Bryn, Abergavenny, Gwent NP7 9AP
☎ 0873 840328   ⊞ 0873 840328

CONTACT   Mrs P. A. Roper-Evans
PRODUCTS   Compost bins
MAIL ORDER   Yes

Unique insulated compost bin which assembles almost instantly. Designed to maintain the high temperatures necessary to kill weed seeds.

Hozelock Ltd
Haddenham, Aylesbury, Buckinghamshire HP17 8JD
☎ 0844 291881   ⊞ 0844 290344

CONTACT   Consumer Services (0844 292002)
PRODUCTS   Watering systems; garden lighting; sprayers; aquatic products
NEW PRODUCTS   Automatic light controller; watering can range; pond lights
CATALOGUE   Trade Catalogue on request
MAIL ORDER   No

Manufacturers and suppliers of a wide range of products and accessories for watering, lighting, spraying and pond care.

Husqvarna Forest & Garden UK
Oldends Lane, Stonehouse, Gloucestershire GL10 3SY
☎ 0453 822382   ⊞ 0453 826936

CONTACT   Heather Gardner
PRODUCTS   Garden machinery; lawnmowers
CATALOGUE   On request
MAIL ORDER   No

A full range of machinery from domestic lawn mowers and lawn tractors to professional brushcutters and chainsaws.

ICI Garden Products
Fernhurst, Haslemere, Surrey GU27 3JE
☎ 0428 645454   ⊞ 0428 657222

CONTACT   Consumer Services
PRODUCTS   Pesticides; fertilisers; herbicides; growing media; house plant care products
MAIL ORDER   No

Manufacturers and suppliers of a wide range of chemicals and gardening sundries, many of them household names.

Ingram Topiary Frames Ltd
15 Freke Road, London SW11 5PU
☎ 071 350 1842

CONTACT   Mrs C. S. Ingram
PRODUCTS   Topiary frames
NEW PRODUCTS   Swan, hare and rabbit topiary figures
CATALOGUE   Sae (50p)
MAIL ORDER   Yes

Wire topiary frames in plastic coated steel. Shapes include obelisks and ornaments for parterre designs.

Interpet Ltd
Interpet House, Vincent Lane, Dorking, Surrey RH4 3YX
☎ 0306 881033   ⊞ 0306 885009

CONTACT   Tracey Masters
PRODUCTS   Aquatic products
NEW PRODUCTS   Pond care kit; 'Sludge-Buster'; squirrel proof bird feeder
CATALOGUE   On request
MAIL ORDER   No

Comprehensive range of aquatic products for ponds and aquariums, including foods, pumps and chemicals. The company also supplies pet products.

Iseki UK
Broadway, Bourn, Cambridge, Cambridgeshire CB3 7TL
☎ 0954 718981   ⊞ 0954 719760

CONTACT   Arthur Wood
PRODUCTS   Lawnmowers; hedge trimmers
CATALOGUE   On request
MAIL ORDER   No

Manufacturers of rotary lawnmowers, including a key start model, and brush cutters, hedge trimmers and pumps.

Jemp Engineering
Canal Estate, Station Road, Langley, Berkshire SL3 6EG
☎ 0753 548327   ⊞ 0753 580137
CONTACT   Mrs Mansford

PRODUCTS   Propagators; greenhouse heaters; greenhouse equipment
CATALOGUE   On request
MAIL ORDER   Yes

Manufacturers of greenhouse heaters and electric propagators, as well as shading and other greenhouse equipment.

Jiffy Products UK Ltd
14 – 16 Commercial Road, March, Cambridgeshire PE15 8QP
☎ 0354 52565   ⊠ 0354 51891

CONTACT   D. Camplin
PRODUCTS   Plant pots; plant trays
NEW PRODUCTS   38mm Jiffy 7, new size
CATALOGUE   On request
MAIL ORDER   No

Manufacturers and suppliers of peat and fibre pots and propagation trays for commercial growers and retail customers. No direct retail trade.

Joanna Sheen Ltd
P O Box 52, Newton Abbot, Devon TQ12 4YF
☎ 0626 872405   ⊠ 0626 872265

CONTACT   Nikki Hadley
PRODUCTS   Dried flowers; floral accessories
NEW PRODUCTS   New craft courses
CATALOGUE   Sae (19p); courses sae (52p)
MAIL ORDER   Yes

Dried flowers and pressed pictures, as well as the components for them. They run courses in these crafts too.

John Deere Ltd
Harby Road, Langar, Nottingham, Nottinghamshire NG13 9HT
☎ 0949 60491   ⊠ 0949 60490

CONTACT   Graham Williams
PRODUCTS   Lawnmowers; lawn tractors
CATALOGUE   Leaflets

Manufacturers of lawn and groundsmanship machinery from garden and commercial lawnmowers, through to lawn tractors and large tractor units.

John McLauchlan Horticulture
50a Market Place, Thirsk, North Yorkshire YO7 1LH
☎ 0845 525585   ⊠ 0845 523133

CONTACT   Mr John McLauchlan
PRODUCTS   Fertilisers; growing media
CATALOGUE   On request
MAIL ORDER   Yes

Specialist suppliers of growing media to trade and retail customers, including vermiculite, perlite, pumice and

biosorb. They also sell fertilisers and some sundries. Mail order service.

Joseph Bentley Ltd
Beck Lane, Barrow on Humber, Humberside DN19 7AQ
☎ 0469 30501   ⊠ 0469 30459

CONTACT   G. H. Moxon
PRODUCTS   Composts; fertilisers
CATALOGUE   On request
MAIL ORDER   Yes

Suppliers of a wide range of general and specialist composts and fertilisers including straight fertilisers, organic granules and compost mixes for chrysanthemum and fuchsia growers.

Kemp's Coconut Products
Kemp's Mushrooms, Chapel Road, Ford, Aylesbury, Buckinghamshire HP17 8XG
☎ 0296 748932

CONTACT   Roger Kemp
PRODUCTS   Composts
CATALOGUE   On request
MAIL ORDER   No

Organic garden composts and growing media including coir, mushroom composts and tree and seed mixes.

King Easton Ltd
The Green, Station Road, Winchmore Hill, London N21 3NB
☎ 081 886 8783   ⊠ 081 882 2685

CONTACT   Brian Easton
PRODUCTS   Garden furniture; parasols
CATALOGUE   On request

A stylish collection of traditional French metal outdoor furniture.

Knight Terrace Pots
West Orchard, Shaftesbury, Dorset SP7 0LJ
☎ 0258 472685

PRODUCTS   Garden ornaments
CATALOGUE   On request
MAIL ORDER   Delivery arranged

Reconstituted stone garden ornaments from simple pots and troughs to elaborate vases, finials and balustrades. The works can be visited by appointment, and they can design or copy originals to order.

Knowles Nets
20 East Road, Bridport, Dorset DT6 4NX
☎ 0308 24342   ⊠ 0308 58186

CONTACT   Sales desk
PRODUCTS   Netting; plant supports; fruit cages

CATALOGUE On request
MAIL ORDER Yes

Manufacturers of protective netting and woven sheeting for plant support, fruit cages and windbreak. They also produce sports nets.

Konstsmide UK Ltd
Yew Tree Farm, Hardstoft, Pilsley, Chesterfield,
Derbyshire S45 8AE
☎ 0246 852140   📠 0246 854297

CONTACT Lisbeth Orum
PRODUCTS Outdoor lighting; garden furniture
CATALOGUE On request
MAIL ORDER Yes

Wholesalers of a large range of Swedish outdoor lighting equipment, garden furniture and barbecues.

Kubota (UK) Ltd
Dormer Road, Thame, Oxfordshire OX9 3UN
☎ 0844 214500   📠 0844 216685

CONTACT Mr Stuart Ellis
PRODUCTS Lawnmowers; lawn tractors; garden machinery

Garden machinery range including lawnmowers, lawn tractors, hedgetrimmers, brushcutters and generators. The range extends to professional and amenity machines.

Kut and Dried
P O Box 50, Penrith, Cumbria CA11 8RY
☎ 0768 892275   📠 0768 892275

CONTACT Steve Smith
PRODUCTS Dried flower arrangements
NEW PRODUCTS Rose arrangements under glass
CATALOGUE £1
MAIL ORDER Yes

Dried flower arrangements in glass boxes and pictures.

L & P Peat Ltd
Tollund House, 8 Abbey Street, Carlisle, Cumbria
CA3 8TX
☎ 0228 22181   📠 0228 41460

CONTACT Alan Armstrong
PRODUCTS Peat; growing media
MAIL ORDER No

Manufacturers and suppliers of peat and peat based composts under the 'Humax' brand name. They also supply growers with professional composts.

Lady Muck
Marshwood House, Whitegate, Forton, Chard,
Somerset TO24 4HL
☎ 0460 220822

CONTACT Lady Muck
PRODUCTS Organic composts
CATALOGUE On request
MAIL ORDER Yes

User-friendly muck which is clean to use and odour free.

Leaky Pipe Systems Ltd
Frith Farm, Dean Street, East Farleigh, Maidstone,
Kent ME15 0PR
☎ 0622 746495   📠 0622 745118
PRODUCTS Irrigation systems
CATALOGUE Leaflets

Porous rubber hose irrigation system which is made from recycled car tyres. Leaky Pipe can be used for horticultural, amenity and agricultural situations.

Lewes Road Sawmills
Standlake, Witney, Oxfordshire OX8 7PR
☎ 0865 300444   📠 0865 300284

PRODUCTS Conservatories; garden buildings
CATALOGUE On request

Timber conservatories and chalets.

Lindum Seeded Turf
West Grange, Thorganby, York YO4 6DJ
☎ 0904 448675   📠 0904 448713

CONTACT David Snowden
PRODUCTS Turf
CATALOGUE On request
MAIL ORDER No

Growers and suppliers nationwide of cultivated turf for sporting, garden and landscaping uses.

Link-Stakes Ltd
30 Warwick Road, Upper Boddington, Daventry,
Northamptonshire NN11 6DH
☎ 0327 60329   📠 0327 62428

CONTACT Madeline Knowles
PRODUCTS Plant supports; stakes
NEW PRODUCTS Cloches; micro-cage plant guards
CATALOGUE On request
MAIL ORDER Yes

Suppliers of interlocking wire plant supports and single stakes. The stakes adapt to a variety of shapes and uses.

M W Horticultural Supplies
P O Box 15, Edenbridge, Kent TN8 6SD
☎ 0732 864967   📠 0732 864967

CONTACT A. Whitlock
PRODUCTS Frames
CATALOGUE On request
MAIL ORDER Yes

Suppliers of the lightweight movable frame, the 'Melbourne' frame.

Machin Conservatories

c/o Amdega, Faverdale, Darlington, Co. Durham
DL3 0PW
☎ 0325 469100   ☏ 0325 489209

CONTACT Mr T. A. Ruddle
PRODUCTS Conservatories
CATALOGUE On request (0800 212072)
MAIL ORDER No

Well known conservatory firm, now under the same ownership as Amdega.

Marston & Langinger Ltd

192 Ebury Street, London SW1W 8UP
☎ 071 824 8818   ☏ 071 824 8757

PRODUCTS Conservatories; conservatory furniture
CATALOGUE On request

Individually designed conservatories with an excellent reputation: the showroom which also displays their range of conservatory fittings is in London. The factory is in Norfolk.

Matthew Eden

Pickwick End, Corsham, Wiltshire SN13 0JB
☎ 0249 713335   ☏ 0249 713644

CONTACT Matthew Eden
PRODUCTS Garden furniture
CATALOGUE £2.50
MAIL ORDER Yes

Wirework pergolas, obelisks and chairs; wrought iron garden furniture; and wooden benches to Lutyens and earlier designs.

Maxicrop International Ltd

Weldon Road, Corby, Northamptonshire NN17 5US
☎ 0536 402182   ☏ 0536 204254

CONTACT Jenny Paxton
PRODUCTS Fertilisers
CATALOGUE On request
MAIL ORDER Yes (10 litres minimum)

Liquid seaweed extract and fertilisers.

Mellors Garden Ceramics

Rosemead, Marshwood, Bridport, Dorset DT6 5QB
☎ 0297 678217

CONTACT Kate Mellors
PRODUCTS Garden ornaments; fountains
CATALOGUE Large sae
MAIL ORDER Yes

Waterproof ceramic planters, fountains and garden ornaments in stony blue and sandstone stoneware.

Metalarts

Park Forge, Coryton, Okehampton, Devon EX20 4PG
☎ 0566 83454   ☏ 0566 83454

CONTACT Sales Office
PRODUCTS Metal pergolas; arches; weather vanes
CATALOGUE On request
MAIL ORDER Yes

Manufacturers and suppliers of wire arches and pergolas, weathervanes and other decorative garden features.

Metpost Ltd

Mardy Road, Cardiff, South Glamorgan CF3 8EQ
☎ 0222 777877   ☏ 0222 779295

CONTACT David Maas
PRODUCTS Fencing; trellis
CATALOGUE On request
MAIL ORDER Yes

Manufacturers of the 'Metpost' fence fixing stake, and a range of maintenance-free trellis made from recycled polystyrene ('Timbron').

Monsanto Garden Care

Thames Tower, Burleys Way, Leicester, Leicestershire LE1 3TP
☎ 0533 620864   ☏ 0533 530320

PRODUCTS Pesticides; herbicides
NEW PRODUCTS Multi purpose insecticide
CATALOGUE Trade catalogue only
MAIL ORDER No

Suppliers of horticultural and agricultural chemicals: they make 'Roundup' and have just introduced a new multipurpose insecticide, 'Polysect'.

Montezumas

9 Oak Road, Ealing, London W5 3SS
☎ 081 579 6293   ☏ 081 566 2758

CONTACT Ingrid Berglund
PRODUCTS Statuary; garden furniture
NEW PRODUCTS Wire work
CATALOGUE On request
MAIL ORDER No

Distinctive Mexican ceramic ornaments for the conservatory and new wire work products.

Natural Pest Control Ltd

Yapton Road, Barnham, Bognor Regis, West Sussex
PO22 0BQ
☎ 0243 553250   ☏ 0243 552879

CONTACT Mr I. E. Worrall
PRODUCTS Biological controls
NEW PRODUCTS Controls for mushroom larval pests and red spider mite on top fruit
CATALOGUE On request

MAIL ORDER Yes

Wide variety of predators and parasites for spider mite, whitefly, mealy bugs, aphids, leaf miners, and thrips. They deal with retail and commercial customers and can arrange advisory visits.

Netlon Ltd
Kelly Street, Blackburn, Lancashire BB2 4PJ
☎ 0254 262431   ℻ 0254 661624

CONTACT   Michael Carr
PRODUCTS   Netting; trellis; sheeting
NEW PRODUCTS   Heavy duty reinforced sheet (roll form)
CATALOGUE   On request

A wide range of netting and sheet products for plant support and protection. They also sell bubble insulation and ties.

New England Gardens Ltd
22 Middle Street, Ashcott, Somerset TA7 9QB
☎ 0458 210821   ℻ 0458 210821

CONTACT   Iain Fraser
PRODUCTS   Garden furniture; fencing; play equipment
NEW PRODUCTS   Wooden play systems; more fencing
CATALOGUE   On request
MAIL ORDER   Yes

Manufacturers and importers of wooden garden furniture, fencing and play equipment. Some items imported from New England, but much made in the UK. No tropical hardwoods used.

Nonington Pottery
Old Court Hill, Nonington, Dover, Kent CT15 4LQ
☎ 0304 840174

CONTACT   David S. Peacock
PRODUCTS   Terracotta pots; garden ornaments
NEW PRODUCTS   Water feature for walls
CATALOGUE   On request
MAIL ORDER   Yes

Frost resistant pots, water features and decorative objects including chimney pots (for display and use): monograms and personal designs can be incorporated into the chimney pots.

Norbark (Northern Bark Ltd)
6 Northern Road, Belfast, Northern Ireland
☎ 0232 754936   ℻ 0232 754937

CONTACT   Jack Arron (0420 85090)
PRODUCTS   Horticultural bark
CATALOGUE   Leaflets on request
MAIL ORDER   No

Producers of horticultural bark in six different grades for propagation and potting as well as amenity use. Technical advice: 0420 85090.

O M Scott & Sons Ltd
115 Princess Street, Chase Terrace, Staffordshire WS7 8JH
☎ 0543 450066   ℻ 0543 450067

CONTACT   Sales Office
PRODUCTS   Fertilisers; lawn spreaders
NEW PRODUCTS   'Patchmaster' lawn repair pack
CATALOGUE   On request
MAIL ORDER   No

Suppliers of controlled release lawn and garden fertilisers, spreaders and a lawn repair patch.

Oak Leaf Conservatories
Clifton Common Industrial Park, Kettlestring Lane, York, North Yorkshire YO3 8XF
☎ 0904 690401   ℻ 0904 690945

CONTACT   Mark Caulfield
PRODUCTS   Conservatories
CATALOGUE   On request

Made to measure conservatories noted for imaginative designs: recent commissions have included domes and two storeys.

Orchid Sundries Ltd
New Gate Farm, Scotchey Lane, Stour Provost, Gillingham, Dorset SP8 5LT
☎ 0747 838368   ℻ 0747 838308

CONTACT   N. J. Heywood
PRODUCTS   Orchid composts
CATALOGUE   Sae
MAIL ORDER   Yes

Bark composts for orchid growers, as well as a list of hardy orchids raised from seed. See Nurseries section, Dorset also.

Organic Concentrates Ltd
3 Broadway Court, Chesham, Buckinghamshire HP5 1EN
☎ 0494 792229   ℻ 0494 792199

CONTACT   C. J. P. Green
PRODUCTS   Organic fertilisers; pesticides; sundries
CATALOGUE   On request
MAIL ORDER   Yes

Suppliers of the concentrated, dried and sterilised poultry manure '6X', a non toxic slug killer and some garden tools.

Original Organics Ltd
Unit 4 – 5 Farthings Lodge Business Centre,
Plymtree, Cullompton, Devon EX15 2JY
☎ 0884 277681   📠 0884 277642

CONTACT   Maureen Gard
PRODUCTS   Compost bins
NEW PRODUCTS   Leafmould kit
CATALOGUE   Leaflets on request
MAIL ORDER   Yes

Composts bins for kitchen and garden waste, including the 'Wormery' for Tiger Worm compost.

Ornate Products
Limecroft Road, Knaphill, Surrey GU23 7EF
☎ 0483 486566   📠 0483 797809

CONTACT   Sheila
PRODUCTS   Garden ornaments
CATALOGUE   On request
MAIL ORDER   Yes

Ornamental wall plaques in classical styles from Ornate Products. A complementary range of containers and plaques in contemporary and whimsical designs is available from Ornate Products International (Unit 48, Tannery House, Tannery Lane, Send, Surrey GU23 7EF: 0483 211474).

Oxley's Garden Furniture
Hardings Yard, Albion Street, Chipping Norton,
Oxfordshire OX7 5BJ
☎ 0608 641569   📠 0608 642216

CONTACT   Simon Hudson
PRODUCTS   Garden furniture
NEW PRODUCTS   New colours
CATALOGUE   On request
MAIL ORDER   Yes

Distinctive cast aluminium garden furniture with maintenance-free finishes. Also attractive slate and oak Versailles tubs.

P J Bridgman & Co Ltd
Barnbridge Works, Lockfield Avenue, Brimsdown,
Enfield, London EN3 7PX
☎ 081 804 7474   📠 081 805 0873

CONTACT   Sales Office
PRODUCTS   Garden furniture
NEW PRODUCTS   Lounger cushion (Victorian and Harvest styles)
CATALOGUE   On request and from stockists
MAIL ORDER   No

Wide range of solidly built Iroko garden furniture in period styles: many include carved details. Wood is derived from sustainable sources.

Pamal
The Cottage, Sproxton, Melton Mowbray,
Leicestershire LE14 4QS
☎ 0476 860266   📠 0476 860523

CONTACT   Mrs Pamela Graham or Mr Malise Graham
PRODUCTS   Garden furniture
CATALOGUE   On request
MAIL ORDER   Yes

Manufacturers and suppliers of wooden garden furniture, including benches and Versailles tubs.

Pan Brittanica Industries Ltd
Brittanica House, Waltham Cross, Hertfordshire
EN8 7DY
☎ 0992 623691   📠 0992 626452

PRODUCTS   Composts; fertilisers; herbicides; garden sundries
NEW PRODUCTS   'Biosafe' vine weevil control
CATALOGUE   Trade only
MAIL ORDER   No

Large garden group with a best-selling range of growing media, garden chemicals and general plant care products, including 'Baby Bio'. They have recently sold their Expert books, written by Dr Hessayon, to Transworld.

Parallax
17 Mapperley Street, Sherwood, Nottingham,
Nottinghamshire NG5 4DE
☎ 0602 606086   📠 0602 626716

CONTACT   Phil Warrior
PRODUCTS   Greenhouses; plastic sheeting
NEW PRODUCTS   Lean-to models
CATALOGUE   On request
MAIL ORDER   Yes

Timber greenhouses and plastic sheeting: all products are available mail order or from garden centres.

Phostrogen
Corwen, Clwyd LL21 0EE
☎ 0490 412662   📠 0490 412177

CONTACT   Mrs Anne Marie Stott
PRODUCTS   Fertilisers
NEW PRODUCTS   Rose food and tonic
CATALOGUE   On request
MAIL ORDER   No

Manufacturers of soluble and slow release fertilisers.

Power Garden Products
3 Daytona Drive, Allesley, Coventry, West
Midlands CU5 9QG
☎ 0676 23062

CONTACT   Mrs S. Smith

PRODUCTS   Plant supports; cloches; footwear
CATALOGUE   Large sae
MAIL ORDER   Yes

Mail order garden supplies including Power plant supports and 'Chase Barn' cloches, both of which are only available from Power. Other products include tools and overshoes.

Practicality Brown Ltd
Iver Stud, Iver, Buckinghamshire SL0 9LA
☎ 0753 652022

CONTACT   Sylvia Reynolds
PRODUCTS   Mulches
CATALOGUE   On request
MAIL ORDER   No

Mulches and bark products in various grades for horticultural and amenity use. Prices from £20 a cubic metre delivered. Tree moving and chipping service available.

Precise Irrigation (UK) Ltd
78 Grove Street, Wantage, Oxfordshire OX12 7BG
☎ 0235 763760   [FAX] 0235 765467

CONTACT   Jeremy Browning and Simon Box
PRODUCTS   Irrigation systems
CATALOGUE   On request
MAIL ORDER   Yes

Designers, suppliers and installers of irrigation systems for domestic and commercial customers. No charge for evaluations and quotations. Starter and hanging basket kits available.

Raffles – Thatched Garden Buildings
Laundry Cottage, Prestwold Hall, Prestwold, Loughborough, Leicestershire LE12 5SQ
☎ 0509 881426   [FAX] 0509 881426

CONTACT   Andrew V. Raffle
PRODUCTS   Summerhouses
CATALOGUE   On request
MAIL ORDER   No

Suppliers of thatched summerhouses and garden buildings built with traditional materials to old designs. They can also restore existing buidings.

Ransomes Consumer Ltd
Bell Close, Newnham Industrial Estate, Plympton, Plymouth, Devon PL7 4JH
☎ 0752 346555   [FAX] 0752 340851

CONTACT   Mr John Burlingham
PRODUCTS   Garden machinery
NEW PRODUCTS   New range of tractors, ride-on and battery mowers
CATALOGUE   On request
MAIL ORDER   Yes

Extensive range of garden machinery including the best selling lawn tractor, Westwood, and Mountfield lawnmowers, shredders, cultivators and garden generators. They also have an alarm to protect garages and garden sheds.

Rayment Wirework
The Forge, Durlock, Minster, Thanet, Kent CT12 4HE
☎ 0843 821628   [FAX] 0843 821635

CONTACT   Ron or Adrian Rayment
PRODUCTS   Planters; wire work; arches
NEW PRODUCTS   Porticos and verandahs
CATALOGUE   Large sae
MAIL ORDER   Yes

Hand painted wire work structures for the garden and conservatory, from plant holders to furniture and intricate gazebos and temples. They accept commissions.

Remanoid
Unit 44, Number One Industrial Estate, Medomsley Road, Consett, Co. Durham DH8 6SZ
☎ 0207 591089   [FAX] 0207 502512

CONTACT   Mrs C. Peart
PRODUCTS   Aquatic products
NEW PRODUCTS   Pumps and accessories
CATALOGUE   On request
MAIL ORDER   No

Suppliers of a wide range of pumps and accessories for water gardens and ponds.

Renaissance Bronzes
79 Pimlico Road, London SW1W 8PH
☎ 071 823 5149   [FAX] 071 730 4598

CONTACT   Simon Jacques
PRODUCTS   Garden statuary
CATALOGUE   On request
MAIL ORDER   No

Classical and classically styled bronzes for indoor and outdoor positions.

Renaissance Casting
19 Cranford Road, Coventry, West Midlands CV5 8JF
☎ 0926 885567

CONTACT   Mr J. A. Healey
PRODUCTS   Garden statuary; fountains
CATALOGUE   £2

Designers and producers of lead garden statuary including fountains, troughs and vases. They accept special commissions.

Roffey Bros Ltd

Throop Road, Throop, Bournemouth, Hampshire
BH8 0DF

☎ 0202 537777   📠 0202 532765

CONTACT   Robert Parsons or Sarah Williams
PRODUCTS   Commercial composts
NEW PRODUCTS   Giant packs of peat based composts
CATALOGUE   On request
MAIL ORDER   No

Composts and materials for commercial growers and garden retailers, including bark, sterilised loam and grit.

Roger Platts

Faircombe, Maresfield, East Sussex TN22 2EH
☎ 0825 764077   📠 0825 764077

CONTACT   Roger Platts
PRODUCTS   Garden furniture
CATALOGUE   On request
MAIL ORDER   Yes

Garden furniture including seats and tables – made from cast iron and wood.

Ryobi Lawn & Garden (UK) Ltd

Cotteswold Road, Tewkesbury, Gloucestershire
GL20 5DJ

☎ 0684 294606   📠 0684 294909

CONTACT   Mr Leslie Mills
PRODUCTS   Powered garden tools
NEW PRODUCTS   New 4 stroke line trimmers and brush cutters
CATALOGUE   On request
MAIL ORDER   No

Manufacturers of powered garden machinery including hedge trimmers, sweeper vacs, cultivators, chainsaws, trimmers and brush cutters.

Samsons

Edwin Avenue, Hoo Farm Industrial Estate,
Kidderminster, Hereford & Worcester DY11 7RA

☎ 0562 825252   📠 0562 820380

CONTACT   Sales Office
PRODUCTS   Wrought iron garden features
NEW PRODUCTS   Flat packed rose arch
CATALOGUE   On request
MAIL ORDER   Yes

Decorative wrought iron garden features including arches, obelisks, gates and panels which can be combined to form pergolas and screens.

Sarah Burgoyne Revivals

Whyly, East Hoathly, East Sussex BN8 6EL
☎ 0825 840738

CONTACT   Sarah Burgoyne

PRODUCTS   Garden furniture
CATALOGUE   On request
MAIL ORDER   Yes

Old-fashioned garden furniture in beech, including a traditional steamer chair with a fringed canopy.

Scarletts Plantcare

Nayland Road, West Bergholt, Colchester, Essex
CO6 3DH

☎ 0206 240466   📠 0206 242530

CONTACT   Carrie Creswell
PRODUCTS   Biological controls
NEW PRODUCTS   Hortinem 12B for vine weevil
CATALOGUE   On request
MAIL ORDER   Yes

Mail order biological controls for whitefly, red spider mite, vine weevil, thrips, mealy bug, aphids and caterpillars. Flat charge per treatment. Ring the number above for advice.

Shamrock Horticulture Ltd

The Crescent Centre, Temple Back, Bristol, Avon
BS1 6EZ

☎ 0272 211666   📠 0272 225501

CONTACT   Anne Pearse
PRODUCTS   Peat; peat-based composts; peat-free composts
NEW PRODUCTS   Suregrow bulb fibre; Shamrock multi-purpose and John Innes compost ranges
CATALOGUE   On request
MAIL ORDER   No

Major peat supplier with an extended range which includes other compost mixes and conditioners. Includes coconut fibre products. Ring for details of your nearest supplier.

Simply Garlands

51 Albion Road, Pitstone, Bedfordshire LU7 9AY
☎ 0296 661425

CONTACT   Kathy Rollings
PRODUCTS   Floral accessories
CATALOGUE   On request
MAIL ORDER   Yes

Plastic cages which link together: used for making floral garlands.

Skyshades

59 St Marys Street, Wallingford, Oxfordshire
OX10 0EL

☎ 0491 834003   📠 0491 825452

CONTACT   Brian Parker
PRODUCTS   Garden furniture
CATALOGUE   On request

MAIL ORDER Yes

Manufacturers of sun canopies and movable pagodas.

Solardome

Rosedale Engineers Ltd, 9 Bridlington Street,
Hunmanby, Filey, North Yorkshire YO14 0BR
☎ 0723 890303   📠 0723 890303

CONTACT Peter Lemke
PRODUCTS Greenhouses
NEW PRODUCTS 1 metre diameter display sphere
CATALOGUE On request
MAIL ORDER Yes

Manufacturers of geodesic domes for use as green-houses and leisure buildings.

Somerset Postal Flowers

Carew Cottage, Crowcombe, Taunton, Somerset
TA4 4AD
☎ 09848 314

CONTACT Mrs Rosalind Gill
PRODUCTS Fresh flowers
CATALOGUE On request
MAIL ORDER Yes

Fresh flowers sent by post to addresses in the United Kingdom.

Spear & Jackson Garden Products

Handsworth Road, Sheffield, South Yorkshire
S13 9BR
☎ 0742 449911

PRODUCTS Hand tools; garden tools
CATALOGUE On request
MAIL ORDER No

Manufacturers of a wide range of hand and garden tools under this well-known brand name.

Specialised Designs Ltd

Unit D7 Taylor Industrial Estate, Risley,
Warrington, Lancashire WA3 6BL
☎ 0925 766265   📠 0925 765029

CONTACT Neil Burns
PRODUCTS Cloches; window baskets
CATALOGUE On request
MAIL ORDER Yes

Manufacturers of Victorian style cloches which are plastic coated for low maintenance. They also make metal window baskets and hayracks.

Sportsmark Group Ltd

Sportsmark House, Ealing Road, Brentford, London
TW8 0LH
☎ 081 560 2010   📠 081 568 2177

CONTACT Sales

PRODUCTS Marking machines; artificial grass
CATALOGUE Leaflet and samples on request
MAIL ORDER Yes

Supplies for groundsmen and sports fields, including marking machines and artificial grass.

Stangwrach Leisure Products

Stangwrach, Llanfynydd, Camarthen, Dyfed
SA32 7TG
☎ 0558 668287

CONTACT Terry or Grace Maidment
PRODUCTS Garden furniture
NEW PRODUCTS Sun lounger; swinging hammock
CATALOGUE £1
MAIL ORDER Yes

Hardwood garden furniture in strong designs. The timber is sourced only from managed forests.

Starkie & Starkie Ltd

118 South Knighton Road, Leicester, Leicestershire
LE2 3LQ
☎ 0533 703212   📠 0533 703426

CONTACT R. A. Starkie
PRODUCTS Tool sharpening systems
CATALOGUE On request
MAIL ORDER Yes

Suppliers of diamond whetstones and tool sharpening systems.

Stephenson Blake

199 Upper Allen Street, Sheffield, South Yorkshire
S3 7GW
☎ 0742 728325   📠 0742 720065

CONTACT Mr T. J. Blake
PRODUCTS Garden furniture
CATALOGUE On request
MAIL ORDER Yes

Yorkshire-made wooden garden furniture in oak: clean designs which fold for storage. Wholesale available.

Store More Garden Buildings

Store More House, Latham Close, Bredbury
Industrial Estate, Stockport, Cheshire SK6 2SD
☎ 061 430 3347   📠 061 406 6054

CONTACT Chris Downes, Julie Breingan and Sharon Winch
PRODUCTS Garden buildings
CATALOGUE On request
MAIL ORDER Yes

Zinc-coated steel sheds and garden buildings which are maintenance free. All items are available mail order, flat-packed for DIY assembly.

Stuart Garden Architecture
Burrow Hill Farm, Wiveliscombe, Somerset
TA4 2RN
☎ 0984 7458   ⊠ 0984 7455

CONTACT   Katherine Boron
PRODUCTS   Trellis; wooden garden features
NEW PRODUCTS   Extended range of modular trellis
CATALOGUE   £2
MAIL ORDER   Yes

Stylish range of trelliswork, gazebos, pergolas, bridges and garden furniture. All constructed from hardwoods from sustainable sources. Custom design and build available.

Sunlight Systems
Unit 3 St Mary's Works, Burnmoor Street, Leicester, Leicestershire LE2 7JJ
☎ 0533 470490   ⊠ 0533 470485
PRODUCTS   Horticultural lighting
CATALOGUE   On request
MAIL ORDER   Yes

Suppliers of artificial lighting products and systems. Other indoor equipment is also sold. There is a counter service also at Unit 347, Stratford Workshops, Burford Road, London E15 2SP.

Super Natural Ltd
Bore Place Farm, Chiddingstone, Edenbridge, Kent TN8 7AR
☎ 0732 463255   ⊠ 0732 740264

CONTACT   Miss Caroline Dunmall
PRODUCTS   Organic composts; organic fertilisers
CATALOGUE   On request
MAIL ORDER   Liquid food from Dig & Delve Organics, Diss (0379 898377)

Organic composts, plant foods and soil conditioners. Also available in commercial sizes. Chiddingstone Brickworks which makes hand made bricks and pavers is under the same ownership.

Thames Valley Wirework Co Ltd
792 Weston Road, Slough Trading Estate, Slough, Berkshire SL1 4HR
☎ 0753 521992   ⊠ 0753 574160

CONTACT   Sales Office
PRODUCTS   Plant supports
NEW PRODUCTS   'Gro-Fleur' wall trellis; indoor bulb supports
CATALOGUE   Sae
MAIL ORDER   Yes

Manufacturers of 'Gro-Thru' plant supports for herbaceous plants and a range of other supports for indoor and outdoor use.

Thermoforce Ltd
Bentalls Complex, Heybridge, Maldon, Essex CM9 7NW
☎ 0621 858797   ⊠ 0621 858496

CONTACT   K. A. Merriman
PRODUCTS   Greenhouse equipment
NEW PRODUCTS   Consul side window vent opener; 250w mercury fluorescent plant lighting luminaire
CATALOGUE   On request
MAIL ORDER   Yes

Manufacturers of greenhouse equipment including soil cables, mist units, automatic vents and lighting.

Town and Country Products
State House, Morledge Street, Leicester LE1 1TA
☎ 0533 536001   ⊠ 0533 513337

CONTACT   Nick Page
PRODUCTS   Tool holders; gloves
CATALOGUE   On request
MAIL ORDER   Yes

Manufacturers and suppliers of pouches and tool holders, and suppliers of Wells Lamont garden and work gloves.

Trade and DIY Products Ltd
The Pump House, Hazelwood Road, Duffield, Belper, Derbyshire DE56 4AA
☎ 0332 842685   ⊠ 0332 842806

CONTACT   Mr R. Barlow
PRODUCTS   Sheeting; weed suppressants
NEW PRODUCTS   Capillary matting
CATALOGUE   On request
MAIL ORDER   Yes

Suppliers of insulating horticultural fleece and 'Plantex' weed suppressant fabric (as used by RBG, Kew) to retail and trade customers.

The Traditional Garden Supply Company Ltd
22 Guildford Park Road, Guildford, Surrey GU2 5ND
☎ 0483 450080   ⊠ 0483 450085

PRODUCTS   Garden supplies
CATALOGUE   On request; 3 a year
MAIL ORDER   Yes

Mail order suppliers of carefully selected garden products: some practical, some decorative.

Trees in Miniature
21 Harrowes Meade, Edgware, London HA8 8RR
☎ 081 958 3574

CONTACT   Burt Coleman
PRODUCTS   Replica bonsai trees

CATALOGUE No
MAIL ORDER No

Preserved wood and foliage crafted into replica bonsai trees.

Two Wests and Elliott Ltd
Unit 4, Carrwood Road, Sheepbridge Industrial Estate, Chesterfield, Derbyshire S41 9RH
☎ 0246 451077   FAX 0246 260115

CONTACT Mrs J. M. West
PRODUCTS Greenhouse equipment; propagators
CATALOGUE On request
MAIL ORDER Yes

Manufacture and sell a wide range of greenhouse and conservatory equipment including staging, heating, watering, propagation equipment and mini greenhouses. For amateur and professional use. Elliott is the dog.

Vale Garden Houses
Melton Road, Harlaxton, Grantham, Lincolnshire NG32 1HQ
☎ 0476 64433   FAX 0476 78555

CONTACT Lisa Morton
PRODUCTS Conservatories
CATALOGUE On request
MAIL ORDER No

Individually designed conservatories in period styles for domestic houses. Vale Conservatories Ltd handles larger and commercial projects.

Wartnaby Gardens
Melton Mowbray, Leicestershire LE14 3HY
☎ 0664 822549   FAX 0664 822231

PRODUCTS Plant labels
NEW PRODUCTS Larger stem label
CATALOGUE On request
MAIL ORDER Yes

Practical zinc plant labels either as tie-ons or with stems; 14 inch stands are available for the tie-on variety and they also sell marking and engraving equipment.

Wells & Winter
Mereworth, Maidstone, Kent ME18 5NB
☎ 0622 813267

CONTACT Sir John Wells
PRODUCTS Labels; tree ties; apron
CATALOGUE On request
MAIL ORDER Yes

Good quality plastic, aluminium, zinc and copper labels, tags, and marking equipment. Labels can be pre-engraved to your order. Mail order and shows only. Some other products, and books (at shows only).

Wessex Horticultural Products Ltd
South Newton, Salisbury, Wiltshire SP2 0QW
☎ 0722 742500   FAX 0722 742571

CONTACT Rosa Henderson
PRODUCTS Growing media; organic products
NEW PRODUCTS Coir growbag
CATALOGUE On request
MAIL ORDER Yes

Manufacturers and suppliers of peat free and traditional growing media. Their sister company Growing Success Organic Ltd sells slug killer, hanging basket liners and insect traps.

West Meters Ltd
Western Bank Industrial Estate, Wigton, Cumbria CA7 9SJ
☎ 06973 44288   FAX 06973 44616

CONTACT John Fisher
PRODUCTS Thermometers; measuring equipment
NEW PRODUCTS Rainfall measure
CATALOGUE On request
MAIL ORDER Yes

A large choice of thermometers, soil test meters and barometers, as well as some household measuring instruments.

Westland Horticulture
97 Moy Road, Dungannon, Co. Tyrone, Northern Ireland
☎ 08687 84007   FAX 08687 84077

CONTACT Seamus McGrane
PRODUCTS Growing media; mulches
CATALOGUE On request

Manufacturers and suppliers of Westland composts and growing media including mulches and chipped bark.

Wetheriggs Pottery
Clifton Dykes, Penrith, Cumbria CA10 2DH
☎ 0768 62946   FAX 0768 899472

CONTACT Chris Merchant
PRODUCTS Terracotta pots
CATALOGUE On request
MAIL ORDER Yes; 6 weeks minimum delivery

Nineteenth century working pottery which supplies hand made pots in many traditional shapes including rhubarb forcers. There are steam engines and a café at the pottery.

Whichford Pottery
Whichford, Shipston on Stour, Warwickshire CV36 5PG
☎ 0608 684416   FAX 0608 684833

CONTACT Jane Lancia

PRODUCTS   Terracotta pots
NEW PRODUCTS   New designs
CATALOGUE   6x 1st class stamps
MAIL ORDER   Yes; £12.50 delivery charge

Hand made, frost free terracotta pots in plain and decorated designs. The pottery, which can be visited, handles some very large pieces.

William Sinclair Horticulture
Firth Road, Lincoln, Lincolnshire LN6 7AH
☎ 0522 537561   📠 0522 513609

CONTACT   Advisory Service
PRODUCTS   Composts; fertilisers; aggregates; lawn care
MAIL ORDER   No

Horticultural conglomerate whose range includes composts, fertilisers and soil conditioners from J. Arthur Bowers; Silvaperl aggregates including sand, gravel and perlite; the Garotta brand compost equipment; and peat-free composts and conditioners.

Wiltshire Summerhouses
The Elms, Millditch, Bratton, Westbury, Wiltshire BA13 4SX
☎ 0380 830235   📠 0380 830235

CONTACT   Sally or Steve Peake
PRODUCTS   Summerhouses; garden buildings
CATALOGUE   On request
MAIL ORDER   Yes; personal delivery

Rotating wooden summerhouses in kit form or ready assembled. All are made to order. Other styles include potting sheds and there is a bespoke service.

WOLF Tools
Alton Road, Ross on Wye, Hereford & Worcester HR9 5NE
☎ 0989 767600   📠 0989 765589

CONTACT   R. Wolf
PRODUCTS   Hand tools; lawnmowers; garden machinery
NEW PRODUCTS   Two small electric lawnmowers; hollow tine aerator; folding pruning saw
CATALOGUE   From Wolf and their stockists
MAIL ORDER   No

An extensive range of tools for the gardener from this well known company. Products include garden tools with interchangeable heads, cultivating tools, pruning equipment, lawnmowers and powered machinery.

Woodgrow Horticulture Ltd
84 Burton Road, Findern, Derby, Derbyshire DE6 6BE
☎ 0332 516392   📠 0332 511481

CONTACT   Arnold or Martin Woodhouse
PRODUCTS   Landscaping materials
NEW PRODUCTS   'Enviromulch' – coloured woodchips for mulching
MAIL ORDER   Some items

Landscape materials for the landscape trade including bark and wood chips, soil and composts, aggregates and plastic tunnels.

20

Organic Gardening

The organic gardening movement has gained remarkable momentum during the latter half of this century.

In the early years it was subjected to much derision, and the phrase 'muck and magic' was seldom uttered without a sneer. The human response to learning new techniques, and to the necessity of changing behaviour was ever thus, but when ecological awareness meets economic necessity, the impetus for change becomes irresistible. The growing evidence of damage to the environment by over-use of chemicals in combination with their spiralling costs has been, in no small measure, a motivating force in the rise of the movement.

Early negative perceptions have now been supplanted to such an extent that many organic practices have regained widespread acceptance as items of good husbandry. Indeed many of the basic tenets were commonplace before the advent of high-input, high-cost agriculture.

Be that as it may, there is no doubt that many of us find the commitment that organic gardening appears to entail most daunting. If we were left to devise tactics and strategies from first principles by ourselves, this would be justifiable. Fortunately, there are several organisations that are not only experienced in the use of organic techniques, but also committed to giving help and advice to the would-be organic grower.

The most fundamental of organic principles lies in the maintenance of soil health and fertility by incorporation of organic materials: feeding the soil rather than the plant. A soil that is humus-rich is better aerated, more likely to have good structure, and is better able to hold moisture and nutrients. Put simply, a healthy soil grows healthy plants that are more likely to resist both pests and diseases.

The Soil Association, 86 Colston St, Bristol BS1 5BB has been one of the prime movers in encouraging such an organic approach to soil management and plant health. It administers the approval scheme for *bona fide* organic growers (by awarding the Soil Association symbol), and although orientated towards larger scale production, can offer advice and information to individuals. They also run a bookshop.

The Good Gardeners Association, Timber Yard, Two Mile Lane, Highnam, Gloucestershire, GL2 8BR; and the Irish Organic Farmers and Growers Association, Killegland Farm, Ashbourne, Co. Meath, Eire, also offer advice and support to growers, and act as contact points for the dissemination of information.

The first port of call for every would-be organic grower, however, should be the Henry Doubleday Research Association (HDRA). Established in 1954 by Lawrence Hills, it has become the largest of such organisations in the world. Its permanent headquarters, since 1985, have been at Ryton Gardens, Ryton on Dunsmore, Coventry CV8 3LG.

Here are demonstration gardens for fruit, vegetables and flowers, with wildflower gardens, and conservation areas; the whole is interspersed with displays of equipment, and integrated with strategies and tactics for natural control of pests.

The maintenance of soil fertility by applying organic matter is widely accepted as good practice, and at Ryton one can see a range of materials and techniques in use, from double-digging to the no-dig deep-bed system. It is probably one of the best places to study the art and science of compost production, that emblem of recycling. The same can be said of their methods of weed control: sheet mulches and loose mulches of every kind. The control of pests and diseases using totally organic methods is the area that appears to present most difficulties to the un-converted gardener. There are several reasons for this. Most of us seek horticultural perfection, and this is compromised by infestations of pests and disease.

Few of us are well-practised in distinguishing between cosmetic damage and damage that seriously and permanently affects the health of the plant. Where beauty and perfection are synonymous, as with roses, for example, even the most sanguine of gardeners takes cosmetic damage as a personal af-front. The instant effect of most modern chemicals makes reaching for the spraygun an easy and appeal-ing solution to pest control. The organic gardener may use selected pesticides but will probably regard their routine use as short-term crisis management.

The primary difference between organic and non-organic approaches lies here, and one can make a neat analogy with the difference between tradi-tional and alternative medicine. The former treats the symptoms, the latter seeks a more holistic solu-tion. When applied to gardens, this means adopting a range of strategies and tactics for pest- and disease-control whose common denominators are that they cause minimum disruption to the ecosystem, and that each tactic employed is coordinated with every other to form a multi-pronged plan of defence.

The tricks, traps, predators and parasitoids that augment sound cultural practices to form a holistic approach can all be seen at Ryton. HDRA's admir-ably practical approach is backed up with advice and information; it also runs a bookshop and specialist library, and coordinates some 30 local groups. The HDRA operates in conjunction with *Chase Or-ganics, Coombelands House, Coombelands Lane, Addlestone, Weybridge, Surrey KT15 1HY.* (0932 820958), and supplies almost everything from bio-controls to books via a joint catalogue.

Whilst a healthy soil may go a long way towards ensuring horticultural success, organic matter alone may not be sufficient to supply all necessary nu-trients, especially for intensive cultivation in the vegetable garden. It is a surprisingly common mis-conception that organic gardeners do not use fer-tilisers. Of course they do, although they *are* selective. Such slow-release fertilisers as bonemeal, hoof and horn, or faster-acting types, such as dried

blood, for example, are organic staples, and are readily available from mainstream suppliers. Gar-deners with vegan tendencies may baulk at such measures, and use rock phosphate, rock potash or seaweed meal instead. Most organic suppliers give guidance in their catalogues on the origin and most appropriate use of their fertiliser products. Many are also happy to advise. Amongst them are:

Cumulus Organics, Pinetum Lodge, Churcham, Gloucestershire GL2 8AD. 0452 750402

All-Gain Organics, 8 Netherlands Road, New Barnet, Hertfordshire EN5 1BN. 081 449 1605;

Other organisations share the ecological prin-ciples of organic gardening, but apply them with a broader brush. Perhaps the best known is the *Centre for Alternative Technology, Machynlleth, Powys, SY20 9AZ.* 0654 2400. This well-established centre demonstrates a range of sustainable techno-logies, including organic food production. It also runs courses, educational visits, and an information service; sells books and environmentally sound pro-ducts; and produces a wide range of information sheets, resource lists and reports.

The Permaculture Association, 8 Hunters Moon, Totnes, Devon TQ9 6JT. 0803 867546, was formed to encourage the practice of permacul-ture, the conscious use of ecological principles for self-sustaining food production. It offers informa-tion and advice on the design of garden and planting to incorporate many different techniques: organic, bio-dynamic and ecological gardening.

The Bio-Dynamic Agriculture Association, Woodman Lane, Clent, Stourbridge, West Mid-lands, DY9 9PX. 0562 884933, promotes bio-dy-namic agriculture, offers help and support to all bio-dynamic growers and operates a postal advice service. Bio-dynamics are based on the anthroposo-phical theories of Rudolph Steiner, and incorporate organic with more celestial principles: the phase of the moon is supposed to influence planting times. It is sometimes regarded as somewhat esoteric, but Virgil would certainly have recognised the prin-ciples.

Aside from the suppliers listed, most of these organisations are charities, so follow the organic maxim: don't take out more than you give back, and dig deep!

21

Buying in Bulk

There are considerable savings to be made by buying wholesale or in bulk, although there are a number of other considerations to be taken into account. The first problem is that many wholesalers simply do not deal with the general public and, if they do, they often stipulate a minimum order that can range from fifty to several hundred pounds. Unwillingness to deal with the public is not a result of bloody-mindedness. There are building regulations and health and safety constraints that may prevent them from opening their premises to the public. Moreover, unlike well-run garden centres, wholesalers seldom have the time (or the inclination) to give horticultural advice. You should have a clear idea of what you need before you order, so always do your homework first.

One approach to bulk buying is to form a 'co-op' – a garden club – to pool financial resources to meet minimum order requirements. There will still be logistical drawbacks to consider. Bulk orders usually need a spacious delivery and distribution centre, and someone willing to organise the process. A good starting point for the would-be bulk buyer is the Yellow Pages Directory; we have given references here for where to look.

Buying Plants and Seeds

(Yellow Pages: Nurseries – Horticultural – Wholesale) For orders of large numbers of plants - hedging, for example - it is always worth considering a direct approach to wholesale nurseries, especially if you are buying as a garden society or group. A number of large country estates, and some local authorities now run forest tree nurseries, with a good selection of native and forestry species. You can only ask, and they can, at worst, refuse to deal with you. If they are willing to deal with you it will probably be on a 'buyer collects' basis, and payment is likely to be required on collection because, as an individual, you are unknown to them as a credit risk.

Give advance notice of your order and fix an appointment for collection, since plants may be field-grown and require lifting. You need to know exactly what you want in terms of species (essential), but also in terms of size, for example whether it be transplant, whip or half standard. You can find guidelines to stock sizes in the British Standard for Nursery Stock: BS3936 Pt. 1, from your local reference library.

Some suppliers are willing to supply bulk orders of seed and sundries at a discount to allotment and garden groups. Among them are:

D T Brown & Co Ltd, Station Road, Poulton le Fylde, Lancs. FY6 7HX, 0253 882371; James Henderson & Sons, Kingholm Quay, Dumfries DG1 4SU, 0387 52234; Seeds-by-Size, 45 Crouchmoor, Boxmoor, Hemel Hempstead HP1 1PA, 0442 251458.

There are also well known seed merchants who offer discount or special terms to clubs and allotment societies, and it is always worth asking the sales department if they run such schemes.

Many schools, and indeed, individuals, are now interested in creating wild flower meadows, or other conservation features. One of the largest suppliers of wild flower seed, *Emorsgate Seeds, Terrington Court, Terrington St Clement, Kings Lynn, Norfolk PE34 4NT, 0553 829028* can supply seed in quantities from 100 kg, down to 1 gm packets, and are experienced in dealing with schools and local authorities.

Should you need to plant up a whole new herbaceous border, it is a good idea to telephone round nurseries for quotes on your planting list.

Composts, Fertilisers and Sundries

(Yellow Pages: Agricultural Wholesalers; DIY Stores) For the range of composts that most gardeners use, retail outlets such as the large chain DIY

superstores can be very competitive since they have a massive buying power. You may find greater reductions at your local Agricultural Wholesalers, but it is worth phoning round to compare prices. The following specialise in bulk supplies:

Joseph Bentley Ltd, Back Lane, Barrow-on-Humber DN19 7AQ, 0469 53 20000. Composts, fertilisers and sundries. Minimum order £75; special terms for gardening and allotment societies. Nationwide delivery.

Gardenland, Bath Rd, Longton, Stockton-on-Trent ST3 2JQ, 0782 598497. Gardenland is a cash and carry outlet, that makes dealing with allotment societies a feature of its business. It can deliver to most of western England. At the same address, *M&D Supplies* specialises in forest bark.

Roffey Bros, Throop Rd, Throop, Bournemouth BH8 0DF, 0202 537777 manufacture and sell a range of composts, fertilisers and chemicals which they will deliver throughout the south and west. They offer special terms to societies, and have no minimum order, but impose a small delivery charge on orders less than £100.

T Dagg & Sons, 16 Bath St, Glasgow G2 1HA, 041 322 2487, Fax 041 332 5044 stock a wide range of composts, fertilisers and sundries. They give discounts to allotment societies, offer free local delivery on orders over £20; at normal carriage cost they supply Shetland and the Western Isles.

Manure

(Yellow Pages: Riding Stables; Dairy Farmers) Rural gardeners need never be short of muck, although farmers are always busy, so you may need charm and persistence to acquire it, especially if you need it delivered. Many farmers will allow you to collect your own. It is, however, always important to offer payment.

The suburban gardener may be lucky enough to live near a riding stables, although it is likely that you will have to make your own arrangements to collect manure. Prospects are fairly bleak for the committed urbanite, in this respect: finding a source, and then collecting sufficient quantities to be worthwhile may be difficult.

Topsoil

(Yellow Pages: Turf Suppliers; Mushroom Growers; Sugar Refiners; Landscapers) Check also the classified section of your local press. Topsoil is sold loose by the tonne, or cubic metre (1.4 tonnes), and you need to check whether the quoted price includes delivery. Before buying, prepare your site, and consider the logistics of how, when and where you will take delivery. A number of substances sold as 'topsoil' are, in reality, amalgams of rubble, roots and subsoil. This is despite the British Standard description, so *caveat emptor* – check on quality *before* delivery.

A void soils that have been stacked high for long periods: they will almost certainly have lost their structure through compaction. The safest procedure is to see the topsoil *in situ*, and to take delivery as and when it is stripped from the original site. Delay planting until any pernicious weeds have shown themselves, and deal with them before you plant.

Spent mushroom compost is a valuable bulking material for growing media and mulching. It has good structure, but do check the pH: it may be very alkaline due to lime used in the casing.

Sugar beet washings are sometimes offered as a substitute for topsoil, but are probably best regarded only as an ameliorant for very heavy soil. Processing destroys the structure; the resulting dirt is nutritionally very poor, light, and liable to be blown about.

Sheet Mulches

(Yellow Pages: Agricultural and Horticultural Wholesalers, Plastics – fabrics, film and sheet) Sheet mulches such as woven polypropylene, black and clear polythene or spun polypropylene fleece (used as floating mulch) can be bought by the roll from agricultural and horticultural wholesalers, or from plastics suppliers. In the long term, this will work out much cheaper, though it may take the average gardener several seasons to use a whole roll. Be sure to store black polythene in cool, dark conditions, since it degenerates in heat and sunlight.

Bark Mulches

(Yellow Pages: Landscapers, Tree Surgeons, Sawmills) Brand name bark mulches can be almost as expensive as best Axminster, though you can usually be sure that you are buying a clean, uniform product. It will have been composted or 'matured' to

drive off terpenes and phenols that would be harmful if applied directly to plant roots. Aside from transport and delivery, this is the major drawback of buying 'raw' bark and woodchips. Unless they are to be used for informal paths, stack for about six months before use. Coarse sawdust or shavings also make good mulches, if composted; be sure that they are not derived from wood that has been treated with preservative. With these qualifications, bark chips, loose bark and sawdust can be had at less than a quarter of the price of branded mulches, from the above sources. The Forestry Commission, and those local authorities that operate an Urban Forestry enterprise, are alternative sources.

Stone, Sand and Gravel

(Yellow Pages: Quarries, Sand and Gravel Merchants, Stone Merchants) There are considerable savings to be made by buying these 'hard' materials direct from source; as little as one tenth of the retail outlet price. This is partly because the more you buy, the cheaper the price per tonne, since transport costs are a major portion of the price. Expect delivery by large tipper lorry and, again, bear in mind that several tonnes can take up horrifying amounts of space. Plan where it will be unloaded; can it be stored there? How far is it from the site? Who will help with the back-breaking barrowing?

Gravel is offered in several grades, so choose one that is appropriate to the site. 3-6 mm will give a beautiful fine-textured surface that will walk into the house and on to the lawn in the cleats of your shoes; 15 mm gravel is hard-wearing, good for driveways but uncomfortable to walk on; 7 -10 mm is probably the most suitable for paths. Base your calculations on 1 m^3 (about 1.9 tonnes) which will cover about 15 m^2 to a depth of 50 mm loose, or 12 m^2 rolled.

If you are buying sand, choose the appropriate type. Fine builders sand is what you require for construction work. It is disastrous for most horticultural purposes, for which you should specify horticultural, sharp silver sand or Bedford sand.

Hard Landscaping Materials

(Yellow Pages: Builders Merchants, DIY Stores, Paving Manufacturers) The bricks, paving and other hard materials that form the structure of your garden are likely to be the single most expensive item in its creation. If chosen well, walls and paving form the foundation and background for plantings, will enhance the architecture of the house, and should last for many years.

Large paving manufacturers seldom deal with the public (it is rather like asking ICI to sell you a bottle of aspirin). You might have more joy with small local manufacturers, but have to collect the paving slabs from their factory.

Builders' Merchants may seem the most logical place to buy, but do not overlook the DIY superstores; they are extremely competitive. As with all bulk orders, consider the logistics of delivery – timing, unloading and space for storage.

Timber

(Yellow Pages: Timber Merchants and Sawmills) Many timber merchants will offer considerable savings over DIY outlets, and may deliver locally. For outdoor use, for example gravel boards and fences, ensure that wood has been pressure treated, and specify rough-sawn or dressed timber (i.e. planed for a smoother surface). Work out the dimensions required in detail before ordering to avoid waste, and be sure that the timber you use is substantial enough for the task in hand. For example, when building a pergola, 225 mm × 75 mm will safely span about 5 m, 125 mm × 50 mm will span less than half that.

Pondliners

(Yellow Pages: Plastics – Manufacturers, Suppliers) Plastics manufacturers and suppliers usually carry a range of butyl, reinforced PVC, and heavy duty plastics that are suitable for pond and bog garden liners. They often, as with many wholesalers, have a minimum order requirement. Calculate your sheet size and get a quote. The area required will be: [(2 × depth) + width + margin for surround] × [(2 × depth) + length + margin for surround]. Add to this equation the dimensions of any marginal shelves. For an irregular shape, use the linear measurements of a square or rectangle that encompasses the widest limits of the shape.

22

Composts

The ecological controversy concerning the use of peat as a growing medium and soil ameliorant has prompted a wide-ranging review of its role as a horticultural panacea. One positive result of this has been a proliferation of 'alternative' composts. Unfortunately, these are early days in the development and trial of 'green mediums', and many of us have yet to learn how to use them with the same confidence as their peat-based predecessors.

There are, however, certain fundamental requirements that *all* growing mediums must fulfil, in order to perform satisfactorily. A compost must have good physical structure, with adequate pore space to hold sufficient air and water for healthy root growth. In addition, it must contain nutrients to sustain growth (requirements vary according to the stage of a plant's development) and have a pH suited to the plant in question. In practice, most composts have a pH between 5.5 and 6.5.

There is one other important caveat to bear in mind when buying compost. Try to ensure that you are not buying old stock (until manufacturers can be persuaded to date stamp this will be difficult). Most soil-less mixes will not deteriorate with age provided that they are stored dry, preferably on pallets off ground. Loam-based and organic mixes may undergo chemical changes that can adversely affect nitrogen content and pH, especially if stored in wet conditions. Look for retailers who store under cover, in cool, dry conditions.

The primary division in compost types is between loam- or soil-based mediums, and soil-less types. The best known of the former is the John Innes range. Based on standardised mixes of sterilised loam, sphagnum moss peat and coarse sand, which provide for aeration, moisture retention and drainage. JI composts are formulated for seed or potting. JI Seed has low nutrient levels for sowing seed or rooting cuttings; JI potting (JIP) mixes have additional 'base' fertilizer. JIP-1 is intended for initial potting on after pricking out, and is sometimes also used for houseplants. JIP-2, and JIP-3, with two and three times the nutrient content respectively, are designed for more vigorous plants, and are especially useful for long-term plantings in large pots, for conservatory or patio. The primary advantage of loam-based compost is that loam has the ability to absorb and release nutrients; this absorptive capacity helps regulate nutrient supply and minimizes the danger of salt build-up. Loam also contains micro-elements, and humus which provides some additional nitrogen as it breaks down. In combination with coarse sand, loam makes re-wetting relatively easy, in comparison with peat-based media. Its weight – not always an advantage – lends stability to potted plants. These properties are invaluable for those of us who manage plants in conditions not noted for control and precision, unlike nursery stock production.

The major disadvantage lies in the variability of loam; if it is of poor quality so is the the compost. Look for the John Innes Manufacturers Association Seal of Approval; the JIMA monitors standards. JI composts are suitable for a wide range of plants, with the exception of acid-loving ericaceous plants. These demand a specially formulated ericaceous mix.

Soil-less mediums have, until recently, been based mainly on peat, mixed with varying proportions of sand, perlite or vermiculite. The most widely used of these have been multi-purpose composts, used for seeds, cuttings and growing on. They usually contain nutrients in slow-release form, so that food becomes available to the plant as it grows. Supplementary feeding should be introduced as soon as plants begin to show the need for it, for example, if they produce smaller than usual leaves, or if existing leaves look pale and feeble. Timing may vary between 4 – 12 weeks after potting. It is difficult to give precise recommendations for additional feeding, since it will depend on both the plant's rate of growth and the individual compost.

Be prepared to observe and respond. Reduced peat or no-peat composts are formulated with a number of alternative substrates. One of the most useful of these is bark, granulated, pulverised or hammer-milled, sometimes amended with vermiculite or per-lite for seed and cutting composts. Bark must be aged or composted to drive off toxic phenolic chemicals. The resulting medium has similar low-nutrient status to that of peat, and additional fertilisers are included in the mix. In use, bark-based mediums have fairly stable structure, adequate aeration and water-hold-ing properties, and produce good root growth. Ex-perienced growers report that bark is not difficult to re-wet, although watering needs more care, because the top layer dries out, disguising adequate moisture below. Bark has great potential as a 'green' growing medium, not least because, as with other timber residues, it is a renewable by-product of the forestry industry.

Great exitement accompanied the revival of coir as a growing medium. Derived from coconut fibre, most is imported from around the Indian ocean. Some environmentalists consider that it may better be used to help prevent soil erosion in its country of origin, and that the use of fuel in transporting it could not be justified by environmental audit. That said, a range of coir-based composts has been developed that has ironed-out initial problems of variability and contaminations with fungi and bacteria. Coir has good aeration and water-holding capacity, re-wets more easily than peat, and contains some NPK and trace elements. Coir composts may be overwatered inadvertently, since they too dry out on the surface, so check below before watering indiscriminately.

Other organic mediums include those based on processed cow slurry, and vermicomposts derived from worms fed on animal manure or plant waste. Pure wormcasts have high nutrient value, and may be used as a fertilizer; they make a valuable compo-nent in the growing mediums, having good structure and nutrient status. Early formulations included peat, but newer types use a variety of alternatives. These mediums appear to be developing rapidly, and may not be readily available from mainstream sup-pliers. The HDRA and Chase Organics catalogue, however, carries a good range; see Organic Garde-ning section.

A range of materials of mineral origin are used in growing mixes, usually as amendments rather than as mediums in their own right. Perlite is a heat-ex-panded aluminosilicate mineral, graded by particle size, that is used to improve drainage and aeration. It has a very stable structure, and holds moisture on the particle surfaces, but has no significant nutrient value, nor can it absorb nutrients from supplemen-tary feeding. The low-nutrient status makes it par-ticularly valuable in propagating mixes. Vermiculite is a micaceous mineral that expands when subjected to high temperature to form a stable lattice structure that holds air and water. Unlike perlite, it contains some potassium and magnesium, and has a useful capacity to absorb and release nutrients, thus reduc-ing loss of fertilizer through leaching.

23

Professional Services

For even the most enthusiastic gardener there comes a time to call on professional help. Others may turn to the experts more often - for large and demanding jobs, for knowledge and expertise, or for their ideas and inspiration. The good news is that there is no shortage of assistance available out there. Choosing the right person for the right task, however, and making sure that what you get is what you actually want are more tricky. The information in this section is designed to help you on your way.

Employing a professional The most important job is to decide what you want. You don't have to make all the decisions yourself, but the nature and extent of the work which you are prepared to pay for must be laid out at the start. For small and well-defined tasks such as the removal of a tree limb this should be straightforward enough. For anything more extensive it's vital to discuss and agree the brief with the professional concerned. Many professionals produce detailed information on the way they carry out their business and what clients can expect. Then you need to spell out your requirements on such matters as time scale, the budget, and the degree of finish. It has to be absolutely clear that the professional understands your terms and is able to fulfil them. This process can be time-consuming. Avoid the temptation to rush it. This will avoid many costly misunderstandings and potential disappointments. Among the questions to ask, satisfy yourself on the following:

What are your qualifications? Do you belong to an appropriate professional body?

What levels of third party insurance and public liability insurance do you carry? This is very important for heavy or hazardous work such as tree surgery or construction.

Can I see a portfolio, inspect completed work or contact previous clients to see whether I like your work?

Will you use your own staff or employ outside contractors? Can a designer recommend contractors?

Notes on the lists Suppliers of professional services have a main entry under one of the following headings: Landscape and Design; Horticultural Consultancy; Arboricultural Services; Water and Riparian Services and Landscape Contractors.

Many of the firms offer more than one of these services: cross-references to the main entry appear under each additional service. A number of the nurseries and garden centres we list also offer garden design and landscaping. These nurseries are marked by a cross-reference from this section to their main entry in the Nurseries section.

Professional bodies For many of the entries we have mentioned the main professional bodies and organisations which they belong to. This information is not definitive, and not everyone has supplied full details, yet it is a useful guide to the sort of service you can expect to find. Firms and practitioners are strictly vetted before they can join these bodies, and this vetting may include inspection of their work and a requirement to carry specified levels of insurance. It is up to you to decide on the level of technical competence and experience you require. For more details about these bodies see the Organisations section.

FHort   Fellow of the Institute of Horticulture
MIHort   Member of the Institute of Horticulture
AIHort   Associate of the Institute of Horticulture
SGD   Fellow or Member of the Society of Garden Designers
ALI   Associate of the Landscape Institute
AAAC   Arboricultural Association Approved Contractor
FAA   Fellow of the Arboricultural Association

Further information   The Institute of Horticulture produces a list of horticultural consultants: to receive a free copy write to the institute at P O Box 313, Vincent Square, London SW1P 2PE. The *Society of Garden Designers* also produces a list of its membership with notes about their careers: free of charge from the Asst Secretary, Society of Garden Designers, 6 Borough Road, Kingston upon Thames, Surrey KT2 6BD. If you contact the *British Association of Landscape Industries* (BALI) at Landscape House, Henry Street, Keighley, West Yorkshire BD21 3DR they can provide a list of BALI members in your area. The *Arboricultural Association*, at Ampfield House, Romsey, Hampshire SO51 9PA can send you a copy of their directory of approved contractors and consultants on request. A *Directory of Registered Landscape Practices*, which includes all the *Landscape Institute's* members, can be obtained from RIBA shops (£10) and by post (£11) from the *Royal Institute of British Architects*.

Caveat Emptor   Our list is based on information which the firms themselves have supplied. Accordingly, the presence in or absence from this list of a firm should not be taken as a judgement on the firm or any sort of recommendation. It's your decision whom you employ in the end - and, as so often, the motto is *Buyer Beware*.

Landscape & Design

Acres Wild (Landscape & Garden Design)
45a High Street, Billingshurst, West Sussex RH14 9PP
☎ 0403 785385
CONTACT   Ian Smith or Debbie Roberts

WORKING AREA   Hampshire, Kent, London, Surrey & Sussex
ASSOCIATIONS   SGD
STARTED TRADING   1988
PROJECTS   Featured on the BBC's *Gardens by Design*; won the Phoenix Award for Memorial Garden Design (Durrington Cemetery) and another award for a wildlife garden for the London & Edinburgh Insurance Group

Both practitioners have degrees in landscape architecture. Acres Wild won the first Hampton Court Trophy for Garden Design.

Agars Nursery, Hampshire
For full details see Nurseries section

Allan Hart Associates
Orchard House, 61 Christchurch Road, East Sheen, London SW14 7AN
☎ 081 878 2017   FAX 081 878 1638

CONTACT   Allan Hart
WORKING AREA   UK, Europe, Middle & Far East, USA
ASSOCIATIONS   ALI; MIHort; MILAM
OTHER SERVICES   Horticultural consultancy; recreation and tourism planning
STARTED TRADING   1968
PROJECTS   Landscape consultancy at Canary Wharf; landscape and horticultural consultancy at Berkeley Square, Mayfair

Landscape architecture practice with particular horticultural expertise. Allan Hart's training includes the Kew diploma. Work includes company headquarters, hospitals, estates and landscape restoration.

Allseasons Landscapes
Spinners, High Street, Upper Beeding, Steyning, West Sussex BN44 3HZ
☎ 0903 815079/ 0273 562160   FAX 0903 813225
CONTACT   Philip Boast
WORKING AREA   East & West Sussex
ASSOCIATIONS   BALI
OTHER SERVICES   Landscape contractors; interior landscaping and maintenance
STARTED TRADING   1982

Andrew Evans, Landscape Designer
5 Nadder Terrace, Churchfields Road, Salisbury, Wiltshire SP2 7NN
☎ 0722 328998

CONTACT   Andrew Evans
WORKING AREA   England and Wales, south of Staffordshire and Leicestershire
STARTED TRADING   1991

Landscape architect offering full survey and design services. Twelve years experience.

Annabel Allhusen

Capstitch House, Compton Abbas, Shaftesbury, Dorset SP7 0NB
☎ 0747 811622

CONTACT Annabel Allhusen
WORKING AREA Devon, Dorset, Hampshire, Somerset & Wiltshire
OTHER SERVICES Horticultural consultancy
STARTED TRADING 1989

Trained at the College of Garden Design. Garden design, including drawings and planting schedules. Consultancy advice and individual border planning also available. Has exhibited recently in the Design Pavilion at Chelsea.

Anthea Sokell

Rickledon, Maddox Lane, Bookham, Leatherhead, Surrey KT23 3BS
☎ 0372 452052

CONTACT Anthea Sokell
WORKING AREA Southern England
STARTED TRADING 1990

Trained at the College of Garden Design. Part of Seven Counties Garden Design.

Anthony Archer-Wills

Broadford Bridge Road, West Chiltington, West Sussex RH20 2LF
☎ 0798 803204   📠 0798 815080
OTHER SERVICES Water and riparian services

Garden designer with particular expertise in water gardens: he can supply the plants and associated products too. His book *The Water Gardener* was published last year. See also the Nurseries section.

Anthony George & Associates

The Old Brick House, Village Road, Dorney, Windsor, Berkshire SL4 6QJ
☎ 0628 604224   📠 0628 604401

CONTACT Anthony George
WORKING AREA London, Midlands & Southern England
ASSOCIATIONS ALI; FRSA
OTHER SERVICES Horticultural consultancy; arboricultural services; architectural consultants
STARTED TRADING 1982

Architectural consultants, planners and landscape architects.

Anthony Short & Partners

34 Church Street, Ashbourne, Derbyshire DE6 1AE
☎ 0335 342345   📠 0335 300624

CONTACT Anthony Short
WORKING AREA 50 mile radius
ASSOCIATIONS ALI; RIBA
STARTED TRADING 1966

Architectural and landscape architectural practice.

Anthos Design

47 Bennerley Road, London SW11 6DR
☎ 071 228 2288   📠 071 978 4148

CONTACT Ian David Dougill
WORKING AREA South east England
ASSOCIATIONS ALI
STARTED TRADING 1976
PROJECTS Design and build projects for gardens in Greater London

Landscape architects.

Antony Young

Ridleys Cheer, Mountain Bower, Chippenham, Wiltshire SN14 7AJ
☎ 0225 891204   📠 0225 891139

CONTACT Antony Young
WORKING AREA UK & Europe
OTHER SERVICES Horticultural consultancy
STARTED TRADING 1990
PROJECTS Extensive new gardens at Ozleworth Park, Gloucestershire, including an arboretum and rose, herb and parterre gardens

Apple Court, Hampshire

For full details see Nurseries section

Architectural Landscape Design Ltd

3 – 5 Kelsey Road, Beckenham, Kent BR3 2LH
☎ 081 658 4455   📠 081 658 2785

CONTACT Chris Coope
WORKING AREA One hour's drive from M25
ASSOCIATIONS BALI
OTHER SERVICES Landscape contractors; irrigation systems
STARTED TRADING 1978
PROJECTS Design and installation of irrigation system at the Tower of London

Complete landscape service from site clearance through to design, planting and construction. Suppliers and installers of Toro sprinkler systems.

Arena Landscapes

50 Grove Hill, Caversham, Reading, Berkshire
RG4 8PR
☎ 0734 475315

CONTACT   Ray Wingrove
WORKING AREA   Berkshire & South Oxfordshire
ASSOCIATIONS   BALI
OTHER SERVICES   Landscape contractors
STARTED TRADING   1988

A small business specialising in garden construction
and maintenance.

Arne Herbs, Avon

For full details see Nurseries section

Arrow Tree Services

See Arboricultural Services section

Artscapes & Theseus Maze Designs

Silk Mill House, 24 Winchester Street, Whitchurch,
Hampshire RG28 7DD
☎ 0256 892837   ☎ 0256 892837

CONTACT   Graham Burgess
WORKING AREA   UK & overseas
OTHER SERVICES   Horticultural consultancy; land-
scape contractors; water and riparian services; maze
and labyrinth design
STARTED TRADING   1981
PROJECTS   Rose maze parterre at Longleat House,
Wiltshire; a country garden in Berkshire; an Eritrean
hill for Christian Aid at Hampton Court, 1993

Kew-trained garden designer whose work includes
symbolic and historic designs, with a special expertise
in mazes. See also Nine Springs Nursery, Hampshire in
Nurseries section.

ASH Consulting Group

21 Carlton Court, Glasgow, Strathclyde G5 9JP
☎ 041 420 3131

CONTACT   Ross Anderson
WORKING AREA   UK & overseas
ASSOCIATIONS   ALI
OTHER SERVICES   Arboricultural services; urban fore-
stry

Substantial landscape design and planning group
formed by the merger of ASH and Cousins Stephens.
There are other branches in Scotland and England. The
practice includes landscape architects, ecologists, fore-
sters, town planners, environmental scientists and
economists.

Auldene Nurseries Ltd, Lancashire

For full details see Nurseries section

Aylett Nurseries Ltd, Hertfordshire

For full details see Nurseries section

Baronscourt Nurseries, Co. Tyrone

For full details see Nurseries section

Barton Grange Landscapes, Lancashire

For full details see Barton Grange Garden Centre
(Preston), Lancashire in Nurseries section

Beechcroft Nurseries, Cumbria

For full details see Nurseries section

Berrys Garden Company Ltd

6 Hodford Road, London NW11 8NP
☎ 081 209 0194   FAX 081 458 6442

CONTACT   Brian Berry
WORKING AREA   Buckinghamshire, Hertfordshire,
Middlesex & north of the Thames
ASSOCIATIONS   BALI
OTHER SERVICES   Horticultural consultancy; land-
scape contractors
STARTED TRADING   1980
PROJECTS   Rhyl School, and numerous large domestic
gardens

Landscape design and build, including garden electrics,
carpentry, and irrigation and drainage.

Birkheads Cottage Garden Nursery, Tyne & Wear

For full details see Nurseries section

Blairhoyle Nursery, Central

For full details see Nurseries section

Bonita Bulaitis

6 Watton Road, Ware, Hertfordshire SG12 0AA
☎ 0920 466466

CONTACT   Bonita Bulaitis
WORKING AREA   UK & Europe
STARTED TRADING   1987
PROJECTS   Three acre garden from a green field site;
contemporary show garden including furniture

Trained in garden design and now studying for a Landscape Architecture degree. Specialities include low
maintenance gardens with bulbs and perennials, and
contemporary garden furniture and structures to her
own design.

Boonwood Garden Centre, Cumbria

For full details see Nurseries section

The Botanic Nursery, Wiltshire
For full details see Nurseries section

brambles
126 Winford Drive, Broxbourne, Hertfordshire
EN10 6PW
☎ 0992 469825/ 0836 587797 📠 0992 451579

CONTACT Richard Baxter
WORKING AREA Nationwide
ASSOCIATIONS BALI
OTHER SERVICES Landscape contractors; water and
riparian services
STARTED TRADING 1982
PROJECTS Four Chelsea Gold medals, and the Fiskars
Sword of Excellence for best garden in show, 1993

Garden services carried out by directly employed
workforce. Experienced in all types of hard and soft
landscaping: they emphasise clean work and attention
to detail.

Brent Surveys & Designs
158a Edenvale Road, Westbury, Wiltshire
BA13 3QG
☎ 0373 827331 📠 0373 777148

CONTACT Mike Osborne
WORKING AREA Nationwide
OTHER SERVICES Horticultural consultancy; land-
scape contractors
STARTED TRADING 1985

Garden design, surveys and construction. Husband and
wife team combine design and estate management experience. The business is based on a postal service:
design and planting plans are created from your sketch,
photographs and soil test. Other services available if
required.

Bressingham Landscapes, Design &
Build, Norfolk
For full details see Bressingham Plant Centre,
Norfolk in Nurseries section

Broadstone Nurseries, Oxfordshire
For full details see Nurseries section

Bunny Guinness
Sibberton Lodge, Thornhaugh, Peterborough,
Cambridgeshire PE8 6NH
☎ 0780 782518

CONTACT Bunny Guinness
WORKING AREA England
ASSOCIATIONS ALI

OTHER SERVICES Horticultural consultancy; arbori-
cultural services; water and riparian services; planning
appeals and public enquiries
STARTED TRADING 1985
PROJECTS Gardens for Stapleford Park Hotel, Melton
Mowbray

Wide experience in public and private practice. Commissions can be phased over several years and an initial
free consultation is offered.

Bybrook Barn Garden & Produce
Centre, Kent
For full details see Nurseries section

Bypass Nurseries, Essex
For full details see Nurseries section

Byrkley Park Centre, Staffordshire
For full details see Nurseries section

Cabbages & Kings
Wilderness Farm, Wilderness Lane, Hadlow Down,
East Sussex TN22 4HU
☎ 0825 830552 📠 0825 830736

CONTACT Andrew or Ryl Nowell
WORKING AREA UK & overseas (design); 100 mile
radius (planting)
ASSOCIATIONS SGD
OTHER SERVICES Horticultural consultancy
STARTED TRADING 1989
PROJECTS Cottage garden for BBC TV's Front Gar-
dens, 1993

Over 30 years experience designing gardens. For local
projects they will supply and plant too. Demonstration
garden open under the National Gardens Scheme, and
for clients by appointment.

Carol Messham
41 Feversham Drive, Kirbymoorside, York, North
Yorkshire YO6 6DH
☎ 0751 432071

CONTACT Carol Messham
WORKING AREA Cheshire, Yorkshire and north west
England
OTHER SERVICES Horticultural consultancy
STARTED TRADING 1988
PROJECTS Private gardens including a small courtyard
in Malton, and a 3½ acre garden at Horwich

Landscape architect and garden design consultant. Services include postal design and supervision of contractors: maintenance schedules are included with all plans.
Before setting up on her own Carol Messham worked
with David Stevens.

Caves Folly Nurseries, Hereford & Worcester

For full details see Nurseries section

Cecily Hazell Garden Design

14 Brudenell Road, London SW17 8DA
☎ 081 767 2380

CONTACT Cecily Hazell
WORKING AREA UK & overseas
OTHER SERVICES Horticultural consultancy; landscape contractors; dried flower and interior decoration
STARTED TRADING 1992
PROJECTS Large gardens in Sussex and Cheshire; garden incorporating an air raid shelter in Aberdeen

Trained at the Kew School of Garden Design. Tackles projects from large country gardens to windowboxes.

Chenies Landscapes Limited

Bramble Lane, London Road East, Amersham, Buckinghamshire HP7 9DH
☎ 0494 728004   ☎ 0494 721403

CONTACT Neil Denton or Brian Toms
WORKING AREA London, south east England & south Midlands
ASSOCIATIONS BALI
OTHER SERVICES Landscape contractors; arboricultural services; interior landscapes
STARTED TRADING 1961
PROJECTS Gold medal, Chelsea Flower Show 1992, for constructing Fisons' garden

A large firm with specialist construction, maintenance and landscape architecture divisions. Chenies Interiorscape designs and maintains interior schemes, and the group also owns a garden centre and a horticultural machinery outlet.

Chris Burnett Associates

New Russia Hall, Tattenhall, Chester, Cheshire CH3 9AH
☎ 0829 71241   ☎ 0829 71152

CONTACT Chris Burnett
WORKING AREA Nationwide
ASSOCIATIONS ALI
STARTED TRADING 1984
PROJECTS Large private garden in Oxfordshire; new deer park in Cheshire

Landscape architects.

Clonmel Garden Centre, Co. Tipperary

For full details see Nurseries section

Colson Stone Partnership

2 Calico House, Clove Hitch Quay, Plantation Wharf, Battersea, London SW11 3TN
☎ 071 924 3257   ☎ 071 978 5220

CONTACT Richard Stone
WORKING AREA Southern England
ASSOCIATIONS ALI
OTHER SERVICES Horticultural consultancy; arboricultural services
STARTED TRADING 1989

Landscape architects with experience of work on historic parks and gardens.

Colvin & Moggridge

Filkins, Lechlade, Gloucestershire GL7 3JQ
☎ 0367 860225   ☎ 0367 860564

CONTACT David McQuitty
WORKING AREA UK & overseas
ASSOCIATIONS ALI; FIHort
STARTED TRADING 1922
PROJECTS Landscape consultants to Central London Royal Parks; masterplan and replanting at Blenheim Park

Landscape consultancy which provides a full range of landscape planning and design services for up to very large scale landscapes. Experienced in designing public and private gardens of all sizes. The late Brenda Colvin's firm.

Compton & Compton

Coombe Cottage, Hanging Langford, Salisbury, Wiltshire SP3 4NW
☎ 0722 790436

CONTACT Tania or James Compton
WORKING AREA UK & overseas
OTHER SERVICES Horticultural consultancy
STARTED TRADING 1990

James Compton is Kew-trained; was head gardener at the Chelsea Physic; taught at the English Gardening School; author of books and many articles; plant collector (in Mexico, S Africa & Korea); advises on suitable plants for gardens. Tania Compton trained at the English Gardening School; gained experience with Rosemary Verey; advises on design and garden style.

Conservatory Gardens

17 Hartington Road, Chiswick, London W4 3TL
☎ 081 994 6109   ☎ 081 547 8241

CONTACT Joan Phelan
WORKING AREA Nationwide
OTHER SERVICES Horticultural consultancy
STARTED TRADING 1991

PROJECTS Conservatory planting at the Hurlingham Club

Help on all aspects of conservatory plants and planting design from a botanist and garden designer team. Pre-building advice and schemes for small gardens are also available, as is a postal service.

Cottage Garden Plants, Dorset
For full details see Nurseries section

Cottage Nurseries, Lincolnshire
For full details see Nurseries section

Courtyard Garden Design
26 Algar Road, Old Isleworth, London TW7 7AG
☎ 081 568 5263   📠 081 568 5263
CONTACT Sally Court
WORKING AREA UK & overseas
STARTED TRADING 1989
PROJECTS Consultancy for the restoration of a 40 acre listed garden

Diploma from the Inchbald School of Design. Service includes advice on specific problems, design and planting plans, and the supervision of their installation. Sally Court has won awards at Hampton Court, and also writes and lectures on garden design and history.

Crowther Landscapes
Ongar Road, Abridge, Essex RM4 1AA
☎ 0708 688581   📠 0708 688677
CONTACT Ross Minterne
WORKING AREA East Anglia, home counties & London
ASSOCIATIONS BALI
OTHER SERVICES Horticultural consultancy; landscape contractors
STARTED TRADING 1966

Complete landscape service including design and maintenance and irrigation. Crowthers has a retail nursery in Essex and another landscape company, Crowther Paysages, at Le Rayol Canadel in the South of France (contact Richard Snell: 010 33 94 05 51 91).

D Wells Landscaping
The Cottage, 15 Park Avenue, Eastbourne, East Sussex BN21 2XG
☎ 0323 502073
CONTACT D. Wells
WORKING AREA 50 mile radius
ASSOCIATIONS BALI
OTHER SERVICES Landscape contractors
STARTED TRADING 1970
PROJECTS St Wilfrid's Hospice, Eastbourne, and work on a BBC TV set

Landscape firm which specialises in water gardens and natural stonework.

Dagenham Landscapes Ltd
Redcrofts Farm, Ockendon Road, Upminster, Essex RM14 2DJ
☎ 0708 222379
CONTACT Colin Byrne
WORKING AREA Essex & North London
ASSOCIATIONS BALI
OTHER SERVICES Landscape contractors; turf suppliers
STARTED TRADING 1968

Garden design and landscape construction service. They also undertake garden maintenance for private and commercial customers, install swimming pools and supply grassland turf.

Daisy Hill Nurseries Ltd, Co. Down
For full details see Nurseries section

David Brown Landscape Design
10 College Road, Impington, Cambridge, Cambridgeshire CB4 4PD
☎ 0223 232366
CONTACT David Brown
WORKING AREA Nationwide
ASSOCIATIONS ALI; MIHort
OTHER SERVICES Horticultural consultancy; arboricultural services
STARTED TRADING 1988
PROJECTS Vision Park, Cambridge and Lucy Cavendish College, Cambridge

Landscape architects whose work ranges from business parks to garden design. Experienced at tree and vegetation surveys, and can undertake historical research and expert witness work.

David Ireland Landscape Architect
Thames Sailing Barge 'Scone', City Harbour, Off East Ferry Road, Isle of Dogs, London E14 9TF
☎ 071 515 8826   📠 071 515 8826
CONTACT David Ireland
WORKING AREA London, home counties & nationwide
ASSOCIATIONS ALI
OTHER SERVICES Horticultural consultancy; landscape contractors; arboricultural services
STARTED TRADING 1991
PROJECTS 17 acre private garden in Hertfordshire; restoration of ancient woodland in Derby; redesign of two London squares

Landscape architect. Working on his own since 1991 offering consultancy and design and build services for domestic gardens and commercial landscapes. Based in London, his work includes small town gardens.

David Stevens International Ltd
Stowe Castle Business Park, Stowe,
Buckinghamshire MK18 5AB
☎ 0280 821097   📠 0280 821150

CONTACT Verna Stewart
WORKING AREA UK & overseas
ASSOCIATIONS SGD; FIHORT
OTHER SERVICES Horticultural consultancy; landscape contractors; arboricultural services; shows consultancy; video and film; product franchising
STARTED TRADING 1972
PROJECTS 10 Gold medals at the Chelsea Flower Show

Undertakes domestic and commercial work all over the UK and abroad. David Stevens is one of the country's best known garden designers, and has recently been appointed professor of garden design at Middlesex University. He is also a broadcaster and writer.

Diana Eldon, Garden Designer
27 Parsons Lane, Bierton, Aylesbury,
Buckinghamshire HP22 5DF
☎ 0296 24138

CONTACT Diana Eldon
WORKING AREA 30 mile radius
ASSOCIATIONS SGD
STARTED TRADING 1991

Large or small scale garden design, which aims to be innovative and appropriate to the house. Will design trellis, screens and gateways and can produce an artist's impression of the finished garden if required.

Designing with Plants, Essex
For full details see Trevor Scott Ornamental Grasses, Essex in Nurseries section

Dolwin & Gray
See Arboricultural Services section

Donaghadee Garden Centre, Co. Down
For full details see Nurseries section

Dream Gardens
Ings Gate, Flaxman Croft, Copmanthorpe, York,
North Yorkshire YO2 3TU
☎ 0904 703833

CONTACT Keith James
WORKING AREA UK & overseas
OTHER SERVICES Horticultural consultancy

STARTED TRADING 1992
PROJECTS Restoration of 16th century garden in Yorkshire dales

Trained in garden design. Specialities include period garden restoration and country house gardens. Handles a wide range of other work including interior landscaping.

Duncan Heather
Heathers of Henley, 34 Kings Road, Henley on Thames, Oxfordshire RG9 2DG
☎ 0491 573577   📠 0491 411161

CONTACT Duncan Heather
WORKING AREA Nationwide
OTHER SERVICES Landscape contractors; garden design courses
STARTED TRADING 1987
PROJECTS Gold medallist at Hampton Court

Duncan Heather is also the director of the Oxford College of Garden Design.

Dobbies Landscape Ltd, Lothian
For full details see Dobbie & Co Ltd in Nurseries section

Eachus Huckson
7 Church Street, Kidderminster, Hereford & Worcester DY10 2AD
☎ 0562 825825   📠 0562 829860

CONTACT Andrew Huckson
ASSOCIATIONS ALI
OTHER SERVICES Horticultural consultancy; arboricultural services
STARTED TRADING 1981

Landscape architects.

Eastern Landscape Service
See Arboricultural Services section

Elaine Horne
Newfield Cottage, Firbank, Sedbergh, Cumbria
LA10 5EN
☎ 05396 20621

CONTACT Elaine Horne
WORKING AREA North west England
OTHER SERVICES Horticultural consultancy; design courses
STARTED TRADING 1988

Trained in landscape design, with experience at Kew and Harlow Carr. She specialises in low maintenance gardens, and also runs design and planting courses.

Elizabeth Banks Associates Ltd
13 Abercorn Place, London NW8 9EA
☎ 071 624 5740   **FAX** 071 372 0964

CONTACT Mrs Elizabeth Banks
WORKING AREA UK & overseas
ASSOCIATIONS ALI; AIHort
OTHER SERVICES Horticultural consultancy
STARTED TRADING 1987
PROJECTS Work includes Hampton Court Palace,
RHS Rosemoor, Devon, and British Embassy, Paris

Landscape practice which has made a name for its work
on historical restoration projects. Also active in designing new gardens and advising on land use and garden
management. Its varied and impressive client list is
matched by EBA's well-qualified personnel, including
director Tom Stuart-Smith (ALI), and Dr Todd Long-
staffe Gowan.

Elizabeth Whateley
48 Glossop Road, Sanderstead, South Croydon,
Surrey CR2 0PU
☎ 081 651 0226

CONTACT Elizabeth Whateley
WORKING AREA Kent, London, Surrey & Sussex
ASSOCIATIONS SGD
STARTED TRADING 1986
PROJECTS Town garden in Clapham; country garden
in Maidstone

A full garden design service, including surveys, plans,
landscaping and planting. Elizabeth Whateley supervises any contractors, and can provide maintenance
schedules and a follow up consultancy visit when required.

Endsleigh Garden Centre, Devon
For full details see Nurseries section

Euro Tree Service
See Arboricultural Services section

Ferndale Nursery and Garden Centre Ltd, South Yorkshire
For full details see Nurseries section

FFC Landscape Architects/ The Garden Design Studio
Birch House, 25 Birch Terrace, Hanley, Stoke on
Trent, Staffordshire ST1 3JN
☎ 0782 283272   **FAX** 0782 283272

CONTACT Francis Colella
WORKING AREA Midlands & north west England
ASSOCIATIONS ALI
STARTED TRADING 1986

PROJECTS Housing Association projects and private
and commercial garden schemes

Landscape architects and garden designers providing
design services, expert witnesses and design consultancy.

Fiona Harrison
23 Course Side, Ascot, Berkshire SL5 7HH
☎ 0344 24543   **FAX** 0344 873505

CONTACT Fiona Harrison
WORKING AREA 50 mile radius
ASSOCIATIONS SGD
OTHER SERVICES Horticultural consultancy
STARTED TRADING 1992

Degree in horticulture, and design course at Pershore.
Carries out garden and landscape design, mostly for
private clients.

FMG Garden Designs
21 Crescent Gardens, London SW19 8AJ
☎ 081 879 3168

CONTACT Nilla Gallanzi
WORKING AREA London & home counties
OTHER SERVICES Horticultural consultancy; land-
scape contractors
PROJECTS Restoration of borders at The Old Rectory,
Wimbledon

Trained in garden design. Creates and supervises the
construction and maintenance of gardens with a special
expertise in perennial borders.

The Fruit Garden, Kent
For full details see Nurseries section

Garden Scents, Suffolk
For full details see Paradise Centre, Suffolk in
Nurseries section

Garden Solutions by Design
43 Park Drive North, Mirfield, West Yorkshire
WF14 9NJ
☎ 0924 495584

CONTACT John Wilson or Elizabeth Wilson
WORKING AREA Lancashire, Yorkshire, Isle of Man
OTHER SERVICES Horticultural consultancy; land-
scape contractors
STARTED TRADING 1992
PROJECTS Garden research for Channel 4's *Gardens
without Borders*

Trained in landscape and horticultural technology.
They provide a full service from design through to
implementation.

Gardens by Graham Evans
20 Grandfield Avenue, Radcliffe on Trent,
Nottinghamshire NG12 1AL
☎ 0602 335737

CONTACT   Graham Evans
WORKING AREA   East Midlands
ASSOCIATIONS   BALI
OTHER SERVICES   Landscape contractors
STARTED TRADING   1986

Garden design and construction.

Gardens of Distinction
The Old Canal Building, East Challow, Wantage,
Oxfordshire OX12 9SY
☎ 0235 769532   ☏ 0235 770040

CONTACT   Michael Branch
WORKING AREA   Central, southern & northern UK
ASSOCIATIONS   ALI
OTHER SERVICES   Horticultural consultancy
STARTED TRADING   1968
PROJECTS   Garden court at Channel 4's new Pimlico
headquarters

Landscape practice with over 25 years of garden design
for private and public clients. Service ranges from horticultural advice to full design. There is a new sub-office
in Warrington (0925 36855).

Gardenscape
Fairview, Smelthouses, Summerbridge, Harrogate,
North Yorkshire HG3 4DH
☎ 0423 780291

CONTACT   Michael D. Myers
ASSOCIATIONS   MIHort
OTHER SERVICES   Horticultural consultancy; land-
scape contractors
STARTED TRADING   1993

Garden maintenance and design, as well as horticultural
consultancy for ornamentals. Michael Myers also holds
three NCCPG national collections, runs a mail order
nursery, and opens his garden for the NGS and
NCCPG. See also Nurseries section.

Geoffrey Coombs
47 Larcombe Road, Petersfield, Hampshire
GU32 3LS
☎ 0730 267417

CONTACT   Geoffrey Coombs
WORKING AREA   30 mile radius
ASSOCIATIONS   SGD
OTHER SERVICES   Horticultural consultancy; botanic
art

Formerly garden adviser for the RHS at Vincent
Square, now retired. Garden design and consultancy:
the latter specialises in trees, shrubs and hardy plants.

Gillian Temple Associates
15 Woodside Avenue, Weston Green, Esher, Surrey
KT10 8JQ
☎ 081 339 0323   ☏ 081 339 0335

CONTACT   Gillian Temple
WORKING AREA   UK & overseas
ASSOCIATIONS   SGD; MIHort
OTHER SERVICES   Horticultural consultancy
STARTED TRADING   1991
PROJECTS   Two large private estates; a London roof
garden; Mediterranean villa development

Landscape and garden design for both private and
commercial clients. Special expertise in interior design
projects.

Goscote Nurseries Ltd, Leicestershire
For full details see Nurseries section

Grace Landscapes Ltd
Knowl Road, Mirfield, West Yorkshire WF19 9UU
☎ 0924 492645   ☏ 0924 480518

CONTACT   Tim Grace or Hugh Pawsey
WORKING AREA   Midlands & northern England
ASSOCIATIONS   BALI
OTHER SERVICES   Landscape contractors
PROJECTS   Design and maintenance at the Arlington
Business Centre, Leeds and work for the National
Rivers Authority at Fenay Beck, Huddersfield

Specialists in design and build contracts for both the
commercial and the domestic garden sectors.

Graham A Pavey & Associates
11 Princes Road, Bromham, Bedfordshire
MK43 8QD
☎ 0243 823860

CONTACT   Chris or Graham Pavey
WORKING AREA   Nationwide
STARTED TRADING   1988
PROJECTS   Courtyard garden at Bedford Hospital; gar-
den of remembrance at St Mark's Church, Bedford

Trained at the English Gardening School. Services include garden and landscape design, planting plans and
advice. In addition to a comprehensive service, they
offer special design packages for smaller gardens.

Graham King Treecare
See Arboricultural Services section

Green Man Landscapes

The Pines, 18 Church Close, Whittlesford,
Cambridgeshire CB2 4NY
☎ 0223 832725

CONTACT Michael or Ann Hood
WORKING AREA East Anglia & Hertfordshire
ASSOCIATIONS BALI; AIHort
OTHER SERVICES Landscape contractors
STARTED TRADING 1982

Small firm specialising in soft landscaping and maintenance by knowledgeable plantsmen.

Green Stock

Church Hill, Pinhoe, Exeter, Devon EX4 9JG
☎ 0392 462988　　📠 0392 462977

CONTACT D. G. Stevenson
WORKING AREA Devon
ASSOCIATIONS BALI
OTHER SERVICES Landscape contractors; water and
riparian services
STARTED TRADING 1984
PROJECTS BALI National Soft Landscaping Premier
Award, 1992

Design, construction and maintenance of gardens, parks
and offices for private and commercial clients.

Greenstone Gardens

14 William Dromey Court, Dyne Road, London
NW6 7XD
☎ 071 625 5347/0831 372 734

CONTACT Christine Drummond
WORKING AREA London & home counties
STARTED TRADING 1989
PROJECTS Exhibited at Chelsea Flower Show and
Hampton Court.

Unique design and construction service by women.

Ground Control Ltd

Ardmore House, London Road, Billericay, Essex
CM12 9HS
☎ 0277 650697/ 081 534 1466　　📠 0277 630746

CONTACT Mr S. Harrod
WORKING AREA 100 mile radius
ASSOCIATIONS BALI
OTHER SERVICES Horticultural consultancy; landscape contractors
STARTED TRADING 1976
PROJECTS BALI award winners in 1993 for work at
the Tower of London

Landscape design and contractors: the firm has an
annual turnover in excess of £1m.

Hambrook Landscapes Ltd

Wangfield Lane, Curdridge, Southampton,
Hampshire S03 2DA
☎ 0489 780505　　📠 0489 785396

CONTACT Norman Hambrook
WORKING AREA South Hampshire
ASSOCIATIONS BALI
OTHER SERVICES Horticultural consultancy; landscape contractors; water and riparian services
STARTED TRADING 1969
PROJECTS Show gardens at their garden centre

Landscaping and maintenance for private and commercial customers, carried out by full time professionals.
Their garden centre is at 135 Southampton Road, Titchfield, Fareham, Hampshire PO14 4PR.

Hardy's Cottage Garden Plants, Hampshire

For full details see Nurseries section

Hazel M. Huddleston, Northumberland

For full details see Northumbria Nurseries,
Northumberland in Nurseries section

Hayes Gardenworld, Cumbria

For full details see Nurseries section

Heath Garden

Heath Hill, Sheriffhales, Shifnal, Shropshire
TF11 8RR
☎ 0952 691341

CONTACT Gordon Malt
WORKING AREA Shropshire, Staffordshire
ASSOCIATIONS MIHort
OTHER SERVICES Horticultural consultancy; landscape contractors; arboricultural services
STARTED TRADING 1989

Trained at RBG Edinburgh, with 25 years of varied
experience in horticulture. Comprehensive range of
services includes garden design, landscaping work and
tree and shrub care.

Heather Goldsmark Partnership

Swallowfield, Eastergate Lane, Eastergate,
Chichester, West Sussex PO20 6SJ
☎ 0243 543834　　📠 0243 543708

CONTACT Heather Goldsmark
WORKING AREA Midlands & southern England
ASSOCIATIONS ALI; MIHort
OTHER SERVICES Horticultural consultancy; landscape contractors
STARTED TRADING 1986

Landscape architects and horticultural consultants, handling design and build contracts, landscape planning advice and all forms of development work and horticultural and environmental consultancy.

Heighley Gate Garden Centre, Northumberland

For full details see Nurseries section

Helen Cahill

15 Richmond Bridge Mansions, Willoughby Road, East Twickenham, London TW1 2QJ
☎ 081 892 2652

CONTACT   Helen Cahill
WORKING AREA   Southern England
STARTED TRADING   1990

Trained at the College of Garden Design. Part of Seven Counties Garden Design.

Hillier Landscapes

Ampfield House, Ampfield, Romsey, Hampshire SO51 9PA
☎ 0794 368733   FAX 0794 368813

CONTACT   Richard Barnard
WORKING AREA   UK & overseas
ASSOCIATIONS   SGD; MIHort; BALI
OTHER SERVICES   Horticultural consultancy; landscape contractors
STARTED TRADING   1864
PROJECTS   Work at the Gothick Villa, Regents Park and for the Downland Housing Association

Landscape architects offering garden design, consultancy and commercial and industrial landscaping. Plants are supplied by their own nurseries. Construction and maintenance is also available in the Hillier heartlands of southern and western England.

Hollington Nurseries, Berkshire

For full details see Nurseries section

Hydon Nurseries, Surrey

For full details see Nurseries section

International Acers, Hereford & Worcester

For full details see Nurseries section

Jakobsen Landscape Architects

Mount Sorrel, West Approach Drive, Pittville, Cheltenham, Gloucestershire GL52 3AD
☎ 0242 241501   FAX 0242 520693

CONTACT   Preben Jakobsen
WORKING AREA   UK & Europe mainly
ASSOCIATIONS   ALI; SGD
OTHER SERVICES   Horticultural consultancy; water and riparian services
STARTED TRADING   1969
PROJECTS   The London Ark, Hammersmith

Landscape architects with a Kew-trained principal. The practice has won numerous awards for landscape, garden and urban design projects for public, commercial and private clients. Experienced in both historic restoration and modern design.

Jan Martinez

Everden Farmhouse, Alkham, Dover, Kent CT15 7EH
☎ 0303 893462

CONTACT   Jan Martinez
WORKING AREA   London & south east England mainly
OTHER SERVICES   Horticultural consultancy; arboricultural services; botanic art
STARTED TRADING   1968
PROJECTS   Landscaping at the Eastern Docks, Port of Dover, and work on a large Surrey garden.

Garden and commercial designer, now operating as a solo designer. All forms of exterior design undertaken, with additional qualifications and experience as an interior designer.

Jane Cordingley Landscape & Garden Design

Southlea, Rillington, Malton, North Yorkshire YO17 8LR
☎ 0944 758943

CONTACT   Jane Cordingley
WORKING AREA   Yorkshire

Jean Harman Garden Design

71 Frog Lane, West Overton, Marlborough, Wiltshire SN8 4ER
☎ 0672 861416

CONTACT   Jean Harman or Judith Woodget
WORKING AREA   Worldwide by post
STARTED TRADING   1982
PROJECTS   Large private garden from a green field, south west Ireland

Garden designer. Operates a special postal service: you supply a plan and photographs prepared to her instructions. Setting up her own garden design course.

Jeanne Paisley

Jacaranda, Wembury Park, Lingfield, Surrey
RH7 6HH
☎ 0342 832561

CONTACT Jeanne Paisley
WORKING AREA Southern England
STARTED TRADING 1990

Trained at the College of Garden Design. Part of Seven Counties Garden Design.

Jill Billington Garden Design

100 Fox Lane, London N13 4AX
☎ 081 886 0898

CONTACT Jill Billington
WORKING AREA Nationwide
ASSOCIATIONS SGD
STARTED TRADING 1983

Degree in Fine Art (sculpture). Has designed at Chelsea, and also teaches and lectures on gardens. Her book on small gardens is due out this year.

Joanna Stay Garden Design & Consultancy

67 Dalton Street, St Albans, Hertfordshire AL3 5QH
☎ 0727 869765

CONTACT Joanna Stay
WORKING AREA Home counties; nationwide & overseas
ASSOCIATIONS SGD
OTHER SERVICES Horticultural consultancy
STARTED TRADING 1981
PROJECTS Modern sunken garden

Trained at Pershore and Oaklands College. Joanna Stay won a Hampton Court Tudor Rose award in 1991.

John A Davies Landscape Consultants

Fernhill Lodge, Llechryd, Cardigan, Dyfed SA43 2QL
☎ 0239 87861   ⊠ 0239 621004

CONTACT John A. Davies
WORKING AREA International
ASSOCIATIONS SGD; MIHort
OTHER SERVICES Horticultural consultancy
STARTED TRADING 1959
PROJECTS Recent work includes the Saudi Arabian embassy and the Umm Al Nassan Park in Bahrain. Currently working on the Jiddah Island development for the Bahrain Ministry of Housing

Chelsea gold medallists. Landscape and garden designers with a subsidiary office in Bahrain, working for private and corporate clients. Bahrain address: Flat 41, Building 437; Road 1805, Area 318; Manama, Bahrain. (010 973 290056).

John A Ford Landscape Architects

8 Church Road, Trull, Taunton, Somerset TA3 7LG
☎ 0823 279817

CONTACT Mr J. A. Ford (Principal)
WORKING AREA UK & overseas
ASSOCIATIONS ALI
STARTED TRADING 1981
PROJECTS Exeter Hospice, and various private gardens.

Landscape architects, working from the South West, but also nationally and overseas. Large and small landscape projects undertaken, including individual gardens. John Ford also teaches and lectures.

John B Rickell

12 College Lane, Apley Park, Wellington, Telford, Shropshire TF1 3DH
☎ 0952 249935

CONTACT John B. Rickell
WORKING AREA Nationwide
ASSOCIATIONS MIHort
OTHER SERVICES Horticultural consultancy
STARTED TRADING 1982
PROJECTS Design of a Victorian estate in Staffordshire

Wisley-trained designer and horticultural consultant. Many years experience including as landscape manager for Telford New Town. His expertise includes wild gardens. Independent professional witness.

John Brookes, Landscape Designer

Clock House, Denmans, Fontwell, Arundel, West Sussex BN18 0SU
☎ 0243 542808   ⊠ 0243 544064

CONTACT John Brookes or Michael Zinn
WORKING AREA UK and overseas

One of the country's best known garden designers. They aim to work with you rather than for you. The practice covers a full service, including specifications and implementation. John Brookes also teaches landscape and garden design, and writes and lectures on the subject.

John H Lucas & Associates

Lansdowne House, 320 Chessington Road, West Ewell, Surrey KT19 9XG
☎ 081 393 9946

CONTACT John Lucas
WORKING AREA Nationwide
ASSOCIATIONS SGD; AIHort; FIDiagE

OTHER SERVICES Horticultural consultancy
STARTED TRADING 1976
PROJECTS Silver medal for Water Conservation Garden at Hampton Court

Provides a landscape and garden design service, and will oversee contractors' work. A postal service is also offered. John Lucas writes and lectures on gardening topics, and his *Low-Water Gardening* was published last year by Dent.

John Medhurst Landscape Consultant
77 Harold Road, Upper Norwood, London SE19 3SP
☎ 081 653 0921

CONTACT John Medhurst
WORKING AREA London & south east England
ASSOCIATIONS ALI; MIHort
STARTED TRADING 1981

Trained in horticulture and conservation, as well as landscape design. Worked for the GLC Architect's department, and is the landscape design tutor at RBG Kew. Offers a complete service for private and public projects of all sizes.

John Moreland
Higher Trevarthen, Sancreed, Penzance, Cornwall TR20 8QY
☎ 0736 788993

CONTACT John Moreland
WORKING AREA Southern England
ASSOCIATIONS SGD
STARTED TRADING 1970
PROJECTS Chelsea gold medal gardens; de Savary's Land's End Project.

Landscape architect and garden designer: works in Britain and abroad on large and small gardens in modern or traditional styles.

Josephine Hindle, Designer and Gardener
11 Beechfield, Newton Tony, Salisbury, Wiltshire SP4 0HQ
☎ 0980 64323

CONTACT Josephine Hindle
OTHER SERVICES Landscape contractors
STARTED TRADING 1992

Trained at the English Gardening School. Garden designer with a fine arts degree: also does consultancy and maintenance work.

Joy Jardine, Garden Designer
Heath House, Alldens Lane, Munstead, Godalming, Surrey GU8 4AP
☎ 0483 416961

CONTACT Joy Jardine
WORKING AREA Hampshire, Surrey, Sussex
STARTED TRADING 1989
PROJECTS Research and restoration of a Jekyll/Lutyens garden in West Surrey; new formal gardens for an eighteenth century manor house

Garden design, including planting plans, maintenance schedules and project supervision.

Judith Walton
The Corner House, Foxcombe Lane, Boars Hill, Oxford, Oxfordshire OX1 5DH
☎ 0865 735179

CONTACT Judith Walton
WORKING AREA Southern England
STARTED TRADING 1990

Trained at the College of Garden Design. Part of Seven Counties Garden Design.

Judy's Country Garden, Lincolnshire
For full details see Nurseries section

Julia Fogg Garden Design
St Osyth's, Parsons Fee, Aylesbury, Buckinghamshire HP20 2QZ
☎ 0296 87502; 0850 381730 ☒ 0296 392825

CONTACT Julia Fogg
WORKING AREA UK & Europe
OTHER SERVICES Horticultural consultancy
STARTED TRADING 1989
PROJECTS Town and family gardens; restoring neglected estates; private sculpture park

Design diplomas. Complete garden design service from survey and planting plans through to overall project management. Also carries out commercial and consultancy work.

Julian Treyer-Evans
Magnolia House, 26 Cuckfield Road, Hurstpierpoint, West Sussex BN6 9SA
☎ 0273 834833   ☒ 0273 834833

CONTACT Julian Treyer-Evans
WORKING AREA Southern England & Australia
ASSOCIATIONS BALI
STARTED TRADING 1977
PROJECTS Gardens for the headquarters of The Body Shop International, and restoration of a large Federation garden in Freemantle, Western Australia

Garden and landscape designer. A Chelsea exhibitor since 1986, whose track record runs from courtyard gardens to golf courses. Carries out overall designs, but has a special taste for herbaceous planting schemes.

Karen Saynor
42 Raleigh Road, Richmond, Surrey TW9 2DX
☎ 081 940 2402

CONTACT   Karen Saynor
WORKING AREA   Southern England
STARTED TRADING   1990

Trained at the College of Garden Design. Part of Seven Counties Garden Design.

Katerina Georgi Landscape & Interior Design
187 Ashmore Road, London W9 3DB
☎ 081 969 2924

CONTACT   Katerina Georgi
WORKING AREA   London and South East; Europe
STARTED TRADING   1991
PROJECTS   Winner of 1992 Bradstone Design Award at Chelsea, for a walled garden

Specialises in integrated designs for interiors and exteriors, although they also do these elements separately. Complete service, including site supervision available when required.

Keepers Nursery, Kent
For full details see Nurseries section

Keith Banyard Tree Surgeons
See Arboricultural Services section

Kelways Nurseries Ltd, Somerset
For full details see Nurseries section

Ken Higginbotham Garden Landscaping
31 Elmfield, Chapel en le Frith, Stockport, Cheshire SK12 6TZ
☎ 0298 813051

CONTACT   K. R. Higginbotham
WORKING AREA   Cheshire, Peak District & south Manchester.
ASSOCIATIONS   BALI
OTHER SERVICES   Landscape contractors; arboricultural services
STARTED TRADING   1979
PROJECTS   1993 BALI award for private gardens in Chinley

Specialise in the design and construction of private gardens, patios and driveways. Experienced in working with difficult sites.

Kinlochlaich House Gardens, Strathclyde
For full details see Nurseries section

Landcare
28 Station Road, Holmfirth, Huddersfield, West Yorkshire HD7 1AB
☎ 0484 686462   📠 0484 688496

CONTACT   Matthew Corder
WORKING AREA   Midlands & Northern England
ASSOCIATIONS   ALI; ILAM
STARTED TRADING   1988

Landscape architects.

Landscape Centre
24 Donegore Hill, Dunadry, Co. Antrim BT41 2QU
☎ 0849 432175   📠 0849 432051

CONTACT   Kaye Campbell
WORKING AREA   Northern Ireland
ASSOCIATIONS   ALI
OTHER SERVICES   Horticultural consultancy; landscape contractors

Professional garden design team located on the same site as a garden centre. Services include consultancy and interior landscapes, and they also do commercial sites.

Landscape Design Studio
3 Hatton Mains Cottages, Dalmahoy, Kirknewton, Midlothian, Lothian EH27 8EB
☎ 031 333 1262

CONTACT   Lucy Eyers
WORKING AREA   Scotland and northern England
STARTED TRADING   1991

Qualified landscape architect: the practice offers landscape architecture and garden design. Postal service available throughout the UK.

Landscape Resource
See Arboricultural Services section

Landskip and Prospect
Talley, Llandeilo, Dyfed SA19 7YH
☎ 0558 685567   📠 0558 685745

CONTACT   Dr Andrew Sclater
WORKING AREA   UK and Europe
ASSOCIATIONS   ALI; MIHort
OTHER SERVICES   Horticultural consultancy; historical landscapes
STARTED TRADING   1987
PROJECTS   Survey and management plan for Culzean Country Park, National Trust for Scotland; many surveys for English Heritage

Specialists in garden and parkland improvement. They have an associated office in Belgium and have an international practice which includes aesthetic assessment, historical research and landscape management.

LDC Ltd
The Courtyard Offices, Hatchlands, East Clandon, Surrey GU4 7RT
☎ 0483 211616   FAX 0483 211548

CONTACT Bridget Purser
WORKING AREA Southern England
ASSOCIATIONS ALI; BALI
OTHER SERVICES Landscape contractors
STARTED TRADING 1983
PROJECTS Hurlingham Club, Fulham; The Deanery, Sonning; and for the National Trust at Hatchlands, Clandon

Specialist design and build service which is led, unusually, by landscape architects.

Lechlade Garden Centre, Gloucestershire
For full details see Nurseries section

Lennox-Boyd Landscape Design
45 Moreton Street, London SW1V 2NY
☎ 071 931 9995   FAX 071 821 6585

CONTACT Thelma Wrightson
WORKING AREA UK & Europe
STARTED TRADING 1971
PROJECTS Chelsea gold medal in 1993 for the *Daily Telegraph*

Undertakes projects of all sizes, including historical gardens. Equal emphasis on architectural design and planting. Arabella Lennox-Boyd is also a trustee of RBG Kew, a council member of the Painshill Park Trust, and has written books on traditional English gardens and London gardens.

Linda Fair – Garden Designer
29 Canons Close, Radlett, Hertfordshire WD7 7ER
☎ 0923 853391   FAX 0923 853391

CONTACT Linda Fair
WORKING AREA Buckinghamshire, North & West London, Hertfordshire
ASSOCIATIONS SGD
STARTED TRADING 1986

Lingard + Styles Landscape
Walpole House, 35 Walpole Street, London SW3 4QS
☎ 071 930 9233   FAX 071 930 9152

CONTACT Peter Styles
WORKING AREA UK, Ireland & Northern Europe
ASSOCIATIONS FLI; MIHort
OTHER SERVICES Horticultural consultancy; architects; architectural historians
STARTED TRADING 1976
PROJECTS Restoration of City garden for the Company of Drapers.

Landscape architects, planning and horticulture consultants. With a Kew-trained senior partner, this award-winning practice has a particular expertise in garden design. Other offices in Cardiff (0222 373140), Llandudno (0492 79892) and Newtown, Powys (0686 27600).

Longacre Nursery, Kent
For full details see Nurseries section

Longstock Park Nursery, Hampshire
For full details see Nurseries section

Lotus Landscapes
9 Beresford Close, Frimley Green, Camberley, Surrey GU16 6LB
☎ 0252 838665   FAX 0252 838665

CONTACT Christine Young
WORKING AREA Berkshire, Hampshire, London & Surrey
ASSOCIATIONS BALI
OTHER SERVICES Landscape contractors
STARTED TRADING 1974

Specialises in the design and construction of private gardens.

Louis Vincent Architectural Garden Designer
2 Ford Cottage, Mamhead Road, Kenton, Exeter, Devon EX6 8LY
☎ 0626 890926

CONTACT Louis Vincent or Anita de Visser
WORKING AREA South west England, Netherlands
OTHER SERVICES Horticultural consultancy
STARTED TRADING 1991

Can provide a full range of design and consultancy services, including fully illustrated plans and architecturally designed garden structures.

Marianne Ford Garden Designs
Manor Farm House, Hulcott, Aylesbury,
Buckinghamshire HP22 5AX
☎ 0296 394364 ☎ 0296 399007

CONTACT Marianne Ford
WORKING AREA Bedfordshire, Buckinghamshire,
Hertfordshire, London & Oxfordshire
ASSOCIATIONS SGD
STARTED TRADING 1987

Marina Adams Landscape Architects
3 Pembroke Studios, Pembroke Gardens, London
W8 6HX
☎ 071 602 5790

CONTACT Marina Adams
WORKING AREA UK & overseas
ASSOCIATIONS ALI
STARTED TRADING 1968

Landscape architect with projects in Britain, Europe,
Africa and the USA.

Mark Ross Landscape Architects
Royal Arcade, Broad Street, Pershore, Hereford &
Worcester WR10 1AG
☎ 0386 561321 ☎ 0386 561961

CONTACT Mark Ross
WORKING AREA England & Wales
ASSOCIATIONS ALI
OTHER SERVICES Horticultural consultancy; water
and riparian services; environmental assessment
STARTED TRADING 1990
PROJECTS Landscaping at the Three Counties Show-
ground, Malvern

Landscape architects and environmental assessors.

Mark Westcott Landscape Architects
14 Dufferin Street, London EC1Y 8PD
☎ 071 251 8789 ☎ 071 490 0102

CONTACT Mark Westcott or Angelos Wideson
WORKING AREA Nationwide
ASSOCIATIONS ALI; RIBA
OTHER SERVICES Horticultural consultancy; arbori-
cultural services; architecture
STARTED TRADING 1988
PROJECTS Wildlife and wetlands garden at Powergen
headquarters, Coventry

Architects and landscape architects with additional
experience of historic gardens work.

Martin Berkley Landscape Architects
40 Berkeley Street, Glasgow, Strathclyde G3 7DW
☎ 041 204 1855 ☎ 041 204 1813

CONTACT Martin Berkley
WORKING AREA Scotland
ASSOCIATIONS ALI; ARICS
STARTED TRADING 1980
PROJECTS M8 road corridor project

Landscape architects.

Mary Ann Lovegrove
Boarden House, Hawkenbury, Staplehurst, Kent
TN12 0EB
☎ 0580 893018

CONTACT Mary Ann Lovegrove
WORKING AREA Southern England
STARTED TRADING 1990

Trained at the College of Garden Design. Part of Seven
Counties Garden Design.

Mary-Jane Hopes, Garden Designer
218 West Malvern Road, West Malvern, Hereford
& Worcester WR14 4BA
☎ 0684 892533 ☎ 0684 892533

CONTACT Mary-Jane Hopes
WORKING AREA Nationwide
ASSOCIATIONS SGD; MIHort
OTHER SERVICES Horticultural consultancy
STARTED TRADING 1984
PROJECTS Essex Wynter Trust Garden, Newbury;
many private gardens

Trained at Pershore and Merrist Wood. Full design
service including survey, drawings and planting plans.
Can supervise contractors' work and also provides
consultancy advice. Specialities include organic and
wildlife gardens. Mary-Jane Hopes also writes and lectures.

Merriments Gardens, East Sussex
For full details see Nurseries section

Michael Ballam Design
66 Marchmont Road, Edinburgh, Lothian EH9 1HS
☎ 031 447 5089

CONTACT Michael Ballam
WORKING AREA Edinburgh and Scotland
STARTED TRADING 1991
PROJECTS Substantial private garden

Qualified landscape architect specialising in garden design. Services include a full survey and supervision of
site works.

Michael Littlewood Landscape Designer

Troutwells, Higher Hayne, Roadwater, Watchet, Somerset TA23 0RN
☎ 0984 41330   ℻ 0984 41330

CONTACT W. M. Littlewood
WORKING AREA UK & overseas
ASSOCIATIONS SGD; FLI
OTHER SERVICES Water and riparian services
PROJECTS Ecological forest gardens and landscapes

Landscape architect since 1960 in UK and New Zealand. Specialises in sustainable developments and permaculture design, including urban forestry. Author of landscaping reference books.

Mickfield Fish and Watergarden Centre, Suffolk

For full details see Nurseries section

Mill Race Landscapes Ltd, Essex

For full details see Mill Race Nursery, Essex in Nurseries section

Monkton Elm Garden Centre, Somerset

For full details see Nurseries section

Muckross Garden Centre, Co. Kerry

For full details see Nurseries section

Nareys Garden Centre, Suffolk

For full details see Nurseries section

Nicholas Roeber Landscapes

38 Wyatt Road, London N5 2JU
☎ 071 354 3762   ℻ 071 359 1996

CONTACT Nicholas Roeber
WORKING AREA London & home counties
OTHER SERVICES Horticultural consultancy
STARTED TRADING 1987
PROJECTS Courtyard for Richard Rogers

Provides a comprehensive design and construction service. The team has experience in all aspects of hard and soft landscaping.

Nigel Jeffries Landscapes

30 Yaverland Drive, Bagshot, Surrey GU19 5DX
☎ 0276 476365

CONTACT Nigel Jeffries
WORKING AREA South east England
ASSOCIATIONS BALI

OTHER SERVICES Landscape and design; landscape contractors
STARTED TRADING 1974

Nigel L Philips Landscape and Garden Design

18a Cliffe High Street, Lewes, East Sussex BN7 2AH
☎ 0273 474948   ℻ 0273 474948

CONTACT Nigel Philips
WORKING AREA Nationwide
ASSOCIATIONS SGD
OTHER SERVICES Horticultural consultancy; landscape contractors
STARTED TRADING 1982

Garden design service is offered nationwide. The landscaping service is restricted to the south and south east.

Noël Kingsbury

Sunbeam Nurseries, Frampton Cotterell, Avon BS17 2AU
☎ 0454 776926   ℻ 0272 245602

CONTACT Noël Kingsbury
WORKING AREA Southern England, south west Midlands
STARTED TRADING 1988
PROJECTS Experimental ecosystem plantings; 4 acre garden in the south of France.

Garden designer. Specialities include wildflower planting and habitat creation, herbaceous plantings and conservatories.

North Devon Garden Centre, Devon

For full details see Nurseries section

Nottcutts Landscapes

Ipswich Road, Woodbridge, Suffolk IP12 4AF
☎ 0394 383344
WORKING AREA See below
ASSOCIATIONS BALI
OTHER SERVICES Landscape contractors

There are four Nottcutts Landscape Centres, including the Woodbridge centre: between them they cover East Anglia, the South East and the West Midlands. All offer a full design and construction service. The other centres are at: Stratford Road, Shirley, Solihull, West Midlands B90 4EN (021 733 6201); Daniels Road, Norwich, Norfolk NR4 6QP (0603 54665); and Tonbridge Road, Pembury, Tunbridge Wells, Kent TN2 4QN (0892 823843).

O Lawson, Warwickshire

For full details see Bernhard's Rugby Garden & Leisure Centre, Warwickshire in Nurseries section

Oak Cottage Herb Garden, Shropshire
For full details see Nurseries section

Oakwood
See Arboricultural Services section

Orchard Nurseries, Lincolnshire
For full details see Nurseries section

Otter Nurseries Ltd, Devon
For full details see Nurseries section

Otter's Court Heathers, Somerset
For full details see Nurseries section

P H Kellett, Kent
For full details see Nurseries section

PMA Plant Specialities, Somerset
For full details see Nurseries section

P W Plants, Norfolk
For full details see Nurseries section

P W Milne Atkinson
Hemington House, Hemington, Derby, Derbyshire
DE74 2RB
☎ 0332 810295

CONTACT Mrs P. W. Milne Atkinson
WORKING AREA Midlands
ASSOCIATIONS FLI
STARTED TRADING 1955
PROJECTS Hospital developments and Business Parks

Landscape architecture practice with expertise in hospital developments, business parks, sports centres and estates. They can arrange and supervise landscape maintenance contracts.

Pantiles Plant & Garden Centre, Surrey
For full details see Nurseries section

Park Garden Centre, Avon
For full details see Nurseries section

Paul Miles
23 Seckford Street, Woodbridge, Suffolk IP12 4LY
☎ 0394 383771

CONTACT Paul Miles
WORKING AREA UK & overseas
ASSOCIATIONS MIHort
OTHER SERVICES Horticultural consultancy

STARTED TRADING 1979
PROJECTS Garden in Majorca; advising at Caserta Reggia, Italy and St Petersburg, Russia

Wisley-trained, but also worked for Ingwersen, Nottcutts Landscapes and the National Trust before going freelance. As well as design and consultancy, Paul Miles is an experienced photographer, writer and lecturer.

Paul Norton
6 Bayard Road, Weymouth, Dorset DT3 6AJ
☎ 0305 832511   FAX 0305 832511

CONTACT Paul Norton
WORKING AREA Southern England
ASSOCIATIONS ALI
STARTED TRADING 1990

Landscape architects offering design and management services, including historic landscape restoration.

Paul Temple Associates
24 Waldegrave Park, Twickenham, London
TW1 4TQ
☎ 081 744 0100   FAX 081 744 0104

CONTACT Paul Temple OBE
WORKING AREA UK & overseas
ASSOCIATIONS SGD; FIHort
OTHER SERVICES Horticultural consultancy; interior landscapes
STARTED TRADING 1950
PROJECTS Organiser of the British garden at Expo '90, in Osaka, Japan

Experienced landscape designer and consultant. Specialities include Japanese gardens and interior landscapes and displays for businesses. For the latter they emphasise their horticultural knowledge and independence from contractors.

Pelham Landscapes
27 Sun Street, Lewes, East Sussex BN7 2QB
☎ 0273 472408

CONTACT Sue Richards
OTHER SERVICES Horticultural consultancy
STARTED TRADING 1990
PROJECTS Redesign of garden at Trinity Hospital, Greenwich for the Mercers Company

Trained at Merrist Wood and the Inchbald School. Services range from verbal consultancy, to full design service and supervision of contractors. Sue Richards is a corresponding member of the Society of Garden Designers.

Penny Bennett Landscape Architects
8 High Peak, Blackstone Peak Old Road,
Littleborough, Lancashire OL15 0LQ
☎ 0706 379378   FAX 0706 371103

CONTACT   Penny Bennett
WORKING AREA   Yorkshire & north west England
ASSOCIATIONS   ALI
OTHER SERVICES   Horticultural consultancy
STARTED TRADING   1992
PROJECTS   Worked at Ebbw Vale Garden Festival 1992

Landscape architects with experience of festival work, garden design and derelict land reclamation.

Perryhill Nurseries, East Sussex
For full details see Nurseries section

Petal Designs Ltd
76 Addison Road, London W14 8EB
☎ 071 602 2599   📠 071 602 7078

CONTACT   Spindrift Al Swaidi
WORKING AREA   England, France, Italy, Jordan & USA
STARTED TRADING   1989
PROJECTS   Private estates

Peter Beales Roses, Norfolk
For full details see Nurseries section

Peter Rogers Associates
Northdowns, Titsey Road, Limpsfield, Surrey RH8 0DF
☎ 0883 715818

CONTACT   Peter Rogers
WORKING AREA   Nationwide
ASSOCIATIONS   SGD; MIHort
OTHER SERVICES   Horticultural consultancy
STARTED TRADING   1973
PROJECTS   Extensive sports facility for the London Borough of Merton

Landscape design services for private, commercial and public clients, including the refurbishment of private gardens.

Plaxtol Nurseries, Kent
For full details see Nurseries section

Professional Tree Services
See Arboricultural Services section

Quartet Design
The Village School, Lillingstone Dayrell, Buckingham, Buckinghamshire MK18 5AP
☎ 0280 860500   📠 0280 860468

CONTACT   David Newman
WORKING AREA   UK & western Europe
ASSOCIATIONS   ALI; MIHort
OTHER SERVICES   Horticultural consultancy

STARTED TRADING   1986

Landscape architects offering full design and construction services.

The Raw Talent Consultancy
56 Fordwater Road, Chertsey, Surrey KT16 8HL
☎ 0932 563613   📠 071 976 5979

CONTACT   Andrew Wilson
WORKING AREA   South east England
ASSOCIATIONS   SGD
STARTED TRADING   1986

Postgraduate landscape qualification. As well as freelance garden design, Mr Wilson writes on gardening and is director of garden design studies at the Inchbald School of Design.

Ray Cheeseborough
The Cottage, Henrietta Mews, Handel Street, Holborn, London WC1N 1PH
☎ 071 837 2553

CONTACT   Ray Cheeseborough
WORKING AREA   UK & overseas
ASSOCIATIONS   SGD; MIHort; FRSA
OTHER SERVICES   Landscape contractors; lectures and workshops
STARTED TRADING   1950

Garden design and construction. Their speciality is rock and water features, for inside and outside.

Ray Pitt Landscape Design
The Rest, Bradden Road, Greens Norton, Towcester, Northamptonshire NN12 8BS
☎ 0327 350520

CONTACT   Ray Pitt
WORKING AREA   London, Midlands & most of southern England
ASSOCIATIONS   ALI
STARTED TRADING   1990
PROJECTS   Landscaping for a new primary school in Tower Hamlets, London and for a housing association in Buckinghamshire

Landscape architect. Services include tree and hedgerow surveys, and site appraisal and assessment. Lectures on landscape design and amenity horticulture.

Robin Williams & Associates
Rowan House, Winterton Drive, Speen, Newbury, Berkshire RG13 1UD
☎ 0635 32910   📠 0635 550254

CONTACT   Robin Williams
WORKING AREA   UK & USA
ASSOCIATIONS   SGD; FIHort; MCSD; M.APLD (USA)

OTHER SERVICES Horticultural consultancy; botanic art
STARTED TRADING 1977

Robin Williams is also co-director of the College of Garden Design Ltd, and is an author and illustrator. His new book *The Garden Designer* is published next year by Frances Lincoln.

The Robinson Penn Partnership

4th Floor, Cathedral Buildings, Dean Street, Newcastle upon Tyne, Tyne & Wear NE1 1PG
☎ 091 230 4339   FAX 091 230 5509

CONTACT Dr Rachel Penn
WORKING AREA UK & overseas
ASSOCIATIONS ALI
OTHER SERVICES Horticultural consultancy; arboricultural services; ecological assessment
STARTED TRADING 1992
PROJECTS Landscaping at St Aidans College, Durham

A partnership of a landscape architect and an environmental scientist. Their work has included large scale habitat creation, formal landscaping and a mannerist garden for a private client.

The Romantic Garden Nursery, Norfolk

For full details see Nurseries section

Romilt Landscape Design & Construction Ltd

North Wyke Farm, Guildford Road, Normandy, Surrey GU3 2AN
☎ 0483 811933

CONTACT R. J. Milton
WORKING AREA Southern England
ASSOCIATIONS BALI
OTHER SERVICES Landscape contractors
STARTED TRADING 1975

Complete design and construction service for gardens and landscapes, including interior landscapes. Note also associated companies Abbey Waters Ltd, Water and Riparian Services, and R. J. Milton (0252 710325), Horticultural Consultancy.

Roots Garden Centre Ltd, Fife

For full details see Nurseries section

Rupert Golby

South View, Cross Hill Road, Adderbury West, Banbury, Oxfordshire OX17 3EG
☎ 0295 810320

CONTACT Rupert Golby
WORKING AREA Central England

OTHER SERVICES Horticultural consultancy
STARTED TRADING 1986
PROJECTS Many Cotswold Manor gardens

Trained at Kew and Wisley. Working from the South Midlands he specialises in recreating the classic English country garden in less maintenance-intensive forms.

Sarah Rycroft Landscape Architects

634 Wilmslow Road, Didsbury, Greater Manchester M20 3QX
☎ 061 445 6375   FAX 061 445 6375

CONTACT Sarah Rycroft
WORKING AREA Nationwide
ASSOCIATIONS ALI
OTHER SERVICES Horticultural consultancy; arboricultural services
STARTED TRADING 1987
PROJECTS Quayside walkway at Trafford Park; gardens at Harrock Hall, Lancashire

Landscape architects and garden designers.

Scotsdale Nursery & Garden Centre, Cambridgeshire

For full details see Nurseries section

Scottlandscape

78 Bousley Rise, Ottershaw, Surrey KT16 0LB
☎ 0932 872667   FAX 0932 872667

CONTACT Robert Scott
WORKING AREA South east England
ASSOCIATIONS BALI
OTHER SERVICES Landscape contractors; irrigation systems
STARTED TRADING 1965
PROJECTS Tudor Rose Award for best garden in show, Hampton Court 1992 & 1993; planting and maintenance at Heathrow airport.

Expanding family firm covering garden design, construction and maintenance. As well as award-winning collaborations with designer Barbara Hunt, they are also involved with Hare Hatch Nursery.

Secret Garden Designs by Christina Oates

Fovant Hut, Fovant, Salisbury, Wiltshire SP3 5LN
☎ 0722 714756

CONTACT Christina Oates
WORKING AREA Dorset, Hampshire, Somerset, Wiltshire
OTHER SERVICES Horticultural consultancy
STARTED TRADING 1990
PROJECTS Adviser to the Hawk Conservancy, Andover

Trained at the English Gardening School. Garden design, including preparation of plans for DIY gardeners and consultancy visits.

Sellet Hall Gardens, Lancashire

For full details see Nurseries section

Seven Counties Garden Design

143 Manor Green Road, Epsom, Surrey KT19 8LL
☎ 0372 724660

CONTACT Sue de Bock Rowles
WORKING AREA Southern England
STARTED TRADING 1990

A chain of affiliated garden designers, all trained at the College of Garden Design. They tackle all sizes and styles of gardens, and can produce surveys, plans and costings. They also run short courses in Garden Design. The eight designers are spread out between Kent and Somerset, and between them cover the south of England. See also under the individual designers: Helen Cahill, Sue de Bock Rowles, Mary Ann Lovegrove, Jeanne Paisley, Karen Saynor, Anthea Sokell, Sonia Stearn and Judith Walton.

Seymours Garden & Leisure Group

Pit House, By-Pass, Ewell, Surrey KT17 1PS
☎ 081 393 0111   FAX 081 393 0237

CONTACT James Seymour
WORKING AREA London, Surrey & adjoining areas
ASSOCIATIONS SGD; BALI
OTHER SERVICES Horticultural consultancy; landscape contractors

James Seymour is a Wisley-trained horticulturist and garden designer, with gold medals at Chelsea and Hampton Court. The firm also acts as contractors, and there is garden centre on the site.

Simon Richards + Associates

17 St Peter's Road, Cirencester, Gloucestershire GL7 1RE
☎ 0285 650828   FAX 0285 650828

CONTACT Simon Richards
WORKING AREA Southern Britain
ASSOCIATIONS ALI; MIHort
STARTED TRADING 1984
PROJECTS Woolgate Shopping Centre, Witney and Stratton House Hotel, Cirencester

Award-winning landscape architecture practice which aims to combine imaginative hard detailing with low maintenance planting schemes. Designs are structured to allowed development in phases.

Simpsons Nursery, Norfolk

For full details see Nurseries section

Smeeden Foreman Partnership

67 Westbourne Road, Huddersfield, West Yorkshire HD1 4LG
☎ 0484 456494   FAX 0484 456495

CONTACT Mark Smeeden or Trevor Foreman
WORKING AREA Nationwide
ASSOCIATIONS ALI; MIHort
OTHER SERVICES Horticultural consultancy; water and riparian services
STARTED TRADING 1992
PROJECTS Design and refurbishment of seventeenth century gardens at Whixley Hall, North Yorkshire

Landscape architects and environmental planners with horticultural qualifications. Retained consultants to the North East division of the National Rivers Authority.

Sol Jordens

Stocksbridge House, Coombe Bissett, Salisbury, Wiltshire SP5 4LZ
☎ 0722 77573

CONTACT Sol Jordens
WORKING AREA Nationwide
STARTED TRADING 1987
PROJECTS Large gardens for country houses

Trained at the College of Garden Design, and worked with John Brookes. Full range of garden design services. Aims to relate the garden to the house and its landscape setting.

Sonia Stearn

10 Belmont Drive, Trull Road, Taunton, Somerset TA1 4QB
☎ 0823 331267

CONTACT Sonia Stearn
WORKING AREA Southern England
STARTED TRADING 1990

Trained at the College of Garden Design. Part of Seven Counties Garden Design.

Southern Tree Surgeons Ltd

See Arboricultural Services section

Stella Caws Associates

Longhope House, 47a Bridge Street, Chepstow, Gwent NP6 5EY
☎ 0291 626645

CONTACT Stella Caws
WORKING AREA Wales, south Midlands & southern England
ASSOCIATIONS SGD; ALI
STARTED TRADING 1990

PROJECTS 3 acre organic display garden in Kent; award winning Potter's Garden at Ebbw Vale Garden Festival, 1992

Undertakes public and private commissions, with a complete service available for projects of all sizes. Currently advising the National Centre for Organic Gardening at Ryton Organic Gardens, West Midlands.

Sue de Bock Rowles Garden Design
143 Manor Green Road, Epsom, Surrey KT19 8LL
☎ 0372 724660

CONTACT Sue de Bock Rowles
WORKING AREA Hampshire, Kent, Surrey, Sussex & Devon
OTHER SERVICES Horticultural consultancy
STARTED TRADING 1991
PROJECTS Children's gardens; long narrow town gardens; informal country gardens

Trained at the College of Garden Design. Won the Bradstone Design Award in 1991, and is a member of Seven Counties Garden Design. Offers a comprehensive garden design service.

Sue Hedger-Brown Landscape Architect
The Rectory, Church Road, Newton Flotman, Norwich, Norfolk NR15 1QB
☎ 0505 470762

CONTACT Sue Hedger-Brown
WORKING AREA East Anglia
ASSOCIATIONS ALI
STARTED TRADING 1983
PROJECTS Campus site for Ridley Hall, Cambridge

Experience in public and private practice (and as a gardener). Sue Hedger-Brown is a sole practitioner who aims at sustainable landscape designs. Work includes commercial sites and private gardens: organic principles used where practicable.

Sue Pack Garden Design
9 Rudchesters, Bancroft, Milton Keynes, Buckinghamshire MK13 0PH
☎ 0908 317029

CONTACT Sue Pack
WORKING AREA Bedfordshire, Buckinghamshire & Oxfordshire mainly
STARTED TRADING 1990
PROJECTS Private gardens for a new house, and a sixteenth century cottage

Garden design and consultancy. Has exhibited in the Chelsea Flower Show Design Pavilion in recent years.

Sue's Garden Designs, Suffolk
For full details see Mrs S. Robinson, Suffolk in Nurseries section

Susan Buckley
124 Ashton Lane, Sale, Cheshire M33 5QJ
☎ 061 905 2327   FAX 061 905 2327

CONTACT Susan Buckley
WORKING AREA North west England
ASSOCIATIONS ALI
STARTED TRADING 1989

Landscape architects with fifteen years experience for private and public sector clients. Full professional service provided. Experienced in conservation of historic gardens, and establishing woodlands and semi-natural habitats.

Sutton, Griffin & Morgan
Albion House, Oxford Street, Newbury, Berkshire RG13 1JE
☎ 0635 521100   FAX 0635 44188

CONTACT Roderick Griffin
WORKING AREA UK & overseas
ASSOCIATIONS SGD; MIHort
OTHER SERVICES Horticultural consultancy; chartered architects
STARTED TRADING 1910

Part of an architectural practice which also accepts garden design commissions. Recently designed for BBC TV's *Front Gardens*.

Syon Courtyard, London
For full details see Nurseries section

Teamwork
Myrtle Cottage, Knellers Lane, Totton, Southampton, Hampshire SO4 2EB
☎ 0703 871919

CONTACT John or Linden Kuyser
WORKING AREA 30 mile radius
ASSOCIATIONS BALI
OTHER SERVICES Landscape contractors
STARTED TRADING 1988

Specialises in the design and construction of domestic gardens.

Tim Brayford Landscapes
The Cliff, Spindlers Road, St Lawrence, Ventnor, Isle of Wight PO38 1XD
☎ 0983 852952   FAX 0983 852952

CONTACT Tim Brayford
WORKING AREA Isle of Wight mainly
ASSOCIATIONS BALI

OTHER SERVICES Horticultural consultancy; landscape contractors
STARTED TRADING 1980
PROJECTS Work at Staplers Nursery, Newport and the Dolphin Sailing Centre, Wootton, Isle of Wight

Design and construction, and redesign and maintenance undertaken. Gardens are tailored exactly to client's requirements including future levels of maintenance.

Tony Benger Landscaping

Burrow Farm Gardens, Dalwood, Axminster, Devon
EX13 7ET
☎ 0404 831844   📠 0404 831844

CONTACT Tony Benger
WORKING AREA Devon, Dorset, Somerset
ASSOCIATIONS BALI
OTHER SERVICES Landscape contractors
STARTED TRADING 1985
PROJECTS Dorchester Hospice, Weston Super Mare Hospital

The five acre garden is open to the public.

Treework Services Ltd

See Arboricultural Services section

Veronica Adams Garden Design

Lower Hopton Farm, Stoke Lacy, Bromyard,
Hereford & Worcester HR7 4HX
☎ 0885 490294

CONTACT Veronica Adams
WORKING AREA Nationwide
OTHER SERVICES Botanic art
STARTED TRADING 1986
PROJECTS Birtsmorton Court, Worcestershire; 4½ acre garden from green field site

Trained at Inchbald School of Design, and in painting at Ruskin School, Oxford. Specialises in gardens for English country houses. Also paints botanical ceramics, porcelain and tiles.

Veronica Ross – Landscape Design

Burnroot Farmhouse, Dinnet, Aboyne, Grampian
AB34 5PN
☎ 03398 86690   📠 03398 86690

CONTACT Veronica Ross
WORKING AREA North east Scotland
ASSOCIATIONS ALI
STARTED TRADING 1989
PROJECTS Parks at Buckpool, Craigellachie and Portgordon

Landscape designer with additional expertise in forest landscape design.

Victor A Shanley

6 Eastry Avenue, Hayes, Bromley, Kent BR2 7PF
☎ 081 462 1864   📠 081 462 0988

CONTACT Victor Shanley
WORKING AREA London and south east England
ASSOCIATIONS SGD
STARTED TRADING 1990
PROJECTS Major work at London Bridge City; Highfield's Grove, London

Vice Chairman of the Society of Garden Designers. Working for himself since 1990 (but 54 years gardening behind him). Designs in varied styles, including roof gardens. Victor Shanley is also a tutor at the English Gardening School.

Water Meadow Nursery & Herb Farm, Hampshire

For full details see Nurseries section

Weaver Vale Garden Centre, Cheshire

For full details see Nurseries section

Webbs of Wychbold, Hereford & Worcester

For full details see Nurseries section

Wendy Wright Landscape & Garden Design

29 Lurline Gardens, London SW11 4DB

CONTACT Mrs Wendy Wright
WORKING AREA Nationwide
ASSOCIATIONS SGD; MIHort
OTHER SERVICES Landscape and design; horticultural consultancy
STARTED TRADING 1982

Experienced garden designer, design consultant and lecturer whose work has appeared frequently at Chelsea. She has lectured at the Inchbald School and the Garden School in the North, and now teaches at the English Gardening School and in Scotland (Country Courses), California and Oxford.

West Kington Nurseries Ltd, Wiltshire

For full details see Nurseries section

Whitehall Garden Centre, Wiltshire

For full details see Nurseries section

Wilkinsons
East Brocks Farm, Eaglescliffe, Stockton on Tees,
Cleveland TS16 0QH
☎ 0642 790409   📠 0642 780372

CONTACT   Peter Wilkinson
WORKING AREA   Cleveland, Durham & North Yorkshire
ASSOCIATIONS   BALI
OTHER SERVICES   Landscape contractors
STARTED TRADING   1981
PROJECTS   Water garden at Middlesborough Botanic Centre

Landscapers and contractors.

Wilmslow Garden Centre, Cheshire
For full details see Nurseries section

Wreford Landscapes
Poulner Hill Nurseries, Forest Corner, Ringwood,
Hampshire BH24 3HP
☎ 0425 478600   📠 0425 480882

CONTACT   Jon Burrows
WORKING AREA   Berkshire, Dorset, Hampshire & Wiltshire
ASSOCIATIONS   BALI; AAAC
OTHER SERVICES   Horticultural consultancy; landscape contractors; arboricultural services
PROJECTS   Maintenance work at Poole Park

Landscape contractors

Allseasons Landscapes
See Landscape and design section

Architectural Landscape Design Ltd
See Landscape and design section

Arena Landscapes
See Landscape and design section

Artscapes & Theseus Maze Designs
See Landscape and design section

Berrys Garden Company Ltd
See Landscape and design section

brambles
See Landscape and design section

Brent Surveys & Designs
See Landscape and design section

Cecily Hazell Garden Design
See Landscape and design section

Chenies Landscapes Limited
See Landscape and design section

Crowther Landscapes
See Landscape and design section

D Wells Landscaping
See Landscape and design section

Dagenham Landscapes Ltd
See Landscape and design section

David Ireland Landscape Architect
See Landscape and design section

David Stevens International Ltd
See Landscape and design section

Dolwin & Gray
See Arboricultural Services section

Duncan Heather
See Landscape and design section

FMG Garden Designs
See Landscape and design section

Garden Solutions by Design
See Landscape and design section

Gardens by Graham Evans
See Landscape and design section

Gardenscape
See Landscape and design section

Grace Landscapes Ltd
See Landscape and design section

Green Man Landscapes
See Landscape and design section

Green Stock
See Landscape and design section

Ground Control Ltd
See Landscape and design section

Hambrook Landscapes Ltd
See Landscape and design section

Heath Garden
See Landscape and design section

Heather Goldsmark Partnership
See Landscape and design section

Hillier Landscapes
See Landscape and design section

Josephine Hindle, Designer and
Gardener
See Landscape and design section

Keith Banyard Tree Surgeons
See Arboricultural Services section

Ken Higginbotham Garden
Landscaping
See Landscape and design section

Landscape Centre
See Landscape and design section

LDC Ltd
See Landscape and design section

Lotus Landscapes
See Landscape and design section

Nigel Jeffries Landscapes
See Landscape and design section

Nigel L Philips Landscape and
Garden Design
See Landscape and design section

Nottcutts Landscapes
See Landscape and design section

Oakwood
See Arboricultural Services section

Ray Cheeseborough
See Landscape and design section

Romilt Landscape Design &
Construction Ltd
See Landscape and design section

Scottlandscape
See Landscape and design section

Seymours Garden & Leisure Group
See Landscape and design section

Teamwork
See Landscape and design section

Tim Brayford Landscapes
See Landscape and design section

Tony Benger Landscaping
See Landscape and design section

Treework Services Ltd
See Arboricultural Services section

Wilkinsons
See Landscape and design section

Wreford Landscapes
See Landscape and design section

Horticultural Consultancy

Allan Hart Associates
See Landscape and design section

Annabel Allhusen
See Landscape and design section

Anthony George & Associates
See Landscape and design section

Antony Young
See Landscape and design section

Artscapes & Theseus Maze Designs
See Landscape and design section

Berrys Garden Company Ltd
See Landscape and design section

Brent Surveys & Designs
See Landscape and design section

Bunny Guinness
See Landscape and design section

Cabbages & Kings
See Landscape and design section

Carol Messham
See Landscape and design section

Cecily Hazell Garden Design
See Landscape and design section

Colson Stone Partnership
See Landscape and design section

Compton & Compton
See Landscape and design section

Conservatory Gardens
See Landscape and design section

Crowther Landscapes
See Landscape and design section

David Brown Landscape Design
See Landscape and design section

David Ireland Landscape Architect
See Landscape and design section

David Stevens International Ltd
See Landscape and design section

Dream Gardens
See Landscape and design section

Eachus Huckson
See Landscape and design section

Elaine Horne
See Landscape and design section

Elizabeth Banks Associates Ltd
See Landscape and design section

Fiona Harrison
See Landscape and design section

FMG Garden Designs
See Landscape and design section

Garden Solutions by Design
See Landscape and design section

Gardens of Distinction
See Landscape and design section

Gardenscape
See Landscape and design section

Geoffrey Coombs
See Landscape and design section

Gillian Temple Associates
See Landscape and design section

Ground Control Ltd
See Landscape and design section

Hambrook Landscapes Ltd
See Landscape and design section

Heath Garden
See Landscape and design section

Heather Goldsmark Partnership
See Landscape and design section

Hillier Landscapes
See Landscape and design section

Jakobsen Landscape Architects
See Landscape and design section

Jan Martinez
See Landscape and design section

**Joanna Stay Garden Design &
Consultancy**
See Landscape and design section

John A Davies Landscape Consultants
See Landscape and design section

John B Rickell
See Landscape and design section

John H Lucas & Associates
See Landscape and design section

Julia Fogg Garden Design
See Landscape and design section

Keith Rushforth
See Arboricultural Services section

Landscape Centre
See Landscape and design section

Landskip and Prospect
See Landscape and design section

Lingard + Styles Landscape
See Landscape and design section

Louis Vincent Architectural Garden Designer
See Landscape and design section

Mark Ross Landscape Architects
See Landscape and design section

Mark Westcott Landscape Architects
See Landscape and design section

Mary-Jane Hopes, Garden Designer
See Landscape and design section

Nicholas Roeber Landscapes
See Landscape and design section

Nigel L Philips Landscape and Garden Design
See Landscape and design section

Oakwood
See Arboricultural Services section

Paul Miles
See Landscape and design section

Paul Temple Associates
See Landscape and design section

Pelham Landscapes
See Landscape and design section

Penny Bennett Landscape Architects
See Landscape and design section

Peter Hemsley
See Arboricultural Services section

Peter Rogers Associates
See Landscape and design section

Quartet Design
See Landscape and design section

Robin Williams & Associates
See Landscape and design section

The Robinson Penn Partnership
See Landscape and design section

Rupert Golby
See Landscape and design section

Sarah Rycroft Landscape Architects
See Landscape and design section

Secret Garden Designs by Christina Oates
See Landscape and design section

Seymours Garden & Leisure Group
See Landscape and design section

Smeeden Foreman Partnership
See Landscape and design section

Sue de Bock Rowles Garden Design
See Landscape and design section

Sutton, Griffin & Morgan
See Landscape and design section

Tim Brayford Landscapes
See Landscape and design section

Treework Services Ltd
See Arboricultural Services section

Wendy Wright Landscape & Garden Design
See Landscape and design section

Wreford Landscapes
See Landscape and design section

Arboricultural Services

Absolute Tree Care
27 Harrison Close, Waltham Chase, Twyford, Berkshire RF10 0LL
☎ 0734 320020

CONTACT Philip Warren
WORKING AREA Berkshire, south Buckinghamshire, south Oxfordshire
ASSOCIATIONS AAAC
STARTED TRADING 1987

All Seasons Tree Service
Paradise Cottage, Sandy Lane, Chew Magna, Avon BS18 8RT
☎ 0275 333401/ 0225 429996   📠 0275 333125

CONTACT Kit or Penny Hogg
WORKING AREA South west England

ASSOCIATIONS AAAC
STARTED TRADING 1984

Tree surgeons specialising in amenity trees; approved contractors for Bath and Bristol city councils.

Anthony George & Associates
See Landscape and design section

Arrow Tree Services
56 St Marys Terrace, Hastings, East Sussex
TN34 3LR
☎ 0424 714376

CONTACT David Archer
WORKING AREA Kent, London, Surrey & Sussex
ASSOCIATIONS AAAC
OTHER SERVICES Landscape and design
STARTED TRADING 1976
PROJECTS Restoration of treescape in a seventeenth century deer park

ASH Consulting Group
See Landscape and design section

Aylmer Addison Associates
Walnut Tree Farm, Kirstead, Brooke, Norwich, Norfolk NR15 1EG
☎ 0508 50402   ᴲᴬˣ 0508 50110

CONTACT Mr Aylmer or Mr Addison
WORKING AREA Cambridgeshire, Norfolk, Suffolk
ASSOCIATIONS AAAC
STARTED TRADING 1979
PROJECTS Re-pollarding fen bank willows in the Norfolk Broads

Arboricultural work including amenity planting, surgery and the conservation and maintenance of small woodlands.

B & B Tree Specialists
Five Mile Lane, Washingborough, Lincoln, Lincolnshire LN4 1AF
☎ 0522 790313/ 0860 915092

CONTACT Harry or Paul Bavin
WORKING AREA Midlands & eastern England
ASSOCIATIONS AAAC
STARTED TRADING 1980

Also offers stump and brushwood chipping, and supply of woodchips.

Branchline Tree Services
23 Charleston Cottages, Glossop, Derbyshire
SK13 8LF
☎ 0457 862954

CONTACT Paul Turkentine

WORKING AREA North west England & Greater Manchester
ASSOCIATIONS AAAC
STARTED TRADING 1988

Approved local and county council contractors.

Bunny Guinness
See Landscape and design section

Channel Island Tree Service
Frenchmans Cottage, Beechvale, St John, Jersey, Channel Islands JE3 4FL
☎ 0534 862343

CONTACT Ian Averty
WORKING AREA Channel Islands
ASSOCIATIONS AAAC
STARTED TRADING 1987
PROJECTS Woodland management St Peter's valley; Queens valley reservoir project

The only Arboricultural Association approved contractor in the islands.

Chenies Landscapes Limited
See Landscape and design section

Chris Yarrow & Associates
Wilderness Wood, Hadlow Down, Uckfield, East Sussex TN22 4HJ
☎ 0825 830509   ᴲᴬˣ 0825 830977

CONTACT Mr Chris Yarrow
WORKING AREA Nationwide
ASSOCIATIONS FAA
STARTED TRADING 1972
PROJECTS Management of award winning Wilderness Wood

Comprehensive forestry advisory service specialising in recreational and tourism aspects.

Colin White Tree Surgeon and Forestry Contractor
The Manor House, Colwell, Hexham, Northumberland NE46 4TL
☎ 0434 681598   ᴲᴬˣ 0434 681598

CONTACT Colin White
WORKING AREA North east England
ASSOCIATIONS AAAC
STARTED TRADING 1978
PROJECTS Tree maintenance at English Heritage sites; trackside planting for Tyneside Metro

Full arboricultural service including planting, maintenance and chipping.

Colson Stone Partnership
See Landscape and design section

Complete Tree Services
Wayside, Kingston Stert, Chinnor, Oxfordshire
OX9 4NL
☎ 0844 351488

CONTACT   Steven Burkitt
WORKING AREA   Thames Valley & home counties
ASSOCIATIONS   AAAC
STARTED TRADING   1982
PROJECTS   Restoration of various private and institutional treescapes

Full range of services including 24 hour emergency call out. Recommended by councils and has worked for the National Trust.

D J Tree and Landscape Specialists
94 Halegate Road, Halebank, Widnes, Cheshire
WA8 8LY
☎ 051 425 3212

CONTACT   John M. Fahey
WORKING AREA   North west England & North Wales
ASSOCIATIONS   AAAC
STARTED TRADING   1985
PROJECTS   Tree clearance for British Rail

Family company with 24 hour emergency service.

D P O'Callaghan & Associates
Valleyfield, 1a Stratford Road, Aigburth, Liverpool, Merseyside L19 3RE
☎ 051 494 1108/ 1525 ⟨FAX⟩ 051 427 4541

CONTACT   D. P. O'Callaghan or M. Lawson
WORKING AREA   UK & Republic of Ireland
ASSOCIATIONS   FAA
STARTED TRADING   1982
PROJECTS   Arboricultural plans and implementation for Fota Island development, Co. Cork

Arboricultural consultancy practice which encompasses planning, litigation, project management and environmental impact studies. Satellite offices in Shrewsbury, Devon and Co. Wicklow.

Dalrymple Ltd
1 Charlwood Place, Charlwood, Surrey RH6 0EB
☎ 0293 862036 ⟨FAX⟩ 0293 863167

CONTACT   Jenny Smithers
WORKING AREA   100 miles radius from Gatwick
ASSOCIATIONS   AAAC
STARTED TRADING   1959

As well as arboricultural work, Dalrymple supplies professional forestry machines and winches, including chippers to the National Trust.

David Brown Landscape Design
See Landscape and design section

David Ireland Landscape Architect
See Landscape and design section

David Stevens International Ltd
See Landscape and design section

David Thorman Arboricultural Consultants
Minerva, Ffestiniog, Gwynedd LL41 4LW
☎ 0766 762712 ⟨FAX⟩ 0766 762590

CONTACT   D. H. Thorman
WORKING AREA   Northern England, north Midlands & Wales
ASSOCIATIONS   FAA
STARTED TRADING   1979

Arboricultural consultant.

Dolwin & Gray
Alpha House, Crowborough Hill, Crowborough, East Sussex TN6 2EG
☎ 0892 664612 ⟨FAX⟩ 0862 663636

CONTACT   F. Noakes or C. Goss
WORKING AREA   South east England
ASSOCIATIONS   AAAC; BALI
OTHER SERVICES   Landscape and design; landscape contractors
STARTED TRADING   1969
PROJECTS   Work in St James' Park, and at the Dartford River Crossing

The firm provides a wide range of arboricultural contracting and consultancy services. It also has a landscape and design capability.

Douglas Lewis Tree Surgeons
11 The Nashes, Clifford Chambers, Stratford upon Avon, Warwickshire CV37 8JB
☎ 0789 295825 ⟨FAX⟩ 0789 261496

CONTACT   Douglas Lewis
WORKING AREA   Midlands
ASSOCIATIONS   AAAC
STARTED TRADING   1979

Full tree service including surveys, written reports and stump grinding.

Eachus Huckson
See Landscape and design section

Eastern Landscape Service

27 High Street, Cottenham, Cambridge,
Cambridgeshire CB4 4SA
☎ 0954 50338

CONTACT   K. Hewitt
WORKING AREA   50 mile radius
ASSOCIATIONS   AAAC
OTHER SERVICES   Landscape and design
STARTED TRADING   1972

Landscape, forestry and tree surgery contractors, including tree and shrub diseases.

Eastern Tree Surgery

71b High Street, Teversham, Cambridgeshire
CB1 5AG
☎ 0223 292110

CONTACT   Paul Cole
WORKING AREA   East Anglia
ASSOCIATIONS   AAAC
STARTED TRADING   1974

Care and preservation of ornamental trees.

Euro Tree Service

Caxton Lodge Farm, Lodge Lane, Cronton, Widnes,
Cheshire WA8 9QA
☎ 051 424 0333   ☎ 051 430 7836

CONTACT   Simon Walton
WORKING AREA   North west England & Wales
ASSOCIATIONS   AAAC
OTHER SERVICES   Landscape and design
STARTED TRADING   1980

Full arboricultural service, including stump grinding and woodland maintenance. Suppliers of timber, logs, mulch and chippings. Garden designs and planting schemes prepared.

Flintshire Woodlands

The Meal House, Iscoyd Park, Redbrook Lane,
Shropshire SY13 3AW
☎ 094873 502   ☎ 094873 412
WORKING AREA   Wales, Midlands & north west
England
ASSOCIATIONS   AAAC

A large group whose activities include woodland management, tree care and environmental consultancy.

Fountain Forestry Ltd

Mollington House, Mollington, Banbury,
Oxfordshire OX17 1AX
☎ 0295 750000   ☎ 0295 750001

CONTACT   T. P. Rose
WORKING AREA   Nationwide
ASSOCIATIONS   AAAC

STARTED TRADING   1957

The largest privately owned independent forestry and land use company in the country. Through ten district offices (and another in New England) their range includes woodland services, timber harvesting, tree care, vegetation control and fencing.

Graham King Treecare

Lucombe House, Condicote, Stow on the Wold,
Cheltenham, Gloucestershire GL54 1ES
☎ 0451 831738

CONTACT   Graham King
WORKING AREA   Gloucestershire, Oxfordshire, Wiltshire & Worcestershire
ASSOCIATIONS   AAAC
OTHER SERVICES   Landscape and design
STARTED TRADING   1981
PROJECTS   Planting a 10 acre arboretum

Arboricultural services and garden design.

Heath Garden

See Landscape and design section

Heritage Tree Services

Redwood Meadow, Stoke Row, Henley on Thames,
Oxfordshire RG9 5QR
☎ 0491 681185   ☎ 0491 681185

CONTACT   Hugo Loudon
WORKING AREA   Berkshire, Buckinghamshire, Oxfordshire
ASSOCIATIONS   AAAC
STARTED TRADING   1985

Honey Brothers

New Pond Road, Peasmarsh, Guildford, Surrey
GU3 1JR
☎ 0483 61362   ☎ 0483 35608

CONTACT   Martyn Honey
WORKING AREA   London & south east England
ASSOCIATIONS   FAA; MIHort
STARTED TRADING   1960

Also sell garden, arboriculture and forestry equipment and organise training courses on tree work and the use of equipment.

Iain Tavendale Arboricultural Consultant

High Bank Farm, Stoney Bank Road, Earby, Colne,
Lancashire BB8 6LD
☎ 0282 844191   ☎ 0282 844191

CONTACT   Iain Tavendale
WORKING AREA   Lancashire, Yorkshire
ASSOCIATIONS   FAA; AAAC

STARTED TRADING 1980

Arboricultural consultant and approved contractor.

J & D Clark Treework Specialists

28 Frances Street, Chesham, Buckinghamshire
HP5 3EQ
☎ 0494 783536

CONTACT John Clark
WORKING AREA 40 mile radius
ASSOCIATIONS AAAC
STARTED TRADING 1953

Full tree service including stump grinding, reports and emergency service. Wood chippings supplied.

Jan Martinez

See Landscape and design section

Jeremy Barrell Treecare

25 Hightown Gardens, Ringwood, Hampshire
BH24 3EG
☎ 0425 479387   FAX 0425 472269

CONTACT Jeremy Barrell
WORKING AREA Southern England
ASSOCIATIONS AAAC
STARTED TRADING 1980

Tree consultancy specialising in reports for insurance and mortgage uses.

Keith Banyard Tree Surgeons

Nettletree Farm, Horton Heath, Wimborne, Dorset
BH21 7JN
☎ 0202 828800   FAX 0202 820128

CONTACT Keith Banyard
WORKING AREA Dorset, Hampshire, Wiltshire
ASSOCIATIONS AAAC; BALI
OTHER SERVICES Landscape and design; landscape contractors
STARTED TRADING 1977
PROJECTS Work at BP Wytch Farm; grass cutting for Broadlands estate

Large firm covering an unusually wide range of disciplines including arboricultural services, tree moving, landscape design and maintenance, fencing and soil improvement.

Keith Rushforth

32 Park Lane, Fareham, Hampshire PO16 7JX
☎ 0329 284738   FAX 0329 284738

CONTACT Keith Rushforth
WORKING AREA Nationwide
ASSOCIATIONS FAA; MIHort
OTHER SERVICES Horticultural consultancy
STARTED TRADING 1984

Arboricultural and horticultural consultant.

Ken Higginbotham Garden Landscaping

See Landscape and design section

Land and Tree Ltd

Ballochyle, Sandbank, Dunoon, Strathclyde
PA23 8RD
☎ 0369 6428

CONTACT Chris Taylor
WORKING AREA Scotland
ASSOCIATIONS AAAC
STARTED TRADING 1987

Carries out all tree work from surveys on amenity woods to commercial forestry.

Landscape Resource

89 Argyll Avenue, Luton, Bedfordshire LU3 1EJ
☎ 0582 452468   FAX 0582 452468

CONTACT John Cromar
WORKING AREA North London & the Chilterns
ASSOCIATIONS AAAC
OTHER SERVICES Landscape and design
STARTED TRADING 1979
PROJECTS Work at IBSA House, London

Mark Collis Tree Service

9 Harrow Road East, Dorking, Surrey RH4 2AX
☎ 0306 881692   FAX 0306 881692

CONTACT Mark Collis
WORKING AREA Surrey, Sussex & South London
ASSOCIATIONS AAAC
STARTED TRADING 1986
PROJECTS Tree planting scheme for Epsom market place

Tree services including stump removal and specialist planting projects. Free quotations.

Mark Westcott Landscape Architects

See Landscape and design section

Midland Tree Surgeons Ltd

Draycott in the Clay, Sudbury, Derbyshire DE6 5BT
☎ 0283 820426   FAX 0283 820086

CONTACT R. I. Kennedy
WORKING AREA Nationwide
ASSOCIATIONS AAAC
STARTED TRADING 1960

Tree surgeons.

North Wales Tree Service

Garmon View, School Hill, Trefriw, Gwynedd
LL27 0NJ
☎ 0492 641009

CONTACT J. R. Butters or K. R. Webber
WORKING AREA North Wales & border counties
ASSOCIATIONS AAAC
STARTED TRADING 1984

General tree works and inspections and reports. They
sell wood and wood chips and run arboricultural and
forestry training courses.

Oakwood

36 Pinewood Grove, New Haw, Addlestone, Surrey
KT15 3BU
☎ 081 669 6056/ 0932 349233 ☎ 081 669 6056

CONTACT N. R. Beardmore or A. Gaynor
WORKING AREA South east England
ASSOCIATIONS AAAC
OTHER SERVICES Landscape and design; horticultural
consultancy; landscape contractors
STARTED TRADING 1987

Design, construction and consultancy work offered by
the unusual combination of a Kew graduate and a
qualified arborist.

P A Searle

85 College Ride, Bagshot, Surrey GU18 5EP
☎ 0276 471586 ☎ 0276 471586

CONTACT Paul Searle
WORKING AREA South east England
ASSOCIATIONS AAAC
STARTED TRADING 1980

P G Biddle

Willowmead, Ickleton Road, Wantage, Oxfordshire
OX12 9JA
☎ 0235 762478 ☎ 0235 768034

CONTACT Dr P. G. Biddle
WORKING AREA Nationwide
ASSOCIATIONS FAA
STARTED TRADING 1972

Arboricultural consultant specialising in root damage
to buildings, and building near trees. Other insurance
and legal work, including expert witness in accident
cases. Dr Biddle is a past Chairman of the Arboricultural Association.

P J Chaffin Tree Surgery

16 The Paddock, Eastbourne, East Sussex BN22 9LJ
☎ 0323 504620 ☎ 0323 504620

CONTACT Pete Chaffin
WORKING AREA South east England

ASSOCIATIONS AAAC
STARTED TRADING 1984

As well as tree services, Mr Chaffin acts as an instruc-
tor and assessor for chainsaw courses.

Peter Hemsley

14 Stonethwaite, Woodthorpe, York, North
Yorkshire YO2 2SY
☎ 0904 705296

CONTACT Peter Hemsley
WORKING AREA Northern England
ASSOCIATIONS MIHort; FAA
OTHER SERVICES Horticultural consultancy; lecturing
STARTED TRADING 1992
PROJECTS Restoration of historic parterre at Hare-
wood House

Tree consultant and lecturer.

Peter Wynn Arboricultural Consultant

Barclays Bank Chambers, Town Hall Street,
Sowerby Bridge, West Yorkshire HX6 2DY
☎ 0422 834587 ☎ 0422 831141

CONTACT Peter Wynn
WORKING AREA Lancashire, Lincolnshire, Midlands,
North Wales & Yorkshire
ASSOCIATIONS FAA
STARTED TRADING 1976

Arboricultural consultant and expert witness. Vice
President of the International Society of Arboriculture,
1993, and President Elect, 1995.

Professional Tree Services

12a Bell Street, Romsey, Hampshire SO51 8GW
☎ 0794 513405 ☎ 0794 513405

CONTACT Bill Kowalczyk
WORKING AREA East Wiltshire & west Hampshire
ASSOCIATIONS AAAC
OTHER SERVICES Landscape and design
STARTED TRADING 1985
PROJECTS Landscaping of a Biblical garden at Romsey
Baptist Church

Full arboricultural service for trees and shrubs, including planting and design, surveys and consultancy work.

Provincial Tree Services Ltd

31 Bridge Street, Heywood, Lancashire OL10 1JF
☎ 0706 369355

CONTACT Mervyn C. Simpson
WORKING AREA Greater Manchester
ASSOCIATIONS AAAC
STARTED TRADING 1979

Also at Elizabeth Street Farm, Heywood, Lancashire.

Raven Tree Services

Florida Close, Hot Lane Industrial Estate, Burslem,
Stoke on Trent, Staffordshire ST6 2DJ
☎ 0782 837755

CONTACT S. A. Coombes
WORKING AREA Midlands (contracting); Nation-
wide (consultancy and stump removal)
ASSOCIATIONS AAAC
STARTED TRADING 1980

As well as contracting services, they offer nationwide
stump removal and arboricultural consultancy. Chain
saw courses and assessment.

Richard Loader Tree Care Specialists

32 Moors Close, Hurn, Christchurch, Dorset
BH23 6AL
☎ 0202 470596   📠 0202 475880

CONTACT Simon Jones
WORKING AREA Dorset, Hampshire, Isle of Wight,
East Sussex & Wiltshire
ASSOCIATIONS AAAC
STARTED TRADING 1977

The Robinson Penn Partnership

See Landscape and design section

Ross Tree Services

The Old Pound, Llangarrow, Ross on Wye,
Hereford & Worcester HR9 6PG
☎ 0989 770383

CONTACT J. P. Ross
WORKING AREA 30 mile radius
ASSOCIATIONS AAAC
STARTED TRADING 1980
PROJECTS Work for English Heritage

Full range of tree surgery and consultancy work, including stump removal.

Roy Finch Tree Care Specialists

Welland Way, Gloucester Road, Welland, Malvern,
Hereford & Worcester WR13 6LD
☎ 0684 310700   📠 0684 310867

CONTACT Roy Finch or Adrian Hope
WORKING AREA 65 mile radius (contracting); nation-
wide (consultancy)
ASSOCIATIONS AAAC; FAA
STARTED TRADING 1970

Full range of arboricultural services and also consultancy work including safety, litigation and conservation
matters.

Ruskins Arboricultural Group

Wolves Farm, Wyatts Green, Brentwood, Essex
CM15 0QE
☎ 0277 353436   📠 0277 353916

CONTACT Robert Wilkins (Operations Manager)
WORKING AREA UK & overseas

Large arboricultural group including tree surgery, consultancy and management services. They supply specimen trees and have the biggest tree moving machinery
in the UK.

Sarah Rycroft Landscape Architects

See Landscape and design section

Southern Tree Surgeons Ltd

Crawley Down, West Sussex RH10 4HL
☎ 0342 712215/ 712771 📠 0342 717662

CONTACT Mr M. Coomber, Area Manager
WORKING AREA South London & south east England
ASSOCIATIONS AAAC; BALI
OTHER SERVICES Landscape and design
STARTED TRADING 1956

Head office of a large firm of tree surgeons and consultants who work nationwide and in Europe. The firm has
a royal warrant, and is the largest of its kind in Europe.

Southern Tree Surgeons Ltd

65a Haywood Street, Leek, Staffordshire ST13 5JH
☎ 0538 384877/ 372682

CONTACT Mr A. Mellor
WORKING AREA Midlands & northern England

Southern Tree Surgeons Ltd

52a Cowick Street, Exeter, Devon EX4 1AP
☎ 0392 214690

CONTACT Mr C. Groves
WORKING AREA South & south west England

Southern Tree Surgeons Ltd

Unit 32, Hardwick Industrial Estate, Hardwick Lane,
Bury St Edmunds, Suffolk IP33 2QH
☎ 0284 762977
WORKING AREA East Anglia

Southern Tree Surgeons Ltd

Hartleys Place, Church Lane, Wexham, Slough,
Berkshire SL3 6LD
☎ 0753 551100   📠 0753 553166

CONTACT Mrs L. Bell
WORKING AREA North London & home counties

Southern Tree Surgeons Ltd
Tring House, 77 High Street, Tring, Hertfordshire
HP23 4AB
☎ 0442 828410
WORKING AREA Bedfordshire, Buckinghamshire &
Hertfordshire

Southern Tree Surgeons Ltd
The Old Kennels, Cirencester Park, Tetbury Road,
Cirencester, Gloucestershire GL7 1UR
☎ 0285 652421/ 654370 ☎ 0285 885800

CONTACT Mr B. Robinson
WORKING AREA Gloucestershire, Oxfordshire &
Wales

Southern Tree Surgeons Ltd
Gaywood, Mulhuddart, Co. Dublin
☎ 010 353 1 821 3150

CONTACT Mr A. Worsnop
WORKING AREA Ireland

Tree Maintenance
Unit 12, Hope Mills, Brinscombe, Stroud,
Gloucestershire GL5 2SA
☎ 0453 731212

CONTACT Geoffrey March
WORKING AREA Avon, Gloucestershire, Hereford-
shire, Oxfordshire, Wiltshire, Worcestershire & South
Wales
ASSOCIATIONS AAAC
STARTED TRADING 1981
PROJECTS Regular maintenance for the National
Trust and Woodland Trust, and of the ninety nine yews
in Painswick churchyard

Tree surgery and maintenance, including hedge trimming, stump removal and chipping.

Treecare
Old Oak Works, 16c Hilary Road, London
W12 0QB
☎ 081 749 4573/ 7712 ☎ 081 749 6805

CONTACT Edward Radziwillowicz or Darryl Parkin
WORKING AREA London & south east England
ASSOCIATIONS AAAC
STARTED TRADING 1982
PROJECTS Contracting work at Tower of London and
Westminster Abbey

Arboricultural contracting and consultancy work.

Treecare
132 Knowsley Road, Norwich, Norfolk NR3 4PU
☎ 0603 612485

CONTACT Nick Coleman or Colin McDonald

WORKING AREA Norfolk
ASSOCIATIONS AAAC
STARTED TRADING 1989
PROJECTS Tree surgery for Norwich City Football
Club

Full arboricultural contracting and consultancy service.

Treemasters
52 Meadow Walk, Walton on the Hill, Surrey
KT20 7UG
☎ 0737 812389 ☎ 081 781 0536

CONTACT John Darter
WORKING AREA London & south east England
ASSOCIATIONS AAAC
STARTED TRADING 1986
PROJECTS Appeared on Channel 4's *Fragile Earth*
programme in 1993

Arboricultural contractors.

Trees
Copse Cottage, Hurst Lane, Sedlescombe, East
Sussex TN33 0PE
☎ 0424 870479 ☎ 0424 870479

CONTACT Mr P. W. Martin
WORKING AREA London and south east England
ASSOCIATIONS AAAC
STARTED TRADING 1971
PROJECTS Contracting work at Hyde Park, Kensing-
ton Gardens and Windsor Castle

All tree work including contracting, consultancy and
planting. 24 hour call out, and free advice and estimates.

Treework Services Ltd
Cheston Combe, Church Town, Backwell, Bristol,
Avon BS19 3JQ
☎ 0275 464466 ☎ 0275 463078

CONTACT Neville Fay
ASSOCIATIONS AAAC; BALI; FAA
OTHER SERVICES Landscape and design; horticultural
consultancy; landscape contractors
PROJECTS Tree maintenance at Bath Royal Victoria
Park and Botanical Gardens.

Tree surgeons, arboricultural consultants, and landscape and garden designers for private and commercial
clients. They combine a wide range of professions with
a strong ecological awareness.

Treeworld Services
14 Portland Gardens, Tilehurst, Reading, Berkshire
RG3 4QH
☎ 0734 419755 ☎ 0734 419755

CONTACT Steven M. Kelleher
WORKING AREA Southern England

ASSOCIATIONS AAAC
STARTED TRADING 1986

Arboricultural services, including fencing and ground maintenance.

W K W Tree Services
The Grange, Old Teversal, Nottinghamshire
NG17 3JW
☎ 0623 512795   📠 0623 442329

CONTACT   William Kew-Winder
WORKING AREA   Derbyshire, Nottinghamshire, South Yorkshire, and adjoining parts of Leicestershire & Lincolnshire
ASSOCIATIONS AAAC
STARTED TRADING 1980
PROJECTS   Woodland management for the Woodland Trust; cable-bracing at Rufford Country Park

Tree contracting and consultancy, including emergency service. Supplies wood chips, bark and logs.

Wessex Tree Surgeons
1 William Road, Lymington, Hampshire SO41 9DZ
☎ 0590 675773

CONTACT   Mr G. Snellgrove
WORKING AREA   Hampshire and adjoining counties
ASSOCIATIONS AAAC
STARTED TRADING 1977

Tree surgery and consultancy work, including planting and stump chipping.

Westside Forestry
Lower Madeley Farm, Harbours Hill, Belbroughton, Stourbridge, West Midlands DY9 9XE
☎ 021 457 9457   📠 021 457 9457

CONTACT   Mr B. Kenward
WORKING AREA   West Midlands
ASSOCIATIONS AAAC
STARTED TRADING 1976

Tree services and fencing.

Willerby Tree Surgeons Ltd
Albion Lane, Willerby, Humberside HU10 6DT
☎ 0482 651185

CONTACT   Mr C. P. Scaife
WORKING AREA   North Humberside, north Lincolnshire & North Yorkshire
ASSOCIATIONS AAAC
STARTED TRADING 1981

Tree surgery and tree consultancy, including surveys and planting.

Wolverhampton Tree Service
150 Lamb Crescent, Wombourn, Wolverhampton, Staffordshire WV5 0ED
☎ 0902 892652/ 0831 367508   📠 0902 892652
CONTACT   Bob Smith
WORKING AREA   Shropshire, Staffordshire & West Midlands
ASSOCIATIONS AAAC
STARTED TRADING 1985

Approved contractor for eight local authorities.

Wreford Landscapes
See Landscape and design section

Water & Riparian Services

Abbey Waters Ltd
See Romilt Landscape Design & Construction Ltd, Landscape and design section

Anthony Archer-Wills
See Landscape and design section

Artscapes & Theseus Maze Designs
See Landscape and design section

brambles
See Landscape and design section

Bunny Guinness
See Landscape and design section

Green Stock
See Landscape and design section

Hambrook Landscapes Ltd
See Landscape and design section

Jakobsen Landscape Architects
See Landscape and design section

Mark Ross Landscape Architects
See Landscape and design section

Michael Littlewood Landscape Designer
See Landscape and design section

Smeeden Foreman Partnership
See Landscape and design section

24

Organisations

ADAS
ADAS Headquarters, Oxford Spires Business Park, The Boulevard, Kidlington, Oxfordshire OX5 1NZ
☎ 0865 842742

All Year Round Chrysanthemum Growers Association
30 Pern Drive, Botley, Hampshire SO3 2GW
☎ 0489 786638
CONTACT The Secretary

Formed to represent the industry and distribute information to growers. Acts as a liaison between the growers, the government and other bodies. In the past their work has included pest control and the new plant passport scheme. They have recently become involved in publicity, and are promoting British Chrysanthemums.

Arboricultural Association
Ampfield House, Romsey, Hampshire SO51 9PA
☎ 0794 368717
CONTACT The Secretariat

A registered charity and the professional body for arboriculturists. The AA publishes a useful directory of consultants and contractors who have met the organisation's stringent standards for training, work and insurance: contact the Secretariat for details. A range of other publications is also available. There is a local group structure, and keen amateurs can join as part of the Tree Club.

Botanic Gardens Conservation International
Descanso House, 199 Kew Road, Richmond, Surrey TW9 3BW
☎ 081 940 0047

British Agricultural & Garden Machinery Association
14 – 16 Church Street, Rickmansworth, Hertfordshire WD3 1RQ
☎ 0923 720241

British Agrochemicals Association
4 Lincoln Court, Lincoln Road, Peterborough
0733 349225

Trade association for manufacturers, distributors and retailers of pesticides. Among many useful publications on using chemicals is a guide to the products available for amateur gardeners.

British Association of Landscape Industries (BALI)
Landscape House, Henry Street, Keighley, West Yorkshire BD21 3DR
☎ 0535 606139

The national body representing Landscape Contractors. BALI promotes the interests of its members at national and regional level, and works to maintain high standards in the industry. Member firms are required to carry adequate insurance, to abide by the code of conduct, and to maintain a certain standard in their work (which is subject to inspection). Probationary membership is available for companies which have been trading for less than two years.

British Association Representing Breeders (BARB)
9 Portland Street, Kings Lynn, Norfolk PE30 1PB

Formerly the British Association of Rose Breeders. Collects payments due under Plant Breeders Rights, and promotes protected varieties.

British Tourist Authority
Thames Tower, Black's Road, Hammersmith, London W6 9EL

A list of British tourist information centres is available. Local centres can often provide information on gardens and events in their area.

British Trust for Conservation Volunteers (BTCV)
36 St Mary's Street, Wallingford, Oxfordshire OX10 0EU
☎ 0491 839766

Carries out practical conservation projects, including tree planting. They run training courses and offer working conservation holidays.

Commercial Horticultural Association
Links View House, 8 Fulwith Avenue, Harrogate, North Yorkshire HG2 8HR
☎ 0423 879208
CONTACT   Mr Brian Dunsby

A trade organisation for manufacturers and suppliers of goods and services to the commercial horticultural industry. The CHA Suppliers Guide is available to professional horticulturists and the trade.

Common Ground
41 Shelton Street, London WC2H 9HJ

Motivating force for projects which preserve and promote links between the environment and social culture. They publicise National Apple Day (21 October), and have worked on the *Flora Britannica* project. Pomologists should investigate their publications list.

The Conservation Foundation
1 Kensington Gore, London SW7 2AR
☎ 071 823 8842

Manages and creates environmental programmes with business sponsorship, and assists conservation groups with publicity and funding.

Council for the Protection of Rural England
Warwick House, 25 Buckingham Palace Road, London SW1W 0PP
☎ 071 976 6433

Country Landowners Association
16 Belgrave Square, London SW1X 8PQ
☎ 071 235 0511

Countryside Commission
John Dower House, Crescent Place, Cheltenham, Gloucestershire GL50 3RA
☎ 0242 521381

Countryside Council for Wales
Plas Penrhos, Ffordd Penrhos, Bangor, Gwynedd LL57 2LQ
☎ 0248 370444

English Nature
Northminster House, Peterborough, Cambridgeshire PE1 1UA
☎ 0733 340345

The English Vineyards Association
38 West Park, London SE9 4RH
☎ 081 857 0452

Federation to Promote Horticulture for the Disabled
252 The Ridgeway, Enfield, London EN2 8AP

Fertiliser Manufacturers Association
Greenhill House, Thorpe Wood, Peterborough PE3 6GF
☎ 0733 331303

Flower Council of Holland
Catherine Chambers, 6 – 8 Catherine Street, Salisbury, Wiltshire SP1 2A
☎ 0722 337505

Flowers & Plants Association
Covent House, New Covent Garden Market, London SW8 5NX
☎ 071 738 8044

The Forestry Authority
Forest Research Station, Alice Holt Lodge, Wrecclesham, Farnham, Surrey GU10 4LH
☎ 0420 23000

Research advisory service operates from the above address, and from: Northern Research Station, Roslin, Lothian EH25 9SY (031 445 2176).

Forestry Commission
231 Corstorphine Road, Edinburgh EH12 7AT
☎ 031 334 0303

The Forestry Trust
The Old Estate Office, Englefield Road, Theale, Reading, Berkshire RG7 5DZ
☎ 0734 323523

Education and conservation trust dedicated to sustainable forestry. They have a network of 'Link Woods' and produce an annual guide, *Woodlands to Visit in England and Wales*.

The Garden Centre Association
38 Carey Street, Reading, Berkshire RG1 7JS
☎ 0734 393900

Industry body: 200 of the best garden centres belong. Members are independently inspected.

Health & Safety Executive (HSE)
Information Centre, Broad Lane, Sheffield S3 7HQ
☎ 0742 892345

Historic Houses Association (HHA)
2 Chester Street, London SW1X 7BB
☎ 071 259 5688

A representative association of private owners which campaigns on their behalf. Of the 1,300 members nearly 300 houses are open to the public. Membership of the Friends of the HHA gives free admission to these properties. The association's brief includes gardens and designed landscapes.

Horticultural Development Council
18 Lavant Street, Petersfield, Hampshire GU32 3EW
☎ 0730 263736

Carries out horticultural research which is funded by an industry levy.

Horticultural Therapy
Goulds Ground, Vallis Way, Frome, Somerset
BA11 3DW
☎ 0373 464782

Horticultural Trades Association (HTA)
Horticulture House, 19 High Street, Theale, Reading, Berkshire RG7 5AH
☎ 0734 303132

The trade association for amenity and leisure horticulture, with around 1,800 members. They publish a magazine, *Nurseryman and Garden Centre* and a useful reference *Yearbook*: both are also available to non-members. Business advice and negotiated discounts are provided to members. They promote horticulture generally, including the HTA National Garden Gift Tokens.

Institute of Groundmanship
19 – 20 Church Street, The Agora, Wolverton, Milton Keynes MK12 5LG
☎ 0908 312511

The Institute of Horticulture (IoH)
P O Box 313, 80 Vincent Square, London
SW1P 2PE
☎ 071 976 5951
CONTACT The Secretary

The professional body for horticulturists of all descriptions. The strict membership requirements demand a combination of education and experience. Membership confers recognised professional status. Student membership and career advice are available. The IoH acts as a forum for the collection and dissemination of horticultural information to its members and the public. It also promotes and represents the horticultural industry.

Institute of Leisure and Amenity Management (ILAM)
Lower Basildon, Reading, Berkshire RG8 9NE
☎ 0491 874222

International Association of Horticultural Producers
Postbus 93099, 2509 AB 's-Gravenhage, Netherlands
☎ 010 31 70 381 4631

International Plant Propagators Society
Longfield Nursery, Cleobury Mortimer, Shropshire
DY14 0TJ
☎ 074632 562
CONTACT Thelma Swash (Secretary)

The Great Britain and Ireland region of an international society. The IPPS is aimed at practical and academic horticulturists. Its motto 'Seek and Share' reflects its aim of bringing together and distributing information about propagation and production techniques.

International Tree Foundation
Sandy Lane, Crawley Down, Crawley, West Sussex
RH10 4HS
☎ 0342 712536

Formerly Men of the Trees. International tree planting and conservation organisation (£10 individual).

John Innes Manufacturers Association
Links View House, 8 Fulwith Avenue, Harrogate, North Yorkshire HG2 8HR
☎ 0423 879208
CONTACT Brian L. Dunsby

The trade organisation for manufacturers of John Innes seed and potting composts. Members have to meet the quality standards: they can then display the seal of approval. JIMA actively promotes the use of loam-based composts by amateur gardeners.

The Landscape Institute
6 – 7 Barnard Mews, London, London SW11 1QU
☎ 071 738 9166

The professional body for the landscape profession: landscape architects, landscape managers and landscape scientists. The LI sets and maintains standards and accredits educational courses. It represents the profession's interests and disseminates information to its members. Members hold the qualification ALI: a directory of firms where at least one of the principals is a registered member is available from RIBA Publications

(071 251 0791). The Landscape Institute can advise potential clients free of charge about suitable firms for large or specialised projects.

Ministry of Agriculture, Fisheries and Food

3 Whitehall Place, London SW1A 2HH
☎ 071 270 8080

General enquiries on the above number. See your local telephone directory (under 'Agriculture') for the addresses of MAFF's regional centres.

National Farmers Union

22 Long Acre, London WC2E 9LY
☎ 071 235 5077

The farmers' trade association has a horticulture section which represents growers. Associated organisations include BGLA Ltd (which organises two trade exhibitions), British Bedding and Pot Plants Association, British Herb Trades Association, and Farm Shop and PYO Association. Specialist advisers can help members with law, taxation, employment and plant health.

National Gardens Scheme

Hatchlands Park, East Clandon, Guildford, Surrey GU4 7RT
☎ 0483 211535

The National Institute of Medical Herbalists

9 Palace Gate, Exeter EX1 1JA
☎ 0392 426022

National Trust

36 Queen Anne's Gate, London SW1H 9AS
☎ 071 222 9251

Conservation body with many outstanding gardens and landscapes under its care. Membership gives admission to all the Trust's properties, and numerous events are organised throughout the year.

National Trust for Scotland

5 Charlotte Square, Edinburgh EH2 4DU
☎ 031 226 5922

This Scottish conservation body has a number of excellent gardens in its care; members also receive free entry to National Trust properties under a reciprocal arrangement. Self-catering and working holidays are available.

NIAB

Huntingdon Road, Cambridge CB3 0LE
☎ 0223 276381

The National Institute of Agricultural Botany carries out testing of seeds and other laboratory and environ-

mental research on behalf of the government and commercial customers. The Wisley Handbook, *Vegetable Varieties for the Gardener*, by J. Chowings and M. J. Day passes on the results of NIAB tests.

The Organic Food & Farming Centre

86 Colston Street, Bristol BS1 5BB
☎ 0272 290661

The Soil Association, British Organic Farmers and the Organic Growers Association are based here.

Plant Breeding International

Maris Lane, Trumpington, Cambridge CB2 2LQ
☎ 0223 840411

Plant Publicity Holland

Goudse Rijweg 1, Postbus 81, 2770 AB Boskoop, Netherlands

Plant Variety Rights Office and Seeds Division

White House Lane, Huntingdon Road, Cambridge CB3 0LF
☎ 0223 277151

Part of the Ministry of Agriculture.

Plantlife

The Natural History Museum, Cromwell Road, London SW7 5BD
☎ 071 938 9111

Wild plant conservation charity (£15 individual). Projects include rescuing individual species, protecting peat bogs, and the Great Hedge Project.

The Professional Gardeners Guild

Gardeners Cottage, Bramdean House, Alresford, Hampshire SO24 0JU
CONTACT Membership Secretary

Rose Growers Association

303 Mile End Road, Colchester, Essex CO4 5EA

Royal Institute of British Architects (RIBA)

66 Portland Place, London W1N 4AD
☎ 071 580 5533

Royal Society for Nature Conservation

The Green, Witham Park, Waterside South, Lincoln LN5 7JR
☎ 0522 544400

The RSNC Wildlife Trusts Partnership is made up of 47 local wildlife trusts, many of whom are listed in our societies section, and 50 Urban groups. They manage nature reserves, campaign on conservation issues, and encourage people to become involved in conservation.

Royal Society for the Protection of Birds

The Lodge, Sandy, Bedfordshire SG19 2DL
☎ 0767 680551

Scotland's Garden Scheme

3 Castle Terrace, Edinburgh EH1 2EL
☎ 031 229 1870

Scottish Natural Heritage

12 Hope Terrace, Edinburgh EH9 2AS
☎ 031 447 4784

Society of Botanical Artists

Burwood House, 15 Union Street, Wells, Somerset BA5 2PU
CONTACT Executive Secretary

The society holds regular open exhibitions and can act as a channel for commissions.

Society of Garden Designers

6 Borough Road, Kingston upon Thames, Surrey KT2 6BD
☎ 081 974 9483
CONTACT Assistant Secretary

A professional body for full-time garden designers. Membership depends upon a combination of training and experience, and work is inspected. The society distributes information about its members to enquirers, and publishes *Vitis*. Members use the initials MSGD and FSGD.

The Society of Floristry

70a Reigate Road, Epsom, Surrey
CONTACT The Secretary

The society, which was started in 1951, works to maintain standards in professional floristry. Part of this work includes professional awards at intermediate level and above. Preliminary qualifications are handled by the NEBAHAI and the City and Guilds of London. The National Diploma of the Society of Floristry is the highest floristry qualification. Members are drawn from all sectors of the industry. The society stages displays and demonstrations, including a stand at the Chelsea Flower Show.

The Tree Council

35 Belgrave Square, London SW1X 8QN
☎ 071 235 8854

Women's Farm & Garden Association

175 Gloucester Street, Cirencester, Gloucestershire GL7 2DP
☎ 0285 658339

Voluntary organisation for women whose livelihood is connected with the land. Among its activities is the Women's Returners to Amenity Gardening Scheme which arranges placements in private gardens for women wishing to return to work.

Woodland Trust

Autumn Park, Dysart Road, Grantham, Lincolnshire NG31 6LL
☎ 0476 74297

World Conifer Data Pool

Treetops, Buzzacott Lane, Combe Martin, Devon EX34 0NL
☎ 0271 883761
CONTACT Humphrey Welch and Gordon Haddow

Acts as a collecting agency for data on new conifer introductions from around the world. They have recently published *The World Checklist of Conifers* through Landsman's Bookshop.

Worshipful Company of Gardeners

25 Luke Street, London EC2A 4AR
☎ 071 739 8200

Colleges and Horticultural Education

From the time when first we become interested in growing plants, we inevitably want to learn more, even if we regard gardening as a leisure pursuit. The routes into horticulture are many and various, with courses suited to every ability, and level of interest. The RHS, and its northern counterpart, the NHS, along with many of the colleges listed here, provide for a diverse range of practical and theoretical studies for the amateur. Most botanic gardens and specialist societies run admirably wide-ranging lectures where both amateur and professional will find much to learn. Perusal of the calendar will illustrate the point. There are, in addition, a number of privately run garden design schools.

For those committed to a career in horticulture the plethora of qualifications available seems horribly complicated. This is partly because the discipline has an almost uniquely wide embrace, encompassing subject areas from micropropagation to landscape design and environmental management on the broadest scale.

The first step is to study the prospectuses of educational establishments which will give an idea of the range of options. An overview can be had from publications of the Institute of Horticulture, Careers Advisory Bureau (see Organisations section). The following is a guide to the scheme of qualifications, and their administering bodies.

NVQ or *National Vocational Qualifications:* developed by the *City and Guilds of London Institute* (*CGLI*) in cooperation with relevant industrial bodies, to meet standards approved by the *National Council for Vocational Qualifications (NCVQ).* The awarding body is the *National Examinations Board for Agriculture, Horticulture and Allied Industries, (NEBAHAI,* whose secretariat is provided by CGLI) in conjunction with the National Proficiency Test Council (NPTC). There are four levels of qualification, which are unit-based, and intended to assess skills and competence in the work situation. Level 1 is suitable for the school leaver at 16 and, although no formal qualifications are required, individual centres have their own selection procedures, and methods of delivery – full-time or part-time. In Scotland and Ireland, examining and validating bodies differ, but the SVQs, developed, awarded and accredited by Scotvec, are equivalent to NVQs.

CGLI also offers a hierarchy of qualifications from City and Guilds Level 1, rising eventually to Fellowship of the C&G Institute. The C&Gs bear comparison with an apprenticeship, and are usually provided via day- and block-release to young people who are working in the horticultural industry. The higher levels incorporate supervisory and management studies.

NEBAHAI also validates the *National Certificate of Horticulture, NCH* which offers a practical craft skills base, and involves a very intensive 1 year course. Requirements vary, but expect to be asked for 3 GCEs or 3 GCSEs, with relevant experience, or a minimum age of 18, with one year in horticultural work. A pass with merit or distinction will count for entry into higher levels, such as NDH, or the Advanced NCH, which includes supervisory and management studies.

BTEC, the *Business and Technology Education Council*, validates a range of courses:

BTEC First Diploma. For the school leaver who wishes to upgrade qualifications to the academic equivalent of 4 GCSEs, at grade C or above, to permit entry to higher level courses, such as the NDH. Formats vary, e.g. one year full time/two years part time, and as well as specialist studies, most curricula include personal development and other work-related skills. Courses may be specific to horticulture, or have a wider remit, e.g. Land-based Industries. The latter may be more suited to those unsure of their area of interest.

BTEC National Diploma, NDH. A three year course, with one year industrial placement, the NDH equips students for skilled and supervisory positions. Courses generally have a greater practical bias than the HND, but in practice, students of both courses will apply for similar positions. The entry requirements are four GCSEs at grade C, usually with relevant experience, but there are exceptional entry courses – good NCH, First Diploma with merit, or C&G II, for example.

BTEC Higher National Diploma. A three year sandwich course, with the industrial middle year of supervised training, the HND is intended as a supervisory, and ultimately, a managerial qualification. Some colleges offer a one year upgrade to a BSc. It is a higher status qualification than the NDH, and some students are surprised by the technical, scientific and economic bias of the syllabus – it is *not* primarily a craft skills course. This is reflected in the entry requirement for two subjects at A-level, 4 GCSEs with science, maths and English among them. Alternative qualifications are considered, especially from mature students.

BSc & BSc Hons. Degrees are validated by Universities; some are offered within Horticultural Colleges. Three and four year courses (respectively) for those intending to enter higher levels of management, or scientific and technological posts; graduates may also consider work in education, research and advisory positions. Degrees are offered in pure horticulture, with a commercial or amenity specialism,

and in a range of ancillary disciplines such as Countryside Management, Landscape Management, Rural Resource Development.

The equivalent awards for the Landscape Architects' profession include: *BA and BA Hons; Dip. Landscape Architecture; Dip. Hons LA*. A BA Hons is also offered in Garden Design at Capel Manor, validated by Middlesex University.

These degree level courses have the normal university entry requirements; a minimum of 2 A-levels, and 5 GCSEs or GCEs, including English and maths. Competition may be fierce, however, and higher grades may be necessary; apply to the university or college in question for details.

Another route to a degree level qualification is the *Master of Horticulture Award (M.Hort.RHS)*, the highest level of award offered by the RHS, and equivalent to a first degree. It is an exacting exam, combining a need for broadly based practical proficiency with high levels of academic ability. That said, it is one of the few high level courses that maintains a connection with horticultural craft skill. It is, therefore, highly respected. Entry requirements are equivalent to A-level standard.

Competition is justifiably fierce for the *Royal Botanic Garden Diploma*, offered by Kew (and Edinburgh). It represents an enviable training in amenity horticulture, at first degree level, not least because the scientific, technical and managerial content of the course goes hand-in-hand with practical experience of an unrivalled diversity of plants. Students need two years of practical experience, with 2 A-levels (one a science) and 4 GCSE/GCE passes.

BERKSHIRE

Berkshire College of Agriculture
Hall Place, Burchetts Green, Maidenhead, Berkshire SL6 6QR
☎ 0628 824444   [FAX] 0628 824695

CONTACT   Steve Gingell
TYPE OF COURSES Professional
RANGE OF COURSES Horticulture; Landscape; Administration and retailing; Floristry; Arboriculture; Garden Design; Garden Centre Retailing (BTEC); Agriculture or Horticulture (BTEC); Conservation and Recreation Garden Design/Interior Landscaping/Parks and Gardens (BTEC); Extensive programme of Short Courses
LEVELS RHS; C&G; NCH; ND; NVQ

Big county agricultural college, well-run and serious. Excellent modern brochure, very inspirational.

University of Reading

Dept of Horticulture, Plant Science Laboratories, Whiteknights, Reading, Berkshire RG6 2AS
☎ 0734 318071   📠 0734 750630

CONTACT   Tony Kendle
TYPE OF COURSES Professional; amateur
RANGE OF COURSES Landscape Management (BSc); Crop Protection (BSc); Certificate in Garden Design (2 year part-time); Amateur courses
LEVELS Postgraduate; Degree

The leading university for horticulture – amenity, commercial, landscape and garden design. The gardens and learning resources are also among the best.

BUCKINGHAMSHIRE

Aylesbury College

Hampden Hall, Stoke Mandeville, Aylesbury, Buckinghamshire MK18 2JA
☎ 0296 434111   📠 0296 614175

CONTACT   Jane Vyse or Ian Cairns (0296 434111 Ext 420)
TYPE OF COURSES Professional; amateur
RANGE OF COURSES Horticulture; Landscape; Floristry; Countryside management; Leisure; CGLI Certificate in Amateur Gardening; Creative Flower Arranging; Bee Keeping; Farm-based Tourism; Agriculture and Conservation; General Examination (RHS); Amenity Horticulture (NVQ); Groundmanship Short courses/one day per week
LEVELS BTEC First Diploma; NVQ I & II; CGLI; RHS

CAMBRIDGESHIRE

Cambridgeshire College of Agriculture and Horticulture

Landbeach Road, Milton, Cambridge, Cambridgeshire CB4 6DB
☎ 0223 860701   📠 0223 860262

CONTACT   Richard Walpole
TYPE OF COURSES Professional
RANGE OF COURSES Horticulture; Landscape; Countryside management; Groundsmanship
LEVELS NCH; BTEC First Diploma

There is an emphasis on fruit and vegetable production at the Milton centre. Floristry courses are based at the College's second centre at Wisbech (Tel: 0945 581024).

Nene Valley Adult Education

Prince William School, Herne Road, Oundle, Cambridgeshire PE8 4BS
☎ 0832 273550   📠 0832 274942

CONTACT   Ian Russell
TYPE OF COURSES Professional; amateur
RANGE OF COURSES Horticulture; Floristry; Countryside management; Leisure; Horticulture (RHS General Certificate, 2 year)
LEVELS C&G; RHS

CHESHIRE

Manchester Metropolitan University

Division of Environmental Science, Crewe and Alsager Faculty, Crewe Green Road, Cheshire CW1 1DU
☎ 0270 500661   📠 0270 251205

CONTACT   Dr Ian W Eastwood (Head of Division)
TYPE OF COURSES Professional
RANGE OF COURSES Environmental Science (BSc); Environmental Analysis and Monitoring (HND); Business Leisure and Recreation (BA)
LEVELS Degree; HND

Reaseheath College (Cheshire College of Agriculture)

Reaseheath, Nantwich, Cheshire CW5 6DF
☎ 0270 625131   📠 0270 625665

CONTACT   Tom Deans
TYPE OF COURSES Professional; amateur
RANGE OF COURSES Horticulture; Arboriculture; Greenkeeping
LEVELS BTEC First Diploma; NC; BTEC National Diploma

Cheshire college for horticulture. In addition to full-time courses, there is a comprehensive range of day- and block-release courses for the industry, including the MHort.

CUMBRIA

Newton Rigg College

Cumbria College of Agriculture and Forestry, Newton Rigg, Penrith, Cumbria CA11 0AH
☎ 0768 63791   📠 0768 67249

CONTACT   The Principal
TYPE OF COURSES Professional; amateur
RANGE OF COURSES Horticulture; Landscape; Administration and retailing; Forestry; Floristry; Countryside management; Leisure; Groundsmanship; Arbori-

culture (C&G); Amateur: Garden Design (RHS); Garden Planning and Planting (10 weeks, Sept.); Bonsai for Beginners (4 weeks, Sept.); RHS courses – Pesticides, Hanging Baskets, Propagation, Interior Landscape; Rural Creative Arts; Leisure (Rural Tourism); Flower Arranging

LEVELS   C&G; NDH; HND; RHS

The college primarily serves the land-based industries and rural economy of Cumbria.

DERBYSHIRE

Broomfield College
Morley, Derby, Derbyshire DE7 6DN
☎ 0332 831345   ℻ 0332 830298

CONTACT   The Principal
TYPE OF COURSES   Professional; amateur
RANGE OF COURSES   Horticulture; Landscape; Administration and retailing; Floristry; Countryside management; Leisure; Botany; Organic Agriculture; Chain Saw use; Pesticide Application; Greenkeeping; Leisure gardening (CGLI 061 series); Master of Horticulture (MHort RHS); smallholders; rural crafts; Flower Arranging – Creative Studies (CGLI)
LEVELS   BTEC First National; HND; HNC; NDH; C&G; RHS & MHort RHS; CGLI

The Derbyshire College of Agriculture and Horticulture, with a full range of residential and sandwich courses at all levels. Wide range of adult, day and evening tuition.

DEVON

Bicton College of Agriculture
East Budleigh, Budleigh Salterton, Devon EX9 7BY
☎ 0395 68353   ℻ 0395 67502

CONTACT   Gordon Hill
TYPE OF COURSES   Professional; amateur
RANGE OF COURSES   Horticulture; Landscape; Administration and retailing; Floristry; Countryside management; Leisure; Conservation; Agriculture
LEVELS   First Diploma; NVQ

Courses to suit all levels, gardens open to the public daily.

DORSET

Kingston Maurward College
Kingston Maurward, Dorchester, Dorset DT2 8PY
☎ 0305 264738   ℻ 0305 250059

CONTACT   Bob Wadey, Head of Horticultural Dept

TYPE OF COURSES   Professional; amateur
RANGE OF COURSES   Horticulture; Landscape; Floristry; Countryside management; Leisure; Groundsmanship; Agriculture; Countryside Skills Amateur: (RHS) Ornamental Horticulture; Fruit; Vegetables; Glasshouse; Hard Landscaping; Design; Sprayers; Bee Keeping; Chainsaws; Flower Arranging; Fun with Flowers; Gardening Demonstrations; Garden Woodwork; Gardening under glass
LEVELS   Degree; C&G; BTEC First Diploma; HNC; ND; NVQ; RHS

A residential county-based horticultural college. 'Dorset's Centre of Excellence' with a wide range of courses.

CO. DURHAM

Finchale Training College
Durham DH1 5RX
☎ 091 3862634   ℻ 091 3864962

CONTACT   Maureen Skelton
TYPE OF COURSES   Professional; amateur
RANGE OF COURSES   Horticulture; Forestry; Horticulture course covers: landscape design; propagation; internal decoration (NVQ I & II, 52 weeks)
LEVELS   NVQ I & II

Finchale is a residential centre offering vocational training to adults who have become or are born disabled.

Houghall College
Houghall, Durham DH1 3SG
☎ 091 386 1351   ℻ 091 386 0419

CONTACT   Ian Webster
TYPE OF COURSES   Professional; amateur
RANGE OF COURSES   Horticulture; Landscape; Administration and retailing; Forestry; Floristry; Leisure; Botany; Arboriculture (NVQ); Wide range of non-vocational courses
LEVELS   NVQ; C&G; HNC; NDH; HND; RHS

ESSEX

Barking College of Technology
Dagenham Road, Romford, Essex RM7 0XU
☎ 0708 66841

CONTACT   G D Chalk
TYPE OF COURSES   Professional; amateur
RANGE OF COURSES   Horticulture; Floristry; Amateur floristry; short courses in horticulture and floristry
LEVELS   NVQ; C&G

Southend Adult Education Centre

Ambleside Drive, Southend on Sea, Essex SS1 2UP
☎ 0702 610196   ⓕ 0702 601529

CONTACT Centre Secretary
TYPE OF COURSES Amateur
RANGE OF COURSES Horticulture; Floristry; Leisure;
RHS General Examination; Flower Arranging
LEVELS RHS

Writtle College

Writtle, Chelmsford, Essex CM1 3RR
☎ 0243 420705   ⓕ 0243 420456

CONTACT Martin Stimson
TYPE OF COURSES Professional; amateur
RANGE OF COURSES Landscape; Administration and
retailing; Forestry; Floristry; Countryside management;
Leisure; Crop Production (MSc); Horticulture (BSc);
Rural Resources (BSc Hons); Leisure Management
(BSc Hons); Landscape & Garden Design (BSc Hons);
Commercial Horticulture (HND); Garden Centre &
Nursery Management (HND); Nursery Stock Produc-
tion/Garden Centres (NDH); Amenity & Decorative
Horticulture (C&G)
LEVELS BSc Hons; C&G; NVQ

One of the top horticultural colleges, with a national
reputation and a commitment to both amenity and
commercial horticulture, as well as floristry and rural
studies. Extensive short courses for the gardener (apply
to Faculty Administrator).

GLOUCESTERSHIRE

Cheltenham & Gloucester College of Higher Education

Francis Close Hall Campus, Swindon Road,
Cheltenham, Gloucestershire GL50 4AZ
☎ 0242 532922   ⓕ 0242 532997

CONTACT James Wilson
TYPE OF COURSES Professional
RANGE OF COURSES Landscape; Countryside man-
agement
LEVELS Postgraduate; Degree

GREATER MANCHESTER

University of Manchester

School of Landscape, Dept of Planning and
Landscape, Manchester M13 9PL

CONTACT Dr M J Emer

TYPE OF COURSES Professional
RANGE OF COURSES Horticulture Plant Sciences
LEVELS BSc; PhD

HAMPSHIRE

Isle of Wight College of Arts & Technology

Medina Way, Newport, Isle of Wight PO30 5TA
☎ 0983 526631   ⓕ 0983 521707

CONTACT Gardening: D Trevan, J Fradgley. Cultivation: R Mew. Floristry: P Gardiner, M Alexander, C Lee
TYPE OF COURSES Professional; amateur
RANGE OF COURSES Horticulture; Landscape; Administration and retailing; Forestry; Botany; Amenity
& Commercial Horticulture (NVQ I & II); Countryside
Studies (BTEC First Diploma, NDH). Amateur courses
include: Certificate in Gardening (C&G); Seeds/Cut-
tings; Garden Pond; Tree and Shrub Cultivation; Garden Design; Christmas Flower Arranging; Gardening
with Nature
LEVELS Degree; BTEC First and National Diplomas;
RHS; C&G

Sparsholt College Hampshire

Sparsholt, Winchester, Hampshire SO21 2NF
☎ 0962 776441   ⓕ 0962 776587

CONTACT General Enquiries: The Courses Adviser;
Plant Identification: C Bird; Domestic Garden Design:
S White
TYPE OF COURSES Professional; amateur
RANGE OF COURSES Horticulture; Landscape; Fore-
stry; Floristry; Countryside management; Leisure; Bo-
tany; Groundsmanship; Greenkeeping; RHS general
exam; Plant Identification; Domestic Garden Design;
Gardening Advice; Gardening Demonstrations; Certi-
ficate of Gardening (C&G)
LEVELS First Diploma/BTEC; National Certificate;
RHS exam

Sparsholt is fast developing as one of the leading county
colleges in England, highly professional and with an
expanding range of part-time and amateur courses, too.
Excellent brochures. Demonstrations on Wednesday
afternoons. (Adults £5.00, OAPs £4.00). Topics include: Pests and Diseases; Autumn Lawn Care; Alpines; Borders; Plant Nutrition; Summer Bedding.

HERTFORDSHIRE

Oaklands College
Hatfield Road, St Albans, Hertfordshire AL4 0JA
☎ 0727 850651   📠 0727 847987

CONTACT Admissions (0727 850651)
TYPE OF COURSES Professional
RANGE OF COURSES Horticulture; Landscape; Administration and retailing; Floristry; Countryside management; Leisure; Amenity & Commercial Horticulture (NC); Horticultural Mechanics; Greenkeeping (NC); Agriculture and Commercial Horticulture Business Management; Amateur: Flower Arranging; Pesticides; Gardening; Tractors; Chain Saws
LEVELS NDH; NCH;

One of the leading national providers of commercial horticultural teaching. Its graduates have long enjoyed a good reputation for professionalism.

KENT

Hadlow College of Agriculture and Horticulture
Hadlow, Tonbridge, Kent TN11 0AL
☎ 0732 850551   📠 0732 851957

CONTACT Admissions Secretary
TYPE OF COURSES Professional; amateur
RANGE OF COURSES Horticulture; Administration and retailing; Floristry, day and evening; Conservation and Environmental studies; Botany; Groundmanship; Amenity; Landscape
LEVELS Degree; C&G; HNC; NDH; HND; RHS

One of the few colleges offering specialist block release courses. There is a wide range of courses at Hadlow, also Maidstone and Canterbury. The horticulture department covers 60ha and houses National Collections of Hellebores and Anemones.

University of Greenwich
School of Architecture and Landscape, Dartford Campus, Oakfield Lane, Dartford, Kent DA1 2SZ
☎ 081 316 8000

CONTACT Tom Turner
TYPE OF COURSES Professional
RANGE OF COURSES Horticulture; Landscape; Botany; Commercial horticulture; Garden Design; Landscape Architecture: all to degree level. HND Garden design
LEVELS BA; HND

The two garden design courses (BA & HND) started in 1993.

Wye College
Wye, Ashford, Kent TN25 5AH
☎ 0233 812401   📠 0233 813320

CONTACT The Academic Registrar
TYPE OF COURSES Professional
RANGE OF COURSES Horticulture; Countryside management; Leisure; Horticultural Business Management
LEVELS All courses lead to a BSc; there are postgraduate courses in fruit production and tropical horticulture leading to a MSc

The horticultural department of London University, and very highly regarded academically and by business.

LANCASHIRE

Myerscough College
Myerscough Hall, Bilsborrow, Preston PR3 0RY
☎ 0995 640611   📠 0995 640842

CONTACT E J Lamont, Head of Horticultural Dept
TYPE OF COURSES Professional; amateur
RANGE OF COURSES Horticulture; Landscape; Floristry; Countryside management; Leisure; Groundsmanship; Leisure Management (BTEC); Amenity Horticulture (NVQ II); Arboriculture (C&G, HND); Chain Saws (NPTC); Agriculture (HND); Nursery Practice (BTEC); Landscape Practice (BTEC, ND); RHS Examination (day release and evening); full Non Vocational Gardening programme; Flower Painting
LEVELS BTEC First Diploma; NCH; HNC; HND; NPTC; NVQ; C&G

A very good range of courses from a college with a good reputation.

LEICESTERSHIRE

University of Nottingham
School of Agriculture, Sutton Nonington, Loughborough, Leicestershire LE1 5RD
☎ 0602 484848   📠 0602 516060

CONTACT Dr Charles Wright
TYPE OF COURSES Professional
RANGE OF COURSES Horticulture; Landscape; Administration and retailing; Botany; Agriculture; Environmental Science in Agriculture; Horticulture with Technology; Plant Sciences
LEVELS Postgraduate; Degree

The undergraduate course in horticulture can be combined with European studies.

LINCOLNSHIRE

Lincolnshire College of Agriculture

Caythorpe Court, Grantham, Lincolnshire NG32 3EP
☎ 0400 72521   ☎ 0400 72722

CONTACT Dr N Cheffins
TYPE OF COURSES Professional; amateur
RANGE OF COURSES Horticulture; Landscape; Administration and retailing; Forestry; Floristry; Countryside management; Master of Horticulture; Agriculture; Agricultural and Horticultural Business Management (12 weeks); Rural Leisure Studies; Garden Design (ANC); Environmental Landscape Management (BTEC); Horticultural Mechanics; Flower Arranging & RHS short courses for amateurs
LEVELS BSc; BA; HND; BTEC First Diploma; NEB

A good range of amateur courses as well as professional tuition leading to the highest levels. There is a General Course in Horticulture for the Visually Impaired available (C&G).

LONDON

Ealing Tertiary College

Norwood Hall Centre, Norwood Green, Southall, London UB2 4LA
☎ 081 574 2261   ☎ 081 571 9479

CONTACT Len Stocks or Margaret Pamment
TYPE OF COURSES Professional
RANGE OF COURSES Horticulture; Floristry; Countryside management; Groundsmanship (Institute of Groundsmanship Cert & Diploma)
LEVELS NVQ

The English Gardening School

Chelsea Physic Garden, 66 Royal Hospital Road, London SW3 4HS
☎ 071 352 3437   ☎ 071 376 3936

CONTACT The Admissions Secretary
TYPE OF COURSES Professional; correspondence
RANGE OF COURSES Horticulture; Landscape, 1 year courses in Garden Design: 2 days a week. Also Practical Horticulture; Plants & Plantsmanship; Botanical Illustration: all 1 day a week. 1 year correspondence course in Garden Design. Range of short courses (1 – 5 days) on such subjects as: The Mixed Border; Plants & Planting; Surveying a Garden; Drawing
LEVELS Own diploma is recognised by the Institute of Horticulture

Inspirational course for (mainly) female and mature students. The venue cannot be bettered and the Principal, Rosemary Alexander, is a brilliant communicator.

The English Gardening School produces confident, stylish garden designers.

Hampstead Garden Suburb Adult Education Centre

The Institute, Central Square, London NW11 7BN
☎ 081 455 9951

CONTACT Faculty Administrator
TYPE OF COURSES Amateur
RANGE OF COURSES Horticulture; Amateur: The Flower Garden (5 weeks) Shrubs and Trees (5 weeks) Elements of Garden Design (4 weeks)

Inchbald School of Design

32 Eccleston Sqaure, London SW1V 1PB
☎ 071 630 9011   ☎ 071 976 5979

CONTACT Andrew Wilson
TYPE OF COURSES Professional; amateur
RANGE OF COURSES Garden Design; Garden Design History
LEVELS Own examinations, recognised by the Society of Garden Designers

Inchbald runs ten-week courses, both full-time and part-time, plus three-week courses in garden-design drawing. There are plans to introduce distance learning courses.

Lambeth College

Norwood Centre, Knights Hill, West Norwood, London SE27 0TX
☎ 081 699 7239   ☎ 081 766 6313

CONTACT Terry Fulham
TYPE OF COURSES Professional; amateur
RANGE OF COURSES Horticulture; Landscape; Decorative Horticulture (NEBAHAI); Creation and Management of Urban Wildlife areas (NVQ); RHS General Exam (Day or Evening)
LEVELS BTEC First Diploma; Training Credits Programme (Horticulture); NEBAHAI; NVQ

Merton Institute of Adult Education

Whatley Avenue, Wimbledon, London SW20 9NS
☎ 081 543 9292   ☎ 081 544 1421

CONTACT General: William Whitham; Flower Arranging: Teresa Liew
TYPE OF COURSES Amateur
RANGE OF COURSES Horticulture; Floristry; General Examination in Horticulture (RHS); Garden Design (Autumn, 1 term, Wisley visit); Starting Your New Garden (1 term, Autumn); Gardening for the Disabled (5 meetings); Herbs for House & Garden (Jan start); Organic Garden (Feb) Flower Arranging (6 weeks); Hanging Baskets; Pruning; Turkish Flowers; Trees of S.E. England

LEVELS   C&G; RHS

A well-run and adventurous Adult Education college.

University College London

Dept of Biology (Darwin), Gower Street, London
WC1E 6BT
☎ 071 387 7050

CONTACT   Dr F B Goldsmith
TYPE OF COURSES   Professional
RANGE OF COURSES   Ecology (BSc); Conservation
(MSc)
LEVELS   Postgraduate Degree

The MSc in conservation is considered an academic
trailblazer.

MERSEYSIDE

Hugh Baird College

Balliol Road, Bootle, Merseyside PR8 3JX
☎ 051 922 6704   FAX 051 934 4469

TYPE OF COURSES   Professional; amateur
RANGE OF COURSES   Floristry; Flower arranging
LEVELS   NVQ Levels I, II and III

Now a further education corporation, independent of
the LEA, but offering a wide range of subjects as well
as horticulture for all ages and standards.

Knowsley Community College, Landbased Industries

The Kennels, Knowsley Park, Prescot, Merseyside
L34 4AQ
☎ 051 549 1500

CONTACT   Ruth Brown
TYPE OF COURSES   Professional; amateur
RANGE OF COURSES   Horticulture; Landscape; Administration and retailing; Floristry; Countryside management; Leisure; Horticulture (C&G); Flower Arranging (College Certificate); Environmental Conservation (NVQ)
LEVELS   C&G; RHS; NVQ I, II & III; College Certificate

Southport College of Art and Technology

Mornington Road, Southport, Merseyside PR9 0TT
☎ 0704 424111/500606 x2629

CONTACT   Vera Hainsworth
TYPE OF COURSES   Professional
RANGE OF COURSES   Horticulture; Leisure
LEVELS   C&G; RHS

St Helens College

Newton Campus, Crow Lane East, Newton le
Willows, Merseyside WA12 9TT
☎ 092524656   FAX 0925 220437

CONTACT   Dr Bob Ashcroft
TYPE OF COURSES   Professional; amateur
RANGE OF COURSES   Horticulture; Landscape; Administration and retailing; Countryside management; Leisure; Botany; Floristry (NVQ/NEBAHAI); Environmental Conservation (C&G); Amenity Horticulture and Commercial Horticulture/Garden Centre Operation (NVQ/NEBAHAI); Society of Floristry (evening); Flower Arranging (CGLI); Amateur Gardening (C&G); Decorative Horticulture (NEBAHAI); Chemical Handling; Groundsmanship
LEVELS   NEBAHAI; C&G; NVQ

The Floristry section has been designated a 'Centre of Excellence' by the Flower Trades Council.

NORFOLK

Easton College

Easton, Norwich, Norfolk NR9 5DX
☎ 0603 742105   FAX 0603 741438

CONTACT   Paul Metcalf
TYPE OF COURSES   Professional; amateur
RANGE OF COURSES   Agriculture (BTEC NDH); Landscaping (NC); Country Skills and Management (BTEC); RHS General Certificate in Amenity Horticulture; Decorative Horticulture (C&G); Agric/Hort Business Management (C&G)
LEVELS   Degree; RHS; C&G; NCH; NDH; HND

Norfolk's College of the Countryside, with a wide range of courses geared to commercial and business opportunities. Short Courses: Gardening; Beekeeping; Floristry and Flower Arranging; Horticulture; Landscape and Estate management. Also Chain Saw course.

NORTHAMPTONSHIRE

Moulton College

West Street, Moulton, Northamptonshire NN3 1RR
☎ 0604 491131   FAX 0604 491127

CONTACT   Stuart Phillips
TYPE OF COURSES   Professional; amateur; correspondence
RANGE OF COURSES   Horticulture; Landscape; Administration and retailing; Floristry; Groundsmanship; Horticultural Therapy (with Coventry University); Business Management (options Horticulture/Floristry); Countryside Management

LEVELS BTEC First Diploma; Preliminary Certificate; C&G; HNC; NDH; RHS; NCH

Moulton College used to be the county agricultural college for Northamptonshire and offers both commercial and amenity courses to a high level, including a MHort by correspondence.

NOTTINGHAMSHIRE

Brackenhurst College
Southwell, Nottinghamshire NG25 0QF
☎ 0636 812252   📠 0636 815404

CONTACT Brian Osborne
TYPE OF COURSES Professional; amateur
RANGE OF COURSES Horticulture; Landscape; Administration and retailing; Floristry; Countryside management; Leisure; Groundsmanship; Arboriculture; Wide range of day/evening courses; Gardening Certificate (C&G); Chain Saw Operation; Spraying (Pesticides)
LEVELS BTEC First Diploma; NDH; HND; NCH; HNC; NVQ; Degree (BSc); NEBAHAI; ANC

A county residential college with a wide range of well-run courses, full-time and part-time. Amateur courses in: Plant Photography; Culinary Horticulture; Victorian Gardens; Gardening skills.

OXFORDSHIRE

West Oxford College
Warren Farm Centre, Horton-cum-Studley, Oxfordshire OX33 1BY
☎ 0865 351794   📠 0865 358931

CONTACT Horticulture: Jeremy Dickson; Short courses: Mary Spiller (Waterperry Horticultural Centre).
TYPE OF COURSES Professional; amateur
RANGE OF COURSES Horticulture; Landscape; Floristry; Leisure; Groundsmanship; Legislative courses e.g. Pesticides; Amenity Horticulture (BTEC/Dipl 2 years/NVQ I & II); wide selection of amateur gardening/horticultural courses
LEVELS BTEC/Diploma; NVQ I & II; RHS General Certificate

Incorporates the Waterperry Horticultural Centre with a strong emphasis on amenity. This is reflected in the amateur courses, which include: Weekend Gardening; Garden Design; Flower Garden; Garden Skills; Down to Earth; Garden Calendar; Pruning Fruit; Growing Under Glass.

SHROPSHIRE

Walford College of Agriculture
Baschurch, Shrewsbury, Shropshire SY11 2HL
☎ 0939 260461   📠 0939 261112

CONTACT M Ford, Horticultural Unit, (0743 360266)
TYPE OF COURSES Professional; amateur
RANGE OF COURSES Horticulture; Landscape; Floristry; Agriculture; Land Use and Recreation; Land Use and Countryside Skills; Amenity Horticulture (NVQ I & II); Decorative Horticulture; Groundsmanship; Amateur: Flower Arranging (day release); Garden and Landscape Design; Gardening for Leisure and Pleasure; General Exam Horticulture (RHS); Pressed Flower Craft
LEVELS IOG; C&G; NVQ I & II; RHS

Walford started as a local authority college and has a wide range of horticultural and floristry courses.

SOMERSET

Cannington College
Cannington, Bridgwater, Somerset TA5 2LS
☎ 0278 652226

CONTACT M Smith, Course Director
TYPE OF COURSES Professional
RANGE OF COURSES Horticulture; Landscape; Administration and retailing; Forestry; Floristry; Countryside management; Leisure; Amenity Horticulture (NVQ I, II & III); Amateur: Landscape and Plantsmanship (RHS; College Diplomas; NVQ)
LEVELS C&G; NVQ I, II, III; Advance National Certificate; RHS; NDH; HND

Perhaps the leading centre for Amenity Horticulture.

College of Garden Design
Cothelstone, Taunton, Somerset TA4 3DP
☎ 0823 433215   📠 0823 433812

CONTACT Francis Huntington, Course Administrator
TYPE OF COURSES Professional
RANGE OF COURSES Horticulture Certificate in Garden Design; Drawing Course for Garden Designers; Planting Design; Managing Your Garden Design Business; Specifications and Costings; Surveys
LEVELS Private certificates

Horticultural Therapy

Goulds Ground, Vallis Way, Frome, Somerset
BA11 3DW
☎ 0373 464782   📠 0373 464782

CONTACT   Jill Thompson
TYPE OF COURSES   Professional; amateur
RANGE OF COURSES   Horticulture; Horticultural
Therapy; Garden Design
LEVELS   Post Professional Diploma

One of the first colleges to develop a range of horticultural activities for therapeutic use, especially for the handicapped, ill, aged or disadvantaged.

Norton Radstock Technical College

South Hill Park, Radstock, Bath, Somerset
BA3 3RW
☎ 0761 433161

CONTACT   Peter Skinner
TYPE OF COURSES   Professional; amateur; correspondence
RANGE OF COURSES   Horticulture; Landscape; Forestry; Floristry; Countryside management; Pesticides; Arboriculture; Amenity Horticulture (NVQ); Amateur Gardening (option C&G); Chain Saw techniques
LEVELS   NVQ; GNVQ; C&G

A further education college concentrating on NVQs. Many short courses e.g. safe use of pesticides. The Garden School has free introductory evenings.

STAFFORDSHIRE

Staffordshire College of Agriculture

Rodbaston, Penkridge, Staffordshire ST19 5PH
☎ 0785 712209   📠 0785 715701

CONTACT   W D D Fowler
TYPE OF COURSES   Professional; amateur
RANGE OF COURSES   Horticulture; Landscape; Administration and retailing; Floristry; Countryside management; Groundsmanship; Garden Design (Diploma)
LEVELS   C&G; NCH; NDH and Diploma

Wide range of short courses, including RHS, either at College or on industrial premises. Day and evening courses.

Stoke-on-Trent College

Burslem Campus, Moorland Road, Burslem,
Staffordshire ST6 1JJ
☎ 0782 208208   📠 0782 828106

CONTACT   Trevor McKeown
TYPE OF COURSES   Professional

RANGE OF COURSES   Horticulture; Floristry; Countryside management; Groundsmanship; Amenity Horticulture; Practical Flower Arranging (C&G)
LEVELS   NVQ I & II; BTEC First Diploma; C&G

Range of full, part-time and evening courses.

SUFFOLK

Otley College of Agriculture and Horticulture

Otley, Ipswich, Suffolk IP6 9EY
☎ 0473 785543   📠 0473 785353

CONTACT   John Blyth
TYPE OF COURSES   Professional; amateur
RANGE OF COURSES   Horticulture; Landscape; Administration and retailing; Forestry; Floristry; Countryside management; Leisure; Arboriculture; Garden Design and Construction; Organic Production; Interior Landscaping
LEVELS   Postgraduate; Degree; C&G; HNC; NDH; BTEC First Diploma; HND; RHS; ANC; NVQ

'Suffolk's Countryside Centre' which offers a MHort in partnership with Writtle College. There is a wide range of courses for young and mature students.

SURREY

Kew School of Horticulture

Royal Botanic Gardens, Kew, Richmond, Surrey
TW9 3AB
☎ 081 940 1171

CONTACT   Ian Leese
TYPE OF COURSES   Professional
RANGE OF COURSES   Horticulture
LEVELS   The Kew Diploma is a three-year course at first degree level in amenity horticulture and horticultural administration. It is recognised as the premier qualification of its kind and vacancies are limited to sixteen a year. The list of 'Old Kewites' reads as a Who's Who of horticulture.

Merrist Wood College

Worplesdon, Guildford, Surrey GU3 3PE
☎ 0483 232424   📠 0483 236518

CONTACT   The Academic Registrar
TYPE OF COURSES   Professional
RANGE OF COURSES   Horticulture; Landscape; Floristry; Leisure; Arboriculture
LEVELS   1 year NCH & 3 year NDH (sandwich course) in arboriculture, landscape & nursery practice. HND in Landscape Contract Management. Part-time

courses leading to NVQ in floristry, arboriculture, landscape and commercial horticulture

Merrist Wood is the Surrey college, and one of the leading centres for amenity horticulture. Both the staff and the pupils are among the most able nationally.

WEST SUSSEX

Brinsbury College
Brinsbury, North Heath, Pulborough, West Sussex RH20 1DL
☎ 0798 873832   📠 0798 873832

CONTACT The Administrator
TYPE OF COURSES Professional; amateur
RANGE OF COURSES Horticulture; Landscape; Forestry; Floristry; Leisure; Groundsmanship; Amenity Horticulture; Rural Business Studies; Countryside Management. Amateur courses include: Amateur Gardening (RHS); Woodland Craft; Woodland Maintenance; Rural Engineering; Landscape (NVQ option); Arboriculture (NVQ option); Glasshouse; Mushroom Production (NVQ); Young Growers; Pesticides
LEVELS NVQ; RHS; C&G; NCH; HNC; NDH; HND

The county agricultural college for West Sussex, offering a wide range of qualifications at most levels.

TYNE & WEAR

University of Newcastle
Faculty of Agriculture, Dept of Town and Country Planning, Newcastle upon Tyne, NE1 7RU
☎ 091 222 7802   📠 091 222 8811

TYPE OF COURSES Professional
RANGE OF COURSES Landscape Master, Diploma, MA, in Landscape Design; Research options to MPhil/PhD; Agriculture; Tropical Agricultural and Environmental Science (MSc); Agricultural Engineering (MSc); International Agricultural Marketing (MSc)
LEVELS Master; Diploma; MA; MSc; PhD

The landscape design course is geared to Town & Country Planning and Urban Landscape design.

WEST MIDLANDS

Bournville College of Further Education
Bristol Road South, Northfield, BirminghamB31 2AJ
☎ 021 411 1414

CONTACT Mike Hill

TYPE OF COURSES Professional; amateur
RANGE OF COURSES Horticulture; Amenity Horticulture (NVQ I & II); RHS Certificate in Horticulture
LEVELS NVQ I & II; RHS

Solihull College of Technology
Blossomfield Road, Solihull, West Midlands B91 1SB
☎ 021 711 2111   📠 021 711 2316

CONTACT Phil Gooding
TYPE OF COURSES Professional; amateur
RANGE OF COURSES Horticulture; Floristry; Amateur Gardening (C&G); Environmental Science (BTEC NDH and A level); Environmental Impact (De Monfort BSc); Flower Arranging (C&G)
LEVELS NVQ I, II & III; C&G; BTEC

Stourbridge College
Horticulture and Conservation Unit, Leasowes Park Nursery, Leasowes Lane, West Midlands B62 8QF
☎ 021 550 0007

CONTACT The Principal
TYPE OF COURSES Professional
RANGE OF COURSES Horticulture; Floristry; Countryside management; Amenity Horticulture (NVQ); Groundsmanship (NVQ); Urban and Countryside Conservation (NDH; FD); Amateur Courses; RHS General Horticulture; Chain Saws; Pesticides
LEVELS BTEC NDH; NVQ; RHS; Society of Floristry exams

Other interesting training modules: Landscape; Drainage; Fencing; Plant Identification; Sowing/Turfing; Walling; Paths/Paving; Pruning; Shrub/Border Maintenance; Diseases; Tractors.

Wulfran College
Paget Road, Wolverhampton, West Midlands WV6 0DU
☎ 0902 312062   📠 0902 23070

CONTACT John Newton
TYPE OF COURSES Professional; amateur
RANGE OF COURSES Horticulture; Landscape Groundsmanship; Spraying Courses for NPTC certificates; C& G Amateur Gardening
LEVELS RHS, C&G

WILTSHIRE

Horticultural Correspondence College
Little Notton Farmhouse, 16 Notton, Lacock, Chippenham, Wiltshire SN15 2NF
☎ 0249 730326   📠 0249 730326

CONTACT Oliver Menhinick (freephone 0800 378918)

TYPE OF COURSES Professional; amateur; correspondence

RANGE OF COURSES Horticulture; Landscape; Administration and retailing; Countryside management; RHS General Examination in Horticulture; Garden Landscape and Design Drawing; Garden Planting and Layout Course; Interior Landscaping; Horticulture Principles; Turf Culture (IOG); Arboriculture Theory; Garden Centre; Leisure Gardening; Organic

LEVELS RHS (MHort); IOG; RFS Certificate; NVQ I & II

This college is one of the great success stories of recent years, largely due to the energy and skills of Oliver Menhinick and his staff. Full (and growing) range of correspondence courses.

Lackham College

Lacock, Chippenham, Wiltshire SN15 2NY
☎ 0249 443111   📠 0249 444474

CONTACT Mrs P J Dickerson
TYPE OF COURSES Professional; amateur
RANGE OF COURSES Horticulture; Forestry; Floristry; Countryside management; Leisure; Groundsmanship; Organic Horticulture (NC); Certificate in Gardening (CGLI); Flower Arranging (CGLI); RHS General Exam (36 weeks)
LEVELS C&G; HNC; NDH; RHS; CGLI

One of the most go-ahead county colleges, with a substantial commitment to horticulture and floristry, and excellent demonstration gardens.

WORCESTERSHIRE

Pershore College of Horticulture

Avonbank, Pershore, Worcestershire WR10 3JP
☎ 0386 552443   📠 0386 556528

CONTACT Garden Design: F S Hardy; RHS Exams: D J Coombs
TYPE OF COURSES Professional
RANGE OF COURSES Horticulture; Floristry; Countryside management; Leisure; Amenity Horticulture; Landscaping (design, construction, maintenance); Arboriculture; Crop Production; Nursery Stock Production; Retail Horticulture; Horticulture and the Environment; Horticultural Technology; Field Tree Production; Container Plants; Bee Keeping; Garden Maintenance. RHS: Greenhouse; Vegetables; Fruit; Garden Design; General Exam
LEVELS Degree; C&G; HNC; NDH; HND; NVQ; RHS

The only specialist college of horticulture (no other subjects are taught), and a clear market leader. It developed to provide education and training for everyone

building a career in this industry. Pershore's contribution to every aspect of commercial and amenity horticulture over the last 35 years has been incalculable.

NORTH YORKSHIRE

Askham Bryan College of Agriculture and Horticulture

Askham Bryan, York YO2 3PR
☎ 0904 702121   📠 0904 702629

CONTACT Dr Bruce Rigby, Director of Education
RANGE OF COURSES Horticulture; Landscape; Arboriculture; Urban Forestry; Countryside management; Administration and Marketing; Leisure; Amenity Horticulture; Landscape and Garden Design; Environment and Conservation; Land Reclamation; Amenity Horticulture with Abor. Option; Green keeping; Land-based Industries; Equitation; Gamekeeping
LEVELS BSc Hons; BSc; HND; NDH; NCH; BTEC First Diploma; Diploma Garden Design; NVQ; C&G

The BTEC National Diploma in Urban Forestry is unique in the country; a BSc Hons in Landscape Management is projected for September 1994.

Craven College of Adult Education

High Street, Skipton, North Yorkshire BD23 1JY
☎ 0756 791411

CONTACT G Hirst
TYPE OF COURSES Professional; amateur
RANGE OF COURSES Horticulture; Landscape; Forestry; Floristry; Countryside management; Groundsmanship; Amateur Gardening (RHS)
LEVELS BTEC First Diploma; NVQ I & II; C&G; RHS

Harlow Carr Botanical Gardens

Crag Lane, Harrogate, North Yorkshire HG3 1QB
☎ 0423 565418

CONTACT Dr S Midgley
TYPE OF COURSES Professional; amateur
RANGE OF COURSES Horticulture; Leisure
LEVELS C&G; RHS

Harlow Carr is the home of the Northern Horticultural Society.

SOUTH YORKSHIRE

Barnsley College of Technology

Church Street, Barnsley, South Yorkshire S70 2AX
☎ 0226 730191   📠 0226 298514

CONTACT John Sheard

TYPE OF COURSES Professional; amateur
RANGE OF COURSES Horticulture Gardening (C&G)
LEVELS NVQ I & II, C&G; RHS

Well planned courses which appeal to amateurs and professionals.

University of Sheffield

Dept of Landscape Architecture, Sheffield, South Yorkshire S10 2TN
☎ 0742 768555

CONTACT Helen Wooley
TYPE OF COURSES Professional
RANGE OF COURSES Landscape design, management and research programmes
LEVELS Postgraduate; Degree

A large landscape teaching unit with over 70 postgraduates: research scholarships available.

WEST YORKSHIRE

Leeds Metropolitan University

Landscape Architecture, Brunswick Building, West Yorkshire LS2 8BU
☎ 0532 832600   ⠀ 0532 833190

CONTACT Landscape Architecture: Alan Simson; Garden Design: Fleur Gethin
TYPE OF COURSES Professional; amateur
RANGE OF COURSES Landscape Architecture (BA Hons, MA and Graduate Diploma); Landscape Conversion Course; Amateurs: The Art of Garden Design (Certificate, no exam, 10 weeks, twice yearly, basic & advanced)
LEVELS BA Hons; MA; Graduate Diploma; Certificate

Shipley College

Exhibition Road, Saltaire, Shipley, West Yorkshire BD18 3JW
☎ 0274 595731   ⠀ 0274 757201

CONTACT John Baker (0274 757222)
TYPE OF COURSES Professional; amateur
RANGE OF COURSES Horticulture; Landscape; Floristry; Leisure; RHS General Certificate; Horticulture NVQ I & II; Day and evening courses
LEVELS NVQ levels I, II, III and IV; RHS; NDH

Wakefield College

Margaret Street, Wakefield, West Yorkshire WS1 2DH
☎ 0924 370501   ⠀ 0924 810610

CONTACT Roger Bennett
TYPE OF COURSES Professional; amateur

RANGE OF COURSES Horticulture; Landscape; Floristry; Various courses for amateurs

LEVELS C&G; NVQ I, II & III; RHS

WALES

CLWYD

Welsh College of Horticulture

Northop, Mold, Clwyd, Wales CH7 6AA
☎ 0352 86861

CONTACT Floristry: Marae Kinread; Correspondence: Graham Wright
TYPE OF COURSES Professional; correspondence
RANGE OF COURSES Horticulture; Landscape; Administration and retailing; Floristry; Environmental Studies (Degree with Chester College); Machinery and Mechanisation (C&G also BTEC NDH); Glasshouse Crop Production & Management (BTEC NDH); Garden Centre Studies (BTEC NDH); Greenkeeping (BTEC NDH)
LEVELS Degrees; C&G; NCH; NDH; HND, HE Access; NVQ levels I, II and III

The leading horticultural college in the Principality – very thorough, professional and go-ahead. The range of courses is impressive, geared to commercial needs. Degree course is 1st year only at WCH, then further 3 years at Chester College. Short Courses: Chain Saws; Pesticides.

SOUTH GLAMORGAN

Cardiff Institute of Higher Education

Llandaff Centre, Western Avenue, Cardiff, South Glamorgan, Wales CF5 2YB
☎ 0222 551111

CONTACT David Thornton
TYPE OF COURSES Professional; amateur
RANGE OF COURSES Horticulture; Groundsmanship (NVQ, 36 weeks, £150); Amenity Horticulture (NVQ II, 36 weeks, £150); AH (BTEC 1st, one year, funded); Certificate in Gardening (C&G, 30 weeks, £63)
LEVELS BTEC First Diploma; NVQ, C&G

The courses are soundly planned and well taught.

WEST GLAMORGAN

Afan College

Margam, Port Talbot, West Glamorgan, Wales
SA13 2AL
☎ 0639 883712   ☎ 0639 891288

CONTACT The Director, Margam Country Park, Port
Talbot
TYPE OF COURSES Professional
RANGE OF COURSES Horticulture; Amateur: Hanging
Baskets (winter/summer); Propagation; Patio Containers; Fuchsias
LEVELS NVQ I & II

GWYNEDD

University College of North Wales

School of Agricultural and Forest Sciences, Bangor,
Gwynedd, Wales LL57 2UW
☎ 0248 382281   ☎ 0248 354997

CONTACT Dr H Omed
TYPE OF COURSES Professional; amateur
RANGE OF COURSES Forestry; Countryside management; Agriculture; Wood Sciences; Rural Resource
Economics; Soil Sciences; BSc in Botany
LEVELS Postgraduate; Degree

SCOTLAND

DUMFRIES & GALLOWAY

The Barony College

Parkgate, Dumfries & Galloway DG1 3NE
☎ 0387 86251   ☎ 0387 86395

CONTACT T Jones
TYPE OF COURSES Professional; amateur
RANGE OF COURSES Horticulture; Landscape; Forestry; Floristry; Countryside management; Botany;
Amateur: RHS; Amateur Gardening
LEVELS C&G; Scotvec National Certificate

Threave School of Horticulture

Threave, Castle Douglas, Dumfries & Galloway,
DG7 1RX
☎ 0556 502575

CONTACT The Principal
TYPE OF COURSES Professional

RANGE OF COURSES Horticulture
LEVELS Scotvec

Full time two-year residential course for all ages: 17/18
year olds to mature students. Aimed at amenity based
professional horticulturists who want to work for the
National Trust for Scotland or private gardens. The
course has a strong practical element.

FIFE

Elmwood College

Carslogie Road, Cupar, Fife, Scotland KY15 4JB
☎ 0334 52781   ☎ 0334 56795

CONTACT Alan Smith
TYPE OF COURSES Professional
RANGE OF COURSES Horticulture; Landscape; Floristry; Golf Greenkeeping; Computer aided landscape
technology
LEVELS HNC; NC; Scottish Vocational Qualification (Scotvec)

The college expects to offer an HND in 1995/96.

GRAMPIAN

Aberdeen College of Further Education

School of Rural Studies, Clinterty, Kinellar,
Aberdeen, Grampian AB2 0TN
☎ 0224 640366   ☎ 0224 790326

CONTACT Bruce Gilliland
TYPE OF COURSES Professional; amateur
RANGE OF COURSES Horticulture; Landscape; Administration and retailing; Countryside management;
Leisure; Agricultural Engineering (NC); Arboriculture
(Scotvec, 1 year); Chainsaw Operation; Forest Tree
Harvesting; Countryside Leisure Recreation & Tourism; Pesticide Application (Scotvec); Evening Classes
for Amateurs
LEVELS NC; Scotvec modules; ND

Aberdeen College incorporates the former Clinterty
Agricultural College.

University of Aberdeen

Department of Agriculture, 581 King Street,
Aberdeen, Grampian AB9 1UD
☎ 0224 480291   ☎ 0224 273731

CONTACT Professor Robert Naylor
TYPE OF COURSES Professional
RANGE OF COURSES Horticulture; Landscape; Administration and retailing; Countryside management;
Leisure; Botany; Soil Science; Tropical Biology; Tropi-

cal Environmental Science; Agriculture (BSc); Agricultural Business Management; Arboriculture; Agroforestry; Rural Resources
LEVELS Postgraduate; Degree

The faculty of science has a good record.

LOTHIAN

Oatridge Agricultural College
Ecclesmachan, Broxburn, Lothian, Scotland
EH52 6NH
☎ 0506 854387   ☒ 0506 853373

CONTACT David Webster
TYPE OF COURSES Professional; amateur
RANGE OF COURSES Horticulture; Landscape; Countryside management; Leisure; Groundsmanship; Greenkeeping and Golf Courses; Non Vocational Horticultural Courses

LEVELS HNC; SVQ

Edinburgh College of Art, Heriot-Watt University
School of Landscape Architecture, Lauriston Place, Lothian, Scotland EH3 9DF
☎ 031 229 9311   ☒ 031 228 8825

CONTACT Anne Watson
TYPE OF COURSES Professional
RANGE OF COURSES Landscape
LEVELS Postgraduate Degree

Noted for stylish and original design; some bursaries available.

University of Edinburgh
School of Forestry and Ecological Science, Darwin Building, Mayfield Road, Edinburgh, Lothian, Scotland EH9 3JU
☎ 031 650 5421   ☒ 031 662 0478

CONTACT BSc: Dr J F Blyth; TropAg courses: G Hilton; Tropical Forests: Dr H McIver; Landscape Architecture: Dr J B Byrom
TYPE OF COURSES Professional
RANGE OF COURSES Landscape; Forestry; Tropical Forest Management; Tropical Agricultural Development; TROPAG (Training for the Tropics) Women in Development; Technology in the Tropics; Sustainable Development; Master of Landscape Architecture
LEVELS BSc in Ecological Science with Honours in Forestry; Postgraduate

A major scientific research institute with a distinguished commitment to tropical botany and husbandry and the highest reputation both among academics and in government.

STRATHCLYDE

Country Courses
Corranmor House, Ardfern, By Lochgilphead, Strathclyde, Scotland PA31 8QN
☎ 08525 609/221   ☒ 08525 627

CONTACT Barbara Service
TYPE OF COURSES Amateur
RANGE OF COURSES Horticulture; Landscape Garden Design & Plant Design (2 – 4 day courses)

International Correspondence Schools
Clydeway Centre, 8 Elliot Place, Glasgow, Strathclyde, Scotland G3 8EF
☎ 041 221 7373   ☒ 041 221 8151 (Glasgow)

CONTACT Course or Career Advisers
TYPE OF COURSES Professional; amateur; correspondence
RANGE OF COURSES Horticulture; Intensive Market Gardening (Diploma); Complete Gardening (Diploma); General Exam in Horticulture (RHS)
LEVELS ICS Diploma; RHS

Offices in Sutton, Surrey, Glasgow and Dublin.

Langside College
Department of Horticulture, Woodburn House, 27 Buchanan Drive, Rutherglen, Strathclyde, Scotland G73 3PF
☎ 041 647 6300

TYPE OF COURSES Professional; amateur
RANGE OF COURSES Horticulture; Landscape; Forestry; Floristry; Countryside management; Leisure Gardening; Flower Arranging
LEVELS C&G; HNC; RHS

Scottish Agricultural College
Auchincruive, Ayr, Strathclyde KA6 5HW
☎ 0292 520331   ☒ 0292 521119

CONTACT Mrs E A Jaffray (Education Liaison Officer) or Professor G R Dixon
TYPE OF COURSES Professional
RANGE OF COURSES Horticulture; Landscape; Countryside management; Leisure; Biotechnology; Applied Plant and Animal Science; Rural Resources; Rural Tourism; Aquaculture
LEVELS Postgraduate; Degree; NCH; NDH; HND; College Diploma (Horticulture)

The major centre for horticulture in Scotland: the degree courses are taught in conjunction with the University of Strathclyde. The emphasis is on commercial horticulture and horticultural management.

TAYSIDE

Angus College

Keptie Road, Arbroath, Tayside, Scotland
DD11 3EA
☎ 0241 72056   🖷 0241 76169

CONTACT Jim Menzies
TYPE OF COURSES Professional; correspondence
RANGE OF COURSES Landscape; Lawns; Garden Machinery; Propagation (Scotvec National Certificate). Correspondence: Wages/PAYE/SSP/Cash Book, etc. (College Certificate); Horticulture (HNC)

Go-ahead local authority college: 'small and friendly'. Courses can be full time or day release.

EIRE

An Grianan College of Horticulture

Termonfechin, Drogheda, Co. Louth, Eire
☎ (010 353) 41 22158

CONTACT Course Administrator
TYPE OF COURSES Professional
RANGE OF COURSES Horticulture
LEVELS HNC; NDH

Kildalton Agricultural and Horticultural College

Piltown, Co. Kilkenny, Eire
☎ (010 353) 51 43105   🖷 (010 353) 51 43446

CONTACT Michael Cowhow
TYPE OF COURSES Professional
RANGE OF COURSES Horticulture; Administration and retailing 3 year course leading to a Diploma in Commercial Horticulture
LEVELS NDH

One of the leading horticultural schools in Eire.

Salesian College of Horticulture

Warrenstown, Drumree, Co. Meath, Eire
☎ (010 353) 1 8259342 🖷 (010 353) 1 8259632

CONTACT Br J O'Hare
TYPE OF COURSES Professional
RANGE OF COURSES Horticulture; Administration and retailing Commercial Horticulture (Diploma, 2-3 years)

Scoil Stiofáin

Naofa, Traore Road, Cork, Co. Cork, Eire
☎ (010 353) 21 961029 🖷 (010 353) 21 961320

CONTACT Bernard Brennan
TYPE OF COURSES Professional
RANGE OF COURSES Horticulture; Landscape
LEVELS C&G; National Certificate

The college has just started a new course in greenkeeping.

Teagasc College of Amenity Horticulture

National Botanic Gardens, Glasnevin, Co. Dublin, Eire
☎ (010 353) 1 374388 🖷 (010 353) 1 377329

CONTACT The Principal
TYPE OF COURSES Professional
RANGE OF COURSES Horticulture; Amenity Horticulture (Diploma); Greenkeeping (Certificate)
LEVELS Diploma; Certificate

The courses have the premier setting in the National Botanic Gardens at Glasnevin. Diploma students demonstrate a high level of competence.

University College Dublin

Dept of Horticulture, Belfield, Dublin, Co. Dublin, Eire
☎ (010 353) 1 2693244 🖷 (010 353) 1 2837328

CONTACT Course Administrator
TYPE OF COURSES Professional
RANGE OF COURSES Horticulture; Landscape; Forestry; Countryside management; Botany; Groundsmanship; Commercial/Landscape Horticulture; Plant Protection; Environmental Resource Management; Landscape Architecture; Agricultural Science; Agribusiness and Rural Development
LEVELS BAgrSc Degrees

Commercial and landscape horticulture are the leading degrees, both geared to getting employment on graduation.

26

Grant-making Trusts

There are hundreds of private charitable trusts which award funds for horticultural projects. Most of the trusts mentioned in this chapter are listed in the 1993 edition of *The Directory of Grant-Making Trusts*, an invaluable reference book which readers are urged to consult in full. Many others are attached to universities, colleges and societies, and only their own students or members are eligible for grants.

All these trusts are known to have supported endeavours which can be classed as 'horticultural'. They may have done so only once, and have no plans to do so again: we cannot tell. If the principal concern of a trust is the welfare of people with disabilities, you can assume that its 'horticultural' interests are limited to projects which help such people.

Most trusts accept applications only from other registered charities, but some are prepared to make an exception to this general rule if an individual puts forward a particularly deserving or imaginative proposal. This list will also be of particular interest to gardening clubs, conservation groups and readers who are active in such areas as horticultural therapy.

The Blunt Trust

C.C. No. 250721
CORRESPONDENT Mrs. J. E. Mustoe, 58 Grafton Terrace, London NW5 4HY
TRUSTEES Mrs. J. E. Mustoe, Mrs. J. M. Blunt

OBJECTS General charitable purposes. The principal areas of interest include historic buildings, conservation and ecology, mainly in Wiltshire. Registered charities only: no applications from individuals or students.
FINANCES Year: 1991; Income: £9,400
NOTES Awards do not normally exceed £100. Only direct applications will be considered.

The H. & L. Cantor Trust

C.C. No. 220300
CORRESPONDENT H. Cantor, Massada, 478 Ecclesall Road South, Sheffield, South Yorkshire S11 9PZ
TRUSTEES L. Cantor, H. Cantor

OBJECTS General charitable purposes with a preference for those charities which are known to the Trustees: registered charities only.
FINANCES Year: 1991; Income: £36,649; Assets: £192,312

The Timothy Colman Charitable Trust

C.C. No 206129
CORRESPONDENT The Administrator, The Timothy Colman Charitable Trust, Coutts & Co., Trustee Dept., 440 Strand, London WC2R 0QS
TRUSTEES Coutts & Co., T. J. A. Colman

OBJECTS General charitable purposes for community life, especially in Norfolk. No grants to individuals.
FINANCES Year: 1991; Income: £9,404; Grants: £10,560; Assets: £201,111
NOTES Small one-off cash grants, primarily for projects within the Norfolk area. Conservation and nautical projects favoured. Applications in writing to Coutts & Co.

The Sarah D'Avigdor Goldsmid Charitable Trust

C.C. No. 233083
CORRESPONDENT Mrs. R. C. Teacher, Hadlow Place, Golden Green, Tonbridge, Kent TN11 0BW
TRUSTEES Lady d'Avigdor Goldsmid, Mrs. R. C. Teacher, A. J. M. Teacher

OBJECTS General charitable purposes. Registered charities only: no applications by individuals. Unsuccessful applications not acknowledged.

FINANCES Year: 1992; Income: £12,078; Grants: £12,475; Assets: £110,732
NOTES Usually one-off grants.

The C. H. Dixon Charitable Trust
C.C. No. 282936
CORRESPONDENT R. M. Robinson, Messrs. Dixon Ward, 16 The Green, Richmond, Surrey TW9 1QD
TRUSTEES Miss A. Dixon, R. M. Robinson

OBJECTS General charitable purposes
FINANCES Year: 1992; Income: £19,819; Grants: £11,098; Assets: £124,223

The Glaxo (1972) Charity Trust
C.C. No. 265241
CORRESPONDENT The Secretary, The Glaxo (1972) Charity Trust, Glaxo House, Berkeley Avenue, Greenford, Middlesex UB6 0NN
TRUSTEES D. J. Derx, Sir Ralf Dahrendorf, J. M. Hignett

OBJECTS General charitable purposes, with priority for appeals which advance science and health care. No grants to individuals.
FINANCES Year: 1992; Income: £396,111; Grants: £294,008
NOTES Single and recurring donations. Some interest in the preservation of the national heritage. Applications are considered four times a year.

The Harry Ibbetson Settlement
C.C. No. 231131
CORRESPONDENT Dr. B. Ibbetson, 39 Cumberland Terrace, Regent's Park, London NW1
TRUSTEES C. Kanter, FCA; Professor W. Fox, CMG

OBJECTS General charitable purposes, especially charities in which the Trustees have a special interest or association. Restricted to welfare organisations and certain cultural and educational purposes.
FINANCES Year: 1986; Income: £5,115; Grants: £2,934; Assets: £61,193
NOTES Recurrent and one-off grants to the handicapped and elderly.

The Kirby Laing Foundation
C.C. No. 264299
CORRESPONDENT R.M. Harley, Box 1, 133 Page Street, Mill Hill, London NW7 2ER
TRUSTEES Sir Kirby Laing, Lady Laing, S. Webley, D. E. Laing

OBJECTS General charitable purposes but not for education or travel
FINANCES Year: 1991; Income: £2,516,199; Grants: £1,843,190; Assets: £15,112,056

NOTES Registered charities only: no gifts to individuals. Meetings approximately quarterly.

The Laspen Trust (formerly The Penrhyn Charitable Trust)
C.C. No. 276043
CORRESPONDENT J. C. Douglas Pennant, Penrhyn, Bangor, Gwynedd LL57 4HN
TRUSTEES Lady Janet Douglas Pennant, (Chair), R. C. H. Douglas Pennant, J. C. Douglas Pennant (Secretary)

OBJECTS General charitable purposes, especially the arts, the handicapped, health, welfare and environmental causes. No grants to individuals. Main area of benefit: north Wales, Merseyside, Northern Ireland.
FINANCES Year: 1992; Income: £8,615; Grants: £8,250; Assets: £117,807
NOTES Usually one-off donations to charities.

The John Spedan Lewis Foundation
C.C. No. 240473
CORRESPONDENT N. Waldemar Brown, The Secretary, The John Spedan Lewis Foundation, 171 Victoria Street, London SW1E 5NN
TRUSTEES P. T. Lewis, W. H. Melly, Miss D. N. Barrett, H. M. J. King, A. D. Page

OBJECTS General charitable purposes, particularly those that reflect John Lewis's interest in education, the arts, the natural sciences (including horticulture) and the encouragement of disadvantaged talent.
FINANCES Year: 1992; Income: £28,922; Grants: £22,500; Assets: £640,734
NOTES Mostly straight donations which may be repeated. Preference is given to smaller, more imaginative appeals (but not normally to local branches, individual students or expeditions).

The W. T. Mattock Charitable Trust
C.C. No. 244038
CORRESPONDENT Messrs Blakemores, Pemberton House, 4 - 6 East Harding Street, London EC4A 3BD
TRUSTEES I. S. Wick, K. G. Coulton, A. C. Salt

OBJECTS General charitable purposes, principally for the blind and disabled. Occasional ecological causes. Registered charities only.
FINANCES Year: 1992; Income: £5,333; Grants: £5,000; Assets: £61,202
NOTES Usually one-off grants for a specific project.

The Nuffield Farming Scholarships Trust
C.C. No. 261823
CORRESPONDENT The Director, Nuffield Farming Scholarships Trust, Uckfield, East Sussex TN22 3AY

OBJECTS The advancement of farming (including horticulture) by the provision of scholarships to study practices and techniques anywhere in the world.

FINANCES Year: 1992; Income: £143,566; Grants: £93,020; Assets: £292,934

NOTES Travelling scholarships only. No grants for courses or conferences. Applicants must be in agriculture, horticulture, forestry or countryside management.

The Rank Prize Funds

C.C. No. 263819

CORRESPONDENT Mrs. Judith Delaney (Administrative Secretary), 12 Warwick Square, London SW1V 2AA

OBJECTS Advancement and promotion of knowledge and education in the sciences of crop husbandry, human nutrition and animal nutrition.

FINANCES Year: 1991; Income: £530,476; Grants: £406,586; Assets: £7,776,820

NOTES The main work of the Funds is organising symposia and awarding prizes. The Trustees do not usually consider unsolicited appeals. Grants are not made for general charitable purposes or to individuals for the furtherance of their education or research.

The Royal Botanical and Horticultural Society of Manchester and the Northern Counties

C.C. No. 226683

CORRESPONDENT A. Pye MA FCA, P.O. Box 498, 12 Booth Street, Manchester M60 2ED

OBJECTS Promotion of science and art in botany and horticulture by giving financial assistance to local gardens or other projects of horticultural interest in the north west.

FINANCES Year: 1989; Income: £10,207; Grants: £7,321; Assets: £108,242

NOTES Mostly cash payments towards prize money or specific expenditure by horticultural societies, show organisers and gardens interest.

Royal Commission for the Exhibition of 1851

C.C. No. 206123

CORRESPONDENT The Secretary, Royal Commission for the Exhibition of 1851, Sherfield Building,

Imperial College of Science Technology and Medicine, London SW7 2AZ

OBJECTS 'To increase the means of industrial education and extend the influence of science and art upon productive industry.'

FINANCES Year: 1991; Income: £1,000,000; Grants: £550,000; Assets: £11,914,000

NOTES Research fellowships in the pure and applied sciences and in engineering, industrial fellowships and industrial design studentships. Young graduates in engineering or science proposing to make their careers in British industry or wishing to develop their knowledge of industrial design.

The Royal Society

C.C. No. 207043

CORRESPONDENT The Executive Secretary, The Royal Society, 6 Carlton House Terrace, London SW1Y 5AG

OBJECTS An independent learned society which promotes national and international activities in the natural sciences. It has over one hundred trust funds.

FINANCES Year: 1992; Income: £20,571,000; Grants: £17,383,000; Assets: £35,000,000

NOTES Principally for the advancement of science through research, mainly to postdoctoral scientists. Information is available on request.

Stanley Smith Horticultural Trust

C.C. No. 261925

CORRESPONDENT Dr James Cullen, Cory Lodge, P O Box 365, Cambridge, CB2 1HR

OBJECT The support of amenity horticulture mainly, but not exclusively, in the United Kingdom

FINANCES Year: 1993; Income: £110,000

NOTES The Trustees welcome applications from individuals, organisations and institutions. They try to maintain a balance between small (up to £1,500) and larger grants at any time. The Trust has recently supported projects concerned with plant collecting, books on horticultural subjects, garden restoration, research on the production of new hybrids, and the maintenance of garden trainees. Grants are awarded twice a year, in April and October. Applications should be sent to the Director, who can also advise applicants as to how their applications should be presented.

27

Horticultural Libraries

Every keen gardener needs to consult reference books and sometimes to borrow them. Most people start their search for a particular book at their local library. Often the volume is not available at that particular branch, in which case the reader's search application form will be referred to other libraries within the same county, metropolitan area or region. Provided that records are readily accessible, and the system is up-to-date, most books are soon found. Those which are not available within the local area are passed to the Local Libraries Bureau, a federation of libraries which holds catalogues from each of its members. If this fails to locate a copy of the book, then the usual course is to refer the request to the British Library at Boston Spa to search through more and better catalogues until a source is found.

The Document Supply Centre of the British Library will also supply copies of articles free of charge to libraries which request them. It is a rule of this service that the copy must be read on the premises of the requesting library and not borrowed by the reader. If the reader wishes to purchase it, the local library will sometimes give permission and levy a small charge.

Sometimes a reader needs to discover whether any books exist on a particular subject. The better libraries have extensive bibliographies and union lists of periodical publications. A good starting point is the British Library's catalogue; better still, that of the Library of Congress.

Specialised collections like the Royal Horticultural Society's Lindley Library have extensive archives and large numbers of older books, especially those which were published before the Copyright Act 1911, came into effect. There are six legal deposit libraries which are entitled under the provisions of the Act to receive a free copy of any book published in the United Kingdom. They are: the British Library, The Bodleian Library at Oxford, the Cambridge University Library, the National Library of Scotland, the National Library of Wales and the library of Trinity College, Dublin. Their post-1911 collections of British gardening books are all complete.

Most of the libraries listed here offer such facilities as photocopying services, computer terminals, video viewers, and full microform and microfiche equipment, but not all are available at some of the smaller, more specialised libraries.

Much of the information in this chapter comes from *The Libraries Directory 1991-93* edited by Richard S Burnell and published by James Clarke & Co Ltd of Cambridge, which gives further details of the services offered by each and by hundreds of other libraries throughout Britain and Ireland.

England

The British Library
2 Sheraton Street, London W1V 4BH
☎ 071 636 1544

OPEN Reading Room, weekdays 9.30 am - 5.30 pm (9 pm on Tuesday - Thursday), Saturday 9.30 am - 1 pm

The British Library is the UK's national library, at the centre of the library and information network. It was established in 1973 to consolidate the library departments of the British Museum, the National Central Library, the National Lending Library for Science and Technology, the British National Bibliography Ltd, and, in 1974, the Office for Scientific and Technical Information. Its services are based on the largest collections in the UK: over 18 million volumes at 18 buildings in

London and the Document Supply Centre in West Yorkshire.

Most books and articles relating to horticulture, apart from more recent issues of popular magazines, can be read at the Humanities and Social Sciences reading rooms at the British Museum. A British Library Reader's Pass is needed: information about eligibility is available from the Reader Admissions Office. Some gardening books, especially those which deal with practical or scientific topics, are stored at the Aldwych and Holborn reading rooms of the Science Reference and Information Service which open to the general public without charge or formality. The great majority of material is at the British Museum.

The British Library is in the process of moving to purpose-built accommodation at St Pancras, London NW1 but the planned opening has been delayed several times and will certainly not take place this year, as once envisaged.

Document Supply Centre
Boston Spa, Wetherby, West Yorkshire LS23 7BQ
☎ 0937 546000

The British Library offers two important services from the Document Supply Centre. The first is, in effect, a book-finding service for readers who apply through their local public or college libraries. The other is a rapid loan and photocopy service. The Document Supply Centre subscribes to 55,000 current journals in addition to acquiring monographs, conference proceedings and scientific reports. Some 88% of the 3,750,000 requests received each year are satisfied from stock.

Library and Archives, Royal Botanic Gardens
Kew, Richmond, Surrey TW9 3AE
☎ 081 940 1171   ᶠᴬˣ 081 332 0920

OPEN Monday - Thursday, 9 am - 5.30 pm

Books are available to *bona fide* researchers by written appointment only. The library's collection includes: plant taxonomy, distribution and conservation, horticulture, economic botany, plant anatomy, genetics, biochemistry and tropical botany. The library has 164,000 volumes (120,000 monographs), 140,000 pamphlets, 1,800 current periodicals and 3,200 no longer current. The archive collection has 250,000 modern and recent items, including the papers of Sir Joseph Banks, Sir William Hooker, Sir Joseph Hooker and George Bentham.

Ministry of Agriculture, Fisheries and Food Library
3 Whitehall Place, London SW1A 3HH
☎ 071 270 8420/21

OPEN Monday - Friday, 9.30 am - 5 pm, by prior appointment giving at least 24 hours notice

The library has 160,000 volumes and subscribes to 2,000 current periodicals. It also publishes a library guide, reading lists and subject bibliographies. We have found it a valuable source, especially for foreign periodicals.

Linnean Society of London Library
Burlington House, Piccadilly, London W1V 0LQ
☎ 071 434 4479   ᶠᴬˣ 071 287 9364

OPEN Monday - Friday, 10 am - 5 pm, by appointment

The library's collection includes: natural history, taxonomy, botany, the history of science, the history of biology, evolutionary theory and some horticultural studies. Its special collections incorporate the Insch Tea Library, the Balfour Bequest Bird Library and the library of Carolus Linnaeus. It has over 100,000 volumes, nearly 1,000 current periodicals and a good collection of pamphlets, photographs and other illustrations.

Chelsea Physic Garden
66 Royal Hospital Road, London SW3 4HS
☎ 071 352 5654

OPEN Monday - Friday, 8 am - 3 pm by appointment

The library concentrates on British and foreign pharmacological, herbal and medicinal studies, and its special collections include historic herbals dating back to 1472, small historic herbaria (e.g. Moore's Clematis), and a general reference collection on medicinal plants.

Consumers' Association Library
2 Marylebone Road, London NW1 4DX
☎ 071 486 5544   ᶠᴬˣ 071 935 1606

OPEN Monday - Friday, 10 am - 6 pm

Admission is at the discretion of the Chief Librarian. Principally concerned with consumer protection, the library has a good collection of gardening sources which are used by the staff of *Gardening Which?* The library has 3,000 volumes and subscribes to 850 current periodicals.

The Natural History Museum
Library Services, Cromwell Road, London SW7 5BD
☎ 071 938 9191   ᶠᴬˣ 071 938 9290

OPEN Monday - Saturday, 10 am - 6 pm

Reader's ticket required. A large collection of books, focused on life and earth sciences: natural history, botany, entomology, palaeontology, mineralogy, geology, anthropology, zoology and horticulture. Also a good collection of drawings, manuscripts, archives, catalogues and papers. There are 800,000 volumes and 10,000 current periodicals.

The Royal Horticultural Society

Lindley Library, 80 Vincent Square, London SW1P 2PE

☎ 071 821 3050

OPEN Monday - Friday, 9.30 am - 5.30 pm

Members of the Society are entitled to use the library at any time during these hours. The library has nearly 50,000 books and the largest collection of nursery catalogues in the UK. It subscribes to a wide range of British and foreign periodicals. It also has an unrivalled collection of horticultural papers and foreign works. Some volumes can be borrowed, by post if the member cannot attend the library in person.

Bodleian Library

Broad Street, Oxford OX1 3BG

☎ 0865 277000   ☎ 0865 277182

OPEN During term time: Monday - Friday, 9 am - 8 pm, Saturday, 9 am - 1 pm. During vacations: Monday - Friday, 9 am - 7 pm, Saturday, 9 am - 1 pm

The library is open to non-University readers on payment for a Reader's Ticket (from £2 for two-day ticket, to £10 for one year). The Bodleian is a copyright library, so the horticultural collection is very comprehensive, although there are comparatively few older works. The Bodleian has a total of 5.5 million volumes and subscribes to 54,800 current periodicals.

Cambridge University Library

West Road, Cambridge CB3 9DR

☎ 0223 333000   ☎ 0223 333160

OPEN Monday to Friday 9 am - 7.15 pm (10 pm during Easter Term), Saturday 9 am - 1 pm; closed for some Bank Holidays and for one week in September. Open to non-members of the University: enquiries in writing to the admissions officer

The library is a copyright library, with a comprehensive collection of 20th century books on gardening. There are 4 million volumes and nearly 60,000 current periodicals, but these include all subjects.

Writtle Agricultural College Library

Writtle College, Chelmsford, Essex CM1 3RR

☎ 0245 420705   ☎ 0245 420456

OPEN Term time: Monday - Thursday, 8.45 am - 8.30 pm, Friday, 8.45 am - 5 pm, Saturday, 9 am - 12 pm. During vacations: Monday - Thursday, 8.45 am - 5.15 pm, Friday, 8.45 am - 4.45 pm

This is a membership library: apply to the chief librarian for details. The collection includes agriculture, horticulture and other land-based subjects, with related science and management, and there are many historical books relating to agriculture and horticulture. The library has 37,000 volumes and subscribes to 375 current periodicals.

University of Reading Library

P O Box 223, Whiteknights, Reading, Berkshire RG6 2AE

☎ 0734 318770   ☎ 0734 312335

OPEN Term time: Monday - Thursday, 9 am - 10.15 pm, Friday, 9 am - 7 pm, Saturday, 9 am - 12.30 pm, Sunday, 2 pm - 6 pm. During vacations: Monday - Friday, 9 am - 5 pm

There is a good natural sciences and agriculture collection as well as horticulture. There are 800,000 volumes and 4,000 current periodicals but these statistics cover all the university's facilities. Nevertheless, Reading has one of the best university collections of horticultural books in the country.

Pershore College of Horticulture Library

Pershore, Worcestershire WR10 3JP

☎ 0386 552443   ☎ 0386 556528

OPEN Monday - Thursday, 9 am - 8 pm, Friday, 9 am - 5 pm by appointment

The horticultural collection covers science, landscaping, management, arboriculture and beekeeping, as well as amenity and commercial horticulture. There are 10,000 volumes, 130 current periodicals and 2,500 pamphlets.

University of Bristol Library

Tyndall Avenue, Bristol BS8 1TJ

☎ 0272 303030   ☎ 0272 255334

OPEN Term time: Monday - Thursday, 8.45 am - 11 pm, Friday and Saturday, 8.45 am - 6 pm, Sunday, 2 pm - 8 pm. Christmas vacation: Monday - Thursday, 8.45 am - 7 pm, Friday, 8.45 am - 4.45 pm. Summer vacation: Monday - Friday, 8.45 am - 4.45 pm, Saturday, 8.45 am - 1 pm.

Applications to use the library should be made in writing to the University Librarian. The library has some rare botany books but, more importantly, houses the book collection of the Garden History Society. There is a total of 940,000 volumes and 6,500 current periodicals, but these figures include all university faculties.

Horticulture Research International

Wellesbourne Library, Wellesbourne, Warwick
CV35 9EF

☎ 0789 470382 📠 0789 470552

Dependent library: Horticulture Research International, East Malling Library, East Malling, Maidstone, Kent ME19 6BJ

OPEN Monday - Friday, 8.30 am - 5 pm, Friday, 8.30 am - 4.30 pm by appointment

Topics covered include horticulture, plant breeding, entomology, plant pathology, seed technology, genetics, vegetable production, soil science, pesticide science and plant physiology. Wellesbourne has 16,000 volumes and subscribes to 400 current periodicals. There is also a small collection of rare 18th and 19th century gardening books and an archive collection of modern books - 'modern' means post 1789.

Wales

Welsh College of Horticulture/Coleg Garddwriaeth Cymru

Northop, Mold, Clwyd CH7 6AA
☎ 0352 86861 📠 0352 86731

OPEN Term time: Monday - Friday, 9 am - 8.30 pm: times variable during the vacation

Reference only: no borrowing. Subjects include horticulture, floristry, interior landscape, landscape, amenity horticulture, garden centres, retail horticulture, commercial horticulture and greenkeeping. The library has 4,000 volumes and subscribes to 50 current periodicals.

The National Library of Wales/ Llyfrgell Genedlaethol Cymru

Aberystwyth, Dyfed SY23 3BU
☎ 0970 623816 📠 0970 615709

OPEN Monday to Friday 9.30 am - 6 pm (5 pm on Saturdays)

Membership open to any person over 18 years of age. A legal deposit library with a large modern collection on horticultural topics. 3 million volumes on all subjects. The library has a good collection of bibliographies on Welsh topics, including aspects of horticulture and garden history.

Scotland

National Library of Scotland

George IV Bridge, Edinburgh EH1 1EW
☎ 031 226 4531

OPEN Reading room, weekdays, 9.30 am - 8.30 pm (Wednesday 10 am - 8.30 pm), Saturday 9.30 am - 1 pm. Scottish Science Library, weekdays 9.30 am - 5 pm (Wednesday 10 am - 8.30 pm)

The Library became the National Library of Scotland by Act of Parliament in 1925. Its collection of printed books and MSS is very large and it has an unrivalled collection of Scottish material. The Reading Room is open to readers for research which cannot conveniently be pursued elsewhere. Admission is by ticket issued to an approved applicant.

The Library, Royal Botanic Garden Edinburgh

Inverleith Row, Edinburgh EH3 5LR
☎ 031 552 7171 📠 031 552 0382

OPEN Monday - Thursday, 9 am - 5 pm, Friday, 9 am - 4.30 pm

Collection includes: systematic botany, amenity horticulture and landscape architecture: there are 180,000 volumes, 25,000 pamphlets, and the library subscribes to 1,500 current periodicals.

Eire

Trinity College Library

College Street, Dublin 2
☎ (010 353) (0)1 772941 📠 (010 353) (0)1 719003

OPEN Monday - Friday 9.30 am - 10 pm (5 pm during vacations, 1 pm on Saturdays)

Members of the public may use the library to consult material not available elsewhere. It is a deposit library for both Ireland and Britain. There are 3 million volumes and the library subscribes to 12,000 current periodicals.

28

Specialist Bookshops

New gardening books appear each year in unrelenting numbers. Some are excellent, most more run of the mill. Nationwide chains such as Waterstones and Dillons, Foyles, and the university booksellers, including Heffers and Blackwells, all carry an impressive selection and usually offer mail order or account facilities. Ordinary secondhand bookshops can prove fruitful for reasonably priced gardening books but much of their stock is out of date and best forgotten. The specialists are your most reliable source for older and more recent classics, floras and affordable but worthwhile titles from overlooked authors. They will also have highly-illustrated and collectable books. The Provincial Booksellers Fairs Association (PBFA) (0763 249212) organises regular sales around the country.

A & PM Books

37b New Cavendish Street, London W1M 8JR
☎ 071 935 0995   ☎ 071 486 4591

CONTACT Philippa Cross
OPEN Mail order only
SPECIALITY Secondhand and antiquarian books; botany; illustrated books or prints
CATALOGUE On request; 2 or 3 a year
MAIL ORDER Yes

This miscellaneous catalogue of rare and collectable works includes botanical and illustrated titles.

Anna Buxton Books

23 Murrayfield Road, Edinburgh, Lothian EH12 6EP
☎ 031 337 1747

CONTACT Mrs Anna Buxton
OPEN By appointment only
SPECIALITY New books; remaindered books; secondhand and antiquarian books; flower arranging; horticulture; illustrated books or prints; Scottish gardening, plant hunters, garden history
CATALOGUE On request; Christmas supplement
MAIL ORDER Yes

An attractively produced and readable list, which includes general titles, collectable works and some new books. All books are described, and appear alphabetically by author.

Berger & Tims

7 Bressenden Place, Victoria, London SW1E 5DE
☎ 071 834 9827   ☎ 071 976 5976

CONTACT Miss Verguin
OPEN 9 am – 6 pm, Monday – Friday
SPECIALITY New books; flower arranging; general gardening
MAIL ORDER Yes
SHOWS Chelsea

Besleys Books

4 Blyburgate, Beccles, Suffolk NR34 9TA
☎ 0502 715762

CONTACT P. Besley
OPEN 9.30 am – 5.30 pm. Closed Wednesdays and Sundays. After hours contact 0502 75649
SPECIALITY Secondhand and antiquarian books; botany; flower arranging; horticulture; illustrated books or prints; natural history; trees and forestry
CATALOGUE On request; 2 a year
MAIL ORDER Yes
SHOWS PBFA

An annotated sectional list: bibliographic details rather than descriptions. A wide selection from general gardening titles to specialist and illustrated books.

BSBI Publications; F & M Perring

Greenacre, Wood Lane, Oundle, Peterborough, Northamptonshire PE8 4JQ
☎ 0832 273388   ☎ 0832 274568

CONTACT Mrs Margaret Perring
OPEN By appointment only
SPECIALITY New books; botany; natural history
CATALOGUE On request; regular supplements

MAIL ORDER Yes

Official agents for the Botanical Society of the British Isles. In addition to the society's publications, they stock local, British and overseas floras and other botanical, conservation and reference titles.

Chantrey Books

24 Cobnar Road, Sheffield, South Yorkshire S8 8QB
☎ 0742 748958

CONTACT Clare Brightman
OPEN By appointment only
SPECIALITY Remaindered books; secondhand and antiquarian books; botany; horticulture; illustrated books or prints; natural history; rural life
CATALOGUE On request: 3 a year
MAIL ORDER Yes
SHOWS Malvern Spring; Harrogate (Spring); PBFA

A pleasing general list, divided into subheadings. Some older books too, as well as natural history and rural titles. They attend several AGS shows.

Ivelet Books Ltd

Church Street Bookshop, 26 Church Street, Godalming, Surrey GU7 1EW
☎ 0483 418878   FAX 0483 418656

CONTACT Mr D. J. and Mrs E. A. Ahern
OPEN 10.30 am – 5.30 pm, Monday – Saturday
SPECIALITY Secondhand and antiquarian books; botany; horticulture; illustrated books or prints; natural history; architecture and interiors
CATALOGUE On request: 3 or 4 a year
MAIL ORDER Yes
SHOWS Chelsea; PBFA

A good range for gardeners and collectors: the list is strongest on twentieth century classics such as Jekyll and Bowles, and is also a source for standard and historical works.

John Henly

Brooklands, Walderton, Chichester, West Sussex PO18 9EE
☎ 0705 631426

CONTACT John Henly
OPEN By appointment only
SPECIALITY Secondhand and antiquarian books; botany; horticulture; natural history; trees and forestry; geology
CATALOGUE On request; 4 a year
MAIL ORDER Yes
SHOWS PBFA

The catalogues are helpfully sub-divided into subjects. Individual entries have full bibliographic notes, but descriptions are kept to a minimum. Good for standard works, especially from the mid twentieth century.

Kew Shop

Mail Order Section, Royal Botanic Gardens, Kew, Richmond, Surrey TW9 3AB
☎ 081 332 5653

OPEN 9 am – 5 pm for telephone orders; Victoria Gate Shop normally open 9.30 am – 5.30 pm (summer and Christmas period) or until last garden admissions
SPECIALITY New books; botany; flower arranging; horticulture; natural history; trees and forestry
CATALOGUE Books and gifts; scientific
MAIL ORDER Yes

An excellent choice of current books, including numerous scientific publications. Entrance is normally through the garden, but you can get in directly if you give advance notice. The closing time changes with the season (information on 081 940 1171).

Landsman's Bookshop Ltd

Buckenhill, Bromyard, Hereford & Worcester HR7 4PH
☎ 0885 483420   FAX 0885 483420

CONTACT K. J. Stewart
OPEN 9 am – 4.30 pm, Monday – Friday
SPECIALITY New and secondhand books; remaindered books; botany; flower arranging; general gardening; natural history; trees and forestry
CATALOGUE £1
MAIL ORDER Yes
SHOWS International Spring Gardening Fair; Malvern Spring; Harrogate (Spring); Southport; Chelsea

Landsman's aims to supply all gardening books which are in print. Mainly mail order and through agricultural and horticultural shows. They also have remaindered and secondhand material. Agriculture is stocked in similar depth, and they publish a few titles of their own.

Lloyds of Kew

9 Mortlake Terrace, Kew, Richmond, Surrey TW9 3DT
☎ 081 940 2512

OPEN 10 am – 4 pm, Monday – Friday; 10 am – 5 pm, Saturdays. Closed Wednesdays and Sundays
SPECIALITY Secondhand and antiquarian books; horticulture; illustrated books or prints
CATALOGUE On request
SHOWS Chelsea

Specialists for secondhand and antiquarian gardening books. Tucked away just off Kew Green, the shop also carries a general secondhand stock. They operate a free finding service (without obligation).

Mary Bland

Augop, Evenjobb, Presteigne, Powys LD8 2PA
☎ 05476 218

CONTACT Mary Bland
OPEN By appointment only
SPECIALITY New books; remaindered books; second-hand and antiquarian books; botany; flower arranging; horticulture; trees and forestry
CATALOGUE On request; about 3 a year
MAIL ORDER Yes
SHOWS RHS Westminster; Chelsea

Good general and collectors stock, with many interesting and reasonably priced titles. The list is divided into sections, with bibliographic details and some descriptions. Prints available at shows. Will search for titles.

Peter M Daly

Thompson Antiques, 20a Jewry Street, Winchester, Hampshire SO23 8RZ
☎ 0962 867732

CONTACT Peter M. Daly
OPEN 10 am – 4.45 pm, Wednesdays, Fridays, Saturdays. Other times by appointment
SPECIALITY Remaindered books; secondhand and antiquarian books; botany; flower arranging; horticulture; illustrated books or prints; natural history; landscape gardening
CATALOGUE No
MAIL ORDER No
SHOWS PBFA

RHS Enterprises Ltd

RHS Garden, Wisley, Woking, Surrey GU23 6QB
☎ 0483 211113   FAX 0483 211003

CONTACT B. M. C. Ambrose
OPEN 10 am – 5.30 pm, Monday – Saturday; 9 am – 6 pm, Sundays. Closes at 6.30 pm in summer
SPECIALITY New books; botany; flower arranging; general gardening; illustrated books or prints; natural history; trees and forestry
CATALOGUE On request; 2 a year
MAIL ORDER Yes (0483 211320)
SHOWS RHS Westminster; International Spring Gardening Fair; Malvern Spring; Harrogate (Spring); Southport; Chelsea; BBC GW Live; Hampton Court; Harrogate (Autumn); Ayr

The range of gardening and botanical books on sale at Wisley is among the best in the country. Twice yearly catalogues detail an extensive part of the stock, and allow for mail order purchase. New books only, including many from overseas. The shop also sells gift items.

Summerfield Books

Summerfield House, High Street, Brough, Kirkby Stephen, Cumbria CA17 4BX
☎ 07683 41577   FAX 07683 41577

CONTACT Jon and Sue Atkins
OPEN By appointment
SPECIALITY New books; remaindered books; second-hand and antiquarian books; botany; horticulture; illustrated books or prints; natural history; trees and forestry; country and foreign floras, cryptogams
CATALOGUE On request; 4 a year
MAIL ORDER Yes

Substantial list with an individual style. Very good for floras, cryptogams and forestry titles. Some interesting general titles also. Free finding service.

W C Cousens

The Leat, Lyme Road, Axminster, Devon EX13 5BL
☎ 0297 32921

CONTACT W. C. Cousens
OPEN By appointment only
SPECIALITY Secondhand and antiquarian books; botany; flower arranging; horticulture; illustrated books or prints; trees and forestry
CATALOGUE sae; 4 a year
SHOWS PBFA

Book search facility available.

Wells & Winter

Mere House Barn, Mereworth, Maidstone, Kent ME18 5NB
☎ 0622 813627

CONTACT Sir John Wells
OPEN Sell from shows only
SPECIALITY New books; remaindered books; second-hand and antiquarian books; botany; general gardening
SHOWS RHS Westminster; International Spring Gardening Fair; Malvern Spring; Chelsea; Hampton Court

Wyseby House Books

1 Elm Cottages, St Mary Bourne, Andover, Hampshire SP11 6BU
☎ 0264 738052   FAX 0264 738052

CONTACT Dr Tim Oldham
OPEN By appointment
SPECIALITY Remaindered books; secondhand and antiquarian books; botany; horticulture; illustrated books or prints; natural history; trees and forestry
CATALOGUE On request; monthly
MAIL ORDER Yes
SHOWS PBFA

The horticultural titles run from affordable classics from the last 150 years to more recent works. Of interest to both gardeners and specialists.

29

Books, Periodicals & Videos

New Books 1993

The 500 Best Garden Plants, Patrick Taylor (Pavilion, 1993) £10.99, pbk.
The title sounds a tall order, but this book is attractively produced, thoughtful, and – more to the point – reliable.

A – Z of Companion Planting, Pamela Allardice (Cassell, 1993) £12.99.

Air Plants and other Bromeliads, Bill Wall (Cassell, 1993) £3.99, Wisley Handbook Series, pbk, 2nd rev edn of Clive Innes, *Bromeliads*.

Alpines, Kenneth A. Beckett (HarperCollins, 1993) £3.99, Collins Garden Guides, pbk, new edn.

'Amateur Gardening' Pocket Fact Finder, Graham Clarke (Hamlyn, 1993) £4.99, pbk.

Annuals and Bedding Plants, Pat Weaver (HarperCollins, 1993) £3.99, Collins Garden Guides, pbk, new edn.

Artists Gardens from Claude Monet to Jennifer Bartlett, Madison Cox (Abrams, 1993) £40.00, Edited by Brooks Adams, and with illustrations by Erica Leonard.

'Bazaar': Budget Gardening Year, Stefan T. Buczacki (BBC Books, 1993) £4.99, pbk.

The Bernard E Harkness Seedlist Handbook, Mabel G. Harkness (ed.) (Batsford, 1993) £25.00.
A new smaller format, easier to read edition which will be welcomed by compulsive propagators from seed. Contains plants which have been offered in the leading specialist seed schemes. Each entry comes with the briefest of descriptions – enough to decide whether or not to order an item.

The Biology of Horticulture: An Introductory Textbook, John E. Preece and Paul Read (Wiley, 1993) £45.50.

Bird Gardening, Brian Loomes (Dalesman, 1993) £8.95.

Bob Flowerdew's Complete Book of Companion Gardening, Bob Flowerdew (Kyle Cathie, 1993) £20.00.

Bonsai, Anne Swinton (HarperCollins, 1993) £3.99, Collins Garden Guides, pbk, new edn.

The Book of Apples, Joan Morgan and Alison Richards (Ebury Press, 1993) £18.99.
Essential reading and self-indulgence for apple addicts. Contains a full catalogue and descriptions of the 2,000 plus varieties at Brogdale, prefaced by a stylishly-illustrated history of apple breeding, cultivation and marketing.

Borders, Penelope Hobhouse (Pavilion, 1993) £9.99, National Trust Gardening Guides, pbk, new edn.
Penelope Hobhouse is also the series editor.

Cacti and Succulents, Ken March (HarperCollins, 1993) £3.99, Collins Garden Guides, pbk, new edn.

Cacti and Succulents, Terry Hewitt (Dorling Kindersley, 1993) £15.99.

Carnations and Pinks: The Complete Guide, Sophie Hughes (Crowood Press, 1993) £9.99, pbk, new edn.

Carnivorous Plants: Care and Cultivation, Marcel Lecoufle (Cassell, 1993) £11.99, pbk, new edn. Translated from the French by P. J. Farrar.

A Century of Kew Plantsmen: Celebration of the Kew Guild, Ray Desmond and F. Nigel Hepper (Kew Guild, 1993) £15.00.

Children's Gardening: A Month by Month Guide Advancing Educational Activities in Schools, Peter Please (V. George & S. Fairhurst, 1993) £5.00, new edn.

'Chinese' Wilson: A Life of Ernest H Wilson, Roy W Briggs (HMSO, 1993) £19.95,
The first in a new series from RBG Kew and Edinburgh, The Great Plant Collectors.

Christopher Lloyd's Flower Garden, Christopher Lloyd (Dorling Kindersley, 1993) £15.99,
Beautifully produced photographic trip round Great Dixter. Relatively brief but characteristically acute text by Lloyd himself. Recommended for its vivid visual counterpart to the author's lively style.

Climbing and Wall Plants, A. G. L. Hellyer (HarperCollins, 1993) £3.99, Collins Garden Guides, pbk, new edn.

Colour Dictionary of Camellias, Stirling Macoboy (ed.) (Stirling Macoboy, Australia, 1993) £27.95, new edn.

Colour Through the Year, Alan R. Toogood (HarperCollins, 1993) £3.99, Collins Garden Guides, pbk, new edn.

The Complete Book of Conservatory Plants, William Davidson and Jane Bland (Ward Lock, 1993) £20.00.

Complete Book of Herbs and Spices, Sarah Garland (Frances Lincoln, 1993) £16.99.

Complete Guide to Conservatory Plants, Ann Bonar (Collins & Brown, 1993) £10.99, pbk, new edn.

Conran Beginner's Guide to Gardening, Stefan Buczacki (Conran Octopus, 1993) £8.99, pbk, new edn.

The Conservatory Gardener, Anne Swithinbank (Frances Lincoln, 1993) £20.00,
Over a thousand plants are described in this substantial guide. Swithinbank, a former glasshouse supervisor at Wisley, will be familiar to many from her television appearances.

Conservatory Gardening: A Complete Practical Guide, Lynn Bryan (Anaya Publishers, 1993) £14.99, Pleasure of Gardening Series.

The Container Garden: A Practical Guide to Planning and Planting, Thomasina Tarling (Conran Octopus, 1993) £15.99, Royal Horticultural Society Collection.
Mixes inspirational photography and practical advice with plant lists and planting plans. Of particular interest to urban gardeners.

Containers and Baskets for Year-Round Colour, Peter McHoy (Ward Lock, 1993) £14.99.

The Cottage Gardener's Companion: A Seasonal Guide to Plants and Plantings, The Cottage Garden Society (David & Charles, 1993) £16.99.

Create a Cottage Garden, Kathleen Brown (Michael Joseph, 1993) £17.99.
Described as garden recipes, this is a pattern book of cottage garden features. Tells you what to plant and how each plant will grow. Looks most useful for those faced with a bare plot.

Creating a Chinese Garden, Engel (Batsford, 1993) £17.99.

Creating a Garden for the Senses, Jeff Cox (Abbeville Press, 1993) £27.00.

Creating Japanese Gardens, Philip Cave (Aurum Press, 1993) £19.95.

Creative Herb Gardening, Geraldene Holt (Conran Octopus, 1993) £12.99.

The Cultivation of Rhododendrons, Peter Cox (Batsford, 1993) £35.00.

The Culture of Flowers, Jack Goody (Cambridge University Press, 1993) £40.00, pbk edn, £13.95.

David Austin's English Roses, David Austin (Conran Octopus, 1993) £18.99.
Austin's English Roses seek to combine the soft shapes and scents of old roses with the wider colour range and repeat flowering of modern kinds. Here he explains how he developed the group, and suggests uses for house and garden. The detailed descriptions of habit and parentage are particularly useful.

Decorate Your Garden, Mary Keen (Conran Octopus, 1993) £17.99.
Clever ideas for 'hard' features to add emphasis and life to your garden. The clear photgraphs of many

examples in England and the Netherlands are accompanied by succinct descriptions.

Designing the Container Garden, Susan McAffer (Anaya Publishers, 1993) £12.99, Pleasure of Gardening series.

Dried Flower Gardening, Joanna Sheen and Caroline Alexander (Ward Lock, 1993) £9.99, pbk, new edn.

The Dry Garden, Beth Chatto (Dent, 1993) £12.99, pbk, 2nd rev edn.

Easy Ways to the Plants of the Bernese Oberland, Philip Talboys and Jean Talboys (Sawd Publications, 1993) £6.99, pbk.

Edible Plants for Temperate Climates, Martin Crawford (Agroforestry Research Trust, 1993) £34.99, spiral bound.

English Private Gardens, Judy Johnson and Susan Berry (Collins & Brown, 1993) £8.99, pbk.
Detailed accounts of 35 gardens which open under the National Gardens Scheme.

An Englishwoman's Garden, Helen Penn (BBC Books, 1993) £18.99.
Through chapters on women gardeners from the early seventeenth century to the present day, and their involvement with style in horticulture, their obsessions with plants, and their love of the highly cultivated and the wild and obscure, this book is full of pleasing surprises. Helen Penn has researched her subject to great effect, but it is all too short a survey of a fascinating area.

The Flower Garden: A Practical Guide to Planning and Planting, Helen Dillon (Conran Octopus, 1993) £15.99, Royal Horticultural Society Collection.

Flowering Plants of the World, Vernon Heywood (Batsford, 1993) £19.99.

The Flowering Year: Guide to Seasonal Planting, Anna Pavord (Chatto & Windus, 1993) £9.99, pbk, new edn.

Forget-Me-Not: A Floral Treasury, Pamela Todd (Little, Brown, 1993) £12.99.

Four-Season Harvest, Eliot Coleman (Chelsea Green, 1993) £12.95.

The Fragrant Year: Growing and Using Scented Plants All Year Round, Jane Newdick (Little, Brown, 1993) £16.99.
More a household than a gardening book, but an attractive theme. Detailed advice on growing and using scented plants in and around the house.

Fruit and Vegetable Clinic, Pippa Greenwood (Ward Lock, 1993) £5.99, pbk.

Fuchsias, Kenneth A. Beckett (HarperCollins, 1993) £3.99, Collins Garden Guides, pbk, new edn.

Fuchsias: The Complete Guide to Cultivation, Propagation and Exhibition, George Bartlett (Crowood Press, 1993) £9.99, pbk.

The Garden at Ashtree Cottage, Wendy Lauderdale (Weidenfeld & Nicolson, 1993) £14.99.
Highly illustrated tale of the making and planting of a cottage garden in Wiltshire. Perhaps not the sort of garden which usually gets written up to this extent, but the size of the plot means most readers can relate better to the tasks and achievements described. Easy to read and easy on the eye.

Garden Graphics, Gemma Nesbitt (Viking, 1993) £17.99.
May herald a trend in DIY garden design. Fun and easy-to-visualise system for recording plantings. There are worked examples matched against photographs. Then in the dictionary section of the book some 900 plants are given a unique symbol and a short description.

The Garden Makers, George Plumptre (Pavilion, 1993) £25.00.

The Garden Sourcebook, Caroline Boisset (ed.) (Mitchell Beazley, 1993) £25.00.
Reference guide to the materials needed to put a garden together.

The Garden Wall, Mirabel Osler (Pavilion, 1993) £4.99, Library of Garden Detail.

The Gardener's Book of Trees, Alan Mitchell (Dent, 1993) £11.99, pbk, new edn.

The Gardener's Guide to Growing Hellebores, Graham Rice and Elizabeth Strangman (David & Charles, 1993) £16.99.
Attractively produced and well-written guide to this genus: the outstanding photographs are by Roger Phillips.

A Gardener's Guide to Plant Life, Susan Berry (Collins & Brown, 1993) £16.99.
The book of the Channel 4 television series. Produced in collaboration with RBG, Kew.

Gardener's Handbook, Tessa Paul and Nigel Chadwick, ed. by Stefan Buczacki (Pan, 1993) £12.99.

The Gardener's Reading Guide, Jan Dean (Facts on File, 1993) £18.95.

'Gardeners' World' Book of Plants for Small Gardens, Sue Fisher (BBC Books, 1993) £8.99, pbk.

'Gardeners' World' Directory, Geoff Hamilton (BBC Books, 1993) £7.99, pbk.

'Gardeners' World' Practical Gardening Course, Geoff Hamilton (BBC Books, 1993) £19.99.
Clear, uncomplicated and thoroughly practical manual which runs from construction and design to plants and maintenance. Something for everyone, but especially recommended for new gardeners.

'Gardeners' World' Vegetables for Small Gardens, Lynda Brown (BBC Books, 1993) £8.99, pbk.

Gardening from 'Which?' Guide to Successful Pruning, Peter McHoy (Hodder & Stoughton, 1993) £16.99.

Gardening Naturally, Ann Reilly (Prion, 1993) £14.95.

Gardening on a Small Scale, (Fraser Stewart, 1993) £6.99, Easy Gardening series.

Gardening with Old Roses, Alan Sinclair and Rosemary Thodey (Cassell, 1993) £16.99.

Gardens of Mexico, Antonio Haas (Rizzoli, 1993) £35.00.

The Gardens of Spain, Consuelo M. Correcher (Abrams, 1993) £45.00.

The Genus Arum, Peter Boyce (HMSO, 1993) £30.00, Kew Magazine monograph.

Geoffrey Jellicoe: The Studies of a Landscape Designer over 80 Years, Sir Geoffrey Jellicoe (Garden Art Press, 1993) £35.00.
This first volume of the collected works of one of the century's most influential landscape designers includes 'Soundings', 'Italian Study: 1923-5', and 'Baroque Gardens of Austria'.

Gertrude Jekyll, Sally Festing (Penguin, 1993) £8.99, pbk.

The Glasshouse Garden: A Practical Guide to Planning and Planting, John Watkins (Conran Octopus, 1993) £15.99, Royal Horticultural Society Collection.

Good Gardens Guide 1994, Graham Rose and Peter King (Vermilion, 1993) £12.99, pbk.

The Good Old-Fashioned Gardener, Nigel Colborn (Letts, 1993) £17.95.

Grapes, Alan R. Toogood (HarperCollins, 1993) £3.99, Collins Garden Guides, pbk, new edn.

Greenhouse Gardening, Ronald H. Menage (HarperCollins, 1993) £3.99, Collins Garden Guides, pbk, new edn.

Greenhouses: Natural Vegetables, Fruit and Flowers all the Year Round, Sue Stickland (Search Press, 1993) £5.95.
Organic production in an unheated greenhouse. Published with the Henry Doubleday Research Association.

Ground Cover Plants, John Negus (HarperCollins, 1993) £3.99, Collins Garden Guides, pbk, new edn.

Growing Indoor Plants, Jane Courtier (Ward Lock, 1993) £5.99, pbk.

Guide to Conservatory Plants, Ken March and Jill Thomas (Kingfisher Books, 1993) £5.99, pbk.

Hamlyn All Colour Greenhouse Gardening, Richard Rosenfeld (Hamlyn, 1993) £7.99.

Hardy Geraniums for the Garden, Joy Jones (ed.) (Hardy Plant Society, 1993) £2.95, pbk, 2nd rev edn.

The Healing Garden: A Natural Haven for Physical and Emotional Well-being, Sue Minter (Headline, 1993) £17.99.

Heaths and Heathers: The Grower's Handbook, Terry Underhill (David & Charles, 1993) £14.99, 2nd rev edn.

Hellebores: Hellebore, Christmas Rose, Lenten Rose, Marlene Sophie Ahlburg (Batsford, 1993) £19.99.

Hellyer Gardening Encyclopedia, A. G. L. Hellyer (Hamlyn, 1993) £14.99.
Revised edition of a classic reference work.

Hemerocallis: The Daylily, R. W. Munson (Timber Press, USA, 1993) £29.99, pbk, £14.99.

The Herb and Kitchen Garden, A. M. Clevely (Letts, 1993) £4.95, Letts Guides to Garden Design.

Herbaceous Perennials, David Joyce (HarperCollins, 1993) £3.99, Collins Garden Guides, pbk, new edn.

Herbs, Mike Janulewicz (HarperCollins, 1993) £3.99, Collins Garden Guides, pbk, new edn.

Hidden Gardens of Ireland, Marianne Heron (Gill & Macmillan, 1993) £7.99, pbk.

Highgrove: Portrait of an Estate, HRH The Prince of Wales and Charles Clover (Chapmans, 1993) £20.00.
High profile and thoughtful work which preaches what has already been practised on Prince Charles's Gloucestershire farm and garden. HRH contributes

a substantial introductory essay to Clover's more dispassionate narrative. Paperback out in June 1994.

'Homes and Gardens': A Year in the Garden, Andi Clevely (Hamlyn, 1993) £16.99.

Houseplants, William Davidson (HarperCollins, 1993) £3.99, Collins Garden Guides, pbk, new edn.

Hugh Johnson on Gardening: The Best of Trad, Hugh Johnson (Mitchell Beazley, 1993) £12.99.
A selection from the 'Tradescant's Diary' column which Hugh Johnson has contributed to the RHS journal, *The Garden*, over the last twenty years.

Illustrated Encyclopedia of Roses, Mary Moody (Headline, 1993) £19.99.

Illustrated Handbook of Bulbs and Perennials, Hugh Redgrove (Cassell, 1993) £20.00.

In My Garden, Christopher Lloyd (Bloomsbury, 1993) £16.99.
Selection of Christopher Lloyd's *Country Life* column, with as much emphasis on the literary as the horticultural. It is arranged month by month for pleasurable dipping, and includes the provocative 'Sweet Disease' (on light-fingered cuttings) and 'Hurrah for Vulgarity'.

Irises, Susan Berry (Pavilion, 1993) £6.99, Garden Flower series.

Italian Gardens, Charles A. Platt (Thames & Hudson, 1993) £20.00, new edn.
Contains a new introduction by Keith N. Morgan and additional illustrations.

The Japanese Garden, Maggie Oster (Cassell, 1993) £19.99.

Japanese Plants: Know Them and Use Them, Betty W. Richards and Anne Kaneko (Shufunomoto, Japan, 1993) £18.95, new edn.

Kew: A World of Plants, Heather Angel (Collins & Brown, and RBG, Kew, 1993) £20.00. Paperback due in 1994.

The Kitchen Gardener, David Pople (Ward Lock, 1993) £9.99, pbk, new edn.

Lawn Craft, Alan R. Toogood (Ward Lock, 1993) £5.99, pbk.

Let's Go Gardening: A Young Person's Guide to the Garden, Ursula Krüger (Lutterworth Press, 1993).

Low-Maintenance Garden, Peter McHoy (Harper-Collins, 1993) £3.99, Collins Garden Guides, pbk, new edn.

Low Water Gardening, John Lucas (Dent, 1993) £15.99, and pbk, £9.99.

Macdonald Encyclopedia of Flowers for Balcony and Garden, Guido Moggi and Luciano Giugnolini (Little, Brown, 1993) £10.99, pbk, new edn.

The National Association of Flower Arranging Societies Complete Step-by-Step Flower Arranging Course, Daphne Vagg (Ebury Press, 1993) £17.99.

The National Plant Collection, John Kelly (Dial Press, 1993) £25.00.
Illustrated account of the history of the NCCPG's National Collections, with chosen collections described in detail.

The New Indoor Plant Book, John Evans (Kyle Cathie, 1993) £18.99.

Orchids, Philip Cribb and Christopher Bailes (Pavilion, 1993) £6.99, Garden Flower Series.

Orchids: An Identifier, Rick Imes (Apple Press, 1993) £4.95, Identifiers series, pbk.

Orchids: Care and Cultivation, Gerald Leroy-Terquem and Jean Parisot (Cassell, 1993) £11.99, pbk, new edn. Translated from the French by J. Gilbert.

The Organic Gardener, Bob Flowerdew (Hamlyn, 1993) £14.99.

Organic Gardening, Roy Lacey (Mitchell Beazley, 1993) £7.99, Royal Horticultural Society Encyclopedia of Practical Gardening, pbk.

Organic Gardening, Richard Bird (Apple Press, 1993) £8.95.

The Ornamental Kitchen Garden, Janet MacDonald (David & Charles, 1993) £16.99.

Pansies, Violas and Violettas: The Complete Guide, Rodney Fuller (Crowood Press, 1993) £9.99, pbk.

Patio Gardening, David Toyne (Ward Lock, 1993) £5.99, pbk.

The Pattern of Landscape, Sylvia Crowe and Mary Mitchell (Packard Publishing, 1993) £15.00, pbk.
A fine introduction to the subject: lucid prose hand-in-hand with telling illustrations. Distributed by the Antique Collectors' Club.

Perennials, Roger Phillips and Martyn Rix (Pan, 1993) £13.99 each, Pan Garden Plants series, pbk, 2 vols; Early Perennials; Late Perennials.

Phylogeny and Classification of the Orchid Family, Robert L. Dressler (Cambridge University Press, 1993) £35.00.

The Plant Growth Planner, Caroline Boisset (Mitchell Beazley, 1993) £9.99, pbk.

Plant Propagation Made Easy, Alan Toogood (Dent, 1993) £11.99.

Plants for Dry Gardens, Jane Taylor (Frances Lincoln, 1993) £18.99.
A descriptive directory of over 1,000 drought-tolerant plants: Taylor's knowledge and expertise is impressive. More photographs would have enhanced the book.

Poppies, Christopher Grey-Wilson (Batsford, 1993) £25.00.

Practical Cacti Growing, Patrick Johns (Crowood Press, 1993) £3.99, Practical Gardening series.

Primula, John Richards (Batsford, 1993) £35.00.
Important monograph on this popular species. Its main section is a systematic treatment of species. It includes taxonomic revisions, and is clearly laid out.

Propagation of Hardy Perennials, Richard Bird (Batsford, 1993) £19.99.

Propagator's Handbook: 50 Foolproof Recipes, Peter Thompson (David & Charles, 1993) £12.99.

The Quest for the Rose: The Most Highly Illustrated Historical Guide to Roses, Roger Phillips and Martyn Rix (BBC Books, 1993) £18.99.
Part horticultural detective work, part pictorial *tour de force*. For the most part a photographic record of the development of cultivated roses: there are many valuable illustrations of little known varieties. This is accompanied by a lively account of the pair's travels in search of the original China roses.

Raising New Plants, (Hardy Plant Society, 1993) £2.50, pbk.

Rock and Water Garden Expert, D. G. Hessayon (PBI, 1993) £4.50, pbk.

Rosemary Verey's Garden Plans, Rosemary Verey (Frances Lincoln, 1993) £18.99.
Garden plans of differing sizes from Rosemary Verey's back catalogue. The fifty designs can be reproduced in whole or in part, or studied for inspiration.

Roses, Janet Browne (Pavilion, 1993) £6.99, Garden Flower series.

Roses, Nancy Gardiner and Peter Harkness (New Holland, 1993) £12.99.

Roses of Great Britain and Ireland, G. Graham and A. Primavesi (BSBI, 1993) £11.50, pbk.

New field guide which covers 20 species and some 83 hybrids. There are line drawings, descriptions and distribution maps for this complex genus.

The Secret Gardens of France, Mirabel Osler (Pavilion, 1993) £16.99.
An engaging account of an idiosyncratic tour of France – seen over the garden fence. Conversational, opinionated, and stylish. Paperback due in 1994.

The Shady Garden: A Practical Guide to Planning and Planting, Jane Taylor (Conran Octopus, 1993) £15.99, Royal Horticultural Society Collection.

Short Cuts to Great Gardens, Nigel Colborn (Conran Octopus, 1993) £16.99.
A provocative title to a well-thought out book. Glossily presented, the advice is clear, sound and to the point.

Shrub Roses and Climbing Roses: With Hybrid Tea and Floribunda Roses, David Austin (Antique Collectors' Club, 1993) £12.95, pbk.

Simply Flowers: Practical Advice and Beautiful Ideas for Creating Flower-filled Rooms, Barbara Milo Ohrbach (Ebury Press, 1993) £14.99.
Rather American in style, but many good ideas nonetheless.

The Small Garden, Roger Grounds (Letts, 1993) £4.95, Letts Guides to Garden Design.

The Small Garden Planner, Graham Rose (Mitchell Beazley, 1993) £12.99, pbk.

Step by Step Guide to Growing and Displaying Orchids, Wilma Rittershausen and others (Gardner's Books, 1993) £5.99, pbk.

The Step by Step Guide to Outdoor Brickwork, Penny Swift and Janek Szymanowski (New Holland, 1993) £7.99.

Step by Step Outdoor Woodwork, Mike Lawrence (New Holland, 1993) £12.99.

Study of Ornamental Nursery Stock and an Investigation into Peat Alternatives, Patrick Glass (Nuffield Farming Scholarships Trust, 1993) £5.00.

Superhints for Gardeners: From the Great and the Green-Fingered, Lady Wardington (ed.) (Michael Joseph, 1993) £8.99.
A collection of tips and hints from experts and public figures. An eclectic compost heap of the potentially useful and the perplexingly useless.

Trees of Britain and Europe, Bob Press and David Hosking (New Holland, 1993) £9.99, pbk.

Thorough and affordable photographic field guide, with some useful supplementary material.

Tulips, Ann Bonar (Pavilion, 1993) £6.99, Garden Flower series.

Urban Permaculture: A Practical Handbook for Sustainable Living, David Watkins (Permanent Productions, 1993) £7.50, pbk.

Vegetables, Roger Phillips and Martyn Rix (Pan, 1993) £17.50, Pan Garden Plants series.

The latest volume in this series which combines a scholarly, readable text with Roger Phillips's excellent photography. Both well-known and less familiar vegetables are included. Good on descriptions and cultivation: more culinary information would have been welcome for the rarer specimens.

The Victorian Garden Album, Elizabeth Drury and Philippa Lewis (Collins & Brown, 1993) £12.99. Attractive period scrapbook.

The Wartime Kitchen and Garden, Jennifer Davies (BBC Books, 1993) £14.99.

This book of the television series chronicles the drive for self-sufficiency in garden and kitchen during the second world war. Personal reminiscences are well illustrated with contemporary photographs. Harry Dodson and Ruth Mott's descriptions of wartime methods add a pleasing mix of nostalgia and social history.

The Water Gardener: A Complete Guide to Designing, Constructing and Planting Water Features, Anthony Archer-Wills (Frances Lincoln, 1993) £25.00.

Water can transform a garden. Here an acknowledged expert on water design and planting gives full advice on everything from bog gardens to waterfalls.

Water Gardening, Philip Swindells (Mitchell Beazley, 1993) £7.99, Royal Horticultural Society Encyclopedia of Practical Gardening, pbk.

Wild Orchids of Scotland, Brian Allan and Patrick Woods (HMSO, 1993) £24.95.

The Royal Botanic Garden, Edinburgh has produced this fully illustrated guide to Scotland's 28 species of orchid. The book includes new photographs, line drawings, a field key and distribution maps. The field key is available separately at £1.95.

Wildflowers of Southern Spain, Betty Molesworth Allen (Mirador Books) £10.25, pbk.

The Wildlife Garden Month-by-Month, Jackie Bennett (David & Charles, 1993) £14.99.

Windowbox Gardening, David Joyce (Conran Octopus, 1993) £12.99.

Winter Garden Glory, Adrian Bloom (HarperCollins, 1993) £14.99.

World Checklist of Conifers, Humphrey Welch and Gordon Haddow (Landsman's Bookshop, 1993) £22.00, pbk.

The World Heritage of Gardens, Dusan Ogrin (Thames & Hudson, 1993) £24.95.

The World of Roses: An Illustrated Guide, Stirling Macoboy (Souvenir Press, 1993) £35.00.

New Books 1994

1994 Gardener's Guide to Britain, Patrick Taylor (Pavilion, 1994) £10.99, pbk.

Alan Toogood's Gardening Under Glass, Alan Toogood (Weidenfeld & Nicolson, 1994) £9.99, pbk, March.

The Alpine Garden: A Practical Guide to Planning and Planting, Christopher Grey-Wilson (Conran Octopus, 1994) £15.99, Royal Horticultural Society Collection, May.

The Basic Arts of Gardening, Jane Fearnley-Whittingstall (Weidenfeld & Nicolson, 1994) £19.99, October.

Bedding Plants, Nigel Colborn (Conran Octopus, 1994) £12.99, March.

Best Borders, Tony Lord (Frances Lincoln, 1994).

This practical guide to planning, planting and maintaining borders comes with twelve planting plans. An appealing combination of successful and famous examples, and the knowledge of a former Gardens Adviser to the National Trust. Published in spring.

Best Climbers, Stefan Buczacki (Hamlyn, 1994) £4.99, pbk, March. In association with *Amateur Gardening*.

Best Foliage Shrubs, Stefan Buczacki (Hamlyn, 1994) £4.99, pbk, March. In association with *Amateur Gardening*.

Best Shade Plants, Stefan Buczacki (Hamlyn, 1994) £4.99, pbk, March. In association with *Amateur Gardening*.

Best Soft Fruit, Stefan Buczacki (Hamlyn, 1994) £4.99, pbk, March. In association with *Amateur Gardening*.

The Book of Primroses, Barbara Shaw (David & Charles, 1994) £14.99, pbk, February.

The Border Book, Anna Pavord (Dorling Kindersley, 1994) £15.99, March.

Border Pinks and Dianthus, Richard Bird (Batsford, 1994) £25.00, May.

The Bulb Expert, Dr D. G. Hessayon (Transworld, 1994) £4.99, October.

Cacti and Succulents in Habitat, Ken Preston-Mafham (Cassell, 1994) £16.99, June. 150 species photographed in the wild.

Clematis: Queen of Climbers, Jim Fisk (Cassell, 1994) £12.99, pbk, new edn, March.

Climbers and Wall Plants for Year Round Colour, Jane Taylor (Ward Lock, 1994) £8.99, pbk, April.

Collins Nature Guide to Wild Flowers, Lippart and Podlech (HarperCollins, 1994) new edn.

Colour in the Winter Garden, Graham Stuart Thomas (Weidenfeld & Nicolson, 1994) £10.99, pbk, March.

Colour your Garden, Mary Keen (Conran Octopus, 1994) £9.99, pbk.

The Complete Book of Garden Design, David Stevens, Lucy Huntington and Richard Key (Ward Lock, 1994) £12.99, pbk, February.

The Complete Book of Pruning, Coombs, Blackburne-Maze, Cracknell and Bentley (Ward Lock, 1994) £12.99, pbk, February.

The Complete Book of Roses, John Mattock, Sean McCann, F. Witchell and P. Wood (Ward Lock, 1994) £20.00, January. Comprehensive illustrated reference book.

The Container Garden Month-by-Month, Jackie Bennett (David & Charles, 1994) £14.99, October.

Cottage Garden, Peter Thurman (Pavilion, 1994) £5.99, February.

The Cottage Garden: A Practical Guide to Planning and Planting, Sue Phillips (Conran Octopus, 1994) £15.99, Royal Horticultural Society Collection, February.

Cottage Gardening, (Ward Lock, 1994) £5.99, Ward Lock Master Gardener series, pbk, March.

Country Houses from the Air, Adrian Tinniswood and Jason Hawkes (Weidenfeld & Nicolson, 1994) £19.99, May.

Creating Wonderful Window Boxes, Martin Baxendale (Ward Lock, 1994) £4.99, pbk, May.

Creative Ideas for Small Gardens, Anthony Paul (HarperCollins, 1994) £16.99, April.

Cultivation of Hardy Perennials, Richard Bird (Batsford, 1994) £20.00, June.

Designing the Small Garden, John Patrick (Anaya Publishers, 1994) £14.99, Pleasure of Gardening series, March.

The English Cottage Garden, Jane Taylor and Andrew Lawson (Weidenfeld & Nicolson, 1994) £14.99, April.

Field Guide to the Trees of Britain and North America, Andrew Cleave (Crowood Press, 1994) £10.99, May.

Field Guide to the Wild Flowers of Britain and North Europe, Bob Gibbons and Paul Davies (Crowood Press, 1994) £9.99, April.

Flora's Gems: Daffodils, Pamela Todd (Little, Brown, 1994) £5.99, March.

Flora's Gems: Tulips, Pamela Todd (Little, Brown, 1994) £5.99, March.

The Flowering Shrub Expert, Dr D. G. Hessayon (Transworld, 1994) £4.99, March. Colourful shrubs given the illustrated and factual 'Expert' treatment.

Fresh Flower Arranging, Wendy Gardiner (Crowood Press, 1994) £7.99, May.

Fuchsias: The Complete Handbook, (Cassell, 1994) £14.99, June.

The Garden Book, David Stevens and Ursula Buchan (Conran Octopus, 1994) £25.00.
In association with the Royal Horticultural Society. A reference resource for design, planting and maintenance.

Garden Design, Sylvia Crowe (Garden Art Press, 1994) £30.00, rev 3rd edn, March.
Long a classic, Dame Sylvia Crowe has updated her study and added new photographs.

The Garden in Flower Month-by-Month, John Kelly (David & Charles, 1994) £14.99, May.

A Gardener's Guide to Bulbs, Brian Mathew and Philip Swindells (Mitchell Beazley, 1994) £19.99, spring.

The Gardener's Guide to Growing Hardy Geraniums, Trevor Bath and Joy Jones (David & Charles, 1994) £16.99, March.

Gardening in the Shade, Alan Toogood (Ward Lock, 1994) £6.99, pbk, May.

The Gardens and Villas of Tuscany, Simon Cobley and David Gallant (Weidenfeld & Nicolson, 1994) £7.99, pbk, April.

Geoffrey Jellicoe: The Studies of a Landscape Designer over 80 Years, Geoffrey Jellicoe (Garden Art Press, 1994) £35.00.
The second volume of this four part series reprints *Gardens and Design* (1927, with J. C. Shepherd) and three lectures given to the Royal Institute of British Architects in 1936 as *Gardens of Europe*.

Geraniums and Pelargoniums, Jan Taylor (Crowood Press, 1994) £9.99, Complete Guide series, February.

The Greenhouse Expert, Dr D. G. Hessayon (Transworld, 1994) £4.99, March. The turn of Greenhouses in this record-breaking series of no-nonsense books.

Growing Carnations and Pinks, Fred C. Smith (Ward Lock, 1994) £8.99, pbk, April.

Growing Clematis, Dr John Howells (Ward Lock, 1994) £8.99, pbk, April.

Growing Fuchsias, Ron Ewart (Ward Lock, 1994) £8.99, pbk, April.

A Handbook for Garden Designers, Rosemary Alexander and Karena Batstone (Ward Lock, 1994) £18.99, March. Practical guide to producing plans and graphics.

Hanging Baskets, Ray Waite (Cassell and the Royal Horticultural Society, 1994) £3.95, Wisley Handbook, pbk, February.

Hardy Euphorbias, Roger Turner (Batsford, 1994) £17.99, May.

Hardy Geraniums, David Hibberd (Cassell and the Royal Horticultural Society, 1994) £3.95, Wisley Handbook, pbk, May.

The Herb Book, Jekka McVicar (Kyle Cathie, 1994) £20.00, October.

The Herb Garden Month-by-Month, Barbara Segall (David & Charles, 1994) £14.99, spring.

Herb Gardens, (Ward Lock, 1994) £5.99, Ward Lock Master Gardener series, pbk, March.

The Hillier Book of Garden Planning, Keith Rushforth, Roderick Griffin and Dennis Woodland (David & Charles, 1994) £17.99, new edn.

Hillier Guide to Connoisseur's Plants, Alan Toogood (David & Charles, 1994) £14.99, pbk, March.

The History of Gardens in Britain and Ireland, Christopher Thacker (Weidenfeld & Nicolson, 1994) £19.99, March.

History of the English Herb Garden, Kay Sanecki (Ward Lock, 1994) £9.99, pbk, February.

Hostas, Sandra Bond (Ward Lock, 1994) £7.99, Foliage Plants in Garden Design series, pbk, February.

How to be a Supergardener, Alan Titchmarsh (Ward Lock, 1994) £9.99, pbk, March.

How to Grow Natural Herbs and Spices for Culinary Uses, Charlotte de la Bédoyère (Search Press, 1994) £4.99, spring.
A practical paperback guide to growing herbs and spices organically.

The Impressionist Garden, Derek Fell (Frances Lincoln, 1994).
This book juxtaposes Impressionist colour theories and their gardens. As well as explaining the relationship between Impressionism and gardening, the book includes planting plans which allow readers to recreate and reinterpret the Impressionist style for themselves.

In the Japanese Garden, Elizabeth Bibb and Michael Yamashita (Cassell, 1994) £10.99, pbk, May.

International Book of Trees, Hugh Johnson (Mitchell Beazley, 1994) £19.99, rev 2nd edn, March.

Ivies, Hazel Key (Cassell and the Royal Horticultural Society, 1994) £3.95, Wisley Handbook, pbk, May.

Lakeland Gardens, Richard Bird (Ward Lock, 1994) £16.99, May.
Detailed guide to 30 gardens which can be visited in the Lake District.

Landscape Design for Elderly and Disabled People, Jane Stoneham and Peter Thoday (Packard Publishing, 1994) £25.00, spring.
Distributed by the Antique Collectors' Club.

Magic Muck, Lady Muck (Pavilion, 1994) £9.99, February.

Magnolias, D. Calloway (Batsford, 1994) £35.00, February.

Orchid Growing Basics, Dr Gustav Schöser (Sterling, 1994) £9.99, pbk.

Ornamental Grasses, Bamboos, Rushes and Sedges, Nigel Taylor (Ward Lock, 1994) £7.99, Foliage Plants in Garden Design series, pbk, February.

The Outdoor Room: Garden Design for Living, David Stevens (Frances Lincoln, 1994).
An attempt to demystify the garden design process by one of the country's most successful garden designers. Planned as 'rooms', or a series of rooms, David Stevens's emphasis is on creating useable spaces. Published in spring.

Palms and Cycads of the World, (Cassell, 1994) £20.00, May.

Pebble Mosaics: Creative Designs and Techniques for Paths, Patios and Walls, Maggy Howarth (Search Press, 1994) £10.95, spring.
A practical paperback guide to a traditional craft.

Penelope Hobhouse on Gardening, Penelope Hobhouse (Frances Lincoln, 1994).
One of our best known garden writers and designers, with a guide to her style. The book is based on Tintinhull, the National Trust garden in Somerset which Penelope Hobhouse worked at for over twelve years. The advice and examples follow three key elements: design, planting and practical skills. Scheduled for the autumn.

A Plantsman in Nepal, Roy Lancaster (Antique Collectors' Club, 1994) £35.00, spring. Revised and updated edition of this account of a modern plant-hunting expedition.

Practical Bedding Plants, Ian Murray (Crowood Press, 1994) £3.99, Practical Gardening series, pbk, March.

Practical Geranium Gardening, Jan Taylor (Crowood Press, 1994) £3.99, Practical Gardening series, pbk, April.

Practical Indoor Gardening, Yvonne Rees (Crowood Press, 1994) £3.99, Practical Gardening series, pbk, March.

Practical Water Gardening, Yvonne Rees (Crowood Press, 1994) £3.99, Practical Gardening series, pbk, February.

Practical Wildflower Gardening, Yvonne Rees (Crowood Press, 1994) £3.99, Practical Gardening series, pbk, April.

Primulas, Mary Robinson (Crowood Press, 1994) £10.99, Complete Guide series, February.

Pruning and Training Plants, David Joyce (Mitchell Beazley, 1994) £19.99, March.

The RHS Index of Garden Plants, Mark Griffiths (ed.) (Macmillan, 1994) £35.00.
Comprehensive lists, including descriptions and taxonomic changes, of garden plants. Based on the new four volume RHS *Dictionary of Gardening*. An instant essential for the reference shelf.

Rock Gardens, (Ward Lock, 1994) £5.99, Ward Lock Master Gardener series, pbk, March.

Rockeries & Alpine Gardens, Mary Moody (Anaya Publishers, 1994) £14.99, Pleasure of Gardening series, March.

Sissinghurst, Jane Brown (Weidenfeld & Nicolson, 1994) £9.99, pbk, June.

Small Gardens with Style, Jill Billington (Ward Lock, 1994) £14.99, June.

Succulents: The Illustrated Dictionary, Maurizio Sajeva and Mariangela Constanzo (Cassell, 1994) £30.00, June.

Traditional Gardens, Graham Rose (Dorling Kindersley, 1994) £12.99, pbk.

Using Foliage Plants in the Garden, Jill Billington (Ward Lock, 1994) £8.99, pbk, March.

Variegated Plants, Susan Conder and Andrew Lawson (Cassell, 1994) £25.00, April.

Water Garden Plants, David Case (Crowood Press, 1994) £9.99, Complete Guide series, February.

Water Gardens, (Ward Lock, 1994) £5.99, Ward Lock Master Gardener series, pbk, March.

Waterside Planting, Philip Swindells (Ward Lock, 1994) £8.99, pbk, June.

Weed Control in the Garden, Richard Chancellor (Cassell and the Royal Horticultural Society, 1994) £3.95, Wisley Handbook, pbk, March.

Weekend Gardener, Anita Perreire (Cassell, 1994) £15.99, June.

The Well-Planned Garden: A Practical Guide to Planning and Planting, Rupert Golby (Conran Octopus, 1994) £15.99, Royal Horticultural Society Collection, February.

The Wild Flower Garden: A Practical Guide to Planning and Planting, Noël Kingsbury (Conran Octopus, 1994) £15.99, Royal Horticultural Society Collection.

Due in May, this book outlines the use of wild flowers in conventional and in wild gardens.

Wildlife Garden, Peter Thurman (Pavilion, 1994) £5.99, February.

Newspapers, magazines & journals

Amateur Gardening
Westover House, West Quay Road, Poole, Dorset BH15 1JG
☎ 0202 680586   📠 0202 674335

CONTACT Janet Salisbury
OWNER IPC Magazines Ltd
PRICE 75p
FREQUENCY Weekly
EDITORS/CORRESPONDENTS Graham Clarke (editor), Stefan Buczacki, Fred Downham, Peter Seabrook, John Kelly

Long running weekly magazine with a distinguished roll call of contributors. Packed with seasonal information and brisk advice for active gardeners.

BBC Gardeners' World
101 Bayham Street, London NW1 0AG
☎ 071 331 8000
OWNER Redwood Publishing Ltd
PRICE £1.60 (£18.60 pa)
FREQUENCY Monthly
EDITORS/CORRESPONDENTS Adam Pascoe (Editor), Kathryn Bradley-Hole (Features)

Good-looking, lavishly illustrated mid-market magazine with a wide readership. The main contributors are the gardening presenters from BBC radio and television.

Country Homes and Interiors
King's Reach Tower, Stamford Street, London SE1 9LS
☎ 071 261 6433   📠 071 261 6895

CONTACT Editor
OWNER SouthBank Publishing Ltd/IPC Magazines Ltd
PRICE £1.95 (£23.40 pa)
FREQUENCY Monthly

There is a monthly garden notebook and commissioned articles on gardening topics in this country lifestyle magazine.

Country Life
King's Reach Tower, Stamford Street, London SE1 9LS
☎ 071 261 7058   📠 071 261 5139
OWNER IPC Magazines Ltd
PRICE £1.80
FREQUENCY Weekly
EDITORS/CORRESPONDENTS Clive Aslet (Editor), Tony Venison (Gardening editor), Christopher Lloyd

Continues to publish the classic articles on gardens and plants which have made it a journal of record. The photography is excellent. The twin columnists are Christopher Lloyd and Tony Venison: both have a following - Lloyd's column tends to be more digressive, Venison's more practical.

Country Living
National Magazine House, 72 Broadwick Street, London W1V 2BP
☎ 071 439 5000   📠 071 439 5093
OWNER National Magazine Co Ltd
PRICE £1.90 (£20.40 pa)
FREQUENCY Monthly
EDITORS/CORRESPONDENTS Francine Lawrence (Editor), Miranda Innes (Gardens editor)

Influential magazine for country and would-be country dwellers. Bright tone and a good mix of photographs and writing.

The Daily Telegraph
1 Canada Square, Canary Wharf, London E14 5DT
☎ 071 538 5000   📠 071 538 6242
OWNER The Telegraph plc
FREQUENCY Daily
EDITORS/CORRESPONDENTS Charles Clover (Environment), Fred Whitsey, Stephen Lacey

A strong gardening team writes for the *Telegraph* on Saturdays, including Fred Whitsey and Stephen Lacey. Its varied and topical articles are recommended reading.

Financial Times
1 Southwark Bridge, London SE1 9HL
☎ 071 873 3000   📠 071 873 3076
OWNER Pearson plc
FREQUENCY Daily
EDITORS/CORRESPONDENTS Robin Lane-Fox (Gardening correspondent), Teresa Maclean

Robin Lane Fox's stylishly idiosyncratic column appears in the weekend section of the Saturday *FT*; Teresa Maclean writes about allotments in an occasional series.

Flora

The Fishing Lodge Studio, 77 Balbridge Road,
Wilton, Wiltshire
☎ 0722 743207

CONTACT Wilton (General Enquiries)
OWNER Maureen Foster
PRICE £1.75
FREQUENCY 6 issues a year
EDITORS/CORRESPONDENTS R. Bennet (Editor)

Bi-monthly magazine for flower arrangers and florists.
The editorial office is in Kent.

The Garden

80 Vincent Square, London SW1P 2PE
☎ 071 834 4333
OWNER EMAP Apex Publications for the RHS
PRICE £2.25 (free to RHS members)
FREQUENCY Monthly
EDITORS/CORRESPONDENTS Ian Hodgson (Editor),
Tradescant (Hugh Johnson), Roy Lancaster, Brent El-
liott, Alan Leslie

The Journal of the Royal Horticultural Society. Indis-
pensable journal both for new articles and for the
repository of information laid up in its back numbers.
Currently on the up, with a varied mixture of serious
but not solemn articles on plants, gardens and horticultural topics. It also contains up to date news of RHS
events.

Garden Answers

Apex House, Oundle Road, Peterborough PE2 9NP
☎ 0733 898100   ☏ 0733 898433
CONTACT Managing editor
OWNER EMAP Apex Publications Ltd
PRICE £1.55
FREQUENCY Monthly
EDITORS/CORRESPONDENTS Adrienne Wild (Editor)

Illustrated monthly magazine with practical information
for keen gardeners.

Garden News

Apex House, Oundle Road, Peterborough,
Cambridgeshire PE2 9NP
☎ 0733 898100   ☏ 0733 898433
OWNER EMAP Apex Publications Ltd
PRICE 67p (£57 pa)
FREQUENCY Weekly
EDITORS/CORRESPONDENTS Andrew Blackford (Edi-
tor), Alan Durose (Gardening editor), Geoff Amos
(Consultant editor), Geoffrey Smith, Geoff Stebbings,
Daphne Ledward

Weekly colour tabloid to read in the potting shed.
Many readers are allotment holders and hobbyists.

No-nonsense hands-on approach, with good product
and club coverage.

The Gardener

Westover House, West Quay Road, Poole, Dorset
BH15 1JG
☎ 0202 687418   ☏ 0202 674335
CONTACT Janet Salisbury
OWNER IPC Magazines Ltd
PRICE £1.60
FREQUENCY Monthly
EDITORS/CORRESPONDENTS Graham Clarke (Group
editor), David Hurrion (Associate editor)

Monthly magazine which has recently joined the *Amateur Gardening* stable. Well illustrated, and aimed at
gardeners with some experience.

Gardening Which?

2 Castlemead, Gascoyne Way, Hertford X SG14 1LH
☎ 0992 587773
OWNER Consumer's Association
PRICE £51 (15 issues)
FREQUENCY 10 issues a year
EDITORS/CORRESPONDENTS Alistair Ayres (Editor)

Consumer led magazine which applies the charac-
teristic *Which?* approach to plants and garden matters.
The number above is for subscriptions.

Gardens Illustrated

The Boathouse, Crabtree Lane, London SW6 6LU
☎ 071 381 6007   ☏ 071 381 3930
CONTACT Editor
OWNER John Brown Publishing Ltd
PRICE £2.95
FREQUENCY 6 issues a year
EDITORS/CORRESPONDENTS Rosie Atkins (Editor),
Penelope Hobhouse (Associate editor), Anna Pavord
(Associate editor), Patrick Taylor

New bi-monthly magazine with glossy articles for smart
gardeners. It is set apart by its international coverage,
distinguished writing and stylish photography.

The Grower

Warwick House, Swanley, Kent BR8 8HY
☎ 0322 660070   ☏ 0322 667633
CONTACT Editor
OWNER Nexus Business Communications Ltd
PRICE £1.05 (£47.50 pa)
FREQUENCY Weekly
EDITORS/CORRESPONDENTS Peter Rogers (Editor)

Trade magazine for those involved in commercial horticulture.

The Guardian

119 Farringdon Road, London EC1R 3ER
☎ 071 278 2332   ☎ 071 837 2114
OWNER Guardian Newspapers Ltd
FREQUENCY Daily
EDITORS/CORRESPONDENTS Hilary Applegate ('Growbag' column)

Good environmental coverage: there is a regular gardening column by Hilary Applegate in the Saturday magazine.

Homes and Gardens

King's Reach Tower, Stamford Street, London SE1 9LS
☎ 071 261 5000   ☎ 071 261 6247
OWNER IPC Magazines Ltd/ Reed Publishing
PRICE £1.80
FREQUENCY Monthly
EDITORS/CORRESPONDENTS Amanda Evans (Editor), A.M. Cleveley (Gardening correspondent)

Reliable monthly magazine with round-ups of garden news items and in-depth features on gardens every month.

Horticulture Week

38 - 42 Hampton Road, Teddington, London TW11 0JE
☎ 081 943 5000   ☎ 081 943 5673
CONTACT Editor
OWNER Haymarket Magazines Ltd
PRICE £55 pa
FREQUENCY Weekly
EDITORS/CORRESPONDENTS Stovin Hayter (Editor)

Informative weekly business news magazine for anyone who works in commercial and ornamental horticulture.

Hortus

Bryan's Ground, Stapleton, Hereford & Worcester LD8 2LP
☎ 0544 260001   ☎ 0544 260015
CONTACT Editor
OWNER David Wheeler
PRICE £25 pa
FREQUENCY Quarterly
EDITORS/CORRESPONDENTS David Wheeler (Editor)

Quarterly journal for thinking gardeners, concentrating on literary and artistic aspects rather than the practical. The tone is gently scholarly; illustrated with original engravings.

House and Gardens

Vogue House, Hanover Square, London WR1 0AD
☎ 071 499 9080   ☎ 071 493 1345
OWNER Condé Nast Publications Ltd

PRICE £2.20
FREQUENCY Monthly
EDITORS/CORRESPONDENTS Robert Harling (Editor), Peter Russell (Gardening correspondent)

This upmarket glossy magazine has a regular column by Peter Russell, and usually profiles a country house garden among other gardening features.

The Independent

40 City Road, London EC1Y 2DB
☎ 071 253 1222   ☎ 071 956 1435
OWNER Newspaper Publishing plc
FREQUENCY Daily
EDITORS/CORRESPONDENTS Anna Pavord (Gardening correspondent)

Anna Pavord's well-written Saturday column is frequently the best of the crop. Chosen topics extend beyond the obvious.

The Independent on Sunday

40 City Road, London EC1Y 2DB
☎ 071 253 1222   ☎ 071 415 1333
OWNER Newspaper Publishing plc
FREQUENCY Weekly
EDITORS/CORRESPONDENTS Mary Keene, Michael Leapman

Interesting though somewhat offbeat gardening articles appear in the Review section.

N & GC

147 - 151 Temple Chambers, Temple Avenue, London EC4 0BP
☎ 071 583 3030   ☎ 071 583 4068
CONTACT Editorial
OWNER Bouverie Publishing Co Ltd
PRICE £44 pa
FREQUENCY Fortnightly
EDITORS/CORRESPONDENTS Peter Dawson (Editor)

Nurseryman & Garden Centre is the official magazine of the Horticultural Trades Association. Contains industry news and features on plants, people and products for retailers.

The New Plantsman

RHS Subscription Service, P O Box 38, Ashford, Kent TN25 6PR
OWNER Royal Horticultural Society
PRICE £25 pa
FREQUENCY Quarterly
EDITORS/CORRESPONDENTS Christopher Brickell (Editorial consultant), Victoria Matthews (Editor)

Relaunched specialist magazine from the RHS for botanists and keen gardeners. Articles by expert contributors will be set off by colour photographs and botanical illustrations. The editor works from Vincent Square.

The Observer
119 Farringdon Road, London EC1R 3ER
☎ 071 278 2332
OWNER   Guardian Newspapers Ltd
FREQUENCY   Weekly
EDITORS/CORRESPONDENTS   John Course (Gardening editor)

There is a regular gardening column written by several different writers.

Organic Gardening
P O Box 4, Wiveliscombe, Taunton, Somerset TA4 2QY
☎ 0984 623998   📠 0984 623998
CONTACT   Editor
OWNER   Organic Garden (Wardnest Ltd)
PRICE   £1.75 (£21 pa)
FREQUENCY   Monthly
EDITORS/CORRESPONDENTS   Basil Kaplan (Editor)

The organic gardening magazine. Covers the whole range of organic approaches, and includes both ornamental and fruit and vegetable gardening.

Pacific Horticulture
P O Box 485, Berkeley, CA 94701, USA
PRICE $20
FREQUENCY   Quarterly

The best of the American gardening magazines: well worth subscribing to.

Period House and Its Garden
Times House, Station Approach, Ruislip, London HA4 8NB
☎ 0895 677677   📠 0895 676027
CONTACT   Editorial Department
OWNER   DMG Home Interest Magazines Ltd
PRICE   £2.20 (£24 pa)
FREQUENCY   Monthly
EDITORS/CORRESPONDENTS   Richard Parker (Editor), Jez Abbott (Assistant Editor)

Colour monthly for people who live in older houses. Gardening coverage consists of news items and case studies of restoring gardens.

Period Living and Traditional Homes
Victory House, 14 Leicester Place, London WC2H 7BP
☎ 071 437 9011   📠 071 434 0656
CONTACT   Editorial department
OWNER   EMAP Elan Publications
PRICE   £2.20

FREQUENCY   Monthly
EDITORS/CORRESPONDENTS   Isobel MacKenzie-Price (Editor), Christine Taylor (Gardens correspondent)

Lifestyle monthly magazine with articles for people who want to make appropriate gardens for a period house, or to create a garden in a period style.

Practical Gardening
Apex House, Oundle Road, Peterborough, Cambridgeshire PE2 9NP
☎ 0733 898100   📠 0733 898433
CONTACT   Editor
OWNER   EMAP Apex Publications
PRICE   £1.90
FREQUENCY   Monthly
EDITORS/CORRESPONDENTS   Adrienne Wild (Editor), Graham Rice

Good-looking monthly magazine with strong photography and some informative special supplements.

The Scotsman
20 North Bridge, Edinburgh EH1 1YT
☎ 031 225 2468   📠 031 226 7420
CONTACT   David Robinson (Weekend section)
OWNER   Scotsman Publications Ltd
FREQUENCY   Daily
EDITORS/CORRESPONDENTS   David Robinson (Editor, weekend section), Dr David Stuart (Columnist)

Dr David Stuart contributes a weekly column every Saturday.

The Spectator
56 Doughty Street, London WC1N 2LL
☎ 071 405 1706   📠 071 242 0603
OWNER   The Spectator (1828) Ltd
PRICE   £1.75
FREQUENCY   Weekly
EDITORS/CORRESPONDENTS   Ursula Buchan (Gardening columnist)

Ursula Buchan writes the more-or-less monthly gardening column in this forthright weekly magazine. Her amusing and intelligent essays should not be missed, and an anthology is surely due soon.

The Sunday Telegraph
1 Canada Square, Canary Wharf, London E14 5DT
☎ 071 538 5000   📠 071 513 2504
OWNER   The Sunday Telegraph plc
FREQUENCY   Weekly
EDITORS/CORRESPONDENTS   Ursula Buchan (Gardening correspondent)

Like its daily sister paper the *Sunday Telegraph* has extensive and interesting gardening coverage.

The Sunday Times
1 Pennington Street, London E1 9XW
☎ 071 782 5000   📠 071 782 5658
OWNER News International
FREQUENCY Weekly
EDITORS/CORRESPONDENTS Graham Rose

Graham Rose writes the regular and authoritative column on gardeners and gardens.

The Times
1 Pennington Street, London E1 9XN
☎ 071 782 5000   📠 071 488 3242
OWNER News International
FREQUENCY Daily
EDITORS/CORRESPONDENTS Francesca Greenoak, Alan Toogood

Francesca Greenoak's Saturday column is intelligent and adventurous. There is also a valuable show report on the Wednesday of the regular RHS shows.

Your Garden
Westover House, West Quay Road, Poole, Dorset BH15 1JG
☎ 0202 680603   📠 0202 674335

CONTACT Janet Salisbury
OWNER IPC Magazines Ltd
PRICE £1 (£15 pa)
FREQUENCY Monthly
EDITORS/CORRESPONDENTS Graham Clarke (Editor)

New glossy monthly with an enthusiastic approach to medium and small gardens: likely to appeal to new gardeners.

Videos

African Violets, Periwinkle Productions (0489 885645) £14.99.

Clematis, Periwinkle Productions (0489 885645) £14.99.

Colour All Year, Consumers' Association (0800 252100) £14.99.

Flower Arranging 1: The Basics, Bill Lomas (MCVC) £10.21.

Flower Arranging 2 : A Step Further, Bill Lomas (MCVC) £10.21.

Fuchsias, Periwinkle Productions (0489 885645) £14.99.

The Gardens and the Gardeners: Spring, Summer, Autumn & Winter, The National Trust (Beckman).

Gardens of England & Wales, Seer TV (0222 751159) £11.99.

The Gardens of England & Wales: Gardeners' Views, Seer TV (0222 751159) £11.95.

Hanging Baskets, Windowboxes & Containers, Periwinkle Productions (0489 885645) £14.99.

House Plants, ICI Garden Products (Beckman) £14.99.

House Plants, Gardening Time Guides, Time-Life Video (P O Box 77, Liverpool L70 1JD).

Pelargoniums, Periwinkle Productions (0489 885645) £14.99.

Peter Beales: A Celebration of Old Roses, Vivian Russell Inc. Ltd (07687 77307) £15.99.

Plants in Containers, Gardening Time, Time-Life.

Ponds and Water Features, Gardening Time, Time-Life.

Roses, ICI Garden Products (Beckman) £14.99.

Trees, Shrubs and Flowering Plants, ICI Garden Products (Beckman) £14.99.

Wisley through the Seasons: Spring, Royal Horticultural Society (0483 211320) £12.99.

Wisley through the Seasons: Summer, Royal Horticultural Society (0483 211320) £12.99.

Wisley through the Seasons: Autumn, Royal Horticultural Society (0483 211320) £12.99.

Wisley through the Seasons: Winter, Royal Horticultural Society (0483 211320) £12.99.

30

Personal Bibliography

(Readers looking for a comprehensive bibliography of plants and gardens will not find one here. There are, however, several works which are very useful sources of further reading. Pre-eminent is The New RHS Dictionary of Gardening: the bibliography at the back of the fourth volume lists over 1,000 books, including a few in French, German and Italian. The Plant Finder is a good source, too: although concerned only with plants, it mentions about 400 books and articles. Also reliable is the bibliography at the back of each volume in the pictorial series by Roger Phillips and Martyn Rix (see below). Finally, we recommend The Oxford Companion to Gardens, whose bibliography includes a number of serious works which are not listed in the other books.)

Every generation has its favourite books (writes Charles Quest-Ritson). Fifty years ago the gardening world was devoted to the writings of Gertrude Jekyll and E A Bowles. It was Vita Sackville-West who moulded my parents' tastes and taught them how to garden, though some of their contemporaries have a special regard for Margery Fish. I have to confess that her writings leave me cold. For me, and for many other members of my generation I suspect, two books stand head and shoulders above all others. The first is Russell Page's The Education of a Gardener which as a young man I read like Holy Writ, pondering the gardening mysteries which lay behind its paragraphs. Page had the knack of never writing in a manner that was too specific, so that he inspired his readers to apply his wisdom to every situation. It is this universality which is his strength. The Education of a Gardener was a cogently argued aesthetic of gardening: I still find it totally convincing. The second book which influenced me beyond reason in those early years could not have been more

different; a compilation called The Well-Tempered Garden based on Christopher Lloyd's weekly articles for Country Life. It was Lloyd's love of plants, his intellect and his willingness to experiment that most enchanted me. Moreover he imparted his great knowledge with humour and style. The young are apt to be influenced by matters of style rather than substance: I recognise now how fortunate I was to fall in with a writer who offered both.

Every beginner needs a how-to-do-it book, a guide that will teach the technical skills. I do not remember how I learnt to take cuttings, prune roses or recognise downy mildew: I suppose I must have learnt it as a child from watching my parents or pestering the gardener. I myself have always been ready to tell people how to perform complicated tasks like saddle-grafting that I have never actually done for myself. However, a most valuable weekly series appeared in about 1970 which built up into an eight volume loose-leaf compendium, parcelled in dark green binders whose edges were dangerously sharp. Published by Marshall Cavendish, The Encyclopaedia of Gardening is still a useful reference source for practical advice. Daniel Lloyd writes that there has never been a series to match it. Daniel Lloyd himself is a name to conjure: I bought a great deal from him in those early days and am very sorry to hear that, twenty years on, he has decided to scale down his activities, for he is a peerless bookseller.

I learnt about trees and shrubs from W J Bean's four-volume Trees and Shrubs Hardy in the British Isles which was just appearing then in its eighth edition. There were long gaps between deliveries: the first volume was given to me by grandmother, the second by my father, the third by my wife, and the fourth by my daughter. The fifth volume was a supplement, and I had to buy it for myself. For easy reference, *Hillier's Manual of Trees and Shrubs* was (and remains) the readiest of reckoners, though I find its descriptions infuriatingly short. Then Graham Thomas published the first edition of his classic work *Perennial Garden Plants*, which opened my eyes to the wealth of herbaceous plants: I had tended to consider them less interesting than trees and shrubs. Thomas is possessed of two sublime gifts: first he catches the distinguishing features which escape lesser men. His second talent is for lucid prose. He has the rare ability, which he shares with an even greater stylist Hugh Johnson, of summing up the character of a plant with succintness, accuracy and wit.

Two other books influenced me strongly: both were plantsman's books, but very different. Sir Frederick Stern's *A Chalk Garden* is learned, original and catholic in its obsession with plants from the tallest tree to the smallest bulb. It remains the best guide to gardening on chalk and, now that we live in the middle of Salisbury Plain, I find it more enthralling than ever. The other book is probably now forgotten - Bertram Anderson's autobiographical *Seven Gardens* which, though badly written and worse edited, was an inspirational testimony to the Englishman's love of plants. But there were many others. E A Bowles' three books on *My Garden in Spring, My Garden in Summer* and *My Garden in Autumn and Winter*; William Robinson's *Flora and Sylva*, short lived but a mine of good ideas; and endless books on foreign gardens - I particularly sought the early A & C Black volumes which dealt with gardens in such exotic locations as the Italian Lakes and the Canary Islands. Then there was Will Ingwersen's *Manual of Alpine Plants*, which has only just been toppled from its premier position by the Alpine Garden Society's brand new *Encyclopaedia of Alpine Plants*. I have, however, long regretted that there are so few books about roses which are either original or well-written, let alone both: Graham Thomas' three volumes on *The Old Shrub Roses, Shrub Roses of Today* and *Climbing Roses Old and New* are now a little out of date.

My education as a gardener was conducted in the 1970s. Those who took to the hobby in the 1980s or 1990s were spoiled for choice. I would advise anyone who is starting to become interested in gardening now to commit several hundred pounds to a supreme act of extravagance and buy the four volume *New RHS Dictionary of Gardening*. There is no better reference work for plants. You will also need *The Plant Finder* (essential reading for every gardener) and *The Oxford Companion to Gardens*, a brilliant compendium of useful information. A modern manual for beginners which has perhaps been rather overlooked is Ursula Buchan's *The Principles of Gardening*: more Elizabeth David than Russell Page in style. But above all you will need picture books. It is only by looking at plants and gardens that you learn how to do things for yourself. I have no hesitation in recommending the Pan Garden Plants series of A4 paperbacks by Roger Phillips and Martyn Rix. More than half the space is taken up by photographs of remarkable clarity. It is the only series which I use with confidence to identify and distinguish different varieties of closely related plants. The titles include *Roses, Shrubs, Bulbs*, and *Perennials*, and all are likely to remain in print for many years. Garden design is more tricky. There is no right way of laying out a garden, and no universal style. The answer is to buy books which have good pictures - photographs, not drawings - and peer at them long and hard. Good examples are Christopher Lloyd's *A Year at Great Dixter* and Alvilde Lees-Milne's three classics - *The Englishwoman's Garden, The Englishman's Garden* and *The New Englishwoman's Garden*.

The best way to decide what to read and what to buy is to visit a really good bookshop or library. I sometimes think that I have learned more from browsing through the Royal Horticultural Society's Lindley Library than from 20 years of building up my own. But I owe more still to Russell Page's incomparable *The Education of a Gardener* and Christopher Lloyd's inspirational *The Well Tempered Garden*, and I am pleased to discover that both are still in print.

The following list includes a number of specialised garden and botanical tour operators. In addition to the companies below, some general tour operators will organise holidays which include a significant number of interesting gardens in their itinerary. Several of the horticultural societies arrange their own trips for their members, notably the Alpine Garden Society and also the Royal Horticultural Society (0394 276276). Members of the International Dendrology Society have access to many otherwise closed gardens through the IDS tours: members only, though. The National Trust and the British Trust for Conservation Volunteers both arrange working conservation holidays (see Section 24). Outside the gardening world, Specialtours (071 730 2297) arranges some very tempting itineraries for the National Art Collections Fund (071 821 0404), including gardens in Cornwall and the Riviera this year.

Abercrombie & Kent Travel
Sloane Square House, Holbein Place, London SW1W 8NS
☎ 071 730 9600　　📠 071 730 9376

CONTACT　Diana Shirley or Janet Andrews
1994 TOURS　UK and Europe
FOUNDED　1962
MEMBER　ABTA; ATOL; IATA

Garden tours will be UK based this year: contact them directly for more details.

Accompanied Cape Tours
Hill House, Much Marcle, Ledbury, Hereford & Worcester HR8 2NX
☎ 0531 84210　　📠 0432 351028

CONTACT　Virginia Carlton
1994 TOURS　Western Cape, South Africa
FOUNDED　1991

Small groups of less than ten allow for a flexible programme which can be altered to suit individual interests. A chance to meet and talk with South Africans is an important feature of the trips.

American Horticultural Society
7931 East Boulevard Drive, Alexandria, Virginia 22308, USA
☎ 0101 703 768 5700　　📠 0101 703 765 6032

CONTACT　Ann Clogan
1994 TOURS　Greek islands, Great Britain, Rhine, Spain and Portugal, Hudson River, Hawaii
FOUNDED　1922

The tours arm of the American Horticultural Society.

Barfield Travel & Tours
14 Chain Lane, Newark, Nottinghamshire NG24 1AU
☎ 0636 705612　　📠 0636 707600

1994 TOURS　Portugal, Jersey, British Columbia, Netherlands and France
MEMBER　ABTA; IATA; ATOL

Tours for gardeners with additional visits to nearby attractions. Specific destinations are subject to confirmation.

Boxwood Tours: Quality Garden Holidays
56 Spring Road, Abingdon, Oxfordshire OX14 1AN
☎ 0235 532791　　📠 0235 532791

CONTACT　Sue Macdonald
1994 TOURS　Great Britain and Europe
FOUNDED　1990
MEMBER　(Client trust account)

Tours to British and European gardens. Distinguished leaders accompany each tour: both partners are themselves Kew-trained.

Carolanka
Rowden House, Brentnor, Tavistock, Devon PL19 0NG
☎ 0822 810230　　📠 0822 810230

CONTACT　Mrs Carol Cameron
1994 TOURS　Sri Lanka

FOUNDED 1991

Guided tours including visits to botanic gardens. Personalised gardens itineraries can also be arranged.

Cox & Kings Travel

St James Court, 45 Buckingham Gate, London
SW1E 6AF
☎ 071 873 5002

CONTACT Caroline Cotton
1994 TOURS Greece, Turkey, Cevennes, Carinthia, Western Australia
FOUNDED 1758
MEMBER ABTA; ATOL; IATA; AITO

Botany and natural history tours are accompanied by Roy Cheek, Mary Briggs and others. Garden tours have now been added to their range. Destinations this year include many of the classic botanical areas of Europe.

David Sayers Travel

10 Barley Mow Passage, London W4 4PH
☎ 081 995 3642   FAX 081 742 1066

CONTACT Andrew Brock Travel
1994 TOURS New Zealand, India, Cyprus, Spain, Azores
FOUNDED 1982
MEMBER ABTA; AITO; ATOL

Specialist garden and botanical tours, operated by Andrew Brock Travel. Kew-trained horticulturist David Sayers accompanies most of the tours.

David Way Associates

Southover, Grove Lane, Hunton, Maidstone Kent
ME15 0SE
☎ 0622 820876   FAX 0622 820645

CONTACT D W Way
1994 TOURS Normandy; Aquitaine; Utrecht; Gelderland; Flanders
FOUNDED 1988

Specialises in the low countries and France. Tours are organised for societies and groups, and are often based on private gardens which are not usually open.

Fine Art Travel Ltd

15 Savile Row, London W1X 1AE
☎ 071 437 8553   FAX 071 437 1733

CONTACT Charles FitzRoy or Jane Rae
1994 TOURS Ravenna and Urbino, Burgundy, Rome
FOUNDED 1984

There are no tours specifically for gardeners, but this top-end of the market firm has the entrée to many fine gardens. High points of this year's itinerary include Ninfa, whilst Robin Lane-Fox later leads a tour to Ravenna and Urbino.

Himalayan Kingdoms Ltd

20 The Mall, Clifton, Bristol BS8 4DR
☎ 0272 237163   FAX 0272 744993

CONTACT Steven Berry
1994 TOURS The Himalaya
FOUNDED 1987
MEMBER AITO; ATOL

No specifically botanical trips this year, but some are planned for 1995. A recent rhododendron hunt found 26 out of 29 available species.

Naturetrek

Chautara, Bighton, Alresford, Hampshire SO24 9RB
☎ 0962 733051   FAX 0962 733368

CONTACT David Mills
1994 TOURS Crete, Sikkim, Bhutan, Pyrenees, Slovakia, New Zealand
FOUNDED 1986
MEMBER AITO; ATOL

Specialist treks to near and far destinations for botanists, ornithologists and naturalists. Treks are graded for difficulty. For the adventurous.

Swan Hellenic Ltd

77 New Oxford Street, London WC1A 1PP
☎ 071 831 1515   FAX 071 497 2832
1994 TOURS Mediterranean; Dutch bulbfields
FOUNDED 1954
MEMBER ATOL; ABTA

Among this well-known company's extensive cruises, those to the Mediterranean in spring and river cruises in the Netherlands are accompanied by distinguished botanists including Dr Phillip Cribb.

Trossachs Garden Tours

Orchardlea House, Callander, Perthshire FK17 8BG
☎ 0877 330798   FAX 0877 330543

CONTACT Mrs Hilary Gunkel
1994 TOURS Dunoon, Callander, St Andrews, Oban, Ayr
FOUNDED 1989

Attractively packaged weekend and midweek visits for small groups to private and public Scottish gardens.

WHEN YOU GO AWAY

Whether you're soaking up sun and sangria in Spain during the winter months, or just cruising the Norfolk Broads for a long weekend, how will the garden manage without you? The answer depends on how well it manages when you are there. Work out how much time you spend tending your plot each week and you'll have a pretty good idea what sort of arrangements, if any, will be needed in your absence. After all, if a grudging hour or so at the weekend is par for the course, then it probably won't even notice you're not there. If, on the other hand, hour upon hour, week in, week out, go to grooming the garden to perfection, then either you'll need some-one else to keep up the standard till you return, or else you should think about going away at a quieter season horticulturally.

Should you fall somewhere in between, then there is a choice of steps you can take to keep the upper hand. So, given that most people go away in summer, the main problem is protecting your plants from English heat and drought. It helps if you can remove pots and hanging baskets to a place of shade and shelter while you are away. Plants in pots fare even better if you plunge them in the ground and water the earth around them well. Consider intro-ducing any or all of the following: mulches on the borders, and especially around newly planted trees and shrubs, to reduce the amount of water lost through evaporation; shade netting; capillary mat-ting or plunge beds for pots, inside and out; a time controlled watering system. This last need not be as expensive as it sounds. Use seepage hoses and/or an electronic clock which switches on after dusk when watering is most effective. And remember that no systems are suitable for long periods.

After water, the main problem is growth. Puri-tanical journalists will advise you to cut the heads off flowers which have not yet faded, or perhaps not even opened, before you leave. Necessary or not, the grass won't cut itself and produce will not pick itself, so you'll have to get a friend or neighbour to fight this battle by proxy. Don't expect them to spare as much time as you would: their little will make all the difference.

For bigger gardens and more intensive cultiva-tion, you will probably need to rely on expert help. Greenhouse gardening is a high-risk activity. Precious specimens are best entrusted to the safe custody of an experienced gardening friend to look after in his or her own greenhouse. If this is im-possible, you must find a knowledgeable person to water and ventilate your greenhouse as frequently as you do yourself. Remember that the usual fault of inexperienced caretakers is to overwater everything. Leave long and detailed instructions in writing, run

through them point by point, and give a practical demonstration of your requirements. If you don't have a gardener already, consider arranging for con-tract gardeners to fill in for you. You will have to set out their duties precisely, and expect to pay from £10 an hour for their time. Alternatively, you can ask one of the specialist agencies to find you a residential houseminder.

Houseminders carry out the basic domestic and garden duties that you would normally perform yourself. These usually involve caring for pets, answering the telephone, and providing the security of a presence in the house, as well as watering the tomatoes and mowing the lawn. Large gardens or greenhouses which demand hours of commitment may require a higher fee. Most agencies are happy to make special arrangements to accommodate your particular needs. Agencies include:

Animal Aunts

45 Fairview Road, Headley Down, Hampshire, GU35 8HQ
☎ 0428 712611   ▣ 0428 717190

Mainly for people with pets and other animals, particu-larly those with special requirements.

Holiday Homewatch

Nursery Cottage, Penybont, Llandrindrod Wells, Powys, LD1 5SP
☎ 0597 851840

Specialise in assignments where there are horses and farm livestock as well as domestic pets to look after.

Homesitters Ltd

Buckland Wharf, Buckland, Aylesbury, Buckinghamshire. HP22 5LQ
☎ 0296 630730

Perhaps the best known agency, Homesitters make a point of emphasising that they recruit mature respon-sible people as caretakers and investigate their back-grounds for the last twenty years, as well as taking up references. Homesitters are particularly conscious of the problems of garden owners who wish to go on holi-day. Their terms of reference run 'from watering and mowing to picking and freezing, and potting and pruning'.

Housewatch Ltd.

Little London, Berden, Bishops Stortford, Hertfordshire, CM23 1BE.
☎ 0279 777412.   ▣ 0279 777049.

Experienced with both houses and gardens.

32

The French Scene

Gardens to Visit

Garden visiting in France is not the popular pastime that it is in England. Nor have the French a tradition of opening gardens to the public: there is, for example, no equivalent to the National Gardens Scheme. The gardens which do open to the public tend to be attached to a big historic house, typically a French formal garden and/or an English-style park.

By far the most useful guide to the types of gardens which interest English visitors is *La guide des jardins botaniques de France* (L'Association des parcs botaniques de France. Pandora, 1991. 190FF.). It is a model of comprehensive and lucid exposition. 'Botanique' means almost any garden whose spirit depends on plants and plantings. The guide gives the address, opening times and a description of each garden's history and principal features.

There is no up-to-date English guide to French gardens, but *The Gardens of Europe* by Penelope Hobhouse & Patrick Taylor is a good introduction to the possibilities. To keep up to date, we recommend you to speak to one of the French bookshops in London before your departure.

Garden Centres

Plants tend to be more expensive at French garden centres than English. The best place to find bargains are ordinary markets, although the quality and range may be indifferent. Terracotta pots, however, are cheap, especially in the south. Generally speaking, everything in France is more expensive for gardeners with the possible exception of small hand tools like trowels.

Large garden centres are spaciously planned but not designed as places to take the family for a day out: there are no cafés or loos. Credit cards are not as widely used as in England, but Visa is accepted more than Access.

Nurseries

France has two 'Plant Finders'. If you wish to know as much as possible about French nurseries, you will need both. The larger of the two is *Où trouver vos plantes* by Anita Pereire & Philippe Bonduel. (Hachette, 1992. Price 98FF). It lists 30,000 plants and 600 nurseries, including a few selected nurseries in Britain and Belgium. The second plant finder is *25,000 Plantes - où et comment les acheter*, promoted by La Société Nationale d'Horticulture de France (Maison Rustique, 1993. Price 98FF). Based on 300 nurseries, it lists 500 varieties of *Prunus*, 700 fuchsias, 1,400 irises and 1,700 roses.

France has some excellent nurseries. Certain plants - irises and paeonies for example - are much more popular than in the UK. Here is a selection of top nurseries:

Pepinières Charentaises, 16310 Montemboeuf, (Charente). Tel: 45 65 02 61. Particularly good for hardy trees and shrubs. Retail and wholesale, mail order and garden centre, bare-root and container-grown stock. Catalogue 40FF.

Eve, Le Bois d'Eve, 77690 La Génévraye, (Seine-et-Marne). Tel: 64 29 00 98. Excellent all-round nurserymen, selling through mail order and on site. Catalogue 60FF, but cost set against purchases.

Les Jardins de Cotelles, 76370 Derchigny-Graincourt, (Seine-Maritime). Tel: 35 83 61 38. Retail and wholesale specialists in herbaceous plants. Mail order and container grown stock sold at their garden centre. Catalogue 25FF.

Cayeux SA, La Carcaudière, 45500 Poilly-lez-Gien, (Loiret). Tel: 38 67 05 08. Prominent iris specialist.

Iris de Thau, 14 Rue des Logis, 34140 Loupian, (Hérault). Tel: 67 43 82 50. Iris nursery with exceptional list of garden varieties.

Les Roses anciennes de André Eve, Morailles, 45300 Pithivier-le Vieil, (Loiret). Tel: 38 30 01 30. Old-fashioned rose specialist. Many unavailable in UK. Mail order only. Good display garden.

Ets Rivière, 'La Plaine', 26400 Crest, (Drôme). Tel: 75 25 44 85. Specialists in paeonies. The present owner Michel Rivière published *Le Monde fabuleux des pivoines* in 1992 (205FF, pp.164: 150 varieties photographed in colour). But there is no substitute for buying *Où trouver vos plantes* or *25,000 Plantes - où et comment les acheter* and finding out about French nurseries for yourself. And remember that, since the beginning of June last year, almost all the restrictions on the import and export of plants within the EC have disappeared. We predict a growth in mail order across the Channel.

Living in France

If you have a holiday house in France, it is often difficult to find out how to plant and maintain a garden. The solution is to read the right magazines and join the right clubs. There is one good monthly publication for keen gardeners: *Mon Jardin et ma Maison*, 20 rue de Billancourt, BP406, 92103 Boulogne-Billancourt. Eleven editions a year - July/August merged as one. 30FF per edition. Principally a garden magazine of the *Practical Gardening* variety. There is a strong English influence in the emphasis on plants and many articles on gardens in the British Isles, but the magazine tries to do justice to all areas and climates of France. It has good class advertising with lots of useful addresses. The magazine also publishes a series of 'How To' guides to special interests like roses, bonsai, climbers, ground cover plants and propagation. The main competition used to come from *L'ami des jardins et de la maison*, which was almost indistinguishable from *Mon Jardin et ma Maison*, but it ceased publication last summer. The market for aspirational gardening magazines in France is still small. We thoroughly recommended any reader with a house in France to join La Société Nationale d'Horticulture de France

(SNHF), 84 Rue de Grenelle, 75007 Paris. Tel: (1) 45 48 81 00. Founded in 1827, the society has eighteen sections: roses, herbaceous plants, floral art, house plants, camellias, ornamental trees & shrubs, garden design, fine arts, bonsai, cacti & succulents, dahlias, cut flowers, fuchsias, geraniums, *jardin d'agréement*, fruit gardens, kitchen garden plants, rhododendrons: each of the groups has regular meetings. 180 local gardening clubs are affiliated to SNHF (like the RHS in England).

SNHF also publishes *Jardins de France*, which is modelled to some extent on *The Garden* and is the only top-quality French gardening magazine. It has ten editions a year. The 1993 cost of an annual subscription was 210FF for non-members or 140FF for members: membership costs 145FF.

There are also specialist societies for such interests as roses and alpines. It is advisable to keep up your membership of British societies and especially of the Royal Horticultural Society.

Journées de Courson

Courson is sometimes described as France's Chelsea, but it is more like a fortnightly Westminster show transported to a château 25 miles south of Paris. Courson's *Journées de Plantes* are more modest than Chelsea, less frequent than the Westminster shows: they happen only twice a year, on 20-22 May and 14-16 October. When Robin Herbert presented Courson's guiding spirit Patrice Fustier with the Veitch Memorial Medal in February 1993, he said 'your creation has been described as an entrancing blend of flower show, garden party and flea market, among the stately planes of a *parc à l'anglaise*'.

Courson's success relies upon the quality of its exhibits. Strict controls are kept on the selection of nurserymen, who are encouraged not just to exhibit plants, but to sell them, too. Societies and institutes also have stands: the NCCPG is a regular attender. The May 1993 *journée* had 169 exhibitors. There are lectures too. Courson has been honing up its scientific credentials by making awards to plants for their beauty, usefulness, rarity. These are assessed by an international jury of experts: Roy Lancaster and Michael Hickson are among the British judges.

Further information from Patrice Fustier, Parc du Domaine de Courson, 91680 Courson-Montloup. Tel: (00-33) (0)1-45-55-41-74 or (00-33) (0)1-64-58-90-12.

Britain in Bloom

This annual competition is probably the largest horticultural event in the country, with over 1,300 entrants last year. Regional competitions take place in seventeen areas each summer and the leading category winners are then entered into the national round. These regional contests often spark off further competitions, so that a town which is entering may award prizes to individuals and businesses within their area as a way of encouraging the community to pull together.

There are ten categories of entrants for the main competition, all based on the size of the population in the villages, towns and cities that take part. Seven special awards are also made each year. Judging for this stage takes place in August and September, with marks for the horticultural display and general tidiness. Potential winners usually combine the collective efforts of the council, local business and private gardeners. Eyesores, areas of neglect and vandalism or graffiti count against the entrants.

Britain in Bloom was started by the late Roy Hay in 1964. Until 1983 it was administered by the British Tourist Authority: the event is now co-ordinated by the Tidy Britain Group at national level. Beautiful Scotland in Bloom and the Wales in Bloom Foundation are responsible for the first stages of the competition in their areas; the regional entrants are completed by twelve English areas and winners from competitions in Northern Ireland (Progressive Ulster), the Isle of Man and Jersey. Entry forms and advice are available from the regional organisers: contact Britain in Bloom, Tidy Britain Group, The Pier, Wigan WN3 4EX. The 1993 winners are:

Large City (150,000)   Birmingham
City (75,000 - 150,000)   Rotherham

Inner City   St Michael's Way, Sunderland
Large Town (25,000 - 70,000)   Perth
Town (10,000 - 25,000)   St Ives and Carbis Bay
Small Town (5,000 - 10,000)   Moira
Small Country Town (2,000 - 5,000)   Kirkby Lonsdale, Cumbria
Large Village (600 - 2,000)   Broughshane
Village (under 600)   Beddgelert, Gwynedd
Urban Community (2,000 - 10,000)   Darley Abbey, Derby

Asmer Trophy   Nottingham
Beautiful Britain Award   Leeds
Bob Hare Award   Bexley, London
Gordon Ford Trophy   Barnstaple
Keep Britain Tidy Award   Christchurch
Moran Memorial Award   Mark Andrew, Cumbria
English Tourist Board Award   Market Bosworth

Regional winners include: *Large City*: Bexley, Nottingham, Westminster; *City*: Aberdeen, Bath, Swansea, Darlington; *Inner City*: Burton on Trent, Leeds, Leicester, Luton, Reading, Sunderland, Southampton; *Large Town*: Abingdon, Armagh, Bury St Edmunds, Douglas, Guildford, Whitehaven; *Town*: Christchurch, Farnham, Ilkley, Prestatyn, Spalding, Stratford upon Avon; *Small Town*: Poulton le Fylde, Ryton, St Brelade, Woodbridge; *Small Country Town*: Holt, Jedburgh, Sedgefield; *Large Village*: Bampton, Beauly, Clare, Cuddington, Eynsford, Harthill with Woodhall, Market Bosworth, Walbottle; *Village*: Cambuskenneth, Chawton, Denbury, Gracehill, Old Ravenfield, Scorton; *Urban Community*: Stanwix.

Nature Reserves

There are more than 3,000 nature reserves in the United Kingdom. Some are concerned primarily with the protection of habitats for specific communities of plants or even individual plants. Others protect the conditions required by particular birds, mammals or insects. Most, however, offer attractions to a greater or lesser degree to followers of all these disciplines, and to those who are attracted by the peace of the countryside and the beauty of the scenery. Public access and conservation do not always go hand in hand. Often the protected habitats will be delicate in structure, as with the raised peat bogs, or vulnerable to destruction by visitors, even those with conservation in mind. Accordingly, many of the country's nature reserves have limited access and entry may be restricted to those with permits.

Reserve ownership is concentrated in the hands of a small number of organisations. The most active is the Royal Society for Nature Conservation, The Green, Witham Park, Waterside South, Lincoln LN5 7JR. Some 47 local wildlife trusts belong to its Wildlife Trusts Partnership, as well as many Urban Wildlife Trusts. All these have an active membership who raise funds for their conservation work and often take part in conservation projects at the reserves. Members of the county trust will be allowed in all or most of its reserves; non-members may be required to obtain a permit before visiting a restricted reserve. We have listed many of the county trusts in our Societies, regional section, and tried to include the names of reserves under their management which are likely to be of interest to botanists. A number of the sites require a permit before they can be visited, and some trusts do not allow non-members to visit the more vulnerable habitats at all. Please contact the relevant trust before visiting its reserves so as to find out the precise conditions which apply. The trusts produce information leaflets for their more popular sites, and most also publish a detailed guide to their reserves for which a charge is made. Note that many trusts retain old county names which are no longer administrative units.

Other major reserve managers include the National Trust, the National Trust for Scotland, the Royal Society for the Protection of Birds, the Wildfowl and Wetlands Trust, English Nature, local authorities, the Ministry of Defence, the regional water companies, and the Forestry Trust. The addresses of some of these bodies are listed in the Organisations section.

The main source of information for reserves managed by RSNC Wildlife Trusts is the handbook which each county trust compiles. In addition we recommend Franklyn Perring's *A Guide to Britain's Conservation Heritage* (Thorsons, 1991) which contains a selection of six of the best sites from each county, including non RSNC sites. Greater detail is available in a series of guides from Macmillan: *A Guide to the Nature Reserves of Southern England*. Other titles cover Northern England, Wales and the West Midlands, Eastern England, and Scotland.

Health &
Safety

Health and safety in the garden is a big topic. We therefore concentrate on two topical areas: the latest European Community legislation on the subject and the problem of pesticides. Then we try to assess the precautions which amateurs should take in their own gardens.

Many of the new rules on health and safety are primarily for the protection of horticultural workers. However, the spirit of the law applies just as much to amateurs. Although there is no statutory obligation on the gardening enthusiast to follow the same procedures personally, he does have a duty to his neighbours and employees to abide by the details of the legislation. It would be foolish to ignore the concern for everyone's safety which underpins the formal requirements. We should therefore all try to work within the codes of practice suggested by the regulations.

Health and Safety Legislation

Many of the regulations which promote health and safety at work were replaced at the beginning of 1993 by new regulations both from the UK parliament and the European Community. These new regulations are important for employers and employees - anyone in the horticultural world who works for someone else. Nevertheless the main law on working practices remains the *Health and Safety at Work Act 1974*, which places a duty on employers to ensure, so far as is reasonably practicable, the health, safety and welfare of employees and others affected by their undertakings. This duty of care is largely achieved by ensuring that the work, work place, machinery and systems are all safe and that employees receive adequate information, train-

ing and supervision. Employees have a corresponding duty to take reasonable care of their own safety and that of fellow employees and visitors.

The *Management of Health and Safety at Work Regulations 1992* came into effect at the beginning of last year. One of its requirements is that employers should make an assessment of the risks to the health and safety of their employees and visitors, so that proper preventative and protective measures can be adopted. Those who employ five or more people must record both the findings of their risk assessment and the health and safety arrangements which they have made as a result. Then there is a duty to reduce the risks posed by hazards. For example, anyone who is working with chemicals must have safe and suitable equipment and systems for their handling, and they must choose the safest appropriate chemical for the task. In the case of a chain saw, for instance, it should be in sound repair and fitted with protective guards. Any electric circuits, wiring and tools must be sound, correctly installed and regularly maintained, and fitted with circuit breakers if appropriate. Employers are under an obligation to provide first aid for employees who are injured or taken ill at work. This extends to seeing that suitable members of staff receive emergency first aid training and that there is good quick transport available in the event of an accident. The regulations are not all one sided. They also place a duty on employees to follow health and safety instructions and report dangers.

The *Provision and Use of Work Equipment Regulations 1992* puts into effect an EC directive to protect workers by regulating the use of work equipment. 'Work equipment' covers everything from a hand tool to a garden tractor. Employers are required to make sure that equipment is correct for the use that will be made of it, used only for operations for which it is suitable, and maintained in an efficient state and good repair. There is a specific responsibility to ensure that all the dangerous parts of machinery have serviceable and effective guards in place so as to prevent accidental contact with any moving component or part. Other specific requirements include protecting equipment against such hazards as catching fire or overheating. The regulations also list the minimum requirements for work equipment in specific situations.

The *Manual Handling Operations Regulations 1992*, are intended to reduce injuries at work caused by the incorrect handling of loads. They apply not only to the lifting of loads but also to lowering, pushing, pulling, carrying or moving them. Employers and employees alike are required to avoid hazardous manual handling operations if possible, assess hazardous operations which cannot be avoided, and reduce the risks of injury as far as reasonably practicable.

The *Workplace (Health, Safety and Welfare) Regulations 1992* consolidate parts of the Factories Act 1961 and the Offices, Shops and Railways Premises Act, 1963. These regulations cover many aspects of health, safety and welfare in the workplace. For example, employees must be supplied with proper lavatories, washing, eating and changing facilities and drinking water.

The *Personal Protective Equipment at Work Regulations* 1992, group together earlier statutory instruments and incorporate a new EC directive on the design, certification and testing of Personal Protective Equipment (PPE). The main point for persons in the horticultural industry to note is that PPE must be suitable for the risks and working conditions, take account of the workers' needs, fit properly, give adequate protection, and be compatible with other items of PPE worn with them. It is important that employees have the correct type of protection. For example, different types of eye protection are needed against the dangers posed by dust, chemical splash and flying objects.

Finally, office workers in the horticultural industry need to know of the recent *Health & Safety (Display Screen Equipment) Regulations 1992* which aim to minimise the problems associated with display screen equipment. Employers should ensure that VDUs and computer monitors do not create eye strain and that the layout of equipment in the office creates the right conditions for use. It is the employer's responsibility to provide eye- and eyesight-tests if required, and special spectacles if needed.

Further information on all aspects of safety regulations may be obtained from: The Health & Safety Executive Information Centre, Broad Lane, Sheffield, S3 7HQ. (Tel: 0742 892345). The Centre also publishes a number of advisory pamphlets and booklets including *Watch Your Back* (avoiding back strain in Timber Handling and chainsaw work), *Working With VDUs* and *Poisoning by Pesticides: First Aid*. These titles are available free from its Information Office.

The Royal National Institute for the Blind, 224 Great Portland Street, London W1N 6AA (Tel: 071 383 0148) in association with *Gardening Which?* has sponsored a helpful pamphlet on *Eye Safety in the Garden*. General advice is also available from the Royal Society for the Prevention of Accidents (ROSPA), Cannon House, Priory Queensway, Birmingham (Tel: 021 200 2461) and from such organisations as the National Union of Farm Workers.

Copies of the six new Statutory Instruments and other regulations which are still in force are available from HMSO and certain booksellers. Details and prices are as follows: *Management of Health and Safety at Work Regulations*, 1992. SI 2051. £2.30.

Provision and Use of Work Equipment Regulations, 1992. SI 2932. £3.10.

Manual Handling Operations Regulations, 1992. SI 2793. £1.50.

Workplace (Health, Safety and Welfare) Regulations, 1992. SI 3004. £3.10.

Personal Protective Equipment at Work Regulations, 1992. SI 2966. £2.70.

Health & Safety (Display Screen Equipment) Regulations, 1992. SI 2792. £1.90.

In addition, HMSO publishes six guides relating to the new regulations which are available from branches of Dillons at a price of £5 each. Details are as follows:

Management of health and safety at work. Approved Code of Practice. ISBN 0 11 886330 4.

Work equipment. Guidance on Regulations. ISBN 0 11 886332 0.

Manual handling. Guidance on Regulations. ISBN 0 11 886335 5.

Workplace health, safety and welfare. Approved Code of Practice. ISBN 0 11 886333 9.

Personal protective equipment at work. Guidance on Regulations. ISBN 0 11 886334 7.

Display screen equipment work. Guidance on Regulations. ISBN 0 11 886331 2.

Pesticides

All pesticides used in agriculture, horticulture, forestry, food storage and gardening must satisfy the safety standards laid down in Part 3 of the *Food and Environment Protection Act* before they can legally be advertised, sold, supplied, stored or used. 'Pesticides' covers most of the chemicals we use in the garden: anything in fact which is intended to kill something, including insecticides, fungicides, algicides, acaricides, weedkillers and mosskillers.

The Pesticides Safety Directorate, an executive agency of the Ministry of Agriculture, Fisheries and Food, has the statutory obligation to regulate the use of pesticides. The Directorate has to protect the health of human beings, creatures and plants, safeguard the environment and secure safe, efficient and humane methods of pest control. Most of its resources are devoted to evaluating and processing applications for pesticide approval.

When that approval is given, the product receives an approval number and is subject to detailed conditions which are intended to ensure that it is used safely. For example, the label must always list: the area of use (agriculture or horticulture, commercial or retail); the crops on which it may be used; the maximum dose rate and number of treatments; details of any limitations of the area to be treated; the latest time of application; how to protect the worker; and any necessary environmental protection.

There are detailed regulations which govern the storage, handling and mixing of pesticides, the disposal of empty containers and the keeping of appropriate records. Commercial pesticides must be kept in a special lockable store, which must be in a suitable site, of adequate capacity and construction, properly lit and ventilated, resistant to fire and frost, clearly marked and designed so that containers can be safely moved in and out. It is also a legal requirement that people should be trained in the proper use of pesticides. An employer has a duty to instruct, inform, train and supervise his or her employees. Moreover, anyone born later than 31st December 1964 who uses pesticides in the course of his em-

ployment must hold a Certificate of Competence unless personally working under the direct supervision of an existing certificate holder. These certificates are issed by the National Proficiency Test Council and are only awarded after training which includes: choosing the right equipment for the job in hand; knowing how to adjust, calibrate and use the equipment safely; carrying out routine maintenance in accordance with the manufacturer's instructions; identifying and correcting common faults; recognising which faults need specialist attention; cleaning and storing equipment properly; using and maintaining the correct clothing and equipment; cleaning protective items which are contaminated; proper disposal of unused chemicals.

The Pesticides Safety Directorate publishes an extremely useful guide called *Pesticides 1993* which gives details of all approved pesticide products, subdivided according to the field of use, active ingredients and whether the product is for professional or amateur use. It is available through HMSO Publications Centre, P O Box 276, London SW8 5DT, price £14.25.

Home Gardeners

How do all these regulations apply to the amateur? Unfortunately, the legal position is far from clear. Domestic servants are specifically excluded from the provisions of the *Health and Safety at Work Act 1974*. Nevertheless, every householder has a duty to ensure that all visitors and people working in his garden are free from danger. He should certainly check that his third party insurance cover extends to the part-time gardener who comes to cut the grass on Saturdays. Contract gardeners and landscapers who are employed by someone else will obviously be covered by their own employers' schemes, but this does not detract from the householder's obligation to provide a safe working environment, proper facilities and safe equipment. Nor is the householder alone in his obligations. Self-employed people have a duty to protect themselves and others who may be affected by what they do. Suppliers and installers must ensure that horticultural equipment does not present a health or safety risk when properly used or serviced. The pesticides legislation is much more clear cut. It applies to all of us individually, whether we are at work or not, inside the garden or outside, amateur or professional. If you have undisposed of stocks of domestic garden chemicals, we suggest you contact the Environmental Health Officer at your local council office for advice. Many councils make periodic collections for disposal. They will take a note of your name and address, the type and quantity of chemical you hold, and keep the information on file until they make their next round of collections.

Otherwise, safety in the garden is all about taking precautions. It means ensuring that machinery is fit for use and that you know how to operate it correctly; following the manufacturer's instructions; wearing protective clothing, including strong shoes and gloves; donning face masks and earplugs when necessary; choosing the right weather conditions; getting expert training before you use such tools as chainsaws; being wary about borrowing tools and equipment from others, even from your friends; fitting RCDs (residual current devices) to all electrical equipment; keeping up your tetanus jabs; knowing how to respond to an emergency; and having first aid at hand for cuts, bruises, stings and other injuries.

We cannot give specific advice. So far as machinery is concerned, it is essential to read the instruction book and make yourself familiar with all the controls before using it, check over the moving sections to ensure that they are in good working order and be certain that important parts like blades are all secure. Chainsaws are a particular concern. Many of the older models do not have the safety features which are now statutory: roll bars and dead-man's brakes, for instance, which cut off in the event of kickback.

Sometimes it is difficult to know where to draw the line between safety and expedience. Do you wear gloves for gardening? Not only do they protect you against thorns and prickles but they also provide some protection against an unwelcome effect of contact with the soil - bacterial and fungal infection. Two such risks are *Trichophyton rubrum* and *Trichophyton mentagrophytes*, soil fungi which infect the bed of a finger and may necessitate an operation to remove the fingernail. But many people refuse to wear gloves. Rightly or wrongly, they say that the risks are smaller than the inconvenience. What about poisonous plants? Some are well known - laburnum and yew trees, for example - while others are lethal even though you never suspected it. You do not hear of people poisoned by lily-of-the-valley, lupins, marsh marigolds, bluebells or wood anemones, but all contain toxic substances. Should you throw them out of your garden? Should they carry health warnings? Obviously not. But the point is this: everyone should be made aware of the dangers inherent in our national pastime and decide what precautions to take. We believe that the Health and Safety legislation is a very good guide to the standards which should regulate an amateur's attitude to the whole subject.

36

Charities

Charitable Gifts

Many people wish to support a horticultural charity but do not know how to do so or which to choose. There are two main welfare charities specifically concerned with gardeners and their families: the Royal Gardeners' Orphan Fund and the Gardeners' Royal Benevolent Society (see below for details of their aims and achievements). Many other horticultural organisations enjoy charitable status - most clubs and societies for instance, as well as educational institutes. An ever-increasing number of gardens are registering as charities, from Achamore on the Isle of Gigha to Trebah in Cornwall.

Donations are always welcome and account for a substantial part of the income of every charity, but the benefit can be enhanced if people are willing to structure their giving in a tax-efficient way rather than leaving it to impulse. Gifts to charity can be exempted from Income Tax, Capital Gains Tax and Inheritance Tax. Take Income Tax, for example. If you put a £10 note in a collecting box, you are giving away money on which you have paid tax and there is no way in which the charity can have the benefit of that tax. But if you use a covenant, gift aid or payroll scheme, the charity can reclaim the basic rate tax which you have already paid so that, with basic rate at 25%, the £10 is worth £13.33.

A Covenant is an undertaking to pay a fixed sum for four or more years. It has to follow the prescribed form and be signed as a deed for the charity to recover the basic rate tax which the giver is deemed to have deducted from the gift. A suitable form would read as follows:

I [Jane Smith] of [13, Acacia Avenue, Newtown, Barsetshire], hereby undertake to pay to [name of charity] for a period of 4 years from the date hereof or during my lifetime, whichever is the shorter, on the [1st] day of [April] in each year such sum as will after the deduction of income tax at the basic rate for the time being in force amount to the sum of £[100] such sum to be paid out of my general fund of taxed income.

Dated this [21st] day of [March] [1994]
Signed as a Deed by [Signature: Jane Smith]
the said [Jane Smith]
in the presence of:
[Signature, name,
address & employment
of witness]

[Date]

Gift Aid is an efficient new way for UK residents to make a one-off cash gift to a charity. The donation should be for more than £250 and you have to sign a form when making the gift so that the charity can reclaim the tax which you have already paid. There is an advantage to the giver as well as the charity if you are a higher-rate tax-payer: the charity reclaims tax at the basic rate but the difference (15%) between higher and basic tax rates is reclaimed by the giver. Gift Aid has proved very beneficial to charities.

Payroll giving has been widely introduced and many employees use it to ensure that a small part of their income goes to charity in the form of a regular donation. The charity can claim back the basic tax which has been deducted from your salary by your employer, at no cost to you. The best way to find out more about payroll giving is to speak to your employer.

Legacies in people's wills can make an enormous difference to the fortunes of a charity. The Anthony Pettit bequest funded the acquisition and maintenance of the Alpine Garden Society's new headquarters at Pershore. The gift of Netherbyres has quite transformed the ability of the Gardeners' Royal Benevolent Society to care for elderly retired gardeners and their spouses in Scotland. We recommend you to seek professional advice when making a legacy. The consequences of getting it wrong can be worse than having no will at all. Equally, it is important not to leave making a will until it is too late. By instructing a solicitor to write your will, you can be sure that your wishes are expressed correctly, so that your executors can put them into effect. Most charities can put you in touch with a suitable person to undertake the legal drafting. Finally, it is worth remembering that the best source of advice on every aspect of giving to charity is the Charities Aid Foundation, 48 Pembury Road, Tonbridge, Kent TN9 2JD (Tel 0732 771333, Fax 0732 350570). The Charities Aid Foundation is itself a charity. It exists to enable individuals and organisations to improve the quality and value of their donations to charity. 'For more than 130,000 private individuals' they claim, 'the Charities Aid Foundation is simply the best way to give '.

Garden Charities

Many gardening organisations are charities. Most of the national horticultural societies are registered charities - the Hardy Plant Society, for instance - and so are such conservation bodies as the National Council for the Conservation of Plants & Gardens. Sometimes an individual garden will belong to a charity, often set up to ensure that it is preserved after the owners who made the garden are dead: Broadleas in Wiltshire and Trebah in Cornwall are two examples. But there are other organisations which are registered charities with a more conventionally charitable purpose. They use their funds to alleviate the needs of people who have been in horticulture for most of their working lives. They are popular with garden owners and rely to a large degree upon funds raised by such bodies as the National Gardens Scheme. The main charities working in this field are The Royal Gardeners' Orphan Fund, The Gardeners' Royal Benevolent Society, The National Gardens Scheme Charitable Trust, Scotland's Gardens Scheme and The Worshipful Company of Gardeners.

The Royal Gardeners' Orphan Fund, 48 St Alban's Road, Codicote, Hertfordshire ST4 8UT (Tel 0428 820783) Secretary: Mrs Kate Wallis. Founded in 1887 to help the orphans of gardeners 'by giving

them regular allowances and grants for special purposes'. Since 1985 the Fund has also offered assistance to needy children, not necessarily orphans, whose parents are employed full-time in horticulture. The Fund's counselling service advises on such problems as may arise when a family which has been living in tied accommodation has to move elsewhere on the death of the bread-winner, sometimes to a different area and far from friends and familiar surroundings. The Fund is supported by many institutions including The National Gardens Scheme, Scotland's Gardens Scheme, The Worshipful Company of Gardeners, The Royal Horticultural Society and many horticultural and flower clubs around the country. Applications from newly bereaved families in 1992 included a two-year old girl whose landscape gardener father died as a result of a brian tumour, and three children who lost their father in a hedging accident. The total value of grants made in 1992 was £30,355.

The Gardeners' Royal Benevolent Society, Bridge House, 139 Kingston Road, Leatherhead, Surrey, KT22 7NT (Tel 0372 373962; Fax 0372 362575). Patron: H M Queen Elizabeth The Queen Mother. President: H R H Princess Alice, Duchess of Gloucester. Secretary-Administrator: C R C Bunce. The Society was founded in 1839 by a group of horticultural growers who were appalled by the fate of men, gardeners all their lives, who became too old to work and had to face starvation or the workhouse. The aim of the Society remains, as it always has been, to help gardeners suffering from ill health and to provide pensions in their old age. Income in 1992 totalled £1,302,564, including £162,293 from donations and £493,535 from investment income and deposits.

The Gardeners' Royal Benevolent Society has been very active in recent years in expanding its activities. Today there are over five hundred pensioners, fifty of whom are resident in the Society's country home, Red Oaks, Henfield, Sussex. Arthur Hellyer spent his last weeks at Red Oaks at the beginning of 1993. The Society also owns a group of seven bungalows at Barton in Cambridgeshire which are used to accommodate retired gardening couples, some of whom have had to vacate tied cottages on retirement. To meet cases of particular difficulty the Society also has a Good Samaritan fund from which grants are made for such specific purposes as fuel, house repairs and special food in cases of illness.

The Society's Scottish home, Netherbyres at Eyemouth near Berwick-on-Tweed, was given to the Society under the terms of the will of Lt Col Simon Furness in 1991 and has grounds of 40 acres. In December 1991 the Society opened a small development of sheltered housing bungalows at Kings Stanley in Gloucestershire. The first tenants moved in at the end of September 1992.

The National Gardens Scheme Charitable Trust, Hatchlands Park, East Clandon, Guildford, Surrey GU4 7RT. Administrator and Director: Lt Col Dennis Carpenter. Despite its high profile, the *National Gardens Scheme* was not originally intended as a horticultural charity: when founded in 1927, its purpose was to help elderly district nurses. Best known for the success of its National Gardens Scheme, over 90% of its income comes from the 3,000 or more gardens which are open to the public, and from the sale of its Yellow Book. In 1992 these accounted for income of £1,374,988, and the scheme paid out a total of £1,136,087 to charities. By far the biggest beneficiary was the Cancer Relief Macmillan Fund (£606,732) and the Gardens Fund of the National Trust (£250,000), but donations were also made to county nursing associations (£33,798), the Queen's Nursing Institute (£67,000), the Nurses' Welfare Service (£35,000), the Gardeners' Royal Benevolent Society (£22,232) and the Royal Gar-

deners' Orphan Fund (£22,116). The balance was shared among other charities nominated by garden owners who are able to specify that up to 25% of their takings should be directed to such organisations as CAFOD and St John's Ambulance.

Scotland's Gardens Scheme, 31 Castle Terrace, Edinburgh EH1 2EL. Tel: 031 229 1870. General Organiser: R S St. Clair-Ford. Over 300 gardens throughout Scotland open for this charity which is closely modelled on the English National Gardens Scheme. Owners are encouraged to open their gardens to the public and the proceeds are then distributed among various charities. In 1992 the total income raised was £212,406, a higher return per garden than the English scheme, and £156,674 was paid out. £43,233 was donated to the Queen's Nursing Institute, Scotland; £47,411 to the Gardens Fund of the National Trust for Scotland; £1,500 to the Gardeners' Royal Benevolent Society; and £1,500 to the Royal Gardeners' Orphan Fund. Owners are able to donate up to 40% to a charity of their choice and, as a result, the balance of £63,030 was made available to help and support over 160 different charities.

The Worshipful Company of Gardeners has a Charities Fund which makes grants to deserving projects, such as horticultural therapy schemes and garden designs for special schools. Details from the Master, 22 Luke Street, London EC2A 4AR

37

Nomenclature Changes

Botanists change scientific names either to reflect their changing view of the plants themselves, or to abide by current rules for naming. A species may be found to be synonymous with another; it may be judged to be a subspecies or variety of another species, and not to deserve full species status. Conversely, a variety or subspecies may be considered sufficiently distinctive to be recognised as a species in its own right. A species may be moved from one genus to another. Genera may be split (as with the break-up of *Chrysanthemum*) or they may be pushed together (as is currently being suggested for *Berberis* and *Mahonia*). If a botanical name emerges which is older than the one in present use, then in keeping with the rules of botanical nomenclature, the older name usually takes precedence, no matter how widespread the use of the present name may be. A name may be found never to have been validly published: in this case it must be rejected for one which has been.

So much for the theory: whatever the reasons for change, the results can be very perplexing for gardeners. The following list shows genera between which there has been some movement of species. Only very seldom does a whole genus change its identity. In most cases only some of the species will have moved into another genus. Some genera have split into several genera (e.g., *Coleus* to *Solenostemon* and *Plectranthus*, leaving no *Coleus*; or *Chrysanthemum* to *Argyranthemum*, *Chrysanthemopsis*, *Dendranthema*, *Leucanthemum* etc., leaving only five species in *Chrysanthemum*). Some of the changes shown are of long-standing; others are more recent. Even botanists can be slow or reluctant to adopt name changes, some of which remain controversial for years. This applies to those

listed below too: not everyone accepts them all, and they are subject to change. We hope that the list will help you if you find yourself stumped by an unfamiliar designation or an absent friend. We suggest you consult *The New RHS Dictionary of Gardening*, *The RHS Index of Garden Plants*, and *The Plant Finder* for more details.

The arrows point in the direction of the genus to which species have moved (the new genus appears in bold type also). Reverse namings are also listed to allow readers to work from the familiar to the new, whether it be 'right' or 'wrong'.

Acacia → **Albizia**
Acacia ← Mimosa
Achillea → **Tanacetum**
Acidanthera → **Gladiolus**
Aconitum → **Eranthis**
Aeonium ← Sempervivum
Agapetes ← Pentapterygium
Agastache ← Cedronella
Albizia ← Acacia
Allium → **Nectaroscordum**
Aloysia ← Lippia
Amaryllis → **Hippeastrum**
Ampelopsis ← Vitis
Amsonia ← Rhazya
Amygdalus → **Prunus**
Anaphalis ← Gnaphalium
Anchusa → **Pentaglottis**
Androsace ← Douglasia
Anemone → **Hepatica**
Anemone → **Pulsatilla**
Anomatheca ← Lapeirousia
Anthemis → **Argyranthemum**

Anthemis → Chamaemelum
Antholyza → Crocosmia
Antirrhinum → Asarina
Aquilegia → Semiaquilegia
Aralia → Fatsia
Arctotis ← Venidium
Argyranthemum ← Anthemis
Argyranthemum ← Chrysanthemum
Argyrocytisus ← Cytisis
Artemisia → Seriphidium
Arum → Dracunculus
Asarina → Maurandya
Asarina ← Antirrhinum
Asparagus ← Smilax
Asperula → Galium
Asphodeline ← Asphodelus
Asphodelus → Asphodeline
Asplenium ← Ceterach
Aster → Boltonia
Aster → Felicia
Aster ← Microglossa
Atragene → Clematis
Austrocedrus ← Libocedrus
Azalea → Rhododendron
Azorina ← Campanula
Balsamita → Tanacetum
Bartlettina ← Eupatorium
Bellevallia ← Muscari
Beloperone → Justicia
Berberis → Mahonia
Betonica → Stachys
Bidens → Cosmos
Bilderdykia → Polygonum
Blechnum ← Lomaria
Bocconia → Macleaya
Boltonia ← Aster
Boykinia → Peltoboykinia
Boykinia ← Telesonix
Brachyglottis ← Senecio
Brimeura ← Hyacinthus
Brodiaea → Triteleia
Brugmansia ← Datura
Bupthalmum → Telekia
Calla → Zantedeschia
Calocedrus ← Libocedrus
Caloscordum ← Nothoscordum
Camellia ← Thea

Campanula → Azorina
Cardamine ← Dentaria
Carduus → Cnicus
Cedrela → Toona
Cedronella → Agastache
Celsia → Verbascum
Centranthus ← Valeriana
Cephalaria ← Scabiosa
Cerasus → Prunus
Ceterach → Asplenium
Chaenomeles → Pseudocydonia
Chaenomeles ← Cydonia
Chaenorrhinum ← Linaria
Chamaecyparis ← Cupressus
Chamaecytisus ← Cytisus
Chamaemelum ← Anthemis
Chamaenerion → Epilobium
Chamaepericlymenum → Cornus
Chamaespartium ← Genista
Cheiranthus → Erysimum
Chelone → Penstemon
Chrysanthemopsis ← Leucanthemum
Chrysanthemopsis ← Pyrethropsis
Chrysanthemum → Argyranthemum
Chrysanthemum → Dendranthema
Chrysanthemum ← Leucanthemum
Chrysanthemum → Nipponanthemum
Chrysanthemum → Tanacetum
Chrysanthemum → Chrysanthemopsis
Cicerbita ← Lactuca
Cineraria → Senecio
Cineraria → Pericallis
Cissus → Parthenocissus
Cistus → × Halimiocistus
Cladothamnus → Elliottia
Clarkia ← Godetia
Clematis ← Atragene
Cleyera ← Eurya
Cnicus ← Carduus
Codariocalyx ← Desmodium
Codiaeum → Croton
Coleus → Plectranthus
Coleus → Solenostemon
Consolida ← Delphinium
Cordyline ← Dracaena
Cornus ← Chamaepericlymenum
Cosmos ← Bidens

Cotinus ← Rhus
Cotula → Leptinella
Crassula ← Sedum
Crinodendron ← Tricuspidaria
Crocosmia → Tritonia
Crocosmia ← Antholyza
Crocosmia ← Curtonus
Crocosmia ← Montbretia
Croton → Codiaeum
Cuitlauzina ← Odontoglossum
Cupressus → Chamaecyparis
Curtonus → Crocosmia
Cydonia → Chaenomeles
Cymbalaria ← Linaria
Cynara ← Scolymus
Cyperus ← Mariscus
Cypripedium → Paphiopedilum
Cytisus → Argyrocytisus
Cytisus → Chamaecytisus
Cytisus → Genista
Dacrycarpus ← Podocarpus
Dacrydium → Lagarostrobus
Dactylorhiza ← Orchis
Daiswa ← Paris
Darmera ← Peltiphyllum
Datura → Brugmansia
Delairea ← Senecio
Delphinium → Consolida
Dendranthema ← Chrysanthemum
Dentaria → Cardamine
Desmodium → Codariocalyx
Desmodium ← Lespedeza
Dichelostemma ← Triteleia
Diervilla → Weigela
Dietes ← Moraea
Dimorphotheca → Osteospermum
Dizygotheca → Schefflera
Douglasia → Androsace
Dracaena ← Pleomele
Dracaena → Cordyline
Dracula ← Masdevallia
Dracunculus ← Arum
Dregea ← Wattakaka
Drimys → Pseudowintera
Dryadella ← Masdevallia
Duchesnea ← Fragaria
Echinacea ← Rudbeckia

Echinospartium ← Genista
Edraianthus ← Wahlenbergia
Egeria ← Elodea
Elliottia ← Cladothamnus
Elodea → Egeria
Elymus → Leymus
Endymion → Hyacinthoides
Ensete ← Musa
Epilobium ← Zauschneria
Epilobium ← Chamaenerion
Epipremnum ← Scindapsus
Eranthis ← Aconitum
Erigeron → Haplopappus
Erysimum ← Cheiranthus
Eupatorium → Bartlettina
Eurya → Cleyera
Eustoma ← Lisianthius
Fallopia → Polygonum
Farfugium ← Ligularia
Fatsia ← Aralia
Felicia ← Aster
Ferula → Foeniculum
Filipendula ← Spiraea
Foeniculum ← Ferula
Fragaria → Duchesnea
Galeobdolon → Lamium
Galium ← Asperula
× Gaulnettya → Gaultheria
Gaultheria ← Pernettya
Gaultheria ← × Gaulnettya
Genista → Chamaespartium
Genista → Echinospartium
Genista → Retama
Genista ← Cytisus
Gentiana → Megacodon
Gladiolus ← Acidanthera
Gladiolus ← Homoglossum
Glechoma ← Nepeta
Gloxinia → Sinningia
Gnaphalium → Anaphalis
Gnaphalium → Helichrysum
Godetia → Clarkia
Goniolimon ← Limonium
Haemaria → Ludisia
Haemanthus → Scadoxus
× Halimiocistus → Cistus
Halimium ← Helianthemum

Haplopappus ← Erigeron
Hebe → Parahebe
Helianthemum → Halimium
Helianthemum → Tuberaria
Helichrysum → Ozothamnus
Helichrysum ← Gnaphalium
Helxine → Soleirolia
Hepatica ← Anemone
Hermodactylus ← Iris
Hippeastrum ← Amaryllis
Hoheria ← Plagianthus
Homoglossum → Gladiolus
Howea ← Kentia
Hyacinthoides ← Endymion
Hyacinthoides ← Scilla
Hyacinthus → Brimeura
Hylotelephium ← Sedum
Hymenocallis ← Ismene
Ipheion ← Triteleia
Ipomoea ← Mina
Ipomoea ← Pharbitis
Iris → Hermodactylus
Ismene → Hymenocallis
Jacobinia → Justicia
Jovibarba ← Sempervivum
Justicia ← Beloperone
Justicia ← Jacobinia
Kentia → Howea
Kleinia ← Senecio
Knautia ← Scabiosa
Lactuca → Cicerbita
Lagarostrobus ← Dacrydium
Lamium ← Galeobdolon
Lapeirousia → Anomatheca
Lavatera ← Malva
Lemboglossum ← Odontoglossum
Leopoldia → Muscari
Leptinella ← Cotula
Lespedeza → Desmodium
Leucanthemopsis → Chrysanthemopsis
Leucanthemum → Chrysanthemopsis
Leucanthemum ← Chrysanthemum
Leymus ← Elymus
Libocedrus → Austrocedrus
Libocedrus → Calocedrus
Ligularia → Farfugium
Ligularia → Sinacalia

Ligularia ← Senecio
Lilium → Nomocharis
Limonium → Goniolimon
Limonium ← Statice
Linaria → Cymbalaria
Linaria ← Chaenorrhinum
Lindera ← Parabenzoin
Lippia → Aloysia
Lippia → Verbena
Lippia → Phyla
Liriope → Ophiopogon
Lisianthius → Eustoma
Lithocarpus ← Quercus
Lithodora ← Lithospermum
Lomaria → Blechnum
Lophomyrtus ← Myrtus
Ludisia ← Haemaria
Luma ← Myrtus
Lychnis → Petrocoptis
Lychnis → Silene
Lychnis ← Viscaria
Macleaya ← Bocconia
Mahonia ← Berberis
Malva → Lavatera
Malvastrum ← Anisodontea
Mariscus → Cyperus
Masdevallia → Dracula
Masdevallia → Dryadella
Maurandya → Asarina
Megacodon ← Gentiana
Microglossa → Aster
Miltonia → Miltoniopsis
Miltoniopsis ← Miltonia
Mimosa → Acacia
Mimulus ← Diplacus
Mina → Ipomoea
Montbretia → Crocosmia
Moraea → Dietes
Musa → Ensete
Muscari → Bellevalia
Muscari ← Leopoldia
Myrtus → Luma
Myrtus → Lophomyrtus
Nectaroscordum ← Allium
Neopanax → Pseudopanax
Nepeta → Glechoma
Nipponanthemum ← Chrysanthemum

Nomocharis ← *Lilium*
Nothoscordum → *Caloscordum*
Odontoglossum → *Cuitlauzina*
Odontoglossum → *Lemboglossum*
Odontoglossum → *Osmoglossum*
Odontoglossum → *Rossioglossum*
Olsynium ← *Sisyrinchium*
Ophiopogon ← *Liriope*
Orchis → *Dactylorhiza*
Osmanthus ← *Phillyrea*
Osmanthus ← × *Osmarea*
× *Osmarea* → *Osmanthus*
Osmoglossum ← *Odontoglossum*
Osteospermum ← *Dimorphotheca*
Othonna ← *Othonnopsis*
Othonnopsis → *Othonna*
Oxycoccus → *Vaccinium*
Oxypetalum → *Tweedia*
Ozothamnus ← *Helichrysum*
Paphiopedilum ← *Cypripedium*
Papilionanthe ← *Vanda*
Parabenzoin → *Lindera*
Parahebe ← *Hebe*
Paraquilegia ← *Semiaquilegia*
Paris → *Daiswa*
Parthenocissus → *Cissus*
Parthenocissus ← *Ampelopsis*
Peltiphyllum → *Darmera*
Peltoboykinia ← *Boykinia*
Penstemon ← *Chelone*
Pentaglottis ← *Anchusa*
Pentapterygium → *Agapetes*
Pericallis ← *Cineraria*
Pericallis ← *Senecio*
Pernettya → *Gaultheria*
Persicaria ← *Polygonum*
Petrocoptis ← *Lychnis*
Pharbitis → *Ipomoea*
Phillyrea → *Osmanthus*
Photinia ← *Stransvaesia*
Phyla ← *Lippia*
Phyteuma ← *Physoplexis*
Plagianthus → *Hoheria*
Platycladus ← *Thuja*
Plectranthus ← *Coleus*
Pleomele → *Dracaena*
Podocarpus → *Dacrycarpus*

Polygonum → *Persicaria*
Polygonum ← *Bilderdykia*
Polygonum ← *Fallopia*
Poterium → *Sanguisorba*
Prunus ← *Amygdalus*
Prunus ← *Cerasus*
Pseudocydonia ← *Chaenomeles*
Pseudopanax ← *Neopanax*
Pseudowintera ← *Drimys*
Pulsatilla ← *Anemone*
Pyrethropsis → *Chrysanthemopsis*
Quercus → *Lithocarpus*
Retama ← *Genista*
Rhazya → *Amsonia*
Rhodiola ← *Sedum*
Rhododendron ← *Azalea*
Rhoeo → *Tradescantia*
Rhus → *Cotinus*
Rossioglossum ← *Odontoglossum*
Rosularia ← *Sedum*
Rudbeckia → *Echinacea*
Sanguisorba ← *Poterium*
Scabiosa → *Cephalaria*
Scabiosa → *Knautia*
Scabiosa → *Succisa*
Scadoxus ← *Haemanthus*
Schefflera ← *Dizygotheca*
Schizocodon → *Shortia*
Scilla → *Hyacinthoides*
Scindapsus → *Epipremnum*
Scolymus → *Cynara*
Sedum → *Crassula*
Sedum → *Hylotelephium*
Sedum → *Rhodiola*
Sedum → *Rosularia*
Semiaquilegia ← *Aquilegia*
Semiaquilegia ← *Paraquilegia*
Sempervivum → *Aeonium*
Sempervivum → *Jovibarba*
Senecio → *Brachyglottis*
Senecio → *Delairea*
Senecio → *Kleinia*
Senecio → *Ligularia*
Senecio → *Sinacalia*
Senecio → *Pericallis*
Senecio ← *Cineraria*
Seriphidium ← *Artemisia*

Setcreasea → Tradescantia

Shortia ← Schizocodon

Silene ← Lychnis

Sinacalia ← Ligularia

Sinacalia ← Senecio

Sinningia ← Gloxinia

Sisyrinchium → Olsynium

Smilax → Asparagus

Soleirolia ← Helxine

Solenostemon ← Coleus

Sorbaria ← Spiraea

Spiraea → Filipendula

Spiraea → Sorbaria

Stachys ← Betonica

Statice → Limonium

Stransvaesia → Photinia

Succisa ← Scabiosa

Tanacetum ← Achillea

Tanacetum ← Balsamita

Tanacetum ← Chrysanthemum

Telekia ← Bupthalmum

Telesonix → Boykinia

Thea → Camellia

Thuja → Platycladus

Toona ← Cedrela

Tradescantia ← Setcreasea

Tradescantia ← Zebrina

Tradescantia ← Rhoeo

Tricuspidaria → Crinodendron

Triteleia → Brodiaea

Triteleia → Dichelostemma

Triteleia → Ipheion

Tritonia ← Crocosmia

Trudelia ← Vanda

Tuberaria ← Helianthemum

Tweedia ← Oxypetalum

Vaccinium ← Oxycoccus

Valeriana → Centranthus

Vanda → Papilionanthe

Vanda → Trudelia

Vanda → Vandopsis

Vandopsis ← Vanda

Index

A & PM Books, 464
Abbey Dore Court Garden, 154, 286
Abbey Plants, 142
Abbots House Garden, The, 159
Abbots Ripton Hall, 251
Abbotsbury Sub-Tropical Gardens, 142, 271
Abbotswood, 276
Aberconwy Nursery, 207
Abercrombie & Kent Travel, 484
Aberdeen College of Further Education, 454
Abriachan Gardens & Nursery, 212
Absolute Tree Care, 427
acaricides, 493
Access Garden Products, 371
Accompanied Cape Tours, 484
acers, 220
Achamore Gardens, 350
Acorn Bank Garden, 263
Acres Wild (Landscape & Garden Design), 401
Adams Garden Design, Veronica, 423
Adams Landscape Architects, Marina, 416
ADAS, 436
Addison Associates, Aylmer, 428
Adlington Hall, 253
Afan College, 454
African Violet Centre, 59, 174
African violets, 220
Agars Nursery, 150, 401
Agriframes, 371
air plants, 220
Aldershot Flower Arrangement Club, 59
algicides, 493
Algoflash UK Ltd, 371
Alitex Ltd, 372
All Seasons Tree Service, 427
All Year Round Chrysanthemum Growers Association, 436
Hart Associates, Allan, 401
Allangrange, 348
Allen and M J Huish, Misses I, 122
Allhusen, Annabel, 402
Allium, 78
allotment and garden groups, 395

Allseasons Landscapes, 401
Allwood Bros, 195
Alpine Garden Society, 59, 66, 98, 238, 483, 484, 495
alpines, 220
Althorp House, 303
Alton Greenhouses, 372
Alton Towers, 316
Altoona Nurseries, 136
Amand Ltd, Jacques, 59, 173
Amateur Gardening, 67, 477
Amdega Ltd, 372
American Camellia Society, 117
American Hemerocallis Society, 117
American Hibiscus Society, 117
American Horticultural Society, 117, 484
American Hosta Society, 117
American Iris Society, 117
American Museum, The, 244
American Orchid Society, 117
American Rhododendron Society, 65, 117
American Rock Garden Society, 117
American Rose Society, 117
Ammerdown Park, 313
An Grianan College of Horticulture, 456
Anderson, Bertram, 483
Andrews Ltd, Bob, 373
Anglesey Abbey, 251
Angus College, 456
Angus Heathers, 214
Animal Aunts, 486
Annes Grove Gardens, 355
Anthos Design, 402
Antony House, 257
Antony Woodland Garden, 258
Apple Court, 150, 402
Apple 'Golden Delicious', 77
apples, 78
Apuldram Roses, 195
Aqua-Soil Products Ltd, 372
aquatic plants, 221
aquatic products, 372, 381, 387
Aquilegia, 77
Arbigland, 345
Arbor Exotica, 126

Arboricultural Association, 401, 436
Arbury Hall, 328
Archer-Wills, Anthony, 402
Archer-Wills Ltd, Anthony, 195
arches, 384, 387, 388
Archibald, Jim & Jenny, 234
Architectural Heritage Ltd, 372
Architectural Landscape Design Ltd, 402
Architectural Plants, 195
Ardencaple Garden Centre, 213
Ardgillan Park, 356
Ardnamona, 355, 364
Ardtornish Garden, 350
Arduaine (Loch Melfort Hotel), 364
Arduaine Gardens, 350
Arena Landscapes, 403
Arivegaig Nursery, 212
Arley Hall, 254
Arlington Court, 267
armillary spheres, 375, 376
Armitage's Garden Centre, 205
Arne Herbs, 121, 403
Arrow Tree Services, 403, 428
artificial grass, 389
Artscapes & Theseus Maze Designs, 403
Ascalon Design, 372
Ascott, 249
ASH Consulting Group, 403
Ashenden Nursery, 162
Ashtree Cottage, 330
Ashwood Nurseries, 199, 232
Askham Bryan College of Agriculture and Horticulture, 452
asters, 221
Atco-Qualcast, 372
Athelhampton, 271
Audley End, 80, 275
Auldene Nurseries Ltd, 166, 403
Austin Roses, David, 59, 199
Australian Garden History Society, 117
Australian plants, 221
Avebury Manor, 331
Avon Bulbs, 59, 182
Avon Gardens Trust, 110
Axletree Nursery, 193
Aylesbury College, 443

Aylett Nurseries Ltd, 159, 403
Ayr Flower Show, 59
B & B Tree Specialists, 428
B & Q, 59
B & T World Seeds, 232
Backwoodsman Horticultural Products, 373
Badminton, 244, 362
Bailey, Steven, 59, 153
Baker, B & H M, 144
Baker Straw Partnership, 154
Bakker Holland, 232
Balcaskie, 346
Ballagan Nursery, 214
Ballam Design, Michael, 416
Ballard, Helen, 156
Ballerina Trees Ltd, 126
Ballydorn Bulb Farm, 216
Ballyrogan Nurseries, 216
bamboos, 221
Bank House, 295
Banks Associates Ltd, Elizabeth, 408
Banyard Tree Surgeons, Keith, 414, 431
Barbados Horticultural Society, 59
Barfield Travel & Tours, 484
bark, 376, 385, 387, 392
Barkers Primrose Nurseries, 167
Barking College of Technology, 444
Barncroft Nurseries, 185
Barningham Park, 274
Barnsley College of Technology, 452
Barnsley House, 277
Baronscourt Nurseries, 217, 403
Barony College, The, 454
Barralets of Ealing, 373
Barratt's Garden Centres, Peter, 130, 198
Barrell Treecare, Jeremy, 431
Barrington Court, 313
Barters Farm Nurseries Ltd, 200
Barton Grange Garden Centre (Bolton), 167
Barton Grange Garden Centre (Preston), 167
Barton Grange Landscapes, 403
Barton Manor, 290
Bateman's, 322
Bates Green Farm, 322
Bath Botanic Gardens, 245
Batsford Arboretum, 277
Battersby Roses, 130
Bawdeswell Garden Centre, 174
Baytree Nurseries, 170
BBC Gardeners' World Live, 58, 60, 477
BBONT, 110
Beach (Nursery) Ltd, John, 199
Beale Arboretum, The, 288
Beales Roses, Peter, 176, 419
Beamish Clematis Nursery, 141

Bean, W J, 482
bedding plants, 221
Bedford sand, 397
Bedgebury National Pinetum, 291, 363
Beechcroft Nurseries, 133, 403
Beechcroft Nursery, 189
beekeeping equipment, 377
Beeston, R F, 157
begonias, 221
Bel Mondo Garden Features, 373
Belgium (ONDAH), 59
Bell Ltd, David, 376
Belmont Park, 292
Beloeil, 80
Belsay Hall, 305
Belton House, 297
Belvoir Castle, 296
Belwood Nurseries Ltd, 213
Benger Landscaping, Tony, 423
Beningbrough Hall, 334
Benington Lordship, 288
Bennett Landscape Architects, Penny, 418
Bennetts Water Lily Farm, 142
Benthall Hall, 311
Bentley Ltd, Joseph, 382
Bents Garden Centre and Nurseries, 127
Berger & Tims, 464
Berkeley Castle, 277
Berkley Landscape Architects, Martin, 416
Berkshire College of Agriculture, 442
Bernhard's Rugby Garden & Leisure Centre, 198
Berri Court, 324
Berry & Saunders, 59
Berrys Garden Company Ltd, 403
Besleys Books, 464
Beth Chatto Gardens Ltd, The, 144, 275
Bettina Floral Artist, 59
Bickerdike's Garden Centre, 123
Bicton College of Agriculture, 444
Bicton Park Gardens, 268
Biddle, P G, 432
Biddulph Grange, 316
Bide-a-Wee Cottage, 305
Biggar Park, 350
Biggs, Ronnie, train robber, 65
Billington Garden Design, Jill, 412
bio-dynamic, 394
biological controls, 376, 377, 379, 384, 388
Birkheads Cottage Garden Nursery, 197, 403
Birmingham Botanical Gardens, 330
Birr Castle Demesne, 358
Blackmore & Langdon, 121
Blackthorn Nursery, 150
Blackwall Products, 373

Blairhoyle, 344
Blairhoyle Nursery, 209, 403
Bland, Mary, 465
Blenheim Palace, 308
Blickling Hall, 301
Blom & Son, Walter, Ltd, 59, 123
Blue Guide to Gardens in England, 243
Bluebell Nursery, 134
Blunt Trust, The, 457
Bockings Exotics, 57
Bodleian Library, 462
Bodnant Garden Nursery Ltd, 207
Bodnant Gardens, 57, 339
Bodysgallen Hall, 342, 364
bog plants, 221
Bolehyde Manor, 331
Bolingbroke, 373
Bond, S & E, 157
Bonhard Nursery, 215
Bonsai, 213
bonsai, 221
Bonsai Clubs International, 117
bonsai, replica, 390
Boonwood Garden Centre, 133, 403
Borde Hill Garden, 325
Bosvigo House, 258
Bosvigo Plants, 130
Botanic Gardens Conservation International, 436
Botanic Nursery, 200, 404
Botanical Society of Scotland, 98
Botanical Society of South Africa, 117
Botanical Society of the British Isles, 66, 98
Boughton Loam Ltd, 373
Bournville College of Further Education, 451
Bourton House, 277
Bouts Cottage Nurseries, 154
Bowden, Ann & Roger, 136
Bowers & Son, Chris, 175
Bowes Museum Garden & Park, The, 274
Bowlby, Rupert, 59, 192
Bowles, E A, 483
Bowood Garden Centre, 200
Bowood House, 331, 360
Boxwood Tours: Quality Garden Holidays, 484
Boyce, J W, 233
Brackenhurst College, 449
Brackenwood Garden Centre, 121
Brackenwood Nurseries, 121
Brackley, S & N, 59, 235
Bradley Batch Cactus Nursery, 182
Bradshaw & Son, J, 163
brambles, 404
Brambling House Alpines, 205
Bramdean House, 282

Brampton Garden Centre, 126
Branchline Tree Services, 428
Brandy Mount House, 283
Branklyn Garden, 352
Brantwood, 80, 264
Brayford Landscapes, Tim, 422
Bregover Plants, 131
Brent Surveys & Designs, 404
Bressingham, Blooms of, 59, 69
Bressingham Gardens, 302
Bressingham Gardens Mail Order, 174
Bressingham Landscapes, 404
Bressingham Plant Centre, 174, 123
Bretby Nurseries, 185
Brickell, Chris, 65
Brickwall House, 322
Bridgemere Garden World, 59, 254
Bridgemere Nurseries, 127
bridges, 377
Bridgman & Co Ltd, P J, 386
Brinkley Nurseries, 179
Brinsbury College, 451
Britain in Bloom, 489
British & European Geranium Society, 99
British Agricultural & Garden Machinery Association, 436
British Agrochemicals Association, 436
British Association of Landscape Industries (BALI), 401, 436
British Association Representing Breeders (BARB), 436
British Bedding & Pot Plant Association, 59
British Bonsai Association, 99
British Clematis Society, 99, 238
British Fuchsia Society, 99
British Gladiolus Society, 56, 99, 239
British Hosta & Hemerocallis Society, 100
British Iris Society, The, 100, 239
British Ivy Society, 100
British Library, The, 460
British Museum Collection, 373
British National Carnation Society, The, 100
British Pelargonium & Geranium Society, The, 100
British Pteridological Society, 101, 239
British Tourist Authority, 436
British Trust for Conservation Volunteers (BTCV), 436, 484
British Wild Plants, 210
Broadlands, 271, 283
Broadleas Gardens Charitable Trust Ltd, 201, 331
Broadleigh Gardens, 183
Broadstone Nurseries, 180, 404
Brockings Exotics, 131
Brodick Castle, 350, 361

Brogdale, Friends of, 111
Brogdale Trust, 57
Bromage & Co Ltd, D N, 189
bromeliads, 221
Brook Cottage, 308
Brook Lodge Farm Cottage, 319
Brookes, Landscape Designer, John, 412
Broomfield College, 444
Broughton Castle, 308
Brown & Co Ltd, D T, 233
Brown Landscape Design, David, 406
Brownthwaite Hardy Plants, 133
BSBI Publications; F & M Perring, 464
BTEC, 442
Buchan, Ursula, 58
Buckingham Nurseries and Garden Centre, 124
Bucklesham Hall, 317
Buckley, Susan, 422
Buczacki, Stefan, 66
Bulaitis, Bonita, 403
Bulbeck Foundry, 374
bulbs, 221
Bulldog Tools Ltd, 374
Burford Garden Centre, 180
Burford House Gardens, 286
Burgess' Alpine Nursery, Jenny, 175
Burgoyne Revivals, Sarah, 388
Burnby Hall Gardens, 289
Burncoose & South Down Nurseries, 56, 59, 131
Burnett Associates, Chris, 405
Burnham Nurseries, 136
Burrough House, 296
Burrows Roses, 134
Burton Constable Foundation, 290
Burton McCall Group, 374
Bury Farm, 251
Buscot Park, 308
Butterfields Nursery, 59, 125
Butterstream, 358
Buxton Books, Anna, 464
Bybrook Barn Garden & Produce Centre, 162, 404
Bypass Nurseries, 144, 404
Byrkley Park Centre, 186, 404
C E & D M Nurseries, 170
C H Dixon Charitable Trust, The, 458
Cabbages & Kings, 404
cacti & succulents, 221
K & C Cacti, 137
Cactus & Succulent Society of America, 117
Caddick's Clematis Nursery, 128
Cae Hir, 340
Caerhays Castle, 258, 362
Cahill, Helen, 411
California Gardens, 161
Calke Abbey, 266
Cally Gardens, 210

Cambrian Controls, 374
Cambridge Glasshouse Co Ltd, 374
Cambridge University, 462
Cambridge University Botanic Garden, 78, 252
Cambridgeshire College of Agriculture and Horticulture, 443
camellias, 222
Canal Gardens, 338
Cannington College, 2, 183, 449
Cannizaro Park, 299
Cants of Colchester, 144
Capel Manor, 299
Capesthorne Hall, 254
Carclew Gardens, 258
Cardiff Institute of Higher Education, 453
Carncairn Daffodils, 215
Carnivorous Plant Society, 101
carnivorous plants, 222
Carnon Downs Garden Centre, 131
Carolanka, 484
Carrog, 340
Carters Tested Seeds Ltd, 232
Carwinion, 258
Case, D J, 150
Castle Ashby Gardens, 304
Castle Bromwich Hall, 330
Castle Drogo, 268
Castle Howard, 335
Castle Kennedy, 345
Castlewellan National Arboretum, 354
Catforth Gardens, 167
Caves Folly Nurseries, 154, 405
Cawdor Castle, 348
Stella Caws Associates, 421
Cawthorne, Richard G M, 165
Cayeux SA, 488
Caythorpe Court, 297
Cecily Hill House, 278
Cefn Bere, 342
Celyn Vale Nurseries, 207
Centre for Alternative Technology, 394
Certificate of Competence, 493
CGLI, 441
Chadwell - Freelance Botanist, Chris, 232
Chaffin Tree Surgery, P J, 432
Chalk Garden, A, 483
Chambers Wild Flower Seeds, John, 58, 234
Champion Trees in the British Isles, 242
Channel Island Tree Service, 428
Chantrey Books, 465
Chapel Knap, 313
charities, 495, 496
Charities Aid Foundation, 496
Charlecote Park, 328
Charleston Farmhouse, 323

Charter House Hardy Plant Nursery, 210
Chartwell, 292
Chase Organics, 371, 374, 398
Chatelherault Garden Centre, 214
Chatsworth, 266
Chatsworth Garden Centre, 135
Cheals Garden Centre, 195
Cheeseborough, Ray, 419
Chelsea Flower Show, 60, 62
Chelsea Physic Garden, 299, 461
Cheltenham & Gloucester College of Higher Education, 445
chemicals, undisposed, 493
Chempak Products, 374
Chenies Garden Centre, 159
Chenies Landscapes Limited, 405
Chenies Manor, 249
Cheshire Herbs, 59, 128, 232
Cheshire Wildlife Trust, 110
Chicheley Hall, 249
Chiffchaffs, 272
children, 360
Chilham Castle Gardens, 292
Chillingham Castle, 305
Chiltern Seeds, 232
Chilworth Manor, 319
chimney pots, 385
Chirk Castle, 339
Chiswick House, 299
Cholmondeley Castle Gardens, 254
Christian Rare Plants, Paul, 208
Christie (Forres) Ltd, T & W, 211
Christie's, 364
chrysanthemums, 222
Church Hill Cottage Gardens, 162
Chyverton, 258
Cilwern Plants, 208
Cimicifuga, 78
Cincinnati Flower Show, 65
CITES, Convention on International Trade in Endangered Species of Wild Fauna and Flora, 229
Clandon Park, 319
Clapton Court Gardens, 313
Clapton Court Plant Centre, 183
Claremont Gardens, 319
Clark (Aberdeen), Findlay, 211
Clark Treework Specialists, J & D, 431
Clay Lane Nursery, 189
Clear Span Ltd, 374
clematis, 222
Cleveland Wildlife Trust, 110
climbers, 222
Clinton Lodge, 323
Cliveden, 249
cloches, 373, 375, 387, 389
Clock House, 309
Clonmel Garden Centre, 219, 405
Clumber Park, 307

Cluny House, 352
Clyne Gardens, 341
CN Seeds, 232
Coates Manor, 325
Cobblers, 323
Coblands Nursery, 162
Cocker & Sons, James, 211
Coghurst Nursery, 193
Coke, John, 56
Colemans Nurseries, 215
Coleton Fishacre Garden, 268
collecting plants, 230
College of Garden Design, 449
Collinwood Nurseries, 128
Collis Tree Service, Mark, 431
Colson Stone Partnership, 405
Colvin & Moggridge, 405
Commercial Horticultural Association, 437
Common Ground, 437
Complete Tree Services, 429
compost bins, 373, 381, 386
composts, 372, 373, 376, 378, 379, 382, 383, 385, 386, 388, 390, 391, 392, 398
Compton & Compton, 405
Compton Acres Gardens, 272
Compton, James, 56
Compton, Robin, 66
Conifer Garden, The, 125
conifers, 222
Connoisseur Sun Dials, 375
Connoisseurs' Cacti, 162
Conock Manor, 331
Conservation Foundation, The, 437
conservatories, 372, 375, 378, 383, 384, 385, 391
Conservatory Gardens, 405
conservatory plants, 222
Constable Daffodils, 189
Consumer Direct Ltd, 375
Consumers' Association, 461
container systems, 379
Cooke's House, 325
Cookson Plantpak Ltd, 375
Coombs, Geoffrey, 409
Cooper Pegler, 375
Copford Bulbs, 144
Copyright Act 1911, 460
Cordingley Landscape & Garden Design, Jane, 411
Cornwall Gardens Society, 110
Cornwall Gardens Trust, 110
Cornwall Trust for Nature Conservation, 110
Corsham Court, 331
Corsley Mill, Brigid Quest-Ritson, 201
Cotehele, 259
Coton Manor, 304
Cotswold Buildings Ltd, 375

Cotswold Garden Flowers, 154
Cottage Garden, The, 144
Cottage Garden Plants, 195, 142, 406
Cottage Garden Society, The, 101, 239
Cottage Herbery, The, 155
Cottage Nurseries, 170, 406
Cottesbrooke Hall, 304
Council for the Protection of Rural England, 437
Country Courses, 455
Country Gardens, 123
Country Homes and Interiors, 477
Country Landowners Association, 437
Country Life, 67, 477
Country Living, 59, 477
Countryside Commission, 437
Countryside Council for Wales, 437
Countryside Wildflowers, 58, 59
County Park Nursery, 145
Courson, 488
Courts, The, 332
Courtyard Designs, 375
Courtyard Garden Design, 406
Courtyard Pottery, 375
Cousens, W C, 466
covenants, 495
Cowcombe Farm Herbs, 147, 233
Cowdray Park, 325, 362
Cowells Garden Centre, 197
Cox & Kings Travel, 485
Crace Designs, Andrew, 372
B J Crafts, 372
Cragside, 306
Craig, David, 376
Craig House Cacti, 167
Craigieburn Classic Plants, 210
Cranborne Manor, 272
Cranborne Manor Garden Centre, 142
Cranesbill Nursery, 155
Crarae Gardens, 351
Crathes Castle, 347
Craven College of Adult Education, 452
Cravens Nursery, 205, 233
Crittenden House, 292
Crocknafeola Nursery, 218
Croftacre Hardy Plants, 175
Croftway Nursery, 195
Crossing House Garden, 252
Crossrigg Hall, 67
Croston Cactus, 167
Crowe Hall, 245
Crown Estate, The, 59
Crown Vegetables, 186
Crowther Landscapes, 406
Crowther of Syon Lodge, 375
Croxden Horticultural Products Ltd, 376
Croxteth Hall & Country Park, 301
Cruck Cottage Cacti, 202

Cruickshank Botanic Garden, 347
Crûg Farm Plants, 208
Culzean Country Park, 351
Cyclamen Society, The, 101, 239
Cymbidium Society of America Inc, 117
daffodils, 222
Dagenham Landscapes Ltd, 406
dahlias, 222
Daily Telegraph, The, 59, 477
Daisy Hill Nurseries Ltd, 216, 406
Daisy Nook Garden Centre, 149
Dalemain, 264
Daleside Nurseries, 202
Dalgety Bay Garden Centre, 211
Dalmeny House, 349
Dalrymple Ltd, 429
Daly, Peter M, 466
Dannell, 376
Darlac Products, 376
Darley House, 266
Dartington Hall, 268
David Sayers Travel, 485
David Way Associates, 485
Davidian, Dr H, 65
Davies Landscape Consultants, John A,
    412
Davis, Kim W, 181
Dawyck Botanic Garden, 344
De Jager & Sons Ltd, P, 165
Deacons Nursery, 161
Dean, Derek Lloyd, 172
Dean's Court, 272
Deanswood Plants, 202
Decorative Foliage, 136
Deelish Garden Centre, 218
Deere Ltd, John, 382
Defenders Ltd, 376
Delphinium Society, The, 101, 239
delphiniums, 223
Denbeigh Heathers, 186
Denmans, 325
Denmans Garden Plant Centre, 196
Denmead Geranium Nurseries, 150
Dennis, 376
Derbyshire Wildlife Trust, 111
Derreen, 357
Designing with Plants, 407
Devon Gardens Trust, 111
DHE Plants, 135
Dianthus, 223
Dibleys, 59, 207
Dickenson's Compost, 376
Dickson Nurseries Ltd, 216
Dingle (Crundale), The, 340
Dingle (Welshpool), The, 343
Diplex Ltd, 376
Directory of Grant-making Trusts, The,
    457
Directory of Registered Landscape
    Practices, 401

Display screen equipment work, 493
DIY Plastics (UK) Ltd, 377
Dobbie & Co Ltd, Melville Garden
    Centre, 213
Dobbies Landscape Ltd, 407
Dobie & Son Ltd, Samuel, 236
Dochfour Gardens, 348
Docton Mill, 268
Document Supply Centre, Boston Spa,
    461
Docwra's Manor, 252
Doddington Hall, 297
Dolwen, 343
Dolwin & Gray, 407, 429
domestic servants, 493
Donaghadee Garden Centre, 216, 407
Donington Plants, 170
Dorfold Hall, 254
Dorothy Clive Garden, The, 316
Dorset Perennial Group, 111
Dorset Trust for Nature Conservation,
    111
dovecotes, 378
Drake Aquilegias, John, 126
Drake, Jack, 212, 234
Dream Gardens, 407
dried flowers, 378, 380, 382, 383
Drummond Castle Gardens, 352
Drysdale Exotics, 151
Duchy of Cornwall, 131
Duncans of Milngavie, 214
Duncombe Park, 335
Dundee University Botanic Garden,
    353
Dunham Massey, 282
Dunrobin Castle Gardens, 348
Dunster Castle, 313
Dupre Vermiculite, 377
Durham Castle Flower Festival, 62
Durston Peat Products, 377
Dyfed Wildlife Trust, 111
Dyffryn Botanic Garden, 81, 341
Dyrham Park, 245
E L F Plants, Cramden Nursery Ltd, 177
Ealing Tertiary College, 447
Earlfarm, 377
East Lambrook Manor, 314
East Midlands Cactus Nursery, 125
Eastern Europe, 77
Eastern Landscape Service, 407, 430
Eastern Tree Surgery, 430
Eastgrove Cottage Garden, 287
Eastgrove Cottage Garden Nursery,
    155
Eastnor Castle, 287
Easton College, 448
Eden, Matthew, 384
Eden Plants, 219

Edinburgh College of Art/Heriot-Watt
    University, 455
Edmondsham House, 272
Edrom Nurseries, 57
The Education of a Gardener, 482
Education of a Gardener, The, 483
Edzell Castle, 353
Eggleston Hall Gardens, 141
Eldon, Garden Designer, Diana, 407
Elliott, Dr Brent, 66
Elly Hill Herbs, 141
Elmwood College, 454
Elsing Hall, 302
Elsworth Herbs, 126
Elton Hall, 252
Elvaston Castle County Park, 266
Elworthy Cottage Garden Plants, 183
Emmetts Garden, 292
Emorsgate, 233
Encyclopaedia of Alpine Plants,
    483
The Encyclopaedia of Gardening,
    482
Endsleigh Garden Centre, 136, 408
English Gardening School, The, 447
English Heritage, 79, 80, 81, 243
English Heritage Garden Grades, 365
English Nature, 437
English Vineyards Association, The,
    437
English Woodlands Biocontrol, 377
Englishman's Garden, The, 483
Englishwoman's Garden, The, 483
engraving equipment, 391
Environmental Health Officers, 494
Equatorial Plant Co, 141
Erddig, 339
Ernest Wilson Memorial Garden, The,
    278
Erway Farm House, 311
Essex House, 245
Essex Wildlife Trust, 111
Ets Rivière, 488
Euro Tree Service, 408, 430
European Commission, 80
European single market, 77
Euston Hall, 317
Evans, Landscape Designer, Andrew,
    401
Evelix Daffodils, 212
Everett, D & M, 155
Eversley Nurseries, 168
Exbury Enterprises Ltd, 151
Exbury Gardens, 283
Exeter University Gardens, 269
exhibitions, 64
Eye Safety in the Garden, 492
Fair - Garden Designer, Linda, 415
Fairfield House, 283
Fairhaven Gardens Trust, 302

Fairweather Ltd, Christopher, 150
Fairy Lane Nurseries, 149
Falkland Palace, 346
Family Trees, 151
Faringdon House, 309
Farnborough Hall, 80, 329
Federation of British Bonsai Societies, 102
Federation of Edinburgh & District Allotments & Gardens, 111
Federation to Promote Horticulture for the Disabled, 437
Felbrigg Hall, 302
Felley Priory, 307
fencing, 384, 385
Fens, The, 145
Fenton House, 299
Ferndale Nursery and Garden Centre Ltd, 205, 408
Fernhill, 356
Fernhill Nursery, 218
ferns, 223
Ferrum Dried Flowers, 378
fertiliser, 371, 372, 374, 376, 377, 379, 382, 384, 385, 386, 392
Fertiliser Manufacturers Association, 437
FFC Landscape Architects/ The Garden Design Studio, 408
ffiske Herbs, Daphne, 175
Fibrex Nurseries Ltd, 198
Field House Alpines, 179, 233
Financial Times, 67, 477
Finch Tree Care Specialists, Roy, 433
Finchale Training College, 444
Findlay Clark Limited, 214
Fine Art Travel Ltd, 485
fine builders sand, 397
Firs Nursery, The, 128
Fish Plant Nursery, Margery, 184
Fiskars UK Ltd, 378
Fisons Horticulture, 378
Fittleworth & District Horticultural Society, 59
Fletcher, M V, 124
Fletcher Moss Botanical Gardens, 282
Fleuroselect, 70, 75
Flintshire Woodlands, 430
Flora, 478
Flora & Fauna Europe Ltd, 378
Flora & Sylva, 483
Flora Exotica, 145, 233
floral accessories, 372, 376, 378, 382, 388
Florence Court, 354
Flower Arrangers Show Shop, The, 378
Flower Centre, 218
Flower Council of Holland, 437
Flower Festival, Sherborne Abbey, 62
Flowers & Plants Association, 437

flowers, postal, 389
FMG Garden Designs, 408
Fogg Garden Design, Julia, 413
Foliage & Unusual Plants, 171
foliage plants, 223
Foliage Scented & Herb Plants, 189
Folly Farm, 247
Food and Environment Protection Act, 493
footwear, 378, 387
Ford Garden Designs, Marianne, 416
Ford Landscape Architects, John A, 412
Forde Abbey, 272
Forestry Authority, The, 437
Forestry Commission, 437
Forestry Trust, The, 437
Forsham Cottage Arks, 378
Forward Nurseries, 162
Fosse Alpines, 169
Fota, 355
Fothergill's Seeds Ltd, Mr, 235
Fountain Forestry Ltd, 430
fountains, 373, 374, 384, 387
Four Counties Nursery, 147
Four Seasons, 175
Foxgrove Farm, 248
Foxgrove Plants, 123
frames, 371, 373, 374, 375, 383
Frampton Court, 278
France, 487
Franshams Ltd, 378
Frolics of Winchester, 378
Fron Nursery, 181
Frost & Co, 378
fruit, 223
Fruit and Vegetable Committee of the RHS, 57
fruit cages, 371, 382
Fruit Garden, The, 163, 408
fuchsias, 223
17 Fulham Park Gardens, 298
fungicides, 493
Furzey Gardens Trust, 283
Gandy's Roses Ltd, 169
Garden, The, 1, 478
Garden Answers, 478
garden buildings, 374, 375, 383, 387, 389, 392
Garden Centre Association, The, 59, 437
Garden Centre at Hounslow Heath, The, 173
garden chemicals, 374, 377, 379, 382, 384, 385, 386
Garden Cottage Nursery, 212
Garden Direct, 371
Garden Events, 1
garden furniture, 372, 373, 376, 378, 379, 380, 382, 383, 384, 385, 386, 388, 389

Garden History Society, The, 65, 102
Garden House, The, 269
garden machinery, 372, 373, 379, 381, 382, 383, 387, 388, 392
Garden News, 59, 478
Garden of the Year Award, 364
garden ornaments, 375, 380, 382, 384, 385, 386
Garden Scents, 188
Garden Solutions by Design, 408
garden statuary, 372, 373, 374, 375, 387
garden tools, 378, 389
Gardena UK Ltd, 379
Gardener, The, 478
Gardener's Guide to Britain, The, 243
Gardeners' Royal Benevolent Society, The, 67, 495 496
gardening clubs, 119
Gardening Which?, 70, 478, 492
Gardens by Graham Evans, 409
Gardens Illustrated, 64, 478
Gardens of Distinction, 409
Gardens of the Rose, The, 288
gardens, French, 487
Gardenscape, 202, 409
Garson Farm, 190
Gascoigne Wild Flowers, Linda, 169
Gateshead Summer Flower Show, 60
Gaulden Manor, 314
Gayways Lawn Mower Centre, 379
GEEBRO Ltd, 379
George & Associates, Anthony, 402
Georgi Landscape & Interior Design, Katerina, 414
Geranium Nursery, The, 197
Gesellschaft der Heidefreunde, 117
Gesellschaft der Staudenfreunde, 117
Gibside, 80
Gidleigh Park, 269, 364
Gift Aid, 495
Gladiolus Breeders Association, 102
Glamorgan Wildlife Trust, 112
Glasgow Botanic Garden, 351
Glaxo (1972) Charity Trust, The, 458
Glebe Cottage Plants, 59, 136
Glenarn, 351
Glendoick Gardens, 353
Glendoick Gardens Ltd, 215
Glendurgan Gardens, 259
Glenhirst Cactus Nursery, 171, 233
Glenveagh, 356, 361
Glenwhan Garden, 345
Global Orange Groves UK, 142
Gloucestershire Gardens & Landscape Trust, 112
gloves, 374, 390
Glowcroft Ltd, 379
Godington Park, 292
Godly's Roses, 159

Godwin (Peat Industries) Ltd, E J, 377
Golby, Rupert, 420
Goldbrook Plants, 59, 187
Golden Acre Park, 338
Goldsmark Partnership, Heather, 410
Goldney Hall, 245
Good Gardens Guide, 243
Good Gardeners Association, The, 393
Goodnestone Park, 293
Gordale Nursery & Garden Centre, 128
Goscote Nurseries Ltd, 169, 409
Goulding's Fuchsias, 187
Gowranes, 353
Grace Landscapes Ltd, 409
Granada Arboretum, 255
Grange Farm Nursery, 155
Grant-making Trusts, 457
grasses, 223
gravel, 397
Gravetye Manor, 326, 364
Grayson - Sweet Pea Seedsman, Peter, 235
Graythwaite Hall, 264
Great Barfield, 250, 363
Great Comp, 293
Great Dixter, 66, 323
Great Dixter Nurseries, 193
Great Garden and Countryside Festival, The, 60
Great Gardens of England Ltd, 125, 159, 173
Green Farm Plants, 56, 190
Green Gardener Products, 379
Green Man Landscapes, 410
Green Stock, 410
Greenacres Horticultural Supplies, 379
Greenbank Garden, 351
Greencombe Garden Trust, 314
greenhouse equipment, 374, 382, 390
greenhouses, 371, 373, 374, 386, 389
Greenleaves Garden Centre Ltd, 135
Greenslacks Nurseries, 205
Greenspan Designs Ltd, 379
Greenstone Gardens, 410
Greenvale Farm Ltd, 379
Greenway Gardens, 136
Greenways, 309
Greystone Cottage, 309
Grimsthorpe Castle Trust Ltd, 298
Ground Control Ltd, 410
ground cover plants, 223
Groves & Son, C W, 142
Grower, The, 478
Growing Carpets, 159
growing media, 391
Guardian, The, 479
Guinness, Bunny, 404
Gunby Hall, 298
Guy Wilson Daffodil Garden, 355
Gwent Wildlife Trust, 112

GWS Ltd, 380
Gwydir Plants, 209
H & L Cantor Trust, The, 457
H₂0, 380
Haddon Hall, 267
Haddonstone Ltd, 380
Hadlow College of Agriculture and Horticulture, 446
Hadspen, 183, 314
Hafod, 81
Haldene, Sheila, legacy, 66
Halecat Garden Nurseries, 133
Hall Farm Nursery, 171, 181
Halls of Heddon, 178
Ham House, 80
Hambrook Landscapes Ltd, 410
Hampshire Gardens Trust, 79, 80, 112
Hampstead Garden Suburb Adult Education Centre, 447
Hampton Court Palace, 300
Hampton Court Palace Flower Show, 58, 60, 62
Hanbury Hall, 80
hand tools, 374, 378, 389, 392
Hanging Garden Pot Holders, 380
Hannays of Bath, 121
Hardwick Hall, 267
Hardwicke House, 252
Hardy, Alan, 66
Hardy Plant Society, The, 57, 69, 102
Hardy's Cottage Garden Plants, 151, 410
Hare Hatch Nursery, 123
Hare Hill Garden, 255
Harewood House, 80, 338
Harkness & Co Ltd, R, 59, 160
Harlow Carr Botanical Gardens, 74, 75, 335, 452
Harman Garden Design, Jean, 411
Harris Garden, The, 248
Harrison, Fiona, 408
Harrogate Great Autumn Flower Show, 61, 62
Harrogate Spring Flower Show, 61, 62
Harry Ibbetson Settlement, The, 458
Hartside Nursery Garden, 133
Harvest Nurseries, 193
Hascombe Court, 319
Hasmead (Landscape) Ltd, 58
Hatchlands, 319
Hatfield House, 289
Haughley Park, 318
Haws Watering Cans, 380
Hayes Gardenworld Ltd, 134, 410
Hayloft Plants, 155
Hayters plc, 380
Huddleston, Hazel M, 410
Hazelby House, 248
Hazeldene Nursery, 59, 163, 233
Hazell Garden Design, Cecily, 405

Heale House, 332
Health & Safety Executive (HSE), 438, 491
Health & Safety at Work Act 1974, 491
Health & Safety (Display Screen Equipment) Regulations 1992, 492
Health & Safety Executive Information Centre, 492
heaters, 381, 382
Heath Garden, 410
Heather, Duncan, 407
Heather Society, The, 102
heathers, 223
Hebe Society, 103
Hedger-Brown Landscape Architect, Sue, 422
hedging, 223
Heighley Gate Garden Centre, 178, 411
Heligan Manor Gardens, 79, 259
Hellyer, Arthur, 67
Helmingham Hall, 318
Hemsley, Peter, 432
Henderson & Sons, James, 234
Henllys Lodge Plants, 209
Henly, John, 465
Henry Doubleday Research Association (HDRA), 103, 393, 394, 398
herbaceous perennials, 224
Herbert, Robin, 64
herbs, 225
Herefordshire Nature Trust, 112
Hergest Croft, 57, 287
Heritage Education Trust, 364
Heritage Tree Services, 430
Heritage Woodcraft, 380
Herons Bonsai Ltd, 59, 190
Herterton House Gardens & Nursery, 178, 306
Herts & Middlesex Wildlife Trust, 113
Hestercombe House, 314
Hever Castle, 293
Hewthorn Herbs & Wild Flowers, 179
Hexham Herbs, 178, 306
Hickson, Michael, 488
Hidcote Manor, 278
Higginbotham Garden Landscaping, Ken, 414
High Banks Nurseries, 163
High Beeches, The, 326
High Garden, The, 137
Highclere Castle, 284
Highdown, 326
Highgates Nursery, 135
Hiley, Brian, 189
Hill House, 289
Hill House Garden, 269
Hillbarn House, 332

Hillier Garden Centre, 121, 124, 151, 190, 196
Hillier Gardens & Arboretum, Sir Harold, 1, 285
Hillier Landscapes, 411
Hillier Nurseries Ltd, 59, 152
Hillier Plant Centre, 152
Hillier's Manual of Trees and Shrubs, 483
Hills, Lawrence, 393
Hillview Hardy Plants, 181
Himalayan Kingdoms Ltd, 485
Hindle, Designer and Gardener, Josephine, 413
Hinton Ampner House, 284
Hippopottering Nursery, 203
Historic Buildings and Monuments Commission for England, 365
Historic Houses Association (HHA), 364, 438
Historic Houses, Castles and Gardens in Great Britain and Ireland, 243
Hodges Barn, 278
Hodgman, Muriel, 66
Hodnet Hall, 312
Hodsock Priory, 307
Hoecroft Plants, 175
Holden Clough Nursery, 168
Holdenby House Gardens, 304
Holehird, 264
holiday companies, 484
Holiday Homewatch, 486
Holker Hall, 264
Holkham Hall, 302
Holland Arms Garden Centre, 209
Hollies Park, The, 338
Hollington Nurseries, 124, 411
Holly Gate Cactus Nursery, 196, 233
Holly Society of America Inc, 118
Home Covert, 332
Home Meadows Nursery Ltd, 187
Homes and Gardens, 479
Homesitters Ltd, 486
Honey Brothers, 430
Hoo House Nursery, 147
Hop Shop, The, 59, 380
Hopes, Garden Designer, Mary-Jane, 416
Hopleys Plants Ltd, 58, 160
Hornby, Sir Simon, 64
Horne, Elaine, 407
Horticultural Abstracts, 76
Horticultural Correspondence College, 451
Horticultural Development Council, 438
horticultural fleece, 371, 390
Horticultural Judges Register, The, 59

horticultural sand, 397
Horticultural Show Handbook, The, 59
Horticultural shows, 59
Horticultural Speakers Register, 119
Horticultural Therapy, 438, 450
Horticultural Trades Association (HTA), 438
Horticulture Research International, Wellesbourne, 463
Horticulture Week, 479
Hortus, 479
Hosford's Geraniums & Garden Centre, 218
Hotbox Heaters Ltd, 381
hotels, 364
Hotterotter Group, 381
Houghall, 274, 444
Houghton Farm Plants, 196
Houghton Lodge, 284
House and Gardens, 479
House of Pitmuies, 353
house plants, 225
householder's obligation, 493
houseminders, 486
Housewatch Ltd, 486
How Caple Court, 287
Howick Hall, 306
Hozelock Ltd, 381
Huckson, Eachus, 407
Hugh Baird College, 448
Hughenden Manor, 250
Hull, Diana, 198
Hull Farm Conifer Centre, 145
Humphrey, V H, 192
Huntington, Lucy, 58
Hunts Court Garden & Nursery, 148
Hurrans Garden Centre Ltd, 148
Husqvarna Forest & Garden UK, 381
Hutton-in-the-Forest, 265
Hyatt, Brenda, 66, 162
Hyde Hall *see* Royal Horticultural Society
Hydon Nurseries, 190, 411
Ichiyo School of Ikebana, 59, 103
ICI Garden Products, 381
Iden Croft Herbs, 163
Iford Manor, 332
IGA Stuttgart '93, 65
importing & exporting plants, 229
Inchbald School of Design, 447
Independent, The, 479
Independent on Sunday, The, 479
Ingram, Tim, 57, 166
Ingram Topiary Frames Ltd, 381
Ingwersen Ltd, W E Th., 57, 197
Ingwersen, Will, 483
insecticides, 493

Institute of Groundsmanship, 438
Institute of Horticulture (IoH), The, 401, 438
Institute of Hydrology, 65
Institute of Leisure and Amenity Management (ILAM), 438
International Acers, 156, 411
International Aroid Society, 118
International Association of Horticultural Producers, 438
International Camellia Society, 103
International Correspondence Schools, 455
International Dendrology Society, 104
International Garden Festival, 65
International Lilac Society, 118
International Orchid Conference, 57
International Palm Society, 118
International Plant Propagators Society, 438
International Spring Gardening Fair, 58, 61
International Tree Foundation, 438
International Violet Association, 104
International Water Lily Society, 104
Interpet Ltd, 381
Inveresk Lodge Garden, 349
Inverewe, 348, 361
Ireland Landscape Architect, David, 406
iris, 225
Iris de Thau, 488
Irish Organic Farmers and Growers Association, 393
irrigation systems, 371, 379, 380, 381, 383, 387
Isabella Plantation, 300
Iseki UK, 381
Isle of Wight College of Arts and Technology, 445
Isle of Wight Gardens Trust, 113
Ivelet Books Ltd, 465
Ivy Cottage, 273
Jack's Patch, 137
Jackson's Nurseries, 186
Jakobsen Landscape Architects, 411
Japanese garden products, 377
Japanese Garden Society, 104
Japanese Gardens, Tully, 358
Jardine, Garden Designer, Joy, 413
Jardins de Cotelles, Les, 487
Jardins de France, 488
Jasper Trees, Paul, 156
Jeffries Landscapes, Nigel, 417
Jekka's Herb Farm, 122
Jemp Engineering, 381
Jenkyn Place, 284
Jersey Lavender Ltd, 217
Jiffy Products UK Ltd, 382
Jodrell Bank Arboretum, 255

John Innes Manufacturers Association, 398, 438
John Spedan Lewis Foundation, The, 458
Johnson, Hugh, 483
Johnsons Seeds, 234
Johnstown Castle Gardens, 359
Jones, C & K, 128, 207
Jones, Clay, 66
Jordan, P A, 214
Jordens, Sol, 421
Judy's Country Garden, 171, 413
Jungle Giants, 156
Juniperus, 78
Just Roses, 193
Kaye Ltd, Reginald, 168
Keepers Nursery, 163, 414
Kellett, P H, 165, 418
Kellie Castle, 346
Kelways Nurseries Ltd, 183, 414
Kemp's Coconut Products, 382
Ken Caro, 259
Kennedy Arboretum, The John F., 359
Kent Street Nurseries, 193
Kent Trust for Nature Conservation, 113
Kenwith Nursery, 137
Kenwood Park, 300
Kew Gardens Gallery, 64
Kew School of Horticulture, 450
Kew Shop, 465
Kiftsgate Court Gardens, 148, 279
Kildalton Agricultural and Horticultural College, 456
Kildrummy Castle, 347, 364
Killerton, 269
King Easton Ltd, 382
King John's House, Romsey, 80
King Treecare, Graham, 409, 430
Kings Crown of Kelvedon, 234
Kingsbury, Noël, 417
Kingston Lacy, 273
Kingston Maurward College, 444
Kingston Maurward Gardens, 273
Kinlochlaich House Gardens, 214, 414
Kinross Garden Centre and Butterfly House, 215
Kirby Laing Foundation, The, 458
Kirstenbosch Botanical Gardens, 59
Knap Hill Nursery Ltd, 190
Knebworth House, 289
Knight, Douglas, 59
Knight Terrace Pots, 382
Knights Garden Centre, 190, 191
Knightshayes, 137, 270
Knowles Nets, 382
Knowsley Community College, Land-based Industries, 448
Konstsmide UK Ltd, 383
Kouwenhoorn, Pieter van, 64

Kubota (UK) Ltd, 383
Kut and Dried, 383
L & P Peat Ltd, 383
labels, 372, 391
Laburnum Nurseries, 169
Lackham College, 452
Ladham House, 293
Lady Muck, 383
Lakeside, 287
Lambeth College, 447
Lamorran House, 260
Lancaster, Roy, 488
Land and Tree Ltd, 431
Landcare, 414
Landford Trees, 201
Landlife Wildflowers Ltd, 174, 234
Landscape Centre, 215, 414
Landscape Design Studio, 414
Landscape Institute, The, 401, 438
Landscape Resource, 414, 431
Landskip and Prospect, 414
Landsman's Bookshop Ltd, 465
Langham Lodge, 296
Langley Boxwood Nursery, 152
Langside College, 455
Langthorns Plantery, 145
Lanhydrock, 132, 260
Laspen Trust, The, 458
late opening hours, 361
lawnmowers, 372, 376, 379, 380, 381, 382, 383, 392
Lawrence, W. J. C., 69
Lawson, O, 417
Layham Garden Centre, 164
LDC Ltd, 415
Lea Gardens, 135, 267
Leaky Pipe Systems Ltd, 383
Lechlade Garden Centre, 148, 415
Lee & Co Ltd, A T, 371
Leeds & Hollingbourne Garden Society, 59
Leeds Castle, 294
Leeds Metropolitan University, 453
Lees-Milne, Alvilde, 483
legacies, 66, 495
Leicestershire and Rutland Trust for Nature Conservation, 113
Leigh Park, 79
Leighton Hall, 295
Leith Hall, 347
Lennox-Boyd Landscape Design, 415
Leonardslee Gardens, 326
Leonardslee Gardens Nurseries, 196
Levens Hall, 265
Lewdon Farm Alpine Nursery, 137
Lewes Road Sawmills, 383
Lewis Tree Surgeons, Douglas, 429
libraries, 460
Libraries Directory 1991-93, The, 460

lighting, 381, 383, 390
lilies, 225
Lime Cross Nursery, 194
Lincolnshire College of Agriculture, 447
Lincolnshire Trust, The, 113
Lindley Library, Royal Horticultural Society, 462, 483
Lindum Seeded Turf, 383
Lingard + Styles Landscape, 415
Lingen Alpine Nursery, 181
Lingholm, 134, 265
Link-Stakes Ltd, 383
Linnean Society, 461
Lisdoonan Herbs, 216
Lismore Castle, 358
Little Brook Fuchsias, 152
Little Creek Nursery, 122
Little Moreton Hall, 255
Littlewood Landscape Designer, Michael, 417
living in France, 488
Llanbrook Alpine & Wildflower Nursery, 182
Lloyd, Christopher, 66, 482, 483
Lloyd, Daniel, 482
Lloyds of Kew, 465
Loader Tree Care Specialists, Richard, 433
Lochalsh Woodland Garden, 348
Lockyer, C S, 121
Logan Botanic Gardens, 345
Long Barn, 294
Long Close, 296
Long Man Gardens, 194
Longacre Nursery, 164, 415
Longhall Nursery, 201
Longleat House, 333
Longstock Park Nursery, 152, 415
Longstock Water Gardens, 284
Loseley Flower Festival, 62
Lotherton Hall, 338
Lotus Landscapes, 415
Lovegrove, Mary Ann, 416
Lowe, Lt Cdr Tony, 66
Lower Hall, 312
Lower House Farm, 341
Lower Severalls Herb Nursery, 184
Lucas & Associates, John H, 412
Luton Hoo, 246
Lydney Park Gardens, 279
Lyme Park, 80, 255
Lyte's Cary Manor, 315
M W Horticultural Supplies, 383
Machin Conservatories, 384
Mackey's Garden Centre, 218, 234
Macpennys Nurseries, 143
Madrona Nursery, 164
Maenllwyd Isaf, 343
Magnolia Society Inc, The, 118

magnolia, 2,000 year old, 64
Malahide Nurseries Ltd, 219
Malleny House, 349
Mallet Court Nursery, 56, 184
Malvern Spring Gardening Show, 61, 62
Mammillaria Society, The, 104, 240
Management of health and safety at work, 492
Management of Health and Safety at Work Regulations 1992, 491
Manchester Metropolitan University, 443
Manderston, 344
Manor House, The, Bledlow, 250
Manor House, Upton Grey, The, 80, 285
Manor House, The, Walton-in-Gordano, 245
Mansell & Hatcher Ltd, 206
Manual handling, 492
Manual Handling Operations Regulations 1992, 492
Manual of Alpine Plants, 483
manure, 396
Marble Hill: A Palladian Rendezvous, 62
Margam Park, 341
marking machines, 389
Marks and Spencer plc, 173
Marle Place Gardens & Nursery, 164
Marley Bank Nursery, 156
Marshall Cavendish, 482
Marshall's Malmaisons, 148
Marshalls, 235
Marston & Langinger Ltd, 384
Marston Exotics, 59, 156
Martel's Garden World, 217
Martin, J E, 233
Martinez, Jan, 411
Marwood Hill Gardens, 137, 270
Matlock Garden Centre Ltd, 135
Matthews Ltd, Frank P, 155
Mattock Roses, 59, 180
Maxicrop International Ltd, 384
Maydencroft Aquatic Nurseries, 160
McArd, S M, 236
McBeans Orchids, 59
McLauchlan Horticulture, John, 371, 382
Mead Nursery, The, 201
Meadowcroft Fuchsias, 126
measuring equipment, 377, 391
Medhurst Landscape Consultant, John, 413
mediterranean plants, 225
Melbourne Hall, 267
Mellerstain, 344
Mellors Garden Ceramics, 384

Melville Nurseries, 213
Mendle Nursery, 161
Merriments Gardens, 194, 416
Merrist Wood College, 450
Merrist Wood College Plant Shop, 191
Merton Institute of Adult Education, 447
Mesemb Study Group, 104, 240
Messham, Carol, 404
Metalarts, 384
Metpost Ltd, 384
Michelham Priory, 323
Mickfield Fish and Watergarden Centre, 187, 417
Middleton Hall, Carmarthen, 81
Midland Tree Surgeons Ltd, 431
Miles, Paul, 418
Mill Cottage Plants, 184
Mill Hill Plants, 179
Mill House, The, 309
Mill Race Nursery, 146, 417
Millais Nurseries, 191
Mills Farm Plants and Gardens, 187
Milne Atkinson, P W, 418
Milton Garden Plants, 143
Milton Lodge, 315
Minature Garden Co of Illminster, 58
Ministry of Agriculture, Fisheries and Food, 70, 71, 439, 493
Ministry of Agriculture, Fisheries and Food Library, 461
Minterne, 273
Miserden Park, 279
Mitchell, Mary & Peter, 196
Molesworth, Barbara, 181
Mon Jardin et ma Maison, 488
Monksilver Nursery, 126
Monkton Elm Garden Centre, 184, 417
Monocot Nursery, 122, 235
Monsanto Garden Care, 384
Montacute House, 315
Montezumas, 384
Montgomeryshire Wildlife Trust, 113
Morehavens, 125
Moreland, John, 413
Morrey & Son, F, 128
Morton Hall, 307
Moseley Old Hall, 316
mosskillers, 493
Mottisfont Abbey, 285, 361
Mottistone Manor, 290
Moulton College, 448
Mount Edgcumbe Gardens, 260
Mount Grace Priory, Northallerton, 81
Mount Perennial Plants, Frances, 145
Mount Pleasant Trees, 148
Mount Skippet, 309
Mount Stewart, 354
Mount Usher Gardens, 359
Muckross Garden Centre, 219, 417

Muckross House & Gardens, 357
Muir Nurseries, Ken, 59, 145
Muncaster Castle, 265
Muncaster Fuchsias, Kathleen, 171
Munstead Wood, 320, 362
Murrel Gardens, The, 346
Museum of Garden History, The, 65, 300
mushroom compost, 396
My Garden in Autumn and Winter, 483
My Garden in Spring, 483
My Garden in Summer, 483
Myddelton House, 300
Myerscough College, 446
N & GC, 479
NAFAS Berks, Bucks & Oxon Flower Festival, 62
NAFAS Devon & Cornwall Area Show and Exhibition, 63
NAFAS Dorset & Guernsey Area Competitions and Exhibition, 63
NAFAS Dorset & Guernsey Conference and Competitions, 63
NAFAS Flower Arranging Competitions and Exhibition, 63
NAFAS Kent Area Show, 63
NAFAS Mercia & North Wales Flower Festival, 63
NAFAS Three Counties & South Wales Area Day, 63
NAFAS Wessex & Jersey Area Competitions, 63
NAFAS Wessex & Jersey Area Exhibition, 63
Naked Cross Nurseries, 143
Nareys Garden Centre, 187, 417
National Art Collections Fund, 484
National Association of Flower Arrangement Societies, The, 105
National Auricula and Primula Society (Southern Section), 105
National Begonia Society, 105
National Bonsai Society, 105
National Botanic Gardens, Dublin, 356
National Chrysanthemum Society, 59, 105
National Collection of Passiflora, 122
National Collections, 66
National Council for the Conservation of Plants & Gardens (NCCPG), 57, 66, 70, 106, 120, 243
National Dahlia Society, 59, 106
National Farmers Union, 439
National Gardens Scheme, 242, 439, 497
National Institute of Medical Herbalists, The, 59, 439
National Library of Scotland, 463
National Library of Wales, 463

National Pot Leek Society, 106
National Proficiency Test Council, 493
National Society of Allotment and Leisure Gardeners, 59, 106
National Sweet Pea Society, The, 106
National Trust, The, 1, 80, 439, 484
National Trust for Scotland, 439
National Trust Gardens Handbook, The, 243
National Union of Farm Workers, 492
National Vegetable Society, 59, 107
National Viola and Pansy Society, 107
Natural History Museum, The, 461
Natural Pest Control Ltd, 384
nature reserves, 490
Naturetrek, 485
NCH, 441
NCVQ, 441
NEBAHAI, 441
Nederlandse Heidervereniging 'Ericultura', 118
Nene Valley Adult Education, 443
Ness Gardens, Cheshire, 1, 89, 90, 91, 256
Nest Nurseries, Martin, 172
Netherbyres, 495, 497
Netlon Ltd, 385
netting, 377, 382, 385
Nettletons Nursery, 191
new books (1993), 467
new books (1994), 473
New England Gardens Ltd, 385
New Englishwoman's Garden, The, 483
New Plantsman, The, 479
New RHS Dictionary of Gardening, 482, 483
New Zealand Alpine Gardening Society, 118
New Zealand Fuchsia Society Inc, 118
New Zealand Gladiolus Council, 118
New Zealand plants, 225
Newby Hall, 335
Newington Nurseries, 180
Newnes, Mary, 66
Newstead Abbey, 307
Newton Hill Alpines, 206
Newton Rigg College, 443
NIAB, 439
Nicky's Rock Garden Nursery, 138
Nicolson, Adam, 65
Nine Springs Nursery, 152
nomenclature changes, 498
Nonington Pottery, 385
Norbark (Northern Bark Ltd), 385
Norden Alpine Nursery, 203
Nordybank Nurseries, 182
Norfield Trees & Seeds, Andrew, 147, 232
Norfolk Lavender Ltd, 175

Norfolk Naturalists Trust, 113
Norman Bonsai, 194
North American Heather Society, 118
North American Lily Society Inc, 118
North Court, 290
North Devon Garden Centre, 138, 417
North End House, 253
North of England Horticultural Society, 113
North of England Rose, Carnation and Sweet Pea Society, The, 113
North Wales Tree Service, 432
North Wales Wildlife Trust, 114
Northamptonshire Wildlife Trust, 114
Northbourne Court, 294
Northern Horticultural Society, 1, 70, 75, 107, 240
Northside Seeds, 235
Northumbria Nurseries, 179
Norton, Paul, 418
Norton Priory Museum & Gardens, 256
Norton Radstock Technical College, 450
Norwich Heather and Conifer Centre, 176
Notcutts Garden Centre, 127, 146, 160, 164, 176, 191, 200
Notcutts Nurseries, 59, 188
Nottcutts Landscapes, 417
Nottinghamshire Wildlife Trust, 114
NPTC, 441
Nuffield Farming Scholarships Trust, The, 458
Nuneham Courtenay Arboretum, 310
Nunwell House, 291
nurseries, French, 487
NVQ, 441
Nymans, 326
O'Callaghan & Associates, D P, 429
Oak Cottage Herb Garden, 182, 418
Oak Leaf Conservatories, 385
Oak Tree Nursery, 203
Oaklands College, 446
Oakleigh Nurseries, 59, 153
Oakwood, 418, 432
Oare House, 333
Oatridge Agricultural College, 455
obituaries, 67
Observer, The, 68, 480
Oddy, J R, 57
Odell Castle, 247
Offham House, 324
Stuart Ogg, 194
Ohara School of Ikebana, 107
Okell's Nurseries, 129
Old Court Nurseries, 156
Old Manor Nursery, The, 148
Old Mill Herbary, The, 132
Old Rectory Cottage, 248
Old Rectory, The, Burghfield, 249

Old Rectory, The, Farnborough, 310
Old Rectory, The, Sudborough, 304
Old Vicarage, The, Edington, 333
Oldbury Nurseries, 59, 165
Olivers, 276
Orchard House Nursery, 203
Orchard Nurseries, 172, 418
Orchardstown Nurseries, 219
Orchid Society of Great Britain, 107
Orchid Sundries Ltd & Hardy Orchids Ltd, 143, 385
orchids, 225, 235
Organic Concentrates Ltd, 385
Organic Food & Farming Centre, The, 439
organic gardening, 393
Organic Gardening, 480
organic products, 374, 376, 377, 380, 382, 383, 385, 390, 391
organisations, 401
Original Organics Ltd, 386
Ornate Products, 386
Osborne House, Isle of Wight, 79
Osterley Park, 301
Otley College of Agriculture and Horticulture, 450
Otter Nurseries Ltd, 138, 418
Otter's Court Heathers, 184, 418
Oulton House, 316
Overbury Court, 288
Owl Cottage, 291
Owlpen Manor, 279, 364
Oxburgh Hall, 302
Oxford Botanic Garden, 310
Oxford Botanic Garden, Friends of, 59
Oxford Companion to Gardens, The, 482, 483
Oxley's Garden Furniture, 386
P M A Plant Specialities, 184, 418
P W Plants, 176, 418
Pacific Horticulture, 480
Pack Garden Design, Sue, 422
Padlock Croft, 127, 253
Padua Botanic Garden, 80
paeonies, 225
Page, Russell, 482, 483
Paignton Zoo & Botanical Gardens, 270
Painshill Park, 80, 320
Painswick Rococo Garden, 279
Paisley, Jeanne, 412
Palm Centre, The, 173
Palmer & Son, A J, 124
palms, 225
Pamal, 386
Pan Brittanica Industries Ltd, 386
Pantiles Plant & Garden Centre, 191, 418
Paradise Centre, 188
Parallax, 386
Parcevall Hall Gardens, 336

Parham, 327
Park Farm, 276
Park Garden Centre, 122, 418
Park Green Nurseries, 188
Parkinson Herbs, 132
Parnham House, 273
Pashley Manor, 324
Pattison (Nurseryman), Chris, 147
Pavey & Associates, Graham A, 409
payroll giving, 495
Peckover House, 253
pelargoniums, 225
Pelham Landscapes, 418
Pencarrow, 260
Penjerrick, 261
Penn, 256
Pennell & Sons Ltd, 161
Penrhyn Castle, 342
Penrhyn Charitable Trust, The, 458
Penshurst Place, 294
Peover Hall, 256
Pepinières Charentaises, 487
Perennial Garden Plants, 483
pergolas, 371, 384, 388, 390
Period House and Its Garden, 480
Period Living and Traditional Homes, 480
periodicals, 477
permaculture, 394
Permaculture Association, The, 394
Perrie Hale Forest Nursery, 138
Perry, Frances, 67
Perry's Plants, 203
Perrybrook Nursery, 182
Perryhill Nurseries, 194, 419
Pershore College of Horticulture, 452, 462
personal allowances, 230
Personal protective equipment at work, 493
Personal Protective Equipment at Work Regulations 1992, 492
Perth Garden Centre, 215
pesticides, 382, 384, 493
Pesticides Safety Directorate, 493
Petal Designs Ltd, 419
Pete & Ken Cactus Nursery, 165
Pettit bequest, the Anthony, 495
Petworth House, 327
Peveril Clematis Nursery, 138
Phedar Nursery, 129, 235
Philips Landscape and Garden Design, Nigel L, 417
Phillips, Roger, 482, 483
Phipps, A & A, 120
Phostrogen, 386
phytosanitary certificates, 230
Picton Castle, 340
Pilkington Garden Centre, 129
Pine Lodge, 261

Pinewood House, 320
Pinks & Carnations, 168
Pitmedden, 347
Pitt Landscape Design, Ray, 419
Plant Breeders Rights, 69, 70, 71
Plant Breeding International, 439
Plant Finder, The, 70, 72, 120, 482, 483
plant hangers, 371
Plant Health (Great Britain) Order 1993, The, 229
Plant Lovers, The, 172, 235
plant passports, 231
plant pots, 382
Plant Publicity Holland, 439
plant supports, 382, 383, 387, 390
Plant Varieties and Seeds Act, 70
Plant Varieties and Seeds Gazette, 70, 71
Plant Variety Rights Office and Seeds Division, 439
Plant World Botanic Gardens, 138, 235
Plantables, 200
Plantasia, 341
Planters Garden Centre, 186
Plantlife, 439
Plantworld, 146
Plas Brondanw Gardens, 342
Plas Newydd, 342
Plas Penhelig, 343, 364
Plas-yn-Rhiw, 343
plastic pots, 375, 377
Platts, Roger, 388
Plaxtol Nurseries, 165, 419
Pleasant View Nursery & Garden, 139
Podington Garden Centre, 178
Poisoning by Pesticides: First Aid, 492
Polesden Lacey, 320
polypropylene fleece, 396
pondliners, 397
Port Lympne Gardens, 294
Porter's Fuchsias, 174
Porthpean House Gardens, 132
Post House Gardens, 340
pot holders, 380
Potterton and Martin, 58, 172, 235
Pound Lane Nurseries, 153
Pounsley Plants, 139
Powderham Castle, 270
Power Garden Products, 386
Powerscourt Gardens, 80, 359
Powis Castle, 343
Poyntzfield Herb Nursery, 212
Practical Gardening, 480
Practicality Brown Ltd, 387
Precise Irrigation (UK) Ltd, 387
Preen Manor, 312
Preston-Mafham Collection, 199
primulas, 226

Pringle Plants, 209
Prior Park, 80
Priory, The, 280
Priory Garden Nursery, 149
Probus, Cornwall, 79
Professional Gardeners Guild, The, 439
professional help, 400
Professional Tree Services, 419, 432
propagators, 374, 381, 382, 391
protected zones, 231
Provincial Booksellers Fairs Association, 464
Provincial Tree Services Ltd, 432
Provision and Use of Work Equipment Regulations 1992, 491, 492
Pruhonice, Czech Republic, 76
public liability insurance, 400
Quartet Design, 419
R D Plants, 139
Radnorshire Wildlife Trust, 114
Rae, Gordon, 65
Raffles - Thatched Garden Buildings, 387
rainfall, 65
Rainthorpe Hall Gardens, 303
Ramster, 320
Rank Prize Funds, The, 459
Ransomes Consumer Ltd, 387
Ransoms Garden Centre, 217
Rarer Plants, 204
Raven Tree Services, 433
Raveningham Gardens, 176
Raveningham Hall, 303
Ravensbourne Floral Society, 59
Ravensthorpe Nursery, 178
Raw Talent Consultancy, The, 419
Rayment Wirework, 387
Reads Nursery, 176
Reaseheath College (Cheshire College of Agriculture), 443
Red Oaks, 496
Regent's Park, 361
regulations, 493
Reid & Co, Ben, 211
Remanoid, 387
Renaissance Bronzes, 387
Renaissance Casting, 387
Renishaw Hall, 267
restoration projects, 79
Reuthe, G, 59, 166
Rhinefield Park, New Forest, 80
Rhodes & Rockliffe, 146
rhododendrons, 65, 76, 226
Richards + Associates, Simon, 421
Rickard's Hardy Ferns Ltd, 157
Rickell, John B, 412
Riley's Chrysanthemums, 135
Ripley Castle, 336
Riseholme Hall, 298

Rivendell Alpines, 143
Rivendell Nursery, 204
Rix, Martyn, 482, 483
Robinson & Sons Ltd, W, 237
Robinson, Dick and Helen, 64
Robinson, Mrs S, 0, 187
Robinson Penn Partnership, The, 420
Robinson, William, 483
Robinsons of Whaley Bridge, 129
Roche Court, 333
Rock Garden Club Prague, The, 118
Rockingham Castle, 305
Rode Hall, 256
Rodgerson, Chris, 205
Rodmarton Manor, 280
Roeber Landscapes, Nicholas, 417
Roffey Bros Ltd, 388
Roger Ltd, R V, 203
Rogers Associates, Peter, 419
Romantic Garden Nursery, The, 177, 420
Romilt Landscape Design & Construction Ltd, 420
Rookhope Nurseries, 141
rooting compounds, 76
Roots Garden Centre Ltd, 211, 420
Rose Growers Association, 439
Rose Hybridizers Association, 118
roses, 64, 66, 76, 226
Roses Anciennes de André Eve, Les, 488
Ross - Landscape Design, Veronica, 423
Ross Landscape Architects, Mark, 416
Ross Tree Services, 433
Rougham Nurseries, 58
Roundstone Garden Centre Ltd, 197
Rousham House, 310
Rowallane Garden, 95, 96, 97, 354
Rowden Gardens, 139
Rowles Garden Design, Sue de Bock, 422
Royal Botanic Garden, Edinburgh, 463, 83, 84, 85, 349
Royal Botanic Gardens, Kew, 461, 79, 56, 66, 321 see also Kew
Royal Botanic Garden, Edinburgh, Friends of the, 112
Royal Botanic Gardens, Kew, Friends of the, 112
Royal Botanical and Horticultural Society of Manchester and the Northern Counties, The, 459
Royal Caledonian Horticultural Society, The, 114
Royal Commission for the Exhibition of 1851, 459
Royal Festival Hall, 1
Royal Gardeners' Orphan Fund, The, 496

Royal Horticultural Society, The, 1, 64, 65, 69, 70, 73, 108, 240, 484; Award of garden Merit, 72, 73; Director General, 65; Education Year, 66; Floral A Committee, 72; member's tickets, 64; RHS Enterprises Ltd, 59, 139, 466; RHS Garden, Hyde Hall, 1, 64, 275; RHS Garden, Rosemoor, 2, 270; RHS Pershore, 1; RHS Garden, Wisley, 2, 72, 86, 87, 88, 321, 363; shows, 56; trials, 72
Royal Institute of British Architects (RIBA), 401, 439
Royal National Institute for the Blind, The, 492
Royal National Rose Society, The, 59, 64, 66, 69, 70, 108; planning appeal, 65; trials, 71
Royal Society for Nature Conservation, 439, 490
Royal Society for the Prevention of Accidents, 492
Royal Society for the Protection of Birds, 440
Royal Society, The, 459
Rumwood Nurseries, 166
Rushfields of Ledbury, 157
Rushforth, Keith, 431
Ruskins Arboricultural Group, 433
Ruthall Manor, 312
Ruxley Manor Garden Centre Ltd, 166
Ryal Nursery, 179
Rycroft Landscape Architects, Sarah, 420
Rydal Mount, 265
Ryobi Lawn & Garden (UK) Ltd, 388
Ryton Organic Gardens, 2, 329, 393
S & S Perennials, 170
Sadler, Mrs J, 196
SAFAS Open Demonstration Day, 63
St Andrews Botanic Garden, 346
St Annes Vineyard, 149
St Helens College, 448
St Michael's Mount, 261
St Paul's Walden Bury, 289
St Peters Garden Centre, 218
Saintpaulia & Houseplant Society, The, 109, 240
Salesian College of Horticulture, 456
Saling Hall, 276
Salley Gardens, 134, 236
Salvia patens 'White Trophy', 58
Sampford Shrubs, 139
Samsons, 388
Sanday (Roses) Ltd, John, 122
Sandford Award, 364
45 Sandford Road, 356
Sandringham House, 303

Sarah D'Avigdor Goldsmid Charitable Trust, The, 457
Savill Garden, The, 58, 321
Sawyers Seeds, 236
Saynor, Karen, 414
Scarletts Plantcare, 388
scientific research, 76
Scoil Stiofáin, 456
Scotland's Garden Scheme, 243, 440, 497
Scotney Castle, 295
Scotsdale Nursery & Garden Centre, 127, 420
Scotsman, The, 480
Scott & Sons Ltd, O M, 385
Scott Ornamental Grasses, Trevor, 146
Scott-Marshall, bequest, John, 66
Scottish Agricultural College, 455
Scottish Allotments and Gardens Society, The, 114
Scottish National Sweet Pea, Rose & Carnation Society, 114
Scottish Natural Heritage, 440
Scottish Rhododendron Society, 109
Scottish Rock Garden Club, The, 109, 240
Scottish Wildlife Trust, 115
Scottlandscape, 420
Scotts Clematis, 140
Scotts Nurseries Ltd, 185
Scotvec, 441
Seaforde Gardens, 217
Searle, P A, 432
Seaside Nursery and Garden Centre, 219
Secret Garden Designs by Christina Oates, 420
Secretts Garden Centre, 192
Seed Bank and Exchange, 147
seed exchange schemes, 238
Seed House, The, 236
Seeds-by-Size, 236
seldom open to the public, 362
Sellet Hall Gardens, 168, 421
Sempervivum Society, The, 109
sempervivums, 226
Serre de la Madone, 80
Seven Counties Garden Design, 421
Seven Gardens, 483
Seymours Garden & Leisure Group, 421
Sezincote, 280
Shackleton Garden, 357
Shamrock Horticulture Ltd, 388
Shanley, Victor A, 423
Sheen Ltd, Joanna, 382
sheet mulches, 396
sheeting, 377, 383, 385, 386, 390
Sheffield Botanical Gardens, 337
Sheffield Park, 324

Sheldon Manor, 333
Shepton Nursery Garden, 185
Sherborne Garden, 246
Sherbourne Park, 329
Sheringham Park, 303
Shipley College, 453
Short & Partners, Anthony, 402
Shrewsbury Flower Show, 61
Shrubland Hall, 318
shrubs, 226
Shugborough Hall, 317
silver sand, 397
Simms, Clive, 170
Simply Garlands, 388
Simply Plants, 127
Simpsons Nursery, 177, 421
Sinclair Horticulture, William, 392
single market, 229
Siskin Plants, 188
Sissinghurst Castle, 295
Sizergh Castle, 266
Skyshades, 388
Sledmere House, 290
Sleightholmedale Lodge, 336
Smallscapes Nursery, 188
Smeeden Foreman Partnership, 421
Smith & Son, John, 169
Smith, Alan C, 161
Smith, Elizabeth, 131
Smith Horticultural Trust, Stanley, 68, 459
Smith's Garden & Leisure, Stephen H, 161, 206
Smithers, Sir Peter, 66
Snowshill Manor, 280
Société Nationale d'Horticulture de France, La, 118, 488
Society for Growing Australian Plants, The, 118
Society of Botanical Artists, 440
Society of Floristry, The, 440
Society of Garden Designers, 401, 440
Société Française des Roses, La, 118
Soil Association, The, 393
Sokell, Anthea, 402
Solardome, 389
Solihull College of Technology, 451
Somerleyton Hall, 318
Somerset Gardens Trust, 115
Somerset Postal Flowers, 389
Somerset Trust for Nature Conservation, 115
Sorbus torminalis, 66
South American plants, 227
South Ockendon Garden Centre, 146
Southend Adult Education Centre, 445
Southern Tree Surgeons Ltd, 421, 433, 434
Southfield Nurseries, 59, 172, 236

Southport College of Art and Technology, 448
Southport Flower Show, 62
Southview Nurseries, 153
Southwick Country Herbs, 140
Sparsholt College Hampshire, 445
Spear & Jackson Garden Products, 389
Special Plants, 201
Specialised Designs Ltd, 389
Specialtours, 484
Spectator, The, 480
Speyside Heather Centre, 212
Spinners, 153, 285
Sportsmark Group Ltd, 389
sprayers, 373, 375, 380, 381
Spreckley, Rosemary, 157
Springfields Show Gardens, 298
Staffordshire College of Agriculture, 450
Staffordshire Gardens & Parks Trust, 115
Staffordshire Wildlife Trust, 115
Stancombe Park, 281
Standen, 324
Stangwrach Leisure Products, 389
Stansfield, 310
Stanway House, 281
Stapeley Water Gardens Ltd, 59, 129, 257
Starborough Nursery, 56, 166
Starkie & Starkie Ltd, 389
statuary, 380, 384
Stay Garden Design & Consultancy, Joanna, 412
Stearn, Sonia, 421
Stephenson Blake, 389
Stern, Sir Frederick, 483
Stevens International Ltd, David, 407
Stewart, Joyce, 66
Stewarts (Nottm) Ltd, 236
Sticky Wicket, 274
Stillingfleet Lodge Nurseries, 204
Stoke-on-Trent College, 450
Ston Easton Park, 315, 364
Stone House Cottage Nurseries, 157
Stone Lane Gardens, 140
Stonehurst, 327
Store More Garden Buildings, 389
Stourbridge College, 451
Stourhead, 333
Stourton House, 334
Stowe Landscape Gardens, 80, 250
Stratfield Saye House, 286
Street, Henry, 124
Strikes Garden Centre, 130, 141, 204, 206
Strong, Sir Roy, 80
Stuart Garden Architecture, 390
Studley Royal, 336
Sudeley Castle, 281

Suffolk Wildlife Trust, 115
sugar beet washings, 396
Sulgrave Manor, 305
Sulman, Pearl, 188
Sulman Pelargoniums, Brian, 186
summer gap, 362
Summerfield Books, 466
summerhouses, 372, 373, 375, 378, 387, 392
sun dials, 375, 380
Sunday Telegraph, The, 480
The Sunday Times, 481
Sunlight Systems, 390
Sunnybank House Nursery, 158
Super Natural Ltd, 390
Surrey Gardens Trust, 115
Surrey Primroses, 192
Surrey Wildlife Trust, 115
Sussex Wildlife Trust, 116
Sutton Park, 336
Sutton, Griffin & Morgan, 422
Suttons Seeds, 236
Suzuki, Hideo, 66
SVQ, 441
Swallow Hayes, 312
Swan Hellenic Ltd, 485
Swiss Garden, The, 247
Syon Courtyard, 173, 422
Syon Park, 301
Talbot Botanic Gardens, 357
Tamarisk Nurseries, 125
Tapeley Park, 271
taps, 373, 378
Tatton Park, 257
Tavendale Arboricultural Consultant, Iain, 430
Taylor, Sir George, 68
Teagasc College of Amenity Horticulture, 456
Teamwork, 422
Telegraph House, 327
Temple Associates, Gillian, 409
Temple Associates, Paul, 418
Temple Newsam Park, 338
terracotta pots, 372, 375, 385, 391
Thacker, Dr Christopher, 365
Thames Valley Wirework Co Ltd, 390
Thermoforce Ltd, 390
thermometers, 376, 379, 391
Theseus Maze Designs, 403
third party insurance, 400, 493
Thoday, Peter, 81
Thomas, Graham, 360, 483
Thompson & Morgan, 69, 237
Thompson's Hill, 334
Thorman Arboricultural Consultants, David, 429
Thorncroft Clematis Nursery, 177
Thorne (Beehives) Ltd, E H, 377
Thornhayes Nursery, 140

Thorp, A & A, 168
Thorp Perrow Arboretum, 337
Threave School of Gardening, 345, 454
Three Counties Nurseries, 143
ties, 377, 379, 391
Tile Barn Nursery, 166
The Times, 481
Timothy Colman Charitable Trust, The, 457
Timpany Nurseries, 217
Tintinhull House, 315
Tirley Garth Trust, 257
Tivey & Son, Philip, 169
Toad Hall Produce, 158
Toll, Julie, 58
Tollgate Cottage Nursery, 199
Tomperrow Farm Nurseries, 132
tool holders, 390
tool sharpening systems, 389
topiary, 227
topiary frames, 381
topsoil, 396
Torbock, Cornish, 67
Totties Nursery, 206
Tough Alpine Nursery, 211
Town and Country Products, 390
Town Farm Nursery, 130
Tracmaster Ltd, BCS, 373
Trade and DIY Products Ltd, 390
Traditional Garden Supply Company Ltd, The, 371, 390
Treasures of Tenbury Ltd, 158
Treasures of the Royal Horticultural Society, 64
Trebah Garden Trust, 261, 360
Tree and Landscape Specialists, D J, 429
Tree Council, The, 440
Tree Maintenance, 434
Treecare (London), 434
Treecare (Norwich), 434
Treemasters, 434
trees, 227, 434
Trees and Shrubs Hardy in the British Isles, 482
Trees in Miniature, 390
Treework Services Ltd, 423, 434
Treeworld Services, 434
Tregrehan, 262
Trehane, 262
Trehane Camellia Nursery, 143
Trelissick (Feock), 92, 93, 94, 262
trellis, 378, 384, 385, 390
Trenear Nurseries, Peter, 153
Trengwainton Gardens, 262, 362
Trentham Park Gardens, 317
Trerice, 262
Tresco Abbey, 263
Treseder, Stephen, 57
Trewidden, 263
Trewidden Estate Nursery, 132

Trewithen, 263
Trewithen Nurseries, 132
Treyer-Evans, Julian, 413
Trinity College, Dublin, 463
Trinity College Botanic Garden, 357
Tropical Rain Forest, 59
Tropical Rain Forest, The, 56
Tropicana Nursery, 140
Trossachs Garden Tours, 485
Tucker & Sons Ltd, Edwin, 233, 377
Tudor House Garden, 286
tunnels, 392
turf, 383
Turn End, 250
Tweedie Fruit Trees, J, 210
Two Wests and Elliott Ltd, 371, 391
Ty'r Orsaf Nursery, 209
Ulverscroft Unusual Plants, 170
underrated gardens, 363
University College Dublin, 456
University College London, 448
University College of North Wales, 454
University of Aberdeen, 454
University of Bristol, 462
University of Bristol Botanic Garden, 246
University of Durham Botanic Garden, 274
University of Edinburgh, 455
University of Greenwich, 446
University of Leicester Botanic Garden, 296
University of Liverpool, 1
University of Manchester, 445
University of Newcastle, 451
University of Nottingham, 446
University of Reading, 443, 462
University of Sheffield, 453
Unwins Seeds Ltd, 237
Upper Mill Cottage, 295
Upton House, 329
Urban Wildlife Trust, The West Midlands Wildlife Campaign, 116
Usual & Unusual Plants, 194
Uzumara Orchids, 213
Vale Garden Houses, 391
Valley Gardens, The, Harrogate, 337
Valley Gardens, The, Windsor, 321, 361
Van Hage Garden Company, The, 160, 237
Vann, 322
Ventnor Botanic Garden, 291
Verein Deutscher Rosenfreunde, 118
Vernon Geranium Nursery, The, 192
Veryans Plants, 140
Vesutor Airplants, 197
Vicarage Gardens, The, 149
Victoria Medal of Honour (VMH), 66

videos, 481
Vincent Architectural Garden Designer, Louis, 415
Vine House, 246
violas, 228
Volpaia, 276
W K W Tree Services, 435
W T Mattock Charitable Trust, The, 458
Waddesdon Manor, 251
Waddesdon Nursery, 125
Wakefield & North of England Tulip Society, 116, 240
Wakefield College, 453
Wakehurst Place, 68, 327
Walford College of Agriculture, 449
Walker, Harold, 129
Walkers Bulbs, J, 171
Wall Cottage Nursery, 133
Wallington Hall, 306
Walpole House, 301
Walton, Judith, 413
Wards Nurseries (Sarratt) Ltd, 160
Ware Ltd, Walter T, 202
Wartnaby Gardens, 297, 371, 391
Warwick Castle, 329
Warwickshire Wildlife Trust, 116
Watch Your Back, 492
Water Meadow Nursery and Herb Farm, 153, 423
water storage granules, 379
watercolours, 372
watering cans, 380
Waterperry Gardens, 180, 311
Waterwheel Nursery, 208
Watsonia, 66
Waveney Fish Farm, 177
Wayford Manor, 315
Weasdale Nurseries, 134
weather vanes, 384
weathervanes, 378
Weaver Vale Garden Centre, 130, 423
Webbs Garden Centre, 134
Webbs of Wychbold, 158, 423
weedkillers, 493
Well-Tempered Garden, The, 482, 483
Wells & Winter, 391, 466, 371
Wells Landscaping, D, 406
Welsh College of Horticulture, 453, 463
Welsh Historic Gardens Trust, 81, 116
Wentworth Castle Gardens, 337
Wessex Horticultural Products Ltd, 391
Wessex Tree Surgeons, 435
West Dean Gardens, 80, 328
West Kington Nurseries Ltd, 202, 423
West Meters Ltd, 391
West Oxford College, 449

West Park Lodge Hotel, 364
West Somerset Garden Centre, 185
West Wycombe Park, 251
Westbury Court, 281
Westcott Landscape Architects, Mark, 416
Western Horticultural Society, 118
Westerwood Garden Centre, 214
Westfield Cacti, 140, 237
Westholme Hall, 275
Westland Horticulture, 391
Weston Park, 313
Westonbirt Arboretum, 282, 363
Westside Forestry, 435
Westwell Manor, 311
Westwood Nursery, 166
Wetheriggs Pottery, 391
Whateley, Elizabeth, 408
Whatton House, 297
Wheatcroft Ltd, 180
Wheeler, A D & N, 198
Whichford Pottery, 391
White Cottage Alpines, 161
White Old Fashioned Roses, Trevor, 177
White Tree Surgeon and Forestry Contractor, Colin, 428
White Windows, 286
Whitehall Garden Centre, 202, 423
Whitehills Nurseries, 210
Whitehouse, C H, 374
Whitehouse Ivies, 146
Whitestone Gardens Ltd, 204
Whitfield, 288
wholesalers, 395
Wightwick Manor, 330
Wilcote House, 311
Wild Flower Centre, The, 177
Wild Flower Society, The, 110
wild flowers, 228
Wild Seeds, 237
Wildlife Gardening Centre, The, 180, 237
The Wildlife Gardening Centre, 237

Wildlife Trust Bedfordshire & Cambridgeshire, The, 116
Wildlife Trust for Bristol, Bath and Avon, 116
Wilkinsons, 424
Willerby Tree Surgeons Ltd, 435
Williams & Associates, Robin, 419
Wills, H & S, 137
Wilmslow Garden Centre, 130, 424
Wilton House, 334, 360
Wiltshire Gardens Trust, 116
Wiltshire Summerhouses, 392
Wiltshire Wildlife Trust, 117
Wimpole Hall, 253
Wincombe Park, 334
Winkworth Arboretum, 322, 361
winter gardens, 363
Wintergreen Nurseries, 158
wire work, 384, 387
Wisley see Royal Horticultural Society
Wisley Flower Festival, 62
Wisley Plant Centre, 192
Withleigh Nurseries, 141
Woburn Abbey, 247
Woking Borough Council, 59
Wolden Nurseries & Garden Centre, 173
WOLF Tools, 392
Wolseley Garden Park, 317
Wolverhampton Tree Service, 435
Women's Farm & Garden Association, 440
Woodfield Bros, 59, 199
Woodgrow Horticulture Ltd, 392
Woodland Trust, 440
Woodperry House, 311
Woolman, H (Dorridge) Ltd, 200
Work equipment, 492
Working with VDUs, 492
Workplace (Health, Safety and Welfare) Regulations 1992, 492
Workplace health, safety and welfare, 493

World Conifer Data Pool, 440
Worshipful Company of Gardeners, The, 440, 497
Worsley Hall Nurseries & Garden Centre, 149
woven polypropylene, 396
Wreford Landscapes, 424
Wrest Park, 247
Wright Landscape & Garden Design, Wendy, 423
Writtle Agricultural College, 1, 445, 462
Wulfran College, 451
Wye College, 446
Wye Valley Herbs, 208
Wyevale Garden Centre, 123, 124, 125, 130, 133, 135, 144, 147, 149, 158, 161, 166, 168, 170, 174, 177, 178, 181, 185, 186, 189, 193, 194, 197, 200, 208
Wyevale Garden Centres plc, 158
Wyken Hall, 518
Wylmington Hayes Gardens, 271
Wynn Arboricultural Consultant, Peter, 432
Wyseby House Books, 466
Wytherstone Nurseries, 204
Yarrow & Associates, Chris, 428
Year at Great Dixter, A, 483
Yellow Book, 242
Yew Tree Cottage, 328
York Gate, 339
Yorkshire Museum Gardens, 337
Yorkshire Wildlife Trust, 117
Young, Antony, 402
young gardens, 361
Young Seeds, Roy, 235
Younger Botanic Garden, The, 352
Your Garden, 481
YSJ Seeds, 185, 237
Zephyrwude Irises, 206
ZimTrade, 59